Residential Costs with RSMeans Data

2017
36th annual edition

Thomas Lane, Senior Editor

Engineering Director
Bob Mewis, CCP

Contributing Editors
Christopher Babbitt
Adrian C. Charest, PE
Cheryl Elsmore
John Gomes (13, 41)
Derrick Hale (2, 31, 32, 33, 34, 35, 44, 46)
Wafaa Hamitou (11, 12)
Joseph Kelble (14, 23)
Charles Kibbee (1, 4)
Robert J. Kuchta (8)
Gerard Lafond, PE
Michael Landry

Thomas Lane (6, 7)
Genevieve Medeiros
Elisa Mello
Ken Monty
Chris Morris (26, 27, 28, 48)
Dale Morris (21, 22)
Marilyn Phelan, AIA (9, 10)
Stephen C. Plotner (3, 5)
Stephen Rosenberg
Matthew Sorrentino
Kevin Souza
Tim Tonello
David Yazbek

Product Manager
Andrea Sillah

Production Manager
Debbie Panarelli

Production
Jonathan Forgit
Mary Lou Geary
Sharon Larsen
Sheryl Rose

Technical Support
Judy Abbruzzese
Gary L. Hoitt

Cover Design
Blaire Gaddis

Numbers in italics are the divisional responsibilities for each editor. Please contact the designated editor directly with any questions.

Gordian RSMeans Data
Construction Publishers & Consultants
1099 Hingham Street, Suite 201
Rockland, MA 02370
United States of America
1-800-448-8182
www.RSMeans.com

Printed in the United States of America
ISSN 0896-8624
ISBN 978-1-943215-64-5

0177 $219.99 per copy (in United States)
Price is subject to change without prior notice.

Related Data and Services

This data set is aimed primarily at single-family and small multi-family housing projects costing up to $1,000,000. For procurement and construction cost data, such as Job Order Contracting and Change Order Management, please refer to Gordian's other offerings.

Our engineers, who are experts in RSMeans data, suggest the following products and services as companion information resources to *Residential Costs with RSMeans Data*:

Construction Cost Data
Square Foot Costs with RSMeans Data 2017
Residential Repair and Remodeling Costs with RSMeans Data 2017

Reference Books
Estimating Building Costs
RSMeans Estimating Handbook
Green Building: Project Planning & Estimating
How to Estimate with RSMeans Data
Plan Reading & Material Takeoff
Project Scheduling & Management for Construction
Universal Design Ideas for Style, Comfort & Safety

Seminars and In-House Training
Unit Price Estimating
Training for our online estimating solution
Practical Project Management for Construction Professionals
Scheduling with MSProject for Construction Professionals
Mechanical & Electrical Estimating

Online Store
Visit www.RSMeans.com for the most reliable and current resources available on the market. Learn more about our more than 20 data sets available in Online, Book, eBook, and CD formats. Our library of reference books is also available, along with professional development seminars aimed at improving cost estimating, project management, administration, and facilities management skills.

RSMeans Electronic Data
Receive the most up-to-date cost information with our online estimating solution. This web-based service is quick, intuitive, and easy to use, giving you instant access to our comprehensive database. Learn more at: **www.RSMeans.com/Online**.

Custom Solutions
Building owners, facility managers, building product manufacturers, attorneys, and even insurance firms across the public and private sectors have engaged in custom solutions to solve their estimating needs including:

Custom Cost Engineering Solutions
Knowing the lifetime maintenance cost of your building, how much it will cost to build a specific building type in different locations across the country and globe, and if the estimate from which you are basing a major decision is accurate are all imperative for building owners and their facility managers.

Market & Custom Analytics
Taking a construction product to market requires accurate market research in order to make critical business development decisions. Once the product goes to market, one way to differentiate your product from the competition is to make any cost saving claims you have to offer.

Third-Party Legal Resources
Natural disasters can lead to reconstruction and repairs just as new developments and expansions can lead to issues of eminent domain. In these cases where one party must pay, it is plausible for legal disputes over costs and estimates to arise.

Construction Costs for Software Applications
More than 25 unit price and assemblies cost databases are available through a number of leading estimating and facilities management software partners.

RSMeans data is also available to federal, state, and local government agencies as multi-year, multi-seat licenses.

For information on our current partners, call 1-800-448-8182.

Table of Contents

Foreword

Who We Are

Gordian was founded in the spirit of innovation and a strong commitment to help our clients reach and exceed their construction goals. In 1982, Gordian's Chairman and Founder, Harry H. Mellon, invented the family of contracting systems known as Job Order Contracting while serving as Chief Engineer at the Supreme Headquarters Allied Powers Europe in Mons, Belgium. Mr. Mellon realized facility and infrastructure owners could greatly benefit from the time and cost saving advantages of this cutting-edge construction procurement solution, and, in 1990, he started Gordian to provide these products and services for that purpose.

Since 1942, RSMeans data has been available for construction cost estimating information and consulting throughout North America, and is the industry standard for estimating. In 2014, Gordian combined two industry-leading construction cost data companies, enhancing the fortitude of its data with the addition of RSMeans. Today, Gordian draws on its highly specialized engineers, software and unique proprietary data sets to solve the construction information, planning and management needs of people in building construction, building products manufacturing, education, healthcare, retail, insurance, legal and government.

Our Offerings

Gordian is the leading provider of construction cost data, software and services to organizations pursuing efficiency and effectiveness throughout all phases of the construction lifecycle. From Planning, Design, and Procurement through Construction and, finally, Operations, Gordian's portfolio of solutions delivers accurate and up-to-date data to meet the needs of contractors, architects, engineers, facility owners, managers and others in the construction industry. Our products and services include Sightlines planning solutions, estimating solutions with RSMeans data and Job Order Contracting offerings from basic online services to enterprise solutions.

Our Commitment

Today at Gordian, we do more than talk about the quality of our data and the usefulness of its application. We stand behind all of our RSMeans data—from historical cost indexes to construction materials and techniques—to craft current costs and predict future trends.

If you have any questions about our products or services, please call us toll-free at 800-448-8182 or visit our website at: www.TheGordianGroup.com.

How the Cost Data Is Built: An Overview

A Powerful Construction Tool

You now have one of the most powerful construction tools available today. A successful project is built on the foundation of an accurate and dependable estimate. This tool will enable you to construct such an estimate.

For the casual user the information is designed to be:

- quickly and easily understood so you can get right to your estimate.
- filled with valuable information so you can understand the necessary factors that go into a cost estimate.

For the professional user, the information is designed to be:

- a handy reference that can be quickly referred to for key costs.
- a comprehensive, fully reliable source of current construction costs and productivity rates so you'll be prepared to estimate any project.
- a source for preliminary project costs, product selections, and alternate materials and methods.

To meet all of these requirements, we have organized the information into the following clearly defined sections.

Estimating with RSMeans Unit Price Cost Data*

Please refer to these steps for guidance on completing an estimate using RSMeans unit price cost data.

How to Use the Cost Data: The Details

This section contains an in-depth explanation of how the information is arranged and how you can use it to determine a reliable construction cost estimate. It includes how we develop our cost figures and how to prepare your estimate.

Unit Prices*

All cost data has been divided into 50 divisions according to the MasterFormat system of classification and numbering.

Assemblies*

The cost data in this section has been organized in an "Assemblies" format. These assemblies are the functional elements of a building and are arranged according to the 7 elements of the UNIFORMAT II classification system. For a complete explanation of a typical "Assembly", see "How RSMeans Assemblies Data Works."

Residential Models*

Model buildings for four classes of construction—economy, average, custom, and luxury—are developed and shown with complete costs per square foot.

Commercial/Industrial/ Institutional Models*

This section contains complete costs for 77 typical model buildings expressed as costs per square foot.

Green Commercial/Industrial/ Institutional Models*

This section contains complete costs for 25 green model buildings expressed as costs per square foot.

References*

This section includes information on Equipment Rental Costs, Crew Listings, Historical Cost Indexes, City Cost Indexes, Location Factors, Reference Tables, and Change Orders, as well as a listing of abbreviations.

- **Equipment Rental Costs:** Included are the average costs to rent and operate hundreds of pieces of construction equipment.
- **Crew Listings:** This section lists all the crews referenced in the cost data. A crew is composed of more than one trade classification and/or the addition of power equipment to any trade classification. Power equipment is included in the cost of the crew. Costs are shown both with bare labor rates and with the installing contractor's overhead and profit added. For each, the total crew cost per eight-hour day and the composite cost per labor-hour are listed.

- **Historical Cost Indexes:** These indexes provide you with data to adjust construction costs over time.
- **City Cost Indexes:** All costs in this data set are U.S. national averages. Costs vary by region. You can adjust for this by CSI Division to over 900 locations throughout the U.S. and Canada by using this data.
- **Location Factors:** You can adjust total project costs to over 900 locations throughout the U.S. and Canada by using the weighted number, which applies across all divisions.
- **Reference Tables:** At the beginning of selected major classifications in the Unit Prices are reference numbers indicators. These numbers refer you to related information in the Reference Section. In this section, you'll find reference tables, explanations, and estimating information that support how we develop the unit price data, technical data, and estimating procedures.
- **Change Orders:** This section includes information on the factors that influence the pricing of change orders.
- **Abbreviations:** A listing of abbreviations used throughout this information, along with the terms they represent, is included.

Index (printed versions only)

A comprehensive listing of all terms and subjects will help you quickly find what you need when you are not sure where it occurs in MasterFormat.

Conclusion

This information is designed to be as comprehensive and easy to use as possible.

The Construction Specifications Institute (CSI) and Construction Specifications Canada (CSC) have produced the 2014 edition of MasterFormat®, a system of titles and numbers used extensively to organize construction information.

All unit prices in the RSMeans cost data are now arranged in the 50-division MasterFormat® 2014 system.

---

* Not all information is available in all data sets

Note: The material prices in RSMeans cost data are "contractor's prices." They are the prices that contractors can expect to pay at the lumberyards, suppliers'/distributors' warehouses, etc. Small orders of specialty items would be higher than the costs shown, while very large orders, such as truckload lots, would be less. The variation would depend on the size, timing, and negotiating power of the contractor. The labor costs are primarily for new construction or major renovation rather than repairs or minor alterations. With reasonable exercise of judgment, the figures can be used for any building work.

Estimating with RSMeans Unit Price Cost Data

Following these steps will allow you to complete an accurate estimate using RSMeans Unit Price cost data.

1. Scope Out the Project

- Think through the project and identify the CSI Divisions needed in your estimate.
- Identify the individual work tasks that will need to be covered in your estimate.
- The Unit Price data has been divided into 50 Divisions according to the CSI MasterFormat® 2014.
- In printed versions, the Unit Price Section Table of Contents on page 1 may also be helpful when scoping out your project.
- Experienced estimators find it helpful to begin with Division 2 and continue through completion. Division 1 can be estimated after the full project scope is known.

2. Quantify

- Determine the number of units required for each work task that you identified.
- Experienced estimators include an allowance for waste in their quantities. (Waste is not included in our Unit Price line items unless otherwise stated.)

3. Price the Quantities

- Use the search tools available to locate individual Unit Price line items for your estimate.
- Reference Numbers indicated within a Unit Price section refer to additional information that you may find useful.
- The crew indicates who is performing the work for that task. Crew codes are expanded in the Crew Listings in the Reference Section to include all trades and equipment that comprise the crew.
- The Daily Output is the amount of work the crew is expected to complete in one day.
- The Labor-Hours value is the amount of time it will take for the crew to install one unit of work.
- The abbreviated Unit designation indicates the unit of measure upon which the crew, productivity, and prices are based.
- Bare Costs are shown for materials, labor, and equipment needed to complete the Unit Price line item. Bare costs do not include waste, project overhead, payroll insurance, payroll taxes, main office overhead, or profit.
- The Total Incl O&P cost is the billing rate or invoice amount of the installing contractor or subcontractor who performs the work for the Unit Price line item.

4. Multiply

- Multiply the total number of units needed for your project by the Total Incl O&P cost for each Unit Price line item.
- Be careful that your take off unit of measure matches the unit of measure in the Unit column.
- The price you calculate is an estimate for a completed item of work.
- Keep scoping individual tasks, determining the number of units required for those tasks, matching each task with individual Unit Price line items, and multiplying quantities by Total Incl O&P costs.
- An estimate completed in this manner is priced as if a subcontractor, or set of subcontractors, is performing the work. The estimate does not yet include Project Overhead or Estimate Summary components such as general contractor markups on subcontracted work, general contractor office overhead and profit, contingency, and location factors.

5. Project Overhead

- Include project overhead items from Division 1–General Requirements.
- These items are needed to make the job run. They are typically, but not always, provided by the general contractor. Items include, but are not limited to, field personnel, insurance, performance bond, permits, testing, temporary utilities, field office and storage facilities, temporary scaffolding and platforms, equipment mobilization and demobilization, temporary roads and sidewalks, winter protection, temporary barricades and fencing, temporary security, temporary signs, field engineering and layout, final cleaning, and commissioning.
- Each item should be quantified and matched to individual Unit Price line items in Division 1, then priced and added to your estimate.
- An alternate method of estimating project overhead costs is to apply a percentage of the total project cost, usually 5% to 15% with an average of 10% (see General Conditions).
- Include other project related expenses in your estimate such as:
  - Rented equipment not itemized in the Crew Listings
  - Rubbish handling throughout the project (see section 02 41 19.19)

6. Estimate Summary

- Include sales tax as required by laws of your state or county.
- Include the general contractor's markup on self-performed work, usually 5% to 15% with an average of 10%.
- Include the general contractor's markup on subcontracted work, usually 5% to 15% with an average of 10%.
- Include the general contractor's main office overhead and profit:
  - RSMeans data provides general guidelines on the general contractor's main office overhead (see section 01 31 13.60 and Reference Number RO13113-50).
  - Markups will depend on the size of the general contractor's operations, projected annual revenue, the level of risk, and the level of competition in the local area and for this project in particular.
- Include a contingency, usually 3% to 5%, if appropriate.
- Adjust your estimate to the project's location by using the City Cost Indexes or the Location Factors in the Reference Section:
  - Look at the rules in "How to Use the City Cost Indexes" to see how to apply the Indexes for your location.
  - When the proper Index or Factor has been identified for the project's location, convert it to a multiplier by dividing it by 100, then multiply that multiplier by your estimated total cost. The original estimated total cost will now be adjusted up or down from the national average to a total that is appropriate for your location.

Editors' Note:
We urge you to spend time reading and
understanding the supporting material. An
accurate estimate requires experience, knowledge,
and careful calculation. The more you know about
how we at RSMeans developed the data, the more
accurate your estimate will be. In addition, it is
important to take into consideration the reference
material such as Equipment Listings, Crew
Listings, City Cost Indexes, Location Factors, and
Reference Tables.

How to Use the Cost Data: The Details

What's Behind the Numbers? The Development of Cost Data

Gordian's RSMeans staff continually monitors developments in the construction industry in order to ensure reliable, thorough, and up-to-date cost information. While overall construction costs may vary relative to general economic conditions, price fluctuations within the industry are dependent upon many factors. Individual price variations may, in fact, be opposite to overall economic trends. Therefore, costs are constantly tracked, and complete updates are performed yearly. Also, new items are frequently added in response to changes in materials and methods.

Costs—$ (U.S.)

All costs represent U.S. national averages and are given in U.S. dollars. The City Cost Index (CCI) with RSMeans data can be used to adjust costs to a particular location. The CCI for Canada can be used to adjust U.S. national averages to local costs in Canadian dollars. No exchange rate conversion is necessary because it has already been factored in.

G The processes or products identified by the green symbol in our publications have been determined to be environmentally responsible and/or resource-efficient solely by Gordian's RSMeans engineering staff. The inclusion of the green symbol does not represent compliance with any specific industry association or standard.

Material Costs

Gordian's RSMeans staff contacts manufacturers, dealers, distributors, and contractors all across the U.S. and Canada to determine national average material costs. If you have access to current material costs for your specific location, you may wish to make adjustments to reflect differences from the national average. Included within material costs are fasteners for a normal installation. Gordian's RSMeans engineers use manufacturers' recommendations, written specifications, and/or standard construction practices for the sizing and spacing of fasteners. Adjustments to material costs may be required for your specific application or location. The manufacturer's warranty is assumed. Extended warranties are not included in the material costs. **Material costs do not include sales tax.**

Labor Costs

Labor costs are based upon a mathematical average of trade-specific wages in 30 major U.S. cities. The type of wage (union, open shop, or residential) is identified on the inside back cover of printed publications or is selected by the estimator when using the electronic products. Markups for the wages can also be found on the inside back cover of printed publications and/or under the labor references found in the electronic products.

- If wage rates in your area vary from those used, or if rate increases are expected within a given year, labor costs should be adjusted accordingly.

Labor costs reflect productivity based on actual working conditions. In addition to actual installation, these figures include time spent during a normal weekday on tasks, such as material receiving and handling, mobilization at site, site movement, breaks, and cleanup.

Productivity data is developed over an extended period so as not to be influenced by abnormal variations and reflects a typical average.

Equipment Costs

Equipment costs include not only rental, but also operating costs for equipment under normal use. The operating costs include parts and labor for routine servicing, such as repair and replacement of pumps, filters, and worn lines. Normal operating expendables, such as fuel, lubricants, tires, and electricity (where applicable), are also included. Extraordinary operating expendables with highly variable wear patterns, such as diamond bits and blades, are excluded. These costs are included under materials. Equipment rental rates are obtained from industry sources throughout North America—contractors, suppliers, dealers, manufacturers, and distributors.

Rental rates can also be treated as reimbursement costs for contractor-owned equipment. Owned equipment costs include depreciation, loan payments, interest, taxes, insurance, storage, and major repairs.

Equipment costs do not include operators' wages.

Equipment Cost/Day—The cost of equipment required for each crew is included in the Crew Listings in the Reference Section (small tools that are considered essential everyday tools are not listed out separately). The Crew Listings itemize specialized tools and heavy equipment along with labor trades. The daily cost of itemized equipment included in a crew is based on dividing the weekly bare rental rate by 5 (number of working days per week), then adding the hourly operating cost times 8 (the number of hours per day). This Equipment Cost/Day is shown in the last column of the Equipment Rental Costs in the Reference Section.

Mobilization, Demobilization—The cost to move construction equipment from an equipment yard or rental company to the job site and back again is not included in equipment costs. Mobilization (to the site) and demobilization (from the site) costs can be found in the Unit Price Section. If a piece of equipment is already at the job site, it is not appropriate to utilize mobilization or demobilization costs again in an estimate.

Overhead and Profit

Total Cost including O&P for the installing contractor is shown in the last column of the Unit Price and/or Assemblies. This figure is the sum of the bare material cost plus 10% for profit, the bare labor cost plus total overhead and profit, and the bare equipment cost plus 10% for profit. Details for the calculation of overhead and profit on labor are shown on the inside back cover of the printed product and in the Reference Section of the electronic product.

General Conditions

Cost data in this data set is presented in two ways: Bare Costs and Total Cost including O&P (Overhead and Profit). General Conditions, or General Requirements, of the contract should also be added to the Total Cost including O&P when applicable. Costs for General Conditions are listed in Division 1 of the Unit Price Section and in the Reference Section.

General Conditions for the installing contractor may range from 0% to 10% of the Total Cost including O&P. For the general or prime contractor, costs for General Conditions may range from 5% to 15% of the Total Cost including O&P, with a figure of 10% as the most typical allowance. If applicable, the Assemblies and Models sections use costs that include the installing contractor's overhead and profit (O&P).

Factors Affecting Costs

Costs can vary depending upon a number of variables. Here's a listing of some factors that affect costs and points to consider.

Quality—The prices for materials and the workmanship upon which productivity is based represent sound construction work. They are also in line with industry standard and manufacturer specifications and are frequently used by federal, state, and local governments.

Overtime—We have made no allowance for overtime. If you anticipate premium time or work beyond normal working hours, be sure to make an appropriate adjustment to your labor costs.

Productivity—The productivity, daily output, and labor-hour figures for each line item are based on working an eight-hour day in daylight hours in moderate temperatures, and up to a 14 foot working height unless otherwise indicated. For work that extends beyond normal work hours or is performed under adverse conditions, productivity may decrease.

Size of Project—The size, scope of work, and type of construction project will have a significant impact on cost. Economies of scale can reduce costs for large projects. Unit costs can often run higher for small projects.

Location—Material prices are for metropolitan areas. However, in dense urban areas, traffic and site storage limitations may increase costs. Beyond a 20-mile radius of metropolitan areas, extra trucking or transportation charges may also increase the material costs slightly. On the other hand, lower wage rates may be in effect. Be sure to consider both of these factors when preparing an estimate, particularly if the job site is located in a central city or remote rural location. In addition, highly specialized subcontract items may require travel and per-diem expenses for mechanics.

Other Factors—

- season of year
- contractor management
- weather conditions
- local union restrictions
- building code requirements
- availability of:
  - □ adequate energy
  - □ skilled labor
  - □ building materials
- owner's special requirements/restrictions
- safety requirements
- environmental considerations
- access

Unpredictable Factors—General business conditions influence "in-place" costs of all items. Substitute materials and construction methods may have to be employed. These may affect the installed cost and/or life cycle costs. Such factors may be difficult to evaluate and cannot necessarily be predicted on the basis of the job's location in a particular section of the country. Thus, where these factors apply, you may find significant but unavoidable cost variations for which you will have to apply a measure of judgment to your estimate.

Rounding of Costs

In printed publications only, all unit prices in excess of $5.00 have been rounded to make them easier to use and still maintain adequate precision of the results.

How Subcontracted Items Affect Costs

A considerable portion of all large construction jobs is usually subcontracted. In fact, the percentage done by subcontractors is constantly increasing and may run over 90%. Since the workers employed by these companies do nothing else but install their particular product, they soon become experts in that line. The result is, installation by these firms is accomplished so efficiently that the total in-place cost, even adding the general contractor's overhead and profit, is no more, and often less, than if the principal contractor had handled the installation. Companies that deal with construction specialties are anxious to have their product perform well and, consequently, the installation will be the best possible.

Contingencies

The allowance for contingencies generally provides for unforeseen construction difficulties. On alterations or repair jobs, 20% is not too much. If drawings are final and only field contingencies are being considered, 2% or 3% is probably sufficient, and often nothing needs to be added. Contractually, changes in plans will be covered by extras. The contractor should consider inflationary price trends and possible material shortages during the course of the job. These escalation factors are dependent upon both economic conditions and the anticipated time between the estimate and actual construction. If drawings are not complete or approved, or a budget cost is wanted, it is wise to add 5% to 10%. Contingencies, then, are a matter of judgment.

Important Estimating Considerations

The productivity, or daily output, of each craftsman or crew assumes a well-managed job where tradesmen with the proper tools and equipment, along with the appropriate construction materials, are present. Included are daily set-up and cleanup time, break time, and plan layout time. Unless otherwise indicated, time for material movement on site (for items that can be transported by hand) of up to 200' into the building and to the first or second floor is also included. If material has to be transported by other means, over greater distances, or to higher floors, an additional allowance should be considered by the estimator.

While horizontal movement is typically a sole function of distances, vertical transport introduces other variables that can significantly impact productivity. In an occupied building, the use of elevators (assuming access, size, and required protective measures are acceptable) must be understood at the time of the estimate. For new construction, hoist wait and cycle times can easily be 15 minutes and may result in scheduled access extending beyond the normal work day. Finally, all vertical transport will impose strict weight limits likely to preclude the use of any motorized material handling.

The productivity, or daily output, also assumes installation that meets manufacturer/designer/ standard specifications. A time allowance for quality control checks, minor adjustments, and any task required to ensure the proper function or operation is also included. For items that require connections to services, time is included for positioning, leveling, securing the unit, and for making all the necessary connections (and start up where applicable), ensuring a complete installation. Estimating of the services themselves (electrical, plumbing, water, steam, hydraulics, dust collection, etc.) is separate.

In some cases, the estimator must consider the use of a crane and an appropriate crew for the installation of large or heavy items. For those situations where a crane is not included in the assigned crew and as part of the line item

cost, equipment rental costs, mobilization and demobilization costs, and operator and support personnel costs must be considered.

Labor-Hours

The labor-hours expressed in this publication are derived by dividing the total daily labor-hours for the crew by the daily output. Based on average installation time and the assumptions listed above, the labor-hours include: direct labor, indirect labor, and nonproductive time. A typical day for a craftsman might include, but is not limited to:

- Direct Work
  - □ Measuring and layout
  - □ Preparing materials
  - □ Actual installation
  - □ Quality assurance/quality control
- Indirect Work
  - □ Reading plans or specifications
  - □ Preparing space
  - □ Receiving materials
  - □ Material movement
  - □ Giving or receiving instruction
  - □ Miscellaneous
- Non-Work
  - □ Chatting
  - □ Personal issues
  - □ Breaks
  - □ Interruptions (i.e., sickness, weather, material or equipment shortages, etc.)

If any of the items for a typical day do not apply to the particular work or project situation, the estimator should make any necessary adjustments.

Final Checklist

Estimating can be a straightforward process provided you remember the basics. Here's a checklist of some of the steps you should remember to complete before finalizing your estimate.

Did you remember to:

- factor in the City Cost Index for your locale?
- take into consideration which items have been marked up and by how much?
- mark up the entire estimate sufficiently for your purposes?
- read the background information on techniques and technical matters that could impact your project time span and cost?
- include all components of your project in the final estimate?
- double check your figures for accuracy?
- call Gordian's RSMeans staff if you have any questions about your estimate or the data you've used? Remember, Gordian stands behind all of our products, including our extensive RSMeans data solutions. If you have any questions about your estimate, about the costs you've used from our data, or even about the technical aspects of the job that may affect your estimate, feel free to call the Gordian RSMeans editors at 1-800-448-8182.

Free Quarterly Updates

Stay up-to-date throughout the year with free RSMeans cost data updates four times a year. Sign up online to make sure you have access to the newest data. Every quarter we provide the city cost adjustment factors for hundreds of cities and updated national average pricing for key materials.

Register at: **http://info.TheGordianGroup.com/ 2017-quarterly-updates.html**.

Square Foot Cost Section

Table of Contents

Introduction to the Square Foot Cost Section

The Square Foot Cost Section contains costs per square foot for four classes of construction in seven building types. Costs are listed for various exterior wall materials which are typical of the class and building type. There are cost tables for wings and ells with modification tables to adjust the base cost of each class of building. Non-standard items can easily be added to the standard structures.

Cost estimating for a residence is a three-step process:
1. Identification
2. Listing dimensions
3. Calculations

Guidelines and a sample cost estimating procedure are shown on the following pages.

Identification
To properly identify a residential building, the class of construction, type, and exterior wall material must be determined. The "Building Classes" information has drawings and guidelines for determining the class of construction. There are also detailed specifications and additional drawings at the beginning of each set of tables to further aid in proper building class and type identification.

Sketches for eight types of residential buildings and their configurations follow. Definitions of living area are next to each sketch. Sketches and definitions of garage types follow.

Living Area
Base cost tables are prepared as costs per square foot of living area. The living area of a residence is that area which is suitable and normally designed for full time living. It does not include basement recreation rooms or finished attics, although these areas are often considered full time living areas by the owners.

Living area is calculated from the exterior dimensions without the need to adjust for exterior wall thickness. When calculating the living area of a 1-1/2 story, two story, three story or tri-level residence, overhangs and other differences in size and shape between floors must be considered.

Only the floor area with a ceiling height of seven feet or more in a 1-1/2 story residence is considered living area. In bi-levels and tri-levels, the areas that are below grade are considered living areas, even when these areas may not be completely finished.

Base Tables and Modifications
Base cost tables show the base cost per square foot without a basement, with one full bath and one full kitchen for economy and average homes, and an additional half bath for custom and luxury models. Adjustments for finished and unfinished basements are part of the base cost tables. Adjustments for multi-family residences, additional bathrooms, townhouses, alternative roofs, and air conditioning and heating systems are listed in Modifications, Adjustments, and Alternatives tables below the base cost tables.

Costs for other modifications, adjustments, and alternatives, including garages, breezeways, and site improvements, follow the base tables.

Listing of Dimensions
To use this section, only the dimensions used to calculate the horizontal area of the building and additions, modifications, adjustments, and alternatives are needed. The dimensions, normally the length and width, can come from drawings or field measurements. For ease in calculation, consider measuring in tenths of feet, i.e., 9 ft. 6 in. = 9.5 ft., 9 ft. 4 in. = 9.3 ft.

In all cases, make a sketch of the building. Any protrusions or other variations in shape should be noted on the sketch with dimensions.

Calculations
The calculations portion of the estimate is a two-step activity:
1. The selection of appropriate costs from the tables
2. Computations

Selection of Appropriate Costs
To select the appropriate cost from the base tables, the following information is needed:
1. Class of construction
   - Economy
   - Average
   - Custom
   - Luxury
2. Type of residence
   - 1 story
   - 1-1/2 story
   - 2 story
   - 2-1/2 story
   - 3 story
   - Bi-level
   - Tri-level
3. Occupancy
   - One family
   - Two family
   - Three family
4. Building configuration
   - Detached
   - Town/Row house
   - Semi-detached
5. Exterior wall construction
   - Wood frame
   - Brick veneer
   - Solid masonry
6. Living areas

Modifications are classified by class, type, and size.

Computations
The computation process should take the following sequence:
1. Multiply the base cost by the area.
2. Add or subtract the modifications, adjustments, and alternatives.
3. Apply the location modifier.

When selecting costs, interpolate or use the cost that most nearly matches the structure under study. This applies to size, exterior wall construction, and class.

How to Use the Residential Square Foot Cost Section

The following is a detailed explanation of a sample entry in the Residential Square Foot Cost Section. Each bold number below corresponds to the item being described in the following list with the appropriate component of the sample entry in parentheses. Prices listed are costs that include overhead and profit of the installing contractor. Total model costs include an additional markup for the general contractor's overhead and profit, and fees specific to the class of construction.

RESIDENTIAL   **Average** ❶   **2 Story** ❷

- Simple design from standard plans
- Single family — 1 full bath, 1 kitchen
- No basement ❸
- Asphalt shingles on roof
- Hot air heat
- Gypsum wallboard interior finishes
- Materials and workmanship are average

Note: The illustration shown may contain some optional components (for example: garages and/or fireplaces) whose costs are shown in the modifications, adjustments, & alternatives below or at the end of the square foot section.

Base cost per square foot of living area

Exterior Wall ❹	Living Area ❺										
	1000	1200	1400	1600	1800	2000	2200	2600	3000	3400	3800
Wood Siding - Wood Frame	148.30	133.95	127.05	122.20	117.25 ❻	112.15	108.75	102.20	96.00	93.00	90.50
Brick Veneer - Wood Frame	156.50	141.50	134.15	128.90	123.65	118.25	114.55	107.50	100.85	97.60	94.85
Stucco on Wood Frame	143.90	129.85	123.25	118.55	113.85	108.80	105.55	99.40	93.30	90.50	88.05
Solid Masonry	171.30	155.20	146.95	141.20	135.15	129.35	125.10	117.00	109.60	106.00	102.80
Finished Basement, Add ❼	23.50	23.20	22.45	21.90	21.35	21.00	20.60 ❽	19.80	19.30	18.95	18.60
Unfinished Basement, Add	9.15	8.55	8.05	7.75	7.40	7.15	6.90	6.45	6.10	5.85	5.65

Modifications

Add to the total cost

Upgrade Kitchen Cabinets ❾	$ + 5823
Solid Surface Countertops (Included)	
Full Bath - including plumbing, wall and floor finishes	+ 8054
Half Bath - including plumbing, wall and floor finishes	+ 4856
One Car Attached Garage	+ 14,940
One Car Detached Garage	+ 19,637
Fireplace & Chimney	+ 7604

Adjustments

For multi family - add to total cost

Additional Kitchen	$ + 10,056
Additional Bath	+ 8054
Additional Entry & Exit	+ 1716
Separate Heating	+ 1421
Separate Electric	+ 1879

**For Townhouse/Rowhouse -
Multiply cost per square foot by**

Inner Unit ❿	.90
End Unit	.95

Alternatives

Add to or deduct from the cost per square foot of living area

Cedar Shake Roof	+ 1.70
Clay Tile Roof	+ 3.45
Slate Roof	+ 3.85
Upgrade Walls to Skim Coat Plaster ⓫	+ .55
Upgrade Ceilings to Textured Finish	+ .60
Air Conditioning, in Heating Ductwork	+ 2.96
In Separate Ductwork	+ 5.70
Heating Systems, Hot Water	+ 1.49
Heat Pump	+ 1.61
Electric Heat	– .63
Not Heated	– 3.28

Additional upgrades or components

Kitchen Cabinets & Countertops	Page 93
Bathroom Vanities	94
Fireplaces & Chimneys	94
Windows, Skylights & Dormers	94
Appliances	95
Breezeways & Porches	95
Finished Attic	95
Garages	96
Site Improvements ⓬	96
Wings & Ells	56

1 Class of Construction (Average)

The class of construction depends upon the design and specifications of the plan. The four classes are economy, average, custom, and luxury.

2 Type of Residence (2 Story)

The building type describes the number of stories or levels in the model. The seven building types are 1 story, 1-1/2 story, 2 story, 2-1/2 story, 3 story, bi-level, and tri-level.

3 Specification Highlights (Hot Air Heat)

These specifications include information concerning the components of the model, including the number of baths, roofing types, HVAC systems, materials, and workmanship. If the components listed are not appropriate, modifications can be made by consulting the information shown below or in the Assemblies section.

4 Exterior Wall System (Wood Siding-Wood Frame)

This section includes the types of exterior wall systems and the structural frames used. The exterior wall systems shown are typical of the class of construction and the building type shown.

5 Living Areas (2000 SF)

The living area is that area of the residence which is suitable and normally designed for full time living. It does not include basement recreation rooms or finished attics. Living area is calculated from the exterior dimensions without the need to adjust for exterior wall thickness. When calculating the living area of a 1-1/2 story, 2 story, 3 story, or tri-level residence, overhangs and other differences in size and shape between floors must be considered. Only the floor area with a ceiling height of seven feet or more in a 1-1/2 story residence is considered living area. In bi-levels and tri-levels, the areas that are below grade are considered living areas, even when these areas may not be completely finished. A range of various living areas for the residential model is shown to aid in the selection of values from the matrix.

6 Base Costs per Square Foot of Living Area ($112.15)

Base cost tables show the cost per square foot of living area without a basement, with one full bath and one full kitchen for economy and average homes, and an additional half bath for custom and luxury models. When selecting costs, interpolate or use the cost that most nearly matches the residence under consideration for size, exterior wall system, and class of construction. Prices listed are costs that include overhead and profit of the installing contractor, a general contractor markup, and an allowance for plans that vary by class of construction. For additional information on contractor overhead and architectural fees, see the Reference Section.

7 Basement Types (Finished)

The two types of basements are finished and unfinished. The specifications and components for both are shown under Building Classes in the Introduction to this section.

8 Additional Costs for Basements ($21.00 or $7.15)

These values indicate the additional cost per square foot of living area for either a finished or an unfinished basement.

9 Modifications and Adjustments (Upgrade Kitchen Cabinets $5823)

Modifications and Adjustments are costs added to or subtracted from the total cost of the residence. The total cost of the residence is equal to the cost per square foot of living area times the living area. Typical modifications and adjustments include kitchens, baths, garages, and fireplaces.

10 Multiplier for Townhouse/Rowhouse (Inner Unit .90)

The multipliers shown adjust the base costs per square foot of living area for the common wall condition encountered in townhouses or rowhouses.

11 Alternatives (Skim Coat Plaster $.55)

Alternatives are costs added to or subtracted from the base cost per square foot of living area. Typical alternatives include variations in kitchens, baths, roofing, and air conditioning and heating systems.

12 Additional Upgrades or Components (Wings & Ells)

Costs for additional upgrades or components, including wings or ells, breezeways, porches, finished attics, and site improvements, are shown at the end of each quality section and at the end of the Square Foot Section.

Average 2 Story

① Living Area - 2000 S.F.
Perimeter - 135 L.F.

		Cost Per Square Foot Of Living Area			% of Total
		Mat.	**Inst.**	**Total**	**(rounded)**
1 Site Work	Site preparation for slab; 4' deep trench excavation for foundation wall.		1.35	1.35	1.2%
2 Foundation	Continuous reinforced concrete footing, 10" deep x 20" wide; damproofed and insulated 8" thick reinforced concrete block foundation wall, 4' deep; trowel finished 4" thick concrete slab on 4" crushed stone base and polyethylene vapor barrier.	3.58	4.75	8.33	7.4%
3 Framing	Exterior walls - 2" x 6" wood studs, 16" O.C.; 1/2" sheathing; gable end roof framing, 2" x 10" rafters, 16" O.C. with 1/2" plywood sheathing; 2" x 10" floor joists, 16" O.C. with bridging and 5/8" subflooring; 2" x 4" interior partitions.	7.14	10.06	17.20	15.3%
4 Exterior Walls	Beveled wood siding and housewrap on insulated wood frame walls; R38 attic insulation; double hung wood windows; flush solid core doors, frame and hardware, painted finish; aluminum storm and screen doors.	14.19	6.09	20.28	18.1%
5 Roofing	25 year asphalt roof shingles; #15 felt building paper; aluminum gutters, downspouts, drip edge and flashings.	1.17	1.41	2.58	2.3%
6 Interiors	Walls & ceilings, 1/2" taped & finished gypsum wallboard, primed & painted with 2 coats of finish paint; birch faced hollow core interior doors, frames & hardware, painted finish; medium weight carpeting with pad, 40%; sheet vinyl, 15%; oak hardwood, 40%; ceramic tile, 5%; hardwood tread stairway.	15.09	15.30	30.39	27.1%
7 Specialties	Average grade kitchen cabinets and countertop; stainless steel kitchen sink; 40 gallon electric water heater.	3.86	1.21	5.07	4.5%
8 Mechanical	Three fixture bathroom: bathtub, water closet, vanity and sink; gas fired hot air heating system.	3.38	3.35	6.73	6.0%
9 Electrical	200 amp electric service; wiring, duplex & GFI receptacles, wall switches, door bell, appliance circuits, fans and communications cabling; average grade lighting fixtures	1.56	2.37	3.93	3.5%
10 Overhead	Contractor's overhead and profit and plans.	8.48	7.81	16.29	14.5%
Total		58.45	53.70	**112.15**	

1 Specifications

The parameters for an example dwelling from the previous pages are listed here. Included are the square foot dimensions of the proposed building. Living Area takes into account the number of floors and other factors needed to define a building's total square footage. Perimeter dimensions are defined in terms of linear feet.

2 Building Type

This is a sketch of a cross section view through the dwelling. It is shown to help define the living area for the building type. For more information, see the Building Types in the Introduction.

3 Components (3 Framing)

This page contains the ten components needed to develop the complete square foot cost of the typical dwelling specified. All components are defined with a description of the materials and/or task involved. Use cost figures from each component to estimate the cost per square foot of that section of the project. The components listed here are typical of all sizes of residences from the facing page. Specific quantities of components required would vary with the size of the dwelling and the exterior wall system.

4 Materials (7.14)

This column gives the amount needed to develop the cost of materials. The figures given here are not bare costs. Ten percent has been added to bare material cost for profit.

5 Installation (10.06)

Installation includes labor and equipment costs. The labor rates included here incorporate the total overhead and profit costs for the installing contractor. The average mark-up used to create these figures is 72.0% over and above bare labor costs. The equipment rates include 10% for profit.

6 Total (17.20)

This column lists the sum of two figures. Use this total to determine the sum of material cost plus installation cost. The result is a convenient total cost for each of the ten components.

7 % of Total (rounded) (15.3%)

This column represents the percent of the total cost for this component group.

8 Overhead

The costs in components 1 through 9 include overhead and profit for the installing contractor. Item 10 is overhead and profit for the general contractor. This is typically a percentage mark-up of all other costs. The amount depends on the size and type of dwelling, building class, and economic conditions. An allowance for plans or design has been included where appropriate.

9 Bottom Line Total (112.15)

This figure is the complete square foot cost for the construction project and equals the sum of total material and total labor costs. To determine total project cost, multiply the bottom line total by the living area.

Building Classes

Economy Class

An economy class residence is usually built from stock plans. The materials and workmanship are sufficient to satisfy building codes. Low construction cost is more important than distinctive features. The overall shape of the foundation and structure is seldom other than square or rectangular.

An unfinished basement includes a 7' high, 8" thick foundation wall composed of either concrete block or cast-in-place concrete.

Included in the finished basement cost are inexpensive paneling or drywall as the interior finish on the foundation walls, a low cost sponge backed carpeting adhered to the concrete floor, a drywall ceiling, and overhead lighting.

Average Class

An average class residence is a simple design and built from standard plans. Materials and workmanship are average but often exceed minimum building codes. There are frequently special features that give the residence some distinctive characteristics.

An unfinished basement includes a 7'-6" high, 8" thick foundation wall composed of either cast-in-place concrete or concrete block.

Included in the finished basement are plywood paneling or drywall on furring that is fastened to the foundation walls, sponge backed carpeting adhered to the concrete floor, a suspended ceiling, overhead lighting, and heating.

Custom Class

A custom class residence is usually built from plans and specifications with enough features to give the building a distinction of design. Materials and workmanship are generally above average with obvious attention given to construction details. Construction normally exceeds building code requirements.

An unfinished basement includes a 7'-6" high, 10" thick cast-in-place concrete foundation wall or a 7'-6" high, 12" thick concrete block foundation wall.

A finished basement includes painted drywall on insulated 2" × 4" wood furring as the interior finish to the concrete walls, a suspended ceiling, carpeting adhered to the concrete floor, overhead lighting, and heating.

Luxury Class

A luxury class residence is built from an architect's plan for a specific owner. It is unique both in design and workmanship. There are many special features, and construction usually exceeds all building codes. It is obvious that primary attention is placed on the owner's comfort and pleasure. Construction is supervised by an architect.

An unfinished basement includes an 8' high, 12" thick foundation wall that is composed of cast-in-place concrete or concrete block.

A finished basement includes painted drywall on 2" × 4" wood furring as the interior finish, a suspended ceiling, tackless carpet on wood subfloor with sleepers, overhead lighting, and heating.

Configurations

Detached House

This category of residence is a free-standing separate building with or without an attached garage. It has four complete walls.

Semi-Detached House

This category of residence has two living units side-by-side. The common wall is fireproof. Semi-detached residences can be treated as a row house with two end units. Semi-detached residences can be any of the building types.

Town/Row House

This category of residence has a number of attached units made up of inner units and end units. The units are joined by common walls. The inner units have only two exterior walls. The common walls are fireproof. The end units have three walls and a common wall. Town houses/row houses can be any of the building types.

Building Types

One Story

This is an example of a one-story dwelling. The living area of this type of residence is confined to the ground floor. The headroom in the attic is usually too low for use as a living area.

One-and-one-half Story

The living area in the upper level of this type of residence is 50% to 90% of the ground floor. This is made possible by a combination of this design's high-peaked roof and/or dormers. Only the upper level area with a ceiling height of seven feet or more is considered living area. The living area of this residence is the sum of the ground floor area plus the area on the second level with a ceiling height of seven feet or more.

One Story with Finished Attic

The main living area in this type of residence is the ground floor. The upper level or attic area has sufficient headroom for use as a living area. This is made possible by a high peaked roof. The living area in the attic is less than 50% of the ground floor. The living area of this type of residence is the ground floor area only. The finished attic is considered an adjustment.

Two Story

This type of residence has a second floor or upper level area which is equal or nearly equal to the ground floor area. The upper level of this type of residence can range from 90% to 110% of the ground floor area, depending on setbacks or overhangs. The living area is the sum of the ground floor area and the upper level floor area.

Two-and-one-half Story

This type of residence has two levels of equal or nearly equal area and a third level which has a living area that is 50% to 90% of the ground floor. This is made possible by a high peaked roof, extended wall heights, and/or dormers. Only the upper level area with a ceiling height of seven feet or more is considered living area. The living area of this residence is the sum of the ground floor area, the second floor area, and the area on the third level with a ceiling height of seven feet or more.

Bi-level

This type of residence has two living areas, one above the other. One area is about four feet below grade and the second is about four feet above grade. Both areas are equal in size. The lower level in this type of residence is designed and built to serve as a living area and not as a basement. Both levels have full ceiling heights. The living area is the sum of the lower level area and the upper level area.

Three Story

This type of residence has three levels which are equal or nearly equal. As in the two story residence, the second and third floor areas may vary slightly depending on setbacks or overhangs. The living area is the sum of the ground floor area and the two upper level floor areas.

Tri-level

This type of residence has three levels of living area: one at grade level, one about four feet below grade, and one about four feet above grade. All levels are designed to serve as living areas. All levels have full ceiling heights. The living area is a sum of the areas of each of the three levels.

Garage Types

Attached Garage

Shares a common wall with the dwelling. Access is typically through a door between the dwelling and garage.

Basement Garage

Constructed under the roof of the dwelling but below the living area.

Built-In Garage

Constructed under the second floor living space and above the basement level of the dwelling. Reduces gross square feet of the living area.

Detached Garage

Constructed apart from the main dwelling. Shares no common area or wall with the dwelling.

Building Components

1. Excavation
2. Sill Plate
3. Basement Window
4. Floor Joist
5. Shoe Plate
6. Studs
7. Drywall
8. Plate
9. Ceiling Joists
10. Rafters
11. Collar Ties
12. Ridge Board
13. Roof Sheathing
14. Roof Felt
15. Roof Shingles
16. Flashing
17. Flue Lining
18. Chimney
19. Roof Shingles
20. Gutter
21. Fascia
22. Downspout
23. Shutter
24. Window
25. Wall Shingles
26. Weather Barrier
27. Wall Sheathing
28. Fire Stop
29. Dampproofing
30. Foundation Wall
31. Backfill
32. Drainage Stone
33. Drainage Tile
34. Wall Footing
35. Gravel
36. Concrete Slab
37. Column Footing
38. Pipe Column
39. Expansion Joint
40. Girder
41. Sub-floor
42. Finish Floor
43. Attic Insulation
44. Soffit
45. Ceiling Strapping
46. Wall Insulation
47. Cross Bridging
48. Bulkhead Stairs

13

Exterior Wall Construction

Typical Frame Construction

Typical wood frame construction consists of wood studs with insulation between them. A typical exterior surface is made up of sheathing, building paper, and exterior siding consisting of wood, vinyl, aluminum, or stucco over the wood sheathing.

Brick Veneer

Typical brick veneer construction consists of wood studs with insulation between them. A typical exterior surface is sheathing, building paper, and an exterior of brick tied to the sheathing with metal strips.

Stone

Typical solid masonry construction consists of a stone or block wall covered on the exterior with brick, stone, or other masonry.

Residential Cost Estimate Worksheet

Worksheet Instructions

The residential cost estimate worksheet can be used as an outline for developing a residential construction or replacement cost. It is also useful for insurance appraisals. The design of the worksheet helps eliminate errors and omissions. To use the worksheet, follow the example below.

1. Fill out the owner's name, residence address, the estimator or appraiser's name, some type of project identifying number or code, and the date.

2. Determine from the plans, specifications, owner's description, photographs, or any other means possible the class of construction. The models in this data set use economy, average, custom, and luxury as classes. Fill in the appropriate box.

3. Fill in the appropriate box for the residence type, configuration, occupancy, and exterior wall. If you require clarification, the pages preceding this worksheet describe each of these.

4. Next, the living area of the residence must be established. The heated or air conditioned space of the residence, not including the basement, should be measured. It is easiest to break the structure up into separate components as shown in the example: the main house (A), a one-and-one-half story wing (B), and a one story wing (C). The breezeway (D), garage (E), and open covered porch (F) will be treated differently. Data entry blocks for the living area are included on the worksheet for your use. Keep each level of each component separate, and fill out the blocks as shown.

5. By using the information on the worksheet, find the model, wing, or ell in the following square foot cost pages that best matches the class, type, exterior finish, and size of the residence being estimated.

Use the Modifications, Adjustments, and Alternatives to determine the adjusted cost per square foot of living area for each component.

6. For each component, multiply the cost per square foot by the living area square footage. If the residence is a townhouse/rowhouse, a multiplier should be applied based upon the configuration.

7. The second page of the residential cost estimate worksheet has space for the additional components of a house. The cost for additional bathrooms, finished attic space, breezeways, porches, fireplaces, appliance or cabinet upgrades, and garages should be added on this page. The information for each of these components is found with the model being used or in the Modifications, Adjustments, and Alternatives.

8. Add the total from page one of the estimate worksheet and the items listed on page two. The sum is the adjusted total building cost.

9. Depending on the use of the final estimated cost, one of the remaining two boxes should be filled out. Any additional items or exclusions should be added or subtracted at this time. The data contained in this data set is a national average. Construction costs are different throughout the country. To allow for this difference, a location factor based upon the first three digits of the residence's zip code must be applied. The location factor is a multiplier that increases or decreases the adjusted total building cost. Find the appropriate location factor and calculate the local cost. If depreciation is a concern, a dollar figure should be subtracted at this point.

10. No residence will match a model exactly. Many differences will be found. At this level of estimating, a variation of plus or minus 10% should be expected.

Adjustments Instructions

No residence matches a model exactly in shape, material, or specifications. The common differences are:

1. Two or more exterior wall systems:
   - Partial basement
   - Partly finished basement
2. Specifications or features that are between two classes
3. Crawl space instead of a basement

Examples

Below are quick examples. See pages 17-19 for complete examples of cost adjustments for these differences:

1. Residence "A" is an average one-story structure with 1,600 S.F. of living area and no basement. Three walls are wood siding on wood frame, and the fourth wall is brick veneer on wood frame. The brick veneer wall is 35% of the exterior wall area.

   Use page 38 to calculate the Base Cost per S.F. of Living Area. Wood Siding for 1,600 S.F. = $115.95 per S.F. Brick Veneer for 1,600 S.F. = $120.90 per S.F.

   .65 ($115.95) + .35 ($120.90) = $117.69 per S.F. of Living Area.

2a. Residence "B" is the same as Residence "A"; However, it has an unfinished basement under 50% of the building. To adjust the $117.69 per S.F. of living area for this partial basement, use page 38.

   $117.69 + .5 ($11.55) = $123.47 per S.F. of Living Area.

2b. Residence "C" is the same as Residence "A"; However, it has a full basement under the entire building. 640 S.F. or 40% of the basement area is finished.

   Using Page 38:

   $117.69 + .40 ($33.80) + .60 ($11.55) = $138.14 per S.F. of Living Area.

3. When specifications or features of a building are between classes, estimate the percent deviation, and use two tables to calculate the cost per S.F.

   A two-story residence with wood siding and 1,800 S.F. of living area has features 30% better than Average, but 70% less than Custom.

   From pages 42 and 64:

Custom 1,800 S.F. Base Cost	=	**$151.30 per S.F.**
Average 1,800 S.F. Base Cost	=	**$117.25 per S.F.**
DIFFERENCE	=	**$34.05 per S.F.**
Cost is $117.25 + .30 ($34.05)	=	**$127.46 per S.F. of Living Area.**

4. To add the cost of a crawl space, use the cost of an unfinished basement as a maximum. For specific costs of components to be added or deducted, such as vapor barrier, underdrain, and floor, see the "Assemblies" section, pages 97 to 281.

Model Residence Example

First Floor Plan

Second Floor Plan

A = Main House
B = 1-1/2 Story Wing
C = 1 Story Wing
D = Breezeway
E = Garage
F = Open Covered Porch

RESIDENTIAL COST ESTIMATE

OWNERS NAME:	Albert Westenberg	APPRAISER:	Nicole Wojtowicz
RESIDENCE ADDRESS:	300 Sygiel Road	PROJECT:	# 55
CITY, STATE, ZIP CODE:	Three Rivers, MA 01080	DATE:	Jan. 1, 2017

CLASS OF CONSTRUCTION	RESIDENCE TYPE	CONFIGURATION	EXTERIOR WALL SYSTEM
☐ ECONOMY	☐ 1 STORY	☒ DETACHED	☒ WOOD SIDING - WOOD FRAME
☒ AVERAGE	☐ 1½ STORY	☐ TOWN/ROW HOUSE	☐ BRICK VENEER - WOOD FRAME
☐ CUSTOM	☒ 2 STORY	☐ SEMI-DETACHED	☐ STUCCO ON WOOD FRAME
☐ LUXURY	☐ 2 1/2 STORY		☐ PAINTED CONCRETE BLOCK
	☐ 3 STORY	OCCUPANCY	☐ SOLID MASONRY (AVERAGE & CUSTOM)
	☐ BI-LEVEL	☒ ONE FAMILY	☐ STONE VENEER - WOOD FRAME
	☐ TRI-LEVEL	☐ TWO FAMILY	☐ SOLID BRICK (LUXURY)
		☐ THREE FAMILY	☐ SOLID STONE (LUXURY)
		☐ OTHER	

* LIVING AREA (Main Building)			* LIVING AREA (Wing or Ell)	(B)		* LIVING AREA (Wing or Ell)	(C)	
First Level	1288	S.F.	First Level	360	S.F.	First Level	192	S.F.
Second level	1288	S.F.	Second level	310	S.F.	Second level		S.F.
Third Level		S.F.	Third Level		S.F.	Third Level		S.F.
Total	2576	S.F.	Total	670	S.F.	Total	192	S.F.

* Basement Area is not part of living area.

MAIN BUILDING			COSTS PER S.F. LIVING AREA	
Cost per Square Foot of Living Area, from Page	42		$	112.15
Basement Addition: _____ % Finished,	100	% Unfinished	+	7.15
Roof Cover Adjustment: **Cedar Shake**	Type, Page 42	(Add or Deduct)	( )	1.65
Central Air Conditioning: ☐ Separate Ducts	☒ Heating Ducts, Page	42	+	2.96
Heating System Adjustment: _____	Type, Page	(Add or Deduct)	( )	
Main Building: Adjusted Cost per S.F. of Living Area			$ #	123.91

MAIN BUILDING TOTAL COST	$ 123.91 /S.F. x	2,576 S.F. x	_____	= $ 319,192
	Cost per S.F. Living Area	Living Area	Town/Row House Multiplier (Use 1 for Detached)	TOTAL COST

WING OR ELL (B)	1 - 1/2	STORY	COSTS PER S.F. LIVING AREA	
Cost per Square Foot of Living Area, from Page	56		$	100.60
Basement Addition: 100 % Finished,		% Unfinished	+	21.00
Roof Cover Adjustment: _____	Type, Page _____	(Add or Deduct)	( )	___
Central Air Conditioning: ☐ Separate Ducts	☒ Heating Ducts, Page	42	+	2.96
Heating System Adjustment: _____	Type, Page	(Add or Deduct)	( )	
Wing or Ell (B): Adjusted Cost per S.F. of Living Area			$ #	124.56

WING OR ELL (B) TOTAL COST	$ 124.56 /S.F. x	670 S.F.		= $ 83,455
	Cost per S.F. Living Area	Living Area		TOTAL COST

WING OR ELL (C)	1	STORY	COSTS PER S.F. LIVING AREA	
Cost per Square Foot of Living Area, from Page	# 56	(WOOD SIDING)	$ #	147.90
Basement Addition: _____ % Finished,		% Unfinished	+	___
Roof Cover Adjustment: -	Type, Page #	(Add or Deduct)	( )	___
Central Air Conditioning: ☐ Separate Ducts	☐ Heating Ducts, Page	_____	+	___
Heating System Adjustment: _____	Type, Page _____	(Add or Deduct)	( )	
Wing or Ell (C) Adjusted Cost per S.F. of Living Area			$ #	147.9

WING OR ELL (C) TOTAL COST	$ 147.90 /S.F. x	192 S.F.		= $ 28,397
	Cost per S.F. Living Area	Living Area		TOTAL COST

		TOTAL THIS PAGE	431,044

RESIDENTIAL COST ESTIMATE

				QUANTITY	UNIT COST		
Total Page 1						$	431,044
Additional Bathrooms:	2	Full, 1 Half	2 @ 7405 1 @ 4331			+	19,141
Finished Attic:	N/A	Ft. x	Ft.		S.F.		
Breezeway: ☑ Open ☐ closed		12 Ft. x 12	Ft.	144	S.F.	40.07 +	5,770
Covered Porch: ☑ Open ☐ Enclosed		18 Ft. x 12	Ft.	216	S.F.	37.81 +	8,167
Fireplace: ☑ Interior Chimney ☐ Exterior Chimney						+	12,746
☑ No. of Flues (2) ☑ Additional Fireplaces		1 - 2nd Story					
Appliances:						+	—
Kitchen Cabinets Adjustments:			(±)				—
☑ Garage ☐ Carport: 2 Car(s) Description Wood, Attached			(±)				25,350
Miscellaneous:						+	

	ADJUSTED TOTAL BUILDING COST	$ 502,218

REPLACEMENT COST

ADJUSTED TOTAL BUILDING COST	$	502,218
Site Improvements		
(A) Paving & Sidewalks	$	
(B) Landscaping	$	
(C) Fences	$	
(D) Swimming Pools	$	
(E) Miscellaneous	$	
TOTAL	$	502,218
Location Factor	x	1.060
Location Replacement Cost	$	532,351
Depreciation	-$	52,592
LOCAL DEPRECIATED COST	$	479,759

INSURANCE COST

ADJUSTED TOTAL BUILDING COST	$	
Insurance Exclusions		
(A) Footings, sitework, Underground Piping	-$	
(B) Architects Fees	-$	
Total Building Cost Less Exclusion	$	
Location Factor	x	
LOCAL INSURABLE REPLACEMENT COST	$	

SKETCH AND ADDITIONAL CALCULATIONS

1 Story

© Home Planners, Inc.

1-1/2 Story

2 Story

Bi-Level

Tri-Level

©Design Basics, Inc.

For customer support on your Residential Costs with RSMeans Data, call 800.448.8182.

23

- **Mass produced from stock plans**
- **Single family — 1 full bath, 1 kitchen**
- **No basement**
- **Asphalt shingles on roof**
- **Hot air heat**
- **Gypsum wallboard interior finishes**
- **Materials and workmanship are sufficient to meet codes**

Note: The illustration shown may contain some optional components (for example: garages and/or fireplaces) whose costs are shown in the modifications, adjustments, & alternatives below or at the end of the square foot section.

©Home Planners, Inc.

Base cost per square foot of living area

Exterior Wall	Living Area										
	600	800	1000	1200	1400	1600	1800	2000	2400	2800	3200
Wood Siding - Wood Frame	146.35	132.00	121.10	112.50	104.95	100.20	97.75	94.50	88.05	83.45	80.25
Brick Veneer - Wood Frame	153.60	138.45	126.90	117.75	109.75	104.70	102.10	98.55	91.80	86.80	83.40
Stucco on Wood Frame	138.45	124.95	114.70	106.75	99.70	95.25	93.05	90.05	84.00	79.65	76.75
Painted Concrete Block	144.30	130.15	119.40	111.00	103.55	98.95	96.50	93.30	87.00	82.45	79.30
Finished Basement, Add	33.50	31.60	30.15	28.90	27.90	27.25	26.90	26.30	25.60	25.00	24.50
Unfinished Basement, Add	14.85	13.25	12.15	11.15	10.35	9.80	9.50	9.05	8.45	8.00	7.60

Modifications

Add to the total cost

Upgrade Kitchen Cabinets	$ + 1313
Solid Surface Countertops	+ 944
Full Bath - including plumbing, wall and floor finishes	+ 6443
Half Bath - including plumbing, wall and floor finishes	+ 3885
One Car Attached Garage	+ 13,851
One Car Detached Garage	+ 17,898
Fireplace & Chimney	+ 6561

Adjustments

For multi family - add to total cost

Additional Kitchen	$ + 5430
Additional Bath	+ 6443
Additional Entry & Exit	+ 1716
Separate Heating	+ 1421
Separate Electric	+ 1169

For Townhouse/Rowhouse - Multiply cost per square foot by

Inner Unit	.95
End Unit	.97

Alternatives

Add to or deduct from the cost per square foot of living area

Composition Roll Roofing	– 1.15
Cedar Shake Roof	+ 3.95
Upgrade Walls and Ceilings to Skim Coat Plaster	+ .76
Upgrade Ceilings to Textured Finish	+ .60
Air Conditioning, in Heating Ductwork	+ 4.73
In Separate Ductwork	+ 6.92
Heating Systems, Hot Water	+ 1.57
Heat Pump	+ 1.33
Electric Heat	– 1.47
Not Heated	– 4.21

Additional upgrades or components

Kitchen Cabinets & Countertops	Page 93
Bathroom Vanities	94
Fireplaces & Chimneys	94
Windows, Skylights & Dormers	94
Appliances	95
Breezeways & Porches	95
Finished Attic	95
Garages	96
Site Improvements	96
Wings & Ells	34

Important: See the Reference Section for Location Factors (to adjust for your city) and Estimating Forms.

		Cost Per Square Foot Of Living Area			% of Total
		Mat.	Inst.	Total	(rounded)
1 Site Work	Site preparation for slab; 4' deep trench excavation for foundation wall.		2.19	2.19	2.1%
2 Foundation	Continuous reinforced concrete footing, 10" deep x 20" wide; damproofed and insulated 8" thick reinforced concrete block foundation wall, 4' deep; trowel finished 4" thick concrete slab on 4" crushed stone base and polyethylene vapor barrier.	6.48	8.50	14.98	14.0%
3 Framing	Exterior walls - 2" x 4" wood studs, 16" O.C.; 1/2" sheathing; wood truss roof frame, 24" O.C. with 1/2" plywood sheating; 2" x 4" interior partitions.	5.49	7.76	13.25	12.4%
4 Exterior Walls	Metal lath reinforced stucco exterior on insulated wood frame walls; R38 attic insulation; sliding wood windows; flush solid core doors, frame and hardware, painted finish; aluminum storm and screen doors.	8.07	7.80	15.87	14.9%
5 Roofing	25 year asphalt roof shingles; #15 felt building paper; aluminum gutters, downspouts, drip edge and flashings.	2.27	2.74	5.01	4.7%
6 Interiors	Walls and ceilings, 1/2" taped and finished gypsum wallboard, primed and painted with 2 coats of finish paint; hollow core wood interior doors, frames and hardware, painted finish; lightweight carpeting with pad, 80%; sheet vinyl flooring, 20%.	11.79	13.29	25.08	23.5%
7 Specialties	Economy grade kitchen cabinets and countertops; stainless steel kitchen sink; 30 gallon electric water heater.	3.58	1.13	4.71	4.4%
8 Mechanical	Three fixture bathroom: bathtub, water closet and wall hung lavatory; gas fired hot air heating system.	4.54	3.91	8.45	7.9%
9 Electrical	100 amp electric service; wiring, duplex & GFI receptacles, wall switches, door bell, appliance circuits and communications cabling; economy grade lighting fixtures.	1.20	2.09	3.29	3.1%
10 Overhead	Contractor's overhead and profit.	6.53	7.39	13.92	13.0%
	Total	49.95	56.80	**106.75**	

For customer support on your Residential Costs with RSMeans Data, call 800.448.8182.

25

- Mass produced from stock plans
- Single family — 1 full bath, 1 kitchen
- No basement
- Asphalt shingles on roof
- Hot air heat
- Gypsum wallboard interior finishes
- Materials and workmanship are sufficient to meet codes

Note: The illustration shown may contain some optional components (for example: garages and/or fireplaces) whose costs are shown in the modifications, adjustments, & alternatives below or at the end of the square foot section.

Base cost per square foot of living area

Exterior Wall	Living Area										
	600	800	1000	1200	1400	1600	1800	2000	2400	2800	3200
Wood Siding - Wood Frame	171.60	142.45	127.90	120.80	115.80	108.00	104.25	100.45	92.40	89.30	86.00
Brick Veneer - Wood Frame	181.95	150.00	134.80	127.30	122.00	113.60	109.60	105.50	96.85	93.55	89.85
Stucco on Wood Frame	160.30	134.25	120.25	113.65	109.05	101.85	98.45	94.90	87.45	84.70	81.70
Painted Concrete Block	168.40	140.20	125.70	118.75	113.90	106.30	102.60	98.85	91.05	88.00	84.75
Finished Basement, Add	25.75	21.85	20.90	20.20	19.70	18.85	18.40	18.05	17.25	16.90	16.50
Unfinished Basement, Add	13.10	10.00	9.20	8.60	8.20	7.60	7.25	6.95	6.30	6.00	5.70

Modifications

Add to the total cost

Upgrade Kitchen Cabinets	$ + 1313
Solid Surface Countertops	+ 944
Full Bath - including plumbing, wall and floor finishes	+ 6443
Half Bath - including plumbing, wall and floor finishes	+ 3885
One Car Attached Garage	+ 13,851
One Car Detached Garage	+ 17,898
Fireplace & Chimney	+ 6561

Adjustments

For multi family - add to total cost

Additional Kitchen	$ + 5430
Additional Bath	+ 6443
Additional Entry & Exit	+ 1716
Separate Heating	+ 1421
Separate Electric	+ 1169

For Townhouse/Rowhouse -
Multiply cost per square foot by

Inner Unit	.95
End Unit	.97

Alternatives

Add to or deduct from the cost per square foot of living area

Composition Roll Roofing	− .80
Cedar Shake Roof	+ 2.85
Upgrade Walls and Ceilings to Skim Coat Plaster	+ .76
Upgrade Ceilings to Textured Finish	+ .60
Air Conditioning, in Heating Ductwork	+ 3.52
In Separate Ductwork	+ 6.07
Heating Systems, Hot Water	+ 1.49
Heat Pump	+ 1.46
Electric Heat	− 1.17
Not Heated	− 3.87

Additional upgrades or components

Kitchen Cabinets & Countertops	Page 93
Bathroom Vanities	94
Fireplaces & Chimneys	94
Windows, Skylights & Dormers	94
Appliances	95
Breezeways & Porches	95
Finished Attic	95
Garages	96
Site Improvements	96
Wings & Ells	34

Important: See the Reference Section for Location Factors (to adjust for your city) and Estimating Forms.

		Cost Per Square Foot Of Living Area			% of Total
		Mat.	Inst.	Total	(rounded)
1 Site Work	Site preparation for slab; 4' deep trench excavation for foundation wall.		1.64	1.64	1.5%
2 Foundation	Continuous reinforced concrete footing, 10" deep x 20" wide; damproofed and insulated 8" thick reinforced concrete block foundation wall, 4' deep; trowel finished 4" thick concrete slab on 4" crushed stone base and polyethylene vapor barrier.	4.35	5.77	10.12	9.4%
3 Framing	Exterior walls - 2" x 4" wood studs, 16" O.C.; 1/2" sheathing; gable end roof framing, steep pitch 2" x 8" rafters, 16" O.C. with 1/2" plywood sheathing; 2" x 8" floor joists, 16" O.C. with bridging and 5/8" subflooring; 2" x 4" interior partitions.	6.31	10.20	16.51	15.3%
4 Exterior Walls	Beveled wood siding and housewrap on insulated wood frame walls; R38 attic insulation; sliding wood windows; flush solid core doors, frame and hardware, painted finish; aluminum storm and screen doors.	14.52	6.01	20.53	19.0%
5 Roofing	25 year asphalt roof shingles; #15 felt building paper; aluminum gutters, downspouts, drip edge and flashings.	1.65	1.99	3.64	3.4%
6 Interiors	Walls and ceilings, 1/2" taped and finished gypsum wallboard, primed and painted with 2 coats of finish paint; hollow core wood interior doors, frames and hardware, painted finish; lightweight carpeting with pad, 80%; sheet vinyl flooring, 20%; hardwood tread stairway.	13.57	14.18	27.75	25.7%
7 Specialties	Economy grade kitchen cabinets and countertops; stainless steel kitchen sink; 30 gallon electric water heater.	2.68	.84	3.52	3.3%
8 Mechanical	Three fixture bathroom: bathtub, water closet and wall hung lavatory; gas fired hot air heating system.	3.66	3.51	7.17	6.6%
9 Electrical	100 amp electric service; wiring, duplex & GFI receptacles, wall switches, door bell, appliance circuits and communications cabling; economy grade lighting fixtures.	1.13	1.92	3.05	2.8%
10 Overhead	Contractor's overhead and profit.	7.18	6.89	14.07	13.0%
Total		55.05	52.95	**108.00**	

- **Mass produced from stock plans**
- **Single family — 1 full bath, 1 kitchen**
- **No basement**
- **Asphalt shingles on roof**
- **Hot air heat**
- **Gypsum wallboard interior finishes**
- **Materials and workmanship are sufficient to meet codes**

Note: The illustration shown may contain some optional components (for example: garages and/or fireplaces) whose costs are shown in the modifications, adjustments, & alternatives below or at the end of the square foot section.

Base cost per square foot of living area

Exterior Wall	Living Area										
	1000	1200	1400	1600	1800	2000	2200	2600	3000	3400	3800
Wood Siding - Wood Frame	130.55	118.15	112.30	108.20	104.05	99.50	96.45	90.75	85.15	82.60	80.40
Brick Veneer - Wood Frame	138.00	125.10	118.75	114.35	109.80	105.05	101.75	95.55	89.60	86.85	84.45
Stucco on Wood Frame	122.40	110.60	105.25	101.45	97.70	93.35	90.65	85.50	80.30	78.00	76.00
Painted Concrete Block	128.65	116.40	110.70	106.60	102.65	98.05	95.15	89.55	84.00	81.60	79.40
Finished Basement, Add	17.50	16.80	16.20	15.80	15.40	15.15	14.80	14.25	13.85	13.55	13.30
Unfinished Basement, Add	8.00	7.40	6.95	6.65	6.30	6.05	5.85	5.40	5.05	4.85	4.60

Modifications

Add to the total cost

Upgrade Kitchen Cabinets	$ + 1313
Solid Surface Countertops	+ 944
Full Bath - including plumbing, wall and floor finishes	+ 6443
Half Bath - including plumbing, wall and floor finishes	+ 3885
One Car Attached Garage	+ 13,851
One Car Detached Garage	+ 17,898
Fireplace & Chimney	+ 7250

Adjustments

For multi family - add to total cost

Additional Kitchen	$ + 5430
Additional Bath	+ 6443
Additional Entry & Exit	+ 1716
Separate Heating	+ 1421
Separate Electric	+ 1169

For Townhouse/Rowhouse - Multiply cost per square foot by

Inner Unit	.93
End Unit	.96

Alternatives

Add to or deduct from the cost per square foot of living area

Composition Roll Roofing	– .55
Cedar Shake Roof	+ 1.95
Upgrade Walls and Ceilings to Skim Coat Plaster	+ .77
Upgrade Ceilings to Textured Finish	+ .60
Air Conditioning, in Heating Ductwork	+ 2.87
In Separate Ductwork	+ 5.57
Heating Systems, Hot Water	+ 1.45
Heat Pump	+ 1.55
Electric Heat	– 1.02
Not Heated	– 3.66

Additional upgrades or components

Kitchen Cabinets & Countertops	Page 93
Bathroom Vanities	94
Fireplaces & Chimneys	94
Windows, Skylights & Dormers	94
Appliances	95
Breezeways & Porches	95
Finished Attic	95
Garages	96
Site Improvements	96
Wings & Ells	34

Important: See the Reference Section for Location Factors (to adjust for your city) and Estimating Forms.

		Cost Per Square Foot Of Living Area			% of Total
		Mat.	Inst.	Total	(rounded)
1 Site Work	Site preparation for slab; 4' deep trench excavation for foundation wall.		1.31	1.31	1.3%
2 Foundation	Continuous reinforced concrete footing, 10" deep x 20" wide; damproofed and insulated 8" thick reinforced concrete block foundation wall, 4' deep; trowel finished 4" thick concrete slab on 4" crushed stone base and polyethylene vapor barrier.	3.48	4.62	8.10	8.1%
3 Framing	Exterior walls - 2" x 4" wood studs, 16" O.C.; 1/2" sheathing; wood truss roof frame, 24" O.C. with 1/2" plywood sheating; 2" x 8" floor joists, 16" O.C. with bridging and 5/8" subflooring; 2" x 4" interior partitions.	5.82	9.00	14.82	14.9%
4 Exterior Walls	Beveled wood siding and housewrap on insulated wood frame walls; R38 attic insulation; sliding wood windows; flush solid core doors, frame and hardware, painted finish; aluminum storm and screen doors.	14.36	5.94	20.30	20.4%
5 Roofing	25 year asphalt roof shingles; #15 felt building paper; aluminum gutters, downspouts, drip edge and flashings.	1.14	1.37	2.51	2.5%
6 Interiors	Walls and ceilings, 1/2" taped and finished gypsum wallboard, primed and painted with 2 coats of finish paint; hollow core wood interior doors, frames and hardware, painted finish; lightweight carpeting with pad, 80%; sheet vinyl flooring, 20%; hardwood tread stairway.	13.24	14.10	27.34	27.5%
7 Specialties	Economy grade kitchen cabinets and countertops; stainless steel kitchen sink; 30 gallon electric water heater.	2.15	.68	2.83	2.8%
8 Mechanical	Three fixture bathroom: bathtub, water closet and wall hung lavatory; gas fired hot air heating system.	3.11	3.27	6.38	6.4%
9 Electrical	100 amp electric service; wiring, duplex & GFI receptacles, wall switches, door bell, appliance circuits and communications cabling; economy grade lighting fixtures.	1.08	1.82	2.90	2.9%
10 Overhead	Contractor's overhead and profit.	6.67	6.34	13.01	13.1%
Total		51.05	48.45	**99.50**	

- **Mass produced from stock plans**
- **Single family — 1 full bath, 1 kitchen**
- **No basement**
- **Asphalt shingles on roof**
- **Hot air heat**
- **Gypsum wallboard interior finishes**
- **Materials and workmanship are sufficient to meet codes**

Note: The illustration shown may contain some optional components (for example: garages and/or fireplaces) whose costs are shown in the modifications, adjustments, & alternatives below or at the end of the square foot section.

Base cost per square foot of living area

Exterior Wall	Living Area										
	1000	1200	1400	1600	1800	2000	2200	2600	3000	3400	3800
Wood Siding - Wood Frame	121.05	109.45	104.20	100.35	96.70	92.40	89.75	84.65	79.50	77.25	75.35
Brick Veneer - Wood Frame	126.75	114.70	109.05	105.05	101.10	96.60	93.80	88.30	82.90	80.50	78.35
Stucco on Wood Frame	114.85	103.70	98.75	95.25	91.90	87.75	85.30	80.65	75.85	73.75	71.95
Painted Concrete Block	119.65	108.05	102.85	99.15	95.55	91.25	88.70	83.70	78.65	76.45	74.55
Finished Basement, Add	17.50	16.80	16.20	15.80	15.40	15.15	14.80	14.25	13.85	13.55	13.30
Unfinished Basement, Add	8.00	7.40	6.95	6.65	6.30	6.05	5.85	5.40	5.05	4.85	4.60

Modifications

Add to the total cost

Upgrade Kitchen Cabinets	$ + 1313
Solid Surface Countertops	+ 944
Full Bath - including plumbing, wall and floor finishes	+ 6443
Half Bath - including plumbing, wall and floor finishes	+ 3885
One Car Attached Garage	+ 13,851
One Car Detached Garage	+ 17,898
Fireplace & Chimney	+ 6561

Adjustments

For multi family - add to total cost

Additional Kitchen	$ + 5430
Additional Bath	+ 6443
Additional Entry & Exit	+ 1716
Separate Heating	+ 1421
Separate Electric	+ 1169

For Townhouse/Rowhouse -
Multiply cost per square foot by

Inner Unit	.94
End Unit	.97

Alternatives

Add to or deduct from the cost per square foot of living area

Composition Roll Roofing	– .55
Cedar Shake Roof	+ 1.95
Upgrade Walls and Ceilings to Skim Coat Plaster	+ .73
Upgrade Ceilings to Textured Finish	+ .60
Air Conditioning, in Heating Ductwork	+ 2.87
In Separate Ductwork	+ 5.57
Heating Systems, Hot Water	+ 1.45
Heat Pump	+ 1.55
Electric Heat	– 1.02
Not Heated	– 3.66

Additional upgrades or components

Important: See the Reference Section for Location Factors (to adjust for your city) and Estimating Forms.

		Cost Per Square Foot Of Living Area			% of Total
		Mat.	Inst.	Total	(rounded)
1 Site Work	Site preparation for slab; 4' deep trench excavation for foundation wall.		1.31	1.31	1.4%
2 Foundation	Continuous reinforced concrete footing, 10" deep x 20" wide; damproofed and insulated 8" thick reinforced concrete block foundation wall, 4' deep; trowel finished 4" thick concrete slab on 4" crushed stone base and polyethylene vapor barrier.	3.48	4.62	8.10	8.8%
3 Framing	Exterior walls - 2" x 4" wood studs, 16" O.C.; 1/2" sheathing; wood truss roof frame, 24" O.C. with 1/2" plywood sheating; 2" x 8" floor joists, 16" O.C. with bridging and 5/8" subflooring; 2" x 4" interior partitions.	5.41	8.34	13.75	14.9%
4 Exterior Walls	Beveled wood siding and housewrap on insulated wood frame walls; R38 attic insulation; sliding wood windows; flush solid core doors, frame and hardware, painted finish; aluminum storm and screen doors.	11.28	4.68	15.96	17.3%
5 Roofing	25 year asphalt roof shingles; #15 felt building paper; aluminum gutters, downspouts, drip edge and flashings.	1.14	1.37	2.51	2.7%
6 Interiors	Walls and ceilings, 1/2" taped and finished gypsum wallboard, primed and painted with 2 coats of finish paint; hollow core wood interior doors, frames and hardware, painted finish; lightweight carpeting with pad, 80%; sheet vinyl flooring, 20%; hardwood tread stairway.	12.94	13.65	26.59	28.8%
7 Specialties	Economy grade kitchen cabinets and countertops; stainless steel kitchen sink; 30 gallon electric water heater.	2.15	.68	2.83	3.1%
8 Mechanical	Three fixture bathroom: bathtub, water closet and wall hung lavatory; gas fired hot air heating system.	3.11	3.27	6.38	6.9%
9 Electrical	100 amp electric service; wiring, duplex & GFI receptacles, wall switches, door bell, appliance circuits and communications cabling; economy grade lighting fixtures.	1.08	1.82	2.90	3.1%
10 Overhead	Contractor's overhead and profit.	6.11	5.96	12.07	13.1%
Total		46.70	45.70	**92.40**	

- **Mass produced from stock plans**
- **Single family — 1 full bath, 1 kitchen**
- **No basement**
- **Asphalt shingles on roof**
- **Hot air heat**
- **Gypsum wallboard interior finishes**
- **Materials and workmanship are sufficient to meet codes**

Note: The illustration shown may contain some optional components (for example: garages and/or fireplaces) whose costs are shown in the modifications, adjustments, & alternatives below or at the end of the square foot section.

©Design Basics, Inc.

Base cost per square foot of living area

Exterior Wall	Living Area										
	1200	1500	1800	2000	2200	2400	2800	3200	3600	4000	4400
Wood Siding - Wood Frame	112.70	103.40	96.45	93.65	89.65	86.35	83.80	80.40	76.35	74.95	71.85
Brick Veneer - Wood Frame	117.95	108.15	100.75	97.80	93.50	90.05	87.35	83.60	79.40	77.85	74.60
Stucco on Wood Frame	106.95	98.15	91.75	89.15	85.35	82.35	79.95	76.75	73.05	71.70	68.85
Solid Masonry	111.30	102.10	95.25	92.55	88.55	85.40	82.80	79.45	75.55	74.15	71.10
Finished Basement, Add*	21.10	20.15	19.30	18.95	18.55	18.15	17.85	17.40	17.05	16.85	16.55
Unfinished Basement, Add*	8.85	8.10	7.45	7.15	6.90	6.55	6.25	5.95	5.65	5.55	5.30

*Basement under middle level only.

Modifications

Add to the total cost

Upgrade Kitchen Cabinets	$ + 1313
Solid Surface Countertops	+ 944
Full Bath - including plumbing, wall and floor finishes	+ 6443
Half Bath - including plumbing, wall and floor finishes	+ 3885
One Car Attached Garage	+ 13,851
One Car Detached Garage	+ 17,898
Fireplace & Chimney	+ 6561

Adjustments

For multi family - add to total cost

Additional Kitchen	$ + 5430
Additional Bath	+ 6443
Additional Entry & Exit	+ 1716
Separate Heating	+ 1421
Separate Electric	+ 1169

For Townhouse/Rowhouse - Multiply cost per square foot by

Inner Unit	.93
End Unit	.96

Alternatives

Add to or deduct from the cost per square foot of living area

Composition Roll Roofing	– .80
Cedar Shake Roof	+ 2.85
Upgrade Walls and Ceilings to Skim Coat Plaster	+ .67
Upgrade Ceilings to Textured Finish	+ .60
Air Conditioning, in Heating Ductwork	+ 2.45
In Separate Ductwork	+ 5.18
Heating Systems, Hot Water	+ 1.39
Heat Pump	+ 1.61
Electric Heat	– .88
Not Heated	– 3.55

Additional upgrades or components

Kitchen Cabinets & Countertops	Page 93
Bathroom Vanities	94
Fireplaces & Chimneys	94
Windows, Skylights & Dormers	94
Appliances	95
Breezeways & Porches	95
Finished Attic	95
Garages	96
Site Improvements	96
Wings & Ells	34

Important: See the Reference Section for Location Factors (to adjust for your city) and Estimating Forms.

Economy Tri-Level

Living Area - 2400 S.F.
Perimeter - 163 L.F.

		Cost Per Square Foot Of Living Area			% of Total
		Mat.	Inst.	Total	(rounded)
1 Site Work	Site preparation for slab; 4' deep trench excavation for foundation wall.		1.09	1.09	1.3%
2 Foundation	Continuous reinforced concrete footing, 10" deep x 20" wide; damproofed and insulated 8" thick reinforced concrete block foundation wall, 4' deep; trowel finished 4" thick concrete slab on 4" crushed stone base and polyethylene vapor barrier.	3.90	5.00	8.90	10.3%
3 Framing	Exterior walls - 2" x 4" wood studs, 16" O.C.; 1/2" sheathing; wood truss roof frame, 24" O.C. with 1/2" plywood sheating; 2" x 8" floor joists, 16" O.C. with bridging and 5/8" subflooring; 2" x 4" interior partitions.	5.04	7.48	12.52	14.5%
4 Exterior Walls	Beveled wood siding and housewrap on insulated wood frame walls; R38 attic insulation; sliding wood windows; flush solid core doors, frame and hardware, painted finish; aluminum storm and screen doors.	9.94	4.08	14.02	16.2%
5 Roofing	25 year asphalt roof shingles; #15 felt building paper; aluminum gutters, downspouts, drip edge and flashings.	1.51	1.83	3.34	3.9%
6 Interiors	Walls and ceilings, 1/2" taped and finished gypsum wallboard, primed and painted with 2 coats of finish paint; hollow core wood interior doors, frames and hardware, painted finish; lightweight carpeting with pad, 80%; sheet vinyl flooring, 20%; hardwood tread stairway.	11.90	12.33	24.23	28.1%
7 Specialties	Economy grade kitchen cabinets and countertops; stainless steel kitchen sink; 30 gallon electric water heater.	1.79	.56	2.35	2.7%
8 Mechanical	Three fixture bathroom: bathtub, water closet and wall hung lavatory; gas fired hot air heating system.	2.75	3.11	5.86	6.8%
9 Electrical	100 amp electric service; wiring, duplex & GFI receptacles, wall switches, door bell, appliance circuits and communications cabling; economy grade lighting fixtures.	1.05	1.75	2.80	3.2%
10 Overhead	Contractor's overhead and profit.	5.67	5.57	11.24	13.0%
Total		43.55	42.80	**86.35**	

1 Story   Base cost per square foot of living area

Exterior Wall	Living Area							
	50	100	200	300	400	500	600	700
Wood Siding - Wood Frame	192.85	146.85	126.95	104.80	98.30	94.40	91.80	92.30
Brick Veneer - Wood Frame	209.45	158.70	136.80	111.40	104.25	99.90	97.05	97.35
Stucco on Wood Frame	174.65	133.85	116.15	97.60	91.85	88.30	86.05	86.70
Painted Concrete Block	189.40	144.40	124.90	103.45	97.05	93.25	90.70	91.20
Finished Basement, Add	51.45	42.00	38.00	31.45	30.10	29.35	28.80	28.40
Unfinished Basement, Add	28.60	21.20	18.15	13.00	12.00	11.35	10.95	10.65

1-1/2 Story   Base cost per square foot of living area

Exterior Wall	Living Area							
	100	200	300	400	500	600	700	800
Wood Siding - Wood Frame	152.40	122.75	104.45	92.90	87.40	84.65	81.25	80.35
Brick Veneer - Wood Frame	167.20	134.60	114.35	100.60	94.50	91.30	87.60	86.60
Stucco on Wood Frame	136.15	109.75	93.70	84.40	79.60	77.25	74.30	73.45
Painted Concrete Block	149.25	120.30	102.45	91.30	85.95	83.25	79.95	79.05
Finished Basement, Add	34.40	30.40	27.80	24.90	24.10	23.60	23.10	23.05
Unfinished Basement, Add	17.60	14.50	12.45	10.20	9.60	9.20	8.80	8.70

2 Story   Base cost per square foot of living area

Exterior Wall	Living Area							
	100	200	400	600	800	1000	1200	1400
Wood Siding - Wood Frame	155.85	115.75	98.35	80.35	74.65	71.20	69.00	69.65
Brick Veneer - Wood Frame	172.50	127.60	108.25	86.90	80.55	76.75	74.20	74.75
Stucco on Wood Frame	137.70	102.80	87.55	73.10	68.15	65.15	63.20	64.10
Painted Concrete Block	152.40	113.35	96.30	78.95	73.40	70.05	67.85	68.60
Finished Basement, Add	25.75	21.00	19.05	15.75	15.10	14.75	14.40	14.25
Unfinished Basement, Add	14.35	10.65	9.05	6.50	6.00	5.70	5.45	5.35

Base costs do not include bathroom or kitchen facilities. Use Modifications/Adjustments/Alternatives on pages 93–96 where appropriate.

1 Story

1-1/2 Story

2 Story

2-1/2 Story

Bi-Level

Tri-Level

For customer support on your Residential Costs with RSMeans Data, call 800.448.8182.

37

- Simple design from standard plans
- Single family — 1 full bath, 1 kitchen
- No basement
- Asphalt shingles on roof
- Hot air heat
- Gypsum wallboard interior finishes
- Materials and workmanship are average

Note: The illustration shown may contain some optional components (for example: garages and/or fireplaces) whose costs are shown in the modifications, adjustments, & alternatives below or at the end of the square foot section.

©Home Planners, Inc.

Base cost per square foot of living area

Exterior Wall	Living Area										
	600	800	1000	1200	1400	1600	1800	2000	2400	2800	3200
Wood Siding - Wood Frame	171.25	153.55	140.50	130.25	121.60	115.95	112.90	109.10	101.75	96.40	92.80
Brick Veneer - Wood Frame	179.10	160.55	146.85	136.00	126.80	120.90	117.55	113.55	105.85	100.20	96.25
Stucco on Wood Frame	166.85	149.55	136.90	127.00	118.70	113.25	110.20	106.55	99.50	94.30	90.90
Solid Masonry	192.50	172.50	157.60	145.75	135.65	129.20	125.60	121.05	112.70	106.55	102.20
Finished Basement, Add	40.95	39.60	37.75	36.05	34.70	33.80	33.30	32.55	31.50	30.75	30.05
Unfinished Basement, Add	16.75	15.15	14.00	13.00	12.10	11.55	11.25	10.85	10.20	9.75	9.35

Modifications

Add to the total cost

Upgrade Kitchen Cabinets	$ + 5823
Solid Surface Countertops (Included)	
Full Bath - including plumbing, wall and floor finishes	+ 8054
Half Bath - including plumbing, wall and floor finishes	+ 4856
One Car Attached Garage	+ 14,940
One Car Detached Garage	+ 19,637
Fireplace & Chimney	+ 6881

Adjustments

For multi family - add to total cost

Additional Kitchen	$ + 10,056
Additional Bath	+ 8054
Additional Entry & Exit	+ 1716
Separate Heating	+ 1421
Separate Electric	+ 1879

For Townhouse/Rowhouse - Multiply cost per square foot by

Inner Unit	.92
End Unit	.96

Alternatives

Add to or deduct from the cost per square foot of living area

Cedar Shake Roof	+ 3.35
Clay Tile Roof	+ 6.90
Slate Roof	+ 7.65
Upgrade Walls to Skim Coat Plaster	+ .47
Upgrade Ceilings to Textured Finish	+ .60
Air Conditioning, in Heating Ductwork	+ 4.89
In Separate Ductwork	+ 7.18
Heating Systems, Hot Water	+ 1.60
Heat Pump	+ 1.38
Electric Heat	− .81
Not Heated	− 3.52

Additional upgrades or components

Kitchen Cabinets & Countertops	Page 93
Bathroom Vanities	94
Fireplaces & Chimneys	94
Windows, Skylights & Dormers	94
Appliances	95
Breezeways & Porches	95
Finished Attic	95
Garages	96
Site Improvements	96
Wings & Ells	56

Important: See the Reference Section for Location Factors (to adjust for your city) and Estimating Forms.

			Cost Per Square Foot Of Living Area			% of Total
			Mat.	Inst.	Total	(rounded)
1	**Site Work**	Site preparation for slab; 4' deep trench excavation for foundation wall.		1.69	1.69	1.5%
2	**Foundation**	Continuous reinforced concrete footing, 10" deep x 20" wide; damproofed and insulated 8" thick reinforced concrete block foundation wall, 4' deep; trowel finished 4" thick concrete slab on 4" crushed stone base and polyethylene vapor barrier.	6.02	7.73	13.75	11.9%
3	**Framing**	Exterior walls - 2" x 6" wood studs, 16" O.C.; 1/2" sheathing; gable end roof framing, 2" x 10" rafters, 16" O.C. with 1/2" plywood sheathing; 2" x 4" interior partitions.	6.80	9.75	16.55	14.3%
4	**Exterior Walls**	Beveled wood siding and housewrap on insulated wood frame walls; R38 attic insulation; double hung wood windows; flush solid core doors, frame and hardware, painted finish; aluminum storm and screen doors.	12.46	5.30	17.76	15.3%
5	**Roofing**	25 year asphalt roof shingles; #15 felt building paper; aluminum gutters, downspouts, drip edge and flashings.	2.33	2.82	5.15	4.4%
6	**Interiors**	Walls & ceilings, 1/2" taped & finished gypsum wallboard, primed & painted with 2 coats of finish paint; birch faced hollow core interior doors, frames & hardware, painted finish; medium weight carpeting with pad, 40%; sheet vinyl, 15%; oak hardwood, 40%; ceramic tile, 5%	12.73	13.38	26.11	22.5%
7	**Specialties**	Average grade kitchen cabinets and countertop; stainless steel kitchen sink; 40 gallon electric water heater.	4.83	1.51	6.34	5.5%
8	**Mechanical**	Three fixture bathroom: bathtub, water closet, vanity and sink; gas fired hot air heating system.	3.99	3.61	7.60	6.6%
9	**Electrical**	200 amp electric service; wiring, duplex & GFI receptacles, wall switches, door bell, appliance circuits, fans and communications cabling; average grade lighting fixtures.	1.63	2.54	4.17	3.6%
10	**Overhead**	Contractor's overhead and profit and plans.	8.61	8.22	16.83	14.5%
	Total		59.40	56.55	**115.95**	

- Simple design from standard plans
- Single family — 1 full bath, 1 kitchen
- No basement
- Asphalt shingles on roof
- Hot air heat
- Gypsum wallboard interior finishes
- Materials and workmanship are average

Note: The illustration shown may contain some optional components (for example: garages and/or fireplaces) whose costs are shown in the modifications, adjustments, & alternatives below or at the end of the square foot section.

©By Designer

Base cost per square foot of living area

Exterior Wall	Living Area										
	600	800	1000	1200	1400	1600	1800	2000	2400	2800	3200
Wood Siding - Wood Frame	195.05	161.80	144.65	136.15	130.15	121.35	116.95	112.55	103.45	99.85	96.00
Brick Veneer - Wood Frame	206.35	170.05	152.25	143.25	136.90	127.55	122.75	118.05	108.35	104.50	100.25
Stucco on Wood Frame	188.60	157.10	140.40	132.10	126.35	117.85	113.60	109.35	100.70	97.25	93.55
Solid Masonry	224.65	183.30	164.55	154.80	147.95	137.45	132.25	127.05	116.25	112.00	107.20
Finished Basement, Add	33.45	29.10	27.85	26.90	26.25	25.15	24.60	24.10	23.00	22.55	21.90
Unfinished Basement, Add	14.50	11.30	10.50	9.95	9.50	8.85	8.50	8.20	7.50	7.25	6.90

Modifications

Add to the total cost

Upgrade Kitchen Cabinets	$ + 5823
Solid Surface Countertops (Included)	
Full Bath - including plumbing, wall and floor finishes	+ 8054
Half Bath - including plumbing, wall and floor finishes	+ 4856
One Car Attached Garage	+ 14,940
One Car Detached Garage	+ 19,637
Fireplace & Chimney	+ 6881

Adjustments

For multi family - add to total cost

Additional Kitchen	$ + 10,056
Additional Bath	+ 8054
Additional Entry & Exit	+ 1716
Separate Heating	+ 1421
Separate Electric	+ 1879

For Townhouse/Rowhouse - Multiply cost per square foot by

Inner Unit	.92
End Unit	.96

Alternatives

Add to or deduct from the cost per square foot of living area

Cedar Shake Roof	+ 2.40
Clay Tile Roof	+ 5
Slate Roof	+ 5.50
Upgrade Walls to Skim Coat Plaster	+ .54
Upgrade Ceilings to Textured Finish	+ .60
Air Conditioning, in Heating Ductwork	+ 3.71
In Separate Ductwork	+ 6.28
Heating Systems, Hot Water	+ 1.52
Heat Pump	+ 1.53
Electric Heat	– .74
Not Heated	– 3.38

Additional upgrades or components

Kitchen Cabinets & Countertops	Page 93
Bathroom Vanities	94
Fireplaces & Chimneys	94
Windows, Skylights & Dormers	94
Appliances	95
Breezeways & Porches	95
Finished Attic	95
Garages	96
Site Improvements	96
Wings & Ells	56

Important: See the Reference Section for Location Factors (to adjust for your city) and Estimating Forms.

		Cost Per Square Foot Of Living Area			% of Total
		Mat.	Inst.	Total	(rounded)
1 Site Work	Site preparation for slab; 4' deep trench excavation for foundation wall.		1.50	1.50	1.3%
2 Foundation	Continuous reinforced concrete footing, 10" deep x 20" wide; damproofed and insulated 8" thick reinforced concrete block foundation wall, 4' deep; trowel finished 4" thick concrete slab on 4" crushed stone base and polyethylene vapor barrier.	4.31	5.68	9.99	8.5%
3 Framing	Exterior walls - 2" x 6" wood studs, 16" O.C.; 1/2" sheathing; gable end roof framing, steep pitch 2" x 10" rafters, 16" O.C. with 1/2" plywood sheathing; 2" x 10" floor joists, 16" O.C. with bridging and 5/8" subflooring; 2" x 4" interior partitions.	7.54	10.62	18.16	15.5%
4 Exterior Walls	Beveled wood siding and housewrap on insulated wood frame walls; R38 attic insulation; double hung wood windows; flush solid core doors, frame and hardware, painted finish; aluminum storm and screen doors.	13.57	5.80	19.37	16.6%
5 Roofing	25 year asphalt roof shingles; #15 felt building paper; aluminum gutters, downspouts, drip edge and flashings.	1.70	2.05	3.75	3.2%
6 Interiors	Walls & ceilings, 1/2" taped & finished gypsum wallboard, primed & painted with 2 coats of finish paint; birch faced hollow core interior doors, frames & hardware, painted finish; medium weight carpeting with pad, 40%; sheet vinyl, 15%; oak hardwood, 40%; ceramic tile, 5%; hardwood tread stairway.	15.18	15.20	30.38	26.0%
7 Specialties	Average grade kitchen cabinets and countertop; stainless steel kitchen sink; 40 gallon electric water heater.	4.29	1.35	5.64	4.8%
8 Mechanical	Three fixture bathroom: bathtub, water closet, vanity and sink; gas fired hot air heating system.	3.65	3.46	7.11	6.1%
9 Electrical	200 amp electric service; wiring, duplex & GFI receptacles, wall switches, door bell, appliance circuits, fans and communications cabling; average grade lighting fixtures.	1.59	2.45	4.04	3.5%
10 Overhead	Contractor's overhead and profit and plans.	8.82	8.19	17.01	14.5%
Total		60.65	56.30	**116.95**	

For customer support on your Residential Costs with RSMeans Data, call 800.448.8182.

41

- Simple design from standard plans
- Single family — 1 full bath, 1 kitchen
- No basement
- Asphalt shingles on roof
- Hot air heat
- Gypsum wallboard interior finishes
- Materials and workmanship are average

Note: The illustration shown may contain some optional components (for example: garages and/or fireplaces) whose costs are shown in the modifications, adjustments, & alternatives below or at the end of the square foot section.

Base cost per square foot of living area

Exterior Wall	Living Area										
	1000	1200	1400	1600	1800	2000	2200	2600	3000	3400	3800
Wood Siding - Wood Frame	148.30	133.95	127.05	122.20	117.25	112.15	108.75	102.20	96.00	93.00	90.50
Brick Veneer - Wood Frame	156.50	141.50	134.15	128.90	123.65	118.25	114.55	107.50	100.85	97.60	94.85
Stucco on Wood Frame	143.90	129.85	123.25	118.55	113.85	108.80	105.55	99.40	93.30	90.50	88.05
Solid Masonry	171.30	155.20	146.95	141.20	135.15	129.35	125.10	117.00	109.60	106.00	102.80
Finished Basement, Add	23.50	23.20	22.45	21.90	21.35	21.00	20.60	19.80	19.30	18.95	18.60
Unfinished Basement, Add	9.15	8.55	8.05	7.75	7.40	7.15	6.90	6.45	6.10	5.85	5.65

Modifications

Add to the total cost

Upgrade Kitchen Cabinets	$ + 5823
Solid Surface Countertops (Included)	
Full Bath - including plumbing, wall and floor finishes	+ 8054
Half Bath - including plumbing, wall and floor finishes	+ 4856
One Car Attached Garage	+ 14,940
One Car Detached Garage	+ 19,637
Fireplace & Chimney	+ 7604

Adjustments

For multi family - add to total cost

Additional Kitchen	$ + 10,056
Additional Bath	+ 8054
Additional Entry & Exit	+ 1716
Separate Heating	+ 1421
Separate Electric	+ 1879

For Townhouse/Rowhouse - Multiply cost per square foot by

Inner Unit	.90
End Unit	.95

Alternatives

Add to or deduct from the cost per square foot of living area

Cedar Shake Roof	+ 1.70
Clay Tile Roof	+ 3.45
Slate Roof	+ 3.85
Upgrade Walls to Skim Coat Plaster	+ .55
Upgrade Ceilings to Textured Finish	+ .60
Air Conditioning, in Heating Ductwork	+ 2.96
In Separate Ductwork	+ 5.70
Heating Systems, Hot Water	+ 1.49
Heat Pump	+ 1.61
Electric Heat	− .63
Not Heated	− 3.28

Additional upgrades or components

Kitchen Cabinets & Countertops	Page 93
Bathroom Vanities	94
Fireplaces & Chimneys	94
Windows, Skylights & Dormers	94
Appliances	95
Breezeways & Porches	95
Finished Attic	95
Garages	96
Site Improvements	96
Wings & Ells	56

Important: See the Reference Section for Location Factors (to adjust for your city) and Estimating Forms.

		Cost Per Square Foot Of Living Area			% of Total
		Mat.	Inst.	Total	(rounded)
1 Site Work	Site preparation for slab; 4' deep trench excavation for foundation wall.		1.35	1.35	1.2%
2 Foundation	Continuous reinforced concrete footing, 10" deep x 20" wide; damproofed and insulated 8" thick reinforced concrete block foundation wall, 4' deep; trowel finished 4" thick concrete slab on 4" crushed stone base and polyethylene vapor barrier.	3.58	4.75	8.33	7.4%
3 Framing	Exterior walls - 2" x 6" wood studs, 16" O.C.; 1/2" sheathing; gable end roof framing, 2" x 10" rafters, 16" O.C. with 1/2" plywood sheathing; 2" x 10" floor joists, 16" O.C. with bridging and 5/8" subflooring; 2" x 4" interior partitions.	7.14	10.06	17.20	15.3%
4 Exterior Walls	Beveled wood siding and housewrap on insulated wood frame walls; R38 attic insulation; double hung wood windows; flush solid core doors, frame and hardware, painted finish; aluminum storm and screen doors.	14.19	6.09	20.28	18.1%
5 Roofing	25 year asphalt roof shingles; #15 felt building paper; aluminum gutters, downspouts, drip edge and flashings.	1.17	1.41	2.58	2.3%
6 Interiors	Walls & ceilings, 1/2" taped & finished gypsum wallboard, primed & painted with 2 coats of finish paint; birch faced hollow core interior doors, frames & hardware, painted finish; medium weight carpeting with pad, 40%; sheet vinyl, 15%; oak hardwood, 40%; ceramic tile, 5%; hardwood tread stairway.	15.09	15.30	30.39	27.1%
7 Specialties	Average grade kitchen cabinets and countertop; stainless steel kitchen sink; 40 gallon electric water heater.	3.86	1.21	5.07	4.5%
8 Mechanical	Three fixture bathroom: bathtub, water closet, vanity and sink; gas fired hot air heating system.	3.38	3.35	6.73	6.0%
9 Electrical	200 amp electric service; wiring, duplex & GFI receptacles, wall switches, door bell, appliance circuits, fans and communications cabling; average grade lighting fixtures	1.56	2.37	3.93	3.5%
10 Overhead	Contractor's overhead and profit and plans.	8.48	7.81	16.29	14.5%
	Total	58.45	53.70	**112.15**	

- **Simple design from standard plans**
- **Single family — 1 full bath, 1 kitchen**
- **No basement**
- **Asphalt shingles on roof**
- **Hot air heat**
- **Gypsum wallboard interior finishes**
- **Materials and workmanship are average**

Note: The illustration shown may contain some optional components (for example: garages and/or fireplaces) whose costs are shown in the modifications, adjustments, & alternatives below or at the end of the square foot section.

Base cost per square foot of living area

Exterior Wall	Living Area										
	1200	1400	1600	1800	2000	2400	2800	3200	3600	4000	4400
Wood Siding - Wood Frame	147.80	138.40	126.20	123.70	118.95	111.55	105.75	99.95	96.95	91.60	89.85
Brick Veneer - Wood Frame	156.75	146.50	133.65	131.10	125.95	117.80	111.75	105.40	102.10	96.40	94.55
Stucco on Wood Frame	142.85	133.95	122.10	119.60	115.10	108.00	102.45	96.90	94.05	88.90	87.30
Solid Masonry	172.20	160.45	146.50	144.05	138.10	128.75	122.25	114.90	111.10	104.75	102.65
Finished Basement, Add	19.90	19.50	18.75	18.70	18.20	17.45	17.10	16.50	16.20	15.80	15.60
Unfinished Basement, Add	7.65	7.05	6.60	6.55	6.20	5.75	5.50	5.15	5.00	4.75	4.65

Modifications

Add to the total cost

Upgrade Kitchen Cabinets	$ + 5823
Solid Surface Countertops (Included)	
Full Bath - including plumbing, wall and floor finishes	+ 8054
Half Bath - including plumbing, wall and floor finishes	+ 4856
One Car Attached Garage	+ 14,940
One Car Detached Garage	+ 19,637
Fireplace & Chimney	+ 8340

Adjustments

For multi family - add to total cost

Additional Kitchen	$ + 10,056
Additional Bath	+ 8054
Additional Entry & Exit	+ 1716
Separate Heating	+ 1421
Separate Electric	+ 1879

For Townhouse/Rowhouse - Multiply cost per square foot by

Inner Unit	.90
End Unit	.95

Alternatives

Add to or deduct from the cost per square foot of living area

Cedar Shake Roof	+ 1.45
Clay Tile Roof	+ 3
Slate Roof	+ 3.30
Upgrade Walls to Skim Coat Plaster	+ .53
Upgrade Ceilings to Textured Finish	+ .60
Air Conditioning, in Heating Ductwork	+ 2.69
In Separate Ductwork	+ 5.51
Heating Systems, Hot Water	+ 1.35
Heat Pump	+ 1.65
Electric Heat	- 1.14
Not Heated	- 3.83

Additional upgrades or components

Kitchen Cabinets & Countertops	Page 93
Bathroom Vanities	94
Fireplaces & Chimneys	94
Windows, Skylights & Dormers	94
Appliances	95
Breezeways & Porches	95
Finished Attic	95
Garages	96
Site Improvements	96
Wings & Ells	56

Important: See the Reference Section for Location Factors (to adjust for your city) and Estimating Forms.

		Cost Per Square Foot Of Living Area			% of Total
		Mat.	Inst.	Total	(rounded)
1 Site Work	Site preparation for slab; 4' deep trench excavation for foundation wall.		.84	.84	0.8%
2 Foundation	Continuous reinforced concrete footing, 10" deep x 20" wide; damproofed and insulated 8" thick reinforced concrete block foundation wall, 4' deep; trowel finished 4" thick concrete slab on 4" crushed stone base and polyethylene vapor barrier.	2.56	3.36	5.92	5.9%
3 Framing	Exterior walls - 2" x 6" wood studs, 16" O.C.; 1/2" sheathing; gable end roof framing, steep pitch 2" x 10" rafters, 16" O.C. with 1/2" plywood sheathing; 2" x 10" floor joists, 16" O.C. with bridging and 5/8" subflooring; 2" x 4" interior partitions.	7.13	9.96	17.09	17.1%
4 Exterior Walls	Beveled wood siding and housewrap on insulated wood frame walls; R38 attic insulation; double hung wood windows; flush solid core doors, frame and hardware, painted finish; aluminum storm and screen doors.	12.15	5.16	17.31	17.3%
5 Roofing	25 year asphalt roof shingles; #15 felt building paper; aluminum gutters, downspouts, drip edge and flashings.	1.04	1.25	2.29	2.3%
6 Interiors	Walls & ceilings, 1/2" taped & finished gypsum wallboard, primed & painted with 2 coats of finish paint; birch faced hollow core interior doors, frames & hardware, painted finish; medium weight carpeting with pad, 40%; sheet vinyl, 15%; oak hardwood, 40%; ceramic tile, 5%; hardwood tread stairway.	14.92	14.81	29.73	29.7%
7 Specialties	Average grade kitchen cabinets and countertop; stainless steel kitchen sink; 40 gallon electric water heater.	2.42	.75	3.17	3.2%
8 Mechanical	Three fixture bathroom: bathtub, water closet, vanity and sink; gas fired hot air heating system.	2.49	2.99	5.48	5.5%
9 Electrical	200 amp electric service; wiring, duplex & GFI receptacles, wall switches, door bell, appliance circuits, fans and communications cabling; average grade lighting fixtures.	1.46	2.11	3.57	3.6%
10 Overhead	Contractor's overhead and profit and plans.	7.53	7.02	14.55	14.6%
Total		51.70	48.25	99.95	

For customer support on your Residential Costs with RSMeans Data, call 800.448.8182.

45

- **Simple design from standard plans**
- **Single family — 1 full bath, 1 kitchen**
- **No basement**
- **Asphalt shingles on roof**
- **Hot air heat**
- **Gypsum wallboard interior finishes**
- **Materials and workmanship are average**

Note: The illustration shown may contain some optional components (for example: garages and/or fireplaces) whose costs are shown in the modifications, adjustments, & alternatives below or at the end of the square foot section.

Base cost per square foot of living area

Exterior Wall	Living Area										
	1500	1800	2100	2500	3000	3500	4000	4500	5000	5500	6000
Wood Siding - Wood Frame	134.15	121.45	115.75	111.10	102.70	98.90	93.85	88.35	86.65	84.60	82.50
Brick Veneer - Wood Frame	142.20	128.90	122.65	117.65	108.70	104.60	99.05	93.10	91.30	89.00	86.70
Stucco on Wood Frame	129.85	117.45	112.00	107.50	99.45	95.85	91.10	85.75	84.10	82.15	80.20
Solid Masonry	157.15	142.70	135.60	130.05	119.85	115.20	108.70	102.00	99.85	97.30	94.45
Finished Basement, Add	17.10	16.90	16.35	16.05	15.45	15.15	14.65	14.30	14.10	13.95	13.70
Unfinished Basement, Add	6.20	5.80	5.50	5.25	4.85	4.65	4.40	4.20	4.10	3.95	3.85

Modifications

Add to the total cost

Upgrade Kitchen Cabinets	$ + 5823
Solid Surface Countertops (Included)	
Full Bath - including plumbing, wall and floor finishes	+ 8054
Half Bath - including plumbing, wall and floor finishes	+ 4856
One Car Attached Garage	+ 14,940
One Car Detached Garage	+ 19,637
Fireplace & Chimney	+ 8340

Adjustments

For multi family - add to total cost

Additional Kitchen	$ + 10,056
Additional Bath	+ 8054
Additional Entry & Exit	+ 1716
Separate Heating	+ 1421
Separate Electric	+ 1879

For Townhouse/Rowhouse - Multiply cost per square foot by

Inner Unit	.88
End Unit	.94

Alternatives

Add to or deduct from the cost per square foot of living area

Cedar Shake Roof	+ 1.10
Clay Tile Roof	+ 2.30
Slate Roof	+ 2.55
Upgrade Walls to Skim Coat Plaster	+ .55
Upgrade Ceilings to Textured Finish	+ .60
Air Conditioning, in Heating Ductwork	+ 2.69
In Separate Ductwork	+ 5.51
Heating Systems, Hot Water	+ 1.35
Heat Pump	+ 1.65
Electric Heat	− .88
Not Heated	− 3.57

Additional upgrades or components

Kitchen Cabinets & Countertops	Page 93
Bathroom Vanities	94
Fireplaces & Chimneys	94
Windows, Skylights & Dormers	94
Appliances	95
Breezeways & Porches	95
Finished Attic	95
Garages	96
Site Improvements	96
Wings & Ells	56

Important: See the Reference Section for Location Factors (to adjust for your city) and Estimating Forms.

			Cost Per Square Foot Of Living Area			% of Total
			Mat.	Inst.	Total	(rounded)
1	**Site Work**	Site preparation for slab; 4' deep trench excavation for foundation wall.		.90	.90	0.9%
2	**Foundation**	Continuous reinforced concrete footing, 10" deep x 20" wide; damproofed and insulated 8" thick reinforced concrete block foundation wall, 4' deep; trowel finished 4" thick concrete slab on 4" crushed stone base and polyethylene vapor barrier.	2.38	3.17	5.55	5.4%
3	**Framing**	Exterior walls - 2" x 6" wood studs, 16" O.C.; 1/2" sheathing; gable end roof framing, 2" x 10" rafters, 16" O.C. with 1/2" plywood sheathing; 2" x 10" floor joists, 16" O.C. with bridging and 5/8" subflooring; 2" x 4" interior partitions.	7.04	9.84	16.88	16.4%
4	**Exterior Walls**	Beveled wood siding and housewrap on insulated wood frame walls; R38 attic insulation; double hung wood windows; flush solid core doors, frame and hardware, painted finish; aluminum storm and screen doors.	13.49	5.77	19.26	18.8%
5	**Roofing**	25 year asphalt roof shingles; #15 felt building paper; aluminum gutters, downspouts, drip edge and flashings.	.78	.94	1.72	1.7%
6	**Interiors**	Walls & ceilings, 1/2" taped & finished gypsum wallboard, primed & painted with 2 coats of finish paint; birch faced hollow core interior doors, frames & hardware, painted finish; medium weight carpeting with pad, 40%; sheet vinyl, 15%; oak hardwood, 40%; ceramic tile, 5%; hardwood tread stairway.	15.46	15.39	30.85	30.0%
7	**Specialties**	Average grade kitchen cabinets and countertop; stainless steel kitchen sink; 40 gallon electric water heater.	2.58	.81	3.39	3.3%
8	**Mechanical**	Three fixture bathroom: bathtub, water closet, vanity and sink; gas fired hot air heating system.	2.58	3.03	5.61	5.5%
9	**Electrical**	200 amp electric service; wiring, duplex & GFI receptacles, wall switches, door bell, appliance circuits, fans and communications cabling; average grade lighting fixtures.	1.47	2.14	3.61	3.5%
10	**Overhead**	Contractor's overhead and profit and plans.	7.77	7.16	14.93	14.5%
	Total		53.55	49.15	**102.70**	

- **Simple design from standard plans**
- **Single family — 1 full bath, 1 kitchen**
- **No basement**
- **Asphalt shingles on roof**
- **Hot air heat**
- **Gypsum wallboard interior finishes**
- **Materials and workmanship are average**

Note: The illustration shown may contain some optional components (for example: garages and/or fireplaces) whose costs are shown in the modifications, adjustments, & alternatives below or at the end of the square foot section.

Base cost per square foot of living area

Exterior Wall	Living Area										
	1000	1200	1400	1600	1800	2000	2200	2600	3000	3400	3800
Wood Siding - Wood Frame	138.50	124.85	118.55	114.00	109.60	104.70	101.75	95.90	90.05	87.40	85.25
Brick Veneer - Wood Frame	144.70	130.55	123.90	119.15	114.45	109.40	106.15	99.90	93.75	90.95	88.50
Stucco on Wood Frame	135.10	121.70	115.60	111.20	107.00	102.15	99.25	93.70	88.05	85.50	83.35
Solid Masonry	155.65	140.80	133.45	128.25	123.05	117.65	113.95	106.95	100.35	97.10	94.45
Finished Basement, Add	23.50	23.20	22.45	21.90	21.35	21.00	20.60	19.80	19.30	18.95	18.60
Unfinished Basement, Add	9.15	8.55	8.05	7.75	7.40	7.15	6.90	6.45	6.10	5.85	5.65

Modifications

Add to the total cost

Upgrade Kitchen Cabinets	$ + 5823
Solid Surface Countertops (Included)	
Full Bath - including plumbing, wall and floor finishes	+ 8054
Half Bath - including plumbing, wall and floor finishes	+ 4856
One Car Attached Garage	+ 14,940
One Car Detached Garage	+ 19,637
Fireplace & Chimney	+ 6881

Adjustments

For multi family - add to total cost

Additional Kitchen	$ + 10,056
Additional Bath	+ 8054
Additional Entry & Exit	+ 1716
Separate Heating	+ 1421
Separate Electric	+ 1879

For Townhouse/Rowhouse - Multiply cost per square foot by

Inner Unit	.91
End Unit	.96

Alternatives

Add to or deduct from the cost per square foot of living area

Cedar Shake Roof	+ 1.70
Clay Tile Roof	+ 3.45
Slate Roof	+ 3.85
Upgrade Walls to Skim Coat Plaster	+ .51
Upgrade Ceilings to Textured Finish	+ .60
Air Conditioning, in Heating Ductwork	+ 2.96
In Separate Ductwork	+ 5.70
Heating Systems, Hot Water	+ 1.49
Heat Pump	+ 1.61
Electric Heat	– .63
Not Heated	– 3.28

Additional upgrades or components

Kitchen Cabinets & Countertops	Page 93
Bathroom Vanities	94
Fireplaces & Chimneys	94
Windows, Skylights & Dormers	94
Appliances	95
Breezeways & Porches	95
Finished Attic	95
Garages	96
Site Improvements	96
Wings & Ells	56

Important: See the Reference Section for Location Factors (to adjust for your city) and Estimating Forms.

		Cost Per Square Foot Of Living Area			% of Total
		Mat.	Inst.	Total	(rounded)
1 Site Work	Site preparation for slab; 4' deep trench excavation for foundation wall.		1.35	1.35	1.3%
2 Foundation	Continuous reinforced concrete footing, 10" deep x 20" wide; damproofed and insulated 8" thick reinforced concrete block foundation wall, 4' deep; trowel finished 4" thick concrete slab on 4" crushed stone base and polyethylene vapor barrier.	3.58	4.75	8.33	8.0%
3 Framing	Exterior walls - 2" x 6" wood studs, 16" O.C.; 1/2" sheathing; gable end roof framing, 2" x 10" rafters, 16" O.C. with 1/2" plywood sheathing; 2" x 10" floor joists, 16" O.C. with bridging and 5/8" subflooring; 2" x 4" interior partitions.	6.63	9.31	15.94	15.2%
4 Exterior Walls	Beveled wood siding and housewrap on insulated wood frame walls; R38 attic insulation; double hung wood windows; flush solid core doors, frame and hardware, painted finish; aluminum storm and screen doors.	11.17	4.80	15.97	15.3%
5 Roofing	25 year roof asphalt shingles; #15 felt building paper; aluminum gutters, downspouts, drip edge and flashings.	1.17	1.41	2.58	2.5%
6 Interiors	Walls & ceilings, 1/2" taped & finished gypsum wallboard, primed & painted with 2 coats of finish paint; birch faced hollow core interior doors, frames & hardware, painted finish; medium weight carpeting with pad, 40%; sheet vinyl, 15%; oak hardwood, 40%; ceramic tile, 5%; hardwood tread stairway.	14.78	14.84	29.62	28.3%
7 Specialties	Average grade kitchen cabinets and countertop; stainless steel kitchen sink; 40 gallon electric water heater.	3.86	1.21	5.07	4.8%
8 Mechanical	Three fixture bathroom: bathtub, water closet, vanity and sink; gas fired hot air heating system.	3.38	3.35	6.73	6.4%
9 Electrical	200 amp electric service; wiring, duplex & GFI receptacles, wall switches, door bell, appliance circuits, fans and communications cabling; average grade lighting fixtures.	1.56	2.37	3.93	3.8%
10 Overhead	Contractor's overhead and profit and plans.	7.82	7.36	15.18	14.5%
Total		53.95	50.75	**104.70**	

- Simple design from standard plans
- Single family — 1 full bath, 1 kitchen
- No basement
- Asphalt shingles on roof
- Hot air heat
- Gypsum wallboard interior finishes
- Materials and workmanship are average

Note: The illustration shown may contain some optional components (for example: garages and/or fireplaces) whose costs are shown in the modifications, adjustments, & alternatives below or at the end of the square foot section.

©Design Basics, Inc.

Base cost per square foot of living area

Exterior Wall	Living Area										
	1200	1500	1800	2100	2400	2700	3000	3400	3800	4200	4600
Wood Siding - Wood Frame	128.80	117.90	109.90	102.95	98.40	95.90	93.00	90.30	86.10	82.50	80.80
Brick Veneer - Wood Frame	134.55	123.15	114.60	107.20	102.45	99.80	96.70	93.85	89.40	85.60	83.75
Stucco on Wood Frame	125.60	115.00	107.25	100.55	96.25	93.80	91.00	88.40	84.30	80.85	79.15
Solid Masonry	144.60	132.25	122.80	114.70	109.45	106.55	103.00	99.95	95.05	91.00	88.90
Finished Basement, Add*	27.05	26.60	25.45	24.60	23.95	23.60	23.20	22.85	22.35	21.95	21.70
Unfinished Basement, Add*	10.20	9.45	8.70	8.20	7.80	7.60	7.35	7.15	6.85	6.65	6.45

*Basement under middle level only.

Modifications

Add to the total cost

Upgrade Kitchen Cabinets	$ + 5823
Solid Surface Countertops (Included)	
Full Bath - including plumbing, wall and floor finishes	+ 8054
Half Bath - including plumbing, wall and floor finishes	+ 4856
One Car Attached Garage	+ 14,940
One Car Detached Garage	+ 19,637
Fireplace & Chimney	+ 6881

Adjustments

For multi family - add to total cost

Additional Kitchen	$ + 10,056
Additional Bath	+ 8054
Additional Entry & Exit	+ 1716
Separate Heating	+ 1421
Separate Electric	+ 1879

For Townhouse/Rowhouse - Multiply cost per square foot by

Inner Unit	.90
End Unit	.95

Alternatives

Add to or deduct from the cost per square foot of living area

Cedar Shake Roof	+ 2.40
Clay Tile Roof	+ 5
Slate Roof	+ 5.50
Upgrade Walls to Skim Coat Plaster	+ .45
Upgrade Ceilings to Textured Finish	+ .60
Air Conditioning, in Heating Ductwork	+ 2.49
In Separate Ductwork	+ 5.37
Heating Systems, Hot Water	+ 1.44
Heat Pump	+ 1.68
Electric Heat	– .54
Not Heated	– 3.16

Additional upgrades or components

Kitchen Cabinets & Countertops	Page 93
Bathroom Vanities	94
Fireplaces & Chimneys	94
Windows, Skylights & Dormers	94
Appliances	95
Breezeways & Porches	95
Finished Attic	95
Garages	96
Site Improvements	96
Wings & Ells	56

Important: See the Reference Section for Location Factors (to adjust for your city) and Estimating Forms.

		Cost Per Square Foot Of Living Area			% of Total
		Mat.	Inst.	Total	(rounded)
1 Site Work	Site preparation for slab; 4' deep trench excavation for foundation wall.		1.12	1.12	1.1%
2 Foundation	Continuous reinforced concrete footing, 10" deep x 20" wide; damproofed and insulated 8" thick reinforced concrete block foundation wall, 4' deep; trowel finished 4" thick concrete slab on 4" crushed stone base and polyethylene vapor barrier.	4.01	5.14	9.15	9.3%
3 Framing	Exterior walls - 2" x 6" wood studs, 16" O.C.; 1/2" sheathing; gable end roof framing, 2" x 10" rafters, 16" O.C. with 1/2" plywood sheathing; 2" x 10" floor joists, 16" O.C. with bridging and 5/8" subflooring; 2" x 4" interior partitions.	6.39	8.92	15.31	15.6%
4 Exterior Walls	Beveled wood siding and housewrap on insulated wood frame walls; R38 attic insulation; double hung wood windows; flush solid core doors, frame and hardware, painted finish; aluminum storm and screen doors.	9.84	4.20	14.04	14.3%
5 Roofing	25 year asphalt roof shingles; #15 felt building paper; aluminum gutters, downspouts, drip edge and flashings.	1.55	1.88	3.43	3.5%
6 Interiors	Walls & ceilings, 1/2" taped & finished gypsum wallboard, primed & painted with 2 coats of finish paint; birch faced hollow core interior doors, frames & hardware, painted finish; medium weight carpeting with pad, 40%; sheet vinyl, 15%; oak hardwood, 40%; ceramic tile, 5%; hardwood tread stairway.	13.57	13.45	27.02	27.5%
7 Specialties	Average grade kitchen cabinets and countertop; stainless steel kitchen sink; 40 gallon electric water heater.	3.21	1.01	4.22	4.3%
8 Mechanical	Three fixture bathroom: bathtub, water closet, vanity and sink; gas fired hot air heating system.	2.88	3.19	6.07	6.2%
9 Electrical	200 amp electric service; wiring, duplex & GFI receptacles, wall switches, door bell, appliance circuits, fans and communications cabling; average grade lighting fixtures.	1.51	2.26	3.77	3.8%
10 Overhead	Contractor's overhead and profit and plans.	7.29	6.98	14.27	14.5%
	Total	50.25	48.15	**98.40**	

- Post and beam frame
- Log exterior walls
- Simple design from standard plans
- Single family — 1 full bath, 1 kitchen
- No basement
- Asphalt shingles on roof
- Hot air heat
- Gypsum wallboard interior finishes
- Materials and workmanship are average

Note: The illustration shown may contain some optional components (for example: garages and/or fireplaces) whose costs are shown in the modifications, adjustments, & alternatives below or at the end of the square foot section.

Base cost per square foot of living area

Exterior Wall	Living Area										
	600	800	1000	1200	1400	1600	1800	2000	2400	2800	3200
6" Log - Solid Wall	192.40	173.55	159.65	148.70	139.30	133.30	129.90	125.80	118.00	112.30	108.25
8" Log - Solid Wall	179.80	162.35	149.50	139.45	130.95	125.45	122.40	118.70	111.55	106.30	102.75
Finished Basement, Add	40.95	39.60	37.75	36.05	34.70	33.80	33.30	32.55	31.50	30.75	30.05
Unfinished Basement, Add	16.75	15.15	14.00	13.00	12.10	11.55	11.25	10.85	10.20	9.75	9.35

Modifications

Add to the total cost

Upgrade Kitchen Cabinets	$ + 5823
Solid Surface Countertops (Included)	
Full Bath - including plumbing, wall and floor finishes	+ 8054
Half Bath - including plumbing, wall and floor finishes	+ 4856
One Car Attached Garage	+ 14,940
One Car Detached Garage	+ 19,637
Fireplace & Chimney	+ 6881

Adjustments

For multi family - add to total cost

Additional Kitchen	$ + 10,056
Additional Bath	+ 8054
Additional Entry & Exit	+ 1716
Separate Heating	+ 1421
Separate Electric	+ 1879

For Townhouse/Rowhouse - Multiply cost per square foot by

Inner Unit	.92
End Unit	.96

Alternatives

Add to or deduct from the cost per square foot of living area

Cedar Shake Roof	+ 3.35
Air Conditioning, in Heating Ductwork	+ 4.89
In Separate Ductwork	+ 7.17
Heating Systems, Hot Water	+ 1.60
Heat Pump	+ 1.37
Electric Heat	– .85
Not Heated	– 3.52

Additional upgrades or components

Kitchen Cabinets & Countertops	Page 93
Bathroom Vanities	94
Fireplaces & Chimneys	94
Windows, Skylights & Dormers	94
Appliances	95
Breezeways & Porches	95
Finished Attic	95
Garages	96
Site Improvements	96
Wings & Ells	56

		Cost Per Square Foot Of Living Area			% of Total
		Mat.	Inst.	Total	(rounded)
1 Site Work	Site preparation for slab; 4' deep trench excavation for foundation wall.		1.69	1.69	1.3%
2 Foundation	Continuous reinforced concrete footing, 10" deep x 20" wide; damproofed and insulated 8" thick reinforced concrete block foundation wall, 4' deep; trowel finished 4" thick concrete slab on 4" crushed stone base and polyethylene vapor barrier.	6.02	7.73	13.75	10.3%
3 Framing	Exterior walls - precut traditional log home, handcrafted white cedar or pine logs, delivery included; heavy timber roof framing with 2" thick tongue and groove decking, rigid insulation with 5/8" sheathing; 2" x 4" interior partitions.	26.72	16.37	43.09	32.3%
4 Exterior Walls	R38 attic insulation; double hung wood windows; flush solid core doors, frame and hardware, painted finish; aluminum storm and screen doors.	5.58	2.80	8.38	6.3%
5 Roofing	25 year asphalt roof shingles; #15 felt building paper; aluminum gutters, downspouts, drip edge and flashings.	2.33	2.82	5.15	3.9%
6 Interiors	Walls & ceilings, 1/2" taped & finished gypsum wallboard, primed & painted with 2 coats of finish paint; birch faced hollow core interior doors, frames & hardware, painted finish; medium weight carpeting with pad, 40%; sheet vinyl, 15%; oak hardwood, 40%; ceramic tile, 5%.	11.79	11.97	23.76	17.8%
7 Specialties	Average grade kitchen cabinets and countertop; stainless steel kitchen sink; 40 gallon electric water heater.	4.83	1.51	6.34	4.8%
8 Mechanical	Three fixture bathroom: bathtub, water closet, vanity and sink; gas fired hot air heating system.	3.99	3.61	7.60	5.7%
9 Electrical	200 amp electric service; wiring, duplex & GFI receptacles, wall switches, door bell, appliance circuits, fans and communications cabling; average grade lighting fixtures.	1.63	2.54	4.17	3.1%
10 Overhead	Contractor's overhead and profit and plans.	10.71	8.66	19.37	14.5%
Total		73.60	59.70	**133.30**	

- Post and beam frame
- Log exterior walls
- Simple design from standard plans
- Single family — 1 full bath, 1 kitchen
- No basement
- Asphalt shingles on roof
- Hot air heat
- Gypsum wallboard interior finishes
- Materials and workmanship are average

Note: The illustration shown may contain some optional components (for example: garages and/or fireplaces) whose costs are shown in the modifications, adjustments, & alternatives below or at the end of the square foot section.

Base cost per square foot of living area

Exterior Wall	Living Area										
	1000	1200	1400	1600	1800	2000	2200	2600	3000	3400	3800
6" Log - Solid Wall	164.10	149.00	141.50	136.20	130.80	125.35	121.60	114.40	107.65	104.40	101.60
8" Log - Solid Wall	151.10	136.95	130.20	125.45	120.70	115.60	112.30	106.00	99.90	97.05	94.60
Finished Basement, Add	23.50	23.20	22.45	21.90	21.35	21.00	20.60	19.80	19.30	18.95	18.60
Unfinished Basement, Add	9.15	8.55	8.05	7.75	7.40	7.15	6.90	6.45	6.10	5.85	5.65

Modifications

Add to the total cost

Upgrade Kitchen Cabinets	$ + 5823
Solid Surface Countertops (Included)	
Full Bath - including plumbing, wall and floor finishes	+ 8054
Half Bath - including plumbing, wall and floor finishes	+ 4856
One Car Attached Garage	+ 14,940
One Car Detached Garage	+ 19,637
Fireplace & Chimney	+ 7604

Adjustments

For multi family - add to total cost

Additional Kitchen	$ + 10,056
Additional Bath	+ 8054
Additional Entry & Exit	+ 1716
Separate Heating	+ 1421
Separate Electric	+ 1879

For Townhouse/Rowhouse -
Multiply cost per square foot by

Inner Unit	.92
End Unit	.96

Alternatives

Add to or deduct from the cost per square foot of living area

Cedar Shake Roof	+ 1.70
Air Conditioning, in Heating Ductwork	+ 2.96
In Separate Ductwork	+ 5.70
Heating Systems, Hot Water	+ 1.49
Heat Pump	+ 1.61
Electric Heat	– .63
Not Heated	– 3.28

Additional upgrades or components

Kitchen Cabinets & Countertops	Page 93
Bathroom Vanities	94
Fireplaces & Chimneys	94
Windows, Skylights & Dormers	94
Appliances	95
Breezeways & Porches	95
Finished Attic	95
Garages	96
Site Improvements	96
Wings & Ells	56

Important: See the Reference Section for Location Factors (to adjust for your city) and Estimating Forms.

Solid Wall 2 Story

Living Area - 2000 S.F.
Perimeter - 135 L.F.

		Cost Per Square Foot Of Living Area			% of Total
		Mat.	Inst.	Total	(rounded)
1 Site Work	Site preparation for slab; 4' deep trench excavation for foundation wall.		1.35	1.35	1.1%
2 Foundation	Continuous reinforced concrete footing, 10" deep x 20" wide; damproofed and insulated 8" thick reinforced concrete block foundation wall, 4' deep; trowel finished 4" thick concrete slab on 4" crushed stone base and polyethylene vapor barrier.	3.58	4.75	8.33	6.6%
3 Framing	Exterior walls - precut traditional log home, handcrafted white cedar or pine logs, delivery included; heavy timber roof framing with 2" thick T.&G. decking, rigid insulation with 5/8" sheathing; heavy timber columns, beams & joists with 2" thick T.&G. decking; 2" x 4" interior partitions.	27.52	15.72	43.24	34.5%
4 Exterior Walls	R38 attic insulation; double hung wood windows; flush solid core doors, frame and hardware, painted finish; aluminum storm and screen doors.	5.61	2.96	8.57	6.8%
5 Roofing	25 year asphalt roof shingles; #15 felt building paper; aluminum gutters, downspouts, drip edge and flashings.	1.17	1.41	2.58	2.1%
6 Interiors	Walls & ceilings, 1/2" taped & finished gypsum wallboard, primed & painted with 2 coats of finish paint; birch faced hollow core interior doors, frames & hardware, painted finish; medium weight carpeting with pad, 40%; sheet vinyl, 15%; oak hardwood, 40%; ceramic tile, 5%; hardwood tread stairway.	13.87	13.47	27.34	21.8%
7 Specialties	Average grade kitchen cabinets and countertop; stainless steel kitchen sink; 40 gallon electric water heater.	3.86	1.21	5.07	4.0%
8 Mechanical	Three fixture bathroom: bathtub, water closet, vanity and sink; gas fired hot air heating system.	3.38	3.35	6.73	5.4%
9 Electrical	200 amp electric service; wiring, duplex & GFI receptacles, wall switches, door bell, appliance circuits, fans and communications cabling; average grade lighting fixtures.	1.56	2.37	3.93	3.1%
10 Overhead	Contractor's overhead and profit and plans.	10.30	7.91	18.21	14.5%
Total		70.85	54.50	125.35	

For customer support on your Residential Costs with RSMeans Data, call 800.448.8182.

55

1 Story — Base cost per square foot of living area

Exterior Wall	Living Area							
	50	100	200	300	400	500	600	700
Wood Siding - Wood Frame	219.80	169.65	147.90	124.30	117.20	112.90	110.10	110.80
Brick Veneer - Wood Frame	224.75	169.45	145.50	118.30	110.50	105.75	102.60	103.20
Stucco on Wood Frame	209.95	162.50	141.90	120.20	113.50	109.45	106.75	107.60
Solid Masonry	276.05	209.80	181.35	146.60	137.30	131.60	129.65	129.50
Finished Basement, Add	66.00	54.60	49.15	39.90	38.10	37.00	36.30	35.75
Unfinished Basement, Add	30.95	23.35	20.15	14.85	13.85	13.20	12.80	12.45

1-1/2 Story — Base cost per square foot of living area

Exterior Wall	Living Area							
	100	200	300	400	500	600	700	800
Wood Siding - Wood Frame	177.35	143.05	122.45	109.85	103.65	100.60	96.85	95.75
Brick Veneer - Wood Frame	236.50	177.50	147.60	129.05	120.05	115.10	109.90	108.05
Stucco on Wood Frame	211.80	157.65	131.10	116.20	108.15	103.90	99.30	97.50
Solid Masonry	270.55	204.70	170.25	146.75	136.40	130.55	124.45	122.45
Finished Basement, Add	44.40	40.15	36.50	32.40	31.30	30.55	29.95	29.85
Unfinished Basement, Add	19.35	16.20	14.05	11.75	11.10	10.70	10.30	10.20

2 Story — Base cost per square foot of living area

Exterior Wall	Living Area							
	100	200	400	600	800	1000	1200	1400
Wood Siding - Wood Frame	176.60	132.65	113.45	94.20	87.95	84.15	81.70	82.70
Brick Veneer - Wood Frame	240.75	168.60	135.75	109.05	100.20	94.85	91.25	91.50
Stucco on Wood Frame	213.05	148.80	119.25	98.05	90.35	85.60	82.45	83.00
Solid Masonry	278.85	195.80	158.45	124.20	113.85	107.50	103.35	103.20
Finished Basement, Add	35.15	29.45	26.70	22.10	21.20	20.65	20.25	20.00
Unfinished Basement, Add	15.60	11.85	10.25	7.60	7.05	6.75	6.55	6.40

Base costs do not include bathroom or kitchen facilities. Use Modifications/Adjustments/Alternatives on pages 93–96 where appropriate.

Important: See the Reference Section for Location Factors (to adjust for your city) and Estimating Forms.

1 Story

1-1/2 Story

2 Story

2-1/2 Story

Bi-Level

Tri-Level

For customer support on your Residential Costs with RSMeans Data, call 800.448.8182.

59

- A distinct residence from designer's plans
- Single family — 1 full bath, 1 half bath, 1 kitchen
- No basement
- Asphalt shingles on roof
- Forced hot air heat/air conditioning
- Gypsum wallboard interior finishes
- Materials and workmanship are above average

Note: The illustration shown may contain some optional components (for example: garages and/or fireplaces) whose costs are shown in the modifications, adjustments, & alternatives below or at the end of the square foot section.

©Design Basics, Inc.

Base cost per square foot of living area

Exterior Wall	Living Area										
	800	1000	1200	1400	1600	1800	2000	2400	2800	3200	3600
Wood Siding - Wood Frame	215.40	194.00	177.55	164.15	155.35	150.00	144.10	133.30	125.55	120.05	114.50
Brick Veneer - Wood Frame	226.25	203.80	186.40	172.20	162.80	157.30	150.90	139.55	131.35	125.35	119.45
Stone Veneer - Wood Frame	235.95	212.70	194.35	179.45	169.65	163.85	157.05	145.20	136.55	130.25	123.95
Solid Masonry	236.85	213.45	195.10	180.15	170.25	164.45	157.60	145.70	137.00	130.60	124.40
Finished Basement, Add	60.05	59.90	57.20	55.15	53.80	52.95	51.85	50.30	49.05	48.00	47.10
Unfinished Basement, Add	26.55	25.10	23.75	22.65	21.95	21.50	20.90	20.10	19.50	18.90	18.45

Modifications

Add to the total cost

Upgrade Kitchen Cabinets	$ + 1842
Solid Surface Countertops (Included)	
Full Bath - including plumbing, wall and floor finishes	+ 9664
Half Bath - including plumbing, wall and floor finishes	+ 5828
Two Car Attached Garage	+ 29,256
Two Car Detached Garage	+ 33,472
Fireplace & Chimney	+ 7234

Adjustments

For multi family - add to total cost

Additional Kitchen	$ + 22,146
Additional Full Bath & Half Bath	+ 15,492
Additional Entry & Exit	+ 1716
Separate Heating & Air Conditioning	+ 7245
Separate Electric	+ 1879

For Townhouse/Rowhouse - Multiply cost per square foot by

Inner Unit	.90
End Unit	.95

Alternatives

Add to or deduct from the cost per square foot of living area

Cedar Shake Roof	+ 2.35
Clay Tile Roof	+ 5.95
Slate Roof	+ 6.65
Upgrade Ceilings to Textured Finish	+ .60
Air Conditioning, in Heating Ductwork	Base System
Heating Systems, Hot Water	+ 1.64
Heat Pump	+ 1.37
Electric Heat	− 2.38
Not Heated	− 4.41

Additional upgrades or components

Kitchen Cabinets & Countertops	Page 93
Bathroom Vanities	94
Fireplaces & Chimneys	94
Windows, Skylights & Dormers	94
Appliances	95
Breezeways & Porches	95
Finished Attic	95
Garages	96
Site Improvements	96
Wings & Ells	74

Important: See the Reference Section for Location Factors (to adjust for your city) and Estimating Forms.

		Cost Per Square Foot Of Living Area			% of Total
		Mat.	Inst.	Total	(rounded)
1 Site Work	Site preparation for slab; 4' deep trench excavation for foundation wall.		1.26	1.26	0.9%
2 Foundation	Continuous reinforced concrete footing, 12" deep x 24" wide; damproofed and insulated 12" thick reinforced concrete block foundation wall, 4' deep; trowel finished 4" thick concrete slab on 4" crushed stone base and polyethylene vapor barrier.	6.62	8.20	14.82	11.1%
3 Framing	Exterior walls - 2" x 6" wood studs, 16" O.C.; 1/2" sheathing; gable end roof framing, 2" x 10" rafters, 16" O.C. with 1/2" plywood sheathing; 2" x 4" interior partitions.	6.55	9.30	15.85	11.9%
4 Exterior Walls	1" x 6" tongue and groove vertical wood siding and housewrap on insulated wood frame walls; R38 attic insulation; plastic clad double hung wood windows; raised panel exterior doors, frames and hardware, painted finish; wood storm and screen door.	11.71	4.15	15.86	11.9%
5 Roofing	Red cedar roof shingles, perfections; #15 felt building paper; aluminum gutters, downspouts and drip edge; copper flashings.	4.82	4.01	8.83	6.6%
6 Interiors	Skim coated 1/2" thick gypsum wallboard walls and ceilings, primed and painted with 2 coats; interior raised panel solid core doors, frames and hardware, painted finish; oak hardwood flooring, 70%; ceramic tile flooring, 30%.	14.39	13.63	28.02	21.0%
7 Specialties	Custom grade kitchen cabinets and countertops; double bowl kitchen sink; 75 gallon gas water heater.	8.65	1.64	10.29	7.7%
8 Mechanical	Three fixture bathroom: bathtub, water closet, vanity and sink; gas fired heating and air conditioning system.	7.21	3.69	10.90	8.2%
9 Electrical	200 amp electric service; wiring, duplex & GFI receptacles, wall switches, door bell, appliance circuits, air conditioning circuit, fans and communications cabling; custom grade lighting fixtures.	2.55	2.72	5.27	4.0%
10 Overhead	Contractor's overhead and profit and design.	12.50	9.70	22.20	16.7%
Total		75.00	58.30	**133.30**	

For customer support on your Residential Costs with RSMeans Data, call 800.448.8182.

61

- **A distinct residence from designer's plans**
- **Single family — 1 full bath, 1 half bath, 1 kitchen**
- **No basement**
- **Asphalt shingles on roof**
- **Forced hot air heat/air conditioning**
- **Gypsum wallboard interior finishes**
- **Materials and workmanship are above average**

Note: The illustration shown may contain some optional components (for example: garages and/or fireplaces) whose costs are shown in the modifications, adjustments, & alternatives below or at the end of the square foot section.

©Donald A. Gardner Architects, Inc.

Base cost per square foot of living area

Exterior Wall	Living Area										
	1000	1200	1400	1600	1800	2000	2400	2800	3200	3600	4000
Wood Siding - Wood Frame	194.60	180.40	170.45	158.60	151.60	145.10	132.65	126.95	121.50	117.60	112.00
Brick Veneer - Wood Frame	206.25	191.35	180.80	168.00	160.60	153.60	140.20	134.00	128.15	123.90	117.90
Stone Veneer - Wood Frame	216.80	201.20	190.20	176.65	168.70	161.30	147.00	140.50	134.05	129.65	123.25
Solid Masonry	217.60	202.00	190.95	177.25	169.30	161.90	147.50	140.95	134.50	130.15	123.60
Finished Basement, Add	39.85	40.10	39.05	37.40	36.50	35.70	34.05	33.30	32.40	31.95	31.25
Unfinished Basement, Add	17.80	17.05	16.55	15.65	15.20	14.80	13.90	13.50	13.05	12.85	12.45

Modifications

Add to the total cost

Upgrade Kitchen Cabinets	$ + 1842
Solid Surface Countertops (Included)	
Full Bath - including plumbing, wall and floor finishes	+ 9664
Half Bath - including plumbing, wall and floor finishes	+ 5828
Two Car Attached Garage	+ 29,256
Two Car Detached Garage	+ 33,472
Fireplace & Chimney	+ 7234

Adjustments

For multi family - add to total cost

Additional Kitchen	$ + 22,146
Additional Full Bath & Half Bath	+ 15,492
Additional Entry & Exit	+ 1716
Separate Heating & Air Conditioning	+ 7245
Separate Electric	+ 1879

For Townhouse/Rowhouse - Multiply cost per square foot by

Inner Unit	.90
End Unit	.95

Alternatives

Add to or deduct from the cost per square foot of living area

Cedar Shake Roof	+ 1.70
Clay Tile Roof	+ 4.30
Slate Roof	+ 4.80
Upgrade Ceilings to Textured Finish	+ .60
Air Conditioning, in Heating Ductwork	Base System
Heating Systems, Hot Water	+ 1.57
Heat Pump	+ 1.43
Electric Heat	– 2.10
Not Heated	– 4.07

Additional upgrades or components

Kitchen Cabinets & Countertops	Page 93
Bathroom Vanities	94
Fireplaces & Chimneys	94
Windows, Skylights & Dormers	94
Appliances	95
Breezeways & Porches	95
Finished Attic	95
Garages	96
Site Improvements	96
Wings & Ells	74

Important: See the Reference Section for Location Factors (to adjust for your city) and Estimating Forms.

		Cost Per Square Foot Of Living Area			% of Total
		Mat.	Inst.	Total	(rounded)
1 Site Work	Site preparation for slab; 4' deep trench excavation for foundation wall.		1.09	1.09	0.9%
2 Foundation	Continuous reinforced concrete footing, 12" deep x 24" wide; damproofed and insulated 12" thick reinforced concrete block foundation wall, 4' deep; trowel finished 4" thick concrete slab on 4" crushed stone base and polyethylene vapor barrier.	4.64	5.86	10.50	8.3%
3 Framing	Exterior walls - 2" x 6" wood studs, 16" O.C.; 1/2" sheathing; gable end roof framing, steep pitch 2" x 10" rafters, 16" O.C. with 1/2" plywood sheathing; 2" x 10" floor joists, 16" O.C. with bridging and 5/8" subflooring; 2" x 4" interior partitions.	7.14	9.95	17.09	13.5%
4 Exterior Walls	1" x 6" tongue and groove vertical wood siding and housewrap on insulated wood frame walls; R38 attic insulation; plastic clad double hung wood windows; raised panel exterior doors, frames and hardware, painted finish; wood storm and screen door.	11.58	4.12	15.70	12.4%
5 Roofing	Red cedar roof shingles, perfections; #15 felt building paper; aluminum gutters, downspouts and drip edge; copper flashings.	3.49	2.91	6.40	5.0%
6 Interiors	Skim coated 1/2" thick gypsum wallboard walls and ceilings, primed and painted with 2 coats; interior raised panel solid core doors, frames and hardware, painted finish; oak hardwood flooring, 70%; ceramic tile flooring, 30%; hardwood tread stairway.	16.29	15.06	31.35	24.7%
7 Specialties	Custom grade kitchen cabinets and countertops; double bowl kitchen sink; 75 gallon gas water heater.	7.40	1.41	8.81	6.9%
8 Mechanical	Three fixture bathroom: bathtub, water closet, vanity and sink; gas fired heating and air conditioning system.	6.22	3.45	9.67	7.6%
9 Electrical	200 amp electric service; wiring, duplex & GFI receptacles, wall switches, door bell, appliance circuits, air conditioning circuit, fans and communications cabling; custom grade lighting fixtures.	2.52	2.64	5.16	4.1%
10 Overhead	Contractor's overhead and profit and design.	11.87	9.31	21.18	16.7%
Total		71.15	55.80	**126.95**	

For customer support on your Residential Costs with RSMeans Data, call 800.448.8182.

63

- A distinct residence from designer's plans
- Single family — 1 full bath, 1 half bath, 1 kitchen
- No basement
- Asphalt shingles on roof
- Forced hot air heat/air conditioning
- Gypsum wallboard interior finishes
- Materials and workmanship are above average

Note: The illustration shown may contain some optional components (for example: garages and/or fireplaces) whose costs are shown in the modifications, adjustments, & alternatives below or at the end of the square foot section.

Base cost per square foot of living area

Exterior Wall	Living Area										
	1200	1400	1600	1800	2000	2400	2800	3200	3600	4000	4400
Wood Siding - Wood Frame	177.50	166.40	158.45	151.30	144.00	133.40	124.45	118.70	115.20	111.35	108.30
Brick Veneer - Wood Frame	189.05	177.20	168.80	161.10	153.35	141.85	132.15	125.90	122.15	117.90	114.60
Stone Veneer - Wood Frame	199.50	187.00	178.15	169.90	161.85	149.55	139.15	132.45	128.45	123.85	120.30
Solid Masonry	200.75	188.20	179.20	170.90	162.80	150.45	139.95	133.15	129.15	124.50	120.95
Finished Basement, Add	32.00	32.25	31.45	30.50	30.00	28.65	27.60	26.90	26.55	25.95	25.65
Unfinished Basement, Add	14.30	13.70	13.25	12.80	12.50	11.85	11.25	10.95	10.75	10.45	10.30

Modifications

Add to the total cost

Upgrade Kitchen Cabinets	$ + 1842
Solid Surface Countertops (Included)	
Full Bath - including plumbing, wall and floor finishes	+ 9664
Half Bath - including plumbing, wall and floor finishes	+ 5828
Two Car Attached Garage	+ 29,256
Two Car Detached Garage	+ 33,472
Fireplace & Chimney	+ 8165

Adjustments

For multi family - add to total cost

Additional Kitchen	$ + 22,146
Additional Full Bath & Half Bath	+ 15,492
Additional Entry & Exit	+ 1716
Separate Heating & Air Conditioning	+ 7245
Separate Electric	+ 1879

For Townhouse/Rowhouse - Multiply cost per square foot by

Inner Unit	.87
End Unit	.93

Alternatives

Add to or deduct from the cost per square foot of living area

Cedar Shake Roof	+ 1.20
Clay Tile Roof	+ 2.95
Slate Roof	+ 3.35
Upgrade Ceilings to Textured Finish	+ .60
Air Conditioning, in Heating Ductwork	Base System
Heating Systems, Hot Water	+ 1.52
Heat Pump	+ 1.60
Electric Heat	– 2.10
Not Heated	– 3.84

Additional upgrades or components

Kitchen Cabinets & Countertops	Page 93
Bathroom Vanities	94
Fireplaces & Chimneys	94
Windows, Skylights & Dormers	94
Appliances	95
Breezeways & Porches	95
Finished Attic	95
Garages	96
Site Improvements	96
Wings & Ells	74

Important: See the Reference Section for Location Factors (to adjust for your city) and Estimating Forms.

		Cost Per Square Foot Of Living Area			% of Total
		Mat.	**Inst.**	**Total**	(rounded)
1 Site Work	Site preparation for slab; 4' deep trench excavation for foundation wall.		1.09	1.09	0.9%
2 Foundation	Continuous reinforced concrete footing, 12" deep x 24" wide; damproofed and insulated 12" thick reinforced concrete block foundation wall, 4' deep; trowel finished 4" thick concrete slab on 4" crushed stone base and polyethylene vapor barrier.	3.94	5.02	8.96	7.2%
3 Framing	Exterior walls - 2" x 6" wood studs, 16" O.C.; 1/2" sheathing; gable end roof framing, 2" x 10" rafters, 16" O.C. with 1/2" plywood sheathing; 2" x 10" floor joists, 16" O.C. with bridging and 5/8" subflooring; 2" x 4" interior partitions.	6.77	9.43	16.20	13.0%
4 Exterior Walls	1" x 6" tongue and groove vertical wood siding and housewrap on insulated wood frame walls; R38 attic insulation; plastic clad double hung wood windows; raised panel exterior doors, frames and hardware, painted finish; wood storm and screen door.	12.55	4.47	17.02	13.7%
5 Roofing	Red cedar roof shingles, perfections; #15 felt building paper; aluminum gutters, downspouts and drip edge; copper flashings.	2.41	2.01	4.42	3.6%
6 Interiors	Skim coated 1/2" thick gypsum wallboard walls and ceilings, primed and painted with 2 coats; interior raised panel solid core doors, frames and hardware, painted finish; oak hardwood flooring, 70%; ceramic tile flooring, 30%; hardwood tread stairway.	16.69	15.49	32.18	25.9%
7 Specialties	Custom grade kitchen cabinets and countertops; double bowl kitchen sink; 75 gallon gas water heater.	7.40	1.41	8.81	7.1%
8 Mechanical	Three fixture bathroom: bathtub, water closet, vanity and sink; gas fired heating and air conditioning system.	6.38	3.50	9.88	7.9%
9 Electrical	200 amp electric service; wiring, duplex & GFI receptacles, wall switches, door bell, appliance circuits, air conditioning circuit, fans and communications cabling; custom grade lighting fixtures.	2.52	2.64	5.16	4.1%
10 Overhead	Contractor's overhead and profit and design.	11.74	8.99	20.73	16.7%
Total		70.40	54.05	**124.45**	

For customer support on your Residential Costs with RSMeans Data, call 800.448.8182.

65

- **A distinct residence from designer's plans**
- **Single family — 1 full bath, 1 half bath, 1 kitchen**
- **No basement**
- **Asphalt shingles on roof**
- **Forced hot air heat/air conditioning**
- **Gypsum wallboard interior finishes**
- **Materials and workmanship are above average**

Note: The illustration shown may contain some optional components (for example: garages and/or fireplaces) whose costs are shown in the modifications, adjustments, & alternatives below or at the end of the square foot section.

Base cost per square foot of living area

Exterior Wall	Living Area										
	1500	1800	2100	2400	2800	3200	3600	4000	4500	5000	5500
Wood Siding - Wood Frame	174.45	157.10	146.55	140.05	131.90	124.30	120.00	113.30	109.70	106.45	103.30
Brick Veneer - Wood Frame	186.80	168.50	156.75	149.70	141.20	132.65	127.90	120.65	116.65	113.10	109.65
Stone Veneer - Wood Frame	198.05	178.80	165.95	158.50	149.55	140.25	135.10	127.25	122.95	119.10	115.35
Solid Masonry	199.20	179.80	166.95	159.35	150.40	141.00	135.85	128.00	123.65	119.70	115.95
Finished Basement, Add	25.40	25.40	24.15	23.50	22.90	22.00	21.50	20.90	20.50	20.10	19.80
Unfinished Basement, Add	11.45	10.90	10.20	9.90	9.60	9.10	8.90	8.55	8.35	8.15	7.95

Modifications

Add to the total cost

Upgrade Kitchen Cabinets	$ + 1842
Solid Surface Countertops (Included)	
Full Bath - including plumbing, wall and floor finishes	+ 9664
Half Bath - including plumbing, wall and floor finishes	+ 5828
Two Car Attached Garage	+ 29,256
Two Car Detached Garage	+ 33,472
Fireplace & Chimney	+ 8165

Adjustments

For multi family - add to total cost

Additional Kitchen	$ + 22,146
Additional Full Bath & Half Bath	+ 15,492
Additional Entry & Exit	+ 1716
Separate Heating & Air Conditioning	+ 7245
Separate Electric	+ 1879

For Townhouse/Rowhouse - Multiply cost per square foot by

Inner Unit	.87
End Unit	.94

Alternatives

Add to or deduct from the cost per square foot of living area

Cedar Shake Roof	+ 1.05
Clay Tile Roof	+ 2.55
Slate Roof	+ 2.90
Upgrade Ceilings to Textured Finish	+ .60
Air Conditioning, in Heating Ductwork	Base System
Heating Systems, Hot Water	+ 1.37
Heat Pump	+ 1.65
Electric Heat	− 3.69
Not Heated	− 3.84

Additional upgrades or components

Kitchen Cabinets & Countertops	Page 93
Bathroom Vanities	94
Fireplaces & Chimneys	94
Windows, Skylights & Dormers	94
Appliances	95
Breezeways & Porches	95
Finished Attic	95
Garages	96
Site Improvements	96
Wings & Ells	74

Important: See the Reference Section for Location Factors (to adjust for your city) and Estimating Forms.

		Cost Per Square Foot Of Living Area			% of Total
		Mat.	Inst.	Total	(rounded)
1 Site Work	Site preparation for slab; 4' deep trench excavation for foundation wall.		.95	.95	0.8%
2 Foundation	Continuous reinforced concrete footing, 12" deep x 24" wide; damproofed and insulated 12" thick reinforced concrete block foundation wall, 4' deep; trowel finished 4" thick concrete slab on 4" crushed stone base and polyethylene vapor barrier.	3.25	4.18	7.43	6.0%
3 Framing	Exterior walls - 2" x 6" wood studs, 16" O.C.; 1/2" sheathing; gable end roof framing, steep pitch 2" x 10" rafters, 16" O.C. with 1/2" plywood sheathing; 2" x 10" floor joists, 16" O.C. with bridging and 5/8" subflooring; 2" x 4" interior partitions.	7.27	10.12	17.39	14.0%
4 Exterior Walls	1" x 6" tongue and groove vertical wood siding and housewrap on insulated wood frame walls; R38 attic insulation; plastic clad double hung wood windows; raised panel exterior doors, frames and hardware, painted finish; wood storm and screen door.	13.00	4.64	17.64	14.2%
5 Roofing	Red cedar roof shingles, perfections; #15 felt building paper; aluminum gutters, downspouts and drip edge; copper flashings.	2.15	1.79	3.94	3.2%
6 Interiors	Skim coated 1/2" thick gypsum wallboard walls and ceilings, primed and painted with 2 coats; interior raised panel solid core doors, frames and hardware, painted finish; oak hardwood flooring, 70%; ceramic tile flooring, 30%; hardwood tread stairway.	17.86	16.46	34.32	27.6%
7 Specialties	Custom grade kitchen cabinets and countertops; double bowl kitchen sink; 75 gallon gas water heater.	6.49	1.23	7.72	6.2%
8 Mechanical	Three fixture bathroom: bathtub, water closet, vanity and sink; gas fired heating and air conditioning system.	5.75	3.37	9.12	7.3%
9 Electrical	200 amp electric service; wiring, duplex & GFI receptacles, wall switches, door bell, appliance circuits, air conditioning circuit, fans and communications cabling; custom grade lighting fixtures.	2.50	2.58	5.08	4.1%
10 Overhead	Contractor's overhead and profit and design.	11.63	9.08	20.71	16.7%
Total		69.90	54.40	**124.30**	

- A distinct residence from designer's plans
- Single family — 1 full bath, 1 half bath, 1 kitchen
- No basement
- Asphalt shingles on roof
- Forced hot air heat/air conditioning
- Gypsum wallboard interior finishes
- Materials and workmanship are above average

Note: The illustration shown may contain some optional components (for example: garages and/or fireplaces) whose costs are shown in the modifications, adjustments, & alternatives below or at the end of the square foot section.

Base cost per square foot of living area

Exterior Wall	Living Area										
	1500	1800	2100	2500	3000	3500	4000	4500	5000	5500	6000
Wood Siding - Wood Frame	171.30	154.15	145.50	138.20	127.35	121.75	115.25	108.40	105.85	103.15	100.40
Brick Veneer - Wood Frame	183.55	165.55	156.15	148.40	136.60	130.50	123.20	115.80	112.95	110.00	106.80
Stone Veneer - Wood Frame	194.75	175.85	165.80	157.65	144.90	138.45	130.35	122.45	119.35	116.15	112.65
Solid Masonry	196.15	177.20	167.05	158.80	145.95	139.40	131.30	123.30	120.15	116.95	113.40
Finished Basement, Add	22.30	22.25	21.45	20.85	20.00	19.40	18.70	18.10	17.85	17.60	17.25
Unfinished Basement, Add	10.10	9.50	9.15	8.85	8.35	8.10	7.70	7.40	7.30	7.15	6.95

Modifications

Add to the total cost

Upgrade Kitchen Cabinets	$ + 1842
Solid Surface Countertops (Included)	
Full Bath - including plumbing, wall and floor finishes	+ 9664
Half Bath - including plumbing, wall and floor finishes	+ 5828
Two Car Attached Garage	+ 29,256
Two Car Detached Garage	+ 33,472
Fireplace & Chimney	+ 9220

Adjustments

For multi family - add to total cost

Additional Kitchen	$ + 22,146
Additional Full Bath & Half Bath	+ 15,492
Additional Entry & Exit	+ 1716
Separate Heating & Air Conditioning	+ 7245
Separate Electric	+ 1879

For Townhouse/Rowhouse - Multiply cost per square foot by

Inner Unit	.85
End Unit	.93

Alternatives

Add to or deduct from the cost per square foot of living area

Cedar Shake Roof	+ .80
Clay Tile Roof	+ 2
Slate Roof	+ 2.20
Upgrade Ceilings to Textured Finish	+ .60
Air Conditioning, in Heating Ductwork	Base System
Heating Systems, Hot Water	+ 1.37
Heat Pump	+ 1.65
Electric Heat	- 3.69
Not Heated	- 3.72

Additional upgrades or components

Kitchen Cabinets & Countertops	Page 93
Bathroom Vanities	94
Fireplaces & Chimneys	94
Windows, Skylights & Dormers	94
Appliances	95
Breezeways & Porches	95
Finished Attic	95
Garages	96
Site Improvements	96
Wings & Ells	74

Important: See the Reference Section for Location Factors (to adjust for your city) and Estimating Forms.

		Cost Per Square Foot Of Living Area			% of Total
		Mat.	Inst.	Total	(rounded)
1 Site Work	Site preparation for slab; 4' deep trench excavation for foundation wall.		1.01	1.01	0.8%
2 Foundation	Continuous reinforced concrete footing, 12" deep x 24" wide; damproofed and insulated 12" thick reinforced concrete block foundation wall, 4' deep; trowel finished 4" thick concrete slab on 4" crushed stone base and polyethylene vapor barrier.	3.04	3.95	6.99	5.5%
3 Framing	Exterior walls - 2" x 6" wood studs, 16" O.C.; 1/2" sheathing; gable end roof framing, 2" x 10" rafters, 16" O.C. with 1/2" plywood sheathing; 2" x 10" floor joists, 16" O.C. with bridging and 5/8" subflooring; 2" x 4" interior partitions.	7.16	9.99	17.15	13.5%
4 Exterior Walls	1" x 6" tongue and groove vertical wood siding and housewrap on insulated wood frame walls; R38 attic insulation; plastic clad double hung wood windows; raised panel exterior doors, frames and hardware, painted finish; wood storm and screen door.	14.48	5.17	19.65	15.4%
5 Roofing	Red cedar roof shingles, perfections; #15 felt building paper; aluminum gutters, downspouts and drip edge; copper flashings.	1.61	1.34	2.95	2.3%
6 Interiors	Skim coated 1/2" thick gypsum wallboard walls and ceilings, primed and painted with 2 coats; interior raised panel solid core doors, frames and hardware, painted finish; oak hardwood flooring, 70%; ceramic tile flooring, 30%; hardwood tread stairway.	18.48	17.05	35.53	27.9%
7 Specialties	Custom grade kitchen cabinets and countertops; double bowl kitchen sink; 75 gallon gas water heater.	6.94	1.32	8.26	6.5%
8 Mechanical	Three fixture bathroom: bathtub, water closet, vanity and sink; gas fired heating and air conditioning system.	6.03	3.43	9.46	7.4%
9 Electrical	200 amp electric service; wiring, duplex & GFI receptacles, wall switches, door bell, appliance circuits, air conditioning circuit, fans and communications cabling; custom grade lighting fixtures.	2.51	2.61	5.12	4.0%
10 Overhead	Contractor's overhead and profit and design.	12.05	9.18	21.23	16.7%
	Total	72.30	55.05	**127.35**	

- A distinct residence from designer's plans
- Single family — 1 full bath, 1 half bath, 1 kitchen
- No basement
- Asphalt shingles on roof
- Forced hot air heat/air conditioning
- Gypsum wallboard interior finishes
- Materials and workmanship are above average

Note: The illustration shown may contain some optional components (for example: garages and/or fireplaces) whose costs are shown in the modifications, adjustments, & alternatives below or at the end of the square foot section.

Base cost per square foot of living area

Exterior Wall	Living Area										
	1200	1400	1600	1800	2000	2400	2800	3200	3600	4000	4400
Wood Siding - Wood Frame	168.05	157.55	150.05	143.40	136.30	126.50	118.15	112.75	109.50	106.05	103.15
Brick Veneer - Wood Frame	176.85	165.85	157.90	150.85	143.45	132.95	124.00	118.30	114.85	111.00	107.95
Stone Veneer - Wood Frame	184.80	173.25	165.00	157.50	149.95	138.80	129.30	123.25	119.55	115.50	112.30
Solid Masonry	185.70	174.05	165.80	158.25	150.60	139.35	129.90	123.80	120.15	116.00	112.75
Finished Basement, Add	32.00	32.25	31.45	30.50	30.00	28.65	27.60	26.90	26.55	25.95	25.65
Unfinished Basement, Add	14.30	13.70	13.25	12.80	12.50	11.85	11.25	10.95	10.75	10.45	10.30

Modifications

Add to the total cost

Upgrade Kitchen Cabinets	$ + 1842
Solid Surface Countertops (Included)	
Full Bath - including plumbing, wall and floor finishes	+ 9664
Half Bath - including plumbing, wall and floor finishes	+ 5828
Two Car Attached Garage	+ 29,256
Two Car Detached Garage	+ 33,472
Fireplace & Chimney	+ 7234

Adjustments

For multi family - add to total cost

Additional Kitchen	$ + 22,146
Additional Full Bath & Half Bath	+ 15,492
Additional Entry & Exit	+ 1716
Separate Heating & Air Conditioning	+ 7245
Separate Electric	+ 1879

For Townhouse/Rowhouse - Multiply cost per square foot by

Inner Unit	.89
End Unit	.95

Alternatives

Add to or deduct from the cost per square foot of living area

Cedar Shake Roof	+ 1.20
Clay Tile Roof	+ 2.95
Slate Roof	+ 3.35
Upgrade Ceilings to Textured Finish	+ .60
Air Conditioning, in Heating Ductwork	Base System
Heating Systems, Hot Water	+ 1.52
Heat Pump	+ 1.60
Electric Heat	– 2.10
Not Heated	– 3.72

Additional upgrades or components

Kitchen Cabinets & Countertops	Page 93
Bathroom Vanities	94
Fireplaces & Chimneys	94
Windows, Skylights & Dormers	94
Appliances	95
Breezeways & Porches	95
Finished Attic	95
Garages	96
Site Improvements	96
Wings & Ells	74

Important: See the Reference Section for Location Factors (to adjust for your city) and Estimating Forms.

		Cost Per Square Foot Of Living Area			% of Total
		Mat.	Inst.	Total	(rounded)
1 Site Work	Site preparation for slab; 4' deep trench excavation for foundation wall.		1.09	1.09	0.9%
2 Foundation	Continuous reinforced concrete footing, 12" deep x 24" wide; dampproofed and insulated 12" thick reinforced concrete block foundation wall, 4' deep; trowel finished 4" thick concrete slab on 4" crushed stone base and polyethylene vapor barrier.	3.94	5.02	8.96	7.6%
3 Framing	Exterior walls - 2" x 6" wood studs, 16" O.C.; 1/2" sheathing; gable end roof framing, 2" x 10" rafters, 16" O.C. with 1/2" plywood sheathing; 2" x 10" floor joists, 16" O.C. with bridging and 5/8" subflooring; 2" x 4" interior partitions.	6.35	8.80	15.15	12.8%
4 Exterior Walls	1" x 6" tongue and groove vertical wood siding and housewrap on insulated wood frame walls; R38 attic insulation; plastic clad double hung wood windows; raised panel exterior doors, frames and hardware, painted finish; wood storm and screen door.	9.96	3.55	13.51	11.4%
5 Roofing	Red cedar roof shingles, perfections; #15 felt building paper; aluminum gutters, downspouts and drip edge; copper flashings.	2.41	2.01	4.42	3.7%
6 Interiors	Skim coated 1/2" thick gypsum wallboard walls and ceilings, primed and painted with 2 coats; interior raised panel solid core doors, frames and hardware, painted finish; oak hardwood flooring, 70%; ceramic tile flooring, 30%; hardwood tread stairway.	16.41	15.08	31.49	26.7%
7 Specialties	Custom grade kitchen cabinets and countertops; double bowl kitchen sink; 75 gallon gas water heater.	7.40	1.41	8.81	7.5%
8 Mechanical	Three fixture bathroom: bathtub, water closet, vanity and sink; gas fired heating and air conditioning system.	6.38	3.50	9.88	8.4%
9 Electrical	200 amp electric service; wiring, duplex & GFI receptacles, wall switches, door bell, appliance circuits, air conditioning circuit, fans and communications cabling; custom grade lighting fixtures.	2.52	2.64	5.16	4.4%
10 Overhead	Contractor's overhead and profit and design.	11.08	8.60	19.68	16.7%
Total		66.45	51.70	**118.15**	

For customer support on your Residential Costs with RSMeans Data, call 800.448.8182.

71

- **A distinct residence from designer's plans**
- **Single family — 1 full bath, 1 half bath, 1 kitchen**
- **No basement**
- **Asphalt shingles on roof**
- **Forced hot air heat/air conditioning**
- **Gypsum wallboard interior finishes**
- **Materials and workmanship are above average**

Note: The illustration shown may contain some optional components (for example: garages and/or fireplaces) whose costs are shown in the modifications, adjustments, & alternatives below or at the end of the square foot section.

eDesign Basics, Inc.

Base cost per square foot of living area

Exterior Wall	Living Area										
	1200	1500	1800	2100	2400	2800	3200	3600	4000	4500	5000
Wood Siding - Wood Frame	173.75	157.05	144.85	134.70	127.85	122.75	117.00	111.10	108.35	102.75	99.55
Brick Veneer - Wood Frame	182.60	165.10	152.05	141.25	134.05	128.65	122.55	116.20	113.30	107.25	103.85
Stone Veneer - Wood Frame	190.60	172.40	158.60	147.25	139.60	134.05	127.50	120.80	117.75	111.35	107.80
Solid Masonry	191.45	173.15	159.30	147.85	140.25	134.60	128.00	121.25	118.20	111.85	108.15
Finished Basement, Add*	40.05	39.90	38.20	36.75	35.85	35.25	34.35	33.55	33.15	32.35	31.85
Unfinished Basement, Add*	17.70	16.70	15.80	15.10	14.60	14.30	13.85	13.40	13.20	12.80	12.55

*Basement under middle level only.

Modifications

Add to the total cost

Upgrade Kitchen Cabinets	$ + 1842
Solid Surface Countertops (Included)	
Full Bath - including plumbing, wall and floor finishes	+ 9664
Half Bath - including plumbing, wall and floor finishes	+ 5828
Two Car Attached Garage	+ 29,256
Two Car Detached Garage	+ 33,472
Fireplace & Chimney	+ 7234

Adjustments

For multi family - add to total cost

Additional Kitchen	$ + 22,146
Additional Full Bath & Half Bath	+ 15,492
Additional Entry & Exit	+ 1716
Separate Heating & Air Conditioning	+ 7245
Separate Electric	+ 1879

*For Townhouse/Rowhouse -
Multiply cost per square foot by*

Inner Unit	.87
End Unit	.94

Alternatives

Add to or deduct from the cost per square foot of living area

Cedar Shake Roof	+ 1.70
Clay Tile Roof	+ 4.30
Slate Roof	+ 4.80
Upgrade Ceilings to Textured Finish	+ .60
Air Conditioning, in Heating Ductwork	Base System
Heating Systems, Hot Water	+ 1.47
Heat Pump	+ 1.67
Electric Heat	− 1.87
Not Heated	− 3.72

Additional upgrades or components

Kitchen Cabinets & Countertops	Page 93
Bathroom Vanities	94
Fireplaces & Chimneys	94
Windows, Skylights & Dormers	94
Appliances	95
Breezeways & Porches	95
Finished Attic	95
Garages	96
Site Improvements	96
Wings & Ells	74

Living Area - 3200 S.F.
Perimeter - 198 L.F.

		Cost Per Square Foot Of Living Area			% of Total
		Mat.	Inst.	Total	(rounded)
1 Site Work	Site preparation for slab; 4' deep trench excavation for foundation wall.		.95	.95	0.8%
2 Foundation	Continuous reinforced concrete footing, 12" deep x 24" wide; damproofed and insulated 12" thick reinforced concrete block foundation wall, 4' deep; trowel finished 4" thick concrete slab on 4" crushed stone base and polyethylene vapor barrier.	4.63	5.77	10.40	8.9%
3 Framing	Exterior walls - 2" x 6" wood studs, 16" O.C.; 1/2" sheathing; gable end roof framing, 2" x 10" rafters, 16" O.C. with 1/2" plywood sheathing; 2" x 10" floor joists, 16" O.C. with bridging and 5/8" subflooring; 2" x 4" interior partitions.	6.32	8.87	15.19	13.0%
4 Exterior Walls	1" x 6" tongue and groove vertical wood siding and housewrap on insulated wood frame walls; R38 attic insulation; plastic clad double hung wood windows; raised panel exterior doors, frames and hardware, painted finish; wood storm and screen door.	9.85	3.49	13.34	11.4%
5 Roofing	Red cedar roof shingles, perfections; #15 felt building paper; aluminum gutters, downspouts and drip edge; copper flashings.	3.21	2.68	5.89	5.0%
6 Interiors	Skim coated 1/2" thick gypsum wallboard walls and ceilings, primed and painted with 2 coats; interior raised panel solid core doors, frames and hardware, painted finish; oak hardwood flooring, 70%; ceramic tile flooring, 30%; hardwood tread stairway.	15.52	14.32	29.84	25.5%
7 Specialties	Custom grade kitchen cabinets and countertops; double bowl kitchen sink; 75 gallon gas water heater.	6.49	1.23	7.72	6.6%
8 Mechanical	Three fixture bathroom: bathtub, water closet, vanity and sink; gas fired heating and air conditioning system.	5.75	3.37	9.12	7.8%
9 Electrical	200 amp electric service; wiring, duplex & GFI receptacles, wall switches, door bell, appliance circuits, air conditioning circuit, fans and communications cabling; custom grade lighting fixtures.	2.50	2.58	5.08	4.3%
10 Overhead	Contractor's overhead and profit and design.	10.83	8.64	19.47	16.6%
	Total	65.10	51.90	**117.00**	

1 Story — Base cost per square foot of living area

Exterior Wall	Living Area							
	50	100	200	300	400	500	600	700
Wood Siding - Wood Frame	254.55	197.85	173.40	146.40	138.40	133.50	130.30	131.05
Brick Veneer - Wood Frame	282.40	217.75	189.95	157.40	148.35	142.75	139.15	139.60
Stone Veneer - Wood Frame	307.60	235.75	204.95	167.45	157.30	151.20	147.15	147.30
Solid Masonry	314.10	240.45	208.85	170.05	159.60	153.35	149.25	149.30
Finished Basement, Add	97.85	83.20	75.20	61.95	59.30	57.70	56.65	55.90
Unfinished Basement, Add	71.55	49.75	39.70	30.50	28.15	26.65	25.65	25.00

1-1/2 Story — Base cost per square foot of living area

Exterior Wall	Living Area							
	100	200	300	400	500	600	700	800
Wood Siding - Wood Frame	202.00	165.90	143.90	130.25	123.65	120.35	116.25	115.10
Brick Veneer - Wood Frame	226.85	185.80	160.50	143.15	135.55	131.65	126.90	125.70
Stone Veneer - Wood Frame	249.35	203.80	175.50	154.90	146.35	141.80	136.55	135.30
Solid Masonry	255.20	208.50	179.35	157.90	149.15	144.50	139.05	137.75
Finished Basement, Add	65.20	60.25	54.90	49.05	47.45	46.40	45.35	45.25
Unfinished Basement, Add	42.95	32.85	28.05	23.90	22.45	21.50	20.65	20.40

2 Story — Base cost per square foot of living area

Exterior Wall	Living Area							
	100	200	400	600	800	1000	1200	1400
Wood Siding - Wood Frame	201.20	153.50	132.75	111.95	105.20	101.10	98.35	99.45
Brick Veneer - Wood Frame	229.10	173.40	149.35	123.00	115.15	110.35	107.15	107.95
Stone Veneer - Wood Frame	254.35	191.45	164.35	133.00	124.15	118.80	115.20	115.65
Solid Masonry	260.80	196.10	168.20	135.60	126.45	120.90	117.25	117.65
Finished Basement, Add	48.95	41.65	37.65	31.00	29.70	28.85	28.40	28.00
Unfinished Basement, Add	35.80	24.85	19.85	15.25	14.05	13.30	12.85	12.50

Base costs do not include bathroom or kitchen facilities. Use Modifications/Adjustments/Alternatives on pages 93–96 where appropriate.

Did you know?

Our online estimating solution gives you the same access to RSMeans' data with 24/7 access:

- Quickly locate costs in the searchable database.

- Build cost lists, estimates, and reports in minutes.

- Adjust costs to any location in the U.S. and Canada with the click of a button.

Start your free trial today at
www.RSMeansOnline.com

1 Story

1-1/2 Story

2 Story

2-1/2 Story

Bi-Level

Tri-Level

For customer support on your Residential Costs with RSMeans Data, call 800.448.8182.

77

- **Unique residence built from an architect's plan**
- **Single family — 1 full bath, 1 half bath, 1 kitchen**
- **No basement**
- **Cedar shakes on roof**
- **Forced hot air heat/air conditioning**
- **Gypsum wallboard interior finishes**
- **Many special features**
- **Extraordinary materials and workmanship**

Note: The illustration shown may contain some optional components (for example: garages and/or fireplaces) whose costs are shown in the modifications, adjustments, & alternatives below or at the end of the square foot section.

©Home Planners, Inc.

Base cost per square foot of living area

Exterior Wall	Living Area										
	1000	1200	1400	1600	1800	2000	2400	2800	3200	3600	4000
Wood Siding - Wood Frame	230.05	210.05	193.95	183.20	176.75	169.40	156.55	147.30	140.65	134.05	128.50
Brick Veneer - Wood Frame	241.00	219.95	202.90	191.55	184.85	177.00	163.45	153.75	146.60	139.60	133.70
Solid Brick	254.30	231.90	213.80	201.80	194.70	186.30	171.95	161.55	153.85	146.40	140.05
Solid Stone	261.70	238.60	219.95	207.50	200.10	191.45	176.65	165.95	157.90	150.10	143.50
Finished Basement, Add	60.15	64.70	62.10	60.40	59.40	58.05	56.10	54.55	53.20	52.10	51.10
Unfinished Basement, Add	26.95	25.35	24.00	23.15	22.65	21.95	20.90	20.15	19.45	18.90	18.40

Modifications

Add to the total cost

Upgrade Kitchen Cabinets	$ + 2594
Solid Surface Countertops (Included)	
Full Bath - including plumbing, wall and floor finishes	+ 11,597
Half Bath - including plumbing, wall and floor finishes	+ 6993
Two Car Attached Garage	+ 33,436
Two Car Detached Garage	+ 37,988
Fireplace & Chimney	+ 10,417

Adjustments

For multi family - add to total cost

Additional Kitchen	$ + 30,167
Additional Full Bath & Half Bath	+ 18,590
Additional Entry & Exit	+ 2418
Separate Heating & Air Conditioning	+ 7245
Separate Electric	+ 1879

For Townhouse/Rowhouse -
Multiply cost per square foot by

Inner Unit	.90
End Unit	.95

Alternatives

Add to or deduct from the cost per square foot of living area

Heavyweight Asphalt Shingles	– 2.35
Clay Tile Roof	+ 3.55
Slate Roof	+ 4.30
Upgrade Ceilings to Textured Finish	+ .60
Air Conditioning, in Heating Ductwork	Base System
Heating Systems, Hot Water	+ 1.77
Heat Pump	+ 1.47
Electric Heat	– 2.10
Not Heated	– 4.80

Additional upgrades or components

Kitchen Cabinets & Countertops	Page 93
Bathroom Vanities	94
Fireplaces & Chimneys	94
Windows, Skylights & Dormers	94
Appliances	95
Breezeways & Porches	95
Finished Attic	95
Garages	96
Site Improvements	96
Wings & Ells	92

Important: See the Reference Section for Location Factors (to adjust for your city) and Estimating Forms.

		Cost Per Square Foot Of Living Area			% of Total
		Mat.	Inst.	Total	(rounded)
1 Site Work	Site preparation for slab; 4' deep trench excavation for foundation wall.		1.18	1.18	0.8%
2 Foundation	Continuous reinforced concrete footing, 12" deep x 24" wide; damproofed and insulated 12" thick reinforced concrete block foundation wall, 4' deep; trowel finished 6" thick concrete slab on 4" crushed stone base and polyethylene vapor barrier.	7.82	8.52	16.34	11.1%
3 Framing	Exterior walls - 2" x 6" wood studs, 16" O.C.; 1/2" sheathing; gable end roof framing, 2" x 10" rafters, 16" O.C. with 1/2" plywood sheathing; 2" x 4" interior partitions.	6.89	9.74	16.63	11.3%
4 Exterior Walls	1" x 6" tongue and groove vertical wood siding and housewrap on insulated wood frame walls; R38 attic insulation; metal clad double hung wood windows; raised panel exterior doors, frame and hardware, painted finish; wood storm and screen door.	12.56	4.22	16.78	11.4%
5 Roofing	Red cedar roof shingles, perfections; #15 felt building paper; aluminum gutters, downspouts and drip edge; copper flashings.	5.21	4.34	9.55	6.5%
6 Interiors	Skim coated 1/2" thick gypsum wallboard walls and ceilings, primed and painted with 2 coats; interior raised panel solid core doors, frames and hardware, painted finish; oak hardwood flooring, 70%; ceramic tile flooring, 30%.	14.29	15.00	29.29	19.9%
7 Specialties	Luxury grade kitchen cabinets and countertops; double bowl kitchen sink; 75 gallon gas water heater.	9.77	1.84	11.61	7.9%
8 Mechanical	Three fixture bathroom: bathtub, water closet, vanity and sink; gas fired heating and air conditioning system.	7.15	3.86	11.01	7.5%
9 Electrical	200 amp electric service; wiring, duplex & GFI receptacles, wall switches, dimmer switches, door bell, appliance circuits, air conditioning circuit, fans and communications cabling; luxury grade lighting fixtures.	3.54	2.86	6.40	4.3%
10 Overhead	Contractor's overhead and profit and architect's fees.	16.12	12.39	28.51	19.4%
Total		83.35	63.95	**147.30**	

For customer support on your Residential Costs with RSMeans Data, call 800.448.8182.

79

- **Unique residence built from an architect's plan**
- **Single family — 1 full bath, 1 half bath, 1 kitchen**
- **No basement**
- **Cedar shakes on roof**
- **Forced hot air heat/air conditioning**
- **Gypsum wallboard interior finishes**
- **Many special features**
- **Extraordinary materials and workmanship**

Note: The illustration shown may contain some optional components (for example: garages and/or fireplaces) whose costs are shown in the modifications, adjustments, & alternatives below or at the end of the square foot section.

©Larry E. Belk Designs

Base cost per square foot of living area

Exterior Wall	Living Area										
	1000	1200	1400	1600	1800	2000	2400	2800	3200	3600	4000
Wood Siding - Wood Frame	231.35	213.90	201.35	187.35	178.85	170.90	156.05	149.00	142.50	137.75	131.10
Brick Veneer - Wood Frame	244.40	226.10	213.00	197.90	188.85	180.35	164.45	156.95	149.85	144.85	137.75
Solid Brick	259.50	240.30	226.50	210.15	200.45	191.45	174.20	166.15	158.40	153.10	145.40
Solid Stone	268.80	249.05	234.85	217.75	207.65	198.30	180.20	171.90	163.65	158.25	150.10
Finished Basement, Add	42.20	45.85	44.50	42.50	41.35	40.30	38.30	37.40	36.25	35.75	34.85
Unfinished Basement, Add	19.45	18.50	17.85	16.90	16.25	15.80	14.70	14.25	13.70	13.45	12.95

Modifications

Add to the total cost

Upgrade Kitchen Cabinets	$ + 2594
Solid Surface Countertops (Included)	
Full Bath - including plumbing, wall and floor finishes	+ 11,597
Half Bath - including plumbing, wall and floor finishes	+ 6993
Two Car Attached Garage	+ 33,436
Two Car Detached Garage	+ 37,988
Fireplace & Chimney	+ 10,417

Adjustments

For multi family - add to total cost

Additional Kitchen	$ + 30,167
Additional Full Bath & Half Bath	+ 18,590
Additional Entry & Exit	+ 2418
Separate Heating & Air Conditioning	+ 7245
Separate Electric	+ 1879

For Townhouse/Rowhouse -
Multiply cost per square foot by

Inner Unit	.90
End Unit	.95

Alternatives

Add to or deduct from the cost per square foot of living area

Heavyweight Asphalt Shingles	– 1.70
Clay Tile Roof	+ 2.55
Slate Roof	+ 3.10
Upgrade Ceilings to Textured Finish	+ .60
Air Conditioning, in Heating Ductwork	Base System
Heating Systems, Hot Water	+ 1.69
Heat Pump	+ 1.64
Electric Heat	– 2.10
Not Heated	– 4.43

Additional upgrades or components

Kitchen Cabinets & Countertops	Page 93
Bathroom Vanities	94
Fireplaces & Chimneys	94
Windows, Skylights & Dormers	94
Appliances	95
Breezeways & Porches	95
Finished Attic	95
Garages	96
Site Improvements	96
Wings & Ells	92

Important: See the Reference Section for Location Factors (to adjust for your city) and Estimating Forms.

		Cost Per Square Foot Of Living Area			% of Total
		Mat.	Inst.	Total	(rounded)
1 Site Work	Site preparation for slab; 4' deep trench excavation for foundation wall.		1.18	1.18	0.8%
2 Foundation	Continuous reinforced concrete footing, 12" deep x 24" wide; damproofed and insulated 12" thick reinforced concrete block foundation wall, 4' deep; trowel finished 6" thick concrete slab on 4" crushed stone base and polyethylene vapor barrier.	5.67	6.44	12.11	8.1%
3 Framing	Exterior walls - 2" x 6" wood studs, 16" O.C.; 1/2" sheathing; gable end roof framing, steep pitch 2" x 10" rafters, 16" O.C. with 1/2" plywood sheathing; 2" x 12" floor joists, 16" O.C. with bridging and 5/8" subflooring; 2" x 4" interior partitions.	7.99	10.81	18.80	12.6%
4 Exterior Walls	1" x 6" tongue and groove vertical wood siding and housewrap on insulated wood frame walls; R38 attic insulation; metal clad double hung wood windows; raised panel exterior doors, frame and hardware, painted finish; wood storm and screen door.	13.45	4.56	18.01	12.1%
5 Roofing	Red cedar roof shingles, perfections; #15 felt building paper; aluminum gutters, downspouts and drip edge; copper flashings.	3.78	3.14	6.92	4.6%
6 Interiors	Skim coated 1/2" thick gypsum wallboard walls and ceilings, primed and painted with 2 coats; interior raised panel solid core doors, frames and hardware, painted finish; oak hardwood flooring, 70%; ceramic tile flooring, 30%; hardwood tread stairway.	16.88	17.24	34.12	22.9%
7 Specialties	Luxury grade kitchen cabinets and countertops; double bowl kitchen sink; 75 gallon gas water heater.	9.77	1.84	11.61	7.8%
8 Mechanical	Three fixture bathroom: bathtub, water closet, vanity and sink; gas fired heating and air conditioning system.	7.15	3.86	11.01	7.4%
9 Electrical	200 amp electric service; wiring, duplex & GFI receptacles, wall switches, dimmer switches, door bell, appliance circuits, air conditioning circuit, fans and communications cabling; luxury grade lighting fixtures.	3.54	2.86	6.40	4.3%
10 Overhead	Contractor's overhead and profit and architect's fees.	16.37	12.47	28.84	19.4%
Total		84.60	64.40	**149.00**	

- Unique residence built from an architect's plan
- Single family — 1 full bath, 1 half bath, 1 kitchen
- No basement
- Cedar shakes on roof
- Forced hot air heat/air conditioning
- Gypsum wallboard interior finishes
- Many special features
- Extraordinary materials and workmanship

Note: The illustration shown may contain some optional components (for example: garages and/or fireplaces) whose costs are shown in the modifications, adjustments, & alternatives below or at the end of the square foot section.

Base cost per square foot of living area

Exterior Wall	Living Area										
	1200	1400	1600	1800	2000	2400	2800	3200	3600	4000	4400
Wood Siding - Wood Frame	210.05	196.40	186.70	178.20	169.35	156.65	146.05	139.05	134.95	130.25	126.60
Brick Veneer - Wood Frame	223.05	208.55	198.30	189.10	179.85	166.10	154.60	147.15	142.70	137.60	133.65
Solid Brick	239.85	224.25	213.30	203.25	193.45	178.40	165.80	157.55	152.80	147.05	142.85
Solid Stone	247.75	231.70	220.35	209.90	199.90	184.20	171.10	162.55	157.60	151.60	147.15
Finished Basement, Add	33.95	36.80	35.85	34.75	34.05	32.40	31.15	30.25	29.80	29.05	28.70
Unfinished Basement, Add	15.60	14.90	14.40	13.85	13.50	12.70	12.00	11.55	11.35	11.00	10.75

Modifications

Add to the total cost

Upgrade Kitchen Cabinets	$ + 2594
Solid Surface Countertops (Included)	
Full Bath - including plumbing, wall and floor finishes	+ 11,597
Half Bath - including plumbing, wall and floor finishes	+ 6993
Two Car Attached Garage	+ 33,436
Two Car Detached Garage	+ 37,988
Fireplace & Chimney	+ 11,420

Adjustments

For multi family - add to total cost

Additional Kitchen	$ + 30,167
Additional Full Bath & Half Bath	+ 18,590
Additional Entry & Exit	+ 2418
Separate Heating & Air Conditioning	+ 7245
Separate Electric	+ 1879

For Townhouse/Rowhouse - Multiply cost per square foot by

Inner Unit	.86
End Unit	.93

Alternatives

Add to or deduct from the cost per square foot of living area

Heavyweight Asphalt Shingles	– 1.20
Clay Tile Roof	+ 1.80
Slate Roof	+ 2.15
Upgrade Ceilings to Textured Finish	+ .60
Air Conditioning, in Heating Ductwork	Base System
Heating Systems, Hot Water	+ 1.64
Heat Pump	+ 1.73
Electric Heat	– 1.90
Not Heated	– 4.19

Additional upgrades or components

Kitchen Cabinets & Countertops	Page 93
Bathroom Vanities	94
Fireplaces & Chimneys	94
Windows, Skylights & Dormers	94
Appliances	95
Breezeways & Porches	95
Finished Attic	95
Garages	96
Site Improvements	96
Wings & Ells	92

Important: See the Reference Section for Location Factors (to adjust for your city) and Estimating Forms.

			Cost Per Square Foot Of Living Area			% of Total
			Mat.	Inst.	Total	(rounded)
1	**Site Work**	Site preparation for slab; 4' deep trench excavation for foundation wall.		1.03	1.03	0.7%
2	**Foundation**	Continuous reinforced concrete footing, 12" deep x 24" wide; damproofed and insulated 12" thick reinforced concrete block foundation wall, 4' deep; trowel finished 6" thick concrete slab on 4" crushed stone base and polyethylene vapor barrier.	4.59	5.23	9.82	7.1%
3	**Framing**	Exterior walls - 2" x 6" wood studs, 16" O.C.; 1/2" sheathing; gable end roof framing, 2" x 10" rafters, 16" O.C. with 1/2" plywood sheathing; 2" x 12" floor joists, 16" O.C. with bridging and 5/8" subflooring; 2" x 4" interior partitions.	7.57	10.09	17.66	12.7%
4	**Exterior Walls**	1" x 6" tongue and groove vertical wood siding and housewrap on insulated wood frame walls; R38 attic insulation; metal clad double hung wood windows; raised panel exterior doors, frame and hardware, painted finish; wood storm and screen door.	13.61	4.62	18.23	13.1%
5	**Roofing**	Red cedar roof shingles, perfections; #15 felt building paper; aluminum gutters, downspouts and drip edge; copper flashings.	2.61	2.17	4.78	3.4%
6	**Interiors**	Skim coated 1/2" thick gypsum wallboard walls and ceilings, primed and painted with 2 coats; interior raised panel solid core doors, frames and hardware, painted finish; oak hardwood flooring, 70%; ceramic tile flooring, 30%; hardwood tread stairway.	16.74	17.25	33.99	24.4%
7	**Specialties**	Luxury grade kitchen cabinets and countertops; double bowl kitchen sink; 75 gallon gas water heater.	8.57	1.60	10.17	7.3%
8	**Mechanical**	Three fixture bathroom: bathtub, water closet, vanity and sink; gas fired heating and air conditioning system.	6.44	3.73	10.17	7.3%
9	**Electrical**	200 amp electric service; wiring, duplex & GFI receptacles, wall switches, dimmer switches, door bell, appliance circuits, air conditioning circuit, fans and communications cabling; luxury grade lighting fixtures.	3.51	2.79	6.30	4.5%
10	**Overhead**	Contractor's overhead and profit and architect's fees.	15.26	11.64	26.90	19.3%
		Total	78.90	60.15	**139.05**	

For customer support on your Residential Costs with RSMeans Data, call 800.448.8182.

83

- Unique residence built from an architect's plan
- Single family — 1 full bath, 1 half bath, 1 kitchen
- No basement
- Cedar shakes on roof
- Forced hot air heat/air conditioning
- Gypsum wallboard interior finishes
- Many special features
- Extraordinary materials and workmanship

Note: The illustration shown may contain some optional components (for example: garages and/or fireplaces) whose costs are shown in the modifications, adjustments, & alternatives below or at the end of the square foot section.

©Larry W. Garnett & Associates, Inc

Base cost per square foot of living area

Exterior Wall	Living Area										
	1500	1800	2100	2500	3000	3500	4000	4500	5000	5500	6000
Wood Siding - Wood Frame	205.10	184.55	171.85	162.45	149.95	140.90	132.35	128.10	124.25	120.55	116.55
Brick Veneer - Wood Frame	218.90	197.30	183.25	173.15	159.70	149.80	140.60	135.85	131.70	127.65	123.30
Solid Brick	236.15	213.20	197.50	186.60	171.85	160.90	150.90	145.60	140.90	136.50	131.75
Solid Stone	245.20	221.50	204.95	193.65	178.30	166.70	156.25	150.75	145.80	141.05	136.20
Finished Basement, Add	27.05	29.10	27.50	26.60	25.35	24.35	23.55	23.00	22.55	22.10	21.80
Unfinished Basement, Add	12.60	11.85	11.05	10.60	9.95	9.45	9.10	8.80	8.55	8.30	8.20

Modifications

Add to the total cost

Upgrade Kitchen Cabinets	$ + 2594
Solid Surface Countertops (Included)	
Full Bath - including plumbing, wall and floor finishes	+ 11,597
Half Bath - including plumbing, wall and floor finishes	+ 6993
Two Car Attached Garage	+ 33,436
Two Car Detached Garage	+ 37,988
Fireplace & Chimney	+ 12,496

Adjustments

For multi family - add to total cost

Additional Kitchen	$ + 30,167
Additional Full Bath & Half Bath	+ 18,590
Additional Entry & Exit	+ 2418
Separate Heating & Air Conditioning	+ 7245
Separate Electric	+ 1879

For Townhouse/Rowhouse - Multiply cost per square foot by

Inner Unit	.86
End Unit	.93

Alternatives

Add to or deduct from the cost per square foot of living area

Heavyweight Asphalt Shingles	– 1.05
Clay Tile Roof	+ 1.55
Slate Roof	+ 1.85
Upgrade Ceilings to Textured Finish	+ .60
Air Conditioning, in Heating Ductwork	Base System
Heating Systems, Hot Water	+ 1.48
Heat Pump	+ 1.78
Electric Heat	– 3.73
Not Heated	– 4.19

Additional upgrades or components

Kitchen Cabinets & Countertops	Page 93
Bathroom Vanities	94
Fireplaces & Chimneys	94
Windows, Skylights & Dormers	94
Appliances	95
Breezeways & Porches	95
Finished Attic	95
Garages	96
Site Improvements	96
Wings & Ells	92

Important: See the Reference Section for Location Factors (to adjust for your city) and Estimating Forms.

			Cost Per Square Foot Of Living Area			% of Total
			Mat.	Inst.	Total	(rounded)
1	**Site Work**	Site preparation for slab; 4' deep trench excavation for foundation wall.		1.10	1.10	0.7%
2	**Foundation**	Continuous reinforced concrete footing, 12" deep x 24" wide; damproofed and insulated 12" thick reinforced concrete block foundation wall, 4' deep; trowel finished 6" thick concrete slab on 4" crushed stone base and polyethylene vapor barrier.	4.02	4.74	8.76	5.8%
3	**Framing**	Exterior walls - 2" x 6" wood studs, 16" O.C.; 1/2" sheathing; gable end roof framing, steep pitch 2" x 10" rafters, 16" O.C. with 1/2" plywood sheathing; 2" x 12" floor joists, 16" O.C. with bridging and 5/8" subflooring; 2" x 4" interior partitions.	8.39	11.16	19.55	13.0%
4	**Exterior Walls**	1" x 6" tongue and groove vertical wood siding and housewrap on insulated wood frame walls; R38 attic insulation; metal clad double hung wood windows; raised panel exterior doors, frame and hardware, painted finish; wood storm and screen door.	15.80	5.37	21.17	14.1%
5	**Roofing**	Red cedar roof shingles, perfections; #15 felt building paper; aluminum gutters, downspouts and drip edge; copper flashings.	2.33	1.93	4.26	2.8%
6	**Interiors**	Skim coated 1/2" thick gypsum wallboard walls and ceilings, primed and painted with 2 coats; interior raised panel solid core doors, frames and hardware, painted finish; oak hardwood flooring, 70%; ceramic tile flooring, 30%; hardwood tread stairway.	19.14	19.20	38.34	25.6%
7	**Specialties**	Luxury grade kitchen cabinets and countertops; double bowl kitchen sink; 75 gallon gas water heater.	9.15	1.71	10.86	7.2%
8	**Mechanical**	Three fixture bathroom: bathtub, water closet, vanity and sink; gas fired heating and air conditioning system.	6.75	3.78	10.53	7.0%
9	**Electrical**	200 amp electric service; wiring, duplex & GFI receptacles, wall switches, dimmer switches, door bell, appliance circuits, air conditioning circuit, fans and communications cabling; luxury grade lighting fixtures.	3.52	2.83	6.35	4.2%
10	**Overhead**	Contractor's overhead and profit and architect's fees.	16.60	12.43	29.03	19.4%
	Total		85.70	64.25	**149.95**	

- **Unique residence built from an architect's plan**
- **Single family — 1 full bath, 1 half bath, 1 kitchen**
- **No basement**
- **Cedar shakes on roof**
- **Forced hot air heat/air conditioning**
- **Gypsum wallboard interior finishes**
- **Many special features**
- **Extraordinary materials and workmanship**

Note: The illustration shown may contain some optional components (for example: garages and/or fireplaces) whose costs are shown in the modifications, adjustments, & alternatives below or at the end of the square foot section.

Base cost per square foot of living area

Exterior Wall	Living Area										
	1500	1800	2100	2500	3000	3500	4000	4500	5000	5500	6000
Wood Siding - Wood Frame	201.55	181.35	170.85	161.95	149.10	142.40	134.65	126.75	123.55	120.50	117.20
Brick Veneer - Wood Frame	215.35	194.10	182.75	173.30	159.45	152.20	143.55	134.95	131.55	128.15	124.35
Solid Brick	233.65	211.10	198.60	188.45	173.15	165.20	155.40	145.95	142.05	138.30	133.95
Solid Stone	241.85	218.55	205.70	195.15	179.25	170.95	160.65	150.75	146.75	142.80	138.20
Finished Basement, Add	23.70	25.55	24.55	23.85	22.70	22.00	21.15	20.45	20.10	19.80	19.35
Unfinished Basement, Add	11.05	10.45	9.90	9.55	9.00	8.70	8.20	7.85	7.75	7.55	7.30

Modifications

Add to the total cost

Upgrade Kitchen Cabinets	$ + 2594
Solid Surface Countertops (Included)	
Full Bath - including plumbing, wall and floor finishes	+ 11,597
Half Bath - including plumbing, wall and floor finishes	+ 6993
Two Car Attached Garage	+ 33,436
Two Car Detached Garage	+ 37,988
Fireplace & Chimney	+ 12,496

Adjustments

For multi family - add to total cost

Additional Kitchen	$ + 30,167
Additional Full Bath & Half Bath	+ 18,590
Additional Entry & Exit	+ 2418
Separate Heating & Air Conditioning	+ 7245
Separate Electric	+ 1879

*For Townhouse/Rowhouse -
Multiply cost per square foot by*

Inner Unit	.84
End Unit	.92

Alternatives

Add to or deduct from the cost per square foot of living area

Heavyweight Asphalt Shingles	– .80
Clay Tile Roof	+ 1.20
Slate Roof	+ 1.45
Upgrade Ceilings to Textured Finish	+ .60
Air Conditioning, in Heating Ductwork	Base System
Heating Systems, Hot Water	+ 1.48
Heat Pump	+ 1.78
Electric Heat	– 3.73
Not Heated	– 4.07

Additional upgrades or components

Kitchen Cabinets & Countertops	Page 93
Bathroom Vanities	94
Fireplaces & Chimneys	94
Windows, Skylights & Dormers	94
Appliances	95
Breezeways & Porches	95
Finished Attic	95
Garages	96
Site Improvements	96
Wings & Ells	92

Important: See the Reference Section for Location Factors (to adjust for your city) and Estimating Forms.

		Mat.	Inst.	Total	% of Total (rounded)
1 Site Work	Site preparation for slab; 4' deep trench excavation for foundation wall.		1.10	1.10	0.7%
2 Foundation	Continuous reinforced concrete footing, 12" deep x 24" wide; damproofed and insulated 12" thick reinforced concrete block foundation wall, 4' deep; trowel finished 6" thick concrete slab on 4" crushed stone base and polyethylene vapor barrier.	3.63	4.32	7.95	5.3%
3 Framing	Exterior walls - 2" x 6" wood studs, 16" O.C.; 1/2" sheathing; gable end roof framing, 2" x 10" rafters, 16" O.C. with 1/2" plywood sheathing; 2" x 12" floor joists, 16" O.C. with bridging and 5/8" subflooring; 2" x 4" interior partitions.	8.23	10.87	19.10	12.8%
4 Exterior Walls	1" x 6" tongue and groove vertical wood siding and housewrap on insulated wood frame walls; R38 attic insulation; metal clad double hung wood windows; raised panel exterior doors, frame and hardware, painted finish; wood storm and screen door.	16.83	5.74	22.57	15.1%
5 Roofing	Red cedar roof shingles, perfections; #15 felt building paper; aluminum gutters, downspouts and drip edge; copper flashings.	1.74	1.45	3.19	2.1%
6 Interiors	Skim coated 1/2" thick gypsum wallboard walls and ceilings, primed and painted with 2 coats; interior raised panel solid core doors, frames and hardware, painted finish; oak hardwood flooring, 70%; ceramic tile flooring, 30%; hardwood tread stairway.	19.22	19.38	38.60	25.9%
7 Specialties	Luxury grade kitchen cabinets and countertops; double bowl kitchen sink; 75 gallon gas water heater.	9.15	1.71	10.86	7.3%
8 Mechanical	Three fixture bathroom: bathtub, water closet, vanity and sink; gas fired heating and air conditioning system.	6.75	3.78	10.53	7.1%
9 Electrical	200 amp electric service; wiring, duplex & GFI receptacles, wall switches, dimmer switches, door bell, appliance circuits, air conditioning circuit, fans and communications cabling; luxury grade lighting fixtures.	3.52	2.83	6.35	4.3%
10 Overhead	Contractor's overhead and profit and architect's fees.	16.58	12.27	28.85	19.3%
	Total	85.65	63.45	**149.10**	

Cost Per Square Foot Of Living Area

For customer support on your Residential Costs with RSMeans Data, call 800.448.8182.

87

- **Unique residence built from an architect's plan**
- **Single family — 1 full bath, 1 half bath, 1 kitchen**
- **No basement**
- **Cedar shakes on roof**
- **Forced hot air heat/air conditioning**
- **Gypsum wallboard interior finishes**
- **Many special features**
- **Extraordinary materials and workmanship**

Note: The illustration shown may contain some optional components (for example: garages and/or fireplaces) whose costs are shown in the modifications, adjustments, & alternatives below or at the end of the square foot section.

Base cost per square foot of living area

Exterior Wall	Living Area										
	1200	1400	1600	1800	2000	2400	2800	3200	3600	4000	4400
Wood Siding - Wood Frame	199.05	186.10	176.90	169.00	160.50	148.65	138.75	132.20	128.35	124.10	120.65
Brick Veneer - Wood Frame	208.95	195.35	185.65	177.25	168.40	155.80	145.25	138.35	134.25	129.65	126.05
Solid Brick	221.40	207.05	196.85	187.75	178.55	164.95	153.60	146.15	141.75	136.70	132.85
Solid Stone	227.70	212.95	202.50	193.05	183.65	169.55	157.75	150.05	145.55	140.30	136.25
Finished Basement, Add	33.95	36.80	35.85	34.75	34.05	32.40	31.15	30.25	29.80	29.05	28.70
Unfinished Basement, Add	15.60	14.90	14.40	13.85	13.50	12.70	12.00	11.55	11.35	11.00	10.75

Modifications

Add to the total cost

Upgrade Kitchen Cabinets	$ + 2594
Solid Surface Countertops (Included)	
Full Bath - including plumbing, wall and floor finishes	+ 11,597
Half Bath - including plumbing, wall and floor finishes	+ 6993
Two Car Attached Garage	+ 33,436
Two Car Detached Garage	+ 37,988
Fireplace & Chimney	+ 10,417

Adjustments

For multi family - add to total cost

Additional Kitchen	$ + 30,167
Additional Full Bath & Half Bath	+ 18,590
Additional Entry & Exit	+ 2418
Separate Heating & Air Conditioning	+ 7245
Separate Electric	+ 1879

For Townhouse/Rowhouse - Multiply cost per square foot by

Inner Unit	.89
End Unit	.94

Alternatives

Add to or deduct from the cost per square foot of living area

Heavyweight Asphalt Shingles	– 1.20
Clay Tile Roof	+ 1.80
Slate Roof	+ 2.15
Upgrade Ceilings to Textured Finish	+ .60
Air Conditioning, in Heating Ductwork	Base System
Heating Systems, Hot Water	+ 1.64
Heat Pump	+ 1.73
Electric Heat	– 1.90
Not Heated	– 4.19

Additional upgrades or components

Kitchen Cabinets & Countertops	Page 93
Bathroom Vanities	94
Fireplaces & Chimneys	94
Windows, Skylights & Dormers	94
Appliances	95
Breezeways & Porches	95
Finished Attic	95
Garages	96
Site Improvements	96
Wings & Ells	92

Important: See the Reference Section for Location Factors (to adjust for your city) and Estimating Forms.

			Cost Per Square Foot Of Living Area			% of Total
			Mat.	Inst.	Total	(rounded)
1	**Site Work**	Site preparation for slab; 4' deep trench excavation for foundation wall.		1.03	1.03	0.8%
2	**Foundation**	Continuous reinforced concrete footing, 12" deep x 24" wide; damproofed and insulated 12" thick reinforced concrete block foundation wall, 4' deep; trowel finished 6" thick concrete slab on 4" crushed stone base and polyethylene vapor barrier.	4.59	5.23	9.82	7.4%
3	**Framing**	Exterior walls - 2" x 6" wood studs, 16" O.C.; 1/2" sheathing; gable end roof framing, 2" x 10" rafters, 16" O.C. with 1/2" plywood sheathing; 2" x 12" floor joists, 16" O.C. with bridging and 5/8" subflooring; 2" x 4" interior partitions.	7.14	9.46	16.60	12.6%
4	**Exterior Walls**	1" x 6" tongue and groove vertical wood siding and housewrap on insulated wood frame walls; R38 attic insulation; metal clad double hung wood windows; raised panel exterior doors, frame and hardware, painted finish; wood storm and screen door.	10.81	3.65	14.46	10.9%
5	**Roofing**	Red cedar roof shingles, perfections: #15 felt building paper; aluminum gutters, downspouts and drip edge; copper flashings.	2.61	2.17	4.78	3.6%
6	**Interiors**	Skim coated 1/2" thick gypsum wallboard walls and ceilings, primed and painted with 2 coats; interior raised panel solid core doors, frames and hardware, painted finish; oak hardwood flooring, 70%; ceramic tile flooring, 30%; hardwood tread stairway.	16.46	16.83	33.29	25.2%
7	**Specialties**	Luxury grade kitchen cabinets and countertops; double bowl kitchen sink; 75 gallon gas water heater.	8.57	1.60	10.17	7.7%
8	**Mechanical**	Three fixture bathroom: bathtub, water closet, vanity and sink; gas fired heating and air conditioning system.	6.44	3.73	10.17	7.7%
9	**Electrical**	200 amp electric service; wiring, duplex & GFI receptacles, wall switches, dimmer switches, door bell, appliance circuits, air conditioning circuit, fans and communications cabling; luxury grade lighting fixtures	3.51	2.79	6.30	4.8%
10	**Overhead**	Contractor's overhead and profit and architect's fees.	14.42	11.16	25.58	19.3%
	Total		74.55	57.65	**132.20**	

- **Unique residence built from an architect's plan**
- **Single family — 1 full bath, 1 half bath, 1 kitchen**
- **No basement**
- **Cedar shakes on roof**
- **Forced hot air heat/air conditioning**
- **Gypsum wallboard interior finishes**
- **Many special features**
- **Extraordinary materials and workmanship**

Note: The illustration shown may contain some optional components (for example: garages and/or fireplaces) whose costs are shown in the modifications, adjustments, & alternatives below or at the end of the square foot section.

©Home Planners, Inc.

Base cost per square foot of living area

Exterior Wall	Living Area										
	1500	1800	2100	2400	2800	3200	3600	4000	4500	5000	5500
Wood Siding - Wood Frame	185.35	170.55	158.40	150.15	144.00	137.10	130.15	126.70	120.15	116.35	112.30
Brick Veneer - Wood Frame	194.30	178.70	165.75	157.05	150.65	143.30	135.80	132.20	125.20	121.15	116.90
Solid Brick	205.55	188.75	175.00	165.70	158.90	150.90	142.95	139.15	131.60	127.10	122.60
Solid Stone	211.45	194.00	179.80	170.15	163.25	154.95	146.60	142.75	134.90	130.30	125.50
Finished Basement, Add*	40.05	43.10	41.40	40.30	39.50	38.35	37.40	37.00	36.00	35.25	34.75
Unfinished Basement, Add*	17.95	16.90	15.95	15.40	15.05	14.45	14.00	13.75	13.25	12.90	12.55

*Basement under middle level only.

Modifications

Add to the total cost

Upgrade Kitchen Cabinets	$ + 2594
Solid Surface Countertops (Included)	
Full Bath - including plumbing, wall and floor finishes	+ 11,597
Half Bath - including plumbing, wall and floor finishes	+ 6993
Two Car Attached Garage	+ 33,436
Two Car Detached Garage	+ 37,988
Fireplace & Chimney	+ 10,417

Adjustments

For multi family - add to total cost

Additional Kitchen	$ + 30,167
Additional Full Bath & Half Bath	+ 18,590
Additional Entry & Exit	+ 2418
Separate Heating & Air Conditioning	+ 7245
Separate Electric	+ 1879

For Townhouse/Rowhouse - Multiply cost per square foot by

Inner Unit	.86
End Unit	.93

Alternatives

Add to or deduct from the cost per square foot of living area

Heavyweight Asphalt Shingles	– 1.70
Clay Tile Roof	+ 2.55
Slate Roof	+ 3.10
Upgrade Ceilings to Textured Finish	+ .60
Air Conditioning, in Heating Ductwork	Base System
Heating Systems, Hot Water	+ 1.59
Heat Pump	+ 1.80
Electric Heat	– 1.67
Not Heated	– 4.07

Additional upgrades or components

Kitchen Cabinets & Countertops	Page 93
Bathroom Vanities	94
Fireplaces & Chimneys	94
Windows, Skylights & Dormers	94
Appliances	95
Breezeways & Porches	95
Finished Attic	95
Garages	96
Site Improvements	96
Wings & Ells	92

Important: See the Reference Section for Location Factors (to adjust for your city) and Estimating Forms.

			Cost Per Square Foot Of Living Area			% of Total
			Mat.	Inst.	Total	(rounded)
1	**Site Work**	Site preparation for slab; 4' deep trench excavation for foundation wall.		.92	.92	0.7%
2	**Foundation**	Continuous reinforced concrete footing, 12" deep x 24" wide; damproofed and insulated 12" thick reinforced concrete block foundation wall, 4' deep; trowel finished 6" thick concrete slab on 4" crushed stone base and polyethylene vapor barrier.	5.47	6.02	11.49	8.8%
3	**Framing**	Exterior walls - 2" x 6" wood studs, 16" O.C.; 1/2" sheathing; gable end roof framing, 2" x 10" rafters, 16" O.C. with 1/2" plywood sheathing; 2" x 12" floor joists, 16" O.C. with bridging and 5/8" subflooring; 2" x 4" interior partitions.	6.90	9.29	16.19	12.4%
4	**Exterior Walls**	1" x 6" tongue and groove vertical wood siding and housewrap on insulated wood frame walls; R38 attic insulation; metal clad double hung wood windows; raised panel exterior doors, frame and hardware, painted finish; wood storm and screen door.	10.64	3.60	14.24	10.9%
5	**Roofing**	Red cedar roof shingles, perfections; #15 felt building paper; aluminum gutters, downspouts and drip edge; copper flashings.	3.47	2.89	6.36	4.9%
6	**Interiors**	Skim coated 1/2" thick gypsum wallboard walls and ceilings, primed and painted with 2 coats; interior raised panel solid core doors, frames and hardware, painted finish; oak hardwood flooring, 70%; ceramic tile flooring, 30%; hardwood tread stairway.	15.33	15.62	30.95	23.8%
7	**Specialties**	Luxury grade kitchen cabinets and countertops; double bowl kitchen sink; 75 gallon gas water heater.	7.64	1.43	9.07	7.0%
8	**Mechanical**	Three fixture bathroom: bathtub, water closet, vanity and sink; gas fired heating and air conditioning system.	5.89	3.60	9.49	7.3%
9	**Electrical**	200 amp electric service; wiring, duplex & GFI receptacles, wall switches, dimmer switches, door bell, appliance circuits, air conditioning circuit, fans and communications cabling; luxury grade lighting fixtures.	3.49	2.75	6.24	4.8%
10	**Overhead**	Contractor's overhead and profit and architect's fees.	14.12	11.08	25.20	19.4%
	Total		72.95	57.20	**130.15**	

For customer support on your Residential Costs with RSMeans Data, call 800.448.8182.

91

1 Story   Base cost per square foot of living area

Exterior Wall	Living Area							
	50	100	200	300	400	500	600	700
Wood Siding - Wood Frame	280.25	217.20	189.85	159.90	151.00	145.65	142.00	142.90
Brick Veneer - Wood Frame	312.15	240.00	208.85	172.55	162.35	156.25	152.15	152.65
Solid Brick	359.85	274.15	237.25	191.50	179.40	172.15	167.30	167.30
Solid Stone	376.90	286.25	247.40	198.20	185.55	177.85	172.70	172.45
Finished Basement, Add	108.30	98.10	88.00	71.05	67.70	65.60	64.35	63.35
Unfinished Basement, Add	56.60	43.60	38.20	29.15	27.40	26.30	25.60	25.05

1-1/2 Story   Base cost per square foot of living area

Exterior Wall	Living Area							
	100	200	300	400	500	600	700	800
Wood Siding - Wood Frame	221.90	181.85	157.25	142.15	134.75	131.15	126.55	125.30
Brick Veneer - Wood Frame	250.40	204.60	176.20	156.95	148.45	144.05	138.70	137.45
Solid Brick	293.00	238.70	204.70	179.15	168.90	163.35	157.05	155.60
Solid Stone	308.15	250.85	214.85	187.00	176.20	170.25	163.55	162.00
Finished Basement, Add	71.25	70.40	63.65	56.20	54.20	52.85	51.60	51.40
Unfinished Basement, Add	35.95	30.55	26.95	22.95	21.90	21.15	20.50	20.40

2 Story   Base cost per square foot of living area

Exterior Wall	Living Area							
	100	200	400	600	800	1000	1200	1400
Wood Siding - Wood Frame	217.95	164.90	141.75	118.70	111.15	106.65	103.55	104.85
Brick Veneer - Wood Frame	249.85	187.70	160.70	131.35	122.55	117.25	113.65	114.60
Solid Brick	297.55	221.80	189.10	150.30	139.55	133.15	128.85	129.25
Solid Stone	314.55	233.90	199.25	157.00	145.70	138.85	134.25	134.40
Finished Basement, Add	54.20	49.10	44.05	35.60	33.90	32.95	32.20	31.75
Unfinished Basement, Add	28.35	21.85	19.10	14.60	13.70	13.15	12.75	12.55

Base costs do not include bathroom or kitchen facilities. Use Modifications/Adjustments/Alternatives on pages 93–96 where appropriate.

Important: See the Reference Section for Location Factors (to adjust for your city) and Estimating Forms.

Kitchen cabinets - Base units, hardwood *(Cost per Unit)*

	Economy	Average	Custom	Luxury
24″ deep, 35″ high,				
One top drawer,				
One door below				
12″ wide	$ 270	$ 360	$ 479	$ 630
15″ wide	281	375	499	656
18″ wide	304	405	539	709
21″ wide	311	415	552	726
24″ wide	360	480	638	840
Four drawers				
12″ wide	285	380	505	665
15″ wide	289	385	512	674
18″ wide	311	415	552	726
24″ wide	341	455	605	796
Two top drawers,				
Two doors below				
27″ wide	390	520	692	910
30″ wide	424	565	751	989
33″ wide	439	585	778	1024
36″ wide	454	605	805	1059
42″ wide	476	635	845	1111
48″ wide	514	685	911	1199
Range or sink base				
(Cost per unit)				
Two doors below				
30″ wide	356	475	632	831
33″ wide	379	505	672	884
36″ wide	398	530	705	928
42″ wide	416	555	738	971
48″ wide	439	585	778	1024
Corner Base Cabinet				
(Cost per unit)				
36″ wide	638	850	1131	1488
Lazy Susan *(Cost per unit)*				
With revolving door	806	1075	1430	1881

Kitchen cabinets - Wall cabinets, hardwood *(Cost per Unit)*

	Economy	Average	Custom	Luxury
12″ deep, 2 doors				
12″ high				
30″ wide	$ 248	$ 330	$ 439	$ 578
36″ wide	289	385	512	674
15″ high				
30″ wide	251	335	446	586
33″ wide	304	405	539	709
36″ wide	296	395	525	691
24″ high				
30″ wide	304	405	539	709
36″ wide	334	445	592	779
42″ wide	375	500	665	875
30″ high, 1 door				
12″ wide	225	300	399	525
15″ wide	236	315	419	551
18″ wide	255	340	452	595
24″ wide	296	395	525	691
30″ high, 2 doors				
27″ wide	345	460	612	805
30″ wide	364	485	645	849
36″ wide	413	550	732	963
42″ wide	443	590	785	1033
48″ wide	495	660	878	1155
Corner wall, 30″ high				
24″ wide	360	480	638	840
30″ wide	383	510	678	893
36″ wide	428	570	758	998
Broom closet				
84″ high, 24″ deep				
18″ wide	671	895	1190	1566
Oven Cabinet				
84″ high, 24″ deep				
27″ wide	994	1325	1762	2319

Kitchen countertops *(Cost per L.F.)*

	Economy	Average	Custom	Luxury
Solid Surface				
24″ wide, no backsplash	$ 119	$ 158	$ 210	$ 277
with backsplash	129	172	229	301
Stock plastic laminate, 24″ wide				
with backsplash	25	33	45	59
Custom plastic laminate, no splash				
7/8″ thick, alum. molding	39	52	69	91
1-1/4″ thick, no splash	44	59	78	103
Marble				
1/2″ - 3/4″ thick w/splash	57	75	100	132
Maple, laminated				
1-1/2″ thick w/splash	90	120	160	210
Stainless steel				
(per S.F.)	146	195	259	341
Cutting blocks, recessed				
16″ x 20″ x 1″ (each)	123	164	218	287

For customer support on your Residential Costs with RSMeans Data, call 800.448.8182.

93

Vanity bases *(Cost per Unit)*

2 door, 30" high, 21" deep	Economy	Average	Custom	Luxury
24" wide	$ 315	$ 420	$ 559	$ 735
30" wide	379	505	672	884
36" wide	379	505	672	884
48" wide	488	650	865	1138

Solid surface vanity tops *(Cost Each)*

Center bowl	Economy	Average	Custom	Luxury
22" x 25"	$ 450	$ 486	$ 525	$ 567
22" x 31"	515	556	600	648
22" x 37"	595	643	694	750
22" x 49"	730	788	851	919

Fireplaces & Chimneys *(Cost per Unit)*

	1-1/2 Story	2 Story	3 Story
Economy (prefab metal)			
Exterior chimney & 1 fireplace	$ 6561	$ 7249	$ 7952
Interior chimney & 1 fireplace	6287	6989	7313
Average (masonry)			
Exterior chimney & 1 fireplace	6881	7603	8340
Interior chimney & 1 fireplace	6594	7331	7670
For more than 1 flue, add	468	797	1336
For more than 1 fireplace, add	4617	4617	4617
Custom (masonry)			
Exterior chimney & 1 fireplace	7233	8165	9220
Interior chimney & 1 fireplace	6782	7677	8274
For more than 1 flue, add	567	982	1644
For more than 1 fireplace, add	5196	5196	5196
Luxury (masonry)			
Exterior chimney & 1 fireplace	10417	11419	12496
Interior chimney & 1 fireplace	9938	10866	11501
For more than 1 flue, add	860	1435	2004
For more than 1 fireplace, add	8211	8211	8211

Windows and Skylights *(Cost Each)*

	Economy	Average	Custom	Luxury
Fixed Picture Windows				
3'-6" x 4'-0"	$ 375	$ 500	$ 665	$ 875
4'-0" x 6'-0"	648	864	1150	1513
5'-0" x 6'-0"	733	977	1300	1711
6'-0" x 6'-0"	761	1015	1350	1776
Bay/Bow Windows				
8'-0" x 5'-0"	874	1165	1550	2039
10'-0" x 5'-0"	930	1240	1650	2171
10'-0" x 6'-0"	1523	2030	2700	3553
12'-0" x 6'-0"	1988	2650	3525	4638
Palladian Windows				
3'-2" x 6'-4"		1522	2025	2664
4'-0" x 6'-0"		1672	2225	2928
5'-5" x 6'-10"		2293	3050	4013
8'-0" x 6'-0"		2763	3675	4836
Skylights				
46" x 21-1/2"	614	945	1145	1260
46" x 28"	631	970	1200	1320
57" x 44"	696	1070	1185	1304

Dormers *(Cost/S.F. of plan area)*

	Economy	Average	Custom	Luxury
Framing and Roofing Only				
Gable dormer, 2" x 6" roof frame	$ 33	$ 37	$ 41	$ 67
2" x 8" roof frame	34	38	42	70
Shed dormer, 2" x 6" roof frame	21	25	28	43
2" x 8" roof frame	23	26	29	44
2" x 10" roof frame	25	28	30	45

Appliances (Cost per Unit)

	Economy	Average	Custom	Luxury
Range				
30" free standing, 1 oven	$ 600	$ 1475	$ 1913	$ 2350
2 oven	1550	2288	2657	3025
30" built-in, 1 oven	1075	1688	1994	2300
2 oven	1700	1955	2083	2210
21" free standing				
1 oven	640	745	798	850
Counter Top Ranges				
4 burner standard	465	1295	1710	2125
As above with griddle	1800	3088	3732	4375
Microwave Oven	263	527	659	790
Compactor				
4 to 1 compaction	855	1140	1283	1425
Deep Freeze				
15 to 23 C.F.	725	863	932	1000
30 C.F.	850	1013	1094	1175
Dehumidifier, portable, auto.				
15 pint	340	391	417	442
30 pint	380	437	466	494
Washing Machine, automatic	795	1498	1849	2200
Water Heater				
Electric, glass lined				
30 gal.	1200	1450	1575	1700
80 gal.	2300	2850	3125	3400
Water Heater, Gas, glass lined				
30 gal.	2100	2550	2775	3000
50 gal.	2475	3025	3300	3575
Dishwasher, built-in				
2 cycles	510	720	825	930
4 or more cycles	625	775	1238	1700
Dryer, automatic	985	1543	1822	2100
Garage Door Opener	530	633	684	735
Garbage Disposal	173	254	295	335
Heater, Electric, built-in				
1250 watt ceiling type	267	329	360	390
1250 watt wall type	330	355	368	380
Wall type w/blower				
1500 watt	330	380	405	429
3000 watt	665	765	815	865
Hood For Range, 2 speed				
30" wide	214	720	973	1225
42" wide	289	1320	1835	2350
Humidifier, portable				
7 gal. per day	173	199	212	225
15 gal. per day	246	283	302	320
Ice Maker, automatic				
13 lb. per day	1275	1467	1563	1658
51 lb. per day	1900	2185	2328	2470
Refrigerator, no frost				
10-12 C.F.	635	673	692	710
14-16 C.F.	730	828	877	925
18-20 C.F.	910	1505	1803	2100
21-29 C.F.	1375	2725	3400	4075
Sump Pump, 1/3 H.P.	330	460	525	590

Breezeway (Cost per S.F.)

Class	Type	Area (S.F.)			
		50	100	150	200
Economy	Open	$ 47.53	$ 39.49	$ 34.66	$ 32.25
	Enclosed	175.06	124.63	102.57	88.20
Average	Open	56.05	45.68	40.07	37.27
	Enclosed	178.66	129.42	107.31	96.00
Custom	Open	67.77	55.62	48.95	45.61
	Enclosed	237.40	171.91	142.20	127.07
Luxury	Open	75.87	62.48	55.40	51.85
	Enclosed	281.36	201.01	164.79	146.41

Porches (Cost per S.F.)

Class	Type	Area (S.F.)				
		25	50	100	200	300
Economy	Open	$ 85.01	$ 63.34	$ 47.39	$ 36.57	$ 32.68
	Enclosed	184.92	146.93	96.77	73.57	63.91
Average	Open	89.13	68.29	49.86	37.81	33.50
	Enclosed	198.95	158.89	102.13	75.63	64.87
Custom	Open	153.84	110.23	84.53	63.20	61.39
	Enclosed	243.08	196.12	129.79	98.73	94.30
Luxury	Open	172.49	123.90	93.92	68.09	61.77
	Enclosed	284.14	255.56	165.24	120.76	100.34

Finished attic (Cost per S.F.)

Class	Area (S.F.)				
	400	500	600	800	1000
Economy	$ 22.98	$ 22.21	$ 21.29	$ 20.93	$ 20.15
Average	35.44	34.67	33.82	33.40	32.46
Custom	45.55	44.53	43.51	42.85	41.97
Luxury	58.42	57.01	55.67	54.35	53.45

Alarm system (Cost per System)

	Burglar Alarm	Smoke Detector
Economy	$ 440	$ 73
Average	500	84
Custom	880	228
Luxury	1525	269

Sauna, prefabricated
(Cost per unit, including heater and controls—7' high)

Size	Cost
6' x 4'	$ 5950
6' x 5'	6525
6' x 6'	6900
6' x 9'	8700
8' x 10'	10,200
8' x 12'	11,900
10' x 12'	13,800

Garages *

(Costs include exterior wall systems comparable with the quality of the residence. Included in the cost is an allowance for one personnel door, manual overhead door(s) and electrical fixture.)

Class	Type									
	Detached			Attached			Built-in		Basement	
	One Car	Two Car	Three Car	One Car	Two Car	Three Car	One Car	Two Car	One Car	Two Car
Economy										
Wood	$17,898	$27,330	$36,763	$13,851	$23,825	$33,257	$-2002	$-4004	$1812	$2483
Masonry	24,397	35,464	46,531	17,918	29,526	40,593	-2800	-5600		
Average										
Wood	19,637	29,507	39,376	14,940	25,350	35,220	-2215	-4431	2066	2991
Masonry	24,521	35,618	46,716	17,995	29,634	40,732	-2815	-4519		
Custom										
Wood	21,828	33,472	45,116	16,922	29,256	40,900	-3464	-3400	2953	4766
Masonry	26,061	38,769	51,477	19,571	32,969	45,677	-3984	-4439		
Luxury										
Wood	24,423	37,988	51,554	19,180	33,436	47,002	-3574	-3620	4016	6381
Masonry	31,866	47,304	62,742	23,838	39,966	55,404	-4488	-5449		

*See the Introduction to this section for definitions of garage types.

Swimming pools (Cost per S.F.)

Residential	
In-ground	$ 40.50 - 97.50
Deck equipment	1.30
Paint pool, preparation & 3 coats (epoxy)	5.40
Rubber base paint	4.72
Pool Cover	1.91
Swimming Pool Heaters	
(not including wiring, external piping, base or pad)	
Gas	
155 MBH	$ 3125.00
190 MBH	3700.00
500 MBH	13,100.
Electric	
15 KW 7200 gallon pool	2875.00
24 KW 9600 gallon pool	3350.00
54 KW 24,000 gallon pool	5250.00

Wood and coal stoves

Wood Only	
Free Standing (minimum)	$ 2175
Fireplace Insert (minimum)	1893
Coal Only	
Free Standing	$ 2139
Fireplace Insert	2342
Wood and Coal	
Free Standing	$ 4400
Fireplace Insert	4509

Sidewalks (Cost per S.F.)

Concrete, 3000 psi with wire mesh	4" thick	$ 4.28
	5" thick	5.22
	6" thick	5.86
Precast concrete patio blocks (natural)	2" thick	6.80
Precast concrete patio blocks (colors)	2" thick	7.20
Flagstone, bluestone	1" thick	20.60
Flagstone, bluestone	1-1/2" thick	28.35
Slate (natural, irregular)	3/4" thick	19.15
Slate (random rectangular)	1/2" thick	29.65
Seeding		
Fine grading & seeding includes lime, fertilizer & seed per S.Y.		3.17
Lawn Sprinkler System	per S.F.	1.12

Fencing (Cost per L.F.)

Chain Link, 4' high, galvanized	$ 16.90
Gate, 4' high (each)	238.00
Cedar Picket, 3' high, 2 rail	15.75
Gate (each)	239.00
3 Rail, 4' high	19.20
Gate (each)	258.00
Cedar Stockade, 3 Rail, 6' high	18.60
Gate (each)	261.00
Board & Battens, 2 sides 6' high, pine	28.50
6' high, cedar	37.00
No. 1 Cedar, basketweave, 6' high	37.00
Gate, 6' high (each)	293.00

Carport (Cost per S.F.)

Economy	$ 10.51
Average	15.65
Custom	23.06
Luxury	26.94

Assemblies Section

Table of Contents

How RSMeans Assemblies Data Works

The following is a detailed explanation of a sample Assemblies Cost Table. Included are an illustration and accompanying system descriptions. Additionally, related systems and price sheets may be included. Next to each bold number below is the item being described with the appropriate component of the sample entry in parentheses. General contractors should add an additional markup to the figures shown in the Assemblies section. Note: Throughout this section, the words assembly and system will be used interchangeably.

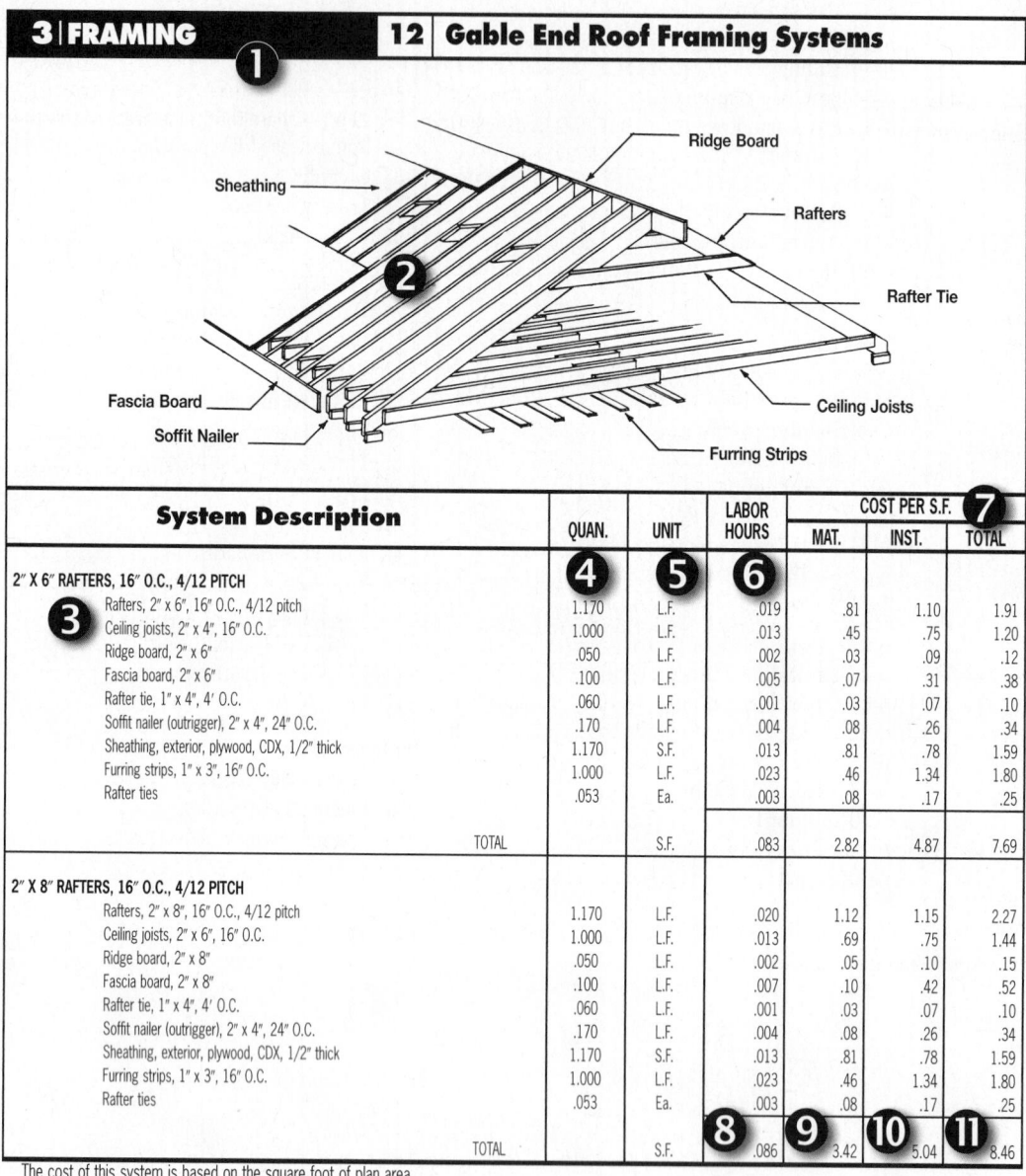

3 | FRAMING ① **12 Gable End Roof Framing Systems**

System Description	QUAN. ④	UNIT ⑤	LABOR HOURS ⑥	COST PER S.F. ⑦		
				MAT.	INST.	TOTAL
2" X 6" RAFTERS, 16" O.C., 4/12 PITCH ③						
Rafters, 2" x 6", 16" O.C., 4/12 pitch	1.170	L.F.	.019	.81	1.10	1.91
Ceiling joists, 2" x 4", 16" O.C.	1.000	L.F.	.013	.45	.75	1.20
Ridge board, 2" x 6"	.050	L.F.	.002	.03	.09	.12
Fascia board, 2" x 6"	.100	L.F.	.005	.07	.31	.38
Rafter tie, 1" x 4", 4' O.C.	.060	L.F.	.001	.03	.07	.10
Soffit nailer (outrigger), 2" x 4", 24" O.C.	.170	L.F.	.004	.08	.26	.34
Sheathing, exterior, plywood, CDX, 1/2" thick	1.170	S.F.	.013	.81	.78	1.59
Furring strips, 1" x 3", 16" O.C.	1.000	L.F.	.023	.46	1.34	1.80
Rafter ties	.053	Ea.	.003	.08	.17	.25
TOTAL		S.F.	.083	2.82	4.87	7.69
2" X 8" RAFTERS, 16" O.C., 4/12 PITCH						
Rafters, 2" x 8", 16" O.C., 4/12 pitch	1.170	L.F.	.020	1.12	1.15	2.27
Ceiling joists, 2" x 6", 16" O.C.	1.000	L.F.	.013	.69	.75	1.44
Ridge board, 2" x 8"	.050	L.F.	.002	.05	.10	.15
Fascia board, 2" x 8"	.100	L.F.	.007	.10	.42	.52
Rafter tie, 1" x 4", 4' O.C.	.060	L.F.	.001	.03	.07	.10
Soffit nailer (outrigger), 2" x 4", 24" O.C.	.170	L.F.	.004	.08	.26	.34
Sheathing, exterior, plywood, CDX, 1/2" thick	1.170	S.F.	.013	.81	.78	1.59
Furring strips, 1" x 3", 16" O.C.	1.000	L.F.	.023	.46	1.34	1.80
Rafter ties	.053	Ea.	.003	.08	.17	.25
TOTAL		S.F.	.086 ⑧	3.42 ⑨	5.04 ⑩	8.46 ⑪

The cost of this system is based on the square foot of plan area.
All quantities have been adjusted accordingly.

Description ⑫	QUAN.	UNIT	LABOR HOURS	COST PER S.F.		
				MAT.	INST.	TOTAL

1 System Identification
(3 Framing 12)
Each Assemblies section has been assigned a unique identification number, component category, system number, and system description.

2 Illustration
Included with most assemblies is an illustration with individual components labeled. Elements involved in the total system function are shown.

3 System Description
(2" x 6" Rafters, 16" O.C., 4/12 Pitch)
The components of a typical system are listed separately to show what has been included in the development of the total system price. Each assembly includes a brief outline of any special conditions to be used when pricing a system. Alternative components can also be found. Simply insert any chosen new element into the chart to develop a custom system.

4 Quantities for Each Component
Each material in a system is shown with the quantity required for the system unit. For example, there are 1.170 L.F. of rafter per S.F. of plan area.

5 Unit of Measure for Each Component
The abbreviated designation indicates the unit of measure as defined by industry standards, upon which the individual component has been priced. In this example, items are priced by the linear foot (L.F.) or the square foot (S.F.).

6 Labor-Hours
This is the amount of time it takes to install the quantity of the individual component.

7 Unit of Measure (Cost per S.F.)
In the three right-hand columns, each cost figure is adjusted to agree with the unit of measure for the entire system. In this case, cost per S.F. is the common unit of measure.

8 Labor-Hours (.086)
The labor-hours column shows the amount of time necessary to install the system per the unit of measure. For example, it takes .086 labor-hours to install one square foot (plan area) of this roof framing system.

9 Materials (3.42)
This column contains the material cost of each element. These cost figures include 10% for profit.

10 Installation (5.04)
This column contains labor and equipment costs. Labor rates include bare cost and the installing contractor's overhead and profit. On the average, the labor cost will be 69.5% over the bare labor cost. Equipment costs include 10% for profit.

11 Totals (8.46)
The figure in this column is the sum of the material and installation costs.

12 Work Sheet
Using the selective price sheet, it is possible to create estimates with alternative items for any number of systems.

Backfill

Excavate

System Description	QUAN.	UNIT	LABOR HOURS	COST EACH		
				MAT.	INST.	TOTAL
BUILDING, 24′ X 38′, 4′ DEEP						
Cut & chip light trees to 6″ diam.	.190	Acre	9.120		807.50	807.50
Excavator, hydraulic, crawler mtd., 1 C.Y. cap. = 100 C.Y./hr.	174.000	C.Y.	3.480		375.84	375.84
Backfill, dozer, 4″ lifts, no compaction	87.000	C.Y.	.580		145.29	145.29
Rough grade, dozer, 30′ from building	87.000	C.Y.	.580		145.29	145.29
Mobilize and demobilize equipment	4.000	Ea.	12.000		970	970
TOTAL		Ea.	25.760		2,443.92	2,443.92
BUILDING, 26′ X 46′, 4′ DEEP						
Cut & chip light trees to 6″ diam.	.210	Acre	10.080		892.50	892.50
Excavator, hydraulic, crawler mtd., 1 C.Y. cap. = 100 C.Y./hr.	201.000	C.Y.	4.020		434.16	434.16
Backfill, dozer, 4″ lifts, no compaction	100.000	C.Y.	.667		167	167
Rough grade, dozer, 30′ from building	100.000	C.Y.	.667		167	167
Mobilize and demobilize equipment	4.000	Ea.	12.000		970	970
TOTAL		Ea.	27.434		2,630.66	2,630.66
BUILDING, 26′ X 60′, 4′ DEEP						
Cut & chip light trees to 6″ diam.	.240	Acre	11.520		1,020	1,020
Excavator, hydraulic, crawler mtd., 1 C.Y. cap. = 100 C.Y./hr.	240.000	C.Y.	4.800		518.40	518.40
Backfill, dozer, 4″ lifts, no compaction	120.000	C.Y.	.800		200.40	200.40
Rough grade, dozer, 30′ from building	120.000	C.Y.	.800		200.40	200.40
Mobilize and demobilize equipment	4.000	Ea.	12.000		970	970
TOTAL		Ea.	29.920		2,909.20	2,909.20
BUILDING, 30′ X 66′, 4′ DEEP						
Cut & chip light trees to 6″ diam.	.260	Acre	12.480		1,105	1,105
Excavator, hydraulic, crawler mtd., 1 C.Y. cap. = 100 C.Y./hr.	268.000	C.Y.	5.360		578.88	578.88
Backfill, dozer, 4″ lifts, no compaction	134.000	C.Y.	.894		223.78	223.78
Rough grade, dozer, 30′ from building	134.000	C.Y.	.894		223.78	223.78
Mobilize and demobilize equipment	4.000	Ea.	12.000		970	970
TOTAL		Ea.	31.628		3,101.44	3,101.44

The costs in this system are on a cost each basis.
Quantities are based on 1′-0″ clearance on each side of footing.

Description	QUAN.	UNIT	LABOR HOURS	COST EACH		
				MAT.	INST.	TOTAL

Footing Excavation Price Sheet	QUAN.	UNIT	LABOR HOURS	COST EACH MAT.	COST EACH INST.	COST EACH TOTAL
Clear and grub, medium brush, 30' from building, 24' x 38'	.190	Acre	9.120		805	805
26' x 46'	.210	Acre	10.080		895	895
26' x 60'	.240	Acre	11.520		1,025	1,025
30' x 66'	.260	Acre	12.480		1,100	1,100
Light trees, to 6" dia. cut & chip, 24' x 38'	.190	Acre	9.120		805	805
26' x 46'	.210	Acre	10.080		895	895
26' x 60'	.240	Acre	11.520		1,025	1,025
30' x 66'	.260	Acre	12.480		1,100	1,100
Medium trees, to 10" dia. cut & chip, 24' x 38'	.190	Acre	13.029		1,150	1,150
26' x 46'	.210	Acre	14.400		1,275	1,275
26' x 60'	.240	Acre	16.457		1,450	1,450
30' x 66'	.260	Acre	17.829		1,575	1,575
Excavation, footing, 24' x 38', 2' deep	68.000	C.Y.	.906		147	147
4' deep	174.000	C.Y.	2.319		375	375
8' deep	384.000	C.Y.	5.119		825	825
26' x 46', 2' deep	79.000	C.Y.	1.053		171	171
4' deep	201.000	C.Y.	2.679		435	435
8' deep	404.000	C.Y.	5.385		875	875
26' x 60', 2' deep	94.000	C.Y.	1.253		203	203
4' deep	240.000	C.Y.	3.199		520	520
8' deep	483.000	C.Y.	6.438		1,050	1,050
30' x 66', 2' deep	105.000	C.Y.	1.400		227	227
4' deep	268.000	C.Y.	3.572		580	580
8' deep	539.000	C.Y.	7.185		1,175	1,175
Backfill, 24' x 38', 2" lifts, no compaction	34.000	C.Y.	.227		56.50	56.50
Compaction, air tamped, add	34.000	C.Y.	2.267		480	480
4" lifts, no compaction	87.000	C.Y.	.580		145	145
Compaction, air tamped, add	87.000	C.Y.	5.800		1,225	1,225
8" lifts, no compaction	192.000	C.Y.	1.281		320	320
Compaction, air tamped, add	192.000	C.Y.	12.801		2,700	2,700
26' x 46', 2" lifts, no compaction	40.000	C.Y.	.267		67	67
Compaction, air tamped, add	40.000	C.Y.	2.667		560	560
4" lifts, no compaction	100.000	C.Y.	.667		167	167
Compaction, air tamped, add	100.000	C.Y.	6.667		1,400	1,400
8" lifts, no compaction	202.000	C.Y.	1.347		340	340
Compaction, air tamped, add	202.000	C.Y.	13.467		2,825	2,825
26' x 60', 2" lifts, no compaction	47.000	C.Y.	.313		78.50	78.50
Compaction, air tamped, add	47.000	C.Y.	3.133		655	655
4" lifts, no compaction	120.000	C.Y.	.800		200	200
Compaction, air tamped, add	120.000	C.Y.	8.000		1,675	1,675
8" lifts, no compaction	242.000	C.Y.	1.614		400	400
Compaction, air tamped, add	242.000	C.Y.	16.134		3,375	3,375
30' x 66', 2" lifts, no compaction	53.000	C.Y.	.354		88.50	88.50
Compaction, air tamped, add	53.000	C.Y.	3.534		745	745
4" lifts, no compaction	134.000	C.Y.	.894		224	224
Compaction, air tamped, add	134.000	C.Y.	8.934		1,875	1,875
8" lifts, no compaction	269.000	C.Y.	1.794		450	450
Compaction, air tamped, add	269.000	C.Y.	17.934		3,750	3,750
Rough grade, 30' from building, 24' x 38'	87.000	C.Y.	.580		145	145
26' x 46'	100.000	C.Y.	.667		167	167
26' x 60'	120.000	C.Y.	.800		200	200
30' x 66'	134.000	C.Y.	.894		224	224
Mobilize and demobilize equipment	4.000	Ea.	12.000		970	970

For customer support on your Residential Costs with RSMeans Data, call 800.448.8182.

103

Backfill

Excavate

System Description	QUAN.	UNIT	LABOR HOURS	COST EACH		
				MAT.	INST.	TOTAL
BUILDING, 24' X 38', 8' DEEP						
Medium clearing	.190	Acre	2.027		301.15	301.15
Excavate, track loader, 1-1/2 C.Y. bucket	550.000	C.Y.	7.860		1,089	1,089
Backfill, dozer, 8" lifts, no compaction	180.000	C.Y.	1.201		300.60	300.60
Rough grade, dozer, 30' from building	280.000	C.Y.	1.868		467.60	467.60
Mobilize and demobilize equipment	4.000	Ea.	12.000		970	970
TOTAL		Ea.	24.956		3,128.35	3,128.35
BUILDING, 26' X 46', 8' DEEP						
Medium clearing	.210	Acre	2.240		332.85	332.85
Excavate, track loader, 1-1/2 C.Y. bucket	672.000	C.Y.	9.603		1,330.56	1,330.56
Backfill, dozer, 8" lifts, no compaction	220.000	C.Y.	1.467		367.40	367.40
Rough grade, dozer, 30' from building	340.000	C.Y.	2.268		567.80	567.80
Mobilize and demobilize equipment	4.000	Ea.	12.000		970	970
TOTAL		Ea.	27.578		3,568.61	3,568.61
BUILDING, 26' X 60', 8' DEEP						
Medium clearing	.240	Acre	2.560		380.40	380.40
Excavate, track loader, 1-1/2 C.Y. bucket	829.000	C.Y.	11.846		1,641.42	1,641.42
Backfill, dozer, 8" lifts, no compaction	270.000	C.Y.	1.801		450.90	450.90
Rough grade, dozer, 30' from building	420.000	C.Y.	2.801		701.40	701.40
Mobilize and demobilzie equipment	4.000	Ea.	12.000		970	970
TOTAL		Ea.	31.008		4,144.12	4,144.12
BUILDING, 30' X 66', 8' DEEP						
Medium clearing	.260	Acre	2.773		412.10	412.10
Excavate, track loader, 1-1/2 C.Y. bucket	990.000	C.Y.	14.147		1,960.20	1,960.20
Backfill dozer, 8" lifts, no compaction	320.000	C.Y.	2.134		534.40	534.40
Rough grade, dozer, 30' from building	500.000	C.Y.	3.335		835	835
Mobilize and demobilize equipment	4.000	Ea.	12.000		970	970
TOTAL		Ea.	34.389		4,711.70	4,711.70

The costs in this system are on a cost each basis.
Quantities are based on 1'-0" clearance beyond footing projection.

Description	QUAN.	UNIT	LABOR HOURS	COST EACH		
				MAT.	INST.	TOTAL

Foundation Excavation Price Sheet

	QUAN.	UNIT	LABOR HOURS	COST EACH MAT.	COST EACH INST.	COST EACH TOTAL
Clear & grub, medium brush, 30' from building, 24' x 38'	.190	Acre	2.027		300	300
26' x 46'	.210	Acre	2.240		335	335
26' x 60'	.240	Acre	2.560		380	380
30' x 66'	.260	Acre	2.773		415	415
Light trees, to 6" dia. cut & chip, 24' x 38'	.190	Acre	9.120		805	805
26' x 46'	.210	Acre	10.080		895	895
26' x 60'	.240	Acre	11.520		1,025	1,025
30' x 66'	.260	Acre	12.480		1,100	1,100
Medium trees, to 10" dia. cut & chip, 24' x 38'	.190	Acre	13.029		1,150	1,150
26' x 46'	.210	Acre	14.400		1,275	1,275
26' x 60'	.240	Acre	16.457		1,450	1,450
30' x 66'	.260	Acre	17.829		1,575	1,575
Excavation, basement, 24' x 38', 2' deep	98.000	C.Y.	1.400		195	195
4' deep	220.000	C.Y.	3.144		435	435
8' deep	550.000	C.Y.	7.860		1,100	1,100
26' x 46', 2' deep	123.000	C.Y.	1.758		244	244
4' deep	274.000	C.Y.	3.915		540	540
8' deep	672.000	C.Y.	9.603		1,325	1,325
26' x 60', 2' deep	157.000	C.Y.	2.244		310	310
4' deep	345.000	C.Y.	4.930		680	680
8' deep	829.000	C.Y.	11.846		1,650	1,650
30' x 66', 2' deep	192.000	C.Y.	2.744		380	380
4' deep	419.000	C.Y.	5.988		830	830
8' deep	990.000	C.Y.	14.147		1,950	1,950
Backfill, 24' x 38', 2" lifts, no compaction	32.000	C.Y.	.213		53.50	53.50
Compaction, air tamped, add	32.000	C.Y.	2.133		450	450
4" lifts, no compaction	72.000	C.Y.	.480		121	121
Compaction, air tamped, add	72.000	C.Y.	4.800		1,000	1,000
8" lifts, no compaction	180.000	C.Y.	1.201		300	300
Compaction, air tamped, add	180.000	C.Y.	12.001		2,525	2,525
26' x 46', 2" lifts, no compaction	40.000	C.Y.	.267		67	67
Compaction, air tamped, add	40.000	C.Y.	2.667		560	560
4" lifts, no compaction	90.000	C.Y.	.600		150	150
Compaction, air tamped, add	90.000	C.Y.	6.000		1,275	1,275
8" lifts, no compaction	220.000	C.Y.	1.467		365	365
Compacton, air tamped, add	220.000	C.Y.	14.667		3,075	3,075
26' x 60', 2" lifts, no compaction	50.000	C.Y.	.334		83.50	83.50
Compaction, air tamped, add	50.000	C.Y.	3.334		705	705
4" lifts, no compaction	110.000	C.Y.	.734		184	184
Compaction, air tamped, add	110.000	C.Y.	7.334		1,550	1,550
8" lifts, no compaction	270.000	C.Y.	1.801		455	455
Compaction, air tamped, add	270.000	C.Y.	18.001		3,800	3,800
30' x 66', 2" lifts, no compaction	60.000	C.Y.	.400		100	100
Compaction, air tamped, add	60.000	C.Y.	4.000		840	840
4" lifts, no compaction	130.000	C.Y.	.867		217	217
Compaction, air tamped, add	130.000	C.Y.	8.667		1,825	1,825
8" lifts, no compaction	320.000	C.Y.	2.134		535	535
Compaction, air tamped, add	320.000	C.Y.	21.334		4,475	4,475
Rough grade, 30' from building, 24' x 38'	280.000	C.Y.	1.868		465	465
26' x 46'	340.000	C.Y.	2.268		565	565
26' x 60'	420.000	C.Y.	2.801		705	705
30' x 66'	500.000	C.Y.	3.335		835	835
Mobilize and demobilize equipment	4.000	Ea.	12.000		970	970

For customer support on your Residential Costs with RSMeans Data, call 800.448.8182.

105

System Description	QUAN.	UNIT	LABOR HOURS	COST PER L.F.		
				MAT.	INST.	TOTAL
2′ DEEP						
Excavation, backhoe	.296	C.Y.	.032		2.46	2.46
Alternate pricing method, 4″ deep	.111	C.Y.	.044	3.66	2.26	5.92
Utility, sewer, 6″ cast iron	1.000	L.F.	.283	39.99	16	55.99
Compaction in 12″ layers, hand tamp, add to above	.185	C.Y.	.044		1.93	1.93
TOTAL		L.F.	.403	43.65	22.65	66.30
4′ DEEP						
Excavation, backhoe	.889	C.Y.	.095		7.37	7.37
Alternate pricing method, 4″ deep	.111	C.Y.	.044	3.66	2.26	5.92
Utility, sewer, 6″ cast iron	1.000	L.F.	.283	39.99	16	55.99
Compaction in 12″ layers, hand tamp, add to above	.778	C.Y.	.183		8.13	8.13
TOTAL		L.F.	.605	43.65	33.76	77.41
6′ DEEP						
Excavation, backhoe	1.770	C.Y.	.189		14.67	14.67
Alternate pricing method, 4″ deep	.111	C.Y.	.044	3.66	2.26	5.92
Utility, sewer, 6″ cast iron	1.000	L.F.	.283	39.99	16	55.99
Compaction in 12″ layers, hand tamp, add to above	1.660	C.Y.	.391		17.35	17.35
TOTAL		L.F.	.907	43.65	50.28	93.93
8′ DEEP						
Excavation, backhoe	2.960	C.Y.	.316		24.54	24.54
Alternate pricing method, 4″ deep	.111	C.Y.	.044	3.66	2.26	5.92
Utility, sewer, 6″ cast iron	1.000	L.F.	.283	39.99	16	55.99
Compaction in 12″ layers, hand tamp, add to above	2.850	C.Y.	.671		29.78	29.78
TOTAL		L.F.	1.314	43.65	72.58	116.23

The costs in this system are based on a cost per linear foot of trench, and based on 2′ wide at bottom of trench up to 6′ deep.

Description	QUAN.	UNIT	LABOR HOURS	COST PER L.F.		
				MAT.	INST.	TOTAL

Utility Trenching Price Sheet	QUAN.	UNIT	LABOR HOURS	COST PER UNIT		
				MAT.	INST.	TOTAL
Excavation, bottom of trench 2' wide, 2' deep	.296	C.Y.	.032		2.46	2.46
4' deep	.889	C.Y.	.095		7.35	7.35
6' deep	1.770	C.Y.	.142		11.25	11.25
8' deep	2.960	C.Y.	.105		21	21
Bedding, sand, bottom of trench 2' wide, no compaction, pipe, 2" diameter	.070	C.Y.	.028	2.31	1.43	3.74
4" diameter	.084	C.Y.	.034	2.77	1.71	4.48
6" diameter	.105	C.Y.	.042	3.47	2.14	5.61
8" diameter	.122	C.Y.	.049	4.03	2.48	6.51
Compacted, pipe, 2" diameter	.074	C.Y.	.030	2.44	1.50	3.94
4" diameter	.092	C.Y.	.037	3.04	1.87	4.91
6" diameter	.111	C.Y.	.044	3.66	2.26	5.92
8" diameter	.129	C.Y.	.052	4.26	2.62	6.88
3/4" stone, bottom of trench 2' wide, pipe, 4" diameter	.082	C.Y.	.033	2.71	1.66	4.37
6" diameter	.099	C.Y.	.040	3.27	2.02	5.29
3/8" stone, bottom of trench 2' wide, pipe, 4" diameter	.084	C.Y.	.034	2.77	1.71	4.48
6" diameter	.102	C.Y.	.041	3.37	2.07	5.44
Utilities, drainage & sewerage, corrugated plastic, 6" diameter	1.000	L.F.	.069	3.61	3.13	6.74
8" diameter	1.000	L.F.	.072	6.50	3.27	9.77
Concrete, non-reinforced, 6" diameter	1.000	L.F.	.181	8.30	10.05	18.35
8" diameter	1.000	L.F.	.214	9.15	11.95	21.10
PVC, SDR 35, 4" diameter	1.000	L.F.	.064	1.71	2.92	4.63
6" diameter	1.000	L.F.	.069	3.61	3.13	6.74
8" diameter	1.000	L.F.	.072	6.50	3.27	9.77
Gas & service, polyethylene, 1-1/4" diameter	1.000	L.F.	.059	1.68	3.08	4.76
Steel sched.40, 1" diameter	1.000	L.F.	.107	5.55	6.80	12.35
2" diameter	1.000	L.F.	.114	8.70	7.35	16.05
Sub-drainage, PVC, perforated, 3" diameter	1.000	L.F.	.064	1.71	2.92	4.63
4" diameter	1.000	L.F.	.064	1.71	2.92	4.63
5" diameter	1.000	L.F.	.069	3.61	3.13	6.74
6" diameter	1.000	L.F.	.069	3.61	3.13	6.74
Water service, copper, type K, 3/4"	1.000	L.F.	.083	6.35	5.45	11.80
1" diameter	1.000	L.F.	.093	10.65	6.10	16.75
PVC, 3/4"	1.000	L.F.	.121	4.50	7.90	12.40
1" diameter	1.000	L.F.	.134	12.20	8.75	20.95
Backfill, bottom of trench 2' wide no compact, 2' deep, pipe, 2" diameter	.226	L.F.	.053		2.36	2.36
4" diameter	.212	L.F.	.050		2.22	2.22
6" diameter	.185	L.F.	.044		1.93	1.93
4' deep, pipe, 2" diameter	.819	C.Y.	.193		8.55	8.55
4" diameter	.805	C.Y.	.189		8.40	8.40
6" diameter	.778	C.Y.	.183		8.15	8.15
6' deep, pipe, 2" diameter	1.700	C.Y.	.400		17.75	17.75
4" diameter	1.690	C.Y.	.398		17.65	17.65
6" diameter	1.660	C.Y.	.391		17.35	17.35
8' deep, pipe, 2" diameter	2.890	C.Y.	.680		30	30
4" diameter	2.870	C.Y.	.675		30	30
6" diameter	2.850	C.Y.	.671		30	30

Asphalt · Brick Edge · Gravel Fill

System Description	QUAN.	UNIT	LABOR HOURS	COST PER S.F.		
				MAT.	INST.	TOTAL
ASPHALT SIDEWALK SYSTEM, 3′ WIDE WALK						
Gravel fill, 4″ deep	1.000	S.F.	.001	.30	.05	.35
Compact fill	.012	C.Y.			.02	.02
Handgrade	1.000	S.F.	.004		.18	.18
Walking surface, bituminous paving, 2″ thick	1.000	S.F.	.007	.85	.38	1.23
Edging, brick, laid on edge	.670	L.F.	.079	2.02	4.22	6.24
TOTAL		S.F.	.091	3.17	4.85	8.02
CONCRETE SIDEWALK SYSTEM, 3′ WIDE WALK						
Gravel fill, 4″ deep	1.000	S.F.	.001	.30	.05	.35
Compact fill	.012	C.Y.			.02	.02
Handgrade	1.000	S.F.	.004		.18	.18
Walking surface, concrete, 4″ thick	1.000	S.F.	.040	2.16	2.12	4.28
Edging, brick, laid on edge	.670	L.F.	.079	2.02	4.22	6.24
TOTAL		S.F.	.124	4.48	6.59	11.07
PAVERS, BRICK SIDEWALK SYSTEM, 3′ WIDE WALK						
Sand base fill, 4″ deep	1.000	S.F.	.001	.50	.09	.59
Compact fill	.012	C.Y.			.02	.02
Handgrade	1.000	S.F.	.004		.18	.18
Walking surface, brick pavers	1.000	S.F.	.160	3.11	8.55	11.66
Edging, redwood, untreated, 1″ x 4″	.670	L.F.	.032	1.66	1.88	3.54
TOTAL		S.F.	.197	5.27	10.72	15.99

The costs in this system are based on a cost per square foot of sidewalk area. Concrete used is 3000 p.s.i.

Description	QUAN.	UNIT	LABOR HOURS	COST PER S.F.		
				MAT.	INST.	TOTAL

Sidewalk Price Sheet	QUAN.	UNIT	LABOR HOURS	COST PER S.F.		
				MAT.	INST.	TOTAL
Base, crushed stone, 3" deep	1.000	S.F.	.001	.31	.11	.42
6" deep	1.000	S.F.	.001	.62	.11	.73
9" deep	1.000	S.F.	.002	.90	.15	1.05
12" deep	1.000	S.F.	.002	1.54	.19	1.73
Bank run gravel, 6" deep	1.000	S.F.	.001	.45	.08	.53
9" deep	1.000	S.F.	.001	.66	.11	.77
12" deep	1.000	S.F.	.001	.90	.14	1.04
Compact base, 3" deep	.009	C.Y.	.001		.01	.01
6" deep	.019	C.Y.	.001		.03	.03
9" deep	.028	C.Y.	.001		.05	.05
Handgrade	1.000	S.F.	.004		.18	.18
Surface, brick, pavers dry joints, laid flat, running bond	1.000	S.F.	.160	3.11	8.55	11.66
Basket weave	1.000	S.F.	.168	4.05	9	13.05
Herringbone	1.000	S.F.	.174	4.05	9.25	13.30
Laid on edge, running bond	1.000	S.F.	.229	4.34	12.20	16.54
Mortar jts. laid flat, running bond	1.000	S.F.	.192	3.73	10.25	13.98
Basket weave	1.000	S.F.	.202	4.86	10.80	15.66
Herringbone	1.000	S.F.	.209	4.86	11.10	15.96
Laid on edge, running bond	1.000	S.F.	.274	5.20	14.65	19.85
Bituminous paving, 1-1/2" thick	1.000	S.F.	.006	.64	.28	.92
2" thick	1.000	S.F.	.007	.85	.38	1.23
2-1/2" thick	1.000	S.F.	.008	1.09	.41	1.50
Sand finish, 3/4" thick	1.000	S.F.	.001	.35	.13	.48
1" thick	1.000	S.F.	.001	.43	.15	.58
Concrete, reinforced, broom finish, 4" thick	1.000	S.F.	.040	2.16	2.12	4.28
5" thick	1.000	S.F.	.044	2.88	2.34	5.22
6" thick	1.000	S.F.	.047	3.36	2.50	5.86
Crushed stone, white marble, 3" thick	1.000	S.F.	.009	.46	.42	.88
Bluestone, 3" thick	1.000	S.F.	.009	.13	.42	.55
Flagging, bluestone, 1"	1.000	S.F.	.198	10.05	10.55	20.60
1-1/2"	1.000	S.F.	.188	18.30	10.05	28.35
Slate, natural cleft, 3/4"	1.000	S.F.	.174	9.90	9.25	19.15
Random rect., 1/2"	1.000	S.F.	.152	21.50	8.15	29.65
Granite blocks	1.000	S.F.	.174	18.65	9.25	27.90
Edging, corrugated aluminum, 4", 3' wide walk	.666	L.F.	.008	1.37	.48	1.85
4' wide walk	.500	L.F.	.006	1.03	.36	1.39
6", 3' wide walk	.666	L.F.	.010	1.71	.57	2.28
4' wide walk	.500	L.F.	.007	1.29	.43	1.72
Redwood-cedar-cypress, 1" x 4", 3' wide walk	.666	L.F.	.021	.85	1.25	2.10
4' wide walk	.500	L.F.	.016	.64	.94	1.58
2" x 4", 3' wide walk	.666	L.F.	.032	1.66	1.88	3.54
4' wide walk	.500	L.F.	.024	1.25	1.42	2.67
Brick, dry joints, 3' wide walk	.666	L.F.	.079	2.02	4.22	6.24
4' wide walk	.500	L.F.	.059	1.51	3.15	4.66
Mortar joints, 3' wide walk	.666	L.F.	.095	2.43	5.05	7.48
4' wide walk	.500	L.F.	.071	1.81	3.78	5.59

System Description		QUAN.	UNIT	LABOR HOURS	COST PER S.F.		
					MAT.	INST.	TOTAL
ASPHALT DRIVEWAY TO 10' WIDE							
Excavation, driveway to 10' wide, 6" deep		.019	C.Y.			.05	.05
Base, 6" crushed stone		1.000	S.F.	.001	.62	.11	.73
Handgrade base		1.000	S.F.	.004		.18	.18
2" thick base		1.000	S.F.	.002	.86	.21	1.07
1" topping		1.000	S.F.	.001	.43	.15	.58
Edging, brick pavers		.200	L.F.	.024	.60	1.26	1.86
	TOTAL		S.F.	.032	2.51	1.96	4.47
CONCRETE DRIVEWAY TO 10' WIDE							
Excavation, driveway to 10' wide, 6" deep		.019	C.Y.			.05	.05
Base, 6" crushed stone		1.000	S.F.	.001	.62	.11	.73
Handgrade base		1.000	S.F.	.004		.18	.18
Surface, concrete, 4" thick		1.000	S.F.	.040	2.16	2.12	4.28
Edging, brick pavers		.200	L.F.	.024	.60	1.26	1.86
	TOTAL		S.F.	.069	3.38	3.72	7.10
PAVERS, BRICK DRIVEWAY TO 10' WIDE							
Excavation, driveway to 10' wide, 6" deep		.019	C.Y.			.05	.05
Base, 6" sand		1.000	S.F.	.001	.79	.14	.93
Handgrade base		1.000	S.F.	.004		.18	.18
Surface, pavers, brick laid flat, running bond		1.000	S.F.	.160	3.11	8.55	11.66
Edging, redwood, untreated, 2" x 4"		.200	L.F.	.010	.50	.57	1.07
	TOTAL		S.F.	.175	4.40	9.49	13.89

Description	QUAN.	UNIT	LABOR HOURS	COST PER S.F.		
				MAT.	INST.	TOTAL

Driveway Price Sheet	QUAN.	UNIT	LABOR HOURS	COST PER S.F.		
				MAT.	INST.	TOTAL
Excavation, by machine, 10' wide, 6" deep	.019	C.Y.	.001		.05	.05
12" deep	.037	C.Y.	.001		.09	.09
18" deep	.055	C.Y.	.001		.12	.12
20' wide, 6" deep	.019	C.Y.	.001		.05	.05
12" deep	.037	C.Y.	.001		.09	.09
18" deep	.055	C.Y.	.001		.12	.12
Base, crushed stone, 10' wide, 3" deep	1.000	S.F.	.001	.31	.06	.37
6" deep	1.000	S.F.	.001	.62	.11	.73
9" deep	1.000	S.F.	.002	.90	.15	1.05
20' wide, 3" deep	1.000	S.F.	.001	.31	.06	.37
6" deep	1.000	S.F.	.001	.62	.11	.73
9" deep	1.000	S.F.	.002	.90	.15	1.05
Bank run gravel, 10' wide, 3" deep	1.000	S.F.	.001	.23	.05	.28
6" deep	1.000	S.F.	.001	.45	.08	.53
9" deep	1.000	S.F.	.001	.66	.11	.77
20' wide, 3" deep	1.000	S.F.	.001	.23	.05	.28
6" deep	1.000	S.F.	.001	.45	.08	.53
9" deep	1.000	S.F.	.001	.66	.11	.77
Handgrade, 10' wide	1.000	S.F.	.004		.18	.18
20' wide	1.000	S.F.	.004		.18	.18
Surface, asphalt, 10' wide, 3/4" topping, 1" base	1.000	S.F.	.002	1.01	.28	1.29
2" base	1.000	S.F.	.003	1.21	.34	1.55
1" topping, 1" base	1.000	S.F.	.002	1.09	.30	1.39
2" base	1.000	S.F.	.003	1.29	.36	1.65
20' wide, 3/4" topping, 1" base	1.000	S.F.	.002	1.01	.28	1.29
2" base	1.000	S.F.	.003	1.21	.34	1.55
1" topping, 1" base	1.000	S.F.	.002	1.09	.30	1.39
2" base	1.000	S.F.	.003	1.29	.36	1.65
Concrete, 10' wide, 4" thick	1.000	S.F.	.040	2.16	2.12	4.28
6" thick	1.000	S.F.	.047	3.36	2.50	5.86
20' wide, 4" thick	1.000	S.F.	.040	2.16	2.12	4.28
6" thick	1.000	S.F.	.047	3.36	2.50	5.86
Paver, brick 10' wide dry joints, running bond, laid flat	1.000	S.F.	.160	3.11	8.55	11.66
Laid on edge	1.000	S.F.	.229	4.34	12.20	16.54
Mortar joints, laid flat	1.000	S.F.	.192	3.73	10.25	13.98
Laid on edge	1.000	S.F.	.274	5.20	14.65	19.85
20' wide, running bond, dry jts., laid flat	1.000	S.F.	.160	3.11	8.55	11.66
Laid on edge	1.000	S.F.	.229	4.34	12.20	16.54
Mortar joints, laid flat	1.000	S.F.	.192	3.73	10.25	13.98
Laid on edge	1.000	S.F.	.274	5.20	14.65	19.85
Crushed stone, 10' wide, white marble, 3"	1.000	S.F.	.009	.46	.42	.88
Bluestone, 3"	1.000	S.F.	.009	.13	.42	.55
20' wide, white marble, 3"	1.000	S.F.	.009	.46	.42	.88
Bluestone, 3"	1.000	S.F.	.009	.13	.42	.55
Soil cement, 10' wide	1.000	S.F.	.007	.36	1.06	1.42
20' wide	1.000	S.F.	.007	.36	1.06	1.42
Granite blocks, 10' wide	1.000	S.F.	.174	18.65	9.25	27.90
20' wide	1.000	S.F.	.174	18.65	9.25	27.90
Asphalt block, solid 1-1/4" thick	1.000	S.F.	.119	8.85	6.30	15.15
Solid 3" thick	1.000	S.F.	.123	12.40	6.55	18.95
Edging, brick, 10' wide	.200	L.F.	.024	.60	1.26	1.86
20' wide	.100	L.F.	.012	.30	.63	.93
Redwood, untreated 2" x 4", 10' wide	.200	L.F.	.010	.50	.57	1.07
20' wide	.100	L.F.	.005	.25	.28	.53
Granite, 4 1/2" x 12" straight, 10' wide	.200	L.F.	.032	1.55	2.12	3.67
20' wide	.100	L.F.	.016	.78	1.06	1.84
Finishes, asphalt sealer, 10' wide	1.000	S.F.	.023	.96	1.04	2
20' wide	1.000	S.F.	.023	.96	1.04	2
Concrete, exposed aggregate 10' wide	1.000	S.F.	.013	.22	.72	.94
20' wide	1.000	S.F.	.013	.22	.72	.94

System Description	QUAN.	UNIT	LABOR HOURS	COST EACH		
				MAT.	INST.	TOTAL
SEPTIC SYSTEM WITH 600 S.F. LEACHING FIELD, 1000 GALLON TANK						
Mobilization	2.000	Ea.	16.000		1,402	1,402
Tank, precast, 1000 gallon	1.000	Ea.	3.500	1,150	186.95	1,336.95
Effluent filter	1.000	Ea.	1.000	47	60	107
Distribution box, precast	1.000	Ea.	1.000	102	44.50	146.50
Flow leveler	3.000	Ea.	.480	7.59	21.30	28.89
PVC pipe, 4" diameter	25.000	L.F.	1.600	42.75	73	115.75
Tee	1.000	Ea.	1.000	17.05	60	77.05
Elbow	2.000	Ea.	1.333	21.60	80	101.60
Viewport cap	1.000	Ea.	.333	7.60	20	27.60
Filter fabric	67.000	S.Y.	.447	112.56	20.10	132.66
Detectable marking tape	1.600	C.L.F.	.085	10.56	3.79	14.35
PVC perforated pipe, 4" diameter	135.000	L.F.	8.640	230.85	394.20	625.05
Excavation	160.000	C.Y.	17.654		1,752	1,752
Backfill	133.000	L.C.Y.	2.660		273.98	273.98
Spoil	55.000	L.C.Y.	3.056		327.25	327.25
Compaction	113.000	E.C.Y.	15.066		742.41	742.41
Stone fill	39.000	C.Y.	6.240	1,716	410.67	2,126.67
TOTAL		Ea.	80.094	3,465.56	5,872.15	9,337.71
SEPTIC SYSTEM WITH 750 S.F. LEACHING FIELD, 1500 GALLON TANK						
Mobilization	2.000	Ea.	16.000		1,402	1,402
Tank, precast, 1500 gallon	1.000	Ea.	4.000	1,800	213.50	2,013.50
Effluent filter	1.000	Ea.	1.000	47	60	107
Distribution box, precast	1.000	Ea.	1.000	102	44.50	146.50
Flow leveler	3.000	Ea.	.480	7.59	21.30	28.89
PVC pipe, 4" diameter	25.000	L.F.	1.600	42.75	73	115.75
Tee	125.000	Ea.	1.000	17.05	60	77.05
Elbow	2.000	Ea.	1.333	21.60	80	101.60
Viewport cap	1.000	Ea.	.333	7.60	20	27.60
Filter fabric	84.000	S.Y.	.560	141.12	25.20	166.32
Detectable marking tape	1.900	C.L.F.	.101	12.54	4.50	17.04
PVC perforated pipe, 4" diameter	165.000	L.F.	10.560	282.15	481.80	763.95
Excavation	199.000	C.Y.	21.958		2,179.05	2,179.05
Backfill	162.000	L.C.Y.	3.240		333.72	333.72
Spoil	73.500	L.C.Y.	4.084		437.33	437.33
Compaction	137.000	E.C.Y.	18.266		900.09	900.09
Stone fill	48.500	C.Y.	7.760	2,134	510.71	2,644.71
TOTAL		Ea.	93.275	4,615.40	6,846.70	11,462.10

The costs in this system include all necessary piping and excavation.

System Description	QUAN.	UNIT	LABOR HOURS	COST EACH		
				MAT.	INST.	TOTAL
SEPTIC SYSTEM WITH 1000 S.F. LEACHING FIELD, 1500 GALLON TANK						
Mobilization	2.000	Ea.	16.000		1,402	1,402
Tank, precast, 1500 gallon	1.000	Ea.	4.000	1,800	213.50	2,013.50
Effluent filter	1.000	Ea.	1.000	47	60	107
Distribution box, precast	1.000	Ea.	1.000	102	44.50	146.50
Flow leveler	4.000	Ea.	.640	10.12	28.40	38.52
PVC pipe, 4" diameter	25.000	L.F.	1.600	42.75	73	115.75
Tee	1.000	Ea.	1.000	17.05	60	77.05
Elbow	4.000	Ea.	2.667	43.20	160	203.20
Viewport cap	1.000	Ea.	.333	7.60	20	27.60
Filter fabric	111.000	S.Y.	.740	186.48	33.30	219.78
Detectable marking tape	2.400	C.L.F.	.128	15.84	5.69	21.53
PVC perforated pipe, 4" diameter	215.000	L.F.	13.760	367.65	627.80	995.45
Excavation	229.000	C.Y.	25.268		2,507.55	2,507.55
Backfill	178.000	L.C.Y.	3.560		366.68	366.68
Spoil	91.500	L.C.Y.	5.084		544.43	544.43
Compaction	151.000	E.C.Y.	20.133		992.07	992.07
Stone fill	64.000	C.Y.	10.240	2,816	673.92	3,489.92
TOTAL		Ea.	107.153	5,455.69	7,812.84	13,268.53

The costs in this system include all necessary piping and excavation.

Septic Systems Price Sheet	QUAN.	UNIT	LABOR HOURS	COST EACH		
				MAT.	INST.	TOTAL
Tank, precast concrete, 1000 gallon	1.000	Ea.	3.500	1,150	187	1,337
1500 gallon	1.000	Ea.	4.000	1,800	214	2,014
Distribution box, concrete, 5 outlets	1.000	Ea.	1.000	102	44.50	146.50
12 outlets	1.000	Ea.	2.000	605	89	694
4" pipe, PVC, solid	25.000	L.F.	1.600	43	73	116
Tank and field excavation, 600 S.F. field	160.000	C.Y.	17.654		1,750	1,750
750 S.F. field	199.000	C.Y.	21.958		2,200	2,200
1000 S.F. field	229.000	C.Y.	25.268		2,525	2,525
Tank excavation only, 1000 gallon tank	20.000	C.Y.	2.206		219	219
1500 gallon tank	26.000	C.Y.	2.869		285	285
Backfill, crushed stone, 600 S.F. field	39.000	C.Y.	12.160	1,725	410	2,135
750 S.F. field	48.500	C.Y.	22.400	2,125	510	2,635
1000 S.F. field	64.000	C.Y.	.240	2,825	670	3,495
Backfill with excavated material, 600 S.F. field	133.000	L.C.Y.	.400		274	274
750 S.F. field	162.000	L.C.Y.	.367		335	335
1000 S.F. field	178.000	L.C.Y.	.280		365	365
Filter fabric, 600 S.F. field	67.000	S.Y.	2.376	113	20	133
750 S.F. field	84.000	S.Y.	4.860	141	25	166
1000 S.F. field	111.000	S.Y.	.740	186	33.50	219.50
4" pipe, PVC, perforated, 600 S.F. field	135.000	L.F.	9.280	231	395	626
750 S.F. field	165.000	L.F.	16.960	282	480	762
1000 S.F. field	215.000	L.F.	1.939	370	630	1,000
Pipe fittings, PVC, 600 S.F. field	2.000	Ea.	3.879	21.50	80	101.50
750 S.F. field	2.000	Ea.		21.50	80	101.50
1000 S.F. field	4.000	Ea.		43	160	203
Mobilization	2.000	Ea.	16.000		1,400	1,400
Effluent filter	1.000	Ea.	1.000	47	60	107
Flow leveler, 600 S.F. field	3.000	Ea.	.480	7.60	21.50	29.10
750 S.F. field	3.000	Ea.	.480	7.60	21.50	29.10
1000 S.F. field	4.000	Ea.	.640	10.10	28.50	38.60
Viewport cap	1.000	Ea.	.333	7.60	20	27.60
Detectable marking tape, 600 S.F. field	1.600	C.L.F.	.085	10.55	3.79	14.34
750 S.F. field	1.900	C.L.F.	.101	12.55	4.50	17.05
1000 S.F. field	2.400	C.L.F.	.128	15.85	5.70	21.55

System Description	QUAN.	UNIT	LABOR HOURS	COST PER UNIT		
				MAT.	INST.	TOTAL
Chain link fence						
Galv.9ga. wire, 1-5/8"post 10'O.C., 1-3/8"top rail, 2"corner post, 3'hi	1.000	L.F.	.130	11.75	5.90	17.65
4' high	1.000	L.F.	.141	10.45	6.45	16.90
6' high	1.000	L.F.	.209	13.50	9.50	23
Add for gate 3' wide 1-3/8" frame 3' high	1.000	Ea.	2.000	113	91	204
4' high	1.000	Ea.	2.400	129	109	238
6' high	1.000	Ea.	2.400	155	109	264
Add for gate 4' wide 1-3/8" frame 3' high	1.000	Ea.	2.667	123	122	245
4' high	1.000	Ea.	2.667	134	122	256
6' high	1.000	Ea.	3.000	163	137	300
Alum.9ga. wire, 1-5/8"post, 10'O.C., 1-3/8"top rail, 2"corner post,3'hi	1.000	L.F.	.130	9.85	5.90	15.75
4' high	1.000	L.F.	.141	10.30	6.45	16.75
6' high	1.000	L.F.	.209	13.40	9.50	22.90
Add for gate 3' wide 1-3/8" frame 3' high	1.000	Ea.	2.000	164	91	255
4' high	1.000	Ea.	2.400	176	109	285
6' high	1.000	Ea.	2.400	223	109	332
Add for gate 4' wide 1-3/8" frame 3' high	1.000	Ea.	2.400	171	109	280
4' high	1.000	Ea.	2.667	163	122	285
6' high	1.000	Ea.	3.000	221	137	358
Vinyl 9ga. wire, 1-5/8"post 10'O.C., 1-3/8"top rail, 2"corner post,3'hi	1.000	L.F.	.130	9.55	5.90	15.45
4' high	1.000	L.F.	.141	8.05	6.45	14.50
6' high	1.000	L.F.	.209	10.75	9.50	20.25
Add for gate 3' wide 1-3/8" frame 3' high	1.000	Ea.	2.000	122	91	213
4' high	1.000	Ea.	2.400	138	109	247
6' high	1.000	Ea.	2.400	171	109	280
Add for gate 4' wide 1-3/8" frame 3' high	1.000	Ea.	2.400	135	109	244
4' high	1.000	Ea.	2.667	141	122	263
6' high	1.000	Ea.	3.000	183	137	320
Tennis court, chain link fence, 10' high						
Galv.11ga.wire, 2"post 10'O.C., 1-3/8"top rail, 2-1/2"corner post	1.000	L.F.	.253	9.95	11.50	21.45
Add for gate 3' wide 1-3/8" frame	1.000	Ea.	2.400	264	109	373
Alum.11ga.wire, 2"post 10'O.C., 1-3/8"top rail, 2-1/2"corner post	1.000	L.F.	.253	12	11.50	23.50
Add for gate 3' wide 1-3/8" frame	1.000	Ea.	2.400	183	109	292
Vinyl 11ga.wire,2"post 10' O.C.,1-3/8"top rail,2-1/2"corner post	1.000	L.F.	.253	10.35	11.50	21.85
Add for gate 3' wide 1-3/8" frame	1.000	Ea.	2.400	365	109	474
Railings, commercial						
Aluminum balcony rail, 1-1/2" posts with pickets	1.000	L.F.	.164	81	12.35	93.35
With expanded metal panels	1.000	L.F.	.164	106	12.35	118.35
With porcelain enamel panel inserts	1.000	L.F.	.164	99	12.35	111.35
Mild steel, ornamental rounded top rail	1.000	L.F.	.164	94	12.35	106.35
As above, but pitch down stairs	1.000	L.F.	.183	122	13.70	135.70
Steel pipe, welded, 1-1/2" round, painted	1.000	L.F.	.160	31	12	43
Galvanized	1.000	L.F.	.160	43.50	12	55.50
Residential, stock units, mild steel, deluxe	1.000	L.F.	.102	17.60	7.60	25.20
Economy	1.000	L.F.	.102	13.15	7.60	20.75

System Description	QUAN.	UNIT	LABOR HOURS	COST PER UNIT		
				MAT.	INST.	TOTAL
Basketweave, 3/8"x4" boards, 2"x4" stringers on spreaders, 4"x4" posts						
No. 1 cedar, 6' high	1.000	L.F.	.150	28.50	8.60	37.10
Treated pine, 6' high	1.000	L.F.	.160	38	9.20	47.20
Board fence, 1"x4" boards, 2"x4" rails, 4"x4" posts						
Preservative treated, 2 rail, 3' high	1.000	L.F.	.166	10.50	9.50	20
4' high	1.000	L.F.	.178	12.35	10.25	22.60
3 rail, 5' high	1.000	L.F.	.185	13.45	10.60	24.05
6' high	1.000	L.F.	.192	15.15	11.05	26.20
Western cedar, No. 1, 2 rail, 3' high	1.000	L.F.	.166	11.55	9.50	21.05
3 rail, 4' high	1.000	L.F.	.178	12.75	10.25	23
5' high	1.000	L.F.	.185	14.30	10.60	24.90
6' high	1.000	L.F.	.192	15.25	11.05	26.30
No. 1 cedar, 2 rail, 3' high	1.000	L.F.	.166	14.65	9.50	24.15
4' high	1.000	L.F.	.178	15.85	10.25	26.10
3 rail, 5' high	1.000	L.F.	.185	19.25	10.60	29.85
6' high	1.000	L.F.	.192	21	11.05	32.05
Shadow box, 1"x6" boards, 2"x4" rails, 4"x4" posts						
Fir, pine or spruce, treated, 3 rail, 6' high	1.000	L.F.	.160	19.50	9.20	28.70
No. 1 cedar, 3 rail, 4' high	1.000	L.F.	.185	20.50	10.60	31.10
6' high	1.000	L.F.	.192	26	11.05	37.05
Open rail, split rails, No. 1 cedar, 2 rail, 3' high	1.000	L.F.	.150	14.20	8.60	22.80
3 rail, 4' high	1.000	L.F.	.160	14.65	9.20	23.85
No. 2 cedar, 2 rail, 3' high	1.000	L.F.	.150	13.05	8.60	21.65
3 rail, 4' high	1.000	L.F.	.160	10.35	9.20	19.55
Open rail, rustic rails, No. 1 cedar, 2 rail, 3' high	1.000	L.F.	.150	11.30	8.60	19.90
3 rail, 4' high	1.000	L.F.	.160	10.85	9.20	20.05
No. 2 cedar, 2 rail, 3' high	1.000	L.F.	.150	10.60	8.60	19.20
3 rail, 4' high	1.000	L.F.	.160	8.85	9.20	18.05
Rustic picket, molded pine pickets, 2 rail, 3' high	1.000	L.F.	.171	9.35	9.85	19.20
3 rail, 4' high	1.000	L.F.	.197	10.75	11.35	22.10
No. 1 cedar, 2 rail, 3' high	1.000	L.F.	.171	10.80	9.85	20.65
3 rail, 4' high	1.000	L.F.	.197	12.40	11.35	23.75
Picket fence, fir, pine or spruce, preserved, treated						
2 rail, 3' high	1.000	L.F.	.171	8.60	9.85	18.45
3 rail, 4' high	1.000	L.F.	.185	9.80	10.60	20.40
Western cedar, 2 rail, 3' high	1.000	L.F.	.171	9.90	9.85	19.75
3 rail, 4' high	1.000	L.F.	.185	10	10.60	20.60
No. 1 cedar, 2 rail, 3' high	1.000	L.F.	.171	15.05	9.85	24.90
3 rail, 4' high	1.000	L.F.	.185	19.60	10.60	30.20
Stockade, No. 1 cedar, 3-1/4" rails, 6' high	1.000	L.F.	.150	14.45	8.60	23.05
8' high	1.000	L.F.	.155	19.90	8.90	28.80
No. 2 cedar, treated rails, 6' high	1.000	L.F.	.150	14.80	8.60	23.40
Treated pine, treated rails, 6' high	1.000	L.F.	.150	15.35	8.60	23.95
Gates, No. 2 cedar, picket, 3'-6" wide 4' high	1.000	Ea.	2.667	87	154	241
No. 2 cedar, rustic round, 3' wide, 3' high	1.000	Ea.	2.667	113	154	267
No. 2 cedar, stockade screen, 3'-6" wide, 6' high	1.000	Ea.	3.000	98.50	172	270.50
General, wood, 3'-6" wide, 4' high	1.000	Ea.	2.400	97	138	235
6' high	1.000	Ea.	3.000	121	172	293

Did you know?

Our online estimating solution gives you the
same access to RSMeans' data with 24/7 access:

- Quickly locate costs in the searchable
  database.
- Build cost lists, estimates, and reports in
  minutes.
- Adjust costs to any location in the U.S. and
  Canada with the click of a button.

Start your free trial today at
www.RSMeansOnline.com

System Description	QUAN.	UNIT	LABOR HOURS	COST PER L.F.		
				MAT.	INST.	TOTAL
8″ THICK BY 18″ WIDE FOOTING						
Concrete, 3000 psi	.040	C.Y.		5.20		5.20
Place concrete, direct chute	.040	C.Y.	.016		.77	.77
Forms, footing, 4 uses	1.330	SFCA	.103	1.05	5.31	6.36
Reinforcing, 1/2″ diameter bars, 2 each	1.380	Lb.	.011	.72	.68	1.40
Keyway, 2″ x 4″, beveled, 4 uses	1.000	L.F.	.015	.24	.88	1.12
Dowels, 1/2″ diameter bars, 2′ long, 6′ O.C.	.166	Ea.	.006	.13	.36	.49
TOTAL		L.F.	.151	7.34	8	15.34
12″ THICK BY 24″ WIDE FOOTING						
Concrete, 3000 psi	.070	C.Y.		9.10		9.10
Place concrete, direct chute	.070	C.Y.	.028		1.36	1.36
Forms, footing, 4 uses	2.000	SFCA	.155	1.58	7.98	9.56
Reinforcing, 1/2″ diameter bars, 2 each	1.380	Lb.	.011	.72	.68	1.40
Keyway, 2″ x 4″, beveled, 4 uses	1.000	L.F.	.015	.24	.88	1.12
Dowels, 1/2″ diameter bars, 2′ long, 6′ O.C.	.166	Ea.	.006	.13	.36	.49
TOTAL		L.F.	.215	11.77	11.26	23.03
12″ THICK BY 36″ WIDE FOOTING						
Concrete, 3000 psi	.110	C.Y.		14.30		14.30
Place concrete, direct chute	.110	C.Y.	.044		2.13	2.13
Forms, footing, 4 uses	2.000	SFCA	.155	1.58	7.98	9.56
Reinforcing, 1/2″ diameter bars, 2 each	1.380	Lb.	.011	.72	.68	1.40
Keyway, 2″ x 4″, beveled, 4 uses	1.000	L.F.	.015	.24	.88	1.12
Dowels, 1/2″ diameter bars, 2′ long, 6′ O.C.	.166	Ea.	.006	.13	.36	.49
TOTAL		L.F.	.231	16.97	12.03	29

The footing costs in this system are on a cost per linear foot basis.

Description	QUAN.	UNIT	LABOR HOURS	COST PER L.F.		
				MAT.	INST.	TOTAL

Footing Price Sheet	QUAN.	UNIT	LABOR HOURS	COST PER L.F.		
				MAT.	INST.	TOTAL
Concrete, 8" thick by 18" wide footing						
2000 psi concrete	.040	C.Y.		4.96		4.96
2500 psi concrete	.040	C.Y.		5.10		5.10
3000 psi concrete	.040	C.Y.		5.20		5.20
3500 psi concrete	.040	C.Y.		5.30		5.30
4000 psi concrete	.040	C.Y.		5.50		5.50
12" thick by 24" wide footing						
2000 psi concrete	.070	C.Y.		8.70		8.70
2500 psi concrete	.070	C.Y.		8.90		8.90
3000 psi concrete	.070	C.Y.		9.10		9.10
3500 psi concrete	.070	C.Y.		9.30		9.30
4000 psi concrete	.070	C.Y.		9.60		9.60
12" thick by 36" wide footing						
2000 psi concrete	.110	C.Y.		13.65		13.65
2500 psi concrete	.110	C.Y.		13.95		13.95
3000 psi concrete	.110	C.Y.		14.30		14.30
3500 psi concrete	.110	C.Y.		14.65		14.65
4000 psi concrete	.110	C.Y.		15.05		15.05
Place concrete, 8" thick by 18" wide footing, direct chute	.040	C.Y.	.016		.77	.77
Pumped concrete	.040	C.Y.	.017		1.07	1.07
Crane & bucket	.040	C.Y.	.032		2.13	2.13
12" thick by 24" wide footing, direct chute	.070	C.Y.	.028		1.36	1.36
Pumped concrete	.070	C.Y.	.030		1.88	1.88
Crane & bucket	.070	C.Y.	.056		3.72	3.72
12" thick by 36" wide footing, direct chute	.110	C.Y.	.044		2.13	2.13
Pumped concrete	.110	C.Y.	.047		2.96	2.96
Crane & bucket	.110	C.Y.	.088		5.85	5.85
Forms, 8" thick footing, 1 use	1.330	SFCA	.140	3.22	7.20	10.42
4 uses	1.330	SFCA	.103	1.05	5.30	6.35
12" thick footing, 1 use	2.000	SFCA	.211	4.84	10.80	15.64
4 uses	2.000	SFCA	.155	1.58	8	9.58
Reinforcing, 3/8" diameter bar, 1 each	.400	Lb.	.003	.21	.20	.41
2 each	.800	Lb.	.006	.42	.39	.81
3 each	1.200	Lb.	.009	.62	.59	1.21
1/2" diameter bar, 1 each	.700	Lb.	.005	.36	.34	.70
2 each	1.380	Lb.	.011	.72	.68	1.40
3 each	2.100	Lb.	.016	1.09	1.03	2.12
5/8" diameter bar, 1 each	1.040	Lb.	.008	.54	.51	1.05
2 each	2.080	Lb.	.016	1.08	1.02	2.10
Keyway, beveled, 2" x 4", 1 use	1.000	L.F.	.030	.48	1.76	2.24
2 uses	1.000	L.F.	.023	.36	1.32	1.68
2" x 6", 1 use	1.000	L.F.	.032	.68	1.88	2.56
2 uses	1.000	L.F.	.024	.51	1.41	1.92
Dowels, 2 feet long, 6' O.C., 3/8" bar	.166	Ea.	.005	.07	.33	.40
1/2" bar	.166	Ea.	.006	.13	.36	.49
5/8" bar	.166	Ea.	.006	.20	.40	.60
3/4" bar	.166	Ea.	.006	.20	.40	.60

For customer support on your Residential Costs with RSMeans Data, call 800.448.8182.

119

Sill Plate
Parging
Dampproofing
Insulation
Anchor Bolts
Masonry Reinforcing
Concrete Blocks
Grout

System Description	QUAN.	UNIT	LABOR HOURS	COST PER S.F.		
				MAT.	INST.	TOTAL
8″ WALL, GROUTED, FULL HEIGHT						
Concrete block, 8″ x 16″ x 8″	1.000	S.F.	.094	3.62	5.10	8.72
Masonry reinforcing, every second course	.750	L.F.	.002	.19	.12	.31
Parging, plastering with portland cement plaster, 1 coat	1.000	S.F.	.014	.33	.80	1.13
Dampproofing, bituminous coating, 1 coat	1.000	S.F.	.012	.25	.66	.91
Insulation, 1″ rigid polystyrene	1.000	S.F.	.010	.63	.58	1.21
Grout, solid, pumped	1.000	S.F.	.059	1.33	3.12	4.45
Anchor bolts, 1/2″ diameter, 8″ long, 4′ O.C.	.060	Ea.	.004	.09	.21	.30
Sill plate, 2″ x 4″, treated	.250	L.F.	.007	.14	.43	.57
TOTAL		S.F.	.202	6.58	11.02	17.60
12″ WALL, GROUTED, FULL HEIGHT						
Concrete block, 8″ x 16″ x 12″	1.000	S.F.	.160	5.45	8.55	14
Masonry reinforcing, every second course	.750	L.F.	.003	.14	.17	.31
Parging, plastering with portland cement plaster, 1 coat	1.000	S.F.	.014	.33	.80	1.13
Dampproofing, bituminous coating, 1 coat	1.000	S.F.	.012	.25	.66	.91
Insulation, 1″ rigid polystyrene	1.000	S.F.	.010	.63	.58	1.21
Grout, solid, pumped	1.000	S.F.	.063	2.17	3.32	5.49
Anchor bolts, 1/2″ diameter, 8″ long, 4′ O.C.	.060	Ea.	.004	.09	.21	.30
Sill plate, 2″ x 4″, treated	.250	L.F.	.007	.14	.43	.57
TOTAL		S.F.	.273	9.20	14.72	23.92

The costs in this system are based on a square foot of wall. Do not subtract for window or door openings.

Description	QUAN.	UNIT	LABOR HOURS	COST PER S.F.		
				MAT.	INST.	TOTAL

Block Wall Price Sheet	QUAN.	UNIT	LABOR HOURS	COST PER S.F.		
				MAT.	INST.	TOTAL
Concrete, block, 8" x 16" x, 6" thick	1.000	S.F.	.089	3.38	4.78	8.16
8" thick	1.000	S.F.	.093	3.62	5.10	8.72
10" thick	1.000	S.F.	.095	4.14	6.20	10.34
12" thick	1.000	S.F.	.122	5.45	8.55	14
Solid block, 8" x 16" x, 6" thick	1.000	S.F.	.091	3.44	4.94	8.38
8" thick	1.000	S.F.	.096	4.81	5.25	10.06
10" thick	1.000	S.F.	.096	4.81	5.25	10.06
12" thick	1.000	S.F.	.126	6.90	7.30	14.20
Masonry reinforcing, wire strips, to 8" wide, every course	1.500	L.F.	.004	.38	.24	.62
Every 2nd course	.750	L.F.	.002	.19	.12	.31
Every 3rd course	.500	L.F.	.001	.13	.08	.21
Every 4th course	.400	L.F.	.001	.10	.06	.16
Wire strips to 12" wide, every course	1.500	L.F.	.006	.29	.35	.64
Every 2nd course	.750	L.F.	.003	.14	.17	.31
Every 3rd course	.500	L.F.	.002	.10	.12	.22
Every 4th course	.400	L.F.	.002	.08	.09	.17
Parging, plastering with portland cement plaster, 1 coat	1.000	S.F.	.014	.33	.80	1.13
2 coats	1.000	S.F.	.022	.51	1.24	1.75
Dampproofing, bituminous, brushed on, 1 coat	1.000	S.F.	.012	.25	.66	.91
2 coats	1.000	S.F.	.016	.49	.88	1.37
Sprayed on, 1 coat	1.000	S.F.	.010	.25	.53	.78
2 coats	1.000	S.F.	.016	.48	.88	1.36
Troweled on, 1/16" thick	1.000	S.F.	.016	.41	.88	1.29
1/8" thick	1.000	S.F.	.020	.73	1.10	1.83
1/2" thick	1.000	S.F.	.023	2.38	1.25	3.63
Insulation, rigid, fiberglass, 1.5#/C.F., unfaced						
1-1/2" thick R 6.2	1.000	S.F.	.008	.43	.47	.90
2" thick R 8.5	1.000	S.F.	.008	.54	.47	1.01
3" thick R 13	1.000	S.F.	.010	.63	.58	1.21
Perlite, 1" thick R 2.77	1.000	S.F.	.010	.50	.58	1.08
2" thick R 5.55	1.000	S.F.	.011	.86	.64	1.50
Polystyrene, extruded, 1" thick R 5.4	1.000	S.F.	.010	.63	.58	1.21
2" thick R 10.8	1.000	S.F.	.011	1.75	.64	2.39
Molded 1" thick R 3.85	1.000	S.F.	.010	.29	.58	.87
2" thick R 7.7	1.000	S.F.	.011	.86	.64	1.50
Grout, concrete block cores, 6" thick	1.000	S.F.	.044	1	2.34	3.34
8" thick	1.000	S.F.	.059	1.33	3.12	4.45
10" thick	1.000	S.F.	.061	1.75	3.22	4.97
12" thick	1.000	S.F.	.063	2.17	3.32	5.49
Anchor bolts, 2' on center, 1/2" diameter, 8" long	.120	Ea.	.005	.18	.43	.61
12" long	.120	Ea.	.005	.20	.43	.63
3/4" diameter, 8" long	.120	Ea.	.006	.54	.44	.98
12" long	.120	Ea.	.006	.68	.45	1.13
4' on center, 1/2" diameter, 8" long	.060	Ea.	.002	.09	.21	.30
12" long	.060	Ea.	.003	.10	.21	.31
3/4" diameter, 8" long	.060	Ea.	.003	.27	.22	.49
12" long	.060	Ea.	.003	.34	.22	.56
Sill plates, treated, 2" x 4"	.250	L.F.	.007	.14	.43	.57
4" x 4"	.250	L.F.	.007	.37	.40	.77

System Description	QUAN.	UNIT	LABOR HOURS	COST PER S.F.		
				MAT.	INST.	TOTAL
8″ THICK, POURED CONCRETE WALL						
Concrete, 8″ thick , 3000 psi	.025	C.Y.		3.25		3.25
Forms, prefabricated plywood, up to 8′ high	2.000	SFCA	.120	2.08	6.26	8.34
Reinforcing, light	.670	Lb.	.004	.35	.23	.58
Placing concrete, direct chute	.025	C.Y.	.013		.65	.65
Dampproofing, brushed on, 2 coats	1.000	S.F.	.016	.49	.88	1.37
Rigid insulation, 1″ polystyrene	1.000	S.F.	.010	.63	.58	1.21
Anchor bolts, 1/2″ diameter, 12″ long, 4′ O.C.	.060	Ea.	.004	.10	.21	.31
Sill plates, 2″ x 4″, treated	.250	L.F.	.007	.14	.43	.57
TOTAL		S.F.	.174	7.04	9.24	16.28
12″ THICK, POURED CONCRETE WALL						
Concrete, 12″ thick, 3000 psi	.040	C.Y.		5.20		5.20
Forms, prefabricated plywood, up to 8′ high	2.000	SFCA	.120	2.08	6.26	8.34
Reinforcing, light	1.000	Lb.	.005	.52	.35	.87
Placing concrete, direct chute	.040	C.Y.	.019		.92	.92
Dampproofing, brushed on, 2 coats	1.000	S.F.	.016	.49	.88	1.37
Rigid insulation, 1″ polystyrene	1.000	S.F.	.010	.63	.58	1.21
Anchor bolts, 1/2″ diameter, 12″ long, 4′ O.C.	.060	Ea.	.004	.10	.21	.31
Sill plates, 2″ x 4″ treated	.250	L.F.	.007	.14	.43	.57
TOTAL		S.F.	.181	9.16	9.63	18.79

The costs in this system are based on sq. ft. of wall. Do not subtract
for window and door openings. The costs assume a 4′ high wall.

Description	QUAN.	UNIT	LABOR HOURS	COST PER S.F.		
				MAT.	INST.	TOTAL

Concrete Wall Price Sheet

Concrete Wall Price Sheet	QUAN.	UNIT	LABOR HOURS	COST PER S.F.		
				MAT.	INST.	TOTAL
Formwork, prefabricated plywood, up to 8' high	2.000	SFCA	.081	2.08	6.25	8.33
Over 8' to 16' high	2.000	SFCA	.076	2.18	8.35	10.53
Job built forms, 1 use per month	2.000	SFCA	.320	5.65	13.50	19.15
4 uses per month	2.000	SFCA	.221	2.14	9.90	12.04
Reinforcing, 8" wall, light reinforcing	.670	Lb.	.004	.35	.23	.58
Heavy reinforcing	1.500	Lb.	.008	.78	.53	1.31
10" wall, light reinforcing	.850	Lb.	.005	.44	.30	.74
Heavy reinforcing	2.000	Lb.	.011	1.04	.70	1.74
12" wall light reinforcing	1.000	Lb.	.005	.52	.35	.87
Heavy reinforcing	2.250	Lb.	.012	1.17	.79	1.96
Placing concrete, 8" wall, direct chute	.025	C.Y.	.013		.65	.65
Pumped concrete	.025	C.Y.	.016		1.02	1.02
Crane & bucket	.025	C.Y.	.023		1.50	1.50
10" wall, direct chute	.030	C.Y.	.016		.77	.77
Pumped concrete	.030	C.Y.	.019		1.22	1.22
Crane & bucket	.030	C.Y.	.027		1.80	1.80
12" wall, direct chute	.040	C.Y.	.019		.92	.92
Pumped concrete	.040	C.Y.	.023		1.47	1.47
Crane & bucket	.040	C.Y.	.032		2.13	2.13
Dampproofing, bituminous, brushed on, 1 coat	1.000	S.F.	.012	.25	.66	.91
2 coats	1.000	S.F.	.016	.49	.88	1.37
Sprayed on, 1 coat	1.000	S.F.	.010	.25	.53	.78
2 coats	1.000	S.F.	.016	.48	.88	1.36
Troweled on, 1/16" thick	1.000	S.F.	.016	.41	.88	1.29
1/8" thick	1.000	S.F.	.020	.73	1.10	1.83
1/2" thick	1.000	S.F.	.023	2.38	1.25	3.63
Insulation rigid, fiberglass, 1.5#/C.F., unfaced						
1-1/2" thick, R 6.2	1.000	S.F.	.008	.43	.47	.90
2" thick, R 8.3	1.000	S.F.	.008	.54	.47	1.01
3" thick, R 12.4	1.000	S.F.	.010	.63	.58	1.21
Perlite, 1" thick R 2.77	1.000	S.F.	.010	.50	.58	1.08
2" thick R 5.55	1.000	S.F.	.011	.86	.64	1.50
Polystyrene, extruded, 1" thick R 5.40	1.000	S.F.	.010	.63	.58	1.21
2" thick R 10.8	1.000	S.F.	.011	1.75	.64	2.39
Molded, 1" thick R 3.85	1.000	S.F.	.010	.29	.58	.87
2" thick R 7.70	1.000	S.F.	.011	.86	.64	1.50
Anchor bolts, 2' on center, 1/2" diameter, 8" long	.120	Ea.	.005	.18	.43	.61
12" long	.120	Ea.	.005	.20	.43	.63
3/4" diameter, 8" long	.120	Ea.	.006	.54	.44	.98
12" long	.120	Ea.	.006	.68	.45	1.13
Sill plates, treated lumber, 2" x 4"	.250	L.F.	.007	.14	.43	.57
4" x 4"	.250	L.F.	.007	.37	.40	.77

System Description	QUAN.	UNIT	LABOR HOURS	COST PER S.F.		
				MAT.	INST.	TOTAL
2″ X 4″ STUDS, 16″ O.C., WALL						
Studs, 2″ x 4″, 16″ O.C., treated	1.000	L.F.	.015	.58	.85	1.43
Plates, double top plate, single bottom plate, treated, 2″ x 4″	.750	L.F.	.011	.44	.64	1.08
Sheathing, 1/2″, exterior grade, CDX, treated	1.000	S.F.	.014	.92	.83	1.75
Asphalt paper, 15# roll	1.100	S.F.	.002	.07	.14	.21
Vapor barrier, 4 mil polyethylene	1.000	S.F.	.002	.04	.13	.17
Fiberglass insulation, 3-1/2″ thick	1.000	S.F.	.007	.36	.41	.77
TOTAL		S.F.	.051	2.41	3	5.41
2″ X 6″ STUDS, 16″ O.C., WALL						
Studs, 2″ x 6″, 16″ O.C., treated	1.000	L.F.	.016	.89	.94	1.83
Plates, double top plate, single bottom plate, treated, 2″ x 6″	.750	L.F.	.012	.67	.71	1.38
Sheathing, 5/8″ exterior grade, CDX, treated	1.000	S.F.	.015	1.42	.89	2.31
Asphalt paper, 15# roll	1.100	S.F.	.002	.07	.14	.21
Vapor barrier, 4 mil polyethylene	1.000	S.F.	.002	.04	.13	.17
Fiberglass insulation, 6″ thick	1.000	S.F.	.007	.50	.41	.91
TOTAL		S.F.	.054	3.59	3.22	6.81
2″ X 8″ STUDS, 16″ O.C., WALL						
Studs, 2″ x 8″, 16″ O.C. treated	1.000	L.F.	.018	1.16	1.04	2.20
Plates, double top plate, single bottom plate, treated, 2″ x 8″	.750	L.F.	.013	.87	.78	1.65
Sheathing, 3/4″ exterior grade, CDX, treated	1.000	S.F.	.016	1.51	.96	2.47
Asphalt paper, 15# roll	1.100	S.F.	.002	.07	.14	.21
Vapor barrier, 4 mil polyethylene	1.000	S.F.	.002	.04	.13	.17
Fiberglass insulation, 9″ thick	1.000	S.F.	.006	.83	.35	1.18
TOTAL		S.F.	.057	4.48	3.40	7.88

The costs in this system are based on a sq. ft. of wall area. Do not subtract for window or door openings. The costs assume a 4′ high wall.

Description	QUAN.	UNIT	LABOR HOURS	COST PER S.F.		
				MAT.	INST.	TOTAL

Wood Wall Foundation Price Sheet

Wood Wall Foundation Price Sheet	QUAN.	UNIT	LABOR HOURS	COST PER S.F.		
				MAT.	INST.	TOTAL
Studs, treated, 2" x 4", 12" O.C.	1.250	L.F.	.018	.73	1.06	1.79
16" O.C.	1.000	L.F.	.015	.58	.85	1.43
2" x 6", 12" O.C.	1.250	L.F.	.020	1.11	1.18	2.29
16" O.C.	1.000	L.F.	.016	.89	.94	1.83
2" x 8", 12" O.C.	1.250	L.F.	.022	1.45	1.30	2.75
16" O.C.	1.000	L.F.	.018	1.16	1.04	2.20
Plates, treated double top single bottom, 2" x 4"	.750	L.F.	.011	.44	.64	1.08
2" x 6"	.750	L.F.	.012	.67	.71	1.38
2" x 8"	.750	L.F.	.013	.87	.78	1.65
Sheathing, treated exterior grade CDX, 1/2" thick	1.000	S.F.	.014	.92	.83	1.75
5/8" thick	1.000	S.F.	.015	1.42	.89	2.31
3/4" thick	1.000	S.F.	.016	1.51	.96	2.47
Asphalt paper, 15# roll	1.100	S.F.	.002	.07	.14	.21
Vapor barrier, polyethylene, 4 mil	1.000	S.F.	.002	.03	.13	.16
10 mil	1.000	S.F.	.002	.09	.13	.22
Insulation, rigid, fiberglass, 1.5#/C.F., unfaced	1.000	S.F.	.008	.33	.47	.80
1-1/2" thick, R 6.2	1.000	S.F.	.008	.43	.47	.90
2" thick, R 8.3	1.000	S.F.	.008	.54	.47	1.01
3" thick, R 12.4	1.000	S.F.	.010	.64	.59	1.23
Perlite 1" thick, R 2.77	1.000	S.F.	.010	.50	.58	1.08
2" thick, R 5.55	1.000	S.F.	.011	.86	.64	1.50
Polystyrene, extruded, 1" thick, R 5.40	1.000	S.F.	.010	.63	.58	1.21
2" thick, R 10.8	1.000	S.F.	.011	1.75	.64	2.39
Molded 1" thick, R 3.85	1.000	S.F.	.010	.29	.58	.87
2" thick, R 7.7	1.000	S.F.	.011	.86	.64	1.50
Non rigid, batts, fiberglass, paper backed, 3-1/2" thick roll, R 11	1.000	S.F.	.005	.36	.41	.77
6", R 19	1.000	S.F.	.006	.50	.41	.91
9", R 30	1.000	S.F.	.006	.83	.35	1.18
12", R 38	1.000	S.F.	.006	1.19	.35	1.54
Mineral fiber, paper backed, 3-1/2", R 13	1.000	S.F.	.005	.77	.29	1.06
6", R 19	1.000	S.F.	.005	1.21	.29	1.50
10", R 30	1.000	S.F.	.006	1.60	.35	1.95

For customer support on your Residential Costs with RSMeans Data, call 800.448.8182.

125

Concrete Slab — | Expansion Material

Bank Run Gravel

Welded Wire Fabric —

Vapor Barrier

System Description	QUAN.	UNIT	LABOR HOURS	COST PER S.F.		
				MAT.	INST.	TOTAL
4″ THICK SLAB						
Concrete, 4″ thick, 3000 psi concrete	.012	C.Y.		1.56		1.56
Place concrete, direct chute	.012	C.Y.	.005		.26	.26
Bank run gravel, 4″ deep	1.000	S.F.	.001	.34	.06	.40
Polyethylene vapor barrier, .006″ thick	1.000	S.F.	.002	.04	.13	.17
Edge forms, expansion material	.100	L.F.	.005	.04	.28	.32
Welded wire fabric, 6 x 6, 10/10 (W1.4/W1.4)	1.100	S.F.	.005	.18	.33	.51
Steel trowel finish	1.000	S.F.	.014		.76	.76
TOTAL		S.F.	.032	2.16	1.82	3.98
6″ THICK SLAB						
Concrete, 6″ thick, 3000 psi concrete	.019	C.Y.		2.47		2.47
Place concrete, direct chute	.019	C.Y.	.008		.40	.40
Bank run gravel, 4″ deep	1.000	S.F.	.001	.34	.06	.40
Polyethylene vapor barrier, .006″ thick	1.000	S.F.	.002	.04	.13	.17
Edge forms, expansion material	.100	L.F.	.005	.04	.28	.32
Welded wire fabric, 6 x 6, 10/10 (W1.4/W1.4)	1.100	S.F.	.005	.18	.33	.51
Steel trowel finish	1.000	S.F.	.014		.76	.76
TOTAL		S.F.	.035	3.07	1.96	5.03

The slab costs in this section are based on a cost per square foot of
floor area.

Description	QUAN.	UNIT	LABOR HOURS	COST PER S.F.		
				MAT.	INST.	TOTAL

Floor Slab Price Sheet	QUAN.	UNIT	LABOR HOURS	COST PER S.F.		
				MAT.	INST.	TOTAL
Concrete, 4" thick slab, 2000 psi concrete	.012	C.Y.		1.49		1.49
2500 psi concrete	.012	C.Y.		1.52		1.52
3000 psi concrete	.012	C.Y.		1.56		1.56
3500 psi concrete	.012	C.Y.		1.60		1.60
4000 psi concrete	.012	C.Y.		1.64		1.64
4500 psi concrete	.012	C.Y.		1.69		1.69
5" thick slab, 2000 psi concrete	.015	C.Y.		1.86		1.86
2500 psi concrete	.015	C.Y.		1.91		1.91
3000 psi concrete	.015	C.Y.		1.95		1.95
3500 psi concrete	.015	C.Y.		2		2
4000 psi concrete	.015	C.Y.		2.06		2.06
4500 psi concrete	.015	C.Y.		2.12		2.12
6" thick slab, 2000 psi concrete	.019	C.Y.		2.36		2.36
2500 psi concrete	.019	C.Y.		2.41		2.41
3000 psi concrete	.019	C.Y.		2.47		2.47
3500 psi concrete	.019	C.Y.		2.53		2.53
4000 psi concrete	.019	C.Y.		2.60		2.60
4500 psi concrete	.019	C.Y.		2.68		2.68
Place concrete, 4" slab, direct chute	.012	C.Y.	.005		.26	.26
Pumped concrete	.012	C.Y.	.006		.38	.38
Crane & bucket	.012	C.Y.	.008		.52	.52
5" slab, direct chute	.015	C.Y.	.007		.32	.32
Pumped concrete	.015	C.Y.	.007		.47	.47
Crane & bucket	.015	C.Y.	.010		.65	.65
6" slab, direct chute	.019	C.Y.	.008		.40	.40
Pumped concrete	.019	C.Y.	.009		.60	.60
Crane & bucket	.019	C.Y.	.012		.83	.83
Gravel, bank run, 4" deep	1.000	S.F.	.001	.34	.06	.40
6" deep	1.000	S.F.	.001	.45	.08	.53
9" deep	1.000	S.F.	.001	.66	.11	.77
12" deep	1.000	S.F.	.001	.90	.14	1.04
3/4" crushed stone, 3" deep	1.000	S.F.	.001	.31	.06	.37
6" deep	1.000	S.F.	.001	.62	.11	.73
9" deep	1.000	S.F.	.002	.90	.15	1.05
12" deep	1.000	S.F.	.002	1.54	.19	1.73
Vapor barrier polyethylene, .004" thick	1.000	S.F.	.002	.03	.13	.16
.006" thick	1.000	S.F.	.002	.04	.13	.17
Edge forms, expansion material, 4" thick slab	.100	L.F.	.004	.02	.18	.20
6" thick slab	.100	L.F.	.005	.04	.28	.32
Welded wire fabric 6 x 6, 10/10 (W1.4/W1.4)	1.100	S.F.	.005	.18	.33	.51
6 x 6, 6/6 (W2.9/W2.9)	1.100	S.F.	.006	.30	.40	.70
4 x 4, 10/10 (W1.4/W1.4)	1.100	S.F.	.006	.26	.36	.62
Finish concrete, screed finish	1.000	S.F.	.009		.31	.31
Float finish	1.000	S.F.	.011		.31	.31
Steel trowel, for resilient floor	1.000	S.F.	.013		.99	.99
For finished floor	1.000	S.F.	.015		.76	.76

For customer support on your Residential Costs with RSMeans Data, call 800.448.8182.

127

System Description	QUAN.	UNIT	LABOR HOURS	COST PER S.F.		
				MAT.	INST.	TOTAL
2″ X 8″, 16″ O.C.						
Wood joists, 2″ x 8″, 16″ O.C.	1.000	L.F.	.015	.96	.85	1.81
Bridging, 1″ x 3″, 6′ O.C.	.080	Pr.	.005	.06	.29	.35
Box sills, 2″ x 8″	.150	L.F.	.002	.14	.13	.27
Concrete filled steel column, 4″ diameter	.125	L.F.	.002	.18	.14	.32
Girder, built up from three 2″ x 8″	.125	L.F.	.013	.36	.78	1.14
Sheathing, plywood, subfloor, 5/8″ CDX	1.000	S.F.	.012	.86	.69	1.55
Furring, 1″ x 3″, 16″ O.C.	1.000	L.F.	.023	.46	1.34	1.80
Joist hangers	.036	Ea.	.002	.05	.10	.15
TOTAL		S.F.	.074	3.07	4.32	7.39
2″ X 10″, 16″ O.C.						
Wood joists, 2″ x 10″, 16″ OC	1.000	L.F.	.018	1.51	1.04	2.55
Bridging, 1″ x 3″, 6′ OC	.080	Pr.	.005	.06	.29	.35
Box sills, 2″ x 10″	.150	L.F.	.003	.23	.16	.39
Concrete filled steel column, 4″ diameter	.125	L.F.	.002	.18	.14	.32
5/8″ thick	.125	L.F.	.014	.57	.83	1.40
Sheathing, plywood, subfloor, 5/8″ CDX	1.000	S.F.	.012	.86	.69	1.55
Furring, 1″ x 3″,16″ OC	1.000	L.F.	.023	.46	1.34	1.80
Joist hangers	.036	Ea.	.002	.05	.10	.15
TOTAL		S.F.	.079	3.92	4.59	8.51
2″ X 12″, 16″ O.C.						
Wood joists, 2″ x 12″, 16″ O.C.	1.000	L.F.	.018	1.93	1.07	3
Bridging, 1″ x 3″, 6′ O.C.	.080	Pr.	.005	.06	.29	.35
Box sills, 2″ x 12″	.150	L.F.	.003	.29	.16	.45
Concrete filled steel column, 4″ diameter	.125	L.F.	.002	.18	.14	.32
Girder, built up from three 2″ x 12″	.125	L.F.	.015	.72	.88	1.60
Sheathing, plywood, subfloor, 5/8″ CDX	1.000	S.F.	.012	.86	.69	1.55
Furring, 1″ x 3″, 16″ O.C.	1.000	L.F.	.023	.46	1.34	1.80
Joist hangers	.036	Ea.	.002	.05	.10	.15
TOTAL		S.F.	.080	4.55	4.67	9.22

Floor costs on this page are given on a cost per square foot basis.

Description	QUAN.	UNIT	LABOR HOURS	COST PER S.F.		
				MAT.	INST.	TOTAL

Floor Framing Price Sheet (Wood)

	QUAN.	UNIT	LABOR HOURS	COST PER S.F. MAT.	COST PER S.F. INST.	COST PER S.F. TOTAL
Joists, #2 or better, pine, 2" x 4", 12" O.C.	1.250	L.F.	.016	.56	.94	1.50
16" O.C.	1.000	L.F.	.013	.45	.75	1.20
2" x 6", 12" O.C.	1.250	L.F.	.016	.86	.94	1.80
16" O.C.	1.000	L.F.	.013	.69	.75	1.44
2" x 8", 12" O.C.	1.250	L.F.	.018	1.20	1.06	2.26
16" O.C.	1.000	L.F.	.015	.96	.85	1.81
2" x 10", 12" O.C.	1.250	L.F.	.022	1.89	1.30	3.19
16" O.C.	1.000	L.F.	.018	1.51	1.04	2.55
2"x 12", 12" O.C.	1.250	L.F.	.023	2.41	1.34	3.75
16" O.C.	1.000	L.F.	.018	1.93	1.07	3
Bridging, wood 1" x 3", joists 12" O.C.	.100	Pr.	.006	.07	.36	.43
16" O.C.	.080	Pr.	.005	.06	.29	.35
Metal, galvanized, joists 12" O.C.	.100	Pr.	.006	.22	.36	.58
16" O.C.	.080	Pr.	.005	.17	.29	.46
Compression type, joists 12" O.C.	.100	Pr.	.004	.10	.23	.33
16" O.C.	.080	Pr.	.003	.08	.19	.27
Box sills, #2 or better, 2" x 4"	.150	L.F.	.002	.07	.11	.18
2" x 6"	.150	L.F.	.002	.10	.11	.21
2" x 8"	.150	L.F.	.002	.14	.13	.27
2" x 10"	.150	L.F.	.003	.23	.16	.39
2" x 12"	.150	L.F.	.003	.29	.16	.45
Girders, including lally columns, 3 pieces spiked together, 2" x 8"	.125	L.F.	.015	.54	.92	1.46
2" x 10"	.125	L.F.	.016	.75	.97	1.72
2" x 12"	.125	L.F.	.017	.90	1.02	1.92
Solid girders, 3" x 8"	.040	L.F.	.004	.31	.24	.55
3" x 10"	.040	L.F.	.004	.34	.25	.59
3" x 12"	.040	L.F.	.004	.37	.26	.63
4" x 8"	.040	L.F.	.004	.33	.26	.59
4" x 10"	.040	L.F.	.004	.40	.27	.67
4" x 12"	.040	L.F.	.004	.42	.28	.70
Steel girders, bolted & including fabrication, wide flange shapes						
12" deep, 14#/l.f.	.040	L.F.	.003	1.04	.28	1.32
10" deep, 15#/l.f.	.040	L.F.	.003	1.04	.28	1.32
8" deep, 10#/l.f.	.040	L.F.	.003	.69	.28	.97
6" deep, 9#/l.f.	.040	L.F.	.003	.62	.28	.90
5" deep, 16#/l.f.	.040	L.F.	.003	1.04	.28	1.32
Sheathing, plywood exterior grade CDX, 1/2" thick	1.000	S.F.	.011	.69	.67	1.36
5/8" thick	1.000	S.F.	.012	.86	.69	1.55
3/4" thick	1.000	S.F.	.013	1.03	.75	1.78
Boards, 1" x 8" laid regular	1.000	S.F.	.016	2.21	.94	3.15
Laid diagonal	1.000	S.F.	.019	2.21	1.10	3.31
1" x 10" laid regular	1.000	S.F.	.015	2.26	.85	3.11
Laid diagonal	1.000	S.F.	.018	2.26	1.04	3.30
Furring, 1" x 3", 12" O.C.	1.250	L.F.	.029	.58	1.68	2.26
16" O.C.	1.000	L.F.	.023	.46	1.34	1.80
24" O.C.	.750	L.F.	.017	.35	1.01	1.36

For customer support on your Residential Costs with RSMeans Data, call 800.448.8182.

131

Labels: CWJ Rim Joist, Plywood Sheathing, Temporary Strut Lines 1" x 4", 8'-0" O.C., Web Stiffener, Girder, Composite Wood Joists (CWJ)

System Description	QUAN.	UNIT	LABOR HOURS	COST PER S.F.		
				MAT.	INST.	TOTAL
9-1/2" COMPOSITE WOOD JOISTS, 16" O.C.						
CWJ, 9-1/2", 16" O.C., 15' span	1.000	L.F.	.018	1.85	1.05	2.90
Temp. strut line, 1" x 4", 8' O.C.	.160	L.F.	.003	.09	.19	.28
CWJ rim joist, 9-1/2"	.150	L.F.	.003	.28	.16	.44
Concrete filled steel column, 4" diameter	.125	L.F.	.002	.18	.14	.32
Girder, built up from three 2" x 8"	.125	L.F.	.013	.36	.78	1.14
Sheathing, plywood, subfloor, 5/8" CDX	1.000	S.F.	.012	.86	.69	1.55
TOTAL		S.F.	.051	3.62	3.01	6.63
11-1/2" COMPOSITE WOOD JOISTS, 16" O.C.						
CWJ, 11-1/2", 16" O.C., 18' span	1.000	L.F.	.018	2.10	1.08	3.18
Temp. strut line, 1" x 4", 8' O.C.	.160	L.F.	.003	.09	.19	.28
CWJ rim joist, 11-1/2"	.150	L.F.	.003	.32	.16	.48
Concrete filled steel column, 4" diameter	.125	L.F.	.002	.18	.14	.32
Girder, built up from three 2" x 10"	.125	L.F.	.014	.57	.83	1.40
Sheathing, plywood, subfloor, 5/8" CDX	1.000	S.F.	.012	.86	.69	1.55
TOTAL		S.F.	.052	4.12	3.09	7.21
14" COMPOSITE WOOD JOISTS, 16" O.C.						
CWJ, 14", 16" O.C., 22' span	1.000	L.F.	.020	2.50	1.15	3.65
Temp. strut line, 1" x 4", 8' O.C.	.160	L.F.	.003	.09	.19	.28
CWJ rim joist, 14"	.150	L.F.	.003	.38	.17	.55
Concrete filled steel column, 4" diameter	.600	L.F.	.002	.18	.14	.32
Girder, built up from three 2" x 12"	.600	L.F.	.015	.72	.88	1.60
Sheathing, plywood, subfloor, 5/8" CDX	1.000	S.F.	.012	.86	.69	1.55
TOTAL		S.F.	.055	4.73	3.22	7.95

Floor costs on this page are given on a cost per square foot basis.

Description	QUAN.	UNIT	LABOR HOURS	COST PER S.F.		
				MAT.	INST.	TOTAL

Floor Framing Price Sheet (Wood)	QUAN.	UNIT	LABOR HOURS	COST PER S.F.		
				MAT.	INST.	TOTAL
Composite wood joist 9-1/2" deep, 12" O.C.	1.250	L.F.	.022	2.31	1.31	3.62
16" O.C.	1.000	L.F.	.018	1.85	1.05	2.90
11-1/2" deep, 12" O.C.	1.250	L.F.	.023	2.63	1.34	3.97
16" O.C.	1.000	L.F.	.018	2.10	1.08	3.18
14" deep, 12" O.C.	1.250	L.F.	.024	3.13	1.44	4.57
16" O.C.	1.000	L.F.	.020	2.50	1.15	3.65
16 " deep, 12" O.C.	1.250	L.F.	.026	5	1.50	6.50
16" O.C.	1.000	L.F.	.021	4	1.20	5.20
CWJ rim joist, 9-1/2"	.150	L.F.	.003	.28	.16	.44
11-1/2"	.150	L.F.	.003	.32	.16	.48
14"	.150	L.F.	.003	.38	.17	.55
16"	.150	L.F.	.003	.60	.18	.78
Girders, including lally columns, 3 pieces spiked together, 2" x 8"	.125	L.F.	.015	.54	.92	1.46
2" x 10"	.125	L.F.	.016	.75	.97	1.72
2" x 12"	.125	L.F.	.017	.90	1.02	1.92
Solid girders, 3" x 8"	.040	L.F.	.004	.31	.24	.55
3" x 10"	.040	L.F.	.004	.34	.25	.59
3" x 12"	.040	L.F.	.004	.37	.26	.63
4" x 8"	.040	L.F.	.004	.33	.26	.59
4" x 10"	.040	L.F.	.004	.40	.27	.67
4" x 12"	.040	L.F.	.004	.42	.28	.70
Steel girders, bolted & including fabrication, wide flange shapes						
12" deep, 14#/l.f.	.040	L.F.	.061	24	6.55	30.55
10" deep, 15#/l.f.	.040	L.F.	.067	26	7.15	33.15
8" deep, 10#/l.f.	.040	L.F.	.067	17.30	7.15	24.45
6" deep, 9#/l.f.	.040	L.F.	.067	15.55	7.15	22.70
5" deep, 16#/l.f.	.040	L.F.	.064	25	6.90	31.90
Sheathing, plywood exterior grade CDX, 1/2" thick	1.000	S.F.	.011	.69	.67	1.36
5/8" thick	1.000	S.F.	.012	.86	.69	1.55
3/4" thick	1.000	S.F.	.013	1.03	.75	1.78
Boards, 1" x 8" laid regular	1.000	S.F.	.016	2.21	.94	3.15
Laid diagonal	1.000	S.F.	.019	2.21	1.10	3.31
1" x 10" laid regular	1.000	S.F.	.015	2.26	.85	3.11
Laid diagonal	1.000	S.F.	.018	2.26	1.04	3.30
Furring, 1" x 3", 12" O.C.	1.250	L.F.	.029	.58	1.68	2.26
16" O.C.	1.000	L.F.	.023	.46	1.34	1.80
24" O.C.	.750	L.F.	.017	.35	1.01	1.36

Cont. 2" x 4" Ribbon

Plywood Sheathing

Girder

Wood Floor Trusses

System Description	QUAN.	UNIT	LABOR HOURS	COST PER S.F.		
				MAT.	INST.	TOTAL
12" OPEN WEB JOISTS, 16" O.C.						
OWJ 12", 16" O.C., 21' span	1.000	L.F.	.018	3.95	1.08	5.03
Continuous ribbing, 2" x 4"	.150	L.F.	.002	.07	.11	.18
Concrete filled steel column, 4" diameter	.125	L.F.	.002	.18	.14	.32
Girder, built up from three 2" x 8"	.125	L.F.	.013	.36	.78	1.14
Sheathing, plywood, subfloor, 5/8" CDX	1.000	S.F.	.012	.86	.69	1.55
Furring, 1" x 3", 16" O.C.	1.000	L.F.	.023	.46	1.34	1.80
TOTAL		S.F.	.070	5.88	4.14	10.02
14" OPEN WEB WOOD JOISTS, 16" O.C.						
OWJ 14", 16" O.C., 22' span	1.000	L.F.	.020	4	1.15	5.15
Continuous ribbing, 2" x 4"	.150	L.F.	.002	.07	.11	.18
Concrete filled steel column, 4" diameter	.125	L.F.	.002	.18	.14	.32
Girder, built up from three 2" x 10"	.125	L.F.	.014	.57	.83	1.40
Sheathing, plywood, subfloor, 5/8" CDX	1.000	S.F.	.012	.86	.69	1.55
Furring, 1" x 3", 16" O.C.	1.000	L.F.	.023	.46	1.34	1.80
TOTAL		S.F.	.073	6.14	4.26	10.40
16" OPEN WEB WOOD JOISTS, 16" O.C.						
OWJ 16", 16" O.C., 24' span	1.000	L.F.	.021	4.30	1.20	5.50
Continuous ribbing, 2" x 4"	.150	L.F.	.002	.07	.11	.18
Concrete filled steel column, 4" diameter	.125	L.F.	.002	.18	.14	.32
Girder, built up from three 2" x 12"	.125	L.F.	.015	.72	.88	1.60
Sheathing, plywood, subfloor, 5/8" CDX	1.000	S.F.	.012	.86	.69	1.55
Furring, 1" x 3", 16" O.C.	1.000	L.F.	.023	.46	1.34	1.80
TOTAL		S.F.	.075	6.59	4.36	10.95

Floor costs on this page are given on a cost per square foot basis.

Description	QUAN.	UNIT	LABOR HOURS	COST PER S.F.		
				MAT.	INST.	TOTAL

Floor Framing Price Sheet (Wood)

Floor Framing Price Sheet (Wood)	QUAN.	UNIT	LABOR HOURS	COST PER S.F.		
				MAT.	INST.	TOTAL
Open web joists, 12" deep, 12" O.C.	1.250	L.F.	.023	4.94	1.34	6.28
16" O.C.	1.000	L.F.	.018	3.95	1.08	5.03
14" deep, 12" O.C.	1.250	L.F.	.024	5	1.44	6.44
16" O.C.	1.000	L.F.	.020	4	1.15	5.15
16 " deep, 12" O.C.	1.250	L.F.	.026	5.40	1.50	6.90
16" O.C.	1.000	L.F.	.021	4.30	1.20	5.50
18" deep, 12" O.C.	1.250	L.F.	.027	5.20	1.59	6.79
16" O.C.	1.000	L.F.	.022	4.18	1.28	5.46
Continuous ribbing, 2" x 4"	.150	L.F.	.002	.07	.11	.18
2" x 6"	.150	L.F.	.002	.10	.11	.21
2" x 8"	.150	L.F.	.002	.14	.13	.27
2" x 10"	.150	L.F.	.003	.23	.16	.39
2" x 12"	.150	L.F.	.003	.29	.16	.45
Girders, including lally columns, 3 pieces spiked together, 2" x 8"	.125	L.F.	.015	.54	.92	1.46
2" x 10"	.125	L.F.	.016	.75	.97	1.72
2" x 12"	.125	L.F.	.017	.90	1.02	1.92
Solid girders, 3" x 8"	.040	L.F.	.004	.31	.24	.55
3" x 10"	.040	L.F.	.004	.34	.25	.59
3" x 12"	.040	L.F.	.004	.37	.26	.63
4" x 8"	.040	L.F.	.004	.33	.26	.59
4" x 10"	.040	L.F.	.004	.40	.27	.67
4" x 12"	.040	L.F.	.004	.42	.28	.70
Steel girders, bolted & including fabrication, wide flange shapes						
12" deep, 14#/l.f.	.040	L.F.	.061	24	6.55	30.55
10" deep, 15#/l.f.	.040	L.F.	.067	26	7.15	33.15
8" deep, 10#/l.f.	.040	L.F.	.067	17.30	7.15	24.45
6" deep, 9#/l.f.	.040	L.F.	.067	15.55	7.15	22.70
5" deep, 16#/l.f.	.040	L.F.	.064	25	6.90	31.90
Sheathing, plywood exterior grade CDX, 1/2" thick	1.000	S.F.	.011	.69	.67	1.36
5/8" thick	1.000	S.F.	.012	.86	.69	1.55
3/4" thick	1.000	S.F.	.013	1.03	.75	1.78
Boards, 1" x 8" laid regular	1.000	S.F.	.016	2.21	.94	3.15
Laid diagonal	1.000	S.F.	.019	2.21	1.10	3.31
1" x 10" laid regular	1.000	S.F.	.015	2.26	.85	3.11
Laid diagonal	1.000	S.F.	.018	2.26	1.04	3.30
Furring, 1" x 3", 12" O.C.	1.250	L.F.	.029	.58	1.68	2.26
16" O.C.	1.000	L.F.	.023	.46	1.34	1.80
24" O.C.	.750	L.F.	.017	.35	1.01	1.36

Sheathing — Top Plates — Studs — Bottom Plate — Corner Bracing

System Description	QUAN.	UNIT	LABOR HOURS	COST PER S.F.		
				MAT.	INST.	TOTAL
2" X 4", 16" O.C.						
2" x 4" studs, 16" O.C.	1.000	L.F.	.015	.44	.85	1.29
Plates, 2" x 4", double top, single bottom	.375	L.F.	.005	.17	.32	.49
Corner bracing, let-in, 1" x 6"	.063	L.F.	.003	.05	.20	.25
Sheathing, 1/2" plywood, CDX	1.000	S.F.	.011	.69	.67	1.36
Framing connectors, holddowns	.013	Ea.	.013	.38	.76	1.14
TOTAL		S.F.	.047	1.73	2.80	4.53
2" X 4", 24" O.C.						
2" x 4" studs, 24" O.C.	.750	L.F.	.011	.33	.64	.97
Plates, 2" x 4", double top, single bottom	.375	L.F.	.005	.17	.32	.49
Corner bracing, let-in, 1" x 6"	.063	L.F.	.002	.05	.13	.18
Sheathing, 1/2" plywood, CDX	1.000	S.F.	.011	.69	.67	1.36
Framing connectors, holddowns	.013	Ea.	.013	.38	.76	1.14
TOTAL		S.F.	.042	1.62	2.52	4.14
2" X 6", 16" O.C.						
2" x 6" studs, 16" O.C.	1.000	L.F.	.016	.69	.94	1.63
Plates, 2" x 6", double top, single bottom	.375	L.F.	.006	.26	.35	.61
Corner bracing, let-in, 1" x 6"	.063	L.F.	.003	.05	.20	.25
Sheathing, 1/2" plywood, CDX	1.000	S.F.	.014	.69	.83	1.52
Framing connectors, holddowns	.013	Ea.	.013	.38	.76	1.14
TOTAL		S.F.	.052	2.07	3.08	5.15
2" X 6", 24" O.C.						
2" x 6" studs, 24" O.C.	.750	L.F.	.012	.52	.71	1.23
Plates, 2" x 6", double top, single bottom	.375	L.F.	.006	.26	.35	.61
Corner bracing, let-in, 1" x 6"	.063	L.F.	.002	.05	.13	.18
Sheathing, 1/2" plywood, CDX	1.000	S.F.	.011	.69	.67	1.36
Framing connectors, holddowns	.013	Ea.	.013	.38	.76	1.14
TOTAL		S.F.	.044	1.90	2.62	4.52

The wall costs on this page are given in cost per square foot of wall.
For window and door openings see below.

Description	QUAN.	UNIT	LABOR HOURS	COST PER S.F.		
				MAT.	INST.	TOTAL

Exterior Wall Framing Price Sheet	QUAN.	UNIT	LABOR HOURS	COST PER S.F.		
				MAT.	INST.	TOTAL
Studs, #2 or better, 2" x 4", 12" O.C.	1.250	L.F.	.018	.55	1.06	1.61
16" O.C.	1.000	L.F.	.015	.44	.85	1.29
24" O.C.	.750	L.F.	.011	.33	.64	.97
32" O.C.	.600	L.F.	.009	.26	.51	.77
2" x 6", 12" O.C.	1.250	L.F.	.020	.86	1.18	2.04
16" O.C.	1.000	L.F.	.016	.69	.94	1.63
24" O.C.	.750	L.F.	.012	.52	.71	1.23
32" O.C.	.600	L.F.	.010	.41	.56	.97
2" x 8", 12" O.C.	1.250	L.F.	.025	1.61	1.46	3.07
16" O.C.	1.000	L.F.	.020	1.29	1.17	2.46
24" O.C.	.750	L.F.	.015	.97	.88	1.85
32" O.C.	.600	L.F.	.012	.77	.70	1.47
Plates, #2 or better, double top, single bottom, 2" x 4"	.375	L.F.	.005	.17	.32	.49
2" x 6"	.375	L.F.	.006	.26	.35	.61
2" x 8"	.375	L.F.	.008	.48	.44	.92
Corner bracing, let-in 1" x 6" boards, studs, 12" O.C.	.070	L.F.	.004	.06	.22	.28
16" O.C.	.063	L.F.	.003	.05	.20	.25
24" O.C.	.063	L.F.	.002	.05	.13	.18
32" O.C.	.057	L.F.	.002	.05	.12	.17
Let-in steel ("T" shape), studs, 12" O.C.	.070	L.F.	.001	.06	.06	.12
16" O.C.	.063	L.F.	.001	.06	.05	.11
24" O.C.	.063	L.F.	.001	.06	.05	.11
32" O.C.	.057	L.F.	.001	.05	.04	.09
Sheathing, plywood CDX, 3/8" thick	1.000	S.F.	.010	.67	.61	1.28
1/2" thick	1.000	S.F.	.011	.69	.67	1.36
5/8" thick	1.000	S.F.	.012	.86	.72	1.58
3/4" thick	1.000	S.F.	.013	1.03	.78	1.81
Boards, 1" x 6", laid regular	1.000	S.F.	.025	1.81	1.44	3.25
Laid diagonal	1.000	S.F.	.027	1.81	1.60	3.41
1" x 8", laid regular	1.000	S.F.	.021	2.21	1.22	3.43
Laid diagonal	1.000	S.F.	.025	2.21	1.44	3.65
Wood fiber, regular, no vapor barrier, 1/2" thick	1.000	S.F.	.013	.70	.78	1.48
5/8" thick	1.000	S.F.	.013	.77	.78	1.55
Asphalt impregnated 25/32" thick	1.000	S.F.	.013	.36	.78	1.14
1/2" thick	1.000	S.F.	.013	.31	.78	1.09
Polystyrene, regular, 3/4" thick	1.000	S.F.	.010	.63	.58	1.21
2" thick	1.000	S.F.	.011	1.75	.64	2.39
Fiberglass, foil faced, 1" thick	1.000	S.F.	.008	.99	.47	1.46
2" thick	1.000	S.F.	.009	1.87	.53	2.40

Window & Door Openings	QUAN.	UNIT	LABOR HOURS	COST EACH		
				MAT.	INST.	TOTAL
The following costs are to be added to the total costs of the wall for each opening. Do not subtract the area of the openings.						
Headers, 2" x 6" double, 2' long	4.000	L.F.	.178	2.76	10.40	13.16
3' long	6.000	L.F.	.267	4.14	15.60	19.74
4' long	8.000	L.F.	.356	5.50	21	26.50
5' long	10.000	L.F.	.444	6.90	26	32.90
2" x 8" double, 4' long	8.000	L.F.	.376	7.70	22	29.70
5' long	10.000	L.F.	.471	9.60	27.50	37.10
6' long	12.000	L.F.	.565	11.50	33	44.50
8' long	16.000	L.F.	.753	15.35	44	59.35
2" x 10" double, 4' long	8.000	L.F.	.400	12.10	23.50	35.60
6' long	12.000	L.F.	.600	18.10	35	53.10
8' long	16.000	L.F.	.800	24	46.50	70.50
10' long	20.000	L.F.	1.000	30	58.50	88.50
2" x 12" double, 8' long	16.000	L.F.	.853	31	50	81
12' long	24.000	L.F.	1.280	46.50	75	121.50

For customer support on your Residential Costs with RSMeans Data, call 800.448.8182.

137

System Description	QUAN.	UNIT	LABOR HOURS	COST PER S.F.		
				MAT.	INST.	TOTAL
2″ X 6″ RAFTERS, 16″ O.C., 4/12 PITCH						
Rafters, 2″ x 6″, 16″ O.C., 4/12 pitch	1.170	L.F.	.019	.81	1.10	1.91
Ceiling joists, 2″ x 4″, 16″ O.C.	1.000	L.F.	.013	.45	.75	1.20
Ridge board, 2″ x 6″	.050	L.F.	.002	.03	.09	.12
Fascia board, 2″ x 6″	.100	L.F.	.005	.07	.31	.38
Rafter tie, 1″ x 4″, 4′ O.C.	.060	L.F.	.001	.03	.07	.10
Soffit nailer (outrigger), 2″ x 4″, 24″ O.C.	.170	L.F.	.004	.08	.26	.34
Sheathing, exterior, plywood, CDX, 1/2″ thick	1.170	S.F.	.013	.81	.78	1.59
Furring strips, 1″ x 3″, 16″ O.C.	1.000	L.F.	.023	.46	1.34	1.80
Rafter ties	.053	Ea.	.003	.08	.17	.25
TOTAL		S.F.	.083	2.82	4.87	7.69
2″ X 8″ RAFTERS, 16″ O.C., 4/12 PITCH						
Rafters, 2″ x 8″, 16″ O.C., 4/12 pitch	1.170	L.F.	.020	1.12	1.15	2.27
Ceiling joists, 2″ x 6″, 16″ O.C.	1.000	L.F.	.013	.69	.75	1.44
Ridge board, 2″ x 8″	.050	L.F.	.002	.05	.10	.15
Fascia board, 2″ x 8″	.100	L.F.	.007	.10	.42	.52
Rafter tie, 1″ x 4″, 4′ O.C.	.060	L.F.	.001	.03	.07	.10
Soffit nailer (outrigger), 2″ x 4″, 24″ O.C.	.170	L.F.	.004	.08	.26	.34
Sheathing, exterior, plywood, CDX, 1/2″ thick	1.170	S.F.	.013	.81	.78	1.59
Furring strips, 1″ x 3″, 16″ O.C.	1.000	L.F.	.023	.46	1.34	1.80
Rafter ties	.053	Ea.	.003	.08	.17	.25
TOTAL		S.F.	.086	3.42	5.04	8.46

The cost of this system is based on the square foot of plan area.
All quantities have been adjusted accordingly.

Description	QUAN.	UNIT	LABOR HOURS	COST PER S.F.		
				MAT.	INST.	TOTAL

Gable End Roof Framing Price Sheet

	QUAN.	UNIT	LABOR HOURS	COST PER S.F. MAT.	COST PER S.F. INST.	COST PER S.F. TOTAL
Rafters, #2 or better, 16″ O.C., 2″ x 6″, 4/12 pitch	1.170	L.F.	.019	.81	1.10	1.91
8/12 pitch	1.330	L.F.	.027	.92	1.56	2.48
2″ x 8″, 4/12 pitch	1.170	L.F.	.020	1.12	1.15	2.27
8/12 pitch	1.330	L.F.	.028	1.28	1.66	2.94
2″ x 10″, 4/12 pitch	1.170	L.F.	.030	1.77	1.73	3.50
8/12 pitch	1.330	L.F.	.043	2.01	2.51	4.52
24″ O.C., 2″ x 6″, 4/12 pitch	.940	L.F.	.015	.65	.88	1.53
8/12 pitch	1.060	L.F.	.021	.73	1.24	1.97
2″ x 8″, 4/12 pitch	.940	L.F.	.016	.90	.92	1.82
8/12 pitch	1.060	L.F.	.023	1.02	1.33	2.35
2″ x 10″, 4/12 pitch	.940	L.F.	.024	1.42	1.39	2.81
8/12 pitch	1.060	L.F.	.034	1.60	2	3.60
Ceiling joist, #2 or better, 2″ x 4″, 16″ O.C.	1.000	L.F.	.013	.45	.75	1.20
24″ O.C.	.750	L.F.	.010	.34	.56	.90
2″ x 6″, 16″ O.C.	1.000	L.F.	.013	.69	.75	1.44
24″ O.C.	.750	L.F.	.010	.52	.56	1.08
2″ x 8″, 16″ O.C.	1.000	L.F.	.015	.96	.85	1.81
24″ O.C.	.750	L.F.	.011	.72	.64	1.36
2″ x 10″, 16″ O.C.	1.000	L.F.	.018	1.51	1.04	2.55
24″ O.C.	.750	L.F.	.013	1.13	.78	1.91
Ridge board, #2 or better, 1″ x 6″	.050	L.F.	.001	.04	.08	.12
1″ x 8″	.050	L.F.	.001	.07	.09	.16
1″ x 10″	.050	L.F.	.002	.09	.09	.18
2″ x 6″	.050	L.F.	.002	.03	.09	.12
2″ x 8″	.050	L.F.	.002	.05	.10	.15
2″ x 10″	.050	L.F.	.002	.08	.12	.20
Fascia board, #2 or better, 1″ x 6″	.100	L.F.	.004	.05	.23	.28
1″ x 8″	.100	L.F.	.005	.06	.27	.33
1″ x 10″	.100	L.F.	.005	.07	.30	.37
2″ x 6″	.100	L.F.	.006	.08	.33	.41
2″ x 8″	.100	L.F.	.007	.10	.42	.52
2″ x 10″	.100	L.F.	.004	.30	.21	.51
Rafter tie, #2 or better, 4′ O.C., 1″ x 4″	.060	L.F.	.001	.03	.07	.10
1″ x 6″	.060	L.F.	.001	.04	.08	.12
2″ x 4″	.060	L.F.	.002	.04	.09	.13
2″ x 6″	.060	L.F.	.002	.05	.12	.17
Soffit nailer (outrigger), 2″ x 4″, 16″ O.C.	.220	L.F.	.006	.10	.33	.43
24″ O.C.	.170	L.F.	.004	.08	.26	.34
2″ x 6″, 16″ O.C.	.220	L.F.	.006	.11	.38	.49
24″ O.C.	.170	L.F.	.005	.09	.30	.39
Sheathing, plywood CDX, 4/12 pitch, 3/8″ thick.	1.170	S.F.	.012	.78	.71	1.49
1/2″ thick	1.170	S.F.	.013	.81	.78	1.59
5/8″ thick	1.170	S.F.	.014	1.01	.84	1.85
8/12 pitch, 3/8″	1.330	S.F.	.014	.89	.81	1.70
1/2″ thick	1.330	S.F.	.015	.92	.89	1.81
5/8″ thick	1.330	S.F.	.016	1.14	.96	2.10
Boards, 4/12 pitch roof, 1″ x 6″	1.170	S.F.	.026	2.12	1.51	3.63
1″ x 8″	1.170	S.F.	.021	2.59	1.25	3.84
8/12 pitch roof, 1″ x 6″	1.330	S.F.	.029	2.41	1.72	4.13
1″ x 8″	1.330	S.F.	.024	2.94	1.42	4.36
Furring, 1″ x 3″, 12″ O.C.	1.200	L.F.	.027	.55	1.61	2.16
16″ O.C.	1.000	L.F.	.023	.46	1.34	1.80
24″ O.C.	.800	L.F.	.018	.37	1.07	1.44

For customer support on your Residential Costs with RSMeans Data, call 800.448.8182.

139

System Description	QUAN.	UNIT	LABOR HOURS	COST PER S.F.		
				MAT.	INST.	TOTAL
TRUSS, 16″ O.C., 4/12 PITCH, 1′ OVERHANG, 26′ SPAN						
Truss, 40# loading, 16″ O.C., 4/12 pitch, 26′ span	.030	Ea.	.021	2.55	1.46	4.01
Fascia board, 2″ x 6″	.100	L.F.	.005	.07	.31	.38
Sheathing, exterior, plywood, CDX, 1/2″ thick	1.170	S.F.	.013	.81	.78	1.59
Furring, 1″ x 3″, 16″ O.C.	1.000	L.F.	.023	.46	1.34	1.80
Rafter ties	.053	Ea.	.003	.08	.17	.25
TOTAL		S.F.	.065	3.97	4.06	8.03
TRUSS, 16″ O.C., 8/12 PITCH, 1′ OVERHANG, 26′ SPAN						
Truss, 40# loading, 16″ O.C., 8/12 pitch, 26′ span	.030	Ea.	.023	3.54	1.59	5.13
Fascia board, 2″ x 6″	.100	L.F.	.005	.07	.31	.38
Sheathing, exterior, plywood, CDX, 1/2″ thick	1.330	S.F.	.015	.92	.89	1.81
Furring, 1″ x 3″, 16″ O.C.	1.000	L.F.	.023	.46	1.34	1.80
Rafter ties	.053	Ea.	.003	.08	.17	.25
TOTAL		S.F.	.069	5.07	4.30	9.37
TRUSS, 24″ O.C., 4/12 PITCH, 1′ OVERHANG, 26′ SPAN						
Truss, 40# loading, 24″ O.C., 4/12 pitch, 26′ span	.020	Ea.	.014	1.70	.97	2.67
Fascia board, 2″ x 6″	.100	L.F.	.005	.07	.31	.38
Sheathing, exterior, plywood, CDX, 1/2″ thick	1.170	S.F.	.013	.81	.78	1.59
Furring, 1″ x 3″, 16″ O.C.	1.000	L.F.	.023	.46	1.34	1.80
Rafter ties	.035	Ea.	.002	.05	.11	.16
TOTAL		S.F.	.057	3.09	3.51	6.60
TRUSS, 24″ O.C., 8/12 PITCH, 1′ OVERHANG, 26′ SPAN						
Truss, 40# loading, 24″ O.C., 8/12 pitch, 26′ span	.020	Ea.	.015	2.36	1.06	3.42
Fascia board, 2″ x 6″	.100	L.F.	.005	.07	.31	.38
Sheathing, exterior, plywood, CDX, 1/2″ thick	1.330	S.F.	.015	.92	.89	1.81
Furring, 1″ x 3″, 16″ O.C.	1.000	L.F.	.023	.46	1.34	1.80
Rafter ties	.035	Ea.	.002	.05	.11	.16
TOTAL		S.F.	.060	3.86	3.71	7.57

The cost of this system is based on the square foot of plan area.
A one foot overhang is included.

Description	QUAN.	UNIT	LABOR HOURS	COST PER S.F.		
				MAT.	INST.	TOTAL

Truss Roof Framing Price Sheet

Truss Roof Framing Price Sheet	QUAN.	UNIT	LABOR HOURS	COST PER S.F.		
				MAT.	INST.	TOTAL
Truss, 40# loading, including 1' overhang, 4/12 pitch, 24' span, 16" O.C.	.033	Ea.	.022	2.85	1.52	4.37
24" O.C.	.022	Ea.	.015	1.90	1.01	2.91
26' span, 16" O.C.	.030	Ea.	.021	2.55	1.46	4.01
24" O.C.	.020	Ea.	.014	1.70	.97	2.67
28' span, 16" O.C.	.027	Ea.	.020	2.84	1.41	4.25
24" O.C.	.019	Ea.	.014	2	1	3
32' span, 16" O.C.	.024	Ea.	.019	2.95	1.33	4.28
24" O.C.	.016	Ea.	.013	1.97	.89	2.86
36' span, 16" O.C.	.022	Ea.	.019	3.12	1.32	4.44
24" O.C.	.015	Ea.	.013	2.13	.91	3.04
8/12 pitch, 24' span, 16" O.C.	.033	Ea.	.024	3.70	1.67	5.37
24" O.C.	.022	Ea.	.016	2.46	1.11	3.57
26' span, 16" O.C.	.030	Ea.	.023	3.54	1.59	5.13
24" O.C.	.020	Ea.	.015	2.36	1.06	3.42
28' span, 16" O.C.	.027	Ea.	.022	3.59	1.52	5.11
24" O.C.	.019	Ea.	.016	2.53	1.07	3.60
32' span, 16" O.C.	.024	Ea.	.021	3.60	1.48	5.08
24" O.C.	.016	Ea.	.014	2.40	.98	3.38
36' span, 16" O.C.	.022	Ea.	.021	4.09	1.48	5.57
24" O.C.	.015	Ea.	.015	2.79	1.01	3.80
Fascia board, #2 or better, 1" x 6"	.100	L.F.	.004	.05	.23	.28
1" x 8"	.100	L.F.	.005	.06	.27	.33
1" x 10"	.100	L.F.	.005	.07	.30	.37
2" x 6"	.100	L.F.	.006	.08	.33	.41
2" x 8"	.100	L.F.	.007	.10	.42	.52
2" x 10"	.100	L.F.	.009	.15	.52	.67
Sheathing, plywood CDX, 4/12 pitch, 3/8" thick	1.170	S.F.	.012	.78	.71	1.49
1/2" thick	1.170	S.F.	.013	.81	.78	1.59
5/8" thick	1.170	S.F.	.014	1.01	.84	1.85
8/12 pitch, 3/8" thick	1.330	S.F.	.014	.89	.81	1.70
1/2" thick	1.330	S.F.	.015	.92	.89	1.81
5/8" thick	1.330	S.F.	.016	1.14	.96	2.10
Boards, 4/12 pitch, 1" x 6"	1.170	S.F.	.026	2.12	1.51	3.63
1" x 8"	1.170	S.F.	.021	2.59	1.25	3.84
8/12 pitch, 1" x 6"	1.330	S.F.	.029	2.41	1.72	4.13
1" x 8"	1.330	S.F.	.024	2.94	1.42	4.36
Furring, 1" x 3", 12" O.C.	1.200	L.F.	.027	.55	1.61	2.16
16" O.C.	1.000	L.F.	.023	.46	1.34	1.80
24" O.C.	.800	L.F.	.018	.37	1.07	1.44

System Description	QUAN.	UNIT	LABOR HOURS	COST PER S.F.		
				MAT.	INST.	TOTAL
2″ X 6″, 16″ O.C., 4/12 PITCH						
Hip rafters, 2″ x 8″, 4/12 pitch	.160	L.F.	.004	.15	.21	.36
Jack rafters, 2″ x 6″, 16″ O.C., 4/12 pitch	1.430	L.F.	.038	.99	2.23	3.22
Ceiling joists, 2″ x 6″, 16″ O.C.	1.000	L.F.	.013	.69	.75	1.44
Fascia board, 2″ x 8″	.220	L.F.	.016	.21	.92	1.13
Soffit nailer (outrigger), 2″ x 4″, 24″ O.C.	.220	L.F.	.006	.10	.33	.43
Sheathing, 1/2″ exterior plywood, CDX	1.570	S.F.	.018	1.08	1.05	2.13
Furring strips, 1″ x 3″, 16″ O.C.	1.000	L.F.	.023	.46	1.34	1.80
Rafter ties	.070	Ea.	.004	.11	.23	.34
TOTAL		S.F.	.122	3.79	7.06	10.85
2″ X 8″, 16″ O.C., 4/12 PITCH						
Hip rafters, 2″ x 10″, 4/12 pitch	.160	L.F.	.004	.24	.26	.50
Jack rafters, 2″ x 8″, 16″ O.C., 4/12 pitch	1.430	L.F.	.047	1.37	2.73	4.10
Ceiling joists, 2″ x 6″, 16″ O.C.	1.000	L.F.	.013	.69	.75	1.44
Fascia board, 2″ x 8″	.220	L.F.	.012	.16	.71	.87
Soffit nailer (outrigger), 2″ x 4″, 24″ O.C.	.220	L.F.	.006	.10	.33	.43
Sheathing, 1/2″ exterior plywood, CDX	1.570	S.F.	.018	1.08	1.05	2.13
Furring strips, 1″ x 3″, 16″ O.C.	1.000	L.F.	.023	.46	1.34	1.80
Rafter ties	.070	Ea.	.004	.11	.23	.34
TOTAL		S.F.	.127	4.21	7.40	11.61

The cost of this system is based on S.F. of plan area. Measurement is area under the hip roof only. See gable roof system for added costs.

Description	QUAN.	UNIT	LABOR HOURS	COST PER S.F.		
				MAT.	INST.	TOTAL

Hip Roof Framing Price Sheet	QUAN.	UNIT	LABOR HOURS	COST PER S.F.		
				MAT.	INST.	TOTAL
Hip rafters, #2 or better, 2" x 6", 4/12 pitch	.160	L.F.	.003	.11	.20	.31
8/12 pitch	.210	L.F.	.006	.14	.34	.48
2" x 8", 4/12 pitch	.160	L.F.	.004	.15	.21	.36
8/12 pitch	.210	L.F.	.006	.20	.36	.56
2" x 10", 4/12 pitch	.160	L.F.	.004	.24	.26	.50
8/12 pitch roof	.210	L.F.	.008	.32	.45	.77
Jack rafters, #2 or better, 16" O.C., 2" x 6", 4/12 pitch	1.430	L.F.	.038	.99	2.23	3.22
8/12 pitch	1.800	L.F.	.061	1.24	3.55	4.79
2" x 8", 4/12 pitch	1.430	L.F.	.047	1.37	2.73	4.10
8/12 pitch	1.800	L.F.	.075	1.73	4.37	6.10
2" x 10", 4/12 pitch	1.430	L.F.	.051	2.16	2.97	5.13
8/12 pitch	1.800	L.F.	.082	2.72	4.81	7.53
24" O.C., 2" x 6", 4/12 pitch	1.150	L.F.	.031	.79	1.79	2.58
8/12 pitch	1.440	L.F.	.048	.99	2.84	3.83
2" x 8", 4/12 pitch	1.150	L.F.	.038	1.10	2.20	3.30
8/12 pitch	1.440	L.F.	.060	1.38	3.50	4.88
2" x 10", 4/12 pitch	1.150	L.F.	.041	1.74	2.39	4.13
8/12 pitch	1.440	L.F.	.066	2.17	3.84	6.01
Ceiling joists, #2 or better, 2" x 4", 16" O.C.	1.000	L.F.	.013	.45	.75	1.20
24" O.C.	.750	L.F.	.010	.34	.56	.90
2" x 6", 16" O.C.	1.000	L.F.	.013	.69	.75	1.44
24" O.C.	.750	L.F.	.010	.52	.56	1.08
2" x 8", 16" O.C.	1.000	L.F.	.015	.96	.85	1.81
24" O.C.	.750	L.F.	.011	.72	.64	1.36
2" x 10", 16" O.C.	1.000	L.F.	.018	1.51	1.04	2.55
24" O.C.	.750	L.F.	.013	1.13	.78	1.91
Fascia board, #2 or better, 1" x 6"	.220	L.F.	.009	.12	.50	.62
1" x 8"	.220	L.F.	.010	.14	.59	.73
1" x 10"	.220	L.F.	.011	.15	.66	.81
2" x 6"	.220	L.F.	.013	.17	.73	.90
2" x 8"	.220	L.F.	.016	.21	.92	1.13
2" x 10"	.220	L.F.	.020	.33	1.14	1.47
Soffit nailer (outrigger), 2" x 4", 16" O.C.	.280	L.F.	.007	.13	.42	.55
24" O.C.	.220	L.F.	.006	.10	.33	.43
2" x 8", 16" O.C.	.280	L.F.	.007	.20	.39	.59
24" O.C.	.220	L.F.	.005	.16	.32	.48
Sheathing, plywood CDX, 4/12 pitch, 3/8" thick	1.570	S.F.	.016	1.05	.96	2.01
1/2" thick	1.570	S.F.	.018	1.08	1.05	2.13
5/8" thick	1.570	S.F.	.019	1.35	1.13	2.48
8/12 pitch, 3/8" thick	1.900	S.F.	.020	1.27	1.16	2.43
1/2" thick	1.900	S.F.	.022	1.31	1.27	2.58
5/8" thick	1.900	S.F.	.023	1.63	1.37	3
Boards, 4/12 pitch, 1" x 6" boards	1.450	S.F.	.032	2.62	1.87	4.49
1" x 8" boards	1.450	S.F.	.027	3.20	1.55	4.75
8/12 pitch, 1" x 6" boards	1.750	S.F.	.039	3.17	2.26	5.43
1" x 8" boards	1.750	S.F.	.032	3.87	1.87	5.74
Furring, 1" x 3", 12" O.C.	1.200	L.F.	.027	.55	1.61	2.16
16" O.C.	1.000	L.F.	.023	.46	1.34	1.80
24" O.C.	.800	L.F.	.018	.37	1.07	1.44

System Description	QUAN.	UNIT	LABOR HOURS	COST PER S.F.		
				MAT.	INST.	TOTAL
2″ X 6″ RAFTERS, 16″ O.C.						
Roof rafters, 2″ x 6″, 16″ O.C.	1.430	L.F.	.029	.99	1.67	2.66
Ceiling joists, 2″ x 6″, 16″ O.C.	.710	L.F.	.009	.49	.53	1.02
Stud wall, 2″ x 4″, 16″ O.C., including plates	.790	L.F.	.012	.36	.73	1.09
Furring strips, 1″ x 3″, 16″ O.C.	.710	L.F.	.016	.33	.95	1.28
Ridge board, 2″ x 8″	.050	L.F.	.002	.05	.10	.15
Fascia board, 2″ x 6″	.100	L.F.	.006	.08	.33	.41
Sheathing, exterior grade plywood, 1/2″ thick	1.450	S.F.	.017	1	.97	1.97
Rafter ties	.106	Ea.	.006	.17	.34	.51
TOTAL		S.F.	.097	3.47	5.62	9.09
2″ X 8″ RAFTERS, 16″ O.C.						
Roof rafters, 2″ x 8″, 16″ O.C.	1.430	L.F.	.031	1.37	1.79	3.16
Ceiling joists, 2″ x 6″, 16″ O.C.	.710	L.F.	.009	.49	.53	1.02
Stud wall, 2″ x 4″, 16″ O.C., including plates	.790	L.F.	.012	.36	.73	1.09
Furring strips, 1″ x 3″, 16″ O.C.	.710	L.F.	.016	.33	.95	1.28
Ridge board, 2″ x 8″	.050	L.F.	.002	.05	.10	.15
Fascia board, 2″ x 8″	.100	L.F.	.007	.10	.42	.52
Sheathing, exterior grade plywood, 1/2″ thick	1.450	S.F.	.017	1	.97	1.97
Rafter ties	.106	Ea.	.006	.17	.34	.51
TOTAL		S.F.	.100	3.87	5.83	9.70

The cost of this system is based on the square foot of plan area on the first floor.

Description	QUAN.	UNIT	LABOR HOURS	COST PER S.F.		
				MAT.	INST.	TOTAL

Gambrel Roof Framing Price Sheet

	QUAN.	UNIT	LABOR HOURS	COST PER S.F. MAT.	COST PER S.F. INST.	COST PER S.F. TOTAL
Roof rafters, #2 or better, 2″ x 6″, 16″ O.C.	1.430	L.F.	.029	.99	1.67	2.66
24″ O.C.	1.140	L.F.	.023	.79	1.33	2.12
2″ x 8″, 16″ O.C.	1.430	L.F.	.031	1.37	1.79	3.16
24″ O.C.	1.140	L.F.	.024	1.09	1.43	2.52
2″ x 10″, 16″ O.C.	1.430	L.F.	.046	2.16	2.70	4.86
24″ O.C.	1.140	L.F.	.037	1.72	2.15	3.87
Ceiling joist, #2 or better, 2″ x 4″, 16″ O.C.	.710	L.F.	.009	.32	.53	.85
24″ O.C.	.570	L.F.	.007	.26	.43	.69
2″ x 6″, 16″ O.C.	.710	L.F.	.009	.49	.53	1.02
24″ O.C.	.570	L.F.	.007	.39	.43	.82
2″ x 8″, 16″ O.C.	.710	L.F.	.010	.68	.60	1.28
24″ O.C.	.570	L.F.	.008	.55	.48	1.03
Stud wall, #2 or better, 2″ x 4″, 16″ O.C.	.790	L.F.	.012	.36	.73	1.09
24″ O.C.	.630	L.F.	.010	.28	.58	.86
2″ x 6″, 16″ O.C.	.790	L.F.	.014	.55	.83	1.38
24″ O.C.	.630	L.F.	.011	.43	.66	1.09
Furring, 1″ x 3″, 16″ O.C.	.710	L.F.	.016	.33	.95	1.28
24″ O.C.	.590	L.F.	.013	.27	.79	1.06
Ridge board, #2 or better, 1″ x 6″	.050	L.F.	.001	.04	.08	.12
1″ x 8″	.050	L.F.	.001	.07	.09	.16
1″ x 10″	.050	L.F.	.002	.09	.09	.18
2″ x 6″	.050	L.F.	.002	.03	.09	.12
2″ x 8″	.050	L.F.	.002	.05	.10	.15
2″ x 10″	.050	L.F.	.002	.08	.12	.20
Fascia board, #2 or better, 1″ x 6″	.100	L.F.	.004	.05	.23	.28
1″ x 8″	.100	L.F.	.005	.06	.27	.33
1″ x 10″	.100	L.F.	.005	.07	.30	.37
2″ x 6″	.100	L.F.	.006	.08	.33	.41
2″ x 8″	.100	L.F.	.007	.10	.42	.52
2″ x 10″	.100	L.F.	.009	.15	.52	.67
Sheathing, plywood, exterior grade CDX, 3/8″ thick	1.450	S.F.	.015	.97	.88	1.85
1/2″ thick	1.450	S.F.	.017	1	.97	1.97
5/8″ thick	1.450	S.F.	.018	1.25	1.04	2.29
3/4″ thick	1.450	S.F.	.019	1.49	1.13	2.62
Boards, 1″ x 6″, laid regular	1.450	S.F.	.032	2.62	1.87	4.49
Laid diagonal	1.450	S.F.	.036	2.62	2.09	4.71
1″ x 8″, laid regular	1.450	S.F.	.027	3.20	1.55	4.75
Laid diagonal	1.450	S.F.	.032	3.20	1.87	5.07

System Description	QUAN.	UNIT	LABOR HOURS	COST PER S.F.		
				MAT.	INST.	TOTAL
2″ X 6″ RAFTERS, 16″ O.C.						
Roof rafters, 2″ x 6″, 16″ O.C.	1.210	L.F.	.033	.83	1.92	2.75
Rafter plates, 2″ x 6″, double top, single bottom	.364	L.F.	.010	.25	.58	.83
Ceiling joists, 2″ x 4″, 16″ O.C.	.920	L.F.	.012	.41	.69	1.10
Hip rafter, 2″ x 6″	.070	L.F.	.002	.05	.13	.18
Jack rafter, 2″ x 6″, 16″ O.C.	1.000	L.F.	.039	.69	2.28	2.97
Ridge board, 2″ x 6″	.018	L.F.	.001	.01	.03	.04
Sheathing, exterior grade plywood, 1/2″ thick	2.210	S.F.	.025	1.52	1.48	3
Furring strips, 1″ x 3″, 16″ O.C.	.920	L.F.	.021	.42	1.23	1.65
Rafter ties	.140	Ea.	.008	.22	.45	.67
TOTAL		S.F.	.151	4.40	8.79	13.19
2″ X 8″ RAFTERS, 16″ O.C.						
Roof rafters, 2″ x 8″, 16″ O.C.	1.210	L.F.	.036	1.16	2.09	3.25
Rafter plates, 2″ x 8″, double top, single bottom	.364	L.F.	.011	.35	.63	.98
Ceiling joists, 2″ x 6″, 16″ O.C.	.920	L.F.	.012	.63	.69	1.32
Hip rafter, 2″ x 8″	.070	L.F.	.002	.07	.14	.21
Jack rafter, 2″ x 8″, 16″ O.C.	1.000	L.F.	.048	.96	2.79	3.75
Ridge board, 2″ x 8″	.018	L.F.	.001	.02	.04	.06
Sheathing, exterior grade plywood, 1/2″ thick	2.210	S.F.	.025	1.52	1.48	3
Furring strips, 1″ x 3″, 16″ O.C.	.920	L.F.	.021	.42	1.23	1.65
Rafter ties	.140	Ea.	.008	.22	.45	.67
TOTAL		S.F.	.164	5.35	9.54	14.89

The cost of this system is based on the square foot of plan area.

Description	QUAN.	UNIT	LABOR HOURS	COST PER S.F.		
				MAT.	INST.	TOTAL

Mansard Roof Framing Price Sheet	QUAN.	UNIT	LABOR HOURS	COST PER S.F.		
				MAT.	INST.	TOTAL
Roof rafters, #2 or better, 2" x 6", 16" O.C.	1.210	L.F.	.033	.83	1.92	2.75
24" O.C.	.970	L.F.	.026	.67	1.54	2.21
2" x 8", 16" O.C.	1.210	L.F.	.036	1.16	2.09	3.25
24" O.C.	.970	L.F.	.029	.93	1.68	2.61
2" x 10", 16" O.C.	1.210	L.F.	.046	1.83	2.66	4.49
24" O.C.	.970	L.F.	.037	1.46	2.13	3.59
Rafter plates, #2 or better double top single bottom, 2" x 6"	.364	L.F.	.010	.25	.58	.83
2" x 8"	.364	L.F.	.011	.35	.63	.98
2" x 10"	.364	L.F.	.014	.55	.80	1.35
Ceiling joist, #2 or better, 2" x 4", 16" O.C.	.920	L.F.	.012	.41	.69	1.10
24" O.C.	.740	L.F.	.009	.33	.56	.89
2" x 6", 16" O.C.	.920	L.F.	.012	.63	.69	1.32
24" O.C.	.740	L.F.	.009	.51	.56	1.07
2" x 8", 16" O.C.	.920	L.F.	.013	.88	.78	1.66
24" O.C.	.740	L.F.	.011	.71	.63	1.34
Hip rafter, #2 or better, 2" x 6"	.070	L.F.	.002	.05	.13	.18
2" x 8"	.070	L.F.	.002	.07	.14	.21
2" x 10"	.070	L.F.	.003	.11	.17	.28
Jack rafter, #2 or better, 2" x 6", 16" O.C.	1.000	L.F.	.039	.69	2.28	2.97
24" O.C.	.800	L.F.	.031	.55	1.82	2.37
2" x 8", 16" O.C.	1.000	L.F.	.048	.96	2.79	3.75
24" O.C.	.800	L.F.	.038	.77	2.23	3
Ridge board, #2 or better, 1" x 6"	.018	L.F.	.001	.01	.03	.04
1" x 8"	.018	L.F.	.001	.03	.03	.06
1" x 10"	.018	L.F.	.001	.03	.03	.06
2" x 6"	.018	L.F.	.001	.01	.03	.04
2" x 8"	.018	L.F.	.001	.02	.04	.06
2" x 10"	.018	L.F.	.001	.03	.04	.07
Sheathing, plywood exterior grade CDX, 3/8" thick	2.210	S.F.	.023	1.48	1.35	2.83
1/2" thick	2.210	S.F.	.025	1.52	1.48	3
5/8" thick	2.210	S.F.	.027	1.90	1.59	3.49
3/4" thick	2.210	S.F.	.029	2.28	1.72	4
Boards, 1" x 6", laid regular	2.210	S.F.	.049	4	2.85	6.85
Laid diagonal	2.210	S.F.	.054	4	3.18	7.18
1" x 8", laid regular	2.210	S.F.	.040	4.88	2.36	7.24
Laid diagonal	2.210	S.F.	.049	4.88	2.85	7.73
Furring, 1" x 3", 12" O.C.	1.150	L.F.	.026	.53	1.54	2.07
24" O.C.	.740	L.F.	.017	.34	.99	1.33

System Description	QUAN.	UNIT	LABOR HOURS	COST PER S.F.		
				MAT.	INST.	TOTAL
2" X 6", 16" O.C., 4/12 PITCH						
Rafters, 2" x 6", 16" O.C., 4/12 pitch	1.170	L.F.	.019	.81	1.10	1.91
Fascia, 2" x 6"	.100	L.F.	.006	.08	.33	.41
Bridging, 1" x 3", 6' O.C.	.080	Pr.	.005	.06	.29	.35
Sheathing, exterior grade plywood, 1/2" thick	1.230	S.F.	.014	.85	.82	1.67
Rafter ties	.053	Ea.	.003	.08	.17	.25
TOTAL		S.F.	.047	1.88	2.71	4.59
2" X 6", 24" O.C., 4/12 PITCH						
Rafters, 2" x 6", 24" O.C., 4/12 pitch	.940	L.F.	.015	.65	.88	1.53
Fascia, 2" x 6"	.100	L.F.	.006	.08	.33	.41
Bridging, 1" x 3", 6' O.C.	.060	Pr.	.004	.04	.22	.26
Sheathing, exterior grade plywood, 1/2" thick	1.230	S.F.	.014	.85	.82	1.67
Rafter ties	.035	Ea.	.002	.05	.11	.16
TOTAL		S.F.	.041	1.67	2.36	4.03
2" X 8", 16" O.C., 4/12 PITCH						
Rafters, 2" x 8", 16" O.C., 4/12 pitch	1.170	L.F.	.020	1.12	1.15	2.27
Fascia, 2" x 8"	.100	L.F.	.007	.10	.42	.52
Bridging, 1" x 3", 6' O.C.	.080	Pr.	.005	.06	.29	.35
Sheathing, exterior grade plywood, 1/2" thick	1.230	S.F.	.014	.85	.82	1.67
Rafter ties	.053	Ea.	.003	.08	.17	.25
TOTAL		S.F.	.049	2.21	2.85	5.06
2" X 8", 24" O.C., 4/12 PITCH						
Rafters, 2" x 8", 24" O.C., 4/12 pitch	.940	L.F.	.016	.90	.92	1.82
Fascia, 2" x 8"	.100	L.F.	.007	.10	.42	.52
Bridging, 1" x 3", 6' O.C.	.060	Pr.	.004	.04	.22	.26
Sheathing, exterior grade plywood, 1/2" thick	1.230	S.F.	.014	.85	.82	1.67
Rafter ties	.035	Ea.	.002	.05	.11	.16
TOTAL		S.F.	.043	1.94	2.49	4.43

The cost of this system is based on the square foot of plan area.
A 1' overhang is assumed. No ceiling joists or furring are included.

Description	QUAN.	UNIT	LABOR HOURS	COST PER S.F.		
				MAT.	INST.	TOTAL

Shed/Flat Roof Framing Price Sheet	QUAN.	UNIT	LABOR HOURS	COST PER S.F.		
				MAT.	INST.	TOTAL
Rafters, #2 or better, 16" O.C., 2" x 4", 0 - 4/12 pitch	1.170	L.F.	.014	.60	.82	1.42
5/12 - 8/12 pitch	1.330	L.F.	.020	.69	1.17	1.86
2" x 6", 0 - 4/12 pitch	1.170	L.F.	.019	.81	1.10	1.91
5/12 - 8/12 pitch	1.330	L.F.	.027	.92	1.56	2.48
2" x 8", 0 - 4/12 pitch	1.170	L.F.	.020	1.12	1.15	2.27
5/12 - 8/12 pitch	1.330	L.F.	.028	1.28	1.66	2.94
2" x 10", 0 - 4/12 pitch	1.170	L.F.	.030	1.77	1.73	3.50
5/12 - 8/12 pitch	1.330	L.F.	.043	2.01	2.51	4.52
24" O.C., 2" x 4", 0 - 4/12 pitch	.940	L.F.	.011	.49	.67	1.16
5/12 - 8/12 pitch	1.060	L.F.	.021	.73	1.24	1.97
2" x 6", 0 - 4/12 pitch	.940	L.F.	.015	.65	.88	1.53
5/12 - 8/12 pitch	1.060	L.F.	.021	.73	1.24	1.97
2" x 8", 0 - 4/12 pitch	.940	L.F.	.016	.90	.92	1.82
5/12 - 8/12 pitch	1.060	L.F.	.023	1.02	1.33	2.35
2" x 10", 0 - 4/12 pitch	.940	L.F.	.024	1.42	1.39	2.81
5/12 - 8/12 pitch	1.060	L.F.	.034	1.60	2	3.60
Fascia, #2 or better,, 1" x 4"	.100	L.F.	.003	.04	.17	.21
1" x 6"	.100	L.F.	.004	.05	.23	.28
1" x 8"	.100	L.F.	.005	.06	.27	.33
1" x 10"	.100	L.F.	.005	.07	.30	.37
2" x 4"	.100	L.F.	.005	.07	.28	.35
2" x 6"	.100	L.F.	.006	.08	.33	.41
2" x 8"	.100	L.F.	.007	.10	.42	.52
2" x 10"	.100	L.F.	.009	.15	.52	.67
Bridging, wood 6' O.C., 1" x 3", rafters, 16" O.C.	.080	Pr.	.005	.06	.29	.35
24" O.C.	.060	Pr.	.004	.04	.22	.26
Metal, galvanized, rafters, 16" O.C.	.080	Pr.	.005	.17	.29	.46
24" O.C.	.060	Pr.	.003	.13	.20	.33
Compression type, rafters, 16" O.C.	.080	Pr.	.003	.08	.19	.27
24" O.C.	.060	Pr.	.002	.06	.14	.20
Sheathing, plywood, exterior grade, 3/8" thick, flat 0 - 4/12 pitch	1.230	S.F.	.013	.82	.75	1.57
5/12 - 8/12 pitch	1.330	S.F.	.014	.89	.81	1.70
1/2" thick, flat 0 - 4/12 pitch	1.230	S.F.	.014	.85	.82	1.67
5/12 - 8/12 pitch	1.330	S.F.	.015	.92	.89	1.81
5/8" thick, flat 0 - 4/12 pitch	1.230	S.F.	.015	1.06	.89	1.95
5/12 - 8/12 pitch	1.330	S.F.	.016	1.14	.96	2.10
3/4" thick, flat 0 - 4/12 pitch	1.230	S.F.	.016	1.27	.96	2.23
5/12 - 8/12 pitch	1.330	S.F.	.018	1.37	1.04	2.41
Boards, 1" x 6", laid regular, flat 0 - 4/12 pitch	1.230	S.F.	.027	2.23	1.59	3.82
5/12 - 8/12 pitch	1.330	S.F.	.041	2.41	2.39	4.80
Laid diagonal, flat 0 - 4/12 pitch	1.230	S.F.	.030	2.23	1.77	4
5/12 - 8/12 pitch	1.330	S.F.	.044	2.41	2.59	5
1" x 8", laid regular, flat 0 - 4/12 pitch	1.230	S.F.	.022	2.72	1.32	4.04
5/12 - 8/12 pitch	1.330	S.F.	.034	2.94	1.96	4.90
Laid diagonal, flat 0 - 4/12 pitch	1.230	S.F.	.027	2.72	1.59	4.31
5/12 - 8/12 pitch	1.330	S.F.	.044	2.41	2.59	5

Valley Rafter — Ridge Board
Sheathing — Rafters
Fascia Board —
Headers — Studs & Plates
Trimmer Rafters

System Description	QUAN.	UNIT	LABOR HOURS	COST PER S.F.		
				MAT.	INST.	TOTAL
2″ X 6″, 16″ O.C.						
Dormer rafter, 2″ x 6″, 16″ O.C.	1.330	L.F.	.036	.92	2.11	3.03
Ridge board, 2″ x 6″	.280	L.F.	.009	.19	.52	.71
Trimmer rafters, 2″ x 6″	.880	L.F.	.014	.61	.83	1.44
Wall studs & plates, 2″ x 4″, 16″ O.C.	3.160	L.F.	.056	1.42	3.25	4.67
Fascia, 2″ x 6″	.220	L.F.	.012	.16	.71	.87
Valley rafter, 2″ x 6″, 16″ O.C.	.280	L.F.	.009	.19	.51	.70
Cripple rafter, 2″ x 6″, 16″ O.C.	.560	L.F.	.022	.39	1.28	1.67
Headers, 2″ x 6″, doubled	.670	L.F.	.030	.46	1.74	2.20
Ceiling joist, 2″ x 4″, 16″ O.C.	1.000	L.F.	.013	.45	.75	1.20
Sheathing, exterior grade plywood, 1/2″ thick	3.610	S.F.	.041	2.49	2.42	4.91
TOTAL		S.F.	.242	7.28	14.12	21.40
2″ X 8″, 16″ O.C.						
Dormer rafter, 2″ x 8″, 16″ O.C.	1.330	L.F.	.039	1.28	2.30	3.58
Ridge board, 2″ x 8″	.280	L.F.	.010	.27	.58	.85
Trimmer rafter, 2″ x 8″	.880	L.F.	.015	.84	.86	1.70
Wall studs & plates, 2″ x 4″, 16″ O.C.	3.160	L.F.	.056	1.42	3.25	4.67
Fascia, 2″ x 8″	.220	L.F.	.016	.21	.92	1.13
Valley rafter, 2″ x 8″, 16″ O.C.	.280	L.F.	.010	.27	.56	.83
Cripple rafter, 2″ x 8″, 16″ O.C.	.560	L.F.	.027	.54	1.56	2.10
Headers, 2″ x 8″, doubled	.670	L.F.	.032	.64	1.84	2.48
Ceiling joist, 2″ x 4″, 16″ O.C.	1.000	L.F.	.013	.45	.75	1.20
Sheathing,, exterior grade plywood, 1/2″ thick	3.610	S.F.	.041	2.49	2.42	4.91
TOTAL		S.F.	.259	8.41	15.04	23.45

The cost in this system is based on the square foot of plan area.
The measurement being the plan area of the dormer only.

Description	QUAN.	UNIT	LABOR HOURS	COST PER S.F.		
				MAT.	INST.	TOTAL

Gable Dormer Framing Price Sheet	QUAN.	UNIT	LABOR HOURS	COST PER S.F.		
				MAT.	INST.	TOTAL
Dormer rafters, #2 or better, 2" x 4", 16" O.C.	1.330	L.F.	.029	.73	1.69	2.42
24" O.C.	1.060	L.F.	.023	.59	1.35	1.94
2" x 6", 16" O.C.	1.330	L.F.	.036	.92	2.11	3.03
24" O.C.	1.060	L.F.	.029	.73	1.69	2.42
2" x 8", 16" O.C.	1.330	L.F.	.039	1.28	2.30	3.58
24" O.C.	1.060	L.F.	.031	1.02	1.83	2.85
Ridge board, #2 or better, 1" x 4"	.280	L.F.	.006	.19	.35	.54
1" x 6"	.280	L.F.	.007	.23	.44	.67
1" x 8"	.280	L.F.	.008	.39	.48	.87
2" x 4"	.280	L.F.	.007	.15	.42	.57
2" x 6"	.280	L.F.	.009	.19	.52	.71
2" x 8"	.280	L.F.	.010	.27	.58	.85
Trimmer rafters, #2 or better, 2" x 4"	.880	L.F.	.011	.49	.66	1.15
2" x 6"	.880	L.F.	.014	.61	.83	1.44
2" x 8"	.880	L.F.	.015	.84	.86	1.70
2" x 10"	.880	L.F.	.022	1.33	1.30	2.63
Wall studs & plates, #2 or better, 2" x 4" studs, 16" O.C.	3.160	L.F.	.056	1.42	3.25	4.67
24" O.C.	2.800	L.F.	.050	1.26	2.88	4.14
2" x 6" studs, 16" O.C.	3.160	L.F.	.063	2.18	3.70	5.88
24" O.C.	2.800	L.F.	.056	1.93	3.28	5.21
Fascia, #2 or better, 1" x 4"	.220	L.F.	.006	.09	.37	.46
1" x 6"	.220	L.F.	.008	.11	.46	.57
1" x 8"	.220	L.F.	.009	.12	.53	.65
2" x 4"	.220	L.F.	.011	.14	.62	.76
2" x 6"	.220	L.F.	.014	.18	.79	.97
2" x 8"	.220	L.F.	.016	.21	.92	1.13
Valley rafter, #2 or better, 2" x 4"	.280	L.F.	.007	.15	.41	.56
2" x 6"	.280	L.F.	.009	.19	.51	.70
2" x 8"	.280	L.F.	.010	.27	.56	.83
2" x 10"	.280	L.F.	.012	.42	.69	1.11
Cripple rafter, #2 or better, 2" x 4", 16" O.C.	.560	L.F.	.018	.31	1.03	1.34
24" O.C.	.450	L.F.	.014	.25	.82	1.07
2" x 6", 16" O.C.	.560	L.F.	.022	.39	1.28	1.67
24" O.C.	.450	L.F.	.018	.31	1.03	1.34
2" x 8", 16" O.C.	.560	L.F.	.027	.54	1.56	2.10
24" O.C.	.450	L.F.	.021	.43	1.26	1.69
Headers, #2 or better double header, 2" x 4"	.670	L.F.	.024	.37	1.40	1.77
2" x 6"	.670	L.F.	.030	.46	1.74	2.20
2" x 8"	.670	L.F.	.032	.64	1.84	2.48
2" x 10"	.670	L.F.	.034	1.01	1.96	2.97
Ceiling joist, #2 or better, 2" x 4", 16" O.C.	1.000	L.F.	.013	.45	.75	1.20
24" O.C.	.800	L.F.	.010	.36	.60	.96
2" x 6", 16" O.C.	1.000	L.F.	.013	.69	.75	1.44
24" O.C.	.800	L.F.	.010	.55	.60	1.15
Sheathing, plywood exterior grade, 3/8" thick	3.610	S.F.	.038	2.42	2.20	4.62
1/2" thick	3.610	S.F.	.041	2.49	2.42	4.91
5/8" thick	3.610	S.F.	.044	3.10	2.60	5.70
3/4" thick	3.610	S.F.	.048	3.72	2.82	6.54
Boards, 1" x 6", laid regular	3.610	S.F.	.089	6.55	5.20	11.75
Laid diagonal	3.610	S.F.	.099	6.55	5.80	12.35
1" x 8", laid regular	3.610	S.F.	.076	8	4.40	12.40
Laid diagonal	3.610	S.F.	.089	8	5.20	13.20

For customer support on your Residential Costs with RSMeans Data, call 800.448.8182.

151

Sheathing
Ceiling Joists
Fascia Board
Studs & Plates
Rafters
Trimmer Rafters

System Description	QUAN.	UNIT	LABOR HOURS	COST PER S.F.		
				MAT.	INST.	TOTAL
2″ X 6″ RAFTERS, 16″ O.C.						
Dormer rafter, 2″ x 6″, 16″ O.C.	1.080	L.F.	.029	.75	1.72	2.47
Trimmer rafter, 2″ x 6″	.400	L.F.	.006	.28	.38	.66
Studs & plates, 2″ x 4″, 16″ O.C.	2.750	L.F.	.049	1.24	2.83	4.07
Fascia, 2″ x 6″	.250	L.F.	.014	.18	.79	.97
Ceiling joist, 2″ x 4″, 16″ O.C.	1.000	L.F.	.013	.45	.75	1.20
Sheathing, exterior grade plywood, CDX, 1/2″ thick	2.940	S.F.	.034	2.03	1.97	4
TOTAL		S.F.	.145	4.93	8.44	13.37
2″ X 8″ RAFTERS, 16″ O.C.						
Dormer rafter, 2″ x 8″, 16″ O.C.	1.080	L.F.	.032	1.04	1.87	2.91
Trimmer rafter, 2″ x 8″	.400	L.F.	.007	.38	.39	.77
Studs & plates, 2″ x 4″, 16″ O.C.	2.750	L.F.	.049	1.24	2.83	4.07
Fascia, 2″ x 8″	.250	L.F.	.018	.24	1.04	1.28
Ceiling joist, 2″ x 6″, 16″ O.C.	1.000	L.F.	.013	.69	.75	1.44
Sheathing, exterior grade plywood, CDX, 1/2″ thick	2.940	S.F.	.034	2.03	1.97	4
TOTAL		S.F.	.153	5.62	8.85	14.47
2″ X 10″ RAFTERS, 16″ O.C.						
Dormer rafter, 2″ x 10″, 16″ O.C.	1.080	L.F.	.041	1.63	2.38	4.01
Trimmer rafter, 2″ x 10″	.400	L.F.	.010	.60	.59	1.19
Studs & plates, 2″ x 4″, 16″ O.C.	2.750	L.F.	.049	1.24	2.83	4.07
Fascia, 2″ x 10″	.250	L.F.	.022	.38	1.30	1.68
Ceiling joist, 2″ x 6″, 16″ O.C.	1.000	L.F.	.013	.69	.75	1.44
Sheathing, exterior grade plywood, CDX, 1/2″ thick	2.940	S.F.	.034	2.03	1.97	4
TOTAL		S.F.	.169	6.57	9.82	16.39

The cost in this system is based on the square foot of plan area.
The measurement is the plan area of the dormer only.

Description	QUAN.	UNIT	LABOR HOURS	COST PER S.F.		
				MAT.	INST.	TOTAL

Shed Dormer Framing Price Sheet	QUAN.	UNIT	LABOR HOURS	COST PER S.F.		
				MAT.	INST.	TOTAL
Dormer rafters, #2 or better, 2" x 4", 16" O.C.	1.080	L.F.	.023	.60	1.37	1.97
24" O.C.	.860	L.F.	.019	.47	1.09	1.56
2" x 6", 16" O.C.	1.080	L.F.	.029	.75	1.72	2.47
24" O.C.	.860	L.F.	.023	.59	1.37	1.96
2" x 8", 16" O.C.	1.080	L.F.	.032	1.04	1.87	2.91
24" O.C.	.860	L.F.	.025	.83	1.49	2.32
2" x 10", 16" O.C.	1.080	L.F.	.041	1.63	2.38	4.01
24" O.C.	.860	L.F.	.032	1.30	1.89	3.19
Trimmer rafter, #2 or better, 2" x 4"	.400	L.F.	.005	.22	.30	.52
2" x 6"	.400	L.F.	.006	.28	.38	.66
2" x 8"	.400	L.F.	.007	.38	.39	.77
2" x 10"	.400	L.F.	.010	.60	.59	1.19
Studs & plates, #2 or better, 2" x 4", 16" O.C.	2.750	L.F.	.049	1.24	2.83	4.07
24" O.C.	2.200	L.F.	.039	.99	2.27	3.26
2" x 6", 16" O.C.	2.750	L.F.	.055	1.90	3.22	5.12
24" O.C.	2.200	L.F.	.044	1.52	2.57	4.09
Fascia, #2 or better, 1" x 4"	.250	L.F.	.006	.09	.37	.46
1" x 6"	.250	L.F.	.008	.11	.46	.57
1" x 8"	.250	L.F.	.009	.12	.53	.65
2" x 4"	.250	L.F.	.011	.14	.62	.76
2" x 6"	.250	L.F.	.014	.18	.79	.97
2" x 8"	.250	L.F.	.018	.24	1.04	1.28
Ceiling joist, #2 or better, 2" x 4", 16" O.C.	1.000	L.F.	.013	.45	.75	1.20
24" O.C.	.800	L.F.	.010	.36	.60	.96
2" x 6", 16" O.C.	1.000	L.F.	.013	.69	.75	1.44
24" O.C.	.800	L.F.	.010	.55	.60	1.15
2" x 8", 16" O.C.	1.000	L.F.	.015	.96	.85	1.81
24" O.C.	.800	L.F.	.012	.77	.68	1.45
Sheathing, plywood exterior grade, 3/8" thick	2.940	S.F.	.031	1.97	1.79	3.76
1/2" thick	2.940	S.F.	.034	2.03	1.97	4
5/8" thick	2.940	S.F.	.036	2.53	2.12	4.65
3/4" thick	2.940	S.F.	.039	3.03	2.29	5.32
Boards, 1" x 6", laid regular	2.940	S.F.	.072	5.30	4.23	9.53
Laid diagonal	2.940	S.F.	.080	5.30	4.70	10
1" x 8", laid regular	2.940	S.F.	.062	6.50	3.59	10.09
Laid diagonal	2.940	S.F.	.072	6.50	4.23	10.73

Window Openings	QUAN.	UNIT	LABOR HOURS	COST EACH		
				MAT.	INST.	TOTAL
The following are to be added to the total cost of the dormers for window openings. Do not subtract window area from the stud wall quantities.						
Headers, 2" x 6" doubled, 2' long	4.000	L.F.	.178	2.76	10.40	13.16
3' long	6.000	L.F.	.267	4.14	15.60	19.74
4' long	8.000	L.F.	.356	5.50	21	26.50
5' long	10.000	L.F.	.444	6.90	26	32.90
2" x 8" doubled, 4' long	8.000	L.F.	.376	7.70	22	29.70
5' long	10.000	L.F.	.471	9.60	27.50	37.10
6' long	12.000	L.F.	.565	11.50	33	44.50
8' long	16.000	L.F.	.753	15.35	44	59.35
2" x 10" doubled, 4' long	8.000	L.F.	.400	12.10	23.50	35.60
6' long	12.000	L.F.	.600	18.10	35	53.10
8' long	16.000	L.F.	.800	24	46.50	70.50
10' long	20.000	L.F.	1.000	30	58.50	88.50

System Description	QUAN.	UNIT	LABOR HOURS	COST PER S.F.		
				MAT.	INST.	TOTAL
2″ X 4″, 16″ O.C.						
2″ x 4″ studs, #2 or better, 16″ O.C.	1.000	L.F.	.015	.44	.85	1.29
Plates, double top, single bottom	.375	L.F.	.005	.17	.32	.49
Cross bracing, let-in, 1″ x 6″	.080	L.F.	.004	.07	.25	.32
TOTAL		S.F.	.024	.68	1.42	2.10
2″ X 4″, 24″ O.C.						
2″ x 4″ studs, #2 or better, 24″ O.C.	.800	L.F.	.012	.35	.68	1.03
Plates, double top, single bottom	.375	L.F.	.005	.17	.32	.49
Cross bracing, let-in, 1″ x 6″	.080	L.F.	.003	.07	.16	.23
TOTAL		S.F.	.020	.59	1.16	1.75
2″ X 6″, 16″ O.C.						
2″ x 6″ studs, #2 or better, 16″ O.C.	1.000	L.F.	.016	.69	.94	1.63
Plates, double top, single bottom	.375	L.F.	.006	.26	.35	.61
Cross bracing, let-in, 1″ x 6″	.080	L.F.	.004	.07	.25	.32
TOTAL		S.F.	.026	1.02	1.54	2.56
2″ X 6″, 24″ O.C.						
2″ x 6″ studs, #2 or better, 24″ O.C.	.800	L.F.	.013	.55	.75	1.30
Plates, double top, single bottom	.375	L.F.	.006	.26	.35	.61
Cross bracing, let-in, 1″ x 6″	.080	L.F.	.003	.07	.16	.23
TOTAL		S.F.	.022	.88	1.26	2.14

The costs in this system are based on a square foot of wall area. Do not subtract for door or window openings.

Description	QUAN.	UNIT	LABOR HOURS	COST PER S.F.		
				MAT.	INST.	TOTAL

Partition Framing Price Sheet	QUAN.	UNIT	LABOR HOURS	COST PER S.F.		
				MAT.	INST.	TOTAL
Wood studs, #2 or better, 2" x 4", 12" O.C.	1.250	L.F.	.018	.55	1.06	1.61
16" O.C.	1.000	L.F.	.015	.44	.85	1.29
24" O.C.	.800	L.F.	.012	.35	.68	1.03
32" O.C.	.650	L.F.	.009	.29	.55	.84
2" x 6", 12" O.C.	1.250	L.F.	.020	.86	1.18	2.04
16" O.C.	1.000	L.F.	.016	.69	.94	1.63
24" O.C.	.800	L.F.	.013	.55	.75	1.30
32" O.C.	.650	L.F.	.010	.45	.61	1.06
Plates, #2 or better double top single bottom, 2" x 4"	.375	L.F.	.005	.17	.32	.49
2" x 6"	.375	L.F.	.006	.26	.35	.61
2" x 8"	.375	L.F.	.005	.36	.32	.68
Cross bracing, let-in, 1" x 6" boards studs, 12" O.C.	.080	L.F.	.005	.08	.31	.39
16" O.C.	.080	L.F.	.004	.07	.25	.32
24" O.C.	.080	L.F.	.003	.07	.16	.23
32" O.C.	.080	L.F.	.002	.05	.13	.18
Let-in steel (T shaped) studs, 12" O.C.	.080	L.F.	.001	.09	.08	.17
16" O.C.	.080	L.F.	.001	.07	.06	.13
24" O.C.	.080	L.F.	.001	.07	.06	.13
32" O.C.	.080	L.F.	.001	.06	.05	.11
Steel straps studs, 12" O.C.	.080	L.F.	.001	.10	.07	.17
16" O.C.	.080	L.F.	.001	.09	.06	.15
24" O.C.	.080	L.F.	.001	.09	.06	.15
32" O.C.	.080	L.F.	.001	.09	.06	.15
Metal studs, load bearing 24" O.C., 20 ga. galv., 2-1/2" wide	1.000	S.F.	.015	.71	.88	1.59
3-5/8" wide	1.000	S.F.	.015	.84	.89	1.73
4" wide	1.000	S.F.	.016	.87	.91	1.78
6" wide	1.000	S.F.	.016	1.12	.93	2.05
16 ga., 2-1/2" wide	1.000	S.F.	.017	.82	1	1.82
3-5/8" wide	1.000	S.F.	.017	.98	1.02	2
4" wide	1.000	S.F.	.018	1.03	1.04	2.07
6" wide	1.000	S.F.	.018	1.30	1.07	2.37
Non-load bearing 24" O.C., 25 ga. galv., 1-5/8" wide	1.000	S.F.	.011	.21	.62	.83
2-1/2" wide	1.000	S.F.	.011	.27	.62	.89
3-5/8" wide	1.000	S.F.	.011	.31	.63	.94
4" wide	1.000	S.F.	.011	.34	.63	.97
6" wide	1.000	S.F.	.011	.41	.64	1.05
20 ga., 2-1/2" wide	1.000	S.F.	.013	.33	.78	1.11
3-5/8" wide	1.000	S.F.	.014	.38	.79	1.17
4" wide	1.000	S.F.	.014	.46	.79	1.25
6" wide	1.000	S.F.	.014	.55	.81	1.36

Window & Door Openings	QUAN.	UNIT	LABOR HOURS	COST EACH		
				MAT.	INST.	TOTAL
The following costs are to be added to the total costs of the walls.						
Do not subtract openings from total wall area.						
Headers, 2" x 6" double, 2' long	4.000	L.F.	.178	2.76	10.40	13.16
3' long	6.000	L.F.	.267	4.14	15.60	19.74
4' long	8.000	L.F.	.356	5.50	21	26.50
5' long	10.000	L.F.	.444	6.90	26	32.90
2" x 8" double, 4' long	8.000	L.F.	.376	7.70	22	29.70
5' long	10.000	L.F.	.471	9.60	27.50	37.10
6' long	12.000	L.F.	.565	11.50	33	44.50
8' long	16.000	L.F.	.753	15.35	44	59.35
2" x 10" double, 4' long	8.000	L.F.	.400	12.10	23.50	35.60
6' long	12.000	L.F.	.600	18.10	35	53.10
8' long	16.000	L.F.	.800	24	46.50	70.50
10' long	20.000	L.F.	1.000	30	58.50	88.50
2" x 12" double, 8' long	16.000	L.F.	.853	31	50	81
12' long	24.000	L.F.	1.280	46.50	75	121.50

Stucco

Paint

Concrete Block

Reinforcing

Furring

Insulation

System Description	QUAN.	UNIT	LABOR HOURS	COST PER S.F.		
				MAT.	INST.	TOTAL
6″ THICK CONCRETE BLOCK WALL						
6″ thick concrete block, 6″ x 8″ x 16″	1.000	S.F.	.100	2.59	5.45	8.04
Masonry reinforcing, truss strips every other course	.625	L.F.	.002	.16	.10	.26
Furring, 1″ x 3″, 16″ O.C.	1.000	L.F.	.016	.49	.94	1.43
Masonry insulation, poured perlite	1.000	S.F.	.013	1.93	.78	2.71
Stucco, 2 coats	1.000	S.F.	.069	.34	3.86	4.20
Masonry paint, 2 coats	1.000	S.F.	.016	.24	.77	1.01
TOTAL		S.F.	.216	5.75	11.90	17.65
8″ THICK CONCRETE BLOCK WALL						
8″ thick concrete block, 8″ x 8″ x 16″	1.000	S.F.	.107	2.77	5.80	8.57
Masonry reinforcing, truss strips every other course	.625	L.F.	.002	.16	.10	.26
Furring, 1″ x 3″, 16″ O.C.	1.000	L.F.	.016	.49	.94	1.43
Masonry insulation, poured perlite	1.000	S.F.	.018	2.55	1.03	3.58
Stucco, 2 coats	1.000	S.F.	.069	.34	3.86	4.20
Masonry paint, 2 coats	1.000	S.F.	.016	.24	.77	1.01
TOTAL		S.F.	.228	6.55	12.50	19.05
12″ THICK CONCRETE BLOCK WALL						
12″ thick concrete block, 12″ x 8″ x 16″	1.000	S.F.	.141	4.59	7.55	12.14
Masonry reinforcing, truss strips every other course	.625	L.F.	.003	.12	.14	.26
Furring, 1″ x 3″, 16″ O.C.	1.000	L.F.	.016	.49	.94	1.43
Masonry insulation, poured perlite	1.000	S.F.	.026	3.77	1.52	5.29
Stucco, 2 coats	1.000	S.F.	.069	.34	3.86	4.20
Masonry paint, 2 coats	1.000	S.F.	.016	.24	.77	1.01
TOTAL		S.F.	.271	9.55	14.78	24.33

Costs for this system are based on a square foot of wall area. Do not subtract for window openings.

Description	QUAN.	UNIT	LABOR HOURS	COST PER S.F.		
				MAT.	INST.	TOTAL

Masonry Block Price Sheet

	QUAN.	UNIT	LABOR HOURS	COST PER S.F. MAT.	COST PER S.F. INST.	COST PER S.F. TOTAL
Block concrete, 8" x 16" regular, 4" thick	1.000	S.F.	.093	1.96	5.05	7.01
6" thick	1.000	S.F.	.100	2.59	5.45	8.04
8" thick	1.000	S.F.	.107	2.77	5.80	8.57
10" thick	1.000	S.F.	.111	3.30	6.05	9.35
12" thick	1.000	S.F.	.141	4.59	7.55	12.14
Solid block, 4" thick	1.000	S.F.	.096	2.25	5.25	7.50
6" thick	1.000	S.F.	.104	2.65	5.65	8.30
8" thick	1.000	S.F.	.111	3.97	6.05	10.02
10" thick	1.000	S.F.	.133	5.40	7.10	12.50
12" thick	1.000	S.F.	.148	6	7.90	13.90
Lightweight, 4" thick	1.000	S.F.	.093	1.96	5.05	7.01
6" thick	1.000	S.F.	.100	2.59	5.45	8.04
8" thick	1.000	S.F.	.107	2.77	5.80	8.57
10" thick	1.000	S.F.	.111	3.30	6.05	9.35
12" thick	1.000	S.F.	.141	4.59	7.55	12.14
Split rib profile, 4" thick	1.000	S.F.	.116	4.35	6.30	10.65
6" thick	1.000	S.F.	.123	4.94	6.70	11.64
8" thick	1.000	S.F.	.131	5.60	7.25	12.85
10" thick	1.000	S.F.	.157	5.85	8.35	14.20
12" thick	1.000	S.F.	.175	6.50	9.30	15.80
Masonry reinforcing, wire truss strips, every course, 8" block	1.375	L.F.	.004	.34	.22	.56
12" block	1.375	L.F.	.006	.26	.32	.58
Every other course, 8" block	.625	L.F.	.002	.16	.10	.26
12" block	.625	L.F.	.003	.12	.14	.26
Furring, wood, 1" x 3", 12" O.C.	1.250	L.F.	.020	.61	1.18	1.79
16" O.C.	1.000	L.F.	.016	.49	.94	1.43
24" O.C.	.800	L.F.	.013	.39	.75	1.14
32" O.C.	.640	L.F.	.010	.31	.60	.91
Steel, 3/4" channels, 12" O.C.	1.250	L.F.	.034	.43	1.90	2.33
16" O.C.	1.000	L.F.	.030	.39	1.69	2.08
24" O.C.	.800	L.F.	.023	.26	1.28	1.54
32" O.C.	.640	L.F.	.018	.21	1.02	1.23
Masonry insulation, vermiculite or perlite poured 4" thick	1.000	S.F.	.009	1.25	.50	1.75
6" thick	1.000	S.F.	.013	1.91	.77	2.68
8" thick	1.000	S.F.	.018	2.55	1.03	3.58
10" thick	1.000	S.F.	.021	3.09	1.25	4.34
12" thick	1.000	S.F.	.026	3.77	1.52	5.29
Block inserts polystyrene, 6" thick	1.000	S.F.		1.34		1.34
8" thick	1.000	S.F.		1.51		1.51
10" thick	1.000	S.F.		1.56		1.56
12" thick	1.000	S.F.		1.73		1.73
Stucco, 1 coat	1.000	S.F.	.057	.28	3.17	3.45
2 coats	1.000	S.F.	.069	.34	3.86	4.20
3 coats	1.000	S.F.	.081	.40	4.53	4.93
Painting, 1 coat	1.000	S.F.	.011	.15	.54	.69
2 coats	1.000	S.F.	.016	.24	.77	1.01
Primer & 1 coat	1.000	S.F.	.013	.22	.63	.85
2 coats	1.000	S.F.	.018	.31	.88	1.19
Lath, metal lath expanded 2.5 lb/S.Y., painted	1.000	S.F.	.010	.45	.58	1.03
Galvanized	1.000	S.F.	.012	.50	.64	1.14

System Description	QUAN.	UNIT	LABOR HOURS	COST PER S.F.		
				MAT.	INST.	TOTAL
SELECT COMMON BRICK						
Brick, select common, running bond	1.000	S.F.	.174	4.77	9.45	14.22
Wall ties, 7/8" x 7", 22 gauge	1.000	Ea.	.008	.17	.45	.62
Building paper, spunbonded polypropylene	1.100	S.F.	.002	.17	.13	.30
Trim, pine, painted	.125	L.F.	.004	.07	.23	.30
TOTAL		S.F.	.188	5.18	10.26	15.44
RED FACED COMMON BRICK						
Brick, common, red faced, running bond	1.000	S.F.	.182	4.56	9.90	14.46
Wall ties, 7/8" x 7", 22 gauge	1.000	Ea.	.008	.17	.45	.62
Building paper, spundbonded polypropylene	1.100	S.F.	.002	.17	.13	.30
Trim, pine, painted	.125	L.F.	.004	.07	.23	.30
TOTAL		S.F.	.196	4.97	10.71	15.68
BUFF OR GREY FACE BRICK						
Brick, buff or grey	1.000	S.F.	.182	4.82	9.90	14.72
Wall ties, 7/8" x 7", 22 gauge	1.000	Ea.	.008	.17	.45	.62
Building paper, spundbonded polypropylene	1.100	S.F.	.002	.17	.13	.30
Trim, pine, painted	.125	L.F.	.004	.07	.23	.30
TOTAL		S.F.	.196	5.23	10.71	15.94
STONE WORK, ROUGH STONE, AVERAGE						
Field stone veneer	1.000	S.F.	.223	9.38	12.13	21.51
Wall ties, 7/8" x 7", 22 gauge	1.000	Ea.	.008	.17	.45	.62
Building paper, spundbonded polypropylene	1.000	S.F.	.002	.17	.13	.30
Trim, pine, painted	.125	L.F.	.004	.07	.23	.30
TOTAL		S.F.	.237	9.79	12.94	22.73

The costs in this system are based on a square foot of wall area. Do not subtract area for window & door openings.

Description	QUAN.	UNIT	LABOR HOURS	COST PER S.F.		
				MAT.	INST.	TOTAL

Brick/Stone Veneer Price Sheet	QUAN.	UNIT	LABOR HOURS	COST PER S.F.		
				MAT.	INST.	TOTAL
Brick						
Select common, running bond	1.000	S.F.	.174	4.77	9.45	14.22
Red faced, running bond	1.000	S.F.	.182	4.56	9.90	14.46
Buff or grey faced, running bond	1.000	S.F.	.182	4.82	9.90	14.72
Header every 6th course	1.000	S.F.	.216	5.30	11.75	17.05
English bond	1.000	S.F.	.286	6.80	15.55	22.35
Flemish bond	1.000	S.F.	.195	4.82	10.60	15.42
Common bond	1.000	S.F.	.267	6.05	14.50	20.55
Stack bond	1.000	S.F.	.182	4.82	9.90	14.72
Jumbo, running bond	1.000	S.F.	.092	5.70	5	10.70
Norman, running bond	1.000	S.F.	.125	7.05	6.80	13.85
Norwegian, running bond	1.000	S.F.	.107	6.25	5.80	12.05
Economy, running bond	1.000	S.F.	.129	4.94	7	11.94
Engineer, running bond	1.000	S.F.	.154	4.38	8.35	12.73
Roman, running bond	1.000	S.F.	.160	7.90	8.70	16.60
Utility, running bond	1.000	S.F.	.089	5.60	6.05	11.65
Glazed, running bond	1.000	S.F.	.190	14.25	10.35	24.60
Stone work, rough stone, average	1.000	S.F.	.179	9.40	12.15	21.55
Maximum	1.000	S.F.	.267	14	18.10	32.10
Wall ties, galvanized, corrugated 7/8" x 7", 22 gauge	1.000	Ea.	.008	.17	.45	.62
16 gauge	1.000	Ea.	.008	.32	.45	.77
Cavity wall, every 3rd course 6" long Z type, 1/4" diameter	1.330	L.F.	.010	.56	.58	1.14
3/16" diameter	1.330	L.F.	.010	.44	.58	1.02
8" long, Z type, 1/4" diameter	1.330	L.F.	.010	.67	.58	1.25
3/16" diameter	1.330	L.F.	.010	.37	.58	.95
Building paper, aluminum and kraft laminated foil, 1 side	1.000	S.F.	.002	.13	.13	.26
2 sides	1.000	S.F.	.002	.15	.13	.28
#15 asphalt paper	1.100	S.F.	.002	.07	.14	.21
Polyethylene, .002" thick	1.000	S.F.	.002	.02	.13	.15
.004" thick	1.000	S.F.	.002	.03	.13	.16
.006" thick	1.000	S.F.	.002	.04	.13	.17
.010" thick	1.000	S.F.	.002	.09	.13	.22
Trim, 1" x 4", cedar	.125	L.F.	.005	.16	.29	.45
Fir	.125	L.F.	.005	.12	.29	.41
Redwood	.125	L.F.	.005	.16	.29	.45
White pine	.125	L.F.	.005	.12	.29	.41

Trim →

Building Paper

Beveled Cedar Siding

System Description	QUAN.	UNIT	LABOR HOURS	COST PER S.F.		
				MAT.	INST.	TOTAL
1/2″ X 6″ BEVELED CEDAR SIDING, "A" GRADE						
1/2″ x 6″ beveled cedar siding	1.000	S.F.	.027	4.82	1.59	6.41
Building wrap, spunbonded polypropylene	1.100	S.F.	.002	.17	.13	.30
Trim, cedar	.125	L.F.	.005	.16	.29	.45
Paint, primer & 2 coats	1.000	S.F.	.017	.23	.83	1.06
TOTAL		S.F.	.051	5.38	2.84	8.22
1/2″ X 8″ BEVELED CEDAR SIDING, "A" GRADE						
1/2″ x 8″ beveled cedar siding	1.000	S.F.	.024	7.35	1.42	8.77
Building wrap, spunbonded polypropylene	1.100	S.F.	.002	.17	.13	.30
Trim, cedar	.125	L.F.	.005	.16	.29	.45
Paint, primer & 2 coats	1.000	S.F.	.017	.23	.83	1.06
TOTAL		S.F.	.048	7.91	2.67	10.58
1″ X 4″ TONGUE & GROOVE, REDWOOD, VERTICAL GRAIN						
Redwood, clear, vertical grain, 1″ x 10″	1.000	S.F.	.020	5.55	1.15	6.70
Building wrap, spunbonded polypropylene	1.100	S.F.	.002	.17	.13	.30
Trim, redwood	.125	L.F.	.005	.16	.29	.45
Sealer, 1 coat, stain, 1 coat	1.000	S.F.	.013	.15	.64	.79
TOTAL		S.F.	.040	6.03	2.21	8.24
1″ X 6″ TONGUE & GROOVE, REDWOOD, VERTICAL GRAIN						
Redwood, clear, vertical grain, 1″ x 10″	1.000	S.F.	.020	5.71	1.18	6.89
Building wrap, spunbonded polypropylene	1.100	S.F.	.002	.17	.13	.30
Trim, redwood	.125	L.F.	.005	.16	.29	.45
Sealer, 1 coat, stain, 1 coat	1.000	S.F.	.013	.15	.64	.79
TOTAL		S.F.	.040	6.19	2.24	8.43

The costs in this system are based on a square foot of wall area.
Do not subtract area for door or window openings.

Description	QUAN.	UNIT	LABOR HOURS	COST PER S.F.		
				MAT.	INST.	TOTAL

Wood Siding Price Sheet	QUAN.	UNIT	LABOR HOURS	COST PER S.F.		
				MAT.	INST.	TOTAL
Siding, beveled cedar, "A" grade, 1/2" x 6"	1.000	S.F.	.028	4.82	1.59	6.41
1/2" x 8"	1.000	S.F.	.023	7.35	1.42	8.77
"B" grade, 1/2" x 6"	1.000	S.F.	.032	5.35	1.77	7.12
1/2" x 8"	1.000	S.F.	.029	8.15	1.58	9.73
Clear grade, 1/2" x 6"	1.000	S.F.	.028	6.05	1.99	8.04
1/2" x 8"	1.000	S.F.	.023	9.20	1.78	10.98
Redwood, clear vertical grain, 1/2" x 6"	1.000	S.F.	.036	5.30	1.59	6.89
1/2" x 8"	1.000	S.F.	.032	5.70	1.42	7.12
Clear all heart vertical grain, 1/2" x 6"	1.000	S.F.	.028	5.90	1.77	7.67
1/2" x 8"	1.000	S.F.	.023	6.35	1.58	7.93
Siding board & batten, cedar, "B" grade, 1" x 10"	1.000	S.F.	.031	4.93	1.11	6.04
1" x 12"	1.000	S.F.	.031	4.93	1.11	6.04
Redwood, clear vertical grain, 1" x 6"	1.000	S.F.	.043	5.35	1.59	6.94
1" x 8"	1.000	S.F.	.018	5.80	1.42	7.22
White pine, #2 & better, 1" x 10"	1.000	S.F.	.029	2.41	1.42	3.83
1" x 12"	1.000	S.F.	.029	2.41	1.42	3.83
Siding vertical, tongue & groove, cedar "B" grade, 1" x 4"	1.000	S.F.	.033	5.65	1.15	6.80
1" x 6"	1.000	S.F.	.024	5.80	1.18	6.98
1" x 8"	1.000	S.F.	.024	5.95	1.21	7.16
1" x 10"	1.000	S.F.	.021	6.15	1.25	7.40
"A" grade, 1" x 4"	1.000	S.F.	.033	5.15	1.05	6.20
1" x 6"	1.000	S.F.	.024	5.30	1.08	6.38
1" x 8"	1.000	S.F.	.024	5.45	1.11	6.56
1" x 10"	1.000	S.F.	.021	5.60	1.14	6.74
Clear vertical grain, 1" x 4"	1.000	S.F.	.033	4.77	.97	5.74
1" x 6"	1.000	S.F.	.024	4.88	.99	5.87
1" x 8"	1.000	S.F.	.024	5	1.02	6.02
1" x 10"	1.000	S.F.	.021	5.15	1.04	6.19
Redwood, clear vertical grain, 1" x 4"	1.000	S.F.	.033	5.55	1.15	6.70
1" x 6"	1.000	S.F.	.024	5.70	1.18	6.88
1" x 8"	1.000	S.F.	.024	5.85	1.21	7.06
1" x 10"	1.000	S.F.	.021	6.05	1.25	7.30
Clear all heart vertical grain, 1" x 4"	1.000	S.F.	.033	5.10	1.05	6.15
1" x 6"	1.000	S.F.	.024	5.20	1.08	6.28
1" x 8"	1.000	S.F.	.024	5.35	1.11	6.46
1" x 10"	1.000	S.F.	.021	5.50	1.14	6.64
White pine, 1" x 10"	1.000	S.F.	.024	3.50	1.25	4.75
Siding plywood, texture 1-11 cedar, 3/8" thick	1.000	S.F.	.024	1.38	1.39	2.77
5/8" thick	1.000	S.F.	.024	2.94	1.39	4.33
Redwood, 3/8" thick	1.000	S.F.	.024	1.38	1.39	2.77
5/8" thick	1.000	S.F.	.024	2.11	1.39	3.50
Fir, 3/8" thick	1.000	S.F.	.024	.99	1.39	2.38
5/8" thick	1.000	S.F.	.024	1.60	1.39	2.99
Southern yellow pine, 3/8" thick	1.000	S.F.	.024	.99	1.39	2.38
5/8" thick	1.000	S.F.	.024	1.51	1.39	2.90
Paper, #15 asphalt felt	1.100	S.F.	.002	.07	.14	.21
Trim, cedar	.125	L.F.	.005	.16	.29	.45
Fir	.125	L.F.	.005	.12	.29	.41
Redwood	.125	L.F.	.005	.16	.29	.45
White pine	.125	L.F.	.005	.12	.29	.41
Painting, primer, & 1 coat	1.000	S.F.	.013	.15	.64	.79
2 coats	1.000	S.F.	.017	.23	.83	1.06
Stain, sealer, & 1 coat	1.000	S.F.	.017	.17	.84	1.01
2 coats	1.000	S.F.	.019	.27	.91	1.18

Trim → ... ← Building Paper

← White Cedar Shingles

System Description	QUAN.	UNIT	LABOR HOURS	COST PER S.F.		
				MAT.	INST.	TOTAL
WHITE CEDAR SHINGLES, 5″ EXPOSURE						
White cedar shingles, 16″ long, grade "A", 5″ exposure	1.000	S.F.	.033	2.15	1.95	4.10
Building wrap, spunbonded polypropylene	1.100	S.F.	.002	.17	.13	.30
Trim, cedar	.125	S.F.	.005	.16	.29	.45
Paint, primer & 1 coat	1.000	S.F.	.017	.17	.84	1.01
TOTAL		S.F.	.057	2.65	3.21	5.86
RESQUARED & REBUTTED PERFECTIONS, 5-1/2″ EXPOSURE						
Resquared & rebutted perfections, 5-1/2″ exposure	1.000	S.F.	.027	3.15	1.56	4.71
Building wrap, spunbonded polypropylene	1.100	S.F.	.002	.17	.13	.30
Trim, cedar	.125	S.F.	.005	.16	.29	.45
Stain, sealer & 1 coat	1.000	S.F.	.017	.17	.84	1.01
TOTAL		S.F.	.051	3.65	2.82	6.47
HAND-SPLIT SHAKES, 8-1/2″ EXPOSURE						
Hand-split red cedar shakes, 18″ long, 8-1/2″ exposure	1.000	S.F.	.040	1.97	2.34	4.31
Building wrap, spunbonded polypropylene	1.100	S.F.	.002	.17	.13	.30
Trim, cedar	.125	S.F.	.005	.16	.29	.45
Stain, sealer & 1 coat	1.000	S.F.	.017	.17	.84	1.01
TOTAL		S.F.	.064	2.47	3.60	6.07

The costs in this system are based on a square foot of wall area.
Do not subtract area for door or window openings.

Description	QUAN.	UNIT	LABOR HOURS	COST PER S.F.		
				MAT.	INST.	TOTAL

Shingle Siding Price Sheet

Shingle Siding Price Sheet	QUAN.	UNIT	LABOR HOURS	COST PER S.F.		
				MAT.	INST.	TOTAL
Shingles wood, white cedar 16" long, "A" grade, 5" exposure	1.000	S.F.	.033	2.15	1.95	4.10
7" exposure	1.000	S.F.	.030	1.94	1.76	3.70
8-1/2" exposure	1.000	S.F.	.032	1.22	1.87	3.09
10" exposure	1.000	S.F.	.028	1.07	1.64	2.71
"B" grade, 5" exposure	1.000	S.F.	.040	1.82	2.34	4.16
7" exposure	1.000	S.F.	.028	1.27	1.64	2.91
8-1/2" exposure	1.000	S.F.	.024	1.09	1.40	2.49
10" exposure	1.000	S.F.	.020	.91	1.17	2.08
Fire retardant, "A" grade, 5" exposure	1.000	S.F.	.033	2.77	1.95	4.72
7" exposure	1.000	S.F.	.028	1.70	1.64	3.34
8-1/2" exposure	1.000	S.F.	.032	1.82	1.87	3.69
10" exposure	1.000	S.F.	.025	1.41	1.46	2.87
Fire retardant, 5" exposure	1.000	S.F.	.029	3.37	1.70	5.07
7" exposure	1.000	S.F.	.036	2.64	2.08	4.72
8-1/2" exposure	1.000	S.F.	.032	2.37	1.87	4.24
10" exposure	1.000	S.F.	.025	1.84	1.46	3.30
Resquared & rebutted, 5-1/2" exposure	1.000	S.F.	.027	3.15	1.56	4.71
7" exposure	1.000	S.F.	.024	2.84	1.40	4.24
8-1/2" exposure	1.000	S.F.	.021	2.52	1.25	3.77
10" exposure	1.000	S.F.	.019	2.21	1.09	3.30
Fire retardant, 5" exposure	1.000	S.F.	.027	3.77	1.56	5.33
7" exposure	1.000	S.F.	.024	3.39	1.40	4.79
8-1/2" exposure	1.000	S.F.	.021	3.01	1.25	4.26
10" exposure	1.000	S.F.	.023	2.06	1.34	3.40
Hand-split, red cedar, 24" long, 7" exposure	1.000	S.F.	.045	4.41	2.62	7.03
8-1/2" exposure	1.000	S.F.	.038	3.78	2.24	6.02
10" exposure	1.000	S.F.	.032	3.15	1.87	5.02
12" exposure	1.000	S.F.	.026	2.52	1.50	4.02
Fire retardant, 7" exposure	1.000	S.F.	.045	5.25	2.62	7.87
8-1/2" exposure	1.000	S.F.	.038	4.52	2.24	6.76
10" exposure	1.000	S.F.	.032	3.77	1.87	5.64
12" exposure	1.000	S.F.	.026	3.01	1.50	4.51
18" long, 5" exposure	1.000	S.F.	.068	3.35	3.98	7.33
7" exposure	1.000	S.F.	.048	2.36	2.81	5.17
8-1/2" exposure	1.000	S.F.	.040	1.97	2.34	4.31
10" exposure	1.000	S.F.	.036	1.77	2.11	3.88
Fire retardant, 5" exposure	1.000	S.F.	.068	4.40	3.98	8.38
7" exposure	1.000	S.F.	.048	3.10	2.81	5.91
8-1/2" exposure	1.000	S.F.	.040	2.59	2.34	4.93
10" exposure	1.000	S.F.	.036	2.32	2.11	4.43
Paper, #15 asphalt felt	1.100	S.F.	.002	.06	.13	.19
Trim, cedar	.125	S.F.	.005	.16	.29	.45
Fir	.125	S.F.	.005	.12	.29	.41
Redwood	.125	S.F.	.005	.16	.29	.45
White pine	.125	S.F.	.005	.12	.29	.41
Painting, primer, & 1 coat	1.000	S.F.	.013	.15	.64	.79
2 coats	1.000	S.F.	.017	.23	.83	1.06
Staining, sealer, & 1 coat	1.000	S.F.	.017	.17	.84	1.01
2 coats	1.000	S.F.	.019	.27	.91	1.18

Aluminum Trim

Building Paper

Alum. Horizontal Siding

Backer Insulation Board

System Description	QUAN.	UNIT	LABOR HOURS	COST PER S.F.		
				MAT.	INST.	TOTAL
ALUMINUM CLAPBOARD SIDING, 8″ WIDE, WHITE						
Aluminum horizontal siding, 8″ clapboard	1.000	S.F.	.031	3.03	1.82	4.85
Backer, insulation board	1.000	S.F.	.008	.43	.47	.90
Trim, aluminum	.600	L.F.	.016	1.13	.92	2.05
Building wrap, spunbonded polypropylene	1.100	S.F.	.002	.17	.13	.30
TOTAL		S.F.	.057	4.76	3.34	8.10
ALUMINUM VERTICAL BOARD & BATTEN, WHITE						
Aluminum vertical board & batten	1.000	S.F.	.027	2.59	1.59	4.18
Backer insulation board	1.000	S.F.	.008	.43	.47	.90
Trim, aluminum	.600	L.F.	.016	1.13	.92	2.05
Building wrap, spunbonded polypropylene	1.100	S.F.	.002	.17	.13	.30
TOTAL		S.F.	.053	4.32	3.11	7.43
VINYL CLAPBOARD SIDING, 8″ WIDE, WHITE						
Vinyl siding, clabboard profile, smooth texture, .042 thick, single 8	1.000	S.F.	.032	.87	1.89	2.76
Backer, insulation board	1.000	S.F.	.008	.43	.47	.90
Vinyl siding, access., outside corner, woodgrain, 4″ face, 3/4″ pocket	.600	L.F.	.014	1.40	.80	2.20
Building wrap, spunbonded polypropylene	1.100	S.F.	.002	.17	.13	.30
TOTAL		S.F.	.056	2.87	3.29	6.16
VINYL VERTICAL BOARD & BATTEN, WHITE						
Vinyl siding, vertical pattern, .046 thick, double 5	1.000	S.F.	.029	1.73	1.70	3.43
Backer, insulation board	1.000	S.F.	.008	.43	.47	.90
Vinyl siding, access., outside corner, woodgrain, 4″ face, 3/4″ pocket	.600	L.F.	.014	1.40	.80	2.20
Building wrap, spunbonded polypropylene	1.100	S.F.	.002	.17	.13	.30
TOTAL		S.F.	.053	3.73	3.10	6.83

The costs in this system are on a square foot of wall basis.
Subtract openings from wall area.

Description	QUAN.	UNIT	LABOR HOURS	COST PER S.F.		
				MAT.	INST.	TOTAL

Metal & Plastic Siding Price Sheet	QUAN.	UNIT	LABOR HOURS	COST PER S.F.		
				MAT.	INST.	TOTAL
Siding, aluminum, .024" thick, smooth, 8" wide, white	1.000	S.F.	.031	3.03	1.82	4.85
Color	1.000	S.F.	.031	3.20	1.82	5.02
Double 4" pattern, 8" wide, white	1.000	S.F.	.031	3.10	1.82	4.92
Color	1.000	S.F.	.031	3.27	1.82	5.09
Double 5" pattern, 10" wide, white	1.000	S.F.	.029	3.03	1.70	4.73
Color	1.000	S.F.	.029	3.20	1.70	4.90
Embossed, single, 8" wide, white	1.000	S.F.	.031	3.04	1.82	4.86
Color	1.000	S.F.	.031	3.21	1.82	5.03
Double 4" pattern, 8" wide, white	1.000	S.F.	.031	3.08	1.82	4.90
Color	1.000	S.F.	.031	3.25	1.82	5.07
Double 5" pattern, 10" wide, white	1.000	S.F.	.029	3.10	1.70	4.80
Color	1.000	S.F.	.029	3.27	1.70	4.97
Alum siding with insulation board, smooth, 8" wide, white	1.000	S.F.	.031	2.72	1.82	4.54
Color	1.000	S.F.	.031	2.89	1.82	4.71
Double 4" pattern, 8" wide, white	1.000	S.F.	.031	2.70	1.82	4.52
Color	1.000	S.F.	.031	2.87	1.82	4.69
Double 5" pattern, 10" wide, white	1.000	S.F.	.029	2.71	1.70	4.41
Color	1.000	S.F.	.029	2.88	1.70	4.58
Embossed, single, 8" wide, white	1.000	S.F.	.031	3.14	1.82	4.96
Color	1.000	S.F.	.031	3.31	1.82	5.13
Double 4" pattern, 8" wide, white	1.000	S.F.	.031	3.16	1.82	4.98
Color	1.000	S.F.	.031	3.33	1.82	5.15
Double 5" pattern, 10" wide, white	1.000	S.F.	.029	3.16	1.70	4.86
Color	1.000	S.F.	.029	3.33	1.70	5.03
Aluminum, shake finish, 10" wide, white	1.000	S.F.	.029	3.41	1.70	5.11
Color	1.000	S.F.	.029	3.58	1.70	5.28
Aluminum, vertical, 12" wide, white	1.000	S.F.	.027	2.59	1.59	4.18
Color	1.000	S.F.	.027	2.76	1.59	4.35
Vinyl siding, 8" wide, smooth, white	1.000	S.F.	.032	.87	1.89	2.76
Color	1.000	S.F.	.032	1.04	1.89	2.93
10" wide, Dutch lap, smooth, white	1.000	S.F.	.029	1.19	1.70	2.89
Color	1.000	S.F.	.029	1.36	1.70	3.06
Double 4" pattern, 8" wide, white	1.000	S.F.	.032	.87	1.89	2.76
Color	1.000	S.F.	.032	1.04	1.89	2.93
Double 5" pattern, 10" wide, white	1.000	S.F.	.029	.87	1.70	2.57
Color	1.000	S.F.	.029	1.04	1.70	2.74
Embossed, single, 8" wide, white	1.000	S.F.	.032	1.51	1.89	3.40
Color	1.000	S.F.	.032	1.68	1.89	3.57
10" wide, white	1.000	S.F.	.029	1.81	1.70	3.51
Color	1.000	S.F.	.029	1.98	1.70	3.68
Double 4" pattern, 8" wide, white	1.000	S.F.	.032	1.17	1.89	3.06
Color	1.000	S.F.	.032	1.34	1.89	3.23
Double 5" pattern, 10" wide, white	1.000	S.F.	.029	1.17	1.70	2.87
Color	1.000	S.F.	.029	1.34	1.70	3.04
Vinyl, shake finish, 10" wide, white	1.000	S.F.	.029	4.03	2.34	6.37
Color	1.000	S.F.	.029	4.20	2.34	6.54
Vinyl, vertical, double 5" pattern, 10" wide, white	1.000	S.F.	.029	1.73	1.70	3.43
Color	1.000	S.F.	.029	1.90	1.70	3.60
Backer board, installed in siding panels 8" or 10" wide	1.000	S.F.	.008	.43	.47	.90
4' x 8' sheets, polystyrene, 3/4" thick	1.000	S.F.	.010	.63	.58	1.21
4' x 8' fiberboard, plain	1.000	S.F.	.008	.43	.47	.90
Trim, aluminum, white	.600	L.F.	.016	1.13	.92	2.05
Color	.600	L.F.	.016	1.22	.92	2.14
Vinyl, white	.600	L.F.	.014	1.40	.80	2.20
Color	.600	L.F.	.014	1.60	.80	2.40
Paper, #15 asphalt felt	1.100	S.F.	.002	.07	.14	.21
Kraft paper, plain	1.100	S.F.	.002	.14	.14	.28
Foil backed	1.100	S.F.	.002	.17	.14	.31

Description	QUAN.	UNIT	LABOR HOURS	COST PER S.F.		
				MAT.	INST.	TOTAL
Poured insulation, cellulose fiber, R3.8 per inch (1" thick)	1.000	S.F.	.003	.06	.19	.25
Fiberglass , R4.0 per inch (1" thick)	1.000	S.F.	.003	.05	.19	.24
Mineral wool, R3.0 per inch (1" thick)	1.000	S.F.	.003	.04	.19	.23
Polystyrene, R4.0 per inch (1" thick)	1.000	S.F.	.003	.15	.19	.34
Vermiculite, R2.7 per inch (1" thick)	1.000	S.F.	.003	.48	.19	.67
Perlite, R2.7 per inch (1" thick)	1.000	S.F.	.003	.48	.19	.67
Reflective insulation, aluminum foil reinforced with scrim	1.000	S.F.	.004	.17	.25	.42
Reinforced with woven polyolefin	1.000	S.F.	.004	.25	.25	.50
With single bubble air space, R8.8	1.000	S.F.	.005	.29	.31	.60
With double bubble air space, R9.8	1.000	S.F.	.005	.35	.31	.66
Rigid insulation, fiberglass, unfaced,						
1-1/2" thick, R6.2	1.000	S.F.	.008	.43	.47	.90
2" thick, R8.3	1.000	S.F.	.008	.54	.47	1.01
2-1/2" thick, R10.3	1.000	S.F.	.010	.63	.58	1.21
3" thick, R12.4	1.000	S.F.	.010	.63	.58	1.21
Foil faced, 1" thick, R4.3	1.000	S.F.	.008	.99	.47	1.46
1-1/2" thick, R6.2	1.000	S.F.	.008	1.49	.47	1.96
2" thick, R8.7	1.000	S.F.	.009	1.87	.53	2.40
2-1/2" thick, R10.9	1.000	S.F.	.010	2.20	.58	2.78
3" thick, R13.0	1.000	S.F.	.010	2.48	.58	3.06
Perlite, 1" thick R2.77	1.000	S.F.	.010	.50	.58	1.08
2" thick R5.55	1.000	S.F.	.011	.86	.64	1.50
Polystyrene, extruded, blue, 2.2#/C.F., 3/4" thick R4	1.000	S.F.	.010	.63	.58	1.21
1-1/2" thick R8.1	1.000	S.F.	.011	1.25	.64	1.89
2" thick R10.8	1.000	S.F.	.011	1.75	.64	2.39
Molded bead board, white, 1" thick R3.85	1.000	S.F.	.010	.29	.58	.87
1-1/2" thick, R5.6	1.000	S.F.	.011	.57	.64	1.21
2" thick, R7.7	1.000	S.F.	.011	.86	.64	1.50
Non-rigid insulation, batts						
Fiberglass, kraft faced, 3-1/2" thick, R13, 11" wide	1.000	S.F.	.005	.36	.41	.77
15" wide	1.000	S.F.	.005	.36	.41	.77
23" wide	1.000	S.F.	.005	.36	.41	.77
6" thick, R19, 11" wide	1.000	S.F.	.006	.50	.41	.91
15" wide	1.000	S.F.	.006	.50	.41	.91
23" wide	1.000	S.F.	.006	.50	.41	.91
9" thick, R30, 15" wide	1.000	S.F.	.006	.83	.35	1.18
23" wide	1.000	S.F.	.006	.83	.35	1.18
12" thick, R38, 15" wide	1.000	S.F.	.006	1.19	.35	1.54
23" wide	1.000	S.F.	.006	1.19	.35	1.54
Fiberglass, foil faced, 3-1/2" thick, R13, 15" wide	1.000	S.F.	.005	.53	.35	.88
23" wide	1.000	S.F.	.005	.53	.35	.88
6" thick, R19, 15" thick	1.000	S.F.	.005	.70	.29	.99
23" wide	1.000	S.F.	.005	.70	.29	.99
9" thick, R30, 15" wide	1.000	S.F.	.006	1.07	.35	1.42
23" wide	1.000	S.F.	.006	1.07	.35	1.42

Insulation Systems	QUAN.	UNIT	LABOR HOURS	COST PER S.F.		
				MAT.	INST.	TOTAL
Non-rigid insulation batts						
Fiberglass unfaced, 3-1/2" thick, R13, 15" wide	1.000	S.F.	.005	.37	.29	.66
23" wide	1.000	S.F.	.005	.37	.29	.66
6" thick, R19, 15" wide	1.000	S.F.	.006	.44	.35	.79
23" wide	1.000	S.F.	.006	.44	.35	.79
9" thick, R19, 15" wide	1.000	S.F.	.007	.68	.41	1.09
23" wide	1.000	S.F.	.007	.68	.41	1.09
12" thick, R38, 15" wide	1.000	S.F.	.007	.85	.41	1.26
23" wide	1.000	S.F.	.007	.85	.41	1.26
Mineral fiber batts, 3" thick, R11	1.000	S.F.	.005	.77	.29	1.06
3-1/2" thick, R13	1.000	S.F.	.005	.77	.29	1.06
6" thick, R19	1.000	S.F.	.005	1.21	.29	1.50
6-1/2" thick, R22	1.000	S.F.	.005	1.21	.29	1.50
10" thick, R30	1.000	S.F.	.006	1.60	.35	1.95

Drip Cap

Snap-in Grille

Caulking

Interior Trim

Window

System Description	QUAN.	UNIT	LABOR HOURS	COST EACH		
				MAT.	INST.	TOTAL
BUILDER'S QUALITY WOOD WINDOW 2' X 3', DOUBLE HUNG						
Window, primed, builder's quality, 2' x 3', insulating glass	1.000	Ea.	.800	264	47	311
Trim, interior casing	11.000	L.F.	.352	17.05	20.57	37.62
Paint, interior & exterior, primer & 2 coats	2.000	Face	1.778	2.72	86	88.72
Caulking	10.000	L.F.	.278	2.50	16.30	18.80
Snap-in grille	1.000	Set	.333	61.50	19.50	81
Drip cap, metal	2.000	L.F.	.040	1.26	2.34	3.60
TOTAL		Ea.	3.581	349.03	191.71	540.74
PLASTIC CLAD WOOD WINDOW 3' X 4', DOUBLE HUNG						
Window, plastic clad, premium, 3' x 4', insulating glass	1.000	Ea.	.889	435	52	487
Trim, interior casing	15.000	L.F.	.480	23.25	28.05	51.30
Paint, interior, primer & 2 coats	1.000	Face	.889	1.36	43	44.36
Caulking	14.000	L.F.	.389	3.50	22.82	26.32
Snap-in grille	1.000	Set	.333	61.50	19.50	81
TOTAL		Ea.	2.980	524.61	165.37	689.98
METAL CLAD WOOD WINDOW, 3' X 5', DOUBLE HUNG						
Window, metal clad, deluxe, 3' x 5', insulating glass	1.000	Ea.	1.000	415	58.50	473.50
Trim, interior casing	17.000	L.F.	.544	26.35	31.79	58.14
Paint, interior, primer & 2 coats	1.000	Face	.889	1.36	43	44.36
Caulking	16.000	L.F.	.444	4	26.08	30.08
Snap-in grille	1.000	Set	.235	154	13.75	167.75
Drip cap, metal	3.000	L.F.	.060	1.89	3.51	5.40
TOTAL		Ea.	3.172	602.60	176.63	779.23

The cost of this system is on a cost per each window basis.

Description	QUAN.	UNIT	LABOR HOURS	COST EACH		
				MAT.	INST.	TOTAL

Double Hung Window Price Sheet	QUAN.	UNIT	LABOR HOURS	COST EACH		
				MAT.	INST.	TOTAL
Windows, double-hung, builder's quality, 2' x 3', single glass	1.000	Ea.	.800	212	47	259
Insulating glass	1.000	Ea.	.800	264	47	311
3' x 4', single glass	1.000	Ea.	.889	310	52	362
Insulating glass	1.000	Ea.	.889	320	52	372
4' x 4'-6", single glass	1.000	Ea.	1.000	365	58.50	423.50
Insulating glass	1.000	Ea.	1.000	390	58.50	448.50
Plastic clad premium insulating glass, 2'-6" x 3'	1.000	Ea.	.800	370	47	417
3' x 3'-6"	1.000	Ea.	.800	370	47	417
3' x 4'	1.000	Ea.	.889	435	52	487
3' x 4'-6"	1.000	Ea.	.889	460	52	512
3' x 5'	1.000	Ea.	1.000	495	58.50	553.50
3'-6" x 6'	1.000	Ea.	1.000	555	58.50	613.50
Metal clad deluxe insulating glass, 2'-6" x 3'	1.000	Ea.	.800	310	47	357
3' x 3'-6"	1.000	Ea.	.800	350	47	397
3' x 4'	1.000	Ea.	.889	370	52	422
3' x 4'-6"	1.000	Ea.	.889	385	52	437
3' x 5'	1.000	Ea.	1.000	415	58.50	473.50
3'-6" x 6'	1.000	Ea.	1.000	505	58.50	563.50
Trim, interior casing, window 2' x 3'	11.000	L.F.	.367	17.05	20.50	37.55
2'-6" x 3'	12.000	L.F.	.400	18.60	22.50	41.10
3' x 3'-6"	14.000	L.F.	.467	21.50	26	47.50
3' x 4'	15.000	L.F.	.500	23.50	28	51.50
3' x 4'-6"	16.000	L.F.	.533	25	30	55
3' x 5'	17.000	L.F.	.567	26.50	32	58.50
3'-6" x 6'	20.000	L.F.	.667	31	37.50	68.50
4' x 4'-6"	18.000	L.F.	.600	28	33.50	61.50
Paint or stain, interior or exterior, 2' x 3' window, 1 coat	1.000	Face	.444	.47	21.50	21.97
2 coats	1.000	Face	.727	.93	35	35.93
Primer & 1 coat	1.000	Face	.727	.90	35	35.90
Primer & 2 coats	1.000	Face	.889	1.36	43	44.36
3' x 4' window, 1 coat	1.000	Face	.667	1.06	32	33.06
2 coats	1.000	Face	.667	1.70	32	33.70
Primer & 1 coat	1.000	Face	.727	1.39	35	36.39
Primer & 2 coats	1.000	Face	.889	1.36	43	44.36
4' x 4'-6" window, 1 coat	1.000	Face	.667	1.06	32	33.06
2 coats	1.000	Face	.667	1.70	32	33.70
Primer & 1 coat	1.000	Face	.727	1.39	35	36.39
Primer & 2 coats	1.000	Face	.889	1.36	43	44.36
Caulking, window, 2' x 3'	10.000	L.F.	.323	2.50	16.30	18.80
2'-6" x 3'	11.000	L.F.	.355	2.75	17.95	20.70
3' x 3'-6"	13.000	L.F.	.419	3.25	21	24.25
3' x 4'	14.000	L.F.	.452	3.50	23	26.50
3' x 4'-6"	15.000	L.F.	.484	3.75	24.50	28.25
3' x 5'	16.000	L.F.	.516	4	26	30
3'-6" x 6'	19.000	L.F.	.613	4.75	31	35.75
4' x 4'-6"	17.000	L.F.	.548	4.25	27.50	31.75
Grilles, glass size to, 16" x 24" per sash	1.000	Set	.333	61.50	19.50	81
32" x 32" per sash	1.000	Set	.235	154	13.75	167.75
Drip cap, aluminum, 2' long	2.000	L.F.	.040	1.26	2.34	3.60
3' long	3.000	L.F.	.060	1.89	3.51	5.40
4' long	4.000	L.F.	.080	2.52	4.68	7.20
Wood, 2' long	2.000	L.F.	.067	3.10	3.74	6.84
3' long	3.000	L.F.	.100	4.65	5.60	10.25
4' long	4.000	L.F.	.133	6.20	7.50	13.70

Drip Cap

Snap-in Grille

Interior Trim

Caulking

Window

System Description	QUAN.	UNIT	LABOR HOURS	COST EACH		
				MAT.	INST.	TOTAL
BUILDER'S QUALITY WINDOW, WOOD, 2' BY 3', CASEMENT						
Window, primed, builder's quality, 2' x 3', insulating glass	1.000	Ea.	.800	293	47	340
Trim, interior casing	11.000	L.F.	.352	17.05	20.57	37.62
Paint, interior & exterior, primer & 2 coats	2.000	Face	1.778	2.72	86	88.72
Caulking	10.000	L.F.	.278	2.50	16.30	18.80
Snap-in grille	1.000	Ea.	.267	37	15.60	52.60
Drip cap, metal	2.000	L.F.	.040	1.26	2.34	3.60
TOTAL		Ea.	3.515	353.53	187.81	541.34
PLASTIC CLAD WOOD WINDOW, 2' X 4', CASEMENT						
Window, plastic clad, premium, 2' x 4', insulating glass	1.000	Ea.	.889	350	52	402
Trim, interior casing	13.000	L.F.	.416	20.15	24.31	44.46
Paint, interior, primer & 2 coats	1.000	Ea.	.889	1.36	43	44.36
Caulking	12.000	L.F.	.333	3	19.56	22.56
Snap-in grille	1.000	Ea.	.267	37	15.60	52.60
TOTAL		Ea.	2.794	411.51	154.47	565.98
METAL CLAD WOOD WINDOW, 2' X 5', CASEMENT						
Window, metal clad, deluxe, 2' x 5', insulating glass	1.000	Ea.	1.000	365	58.50	423.50
Trim, interior casing	15.000	L.F.	.480	23.25	28.05	51.30
Paint, interior, primer & 2 coats	1.000	Ea.	.889	1.36	43	44.36
Caulking	14.000	L.F.	.389	3.50	22.82	26.32
Snap-in grille	1.000	Ea.	.250	51	14.60	65.60
Drip cap, metal	12.000	L.F.	.040	1.26	2.34	3.60
TOTAL		Ea.	3.048	445.37	169.31	614.68

The cost of this system is on a cost per each window basis.

Description	QUAN.	UNIT	LABOR HOURS	COST EACH		
				MAT.	INST.	TOTAL

Casement Window Price Sheet

Casement Window Price Sheet	QUAN.	UNIT	LABOR HOURS	COST EACH		
				MAT.	INST.	TOTAL
Window, casement, builders quality, 2' x 3', double insulated glass	1.000	Ea.	.800	300	47	347
Insulating glass	1.000	Ea.	.800	293	47	340
2' x 4'-6", double insulated glass	1.000	Ea.	.727	980	42.50	1,022.50
Insulating glass	1.000	Ea.	.727	600	42.50	642.50
2' x 6', double insulated glass	1.000	Ea.	.889	490	58.50	548.50
Insulating glass	1.000	Ea.	.889	485	58.50	543.50
Plastic clad premium insulating glass, 2' x 3'	1.000	Ea.	.800	297	47	344
2' x 4'	1.000	Ea.	.889	455	52	507
2' x 5'	1.000	Ea.	1.000	610	58.50	668.50
2' x 6'	1.000	Ea.	1.000	430	58.50	488.50
Metal clad deluxe insulating glass, 2' x 3'	1.000	Ea.	.800	315	47	362
2' x 4'	1.000	Ea.	.889	310	52	362
2' x 5'	1.000	Ea.	1.000	355	58.50	413.50
2' x 6'	1.000	Ea.	1.000	405	58.50	463.50
Trim, interior casing, window 2' x 3'	11.000	L.F.	.367	17.05	20.50	37.55
2' x 4'	13.000	L.F.	.433	20	24.50	44.50
2' x 4'-6"	14.000	L.F.	.467	21.50	26	47.50
2' x 5'	15.000	L.F.	.500	23.50	28	51.50
2' x 6'	17.000	L.F.	.567	26.50	32	58.50
Paint or stain, interior or exterior, 2' x 3' window, 1 coat	1.000	Face	.444	.47	21.50	21.97
2 coats	1.000	Face	.727	.93	35	35.93
Primer & 1 coat	1.000	Face	.727	.90	35	35.90
Primer & 2 coats	1.000	Face	.889	1.36	43	44.36
2' x 4' window, 1 coat	1.000	Face	.444	.47	21.50	21.97
2 coats	1.000	Face	.727	.93	35	35.93
Primer & 1 coat	1.000	Face	.727	.90	35	35.90
Primer & 2 coats	1.000	Face	.889	1.36	43	44.36
2' x 6' window, 1 coat	1.000	Face	.667	1.06	32	33.06
2 coats	1.000	Face	.667	1.70	32	33.70
Primer & 1 coat	1.000	Face	.727	1.39	35	36.39
Primer & 2 coats	1.000	Face	.889	1.36	43	44.36
Caulking, window, 2' x 3'	10.000	L.F.	.323	2.50	16.30	18.80
2' x 4'	12.000	L.F.	.387	3	19.55	22.55
2' x 4'-6"	13.000	L.F.	.419	3.25	21	24.25
2' x 5'	14.000	L.F.	.452	3.50	23	26.50
2' x 6'	16.000	L.F.	.516	4	26	30
Grilles, glass size, to 20" x 36"	1.000	Ea.	.267	37	15.60	52.60
To 20" x 56"	1.000	Ea.	.250	51	14.60	65.60
Drip cap, metal, 2' long	2.000	L.F.	.040	1.26	2.34	3.60
Wood, 2' long	2.000	L.F.	.067	3.10	3.74	6.84

Drip Cap — Interior Trim
Snap-in Grille
Caulking — Window

System Description	QUAN.	UNIT	LABOR HOURS	COST EACH		
				MAT.	INST.	TOTAL
BUILDER'S QUALITY WINDOW, WOOD, 34" X 22", AWNING						
Window, 34" x 22", insulating glass	1.000	Ea.	.800	330	47	377
Trim, interior casing	10.500	L.F.	.336	16.28	19.64	35.92
Paint, interior & exterior, primer & 2 coats	2.000	Face	1.778	2.72	86	88.72
Caulking	9.500	L.F.	.264	2.38	15.49	17.87
Snap-in grille	1.000	Ea.	.267	33.50	15.60	49.10
Drip cap, metal	3.000	L.F.	.060	1.89	3.51	5.40
TOTAL		Ea.	3.505	386.77	187.24	574.01
PLASTIC CLAD WOOD WINDOW, 40" X 28", AWNING						
Window, plastic clad, premium, 40" x 28", insulating glass	1.000	Ea.	.889	385	52	437
Trim interior casing	13.500	L.F.	.432	20.93	25.25	46.18
Paint, interior, primer & 2 coats	1.000	Face	.889	1.36	43	44.36
Caulking	12.500	L.F.	.347	3.13	20.38	23.51
Snap-in grille	1.000	Ea.	.267	33.50	15.60	49.10
TOTAL		Ea.	2.824	443.92	156.23	600.15
METAL CLAD WOOD WINDOW, 48" X 36", AWNING						
Window, metal clad, deluxe, 48" x 36", insulating glass	1.000	Ea.	1.000	410	58.50	468.50
Trim, interior casing	15.000	L.F.	.480	23.25	28.05	51.30
Paint, interior, primer & 2 coats	1.000	Face	.889	1.36	43	44.36
Caulking	14.000	L.F.	.389	3.50	22.82	26.32
Snap-in grille	1.000	Ea.	.250	48.50	14.60	63.10
Drip cap, metal	4.000	L.F.	.080	2.52	4.68	7.20
TOTAL		Ea.	3.088	489.13	171.65	660.78

The cost of this system is on a cost per each window basis.

Description	QUAN.	UNIT	LABOR HOURS	COST EACH		
				MAT.	INST.	TOTAL

Awning Window Price Sheet

Awning Window Price Sheet	QUAN.	UNIT	LABOR HOURS	COST EACH MAT.	COST EACH INST.	COST EACH TOTAL
Windows, awning, builder's quality, 34" x 22", insulated glass	1.000	Ea.	.800	305	47	352
Low E glass	1.000	Ea.	.800	330	47	377
40" x 28", insulated glass	1.000	Ea.	.889	345	52	397
Low E glass	1.000	Ea.	.889	380	52	432
48" x 36", insulated glass	1.000	Ea.	1.000	515	58.50	573.50
Low E glass	1.000	Ea.	1.000	545	58.50	603.50
Plastic clad premium insulating glass, 34" x 22"	1.000	Ea.	.800	294	47	341
40" x 22"	1.000	Ea.	.800	325	47	372
36" x 28"	1.000	Ea.	.889	340	52	392
36" x 36"	1.000	Ea.	.889	385	52	437
48" x 28"	1.000	Ea.	1.000	410	58.50	468.50
60" x 36"	1.000	Ea.	1.000	570	58.50	628.50
Metal clad deluxe insulating glass, 34" x 22"	1.000	Ea.	.800	281	52	333
40" x 22"	1.000	Ea.	.800	325	52	377
36" x 25"	1.000	Ea.	.889	305	52	357
40" x 30"	1.000	Ea.	.889	375	52	427
48" x 28"	1.000	Ea.	1.000	385	58.50	443.50
60" x 36"	1.000	Ea.	1.000	410	58.50	468.50
Trim, interior casing window, 34" x 22"	10.500	L.F.	.350	16.30	19.65	35.95
40" x 22"	11.500	L.F.	.383	17.85	21.50	39.35
36" x 28"	12.500	L.F.	.417	19.40	23.50	42.90
40" x 28"	13.500	L.F.	.450	21	25.50	46.50
48" x 28"	14.500	L.F.	.483	22.50	27	49.50
48" x 36"	15.000	L.F.	.500	23.50	28	51.50
Paint or stain, interior or exterior, 34" x 22", 1 coat	1.000	Face	.444	.47	21.50	21.97
2 coats	1.000	Face	.727	.93	35	35.93
Primer & 1 coat	1.000	Face	.727	.90	35	35.90
Primer & 2 coats	1.000	Face	.889	1.36	43	44.36
36" x 28", 1 coat	1.000	Face	.444	.47	21.50	21.97
2 coats	1.000	Face	.727	.93	35	35.93
Primer & 1 coat	1.000	Face	.727	.90	35	35.90
Primer & 2 coats	1.000	Face	.889	1.36	43	44.36
48" x 36", 1 coat	1.000	Face	.667	1.06	32	33.06
2 coats	1.000	Face	.667	1.70	32	33.70
Primer & 1 coat	1.000	Face	.727	1.39	35	36.39
Primer & 2 coats	1.000	Face	.889	1.36	43	44.36
Caulking, window, 34" x 22"	9.500	L.F.	.306	2.38	15.50	17.88
40" x 22"	10.500	L.F.	.339	2.63	17.10	19.73
36" x 28"	11.500	L.F.	.371	2.88	18.75	21.63
40" x 28"	12.500	L.F.	.403	3.13	20.50	23.63
48" x 28"	13.500	L.F.	.436	3.38	22	25.38
48" x 36"	14.000	L.F.	.452	3.50	23	26.50
Grilles, glass size, to 28" by 16"	1.000	Ea.	.267	33.50	15.60	49.10
To 44" by 24"	1.000	Ea.	.250	48.50	14.60	63.10
Drip cap, aluminum, 3' long	3.000	L.F.	.060	1.89	3.51	5.40
3'-6" long	3.500	L.F.	.070	2.21	4.10	6.31
4' long	4.000	L.F.	.080	2.52	4.68	7.20
Wood, 3' long	3.000	L.F.	.100	4.65	5.60	10.25
3'-6" long	3.500	L.F.	.117	5.45	6.55	12
4' long	4.000	L.F.	.133	6.20	7.50	13.70

Drip Cap
Snap-in Grille
Caulking
Interior Trim
Window

System Description	QUAN.	UNIT	LABOR HOURS	COST EACH		
				MAT.	INST.	TOTAL
BUILDER'S QUALITY WOOD WINDOW, 3' X 2', SLIDING						
Window, primed, builder's quality, 3' x 3', insul. glass	1.000	Ea.	.800	350	47	397
Trim, interior casing	11.000	L.F.	.352	17.05	20.57	37.62
Paint, interior & exterior, primer & 2 coats	2.000	Face	1.778	2.72	86	88.72
Caulking	10.000	L.F.	.278	2.50	16.30	18.80
Snap-in grille	1.000	Set	.333	41.50	19.50	61
Drip cap, metal	3.000	L.F.	.060	1.89	3.51	5.40
TOTAL		Ea.	3.601	415.66	192.88	608.54
PLASTIC CLAD WOOD WINDOW, 4' X 3'-6", SLIDING						
Window, plastic clad, premium, 4' x 3'-6", insulating glass	1.000	Ea.	.889	760	52	812
Trim, interior casing	16.000	L.F.	.512	24.80	29.92	54.72
Paint, interior, primer & 2 coats	1.000	Face	.889	1.36	43	44.36
Caulking	17.000	L.F.	.472	4.25	27.71	31.96
Snap-in grille	1.000	Set	.333	41.50	19.50	61
TOTAL		Ea.	3.095	831.91	172.13	1,004.04
METAL CLAD WOOD WINDOW, 6' X 5', SLIDING						
Window, metal clad, deluxe, 6' x 5', insulating glass	1.000	Ea.	1.000	820	58.50	878.50
Trim, interior casing	23.000	L.F.	.736	35.65	43.01	78.66
Paint, interior, primer & 2 coats	1.000	Face	.889	1.36	43	44.36
Caulking	22.000	L.F.	.611	5.50	35.86	41.36
Snap-in grille	1.000	Set	.364	49.50	21.50	71
Drip cap, metal	6.000	L.F.	.120	3.78	7.02	10.80
TOTAL		Ea.	3.720	915.79	208.89	1,124.68

The cost of this system is on a cost per each window basis.

Description	QUAN.	UNIT	LABOR HOURS	COST EACH		
				MAT.	INST.	TOTAL

Sliding Window Price Sheet

Sliding Window Price Sheet	QUAN.	UNIT	LABOR HOURS	COST EACH MAT.	INST.	TOTAL
Windows, sliding, builder's quality, 3' x 3', single glass	1.000	Ea.	.800	320	47	367
Insulating glass	1.000	Ea.	.800	350	47	397
4' x 3'-6", single glass	1.000	Ea.	.889	420	52	472
Insulating glass	1.000	Ea.	.889	420	52	472
6' x 5', single glass	1.000	Ea.	1.000	555	58.50	613.50
Insulating glass	1.000	Ea.	1.000	605	58.50	663.50
Plastic clad premium insulating glass, 3' x 3'	1.000	Ea.	.800	685	47	732
4' x 3'-6"	1.000	Ea.	.889	760	52	812
5' x 4'	1.000	Ea.	.889	1,000	52	1,052
6' x 5'	1.000	Ea.	1.000	1,275	58.50	1,333.50
Metal clad deluxe insulating glass, 3' x 3'	1.000	Ea.	.800	360	47	407
4' x 3'-6"	1.000	Ea.	.889	440	52	492
5' x 4'	1.000	Ea.	.889	525	52	577
6' x 5'	1.000	Ea.	1.000	820	58.50	878.50
Trim, interior casing, window 3' x 2'	11.000	L.F.	.367	17.05	20.50	37.55
3' x 3'	13.000	L.F.	.433	20	24.50	44.50
4' x 3'-6"	16.000	L.F.	.533	25	30	55
5' x 4'	19.000	L.F.	.633	29.50	35.50	65
6' x 5'	23.000	L.F.	.767	35.50	43	78.50
Paint or stain, interior or exterior, 3' x 2' window, 1 coat	1.000	Face	.444	.47	21.50	21.97
2 coats	1.000	Face	.727	.93	35	35.93
Primer & 1 coat	1.000	Face	.727	.90	35	35.90
Primer & 2 coats	1.000	Face	.889	1.36	43	44.36
4' x 3'-6" window, 1 coat	1.000	Face	.667	1.06	32	33.06
2 coats	1.000	Face	.667	1.70	32	33.70
Primer & 1 coat	1.000	Face	.727	1.39	35	36.39
Primer & 2 coats	1.000	Face	.889	1.36	43	44.36
6' x 5' window, 1 coat	1.000	Face	.889	2.64	43	45.64
2 coats	1.000	Face	1.333	4.82	64.50	69.32
Primer & 1 coat	1.000	Face	1.333	4.79	64.50	69.29
Primer & 2 coats	1.000	Face	1.600	7.25	77	84.25
Caulking, window, 3' x 2'	10.000	L.F.	.323	2.50	16.30	18.80
3' x 3'	12.000	L.F.	.387	3	19.55	22.55
4' x 3'-6"	15.000	L.F.	.484	3.75	24.50	28.25
5' x 4'	18.000	L.F.	.581	4.50	29.50	34
6' x 5'	22.000	L.F.	.710	5.50	36	41.50
Grilles, glass size, to 14" x 36"	1.000	Set	.333	41.50	19.50	61
To 36" x 36"	1.000	Set	.364	49.50	21.50	71
Drip cap, aluminum, 3' long	3.000	L.F.	.060	1.89	3.51	5.40
4' long	4.000	L.F.	.080	2.52	4.68	7.20
5' long	5.000	L.F.	.100	3.15	5.85	9
6' long	6.000	L.F.	.120	3.78	7	10.78
Wood, 3' long	3.000	L.F.	.100	4.65	5.60	10.25
4' long	4.000	L.F.	.133	6.20	7.50	13.70
5' long	5.000	L.F.	.167	7.75	9.35	17.10
6' long	6.000	L.F.	.200	9.30	11.20	20.50

For customer support on your Residential Costs with RSMeans Data, call 800.448.8182.

177

Drip Cap

Caulking

Snap-in Grille

Window

System Description	QUAN.	UNIT	LABOR HOURS	COST EACH		
				MAT.	INST.	TOTAL
AWNING TYPE BOW WINDOW, BUILDER'S QUALITY, 8' X 5'						
Window, primed, builder's quality, 8' x 5', insulating glass	1.000	Ea.	1.600	1,450	93.50	1,543.50
Trim, interior casing	27.000	L.F.	.864	41.85	50.49	92.34
Paint, interior & exterior, primer & 1 coat	2.000	Face	3.200	14.50	154	168.50
Caulking	26.000	L.F.	.722	6.50	42.38	48.88
Snap-in grilles	1.000	Set	1.067	148	62.40	210.40
TOTAL		Ea.	7.453	1,660.85	402.77	2,063.62
CASEMENT TYPE BOW WINDOW, PLASTIC CLAD, 10' X 6'						
Window, plastic clad, premium, 10' x 6', insulating glass	1.000	Ea.	2.286	3,075	134	3,209
Trim, interior casing	33.000	L.F.	1.056	51.15	61.71	112.86
Paint, interior, primer & 1 coat	1.000	Face	1.778	2.72	86	88.72
Caulking	32.000	L.F.	.889	8	52.16	60.16
Snap-in grilles	1.000	Set	1.333	185	78	263
TOTAL		Ea.	7.342	3,321.87	411.87	3,733.74
DOUBLE HUNG TYPE, METAL CLAD, 9' X 5'						
Window, metal clad, deluxe, 9' x 5', insulating glass	1.000	Ea.	2.667	1,625	156	1,781
Trim, interior casing	29.000	L.F.	.928	44.95	54.23	99.18
Paint, interior, primer & 1 coat	1.000	Face	1.778	2.72	86	88.72
Caulking	28.000	L.F.	.778	7	45.64	52.64
Snap-in grilles	1.000	Set	1.067	148	62.40	210.40
TOTAL		Ea.	7.218	1,827.67	404.27	2,231.94

The cost of this system is on a cost per each window basis.

Description	QUAN.	UNIT	LABOR HOURS	COST EACH		
				MAT.	INST.	TOTAL

Bow/Bay Window Price Sheet

Bow/Bay Window Price Sheet	QUAN.	UNIT	LABOR HOURS	COST EACH		
				MAT.	INST.	TOTAL
Windows, bow awning type, builder's quality, 8' x 5', insulating glass	1.000	Ea.	1.600	1,725	93.50	1,818.50
Low E glass	1.000	Ea.	1.600	1,450	93.50	1,543.50
12' x 6', insulating glass	1.000	Ea.	2.667	1,500	156	1,656
Low E glass	1.000	Ea.	2.667	1,600	156	1,756
Plastic clad premium insulating glass, 6' x 4'	1.000	Ea.	1.600	1,150	93.50	1,243.50
9' x 4'	1.000	Ea.	2.000	1,575	117	1,692
10' x 5'	1.000	Ea.	2.286	2,575	134	2,709
12' x 6'	1.000	Ea.	2.667	3,375	156	3,531
Metal clad deluxe insulating glass, 6' x 4'	1.000	Ea.	1.600	1,325	93.50	1,418.50
9' x 4'	1.000	Ea.	2.000	1,700	117	1,817
10' x 5'	1.000	Ea.	2.286	2,325	134	2,459
12' x 6'	1.000	Ea.	2.667	2,950	156	3,106
Bow casement type, builder's quality, 8' x 5', single glass	1.000	Ea.	1.600	2,100	93.50	2,193.50
Insulating glass	1.000	Ea.	1.600	2,550	93.50	2,643.50
12' x 6', single glass	1.000	Ea.	2.667	2,625	156	2781
Insulating glass	1.000	Ea.	2.667	3,575	156	3,731
Plastic clad premium insulating glass, 8' x 5'	1.000	Ea.	1.600	1,975	93.50	2,068.50
10' x 5'	1.000	Ea.	2.000	2,650	117	2,767
10' x 6'	1.000	Ea.	2.286	3,075	134	3,209
12' x 6'	1.000	Ea.	2.667	3,700	156	3,856
Metal clad deluxe insulating glass, 8' x 5'	1.000	Ea.	1.600	1,875	93.50	1,968.50
10' x 5'	1.000	Ea.	2.000	2,000	117	2,117
10' x 6'	1.000	Ea.	2.286	2,375	134	2,509
12' x 6'	1.000	Ea.	2.667	3,225	156	3,381
Bow, double hung type, builder's quality, 8' x 4', single glass	1.000	Ea.	1.600	1,475	93.50	1,568.50
Insulating glass	1.000	Ea.	1.600	1,600	93.50	1,693.50
9' x 5', single glass	1.000	Ea.	2.667	1,600	156	1,756
Insulating glass	1.000	Ea.	2.667	1,675	156	1,831
Plastic clad premium insulating glass, 7' x 4'	1.000	Ea.	1.600	1,525	93.50	1,618.50
8' x 4'	1.000	Ea.	2.000	1,550	117	1,667
8' x 5'	1.000	Ea.	2.286	1,650	134	1,784
9' x 5'	1.000	Ea.	2.667	1,675	156	1,831
Metal clad deluxe insulating glass, 7' x 4'	1.000	Ea.	1.600	1,425	93.50	1,518.50
8' x 4'	1.000	Ea.	2.000	1,475	117	1,592
8' x 5'	1.000	Ea.	2.286	1,525	134	1,659
9' x 5'	1.000	Ea.	2.667	1,625	156	1,781
Trim, interior casing, window 7' x 4'	1.000	Ea.	.767	35.50	43	78.50
8' x 5'	1.000	Ea.	.900	42	50.50	92.50
10' x 6'	1.000	Ea.	1.100	51	61.50	112.50
12' x 6'	1.000	Ea.	1.233	57.50	69	126.50
Paint or stain, interior, or exterior, 7' x 4' window, 1 coat	1.000	Face	.889	2.64	43	45.64
Primer & 1 coat	1.000	Face	1.333	4.79	64.50	69.29
8' x 5' window, 1 coat	1.000	Face	.889	2.64	43	45.64
Primer & 1 coat	1.000	Face	1.333	4.79	64.50	69.29
10' x 6' window, 1 coat	1.000	Face	1.333	2.12	64	66.12
Primer & 1 coat	1.000	Face	1.778	2.72	86	88.72
12' x 6' window, 1 coat	1.000	Face	1.778	5.30	86	91.30
Primer & 1 coat	1.000	Face	2.667	9.60	129	138.60
Drip cap, vinyl moulded window, 7' long	1.000	Ea.	.533	125	24.50	149.50
8' long	1.000	Ea.	.533	143	28	171
Caulking, window, 7' x 4'	1.000	Ea.	.710	5.50	36	41.50
8' x 5'	1.000	Ea.	.839	6.50	42.50	49
10' x 6'	1.000	Ea.	1.032	8	52	60
12' x 6'	1.000	Ea.	1.161	9	58.50	67.50
Grilles, window, 7' x 4'	1.000	Set	.800	111	47	158
8' x 5'	1.000	Set	1.067	148	62.50	210.50
10' x 6'	1.000	Set	1.333	185	78	263
12' x 6'	1.000	Set	1.600	222	93.50	315.50

System Description	QUAN.	UNIT	LABOR HOURS	COST EACH		
				MAT.	INST.	TOTAL
BUILDER'S QUALITY PICTURE WINDOW, 4' X 4'						
Window, primed, builder's quality, 3'-0" x 4', insulating glass	1.000	Ea.	1.333	490	78	568
Trim, interior casing	17.000	L.F.	.544	26.35	31.79	58.14
Paint, interior & exterior, primer & 2 coats	2.000	Face	1.778	2.72	86	88.72
Caulking	16.000	L.F.	.444	4	26.08	30.08
Snap-in grille	1.000	Ea.	.267	141	15.60	156.60
Drip cap, metal	4.000	L.F.	.080	2.52	4.68	7.20
TOTAL		Ea.	4.446	666.59	242.15	908.74
PLASTIC CLAD WOOD WINDOW, 4'-6" X 6'-6"						
Window, plastic clad, prem., 4'-6" x 6'-6", insul. glass	1.000	Ea.	1.455	1,075	85	1,160
Trim, interior casing	23.000	L.F.	.736	35.65	43.01	78.66
Paint, interior, primer & 2 coats	1.000	Face	.889	1.36	43	44.36
Caulking	22.000	L.F.	.611	5.50	35.86	41.36
Snap-in grille	1.000	Ea.	.267	141	15.60	156.60
TOTAL		Ea.	3.958	1,258.51	222.47	1,480.98
METAL CLAD WOOD WINDOW, 6'-6" X 6'-6"						
Window, metal clad, deluxe, 6'-0" x 6'-0", insulating glass	1.000	Ea.	1.600	780	93.50	873.50
Trim interior casing	27.000	L.F.	.864	41.85	50.49	92.34
Paint, interior, primer & 2 coats	1.000	Face	1.600	7.25	77	84.25
Caulking	26.000	L.F.	.722	6.50	42.38	48.88
Snap-in grille	1.000	Ea.	.267	141	15.60	156.60
Drip cap, metal	6.500	L.F.	.130	4.10	7.61	11.71
TOTAL		Ea.	5.183	980.70	286.58	1,267.28

The cost of this system is on a cost per each window basis.

Description	QUAN.	UNIT	LABOR HOURS	COST EACH		
				MAT.	INST.	TOTAL

Fixed Window Price Sheet

	QUAN.	UNIT	LABOR HOURS	COST EACH MAT.	COST EACH INST.	COST EACH TOTAL
Window-picture, builder's quality, 4' x 4', single glass	1.000	Ea.	1.333	480	78	558
Insulating glass	1.000	Ea.	1.333	490	78	568
4' x 4'-6", single glass	1.000	Ea.	1.455	605	85	690
Insulating glass	1.000	Ea.	1.455	585	85	670
5' x 4', single glass	1.000	Ea.	1.455	640	85	725
Insulating glass	1.000	Ea.	1.455	665	85	750
6' x 4'-6", single glass	1.000	Ea.	1.600	700	93.50	793.50
Insulating glass	1.000	Ea.	1.600	705	93.50	798.50
Plastic clad premium insulating glass, 4' x 4'	1.000	Ea.	1.333	585	78	663
4'-6" x 6'-6"	1.000	Ea.	1.455	1,075	85	1,160
5'-6" x 6'-6"	1.000	Ea.	1.600	1,200	93.50	1,293.50
6'-6" x 6'-6"	1.000	Ea.	1.600	1,250	93.50	1,343.50
Metal clad deluxe insulating glass, 4' x 4'	1.000	Ea.	1.333	420	78	498
4'-6" x 6'-6"	1.000	Ea.	1.455	615	85	700
5'-6" x 6'-6"	1.000	Ea.	1.600	680	93.50	773.50
6'-6" x 6'-6"	1.000	Ea.	1.600	780	93.50	873.50
Trim, interior casing, window 4' x 4'	17.000	L.F.	.567	26.50	32	58.50
4'-6" x 4'-6"	19.000	L.F.	.633	29.50	35.50	65
5'-0" x 4'-0"	19.000	L.F.	.633	29.50	35.50	65
4'-6" x 6'-6"	23.000	L.F.	.767	35.50	43	78.50
5'-6" x 6'-6"	25.000	L.F.	.833	39	47	86
6'-6" x 6'-6"	27.000	L.F.	.900	42	50.50	92.50
Paint or stain, interior or exterior, 4' x 4' window, 1 coat	1.000	Face	.667	1.06	32	33.06
2 coats	1.000	Face	.667	1.70	32	33.70
Primer & 1 coat	1.000	Face	.727	1.39	35	36.39
Primer & 2 coats	1.000	Face	.889	1.36	43	44.36
4'-6" x 6'-6" window, 1 coat	1.000	Face	.667	1.06	32	33.06
2 coats	1.000	Face	.667	1.70	32	33.70
Primer & 1 coat	1.000	Face	.727	1.39	35	36.39
Primer & 2 coats	1.000	Face	.889	1.36	43	44.36
6'-6" x 6'-6" window, 1 coat	1.000	Face	.889	2.64	43	45.64
2 coats	1.000	Face	1.333	4.82	64.50	69.32
Primer & 1 coat	1.000	Face	1.333	4.79	64.50	69.29
Primer & 2 coats	1.000	Face	1.600	7.25	77	84.25
Caulking, window, 4' x 4'	1.000	Ea.	.516	4	26	30
4'-6" x 4'-6"	1.000	Ea.	.581	4.50	29.50	34
5'-0" x 4'-0"	1.000	Ea.	.581	4.50	29.50	34
4'-6" x 6'-6"	1.000	Ea.	.710	5.50	36	41.50
5'-6" x 6'-6"	1.000	Ea.	.774	6	39	45
6'-6" x 6'-6"	1.000	Ea.	.839	6.50	42.50	49
Grilles, glass size, to 48" x 48"	1.000	Ea.	.267	141	15.60	156.60
To 60" x 68"	1.000	Ea.	.286	216	16.70	232.70
Drip cap, aluminum, 4' long	4.000	L.F.	.080	2.52	4.68	7.20
4'-6" long	4.500	L.F.	.090	2.84	5.25	8.09
5' long	5.000	L.F.	.100	3.15	5.85	9
6' long	6.000	L.F.	.120	3.78	7	10.78
Wood, 4' long	4.000	L.F.	.133	6.20	7.50	13.70
4'-6" long	4.500	L.F.	.150	7	8.40	15.40
5' long	5.000	L.F.	.167	7.75	9.35	17.10
6' long	6.000	L.F.	.200	9.30	11.20	20.50

Drip Cap

Door

Frame & Exterior Casing

Interior Casing

Sill

System Description	QUAN.	UNIT	LABOR HOURS	COST EACH		
				MAT.	INST.	TOTAL
COLONIAL, 6 PANEL, 3′ X 6′-8″, WOOD						
Door, 3′ x 6′-8″ x 1-3/4″ thick, pine, 6 panel colonial	1.000	Ea.	1.067	480	62.50	542.50
Frame, 5-13/16″ deep, incl. exterior casing & drip cap	17.000	L.F.	.725	154.70	42.33	197.03
Interior casing, 2-1/2″ wide	18.000	L.F.	.576	27.90	33.66	61.56
Sill, 8/4 x 8″ deep	3.000	L.F.	.480	67.50	28.05	95.55
Butt hinges, brass, 4-1/2″ x 4-1/2″	1.500	Pr.		36		36
Average quality	1.000	Ea.	.571	55	33.50	88.50
Weatherstripping, metal, spring type, bronze	1.000	Set	1.053	26	61.50	87.50
Paint, interior & exterior, primer & 2 coats	2.000	Face	1.778	14.30	86	100.30
TOTAL		Ea.	6.250	861.40	347.54	1,208.94
SOLID CORE BIRCH, FLUSH, 3′ X 6′-8″						
Door, 3′ x 6′-8″, 1-3/4″ thick, birch, flush solid core	1.000	Ea.	1.067	130	62.50	192.50
Frame, 5-13/16″ deep, incl. exterior casing & drip cap	17.000	L.F.	.725	154.70	42.33	197.03
Interior casing, 2-1/2″ wide	18.000	L.F.	.576	27.90	33.66	61.56
Sill, 8/4 x 8″ deep	3.000	L.F.	.480	67.50	28.05	95.55
Butt hinges, brass, 4-1/2″ x 4-1/2″	1.500	Pr.		36		36
Average quality	1.000	Ea.	.571	55	33.50	88.50
Weatherstripping, metal, spring type, bronze	1.000	Set	1.053	26	61.50	87.50
Paint, Interior & exterior, primer & 2 coats	2.000	Face	1.778	13.40	86	99.40
TOTAL		Ea.	6.250	510.50	347.54	858.04

These systems are on a cost per each door basis.

Description	QUAN.	UNIT	LABOR HOURS	COST EACH		
				MAT.	INST.	TOTAL

Entrance Door Price Sheet	QUAN.	UNIT	LABOR HOURS	COST EACH		
				MAT.	INST.	TOTAL
Door exterior wood 1-3/4" thick, pine, dutch door, 2'-8" x 6'-8" minimum	1.000	Ea.	1.333	820	78	898
Maximum	1.000	Ea.	1.600	1,025	93.50	1,118.50
3'-0" x 6'-8", minimum	1.000	Ea.	1.333	820	78	898
Maximum	1.000	Ea.	1.600	965	93.50	1,058.50
Colonial, 6 panel, 2'-8" x 6'-8"	1.000	Ea.	1.000	615	58.50	673.50
3'-0" x 6'-8"	1.000	Ea.	1.067	480	62.50	542.50
8 panel, 2'-6" x 6'-8"	1.000	Ea.	1.000	670	58.50	728.50
3'-0" x 6'-8"	1.000	Ea.	1.067	660	62.50	722.50
Flush, birch, solid core, 2'-8" x 6'-8"	1.000	Ea.	1.000	122	58.50	180.50
3'-0" x 6'-8"	1.000	Ea.	1.067	130	62.50	192.50
Porch door, 2'-8" x 6'-8"	1.000	Ea.	1.000	680	58.50	738.50
3'-0" x 6'-8"	1.000	Ea.	1.067	700	62.50	762.50
Hand carved mahogany, 2'-8" x 6'-8"	1.000	Ea.	1.067	1,550	62.50	1,612.50
3'-0" x 6'-8"	1.000	Ea.	1.067	1,525	62.50	1,587.50
Rosewood, 2'-8" x 6'-8"	1.000	Ea.	1.067	825	57.50	882.50
3'-0" x 6-8"	1.000	Ea.	1.067	780	62.50	842.50
Door, metal clad wood 1-3/8" thick raised panel, 2'-8" x 6'-8"	1.000	Ea.	1.067	355	55	410
3'-0" x 6'-8"	1.000	Ea.	1.067	310	62.50	372.50
Deluxe metal door, 3'-0" x 6'-8"	1.000	Ea.	1.231	310	62.50	372.50
3'-0" x 6'-8"	1.000	Ea.	1.231	310	62.50	372.50
Frame, pine, including exterior trim & drip cap, 5/4, x 4-9/16" deep	17.000	L.F.	.725	127	42.50	169.50
5-13/16" deep	17.000	L.F.	.725	155	42.50	197.50
6-9/16" deep	17.000	L.F.	.725	183	42.50	225.50
Safety glass lites, add	1.000	Ea.		88		88
Interior casing, 2'-8" x 6'-8" door	18.000	L.F.	.600	28	33.50	61.50
3'-0" x 6'-8" door	19.000	L.F.	.633	29.50	35.50	65
Sill, oak, 8/4 x 8" deep	3.000	L.F.	.480	67.50	28	95.50
8/4 x 10" deep	3.000	L.F.	.533	87	31	118
Butt hinges, steel plated, 4-1/2" x 4-1/2", plain	1.500	Pr.		36		36
Ball bearing	1.500	Pr.		62.50		62.50
Bronze, 4-1/2" x 4-1/2", plain	1.500	Pr.		48		48
Ball bearing	1.500	Pr.		65.50		65.50
Lockset, minimum	1.000	Ea.	.571	55	33.50	88.50
Maximum	1.000	Ea.	1.000	242	58.50	300.50
Weatherstripping, metal, interlocking, zinc	1.000	Set	2.667	48.50	156	204.50
Bronze	1.000	Set	2.667	61.50	156	217.50
Spring type, bronze	1.000	Set	1.053	26	61.50	87.50
Rubber, minimum	1.000	Set	1.053	10.20	61.50	71.70
Maximum	1.000	Set	1.143	12.50	67	79.50
Felt minimum	1.000	Set	.571	4.40	33.50	37.90
Maximum	1.000	Set	.615	5.10	36	41.10
Paint or stain, flush door, interior or exterior, 1 coat	2.000	Face	.941	5	45	50
2 coats	2.000	Face	1.455	10.10	70	80.10
Primer & 1 coat	2.000	Face	1.455	8.70	70	78.70
Primer & 2 coats	2.000	Face	1.778	13.40	86	99.40
Paneled door, interior & exterior, 1 coat	2.000	Face	1.143	5.40	55	60.40
2 coats	2.000	Face	2.000	10.70	96	106.70
Primer & 1 coat	2.000	Face	1.455	9.30	70	79.30
Primer & 2 coats	2.000	Face	1.778	14.30	86	100.30

System Description	QUAN.	UNIT	LABOR HOURS	COST EACH		
				MAT.	INST.	TOTAL
WOOD SLIDING DOOR, 8′ WIDE, PREMIUM						
Wood, 5/8″ thick tempered insul. glass, 8′ wide, premium	1.000	Ea.	5.333	2,025	310	2,335
Interior casing	22.000	L.F.	.704	34.10	41.14	75.24
Exterior casing	22.000	L.F.	.704	34.10	41.14	75.24
Sill, oak, 8/4 x 8″ deep	8.000	L.F.	1.280	180	74.80	254.80
Drip cap	8.000	L.F.	.160	5.04	9.36	14.40
Paint, interior & exterior, primer & 2 coats	2.000	Face	2.816	20.24	135.52	155.76
TOTAL		Ea.	10.997	2,298.48	611.96	2,910.44
ALUMINUM SLIDING DOOR, 8′ WIDE, PREMIUM						
Aluminum, 5/8″ tempered insul. glass, 8′ wide, premium	1.000	Ea.	5.333	1,825	310	2,135
Interior casing	22.000	L.F.	.704	34.10	41.14	75.24
Exterior casing	22.000	L.F.	.704	34.10	41.14	75.24
Sill, oak, 8/4 x 8″ deep	8.000	L.F.	1.280	180	74.80	254.80
Drip cap	8.000	L.F.	.160	5.04	9.36	14.40
Paint, interior & exterior, primer & 2 coats	2.000	Face	2.816	20.24	135.52	155.76
TOTAL		Ea.	10.997	2,098.48	611.96	2,710.44

The cost of this system is on a cost per each door basis.

Description	QUAN.	UNIT	LABOR HOURS	COST EACH		
				MAT.	INST.	TOTAL

Sliding Door Price Sheet	QUAN.	UNIT	LABOR HOURS	COST PER UNIT		
				MAT.	INST.	TOTAL
Sliding door, wood, 5/8" thick, tempered insul. glass, 6' wide, premium	1.000	Ea.	4.000	1,600	234	1,834
Economy	1.000	Ea.	4.000	1,325	234	1,559
8'wide, wood premium	1.000	Ea.	5.333	2,025	310	2,335
Economy	1.000	Ea.	5.333	1,675	310	1,985
12' wide, wood premium	1.000	Ea.	6.400	3,400	375	3,775
Economy	1.000	Ea.	6.400	2,725	375	3,100
Aluminum, 5/8" thick, tempered insul. glass, 6'wide, premium	1.000	Ea.	4.000	1,700	234	1,934
Economy	1.000	Ea.	4.000	905	234	1,139
8'wide, premium	1.000	Ea.	5.333	1,825	310	2,135
Economy	1.000	Ea.	5.333	1,575	310	1,885
12' wide, premium	1.000	Ea.	6.400	3,300	375	3,675
Economy	1.000	Ea.	6.400	1,725	375	2,100
Interior casing, 6' wide door	20.000	L.F.	.667	31	37.50	68.50
8' wide door	22.000	L.F.	.733	34	41	75
12' wide door	26.000	L.F.	.867	40.50	48.50	89
Exterior casing, 6' wide door	20.000	L.F.	.667	31	37.50	68.50
8' wide door	22.000	L.F.	.733	34	41	75
12' wide door	26.000	L.F.	.867	40.50	48.50	89
Sill, oak, 8/4 x 8" deep, 6' wide door	6.000	L.F.	.960	135	56	191
8' wide door	8.000	L.F.	1.280	180	75	255
12' wide door	12.000	L.F.	1.920	270	112	382
8/4 x 10" deep, 6' wide door	6.000	L.F.	1.067	174	62.50	236.50
8' wide door	8.000	L.F.	1.422	232	83	315
12' wide door	12.000	L.F.	2.133	350	125	475
Drip cap, 6' wide door	6.000	L.F.	.120	3.78	7	10.78
8' wide door	8.000	L.F.	.160	5.05	9.35	14.40
12' wide door	12.000	L.F.	.240	7.55	14.05	21.60
Paint or stain, interior & exterior, 6' wide door, 1 coat	2.000	Face	1.600	7.20	77	84.20
2 coats	2.000	Face	1.600	7.20	77	84.20
Primer & 1 coat	2.000	Face	1.778	12	85.50	97.50
Primer & 2 coats	2.000	Face	2.560	18.40	123	141.40
8' wide door, 1 coat	2.000	Face	1.760	7.90	84.50	92.40
2 coats	2.000	Face	1.760	7.90	84.50	92.40
Primer & 1 coat	2.000	Face	1.955	13.20	94	107.20
Primer & 2 coats	2.000	Face	2.816	20	136	156
12' wide door, 1 coat	2.000	Face	2.080	9.35	100	109.35
2 coats	2.000	Face	2.080	9.35	100	109.35
Primer & 1 coat	2.000	Face	2.311	15.60	111	126.60
Primer & 2 coats	2.000	Face	3.328	24	160	184
Aluminum door, trim only, interior & exterior, 6' door, 1 coat	2.000	Face	.800	3.60	38.50	42.10
2 coats	2.000	Face	.800	3.60	38.50	42.10
Primer & 1 coat	2.000	Face	.889	6	43	49
Primer & 2 coats	2.000	Face	1.280	9.20	61.50	70.70
8' wide door, 1 coat	2.000	Face	.880	3.96	42	45.96
2 coats	2.000	Face	.880	3.96	42	45.96
Primer & 1 coat	2.000	Face	.978	6.60	47	53.60
Primer & 2 coats	2.000	Face	1.408	10.10	68	78.10
12' wide door, 1 coat	2.000	Face	1.040	4.68	50	54.68
2 coats	2.000	Face	1.040	4.68	50	54.68
Primer & 1 coat	2.000	Face	1.155	7.80	55.50	63.30
Primer & 2 coats	2.000	Face	1.664	11.95	80	91.95

For customer support on your Residential Costs with RSMeans Data, call 800.448.8182.

185

System Description	QUAN.	UNIT	LABOR HOURS	COST EACH		
				MAT.	INST.	TOTAL
OVERHEAD, SECTIONAL GARAGE DOOR, 9′ X 7′						
Wood, overhead sectional door, std., incl. hardware, 9′ x 7′	1.000	Ea.	2.000	1,075	117	1,192
Jamb & header blocking, 2″ x 6″	25.000	L.F.	.901	17.25	52.75	70
Exterior trim	25.000	L.F.	.800	38.75	46.75	85.50
Paint, interior & exterior, primer & 2 coats	2.000	Face	3.556	28.60	172	200.60
Weatherstripping, molding type	1.000	Set	.736	35.65	43.01	78.66
Drip cap	9.000	L.F.	.180	5.67	10.53	16.20
TOTAL		Ea.	8.173	1,200.92	442.04	1,642.96
OVERHEAD, SECTIONAL GARAGE DOOR, 16′ X 7′						
Wood, overhead sectional, std., incl. hardware, 16′ x 7′	1.000	Ea.	2.667	1,800	156	1,956
Jamb & header blocking, 2″ x 6″	30.000	L.F.	1.081	20.70	63.30	84
Exterior trim	30.000	L.F.	.960	46.50	56.10	102.60
Paint, interior & exterior, primer & 2 coats	2.000	Face	5.333	42.90	258	300.90
Weatherstripping, molding type	1.000	Set	.960	46.50	56.10	102.60
Drip cap	16.000	L.F.	.320	10.08	18.72	28.80
TOTAL		Ea.	11.321	1,966.68	608.22	2,574.90
OVERHEAD, SWING-UP TYPE, GARAGE DOOR, 16′ X 7′						
Wood, overhead, swing-up, std., incl. hardware, 16′ x 7′	1.000	Ea.	2.667	990	156	1,146
Jamb & header blocking, 2″ x 6″	30.000	L.F.	1.081	20.70	63.30	84
Exterior trim	30.000	L.F.	.960	46.50	56.10	102.60
Paint, interior & exterior, primer & 2 coats	2.000	Face	5.333	42.90	258	300.90
Weatherstripping, molding type	1.000	Set	.960	46.50	56.10	102.60
Drip cap	16.000	L.F.	.320	10.08	18.72	28.80
TOTAL		Ea.	11.321	1,156.68	608.22	1,764.90

This system is on a cost per each door basis.

Description	QUAN.	UNIT	LABOR HOURS	COST EACH		
				MAT.	INST.	TOTAL

Resi Garage Door Price Sheet	QUAN.	UNIT	LABOR HOURS	COST EACH		
				MAT.	INST.	TOTAL
Overhead, sectional, including hardware, fiberglass, 9' x 7', standard	1.000	Ea.	3.030	1,075	187	1,262
Deluxe	1.000	Ea.	3.030	1,275	187	1,462
16' x 7', standard	1.000	Ea.	2.667	1,725	156	1,881
Deluxe	1.000	Ea.	2.667	2,350	156	2,506
Hardboard, 9' x 7', standard	1.000	Ea.	2.000	755	117	872
Deluxe	1.000	Ea.	2.000	900	117	1,017
16' x 7', standard	1.000	Ea.	2.667	1,350	156	1,506
Deluxe	1.000	Ea.	2.667	1,575	156	1,731
Metal, 9' x 7', standard	1.000	Ea.	3.030	920	117	1,037
Deluxe	1.000	Ea.	2.000	1,050	156	1,206
16' x 7', standard	1.000	Ea.	5.333	1,125	156	1,281
Deluxe	1.000	Ea.	2.667	1,550	187	1,737
Wood, 9' x 7', standard	1.000	Ea.	2.000	1,075	117	1,192
Deluxe	1.000	Ea.	2.000	2,350	117	2,467
16' x 7', standard	1.000	Ea.	2.667	1,800	156	1,956
Deluxe	1.000	Ea.	2.667	3,325	156	3,481
Overhead swing-up type including hardware, fiberglass, 9' x 7', standard	1.000	Ea.	2.000	1,100	117	1,217
Deluxe	1.000	Ea.	2.000	1,200	117	1,317
16' x 7', standard	1.000	Ea.	2.667	1,375	156	1,531
Deluxe	1.000	Ea.	2.667	1,750	156	1,906
Hardboard, 9' x 7', standard	1.000	Ea.	2.000	605	117	722
Deluxe	1.000	Ea.	2.000	715	117	832
16' x 7', standard	1.000	Ea.	2.667	735	156	891
Deluxe	1.000	Ea.	2.667	935	156	1,091
Metal, 9' x 7', standard	1.000	Ea.	2.000	660	117	777
Deluxe	1.000	Ea.	2.000	1,075	117	1,192
16' x 7', standard	1.000	Ea.	2.667	880	156	1,036
Deluxe	1.000	Ea.	2.667	1,200	156	1,356
Wood, 9' x 7', standard	1.000	Ea.	2.000	770	117	887
Deluxe	1.000	Ea.	2.000	1,250	117	1,367
16' x 7', standard	1.000	Ea.	2.667	990	156	1,146
Deluxe	1.000	Ea.	2.667	2,300	156	2,456
Jamb & header blocking, 2" x 6", 9' x 7' door	25.000	L.F.	.901	17.25	53	70.25
16' x 7' door	30.000	L.F.	1.081	20.50	63.50	84
2" x 8", 9' x 7' door	25.000	L.F.	1.000	24	58.50	82.50
16' x 7' door	30.000	L.F.	1.200	29	70	99
Exterior trim, 9' x 7' door	25.000	L.F.	.833	39	47	86
16' x 7' door	30.000	L.F.	1.000	46.50	56	102.50
Paint or stain, interior & exterior, 9' x 7' door, 1 coat	1.000	Face	2.286	10.75	110	120.75
2 coats	1.000	Face	4.000	21.50	192	213.50
Primer & 1 coat	1.000	Face	2.909	18.55	140	158.55
Primer & 2 coats	1.000	Face	3.556	28.50	172	200.50
16' x 7' door, 1 coat	1.000	Face	3.429	16.15	165	181.15
2 coats	1.000	Face	6.000	32	288	320
Primer & 1 coat	1.000	Face	4.364	28	210	238
Primer & 2 coats	1.000	Face	5.333	43	258	301
Weatherstripping, molding type, 9' x 7' door	1.000	Set	.767	35.50	43	78.50
16' x 7' door	1.000	Set	1.000	46.50	56	102.50
Drip cap, 9' door	9.000	L.F.	.180	5.65	10.55	16.20
16' door	16.000	L.F.	.320	10.10	18.70	28.80
Garage door opener, economy	1.000	Ea.	1.000	470	58.50	528.50
Deluxe, including remote control	1.000	Ea.	1.000	675	58.50	733.50

For customer support on your Residential Costs with RSMeans Data, call 800.448.8182.

187

Drywall → ← Finish Drywall

← Window

Corner Bead →

Sill

System Description	QUAN.	UNIT	LABOR HOURS	COST EACH		
				MAT.	INST.	TOTAL
SINGLE HUNG, 2' X 3' OPENING						
Window, 2' x 3' opening, enameled, insulating glass	1.000	Ea.	1.600	283	111	394
Blocking, 1" x 3" furring strip nailers	10.000	L.F.	.146	4.60	8.50	13.10
Drywall, 1/2" thick, standard	5.000	S.F.	.040	1.85	2.35	4.20
Corner bead, 1" x 1", galvanized steel	8.000	L.F.	.160	1.44	9.36	10.80
Finish drywall, tape and finish corners inside and outside	16.000	L.F.	.269	1.76	15.68	17.44
Sill, slate	2.000	L.F.	.400	26.80	21.30	48.10
TOTAL		Ea.	2.615	319.45	168.19	487.64
SLIDING, 3' X 2' OPENING						
Window, 3' x 2' opening, enameled, insulating glass	1.000	Ea.	1.600	260	111	371
Blocking, 1" x 3" furring strip nailers	10.000	L.F.	.146	4.60	8.50	13.10
Drywall, 1/2" thick, standard	5.000	S.F.	.040	1.85	2.35	4.20
Corner bead, 1" x 1", galvanized steel	7.000	L.F.	.140	1.26	8.19	9.45
Finish drywall, tape and finish corners inside and outside	14.000	L.F.	.236	1.54	13.72	15.26
Sill, slate	3.000	L.F.	.600	40.20	31.95	72.15
TOTAL		Ea.	2.762	309.45	175.71	485.16
AWNING, 3'-1" X 3'-2"						
Window, 3'-1" x 3'-2" opening, enameled, insul. glass	1.000	Ea.	1.600	425	111	536
Blocking, 1" x 3" furring strip, nailers	12.500	L.F.	.182	5.75	10.63	16.38
Drywall, 1/2" thick, standard	4.500	S.F.	.036	1.67	2.12	3.79
Corner bead, 1" x 1", galvanized steel	9.250	L.F.	.185	1.67	10.82	12.49
Finish drywall, tape and finish corners, inside and outside	18.500	L.F.	.312	2.04	18.13	20.17
Sill, slate	3.250	L.F.	.650	43.55	34.61	78.16
TOTAL		Ea.	2.965	479.68	187.31	666.99

Description	QUAN.	UNIT	LABOR HOURS	COST EACH		
				MAT.	INST.	TOTAL

Aluminum Window Price Sheet

Aluminum Window Price Sheet	QUAN.	UNIT	LABOR HOURS	COST EACH MAT.	COST EACH INST.	COST EACH TOTAL
Window, aluminum, awning, 3'-1" x 3'-2", standard glass	1.000	Ea.	1.600	395	111	506
Insulating glass	1.000	Ea.	1.600	425	111	536
4'-5" x 5'-3", standard glass	1.000	Ea.	2.000	450	139	589
Insulating glass	1.000	Ea.	2.000	525	139	664
Casement, 3'-1" x 3'-2", standard glass	1.000	Ea.	1.600	420	111	531
Insulating glass	1.000	Ea.	1.600	565	111	676
Single hung, 2' x 3', standard glass	1.000	Ea.	1.600	233	111	344
Insulating glass	1.000	Ea.	1.600	283	111	394
2'-8" x 6'-8", standard glass	1.000	Ea.	2.000	405	139	544
Insulating glass	1.000	Ea.	2.000	530	139	669
3'-4" x 5'-0", standard glass	1.000	Ea.	1.778	335	124	459
Insulating glass	1.000	Ea.	1.778	375	124	499
Sliding, 3' x 2', standard glass	1.000	Ea.	1.600	242	111	353
Insulating glass	1.000	Ea.	1.600	260	111	371
5' x 3', standard glass	1.000	Ea.	1.778	370	124	494
Insulating glass	1.000	Ea.	1.778	430	124	554
8' x 4', standard glass	1.000	Ea.	2.667	395	186	581
Insulating glass	1.000	Ea.	2.667	635	186	821
Blocking, 1" x 3" furring, opening 3' x 2'	10.000	L.F.	.146	4.60	8.50	13.10
3' x 3'	12.500	L.F.	.182	5.75	10.65	16.40
3' x 5'	16.000	L.F.	.233	7.35	13.60	20.95
4' x 4'	16.000	L.F.	.233	7.35	13.60	20.95
4' x 5'	18.000	L.F.	.262	8.30	15.30	23.60
4' x 6'	20.000	L.F.	.291	9.20	17	26.20
4' x 8'	24.000	L.F.	.349	11.05	20.50	31.55
6'-8" x 2'-8"	19.000	L.F.	.276	8.75	16.15	24.90
Drywall, 1/2" thick, standard, opening 3' x 2'	5.000	S.F.	.040	1.85	2.35	4.20
3' x 3'	6.000	S.F.	.048	2.22	2.82	5.04
3' x 5'	8.000	S.F.	.064	2.96	3.76	6.72
4' x 4'	8.000	S.F.	.064	2.96	3.76	6.72
4' x 5'	9.000	S.F.	.072	3.33	4.23	7.56
4' x 6'	10.000	S.F.	.080	3.70	4.70	8.40
4' x 8'	12.000	S.F.	.096	4.44	5.65	10.09
6'-8" x 2'	9.500	S.F.	.076	3.52	4.47	7.99
Corner bead, 1" x 1", galvanized steel, opening 3' x 2'	7.000	L.F.	.140	1.26	8.20	9.46
3' x 3'	9.000	L.F.	.180	1.62	10.55	12.17
3' x 5'	11.000	L.F.	.220	1.98	12.85	14.83
4' x 4'	12.000	L.F.	.240	2.16	14.05	16.21
4' x 5'	13.000	L.F.	.260	2.34	15.20	17.54
4' x 6'	14.000	L.F.	.280	2.52	16.40	18.92
4' x 8'	16.000	L.F.	.320	2.88	18.70	21.58
6'-8" x 2'	15.000	L.F.	.300	2.70	17.55	20.25
Tape and finish corners, inside and outside, opening 3' x 2'	14.000	L.F.	.204	1.54	13.70	15.24
3' x 3'	18.000	L.F.	.262	1.98	17.65	19.63
3' x 5'	22.000	L.F.	.320	2.42	21.50	23.92
4' x 4'	24.000	L.F.	.349	2.64	23.50	26.14
4' x 5'	26.000	L.F.	.378	2.86	25.50	28.36
4' x 6'	28.000	L.F.	.407	3.08	27.50	30.58
4' x 8'	32.000	L.F.	.466	3.52	31.50	35.02
6'-8" x 2'	30.000	L.F.	.437	3.30	29.50	32.80
Sill, slate, 2' long	2.000	L.F.	.400	27	21.50	48.50
3' long	3.000	L.F.	.600	40	32	72
4' long	4.000	L.F.	.800	53.50	42.50	96
Wood, 1-5/8" x 6-1/4", 2' long	2.000	L.F.	.128	11.70	7.50	19.20
3' long	3.000	L.F.	.192	17.55	11.20	28.75
4' long	4.000	L.F.	.256	23.50	14.95	38.45

Aluminum Window

Aluminum Door

System Description	QUAN.	UNIT	LABOR HOURS	COST EACH		
				MAT.	INST.	TOTAL
Storm door, aluminum, combination, storm & screen, anodized, 2'-6" x 6'-8"	1.000	Ea.	1.067	228	62.50	290.50
2'-8" x 6'-8"	1.000	Ea.	1.143	228	67	295
3'-0" x 6'-8"	1.000	Ea.	1.143	198	67	265
Mill finish, 2'-6" x 6'-8"	1.000	Ea.	1.067	270	62.50	332.50
2'-8" x 6'-8"	1.000	Ea.	1.143	270	67	337
3'-0" x 6'-8"	1.000	Ea.	1.143	292	67	359
Painted, 2'-6" x 6'-8"	1.000	Ea.	1.067	305	62.50	367.50
2'-8" x 6'-8"	1.000	Ea.	1.143	315	67	382
3'-0" x 6'-8"	1.000	Ea.	1.143	330	67	397
Wood, combination, storm & screen, crossbuck, 2'-6" x 6'-9"	1.000	Ea.	1.455	345	85	430
2'-8" x 6'-9"	1.000	Ea.	1.600	345	93.50	438.50
3'-0" x 6'-9"	1.000	Ea.	1.778	350	104	454
Full lite, 2'-6" x 6'-9"	1.000	Ea.	1.455	355	85	440
2'-8" x 6'-9"	1.000	Ea.	1.600	360	93.50	453.50
3'-0" x 6'-9"	1.000	Ea.	1.778	365	104	469
Windows, aluminum, combination storm & screen, basement, 1'-10" x 1'-0"	1.000	Ea.	.533	39.50	31	70.50
2'-9" x 1'-6"	1.000	Ea.	.533	43	31	74
3'-4" x 2'-0"	1.000	Ea.	.533	50.50	31	81.50
Double hung, anodized, 2'-0" x 3'-5"	1.000	Ea.	.533	109	31	140
2'-6" x 5'-0"	1.000	Ea.	.571	132	33.50	165.50
4'-0" x 6'-0"	1.000	Ea.	.640	259	37.50	296.50
Painted, 2'-0" x 3'-5"	1.000	Ea.	.533	127	31	158
2'-6" x 5'-0"	1.000	Ea.	.571	193	33.50	226.50
4'-0" x 6'-0"	1.000	Ea.	.640	320	37.50	357.50
Fixed window, anodized, 4'-6" x 4'-6"	1.000	Ea.	.640	154	37.50	191.50
5'-8" x 4'-6"	1.000	Ea.	.800	171	47	218
Painted, 4'-6" x 4'-6"	1.000	Ea.	.640	154	37.50	191.50
5'-8" x 4'-6"	1.000	Ea.	.800	176	47	223

Aluminum Louvered →

← Raised Panel

Wood Louvered

System Description	QUAN.	UNIT	LABOR HOURS	COST PER PAIR		
				MAT.	INST.	TOTAL
Shutters, exterior blinds, aluminum, louvered, 1'-4" wide, 3"-0" long	1.000	Set	.800	222	47	269
4'-0" long	1.000	Set	.800	268	47	315
5'-4" long	1.000	Set	.800	315	47	362
6'-8" long	1.000	Set	.889	390	52	442
Wood, louvered, 1'-2" wide, 3'-3" long	1.000	Set	.800	236	47	283
4'-7" long	1.000	Set	.800	305	47	352
5'-3" long	1.000	Set	.800	355	47	402
1'-6" wide, 3'-3" long	1.000	Set	.800	280	47	327
4'-7" long	1.000	Set	.800	350	47	397
Polystyrene, louvered, 1'-2" wide, 3'-3" long	1.000	Set	.800	39.50	47	86.50
4'-7" long	1.000	Set	.800	53	47	100
5'-3" long	1.000	Set	.800	65	47	112
6'-8" long	1.000	Set	.889	72	52	124
Vinyl, louvered, 1'-2" wide, 4'-7" long	1.000	Set	.720	63.50	42.50	106
1'-4" x 6'-8" long	1.000	Set	.889	91.50	52	143.50

System Description	QUAN.	UNIT	LABOR HOURS	COST PER S.F.		
				MAT.	INST.	TOTAL
ASPHALT, ROOF SHINGLES, CLASS A						
Shingles, inorganic class A, 210-235 lb./sq., 4/12 pitch	1.160	S.F.	.017	1.07	.95	2.02
Drip edge, metal, 5" wide	.150	L.F.	.003	.10	.18	.28
Building paper, #15 felt	1.300	S.F.	.002	.08	.10	.18
Ridge shingles, asphalt	.042	L.F.	.001	.10	.06	.16
Soffit & fascia, white painted aluminum, 1' overhang	.083	L.F.	.012	.41	.71	1.12
Rake trim, 1" x 6"	.040	L.F.	.002	.05	.09	.14
Rake trim, prime and paint	.040	L.F.	.002	.01	.09	.10
Gutter, seamless, aluminum painted	.083	L.F.	.005	.26	.34	.60
Downspouts, aluminum painted	.035	L.F.	.002	.08	.10	.18
Ridge vent	.042	L.F.	.002	.11	.12	.23
TOTAL		S.F.	.048	2.27	2.74	5.01
WOOD, CEDAR SHINGLES NO. 1 PERFECTIONS, 18" LONG						
Shingles, wood, cedar, No. 1 perfections, 4/12 pitch	1.160	S.F.	.035	3.30	2.04	5.34
Drip edge, metal, 5" wide	.150	L.F.	.003	.10	.18	.28
Building paper, #15 felt	1.300	S.F.	.002	.08	.10	.18
Ridge shingles, cedar	.042	L.F.	.001	.21	.07	.28
Soffit & fascia, white painted aluminum, 1' overhang	.083	L.F.	.012	.41	.71	1.12
Rake trim, 1" x 6"	.040	L.F.	.002	.05	.09	.14
Rake trim, prime and paint	.040	L.F.	.002	.01	.09	.10
Gutter, seamless, aluminum, painted	.083	L.F.	.005	.26	.34	.60
Downspouts, aluminum, painted	.035	L.F.	.002	.08	.10	.18
Ridge vent	.042	L.F.	.002	.11	.12	.23
TOTAL		S.F.	.066	4.61	3.84	8.45

The prices in these systems are based on a square foot of plan area.
All quantities have been adjusted accordingly.

Description	QUAN.	UNIT	LABOR HOURS	COST PER S.F.		
				MAT.	INST.	TOTAL

Gable End Roofing Price Sheet

	QUAN.	UNIT	LABOR HOURS	COST PER S.F. MAT.	COST PER S.F. INST.	COST PER S.F. TOTAL
Shingles, asphalt, inorganic, class A, 210-235 lb./sq., 4/12 pitch	1.160	S.F.	.017	1.07	.95	2.02
8/12 pitch	1.330	S.F.	.019	1.16	1.03	2.19
Laminated, multi-layered, 240-260 lb./sq., 4/12 pitch	1.160	S.F.	.021	1.44	1.17	2.61
8/12 pitch	1.330	S.F.	.023	1.56	1.27	2.83
Premium laminated, multi-layered, 260-300 lb./sq., 4/12 pitch	1.160	S.F.	.027	2.09	1.50	3.59
8/12 pitch	1.330	S.F.	.030	2.26	1.63	3.89
Clay tile, Spanish tile, red, 4/12 pitch	1.160	S.F.	.053	6.65	2.88	9.53
8/12 pitch	1.330	S.F.	.058	7.20	3.12	10.32
Mission tile, red, 4/12 pitch	1.160	S.F.	.083	5.45	2.88	8.33
8/12 pitch	1.330	S.F.	.090	5.90	3.12	9.02
French tile, red, 4/12 pitch	1.160	S.F.	.071	15.30	2.64	17.94
8/12 pitch	1.330	S.F.	.077	16.60	2.86	19.46
Slate, Buckingham, Virginia, black, 4/12 pitch	1.160	S.F.	.055	7.25	3.01	10.26
8/12 pitch	1.330	S.F.	.059	7.85	3.26	11.11
Vermont, black or grey, 4/12 pitch	1.160	S.F.	.055	6.30	3.01	9.31
8/12 pitch	1.330	S.F.	.059	6.85	3.26	10.11
Wood, No. 1 red cedar, 5X, 16" long, 5" exposure, 4/12 pitch	1.160	S.F.	.038	3.72	2.24	5.96
8/12 pitch	1.330	S.F.	.042	4.03	2.43	6.46
Fire retardant, 4/12 pitch	1.160	S.F.	.038	4.46	2.24	6.70
8/12 pitch	1.330	S.F.	.042	4.83	2.43	7.26
18" long, No.1 perfections, 5" exposure, 4/12 pitch	1.160	S.F.	.035	3.30	2.04	5.34
8/12 pitch	1.330	S.F.	.038	3.58	2.21	5.79
Fire retardant, 4/12 pitch	1.160	S.F.	.035	4.04	2.04	6.08
8/12 pitch	1.330	S.F.	.038	4.38	2.21	6.59
Resquared & rebutted, 18" long, 6" exposure, 4/12 pitch	1.160	S.F.	.032	3.78	1.87	5.65
8/12 pitch	1.330	S.F.	.035	4.10	2.03	6.13
Fire retardant, 4/12 pitch	1.160	S.F.	.032	4.52	1.87	6.39
8/12 pitch	1.330	S.F.	.035	4.90	2.03	6.93
Wood shakes hand split, 24" long, 10" exposure, 4/12 pitch	1.160	S.F.	.038	3.78	2.24	6.02
8/12 pitch	1.330	S.F.	.042	4.10	2.43	6.53
Fire retardant, 4/12 pitch	1.160	S.F.	.038	4.52	2.24	6.76
8/12 pitch	1.330	S.F.	.042	4.90	2.43	7.33
18" long, 8" exposure, 4/12 pitch	1.160	S.F.	.048	2.36	2.81	5.17
8/12 pitch	1.330	S.F.	.052	2.56	3.04	5.60
Fire retardant, 4/12 pitch	1.160	S.F.	.048	3.10	2.81	5.91
8/12 pitch	1.330	S.F.	.052	3.36	3.04	6.40
Drip edge, metal, 5" wide	.150	L.F.	.003	.10	.18	.28
8" wide	.150	L.F.	.003	.14	.18	.32
Building paper, #15 asphalt felt	1.300	S.F.	.002	.08	.10	.18
Ridge shingles, asphalt	.042	L.F.	.001	.10	.06	.16
Clay	.042	L.F.	.002	.23	.28	.51
Slate	.042	L.F.	.002	.46	.09	.55
Wood, shingles	.042	L.F.	.001	.21	.07	.28
Shakes	.042	L.F.	.001	.21	.07	.28
		L.F.				
Soffit & fascia, aluminum, vented, 1' overhang	.083	L.F.	.012	.41	.71	1.12
2' overhang	.083	L.F.	.013	.59	.78	1.37
Vinyl, vented, 1' overhang	.083	L.F.	.011	.43	.65	1.08
2' overhang	.083	L.F.	.012	.57	.78	1.35
Wood, board fascia, plywood soffit, 1' overhang	.083	L.F.	.004	.02	.18	.20
2' overhang	.083	L.F.	.006	.04	.27	.31
Rake trim, painted, 1" x 6"	.040	L.F.	.004	.06	.18	.24
1" x 8"	.040	L.F.	.004	.24	.17	.41
Gutter, 5" box, aluminum, seamless, painted	.083	L.F.	.006	.26	.34	.60
Vinyl	.083	L.F.	.006	.15	.34	.49
Downspout, 2" x 3", aluminum, one story house	.035	L.F.	.001	.05	.09	.14
Two story house	.060	L.F.	.003	.09	.16	.25
Vinyl, one story house	.035	L.F.	.002	.08	.10	.18
Two story house	.060	L.F.	.003	.09	.16	.25

System Description	QUAN.	UNIT	LABOR HOURS	COST PER S.F.		
				MAT.	INST.	TOTAL
ASPHALT, ROOF SHINGLES, CLASS A						
Shingles, inorganic, class A, 210-235 lb./sq. 4/12 pitch	1.570	S.F.	.023	1.43	1.27	2.70
Drip edge, metal, 5" wide	.122	L.F.	.002	.08	.14	.22
Building paper, #15 asphalt felt	1.800	S.F.	.002	.11	.14	.25
Ridge shingles, asphalt	.075	L.F.	.002	.19	.10	.29
Soffit & fascia, white painted aluminum, 1' overhang	.120	L.F.	.017	.59	1.02	1.61
Gutter, seamless, aluminum, painted	.120	L.F.	.008	.38	.49	.87
Downspouts, aluminum, painted	.035	L.F.	.002	.08	.10	.18
Ridge vent	.028	L.F.	.001	.07	.08	.15
TOTAL		S.F.	.057	2.93	3.34	6.27
WOOD, CEDAR SHINGLES, NO. 1 PERFECTIONS, 18" LONG						
Shingles, red cedar, No. 1 perfections, 5" exp., 4/12 pitch	1.570	S.F.	.047	4.40	2.72	7.12
Drip edge, metal, 5" wide	.122	L.F.	.002	.08	.14	.22
Building paper, #15 asphalt felt	1.800	S.F.	.002	.11	.14	.25
Ridge shingles, wood, cedar	.075	L.F.	.002	.37	.13	.50
Soffit & fascia, white painted aluminum, 1' overhang	.120	L.F.	.017	.59	1.02	1.61
Gutter, seamless, aluminum, painted	.120	L.F.	.008	.38	.49	.87
Downspouts, aluminum, painted	.035	L.F.	.002	.08	.10	.18
Ridge vent	.028	L.F.	.001	.07	.08	.15
TOTAL		S.F.	.081	6.08	4.82	10.90

The prices in these systems are based on a square foot of plan area.
All quantities have been adjusted accordingly.

Description	QUAN.	UNIT	LABOR HOURS	COST PER S.F.		
				MAT.	INST.	TOTAL

Hip Roof - Roofing Price Sheet

	QUAN.	UNIT	LABOR HOURS	MAT.	INST.	TOTAL
Shingles, asphalt, inorganic, class A, 210-235 lb./sq., 4/12 pitch	1.570	S.F.	.023	1.43	1.27	2.70
8/12 pitch	1.850	S.F.	.028	1.70	1.51	3.21
Laminated, multi-layered, 240-260 lb./sq., 4/12 pitch	1.570	S.F.	.028	1.92	1.56	3.48
8/12 pitch	1.850	S.F.	.034	2.28	1.85	4.13
Prem. laminated, multi-layered, 260-300 lb./sq., 4/12 pitch	1.570	S.F.	.037	2.78	2	4.78
8/12 pitch	1.850	S.F.	.043	3.31	2.38	5.69
Clay tile, Spanish tile, red, 4/12 pitch	1.570	S.F.	.071	8.90	3.84	12.74
8/12 pitch	1.850	S.F.	.084	10.55	4.56	15.11
Mission tile, red, 4/12 pitch	1.570	S.F.	.111	7.30	3.84	11.14
8/12 pitch	1.850	S.F.	.132	8.65	4.56	13.21
French tile, red, 4/12 pitch	1.570	S.F.	.095	20.50	3.52	24.02
8/12 pitch	1.850	S.F.	.113	24	4.18	28.18
Slate, Buckingham, Virginia, black, 4/12 pitch	1.570	S.F.	.073	9.70	4.02	13.72
8/12 pitch	1.850	S.F.	.087	11.50	4.77	16.27
Vermont, black or grey, 4/12 pitch	1.570	S.F.	.073	8.40	4.02	12.42
8/12 pitch	1.850	S.F.	.087	10	4.77	14.77
Wood, red cedar, No.1 5X, 16" long, 5" exposure, 4/12 pitch	1.570	S.F.	.051	4.96	2.99	7.95
8/12 pitch	1.850	S.F.	.061	5.90	3.55	9.45
Fire retardant, 4/12 pitch	1.570	S.F.	.051	5.95	2.99	8.94
8/12 pitch	1.850	S.F.	.061	7.05	3.55	10.60
18" long, No.1 perfections, 5" exposure, 4/12 pitch	1.570	S.F.	.047	4.40	2.72	7.12
8/12 pitch	1.850	S.F.	.055	5.25	3.23	8.48
Fire retardant, 4/12 pitch	1.570	S.F.	.047	5.40	2.72	8.12
8/12 pitch	1.850	S.F.	.055	6.40	3.23	9.63
Resquared & rebutted, 18" long, 6" exposure, 4/12 pitch	1.570	S.F.	.043	5.05	2.50	7.55
8/12 pitch	1.850	S.F.	.051	6	2.96	8.96
Fire retardant, 4/12 pitch	1.570	S.F.	.043	6	2.50	8.50
8/12 pitch	1.850	S.F.	.051	7.15	2.96	10.11
Wood shakes hand split, 24" long, 10" exposure, 4/12 pitch	1.570	S.F.	.051	5.05	2.99	8.04
8/12 pitch	1.850	S.F.	.061	6	3.55	9.55
Fire retardant, 4/12 pitch	1.570	S.F.	.051	6	2.99	8.99
8/12 pitch	1.850	S.F.	.061	7.15	3.55	10.70
18" long, 8" exposure, 4/12 pitch	1.570	S.F.	.064	3.15	3.74	6.89
8/12 pitch	1.850	S.F.	.076	3.74	4.45	8.19
Fire retardant, 4/12 pitch	1.570	S.F.	.064	4.13	3.74	7.87
8/12 pitch	1.850	S.F.	.076	4.91	4.45	9.36
Drip edge, metal, 5" wide	.122	L.F.	.002	.08	.14	.22
8" wide	.122	L.F.	.002	.11	.14	.25
Building paper, #15 asphalt felt	1.800	S.F.	.002	.11	.14	.25
Ridge shingles, asphalt	.075	L.F.	.002	.19	.10	.29
Clay	.075	L.F.	.003	.41	.50	.91
Slate	.075	L.F.	.003	.83	.17	1
Wood, shingles	.075	L.F.	.002	.37	.13	.50
Shakes	.075	L.F.	.002	.37	.13	.50
		L.F.				
Soffit & fascia, aluminum, vented, 1' overhang	.120	L.F.	.017	.59	1.02	1.61
2' overhang	.120	L.F.	.019	.86	1.12	1.98
Vinyl, vented, 1' overhang	.120	L.F.	.016	.62	.94	1.56
2' overhang	.120	L.F.	.017	.82	1.12	1.94
Wood, board fascia, plywood soffit, 1' overhang	.120	L.F.	.004	.02	.18	.20
2' overhang	.120	L.F.	.006	.04	.27	.31
Gutter, 5" box, aluminum, seamless, painted	.120	L.F.	.008	.38	.49	.87
Vinyl	.120	L.F.	.009	.21	.49	.70
Downspout, 2" x 3", aluminum, one story house	.035	L.F.	.002	.08	.10	.18
Two story house	.060	L.F.	.003	.09	.16	.25
Vinyl, one story house	.035	L.F.	.001	.05	.09	.14
Two story house	.060	L.F.	.003	.09	.16	.25

System Description	QUAN.	UNIT	LABOR HOURS	COST PER S.F.		
				MAT.	INST.	TOTAL
ASPHALT, ROOF SHINGLES, CLASS A						
Shingles, asphalt, inorganic, class A, 210-235 lb./sq.	1.450	S.F.	.022	1.34	1.19	2.53
Drip edge, metal, 5" wide	.146	L.F.	.003	.10	.17	.27
Building paper, #15 asphalt felt	1.500	S.F.	.002	.09	.11	.20
Ridge shingles, asphalt	.042	L.F.	.001	.10	.06	.16
Soffit & fascia, painted aluminum, 1' overhang	.083	L.F.	.012	.41	.71	1.12
Rake trim, 1" x 6"	.063	L.F.	.003	.08	.15	.23
Rake trim, prime and paint	.063	L.F.	.003	.02	.13	.15
Gutter, seamless, alumunum, painted	.083	L.F.	.005	.26	.34	.60
Downspouts, aluminum, painted	.042	L.F.	.002	.10	.12	.22
Ridge vent	.042	L.F.	.002	.11	.12	.23
TOTAL		S.F.	.055	2.61	3.10	5.71
WOOD, CEDAR SHINGLES, NO. 1 PERFECTIONS, 18" LONG						
Shingles, wood, red cedar, No. 1 perfections, 5" exposure	1.450	S.F.	.044	4.13	2.55	6.68
Drip edge, metal, 5" wide	.146	L.F.	.003	.10	.17	.27
Building paper, #15 asphalt felt	1.500	S.F.	.002	.09	.11	.20
Ridge shingles, wood	.042	L.F.	.001	.21	.07	.28
Soffit & fascia, white painted aluminum, 1' overhang	.083	L.F.	.012	.41	.71	1.12
Rake trim, 1" x 6"	.063	L.F.	.003	.08	.15	.23
Rake trim, prime and paint	.063	L.F.	.001	.02	.06	.08
Gutter, seamless, aluminum, painted	.083	L.F.	.005	.26	.34	.60
Downspouts, aluminum, painted	.042	L.F.	.002	.10	.12	.22
Ridge vent	.042	L.F.	.002	.11	.12	.23
TOTAL		S.F.	.075	5.51	4.40	9.91

The prices in this system are based on a square foot of plan area.
All quantities have been adjusted accordingly.

Description	QUAN.	UNIT	LABOR HOURS	COST PER S.F.		
				MAT.	INST.	TOTAL

Gambrel Roofing Price Sheet

	QUAN.	UNIT	LABOR HOURS	MAT.	INST.	TOTAL
				COST PER S.F.		
Shingles, asphalt, standard, inorganic, class A, 210-235 lb./sq.	1.450	S.F.	.022	1.34	1.19	2.53
Laminated, multi-layered, 240-260 lb./sq.	1.450	S.F.	.027	1.80	1.46	3.26
Premium laminated, multi-layered, 260-300 lb./sq.	1.450	S.F.	.034	2.61	1.88	4.49
Slate, Buckingham, Virginia, black	1.450	S.F.	.069	9.10	3.77	12.87
Vermont, black or grey	1.450	S.F.	.069	7.90	3.77	11.67
Wood, red cedar, No.1 5X, 16" long, 5" exposure, plain	1.450	S.F.	.048	4.65	2.81	7.46
Fire retardant	1.450	S.F.	.048	5.55	2.81	8.36
18" long, No.1 perfections, 6" exposure, plain	1.450	S.F.	.044	4.13	2.55	6.68
Fire retardant	1.450	S.F.	.044	5.05	2.55	7.60
Resquared & rebutted, 18" long, 6" exposure, plain	1.450	S.F.	.040	4.73	2.34	7.07
Fire retardant	1.450	S.F.	.040	5.70	2.34	8.04
Shakes, hand split, 24" long, 10" exposure, plain	1.450	S.F.	.048	4.73	2.81	7.54
Fire retardant	1.450	S.F.	.048	5.65	2.81	8.46
18" long, 8" exposure, plain	1.450	S.F.	.060	2.96	3.51	6.47
Fire retardant	1.450	S.F.	.060	3.88	3.51	7.39
Drip edge, metal, 5" wide	.146	L.F.	.003	.10	.17	.27
8" wide	.146	L.F.	.003	.13	.17	.30
Building paper, #15 asphalt felt	1.500	S.F.	.002	.09	.11	.20
Ridge shingles, asphalt	.042	L.F.	.001	.10	.06	.16
Slate	.042	L.F.	.002	.46	.09	.55
Wood, shingles	.042	L.F.	.001	.21	.07	.28
Soffit & fascia, aluminum, vented, 1' overhang	.083	L.F.	.012	.41	.71	1.12
2' overhang	.083	L.F.	.013	.59	.78	1.37
Vinyl vented, 1' overhang	.083	L.F.	.011	.43	.65	1.08
2' overhang	.083	L.F.	.012	.57	.78	1.35
Wood board fascia, plywood soffit, 1' overhang	.083	L.F.	.004	.02	.18	.20
2' overhang	.083	L.F.	.006	.04	.27	.31
Rake trim, painted, 1" x 6"	.063	L.F.	.006	.10	.28	.38
1" x 8"	.063	L.F.	.007	.13	.37	.50
Gutter, 5" box, aluminum, seamless, painted	.083	L.F.	.006	.26	.34	.60
Vinyl	.083	L.F.	.006	.15	.34	.49
Downspout 2" x 3", aluminum, one story house	.042	L.F.	.002	.07	.11	.18
Two story house	.070	L.F.	.003	.11	.19	.30
Vinyl, one story house	.042	L.F.	.002	.07	.11	.18
Two story house	.070	L.F.	.003	.11	.19	.30

Ridge Shingles

Shingles

Building Paper

Drip Edge

Soffit

System Description	QUAN.	UNIT	LABOR HOURS	COST PER S.F.		
				MAT.	INST.	TOTAL
ASPHALT, ROOF SHINGLES, CLASS A						
Shingles, standard inorganic class A 210-235 lb./sq.	2.210	S.F.	.032	1.97	1.75	3.72
Drip edge, metal, 5″ wide	.122	L.F.	.002	.08	.14	.22
Building paper, #15 asphalt felt	2.300	S.F.	.003	.13	.17	.30
Ridge shingles, asphalt	.090	L.F.	.002	.22	.12	.34
Soffit & fascia, white painted aluminum, 1′ overhang	.122	L.F.	.018	.60	1.04	1.64
Gutter, seamless, aluminum, painted	.122	L.F.	.008	.38	.50	.88
Downspouts, aluminum, painted	.042	L.F.	.002	.10	.12	.22
Ridge vent	.028	L.F.	.001	.07	.08	.15
TOTAL		S.F.	.068	3.55	3.92	7.47
WOOD, CEDAR SHINGLES, NO. 1 PERFECTIONS, 18″ LONG						
Shingles, wood, red cedar, No. 1 perfections, 5″ exposure	2.210	S.F.	.064	6.05	3.74	9.79
Drip edge, metal, 5″ wide	.122	L.F.	.002	.08	.14	.22
Building paper, #15 asphalt felt	2.300	S.F.	.003	.13	.17	.30
Ridge shingles, wood	.090	L.F.	.003	.45	.15	.60
Soffit & fascia, white painted aluminum, 1′ overhang	.122	L.F.	.018	.60	1.04	1.64
Gutter, seamless, aluminum, painted	.122	L.F.	.008	.38	.50	.88
Downspouts, aluminum, painted	.042	L.F.	.002	.10	.12	.22
Ridge vent	.028	L.F.	.001	.07	.08	.15
TOTAL		S.F.	.101	7.86	5.94	13.80

The prices in these systems are based on a square foot of plan area.
All quantities have been adjusted accordingly.

Description	QUAN.	UNIT	LABOR HOURS	COST PER S.F.		
				MAT.	INST.	TOTAL

Mansard Roofing Price Sheet	QUAN.	UNIT	LABOR HOURS	COST PER S.F.		
				MAT.	INST.	TOTAL
Shingles, asphalt, standard, inorganic, class A, 210-235 lb./sq.	2.210	S.F.	.032	1.97	1.75	3.72
Laminated, multi-layered, 240-260 lb./sq.	2.210	S.F.	.039	2.64	2.15	4.79
Premium laminated, multi-layered, 260-300 lb./sq.	2.210	S.F.	.050	3.83	2.75	6.58
Slate Buckingham, Virginia, black	2.210	S.F.	.101	13.30	5.50	18.80
Vermont, black or grey	2.210	S.F.	.101	11.55	5.50	17.05
Wood, red cedar, No.1 5X, 16" long, 5" exposure, plain	2.210	S.F.	.070	6.80	4.11	10.91
Fire retardant	2.210	S.F.	.070	8.15	4.11	12.26
18" long, No.1 perfections 6" exposure, plain	2.210	S.F.	.064	6.05	3.74	9.79
Fire retardant	2.210	S.F.	.064	7.40	3.74	11.14
Resquared & rebutted, 18" long, 6" exposure, plain	2.210	S.F.	.059	6.95	3.43	10.38
Fire retardant	2.210	S.F.	.059	8.30	3.43	11.73
Shakes, hand split, 24" long 10" exposure, plain	2.210	S.F.	.070	6.95	4.11	11.06
Fire retardant	2.210	S.F.	.070	8.30	4.11	12.41
18" long, 8" exposure, plain	2.210	S.F.	.088	4.33	5.15	9.48
Fire retardant	2.210	S.F.	.088	5.70	5.15	10.85
Drip edge, metal, 5" wide	.122	S.F.	.002	.08	.14	.22
8" wide	.122	S.F.	.002	.11	.14	.25
Building paper, #15 asphalt felt	2.300	S.F.	.003	.13	.17	.30
Ridge shingles, asphalt	.090	L.F.	.002	.22	.12	.34
Slate	.090	L.F.	.004	.99	.20	1.19
Wood, shingles	.090	L.F.	.003	.45	.15	.60
Soffit & fascia, aluminum vented, 1' overhang	.122	L.F.	.018	.60	1.04	1.64
2' overhang	.122	L.F.	.020	.87	1.14	2.01
Vinyl vented, 1' overhang	.122	L.F.	.016	.63	.95	1.58
2' overhang	.122	L.F.	.018	.84	1.14	1.98
Wood board fascia, plywood soffit, 1' overhang	.122	L.F.	.013	.38	.72	1.10
2' overhang	.122	L.F.	.019	.53	1.09	1.62
Gutter, 5" box, aluminum, seamless, painted	.122	L.F.	.008	.38	.50	.88
Vinyl	.122	L.F.	.009	.22	.50	.72
Downspout 2" x 3", aluminum, one story house	.042	L.F.	.002	.07	.11	.18
Two story house	.070	L.F.	.003	.11	.19	.30
Vinyl, one story house	.042	L.F.	.002	.07	.11	.18
Two story house	.070	L.F.	.003	.11	.19	.30

For customer support on your Residential Costs with RSMeans Data, call 800.448.8182.

201

System Description	QUAN.	UNIT	LABOR HOURS	COST PER S.F.		
				MAT.	INST.	TOTAL
ASPHALT, ROOF SHINGLES, CLASS A						
Shingles, inorganic class A 210-235 lb./sq. 4/12 pitch	1.230	S.F.	.019	1.16	1.03	2.19
Drip edge, metal, 5" wide	.100	L.F.	.002	.07	.12	.19
Building paper, #15 asphalt felt	1.300	S.F.	.002	.08	.10	.18
Soffit & fascia, white painted aluminum, 1' overhang	.080	L.F.	.012	.40	.68	1.08
Rake trim, 1" x 6"	.043	L.F.	.002	.06	.10	.16
Rake trim, prime and paint	.043	L.F.	.002	.01	.09	.10
Gutter, seamless, aluminum, painted	.040	L.F.	.003	.13	.16	.29
Downspouts, painted aluminum	.020	L.F.	.001	.05	.06	.11
TOTAL		S.F.	.043	1.96	2.34	4.30
WOOD, CEDAR SHINGLES, NO. 1 PERFECTIONS, 18" LONG						
Shingles, red cedar, No. 1 perfections, 5" exp., 4/12 pitch	1.230	S.F.	.035	3.30	2.04	5.34
Drip edge, metal, 5" wide	.100	L.F.	.002	.07	.12	.19
Building paper, #15 asphalt felt	1.300	S.F.	.002	.08	.10	.18
Soffit & fascia, white painted aluminum, 1' overhang	.080	L.F.	.012	.40	.68	1.08
Rake trim, 1" x 6"	.043	L.F.	.002	.06	.10	.16
Rake trim, prime and paint	.043	L.F.	.001	.01	.04	.05
Gutter, seamless, aluminum, painted	.040	L.F.	.003	.13	.16	.29
Downspouts, painted aluminum	.020	L.F.	.001	.05	.06	.11
TOTAL		S.F.	.058	4.10	3.30	7.40

The prices in these systems are based on a square foot of plan area.
All quantities have been adjusted accordingly.

Description	QUAN.	UNIT	LABOR HOURS	COST PER S.F.		
				MAT.	INST.	TOTAL

Shed Roofing Price Sheet

Shed Roofing Price Sheet	QUAN.	UNIT	LABOR HOURS	COST PER S.F.		
				MAT.	INST.	TOTAL
Shingles, asphalt, inorganic, class A, 210-235 lb./sq., 4/12 pitch	1.230	S.F.	.017	1.07	.95	2.02
8/12 pitch	1.330	S.F.	.019	1.16	1.03	2.19
Laminated, multi-layered, 240-260 lb./sq. 4/12 pitch	1.230	S.F.	.021	1.44	1.17	2.61
8/12 pitch	1.330	S.F.	.023	1.56	1.27	2.83
Premium laminated, multi-layered, 260-300 lb./sq. 4/12 pitch	1.230	S.F.	.027	2.09	1.50	3.59
8/12 pitch	1.330	S.F.	.030	2.26	1.63	3.89
Clay tile, Spanish tile, red, 4/12 pitch	1.230	S.F.	.053	6.65	2.88	9.53
8/12 pitch	1.330	S.F.	.058	7.20	3.12	10.32
Mission tile, red, 4/12 pitch	1.230	S.F.	.083	5.45	2.88	8.33
8/12 pitch	1.330	S.F.	.090	5.90	3.12	9.02
French tile, red, 4/12 pitch	1.230	S.F.	.071	15.30	2.64	17.94
8/12 pitch	1.330	S.F.	.077	16.60	2.86	19.46
Slate, Buckingham, Virginia, black, 4/12 pitch	1.230	S.F.	.055	7.25	3.01	10.26
8/12 pitch	1.330	S.F.	.059	7.85	3.26	11.11
Vermont, black or grey, 4/12 pitch	1.230	S.F.	.055	6.30	3.01	9.31
8/12 pitch	1.330	S.F.	.059	6.85	3.26	10.11
Wood, red cedar, No.1 5X, 16" long, 5" exposure, 4/12 pitch	1.230	S.F.	.038	3.72	2.24	5.96
8/12 pitch	1.330	S.F.	.042	4.03	2.43	6.46
Fire retardant, 4/12 pitch	1.230	S.F.	.038	4.46	2.24	6.70
8/12 pitch	1.330	S.F.	.042	4.83	2.43	7.26
18" long, 6" exposure, 4/12 pitch	1.230	S.F.	.035	3.30	2.04	5.34
8/12 pitch	1.330	S.F.	.038	3.58	2.21	5.79
Fire retardant, 4/12 pitch	1.230	S.F.	.035	4.04	2.04	6.08
8/12 pitch	1.330	S.F.	.038	4.38	2.21	6.59
Resquared & rebutted, 18" long, 6" exposure, 4/12 pitch	1.230	S.F.	.032	3.78	1.87	5.65
8/12 pitch	1.330	S.F.	.035	4.10	2.03	6.13
Fire retardant, 4/12 pitch	1.230	S.F.	.032	4.52	1.87	6.39
8/12 pitch	1.330	S.F.	.035	4.90	2.03	6.93
Wood shakes, hand split, 24" long, 10" exposure, 4/12 pitch	1.230	S.F.	.038	3.78	2.24	6.02
8/12 pitch	1.330	S.F.	.042	4.10	2.43	6.53
Fire retardant, 4/12 pitch	1.230	S.F.	.038	4.52	2.24	6.76
8/12 pitch	1.330	S.F.	.042	4.90	2.43	7.33
18" long, 8" exposure, 4/12 pitch	1.230	S.F.	.048	2.36	2.81	5.17
8/12 pitch	1.330	S.F.	.052	2.56	3.04	5.60
Fire retardant, 4/12 pitch	1.230	S.F.	.048	3.10	2.81	5.91
8/12 pitch	1.330	S.F.	.052	3.36	3.04	6.40
Drip edge, metal, 5" wide	.100	L.F.	.002	.07	.12	.19
8" wide	.100	L.F.	.002	.09	.12	.21
Building paper, #15 asphalt felt	1.300	S.F.	.002	.08	.10	.18
Soffit & fascia, aluminum vented, 1' overhang	.080	L.F.	.012	.40	.68	1.08
2' overhang	.080	L.F.	.013	.57	.75	1.32
Vinyl vented, 1' overhang	.080	L.F.	.011	.41	.62	1.03
2' overhang	.080	L.F.	.012	.55	.75	1.30
Wood board fascia, plywood soffit, 1' overhang	.080	L.F.	.010	.25	.52	.77
2' overhang	.080	L.F.	.014	.36	.79	1.15
Rake, trim, painted, 1" x 6"	.043	L.F.	.004	.07	.19	.26
1" x 8"	.043	L.F.	.004	.07	.19	.26
Gutter, 5" box, aluminum, seamless, painted	.040	L.F.	.003	.13	.16	.29
Vinyl	.040	L.F.	.003	.07	.16	.23
Downspout 2" x 3", aluminum, one story house	.020	L.F.	.001	.03	.05	.08
Two story house	.020	L.F.	.001	.05	.09	.14
Vinyl, one story house	.020	L.F.	.001	.03	.05	.08
Two story house	.020	L.F.	.001	.05	.09	.14

Ridge Shingles — Building Paper
Shingles — Rake Boards
— Drip Edge
— Soffit & Fascia
Flashing

System Description	QUAN.	UNIT	LABOR HOURS	COST PER S.F.		
				MAT.	INST.	TOTAL
ASPHALT, ROOF SHINGLES, CLASS A						
Shingles, standard inorganic class A 210-235 lb./sq	1.400	S.F.	.020	1.25	1.11	2.36
Drip edge, metal, 5″ wide	.220	L.F.	.004	.15	.26	.41
Building paper, #15 asphalt felt	1.500	S.F.	.002	.09	.11	.20
Ridge shingles, asphalt	.280	L.F.	.007	.69	.37	1.06
Soffit & fascia, aluminum, vented	.220	L.F.	.032	1.09	1.87	2.96
Flashing, aluminum, mill finish, .013″ thick	1.500	S.F.	.083	1.37	4.53	5.90
TOTAL		S.F.	.148	4.64	8.25	12.89
WOOD, CEDAR, NO. 1 PERFECTIONS						
Shingles, red cedar, No.1 perfections, 18″ long, 5″ exp.	1.400	S.F.	.041	3.85	2.38	6.23
Drip edge, metal, 5″ wide	.220	L.F.	.004	.15	.26	.41
Building paper, #15 asphalt felt	1.500	S.F.	.002	.09	.11	.20
Ridge shingles, wood	.280	L.F.	.008	1.39	.47	1.86
Soffit & fascia, aluminum, vented	.220	L.F.	.032	1.09	1.87	2.96
Flashing, aluminum, mill finish, .013″ thick	1.500	S.F.	.083	1.37	4.53	5.90
TOTAL		S.F.	.170	7.94	9.62	17.56
SLATE, BUCKINGHAM, BLACK						
Shingles, Buckingham, Virginia, black	1.400	S.F.	.064	8.47	3.51	11.98
Drip edge, metal, 5″ wide	.220	L.F.	.004	.15	.26	.41
Building paper, #15 asphalt felt	1.500	S.F.	.002	.09	.11	.20
Ridge shingles, slate	.280	L.F.	.011	3.08	.62	3.70
Soffit & fascia, aluminum, vented	.220	L.F.	.032	1.09	1.87	2.96
Flashing, copper, 16 oz.	1.500	S.F.	.104	13.05	5.72	18.77
TOTAL		S.F.	.217	25.93	12.09	38.02

The prices in these systems are based on a square foot of plan area under the dormer roof.

Description	QUAN.	UNIT	LABOR HOURS	COST PER S.F.		
				MAT.	INST.	TOTAL

Gable Dormer Roofing Price Sheet	QUAN.	UNIT	LABOR HOURS	COST PER S.F.		
				MAT.	INST.	TOTAL
Shingles, asphalt, standard, inorganic, class A, 210-235 lb./sq.	1.400	S.F.	.020	1.25	1.11	2.36
Laminated, multi-layered, 240-260 lb./sq.	1.400	S.F.	.025	1.68	1.37	3.05
Premium laminated, multi-layered, 260-300 lb./sq.	1.400	S.F.	.032	2.44	1.75	4.19
Clay tile, Spanish tile, red	1.400	S.F.	.062	7.75	3.36	11.11
Mission tile, red	1.400	S.F.	.097	6.35	3.36	9.71
French tile, red	1.400	S.F.	.083	17.85	3.08	20.93
Slate Buckingham, Virginia, black	1.400	S.F.	.064	8.45	3.51	11.96
Vermont, black or grey	1.400	S.F.	.064	7.35	3.51	10.86
Wood, red cedar, No.1 5X, 16" long, 5" exposure	1.400	S.F.	.045	4.34	2.62	6.96
Fire retardant	1.400	S.F.	.045	5.20	2.62	7.82
18" long, No.1 perfections, 5" exposure	1.400	S.F.	.041	3.85	2.38	6.23
Fire retardant	1.400	S.F.	.041	4.71	2.38	7.09
Resquared & rebutted, 18" long, 5" exposure	1.400	S.F.	.037	4.41	2.18	6.59
Fire retardant	1.400	S.F.	.037	5.25	2.18	7.43
Shakes hand split, 24" long, 10" exposure	1.400	S.F.	.045	4.41	2.62	7.03
Fire retardant	1.400	S.F.	.045	5.25	2.62	7.87
18" long, 8" exposure	1.400	S.F.	.056	2.76	3.28	6.04
Fire retardant	1.400	S.F.	.056	3.62	3.28	6.90
Drip edge, metal, 5" wide	.220	L.F.	.004	.15	.26	.41
8" wide	.220	L.F.	.004	.20	.26	.46
Building paper, #15 asphalt felt	1.500	S.F.	.002	.09	.11	.20
Ridge shingles, asphalt	.280	L.F.	.007	.69	.37	1.06
Clay	.280	L.F.	.011	1.53	1.85	3.38
Slate	.280	L.F.	.011	3.08	.62	3.70
Wood	.280	L.F.	.008	1.39	.47	1.86
Soffit & fascia, aluminum, vented	.220	L.F.	.032	1.09	1.87	2.96
Vinyl, vented	.220	L.F.	.029	1.13	1.72	2.85
Wood, board fascia, plywood soffit	.220	L.F.	.026	.70	1.43	2.13
Flashing, aluminum, .013" thick	1.500	S.F.	.083	1.37	4.53	5.90
.032" thick	1.500	S.F.	.083	2.28	4.53	6.81
.040" thick	1.500	S.F.	.083	3.89	4.53	8.42
.050" thick	1.500	S.F.	.083	4.55	4.53	9.08
Copper, 16 oz.	1.500	S.F.	.104	13.05	5.70	18.75
20 oz.	1.500	S.F.	.109	17.35	5.95	23.30
24 oz.	1.500	S.F.	.114	24.50	6.25	30.75
32 oz.	1.500	S.F.	.120	31.50	6.55	38.05

System Description	QUAN.	UNIT	LABOR HOURS	COST PER S.F.		
				MAT.	INST.	TOTAL
ASPHALT, ROOF SHINGLES, CLASS A						
Shingles, standard inorganic class A 210-235 lb./sq.	1.100	S.F.	.016	.98	.87	1.85
Drip edge, aluminum, 5" wide	.250	L.F.	.005	.16	.29	.45
Building paper, #15 asphalt felt	1.200	S.F.	.002	.07	.09	.16
Soffit & fascia, aluminum, vented, 1' overhang	.250	L.F.	.036	1.24	2.13	3.37
Flashing, aluminum, mill finish, 0.013" thick	.800	L.F.	.044	.73	2.42	3.15
TOTAL		S.F.	.103	3.18	5.80	8.98
WOOD, CEDAR, NO. 1 PERFECTIONS, 18" LONG						
Shingles, wood, red cedar, #1 perfections, 5" exposure	1.100	S.F.	.032	3.03	1.87	4.90
Drip edge, aluminum, 5" wide	.250	L.F.	.005	.16	.29	.45
Building paper, #15 asphalt felt	1.200	S.F.	.002	.07	.09	.16
Soffit & fascia, aluminum, vented, 1' overhang	.250	L.F.	.036	1.24	2.13	3.37
Flashing, aluminum, mill finish, 0.013" thick	.800	L.F.	.044	.73	2.42	3.15
TOTAL		S.F.	.119	5.23	6.80	12.03
SLATE, BUCKINGHAM, BLACK						
Shingles, slate, Buckingham, black	1.100	S.F.	.050	6.66	2.76	9.42
Drip edge, aluminum, 5" wide	.250	L.F.	.005	.16	.29	.45
Building paper, #15 asphalt felt	1.200	S.F.	.002	.07	.09	.16
Soffit & fascia, aluminum, vented, 1' overhang	.250	L.F.	.036	1.24	2.13	3.37
Flashing, copper, 16 oz.	.800	L.F.	.056	6.96	3.05	10.01
TOTAL		S.F.	.149	15.09	8.32	23.41

The prices in this system are based on a square foot of plan area under the dormer roof.

Description	QUAN.	UNIT	LABOR HOURS	COST PER S.F.		
				MAT.	INST.	TOTAL

Shed Dormer Roofing Price Sheet	QUAN.	UNIT	LABOR HOURS	COST PER S.F.		
				MAT.	INST.	TOTAL
Shingles, asphalt, standard, inorganic, class A, 210-235 lb./sq.	1.100	S.F.	.016	.98	.87	1.85
Laminated, multi-layered, 240-260 lb./sq.	1.100	S.F.	.020	1.32	1.07	2.39
Premium laminated, multi-layered, 260-300 lb./sq.	1.100	S.F.	.025	1.91	1.38	3.29
Clay tile, Spanish tile, red	1.100	S.F.	.049	6.10	2.64	8.74
Mission tile, red	1.100	S.F.	.077	5	2.64	7.64
French tile, red	1.100	S.F.	.065	14.05	2.42	16.47
Slate Buckingham, Virginia, black	1.100	S.F.	.050	6.65	2.76	9.41
Vermont, black or grey	1.100	S.F.	.050	5.80	2.76	8.56
Wood, red cedar, No. 1 5X, 16" long, 5" exposure	1.100	S.F.	.035	3.41	2.06	5.47
Fire retardant	1.100	S.F.	.035	4.09	2.06	6.15
18" long, No.1 perfections, 5" exposure	1.100	S.F.	.032	3.03	1.87	4.90
Fire retardant	1.100	S.F.	.032	3.71	1.87	5.58
Resquared & rebutted, 18" long, 5" exposure	1.100	S.F.	.029	3.47	1.72	5.19
Fire retardant	1.100	S.F.	.029	4.15	1.72	5.87
Shakes hand split, 24" long, 10" exposure	1.100	S.F.	.035	3.47	2.06	5.53
Fire retardant	1.100	S.F.	.035	4.15	2.06	6.21
18" long, 8" exposure	1.100	S.F.	.044	2.17	2.57	4.74
Fire retardant	1.100	S.F.	.044	2.85	2.57	5.42
Drip edge, metal, 5" wide	.250	L.F.	.005	.16	.29	.45
8" wide	.250	L.F.	.005	.23	.29	.52
Building paper, #15 asphalt felt	1.200	S.F.	.002	.07	.09	.16
Soffit & fascia, aluminum, vented	.250	L.F.	.036	1.24	2.13	3.37
Vinyl, vented	.250	L.F.	.033	1.29	1.95	3.24
Wood, board fascia, plywood soffit	.250	L.F.	.030	.81	1.64	2.45
Flashing, aluminum, .013" thick	.800	L.F.	.044	.73	2.42	3.15
.032" thick	.800	L.F.	.044	1.22	2.42	3.64
.040" thick	.800	L.F.	.044	2.07	2.42	4.49
.050" thick	.800	L.F.	.044	2.42	2.42	4.84
Copper, 16 oz.	.800	L.F.	.056	6.95	3.05	10
20 oz.	.800	L.F.	.058	9.25	3.18	12.43
24 oz.	.800	L.F.	.061	13	3.34	16.34
32 oz.	.800	L.F.	.064	16.80	3.50	20.30

For customer support on your Residential Costs with RSMeans Data, call 800.448.8182.

207

System Description	QUAN.	UNIT	LABOR HOURS	COST EACH		
				MAT.	INST.	TOTAL
SKYLIGHT, FIXED, 32″ X 32″						
Skylight, fixed bubble, insulating, 32″ x 32″	1.000	Ea.	1.422	234.66	77.15	311.81
Trimmer rafters, 2″ x 6″	28.000	L.F.	.448	19.32	26.32	45.64
Headers, 2″ x 6″	6.000	L.F.	.267	4.14	15.60	19.74
Curb, 2″ x 4″	12.000	L.F.	.154	5.40	9	14.40
Flashing, aluminum, .013″ thick	13.500	S.F.	.745	12.29	40.77	53.06
Moldings, casing, ogee, 11/16″ x 2-1/2″, pine	12.000	L.F.	.384	18.60	22.44	41.04
Trim primer coat, oil base, brushwork	12.000	L.F.	.148	.48	7.08	7.56
Trim paint, 1 coat, brushwork	12.000	L.F.	.148	.72	7.08	7.80
TOTAL		Ea.	3.716	295.61	205.44	501.05
SKYLIGHT, FIXED, 48″ X 48″						
Skylight, fixed bubble, insulating, 48″ x 48″	1.000	Ea.	1.296	560	70.24	630.24
Trimmer rafters, 2″ x 6″	28.000	L.F.	.448	19.32	26.32	45.64
Headers, 2″ x 6″	8.000	L.F.	.356	5.52	20.80	26.32
Curb, 2″ x 4″	16.000	L.F.	.205	7.20	12	19.20
Flashing, aluminum, .013″ thick	16.000	S.F.	.883	14.56	48.32	62.88
Moldings, casing, ogee, 11/16″ x 2-1/2″, pine	16.000	L.F.	.512	24.80	29.92	54.72
Trim primer coat, oil base, brushwork	16.000	L.F.	.197	.64	9.44	10.08
Trim paint, 1 coat, brushwork	16.000	L.F.	.197	.96	9.44	10.40
TOTAL		Ea.	4.094	633	226.48	859.48
SKYWINDOW, OPERATING, 24″ X 48″						
Skywindow, operating, thermopane glass, 24″ x 48″	1.000	Ea.	3.200	645	174	819
Trimmer rafters, 2″ x 6″	28.000	L.F.	.448	19.32	26.32	45.64
Headers, 2″ x 6″	8.000	L.F.	.267	4.14	15.60	19.74
Curb, 2″ x 4″	14.000	L.F.	.179	6.30	10.50	16.80
Flashing, aluminum, .013″ thick	14.000	S.F.	.772	12.74	42.28	55.02
Moldings, casing, ogee, 11/16″ x 2-1/2″, pine	14.000	L.F.	.448	21.70	26.18	47.88
Trim primer coat, oil base, brushwork	14.000	L.F.	.172	.56	8.26	8.82
Trim paint, 1 coat, brushwork	14.000	L.F.	.172	.84	8.26	9.10
TOTAL		Ea.	5.658	710.60	311.40	1,022

The prices in these systems are on a cost each basis.

Description	QUAN.	UNIT	LABOR HOURS	COST EACH		
				MAT.	INST.	TOTAL

Skylight/Skywindow Price Sheet	QUAN.	UNIT	LABOR HOURS	COST EACH		
				MAT.	INST.	TOTAL
Skylight, fixed bubble insulating, 24" x 24"	1.000	Ea.	.800	132	43.50	175.50
32" x 32"	1.000	Ea.	1.422	235	77	312
32" x 48"	1.000	Ea.	.864	375	47	422
48" x 48"	1.000	Ea.	1.296	560	70	630
Ventilating bubble insulating, 36" x 36"	1.000	Ea.	2.667	530	145	675
52" x 52"	1.000	Ea.	2.667	735	145	880
28" x 52"	1.000	Ea.	3.200	540	174	714
36" x 52"	1.000	Ea.	3.200	595	174	769
Skywindow, operating, thermopane glass, 24" x 48"	1.000	Ea.	3.200	645	174	819
32" x 48"	1.000	Ea.	3.556	675	193	868
Trimmer rafters, 2" x 6"	28.000	L.F.	.448	19.30	26.50	45.80
2" x 8"	28.000	L.F.	.472	27	27.50	54.50
2" x 10"	28.000	L.F.	.711	42.50	41.50	84
Headers, 24" window, 2" x 6"	4.000	L.F.	.178	2.76	10.40	13.16
2" x 8"	4.000	L.F.	.188	3.84	11	14.84
2" x 10"	4.000	L.F.	.200	6.05	11.70	17.75
32" window, 2" x 6"	6.000	L.F.	.267	4.14	15.60	19.74
2" x 8"	6.000	L.F.	.282	5.75	16.50	22.25
2" x 10"	6.000	L.F.	.300	9.05	17.50	26.55
48" window, 2" x 6"	8.000	L.F.	.356	5.50	21	26.50
2" x 8"	8.000	L.F.	.376	7.70	22	29.70
2" x 10"	8.000	L.F.	.400	12.10	23.50	35.60
Curb, 2" x 4", skylight, 24" x 24"	8.000	L.F.	.102	3.60	6	9.60
32" x 32"	12.000	L.F.	.154	5.40	9	14.40
32" x 48"	14.000	L.F.	.179	6.30	10.50	16.80
48" x 48"	16.000	L.F.	.205	7.20	12	19.20
Flashing, aluminum .013" thick, skylight, 24" x 24"	9.000	S.F.	.497	8.20	27	35.20
32" x 32"	13.500	S.F.	.745	12.30	41	53.30
32" x 48"	14.000	S.F.	.772	12.75	42.50	55.25
48" x 48"	16.000	S.F.	.883	14.55	48.50	63.05
Copper 16 oz., skylight, 24" x 24"	9.000	S.F.	.626	78.50	34.50	113
32" x 32"	13.500	S.F.	.939	117	51.50	168.50
32" x 48"	14.000	S.F.	.974	122	53.50	175.50
48" x 48"	16.000	S.F.	1.113	139	61	200
Trim, interior casing painted, 24" x 24"	8.000	L.F.	.347	13.60	18.80	32.40
32" x 32"	12.000	L.F.	.520	20.50	28	48.50
32" x 48"	14.000	L.F.	.607	24	33	57
48" x 48"	16.000	L.F.	.693	27	37.50	64.50

Flashing
4" x 4" Cant
6" x 2-1/4" Wood Blocking
Gravel
Asphalt
Felt
Insulation Board

System Description	QUAN.	UNIT	LABOR HOURS	COST PER S.F.		
				MAT.	INST.	TOTAL
ASPHALT, ORGANIC, 4-PLY, INSULATED DECK						
Membrane, asphalt, 4-plies #15 felt, gravel surfacing	1.000	S.F.	.025	1.45	1.58	3.03
Insulation board, 2-layers of 1-1/16" glass fiber	2.000	S.F.	.012	2.28	.68	2.96
Roof deck insulation, fastening alternatives, coated screws, 4" long	1.000	S.F	.003	.12	.14	.26
Wood blocking, 2" x 6"	.040	L.F.	.004	.08	.25	.33
Treated 4" x 4" cant strip	.040	L.F.	.001	.08	.06	.14
Flashing, aluminum, 0.040" thick	.050	S.F.	.003	.13	.15	.28
TOTAL		S.F.	.048	4.14	2.86	7
ASPHALT, INORGANIC, 3-PLY, INSULATED DECK						
Membrane, asphalt, 3-plies type IV glass felt, gravel surfacing	1.000	S.F.	.028	1.49	1.73	3.22
Insulation board, 2-layers of 1-1/16" glass fiber	2.000	S.F.	.012	2.28	.68	2.96
Roof deck insulation, fastening alternatives, coated screws, 4" long	1.000	S.F	.003	.12	.14	.26
Wood blocking, 2" x 6"	.040	L.F.	.004	.08	.25	.33
Treated 4" x 4" cant strip	.040	L.F.	.001	.08	.06	.14
Flashing, aluminum, 0.040" thick	.050	S.F.	.003	.13	.15	.28
TOTAL		S.F.	.051	4.18	3.01	7.19
COAL TAR, ORGANIC, 4-PLY, INSULATED DECK						
Membrane, coal tar, 4-plies #15 felt, gravel surfacing	1.000	S.F.	.027	2.21	1.65	3.86
Insulation board, 2-layers of 1-1/16" glass fiber	2.000	S.F.	.012	2.28	.68	2.96
Roof deck insulation, fastening alternatives, coated screws, 4" long	1.000	S.F	.003	.12	.14	.26
Wood blocking, 2" x 6"	.040	L.F.	.004	.08	.25	.33
Treated 4" x 4" cant strip	.040	L.F.	.001	.08	.06	.14
Flashing, aluminum, 0.040" thick	.050	S.F.	.003	.13	.15	.28
TOTAL		S.F.	.050	4.90	2.93	7.83
COAL TAR, INORGANIC, 3-PLY, INSULATED DECK						
Membrane, coal tar, 3-plies type IV glass felt, gravel surfacing	1.000	S.F.	.029	1.82	1.83	3.65
Insulation board, 2-layers of 1-1/16" glass fiber	2.000	S.F.	.012	2.28	.68	2.96
Roof deck insulation, fastening alternatives, coated screws, 4" long	1.000	S.F	.003	.12	.14	.26
Wood blocking, 2" x 6"	.040	L.F.	.004	.08	.25	.33
Treated 4" x 4" cant strip	.040	L.F.	.001	.08	.06	.14
Flashing, aluminum, 0.040" thick	.050	S.F.	.003	.13	.15	.28
TOTAL		S.F.	.052	4.51	3.11	7.62

Built-Up Roofing Price Sheet	QUAN.	UNIT	LABOR HOURS	COST PER S.F.		
				MAT.	INST.	TOTAL
Membrane, asphalt, 4-plies #15 organic felt, gravel surfacing	1.000	S.F.	.025	1.45	1.58	3.03
Asphalt base sheet & 3-plies #15 asphalt felt	1.000	S.F.	.025	1.11	1.58	2.69
3-plies type IV glass fiber felt	1.000	S.F.	.028	1.49	1.73	3.22
4-plies type IV glass fiber felt	1.000	S.F.	.028	1.85	1.73	3.58
Coal tar, 4-plies #15 organic felt, gravel surfacing	1.000	S.F.	.027			
4-plies tarred felt	1.000	S.F.	.027	2.21	1.65	3.86
3-plies type IV glass fiber felt	1.000	S.F.	.029	1.82	1.83	3.65
4-plies type IV glass fiber felt	1.000	S.F.	.027	2.53	1.65	4.18
Roll, asphalt, 1-ply #15 organic felt, 2-plies mineral surfaced	1.000	S.F.	.021	.84	1.29	2.13
3-plies type IV glass fiber, 1-ply mineral surfaced	1.000	S.F.	.022	1.45	1.39	2.84
Insulation boards, glass fiber, 1-1/16" thick	1.000	S.F.	.008	1.26	.48	1.74
2-1/16" thick	1.000	S.F.	.010	1.77	.56	2.33
2-7/16" thick	1.000	S.F.	.010	1.99	.56	2.55
Expanded perlite, 1" thick	1.000	S.F.	.010	.70	.56	1.26
1-1/2" thick	1.000	S.F.	.010	.98	.56	1.54
2" thick	1.000	S.F.	.011	1.30	.62	1.92
Fiberboard, 1" thick	1.000	S.F.	.010	.74	.56	1.30
1-1/2" thick	1.000	S.F.	.010	1.06	.56	1.62
2" thick	1.000	S.F.	.010	1.33	.56	1.89
Extruded polystyrene, 15 PSI compressive strength, 2" thick R10	1.000	S.F.	.006	.99	.41	1.40
3" thick R15	1.000	S.F.	.008	1.86	.48	2.34
4" thick R20	1.000	S.F.	.008	2.47	.48	2.95
Tapered for drainage	1.000	S.F.	.005	.81	.36	1.17
40 PSI compressive strength, 1" thick R5	1.000	S.F.	.005	.71	.36	1.07
2" thick R10	1.000	S.F.	.006	1.25	.41	1.66
3" thick R15	1.000	S.F.	.008	1.75	.48	2.23
4" thick R20	1.000	S.F.	.008	2.26	.48	2.74
Fiberboard high density, 1/2" thick R1.3	1.000	S.F.	.008	.45	.48	.93
1" thick R2.5	1.000	S.F.	.010	.74	.56	1.30
1 1/2" thick R3.8	1.000	S.F.	.010	1.07	.56	1.63
Polyisocyanurate, 1 1/2" thick	1.000	S.F.	.006	.77	.41	1.18
2" thick	1.000	S.F.	.007	.95	.45	1.40
3 1/2" thick	1.000	S.F.	.008	2.03	.48	2.51
Tapered for drainage	1.000	S.F.	.006	.77	.38	1.15
Expanded polystyrene, 1" thick	1.000	S.F.	.005	.41	.36	.77
2" thick R10	1.000	S.F.	.006	.69	.41	1.10
3" thick	1.000	S.F.	.006	.98	.41	1.39
Wood blocking, treated, 6" x 2" & 4" x 4" cant	.040	L.F.	.002	.14	.14	.28
6" x 4-1/2" & 4" x 4" cant	.040	L.F.	.005	.20	.31	.51
6" x 5" & 4" x 4" cant	.040	L.F.	.007	.24	.40	.64
Flashing, aluminum, 0.019" thick	.050	S.F.	.003	.07	.15	.22
0.032" thick	.050	S.F.	.003	.08	.15	.23
0.040" thick	.050	S.F.	.003	.13	.15	.28
Copper sheets, 16 oz., under 500 lbs.	.050	S.F.	.003	.44	.19	.63
Over 500 lbs.	.050	S.F.	.003	.44	.14	.58
20 oz., under 500 lbs.	.050	S.F.	.004	.58	.20	.78
Over 500 lbs.	.050	S.F.	.003	.55	.15	.70
Stainless steel, 32 gauge	.050	S.F.	.003	.18	.14	.32
28 gauge	.050	S.F.	.003	.23	.14	.37
26 gauge	.050	S.F.	.003	.25	.14	.39
24 gauge	.050	S.F.	.003	.28	.14	.42

Corners — Finish

Paint

Trim — Drywall

System Description	QUAN.	UNIT	LABOR HOURS	COST PER S.F.		
				MAT.	INST.	TOTAL
1/2″ DRYWALL, TAPED & FINISHED						
Gypsum wallboard, 1/2″ thick, standard	1.000	S.F.	.008	.37	.47	.84
Finish, taped & finished joints	1.000	S.F.	.008	.05	.47	.52
Corners, taped & finished, 32 L.F. per 12′ x 12′ room	.083	L.F.	.002	.01	.09	.10
Painting, primer & 2 coats	1.000	S.F.	.011	.22	.51	.73
Paint trim, to 6″ wide, primer + 1 coat enamel	.125	L.F.	.001	.02	.06	.08
Moldings, base, ogee profile, 9/16″ x 4-1/2, red oak	.125	L.F.	.005	.58	.27	.85
TOTAL		S.F.	.035	1.25	1.87	3.12
THINCOAT, SKIM-COAT, ON 1/2″ BACKER DRYWALL						
Gypsum wallboard, 1/2″ thick, thincoat backer	1.000	S.F.	.008	.37	.47	.84
Thincoat plaster	1.000	S.F.	.011	.12	.62	.74
Corners, taped & finished, 32 L.F. per 12′ x 12′ room	.083	L.F.	.002	.01	.09	.10
Painting, primer & 2 coats	1.000	S.F.	.011	.22	.51	.73
Paint trim, to 6″ wide, primer + 1 coat enamel	.125	L.F.	.001	.02	.06	.08
Moldings, base, ogee profile, 9/16″ x 4-1/2, red oak	.125	L.F.	.005	.58	.27	.85
TOTAL		S.F.	.038	1.32	2.02	3.34
5/8″ DRYWALL, TAPED & FINISHED						
Gypsum wallboard, 5/8″ thick, standard	1.000	S.F.	.008	.39	.47	.86
Finish, taped & finished joints	1.000	S.F.	.008	.05	.47	.52
Corners, taped & finished, 32 L.F. per 12′ x 12′ room	.083	L.F.	.002	.01	.09	.10
Painting, primer & 2 coats	1.000	S.F.	.011	.22	.51	.73
Moldings, base, ogee profile, 9/16″ x 4-1/2, red oak	.125	L.F.	.005	.58	.27	.85
Paint trim, to 6″ wide, primer + 1 coat enamel	.125	L.F.	.001	.02	.06	.08
TOTAL		S.F.	.035	1.27	1.87	3.14

The costs in this system are based on a square foot of wall.
Do not deduct for openings.

Description	QUAN.	UNIT	LABOR HOURS	COST PER S.F.		
				MAT.	INST.	TOTAL

Drywall & Thincoat Wall Price Sheet

	QUAN.	UNIT	LABOR HOURS	COST PER S.F.		
				MAT.	INST.	TOTAL
Gypsum wallboard, 1/2" thick, standard	1.000	S.F.	.008	.37	.47	.84
Fire resistant	1.000	S.F.	.008	.41	.47	.88
Water resistant	1.000	S.F.	.008	.46	.47	.93
5/8" thick, standard	1.000	S.F.	.008	.39	.47	.86
Fire resistant	1.000	S.F.	.008	.40	.47	.87
Water resistant	1.000	S.F.	.008	.48	.47	.95
Gypsum wallboard backer for thincoat system, 1/2" thick	1.000	S.F.	.008	.37	.47	.84
5/8" thick	1.000	S.F.	.008	.39	.47	.86
Gypsum wallboard, taped & finished	1.000	S.F.	.008	.05	.47	.52
Texture spray	1.000	S.F.	.010	.04	.56	.60
Thincoat plaster, including tape	1.000	S.F.	.011	.12	.62	.74
Gypsum wallboard corners, taped & finished, 32 L.F. per 4' x 4' room	.250	L.F.	.004	.03	.25	.28
6' x 6' room	.110	L.F.	.002	.01	.11	.12
10' x 10' room	.100	L.F.	.001	.01	.10	.11
12' x 12' room	.083	L.F.	.001	.01	.08	.09
16' x 16' room	.063	L.F.	.001	.01	.06	.07
Thincoat system, 32 L.F. per 4' x 4' room	.250	L.F.	.003	.03	.16	.19
6' x 6' room	.110	L.F.	.001	.01	.06	.07
10' x 10' room	.100	L.F.	.001	.01	.06	.07
12' x 12' room	.083	L.F.	.001	.01	.05	.06
16' x 16' room	.063	L.F.	.001	.01	.04	.05
Painting, primer, & 1 coat	1.000	S.F.	.008	.14	.40	.54
& 2 coats	1.000	S.F.	.011	.22	.51	.73
Wallpaper, $7/double roll	1.000	S.F.	.013	.65	.60	1.25
$17/double roll	1.000	S.F.	.015	1.29	.72	2.01
$40/double roll	1.000	S.F.	.018	2	.89	2.89
Wallcovering, medium weight vinyl		S.F.	.017	1	.81	1.81
Tile, ceramic adhesive thin set, 4 1/4" x 4 1/4" tiles	1.000	S.F.	.084	2.87	4.07	6.94
6" x 6" tiles	1.000	S.F.	.080	3.94	4.42	8.36
Pregrouted sheets	1.000	S.F.	.067	6.20	3.23	9.43
Trim, painted or stained, baseboard	.125	L.F.	.006	.60	.33	.93
Base shoe	.125	L.F.	.005	.07	.30	.37
Chair rail	.125	L.F.	.005	.22	.28	.50
Cornice molding	.125	L.F.	.004	.15	.28	.43
Cove base, vinyl	.125	L.F.	.003	.16	.17	.33
Paneling, not including furring or trim						
Plywood, prefinished, 1/4" thick, 4' x 8' sheets, vert. grooves						
Birch faced, minimum	1.000	S.F.	.032	1.62	1.87	3.49
Average	1.000	S.F.	.038	1.32	2.23	3.55
Maximum	1.000	S.F.	.046	1.40	2.67	4.07
Mahogany, African	1.000	S.F.	.040	2.70	2.34	5.04
Philippine (lauan)	1.000	S.F.	.032	.72	1.87	2.59
Oak or cherry, minimum	1.000	S.F.	.032	1.47	1.87	3.34
Maximum	1.000	S.F.	.040	2.20	2.34	4.54
Rosewood	1.000	S.F.	.050	3.41	2.92	6.33
Teak	1.000	S.F.	.040	3.43	2.34	5.77
Chestnut	1.000	S.F.	.043	5.80	2.49	8.29
Pecan	1.000	S.F.	.040	2.75	2.34	5.09
Walnut, minimum	1.000	S.F.	.032	2.72	1.87	4.59
Maximum	1.000	S.F.	.040	5.55	2.34	7.89

System Description	QUAN.	UNIT	LABOR HOURS	COST PER S.F.		
				MAT.	INST.	TOTAL
1/2″ GYPSUM WALLBOARD, TAPED & FINISHED						
Gypsum wallboard, 1/2″ thick, standard	1.000	S.F.	.008	.37	.47	.84
Finish, taped & finished	1.000	S.F.	.008	.05	.47	.52
Corners, taped & finished, 12′ x 12′ room	.333	L.F.	.006	.04	.32	.36
Paint, primer & 2 coats	1.000	S.F.	.011	.22	.51	.73
TOTAL		S.F.	.033	.68	1.77	2.45
THINCOAT, SKIM COAT ON 1/2″ GYPSUM WALLBOARD						
Gypsum wallboard, 1/2″ thick, thincoat backer	1.000	S.F.	.008	.37	.47	.84
Thincoat plaster	1.000	S.F.	.011	.12	.62	.74
Corners, taped & finished, 12′ x 12′ room	.333	L.F.	.006	.04	.32	.36
Paint, primer & 2 coats	1.000	S.F.	.011	.22	.51	.73
TOTAL		S.F.	.036	.75	1.92	2.67
WATER-RESISTANT GYPSUM WALLBOARD, 1/2″ THICK, TAPED & FINISHED						
Gypsum wallboard, 1/2″ thick, water-resistant	1.000	S.F.	.008	.46	.47	.93
Finish, taped & finished	1.000	S.F.	.008	.05	.47	.52
Corners, taped & finished, 12′ x 12′ room	.333	L.F.	.006	.04	.32	.36
Paint, primer & 2 coats	1.000	S.F.	.011	.22	.51	.73
TOTAL		S.F.	.033	.77	1.77	2.54
5/8″ GYPSUM WALLBOARD, TAPED & FINISHED						
Gypsum wallboard, 5/8″ thick, standard	1.000	S.F.	.008	.39	.47	.86
Finish, taped & finished	1.000	S.F.	.008	.05	.47	.52
Corners, taped & finished, 12′ x 12′ room	.333	L.F.	.006	.04	.32	.36
Paint, primer & 2 coats	1.000	S.F.	.011	.22	.51	.73
TOTAL		S.F.	.033	.70	1.77	2.47

The costs in this system are based on a square foot of ceiling.

Description	QUAN.	UNIT	LABOR HOURS	COST PER S.F.		
				MAT.	INST.	TOTAL

Drywall & Thincoat Ceilings Price Sheet	QUAN.	UNIT	LABOR HOURS	COST PER S.F.		
				MAT.	INST.	TOTAL
Gypsum wallboard ceilings, 1/2" thick, standard	1.000	S.F.	.008	.37	.47	.84
Fire resistant	1.000	S.F.	.008	.41	.47	.88
Water resistant	1.000	S.F.	.008	.46	.47	.93
5/8" thick, standard	1.000	S.F.	.008	.39	.47	.86
Fire resistant	1.000	S.F.	.008	.40	.47	.87
Water resistant	1.000	S.F.	.008	.48	.47	.95
Gypsum wallboard backer for thincoat ceiling system, 1/2" thick	1.000	S.F.	.016	.78	.94	1.72
5/8" thick	1.000	S.F.	.016	.80	.94	1.74
Gypsum wallboard ceilings, taped & finished	1.000	S.F.	.008	.05	.47	.52
Texture spray	1.000	S.F.	.010	.04	.56	.60
Thincoat plaster	1.000	S.F.	.011	.12	.62	.74
Corners taped & finished, 4' x 4' room	1.000	L.F.	.015	.11	.98	1.09
6' x 6' room	.667	L.F.	.010	.07	.66	.73
10' x 10' room	.400	L.F.	.006	.04	.39	.43
12' x 12' room	.333	L.F.	.005	.04	.32	.36
16' x 16' room	.250	L.F.	.003	.02	.18	.20
Thincoat system, 4' x 4' room	1.000	L.F.	.011	.12	.62	.74
6' x 6' room	.667	L.F.	.007	.08	.42	.50
10' x 10' room	.400	L.F.	.004	.05	.25	.30
12' x 12' room	.333	L.F.	.004	.04	.20	.24
16' x 16' room	.250	L.F.	.002	.02	.12	.14
Painting, primer & 1 coat	1.000	S.F.	.008	.14	.40	.54
& 2 coats	1.000	S.F.	.011	.22	.51	.73
Wallpaper, double roll, solid pattern, avg. workmanship	1.000	S.F.	.013	.65	.60	1.25
Basic pattern, avg. workmanship	1.000	S.F.	.015	1.29	.72	2.01
Basic pattern, quality workmanship	1.000	S.F.	.018	2	.89	2.89
Tile, ceramic adhesive thin set, 4 1/4" x 4 1/4" tiles	1.000	S.F.	.084	2.87	4.07	6.94
6" x 6" tiles	1.000	S.F.	.080	3.94	4.42	8.36
Pregrouted sheets	1.000	S.F.	.067	6.20	3.23	9.43

System Description	QUAN.	UNIT	LABOR HOURS	COST PER S.F.		
				MAT.	INST.	TOTAL
PLASTER ON GYPSUM LATH						
Plaster, gypsum or perlite, 2 coats	1.000	S.F.	.053	.45	2.99	3.44
Lath, 3/8" gypsum	1.000	S.F.	.010	.39	.58	.97
Corners, expanded metal, 32 L.F. per 12' x 12' room	.083	L.F.	.002	.01	.10	.11
Painting, primer & 2 coats	1.000	S.F.	.011	.22	.51	.73
Paint trim, to 6" wide, primer + 1 coat enamel	.125	L.F.	.001	.02	.06	.08
Moldings, base, ogee profile, 9/16" x 4-1/2, red oak	.125	L.F.	.005	.58	.27	.85
TOTAL		S.F.	.082	1.67	4.51	6.18
PLASTER ON METAL LATH						
Plaster, gypsum or perlite, 2 coats	1.000	S.F.	.053	.45	2.99	3.44
Lath, 2.5 Lb. diamond, metal	1.000	S.F.	.010	.45	.58	1.03
Corners, expanded metal, 32 L.F. per 12' x 12' room	.083	L.F.	.002	.01	.10	.11
Painting, primer & 2 coats	1.000	S.F.	.011	.22	.51	.73
Paint trim, to 6" wide, primer + 1 coat enamel	.125	L.F.	.001	.02	.06	.08
Moldings, base, ogee profile, 9/16" x 4-1/2, red oak	.125	L.F.	.005	.58	.27	.85
TOTAL		S.F.	.082	1.73	4.51	6.24
STUCCO ON METAL LATH						
Stucco, 2 coats	1.000	S.F.	.041	.39	2.29	2.68
Lath, 2.5 Lb. diamond, metal	1.000	S.F.	.010	.45	.58	1.03
Corners, expanded metal, 32 L.F. per 12' x 12' room	.083	L.F.	.002	.01	.10	.11
Painting, primer & 2 coats	1.000	S.F.	.011	.22	.51	.73
Paint trim, to 6" wide, primer + 1 coat enamel	.125	L.F.	.001	.02	.06	.08
Moldings, base, ogee profile, 9/16" x 4-1/2, red oak	.125	L.F.	.005	.58	.27	.85
TOTAL		S.F.	.070	1.67	3.81	5.48

The costs in these systems are based on a per square foot of wall area.
Do not deduct for openings.

Description	QUAN.	UNIT	LABOR HOURS	COST PER S.F.		
				MAT.	INST.	TOTAL

Plaster & Stucco Wall Price Sheet	QUAN.	UNIT	LABOR HOURS	COST PER S.F.		
				MAT.	INST.	TOTAL
Plaster, gypsum or perlite, 2 coats	1.000	S.F.	.053	.45	2.99	3.44
3 coats	1.000	S.F.	.065	.65	3.62	4.27
Lath, gypsum, standard, 3/8″ thick	1.000	S.F.	.010	.39	.58	.97
Fire resistant, 3/8″ thick	1.000	S.F.	.013	.31	.71	1.02
1/2″ thick	1.000	S.F.	.014	.36	.76	1.12
Metal, diamond, 2.5 Lb.	1.000	S.F.	.010	.45	.58	1.03
3.4 Lb.	1.000	S.F.	.012	.50	.66	1.16
Rib, 2.75 Lb.	1.000	S.F.	.012	.40	.66	1.06
3.4 Lb.	1.000	S.F.	.013	.50	.71	1.21
Corners, expanded metal, 32 L.F. per 4′ x 4′ room	.250	L.F.	.005	.05	.29	.34
6′ x 6′ room	.110	L.F.	.002	.02	.13	.15
10′ x 10′ room	.100	L.F.	.002	.02	.12	.14
12′ x 12′ room	.083	L.F.	.002	.01	.10	.11
16′ x 16′ room	.063	L.F.	.001	.01	.07	.08
Painting, primer & 1 coats	1.000	S.F.	.008	.14	.40	.54
Primer & 2 coats	1.000	S.F.	.011	.22	.51	.73
Wallpaper, low price double roll	1.000	S.F.	.013	.65	.60	1.25
Medium price double roll	1.000	S.F.	.015	1.29	.72	2.01
High price double roll	1.000	S.F.	.018	2	.89	2.89
Tile, ceramic thin set, 4-1/4″ x 4-1/4″ tiles	1.000	S.F.	.084	2.87	4.07	6.94
6″ x 6″ tiles	1.000	S.F.	.080	3.94	4.42	8.36
Pregrouted sheets	1.000	S.F.	.067	6.20	3.23	9.43
Trim, painted or stained, baseboard	.125	L.F.	.006	.60	.33	.93
Base shoe	.125	L.F.	.005	.07	.30	.37
Chair rail	.125	L.F.	.005	.22	.28	.50
Cornice molding	.125	L.F.	.004	.15	.28	.43
Cove base, vinyl	.125	L.F.	.003	.16	.17	.33
Paneling not including furring or trim						
Plywood, prefinished, 1/4″ thick, 4′ x 8′ sheets, vert. grooves						
Birch faced, minimum	1.000	S.F.	.032	1.62	1.87	3.49
Average	1.000	S.F.	.038	1.32	2.23	3.55
Maximum	1.000	S.F.	.046	1.40	2.67	4.07
Mahogany, African	1.000	S.F.	.040	2.70	2.34	5.04
Philippine (lauan)	1.000	S.F.	.032	.72	1.87	2.59
Oak or cherry, minimum	1.000	S.F.	.032	1.47	1.87	3.34
Maximum	1.000	S.F.	.040	2.20	2.34	4.54
Rosewood	1.000	S.F.	.050	3.41	2.92	6.33
Teak	1.000	S.F.	.040	3.43	2.34	5.77
Chestnut	1.000	S.F.	.043	5.80	2.49	8.29
Pecan	1.000	S.F.	.040	2.75	2.34	5.09
Walnut, minimum	1.000	S.F.	.032	2.72	1.87	4.59
Maximum	1.000	S.F.	.040	5.55	2.34	7.89

System Description	QUAN.	UNIT	LABOR HOURS	COST PER S.F.		
				MAT.	INST.	TOTAL
PLASTER ON GYPSUM LATH						
Plaster, gypsum or perlite, 2 coats	1.000	S.F.	.061	.45	3.39	3.84
Gypsum lath, plain or perforated, nailed, 3/8" thick	1.000	S.F.	.010	.39	.58	.97
Gypsum lath, ceiling installation adder	1.000	S.F.	.004		.23	.23
Corners, expanded metal, 12' x 12' room	.330	L.F.	.007	.06	.39	.45
Painting, primer & 2 coats	1.000	S.F.	.011	.22	.51	.73
TOTAL		S.F.	.093	1.12	5.10	6.22
PLASTER ON METAL LATH						
Plaster, gypsum or perlite, 2 coats	1.000	S.F.	.061	.45	3.39	3.84
Lath, 2.5 Lb. diamond, metal	1.000	S.F.	.012	.45	.66	1.11
Corners, expanded metal, 12' x 12' room	.330	L.F.	.007	.06	.39	.45
Painting, primer & 2 coats	1.000	S.F.	.011	.22	.51	.73
TOTAL		S.F.	.091	1.18	4.95	6.13
STUCCO ON GYPSUM LATH						
Stucco, 2 coats	1.000	S.F.	.041	.39	2.29	2.68
Gypsum lath, plain or perforated, nailed, 3/8" thick	1.000	S.F.	.010	.39	.58	.97
Gypsum lath, ceiling installation adder	1.000	S.F.	.004		.23	.23
Corners, expanded metal, 12' x 12' room	.330	L.F.	.007	.06	.39	.45
Painting, primer & 2 coats	1.000	S.F.	.011	.22	.51	.73
TOTAL		S.F.	.073	1.06	4	5.06
STUCCO ON METAL LATH						
Stucco, 2 coats	1.000	S.F.	.041	.39	2.29	2.68
Lath, 2.5 Lb. diamond, metal	1.000	S.F.	.012	.45	.66	1.11
Corners, expanded metal, 12' x 12' room	.330	L.F.	.007	.06	.39	.45
Painting, primer & 2 coats	1.000	S.F.	.011	.22	.51	.73
TOTAL		S.F.	.071	1.12	3.85	4.97

The costs in these systems are based on a square foot of ceiling area.

Description	QUAN.	UNIT	LABOR HOURS	COST PER S.F.		
				MAT.	INST.	TOTAL

Plaster & Stucco Ceiling Price Sheet	QUAN.	UNIT	LABOR HOURS	COST PER S.F.		
				MAT.	INST.	TOTAL
Plaster, gypsum or perlite, 2 coats	1.000	S.F.	.061	.45	3.39	3.84
3 coats	1.000	S.F.	.065	.65	3.62	4.27
Lath, gypsum, standard, 3/8″ thick	1.000	S.F.	.014	.39	.81	1.20
Fire resistant, 3/8″ thick	1.000	S.F.	.017	.31	.94	1.25
1/2″ thick	1.000	S.F.	.018	.36	.99	1.35
Metal, diamond, 2.5 Lb.	1.000	S.F.	.012	.45	.66	1.11
3.4 Lb.	1.000	S.F.	.015	.50	.83	1.33
Rib, 2.75 Lb.	1.000	S.F.	.012	.40	.66	1.06
3.4 Lb.	1.000	S.F.	.013	.50	.71	1.21
Corners expanded metal, 4′ x 4′ room	1.000	L.F.	.020	.18	1.17	1.35
6′ x 6′ room	.667	L.F.	.013	.12	.78	.90
10′ x 10′ room	.400	L.F.	.008	.07	.47	.54
12′ x 12′ room	.333	L.F.	.007	.06	.39	.45
16′ x 16′ room	.250	L.F.	.004	.03	.22	.25
Painting, primer & 1 coat	1.000	S.F.	.008	.14	.40	.54
Primer & 2 coats	1.000	S.F.	.011	.22	.51	.73

System Description	QUAN.	UNIT	LABOR HOURS	COST PER S.F.		
				MAT.	INST.	TOTAL
2' X 2' GRID, FILM FACED FIBERGLASS, 5/8" THICK						
Suspension system, 2' x 2' grid, T bar	1.000	S.F.	.012	1.12	.72	1.84
Ceiling board, film faced fiberglass, 5/8" thick	1.000	S.F.	.013	1.42	.75	2.17
Carrier channels, 1-1/2" x 3/4"	1.000	S.F.	.017	.13	.99	1.12
Hangers, #12 wire	1.000	S.F.	.002		.10	.10
TOTAL		S.F.	.044	2.67	2.56	5.23
2' X 4' GRID, FILM FACED FIBERGLASS, 5/8" THICK						
Suspension system, 2' x 4' grid, T bar	1.000	S.F.	.010	.87	.58	1.45
Ceiling board, film faced fiberglass, 5/8" thick	1.000	S.F.	.013	1.42	.75	2.17
Carrier channels, 1-1/2" x 3/4"	1.000	S.F.	.017	.13	.99	1.12
Hangers, #12 wire	1.000	S.F.	.002		.10	.10
TOTAL		S.F.	.042	2.42	2.42	4.84
2' X 2' GRID, MINERAL FIBER, REVEAL EDGE, 1" THICK						
Suspension system, 2' x 2' grid, T bar	1.000	S.F.	.012	1.12	.72	1.84
Ceiling board, mineral fiber, reveal edge, 1" thick	1.000	S.F.	.013	2.33	.78	3.11
Carrier channels, 1-1/2" x 3/4"	1.000	S.F.	.017	.13	.99	1.12
Hangers, #12 wire	1.000	S.F.	.002		.10	.10
TOTAL		S.F.	.044	3.58	2.59	6.17
2' X 4' GRID, MINERAL FIBER, REVEAL EDGE, 1" THICK						
Suspension system, 2' x 4' grid, T bar	1.000	S.F.	.010	.87	.58	1.45
Ceiling board, mineral fiber, reveal edge, 1" thick	1.000	S.F.	.013	2.33	.78	3.11
Carrier channels, 1-1/2" x 3/4"	1.000	S.F.	.017	.13	.99	1.12
Hangers, #12 wire	1.000	S.F.	.002		.10	.10
TOTAL		S.F.	.042	3.33	2.45	5.78

Description	QUAN.	UNIT	LABOR HOURS	COST PER S.F.		
				MAT.	INST.	TOTAL

Suspended Ceiling Price Sheet

	QUAN.	UNIT	LABOR HOURS	COST PER S.F. MAT.	COST PER S.F. INST.	COST PER S.F. TOTAL
Suspension systems, T bar, 2' x 2' grid	1.000	S.F.	.012	1.12	.72	1.84
2' x 4' grid	1.000	S.F.	.010	.87	.58	1.45
Concealed Z bar, 12" module	1.000	S.F.	.015	.98	.90	1.88
Ceiling boards, fiberglass, film faced, 2' x 2' or 2' x 4', 5/8" thick	1.000	S.F.	.013	1.42	.75	2.17
3/4" thick	1.000	S.F.	.013	2.93	.78	3.71
3" thick thermal R11	1.000	S.F.	.018	3.85	1.04	4.89
Glass cloth faced, 3/4" thick	1.000	S.F.	.016	3.09	.94	4.03
1" thick	1.000	S.F.	.016	3.75	.96	4.71
1-1/2" thick, nubby face	1.000	S.F.	.017	2.94	.98	3.92
Mineral fiber boards, 5/8" thick, aluminum face 2' x 2'	1.000	S.F.	.013	4.17	.78	4.95
2' x 4'	1.000	S.F.	.012	4.17	.72	4.89
Standard faced, 2' x 2' or 2' x 4'	1.000	S.F.	.012	.86	.69	1.55
Plastic coated face, 2' x 2' or 2' x 4'	1.000	S.F.	.020	2.86	1.17	4.03
Fire rated, 2 hour rating, 5/8" thick	1.000	S.F.	.012	1.38	.69	2.07
Tegular edge, 2' x 2' or 2' x 4', 5/8" thick, fine textured	1.000	S.F.	.013	1.19	.99	2.18
Rough textured	1.000	S.F.	.015	1.45	.99	2.44
3/4" thick, fine textured	1.000	S.F.	.016	2.48	1.04	3.52
Rough textured	1.000	S.F.	.018	1.60	1.04	2.64
Luminous panels, prismatic, acrylic	1.000	S.F.	.020	3.20	1.17	4.37
Polystyrene	1.000	S.F.	.020	1.78	1.17	2.95
Flat or ribbed, acrylic	1.000	S.F.	.020	4.61	1.17	5.78
Polystyrene	1.000	S.F.	.020	2.60	1.17	3.77
Drop pan, white, acrylic	1.000	S.F.	.020	6.35	1.17	7.52
Polystyrene	1.000	S.F.	.020	5	1.17	6.17
Carrier channels, 4'-0" on center, 3/4" x 1-1/2"	1.000	S.F.	.017	.13	.99	1.12
1-1/2" x 3-1/2"	1.000	S.F.	.017	.35	.99	1.34
Hangers, #12 wire	1.000	S.F.	.002		.10	.10

System Description	QUAN.	UNIT	LABOR HOURS	COST EACH		
				MAT.	INST.	TOTAL
LAUAN, FLUSH DOOR, HOLLOW CORE						
Door, flush, lauan, hollow core, 2'-8" wide x 6'-8" high	1.000	Ea.	.889	45.50	52	97.50
Frame, pine, 4-5/8" jamb	17.000	L.F.	.725	94.35	42.33	136.68
Moldings, casing, ogee, 11/16" x 2-1/2", pine	34.000	L.F.	1.088	52.70	63.58	116.28
Paint trim, to 6" wide, primer + 1 coat enamel	34.000	L.F.	.340	5.10	16.32	21.42
Butt hinges, chrome, 3-1/2" x 3-1/2"	1.500	Pr.		50.25		50.25
Lockset, passage	1.000	Ea.	.500	38.50	29	67.50
Prime door & frame, oil, primer, brushwork	2.000	Face	1.600	8.22	77	85.22
Paint door and frame, oil, 2 coats	2.000	Face	2.667	10.10	129	139.10
TOTAL		Ea.	7.809	304.72	409.23	713.95
BIRCH, FLUSH DOOR, HOLLOW CORE						
Door, flush, birch, hollow core, 2'-8" wide x 6'-8" high	1.000	Ea.	.889	56.50	52	108.50
Frame, pine, 4-5/8" jamb	17.000	L.F.	.725	94.35	42.33	136.68
Moldings, casing, ogee, 11/16" x 2-1/2", pine	34.000	L.F.	1.088	52.70	63.58	116.28
Butt hinges, chrome, 3-1/2" x 3-1/2"	1.500	Pr.		50.25		50.25
Lockset, passage	1.000	Ea.	.500	38.50	29	67.50
Prime door & frame, oil, primer, brushwork	2.000	Face	1.600	8.22	77	85.22
Paint door and frame, oil, 2 coats	2.000	Face	2.667	10.10	129	139.10
TOTAL		Ea.	7.469	310.62	392.91	703.53
RAISED PANEL, SOLID, PINE DOOR						
Door, pine, raised panel, 2'-8" wide x 6'-8" high	1.000	Ea.	.889	202	52	254
Frame, pine, 4-5/8" jamb	17.000	L.F.	.725	94.35	42.33	136.68
Moldings, casing, ogee, 11/16" x 2-1/2", pine	34.000	L.F.	1.088	52.70	63.58	116.28
Butt hinges, bronze, 3-1/2" x 3-1/2"	1.500	Pr.		57.75		57.75
Lockset, passage	1.000	Ea.	.500	38.50	29	67.50
Prime door & frame, oil, primer, brushwork	2.000	Face	1.600	8.22	77	85.22
Paint door and frame, oil, 2 coats	2.000	Face	2.667	10.10	129	139.10
TOTAL		Ea.	7.469	463.62	392.91	856.53

The costs in these systems are based on a cost per each door.

Description	QUAN.	UNIT	LABOR HOURS	COST EACH		
				MAT.	INST.	TOTAL

Interior Door Price Sheet	QUAN.	UNIT	LABOR HOURS	COST EACH		
				MAT.	INST.	TOTAL
Door, hollow core, lauan 1-3/8" thick, 6'-8" high x 1'-6" wide	1.000	Ea.	.889	40.50	52	92.50
2'-0" wide	1.000	Ea.	.889	39.50	52	91.50
2'-6" wide	1.000	Ea.	.889	43.50	52	95.50
2'-8" wide	1.000	Ea.	.889	45.50	52	97.50
3'-0" wide	1.000	Ea.	.941	48	55	103
Birch 1-3/8" thick, 6'-8" high x 1'-6" wide	1.000	Ea.	.889	48	52	100
2'-0" wide	1.000	Ea.	.889	42.50	52	94.50
2'-6" wide	1.000	Ea.	.889	56.50	52	108.50
2'-8" wide	1.000	Ea.	.889	56.50	52	108.50
3'-0" wide	1.000	Ea.	.941	57.50	55	112.50
Louvered pine 1-3/8" thick, 6'-8" high x 1'-6" wide	1.000	Ea.	.842	123	49	172
2'-0" wide	1.000	Ea.	.889	144	52	196
2'-6" wide	1.000	Ea.	.889	163	52	215
2'-8" wide	1.000	Ea.	.889	172	52	224
3'-0" wide	1.000	Ea.	.941	185	55	240
Paneled pine 1-3/8" thick, 6'-8" high x 1'-6" wide	1.000	Ea.	.842	133	49	182
2'-0" wide	1.000	Ea.	.889	179	52	231
2'-6" wide	1.000	Ea.	.889	202	52	254
2'-8" wide	1.000	Ea.	.889	202	52	254
3'-0" wide	1.000	Ea.	.941	215	55	270
Frame, pine, 1'-6" thru 2'-0" wide door, 3-5/8" deep	16.000	L.F.	.683	79	40	119
4-5/8" deep	16.000	L.F.	.683	89	40	129
5-5/8" deep	16.000	L.F.	.683	82.50	40	122.50
2'-6" thru 3'0" wide door, 3-5/8" deep	17.000	L.F.	.725	84	42.50	126.50
4-5/8" deep	17.000	L.F.	.725	94.50	42.50	137
5-5/8" deep	17.000	L.F.	.725	87.50	42.50	130
Trim, casing, painted, both sides, 1'-6" thru 2'-6" wide door	32.000	L.F.	1.855	53	97.50	150.50
2'-6" thru 3'-0" wide door	34.000	L.F.	1.971	56	104	160
Butt hinges 3-1/2" x 3-1/2", steel plated, chrome	1.500	Pr.		50.50		50.50
Bronze	1.500	Pr.		58		58
Locksets, passage, minimum	1.000	Ea.	.500	38.50	29	67.50
Maximum	1.000	Ea.	.575	44.50	33.50	78
Privacy, miniumum	1.000	Ea.	.625	48	36.50	84.50
Maximum	1.000	Ea.	.675	52	39	91
Paint 2 sides, primer & 2 cts., flush door, 1'-6" to 2'-0" wide	2.000	Face	5.547	24.50	268	292.50
2'-6" thru 3'-0" wide	2.000	Face	6.933	31	335	366
Louvered door, 1'-6" thru 2'-0" wide	2.000	Face	6.400	22.50	310	332.50
2'-6" thru 3'-0" wide	2.000	Face	8.000	28	385	413
Paneled door, 1'-6" thru 2'-0" wide	2.000	Face	6.400	22.50	310	332.50
2'-6" thru 3'-0" wide	2.000	Face	8.000	28	385	413

Trim

Door

Frame

System Description	QUAN.	UNIT	LABOR HOURS	COST EACH		
				MAT.	INST.	TOTAL
BI-PASSING, FLUSH, LAUAN, HOLLOW CORE, 4'-0" X 6'-8"						
Door, flush, lauan, hollow core, 4'-0" x 6'-8" opening	1.000	Ea.	1.333	198	78	276
Frame, pine, 4-5/8" jamb	18.000	L.F.	.768	99.90	44.82	144.72
Moldings, casing, ogee, 11/16" x 2-1/2", pine	36.000	L.F.	1.152	55.80	67.32	123.12
Prime door & frame, oil, primer, brushwork	2.000	Face	1.600	8.22	77	85.22
Paint door and frame, oil, 2 coats	2.000	Face	2.667	10.10	129	139.10
TOTAL		Ea.	7.520	372.02	396.14	768.16
BI-PASSING, FLUSH, BIRCH, HOLLOW CORE, 6'-0" X 6'-8"						
Door, flush, birch, hollow core, 6'-0" x 6'-8" opening	1.000	Ea.	1.600	320	93.50	413.50
Frame, pine, 4-5/8" jamb	19.000	L.F.	.811	105.45	47.31	152.76
Moldings, casing, ogee, 11/16" x 2-1/2", pine	38.000	L.F.	1.216	58.90	71.06	129.96
Prime door & frame, oil, primer, brushwork	2.000	Face	2.000	10.28	96.25	106.53
Paint door and frame, oil, 2 coats	2.000	Face	3.333	12.63	161.25	173.88
TOTAL		Ea.	8.960	507.26	469.37	976.63
BI-FOLD, PINE, PANELED, 3'-0" X 6'-8"						
Door, pine, paneled, 3'-0" x 6'-8" opening	1.000	Ea.	1.231	251	72	323
Frame, pine, 4-5/8" jamb	17.000	L.F.	.725	94.35	42.33	136.68
Moldings, casing, ogee, 11/16" x 2-1/2", pine	34.000	L.F.	1.088	52.70	63.58	116.28
Prime door & frame, oil, primer, brushwork	2.000	Face	1.600	8.22	77	85.22
Paint door and frame, oil, 2 coats	2.000	Face	2.667	10.10	129	139.10
TOTAL		Ea.	7.311	416.37	383.91	800.28
BI-FOLD, PINE, LOUVERED, 6'-0" X 6'-8"						
Door, pine, louvered, 6'-0" x 6'-8" opening	1.000	Ea.	1.600	330	93.50	423.50
Frame, pine, 4-5/8" jamb	19.000	L.F.	.811	105.45	47.31	152.76
Moldings, casing, ogee, 11/16" x 2-1/2", pine	38.000	L.F.	1.216	58.90	71.06	129.96
Prime door & frame, oil, primer, brushwork	2.500	Face	2.000	10.28	96.25	106.53
Paint door and frame, oil, 2 coats	2.500	Face	3.333	12.63	161.25	173.88
TOTAL		Ea.	8.960	517.26	469.37	986.63

The costs in this system are based on a cost per each door.

Description	QUAN.	UNIT	LABOR HOURS	COST EACH		
				MAT.	INST.	TOTAL

226

Closet Door Price Sheet

Closet Door Price Sheet	QUAN.	UNIT	LABOR HOURS	COST EACH MAT.	COST EACH INST.	COST EACH TOTAL
Doors, bi-passing, pine, louvered, 4'-0" x 6'-8" opening	1.000	Ea.	1.333	535	78	613
6'-0" x 6'-8" opening	1.000	Ea.	1.600	695	93.50	788.50
Paneled, 4'-0" x 6'-8" opening	1.000	Ea.	1.333	520	78	598
6'-0" x 6'-8" opening	1.000	Ea.	1.600	810	93.50	903.50
Flush, birch, hollow core, 4'-0" x 6'-8" opening	1.000	Ea.	1.333	273	78	351
6'-0" x 6'-8" opening	1.000	Ea.	1.600	320	93.50	413.50
Flush, lauan, hollow core, 4'-0" x 6'-8" opening	1.000	Ea.	1.333	198	78	276
6'-0" x 6'-8" opening	1.000	Ea.	1.600	238	93.50	331.50
Bi-fold, pine, louvered, 3'-0" x 6'-8" opening	1.000	Ea.	1.231	251	72	323
6'-0" x 6'-8" opening	1.000	Ea.	1.600	330	93.50	423.50
Paneled, 3'-0" x 6'-8" opening	1.000	Ea.	1.231	251	72	323
6'-0" x 6'-8" opening	1.000	Ea.	1.600	330	93.50	423.50
Flush, birch, hollow core, 3'-0" x 6'-8" opening	1.000	Ea.	1.231	80	72	152
6'-0" x 6'-8" opening	1.000	Ea.	1.600	145	93.50	238.50
Flush, lauan, hollow core, 3'-0" x 6'8" opening	1.000	Ea.	1.231	310	72	382
6'-0" x 6'-8" opening	1.000	Ea.	1.600	475	93.50	568.50
Frame pine, 3'-0" door, 3-5/8" deep	17.000	L.F.	.725	84	42.50	126.50
4-5/8" deep	17.000	L.F.	.725	94.50	42.50	137
5-5/8" deep	17.000	L.F.	.725	87.50	42.50	130
4'-0" door, 3-5/8" deep	18.000	L.F.	.768	89	45	134
4-5/8" deep	18.000	L.F.	.768	100	45	145
5-5/8" deep	18.000	L.F.	.768	92.50	45	137.50
6'-0" door, 3-5/8" deep	19.000	L.F.	.811	94	47.50	141.50
4-5/8" deep	19.000	L.F.	.811	105	47.50	152.50
5-5/8" deep	19.000	L.F.	.811	98	47.50	145.50
Trim both sides, painted 3'-0" x 6'-8" door	34.000	L.F.	1.971	56	104	160
4'-0" x 6'-8" door	36.000	L.F.	2.086	59.50	110	169.50
6'-0" x 6'-8" door	38.000	L.F.	2.203	62.50	116	178.50
Paint 2 sides, primer & 2 cts., flush door & frame, 3' x 6'-8" opng	2.000	Face	2.914	13.75	155	168.75
4'-0" x 6'-8" opening	2.000	Face	3.886	18.30	206	224.30
6'-0" x 6'-8" opening	2.000	Face	4.857	23	258	281
Paneled door & frame, 3'-0" x 6'-8" opening	2.000	Face	6.000	21	290	311
4'-0" x 6'-8" opening	2.000	Face	8.000	28	385	413
6'-0" x 6'-8" opening	2.000	Face	10.000	35	485	520
Louvered door & frame, 3'-0" x 6'-8" opening	2.000	Face	6.000	21	290	311
4'-0" x 6'-8" opening	2.000	Face	8.000	28	385	413
6'-0" x 6'-8" opening	2.000	Face	10.000	35	485	520

System Description	QUAN.	UNIT	LABOR HOURS	COST PER S.F.		
				MAT.	INST.	TOTAL
Carpet, direct glue-down, nylon, level loop, 26 oz.	1.000	S.F.	.018	2.65	.64	3.29
32 oz.	1.000	S.F.	.018	4.83	.64	5.47
40 oz.	1.000	S.F.	.018	5.50	.64	6.14
Nylon, plush, 20 oz.	1.000	S.F.	.018	2.24	.64	2.88
24 oz.	1.000	S.F.	.018	2.33	.64	2.97
30 oz.	1.000	S.F.	.018	3.78	.64	4.42
42 oz.	1.000	S.F.	.022	5.50	.69	6.19
48 oz.	1.000	S.F.	.022	6.45	.69	7.14
54 oz.	1.000	S.F.	.022	7.10	.69	7.79
Olefin, 15 oz.	1.000	S.F.	.018	1.84	.64	2.48
22 oz.	1.000	S.F.	.018	1.81	.64	2.45
Tile, foam backed, needle punch	1.000	S.F.	.014	4.85	.76	5.61
Tufted loop or shag	1.000	S.F.	.014	3.62	.76	4.38
Wool, 36 oz., level loop	1.000	S.F.	.018	12.30	.69	12.99
32 oz., patterned	1.000	S.F.	.020	11.15	.69	11.84
48 oz., patterned	1.000	S.F.	.020	12.30	.69	12.99
Padding, sponge rubber cushion, minimum	1.000	S.F.	.006	.57	.32	.89
Maximum	1.000	S.F.	.006	1.07	.32	1.39
Felt, 32 oz. to 56 oz., minimum	1.000	S.F.	.006	.72	.32	1.04
Maximum	1.000	S.F.	.006	1.30	.32	1.62
Bonded urethane, 3/8" thick, minimum	1.000	S.F.	.006	.73	.32	1.05
Maximum	1.000	S.F.	.006	.98	.32	1.30
Prime urethane, 1/4" thick, minimum	1.000	S.F.	.006	.43	.32	.75
Maximum	1.000	S.F.	.006	.81	.32	1.13
Stairs, for stairs, add to above carpet prices	1.000	Riser	.267		14.50	14.50
Underlayment plywood, 3/8" thick	1.000	S.F.	.011	1.16	.62	1.78
1/2" thick	1.000	S.F.	.011	1.38	.64	2.02
5/8" thick	1.000	S.F.	.011	1.52	.67	2.19
3/4" thick	1.000	S.F.	.012	1.64	.72	2.36
Particle board, 3/8" thick	1.000	S.F.	.011	.44	.62	1.06
1/2" thick	1.000	S.F.	.011	.50	.64	1.14
5/8" thick	1.000	S.F.	.011	.59	.67	1.26
3/4" thick	1.000	S.F.	.012	.77	.72	1.49
Hardboard, 4' x 4', 0.215" thick	1.000	S.F.	.011	.69	.62	1.31

System Description	QUAN.	UNIT	LABOR HOURS	COST PER S.F.		
				MAT.	INST.	TOTAL
Resilient flooring, asphalt tile on concrete, 1/8" thick						
Color group B	1.000	S.F.	.020	1.33	1.09	2.42
Color group C & D	1.000	S.F.	.020	1.46	1.09	2.55
Asphalt tile on wood subfloor, 1/8" thick						
Color group B	1.000	S.F.	.020	1.62	1.09	2.71
Color group C & D	1.000	S.F.	.020	1.75	1.09	2.84
Vinyl composition tile, 12" x 12", 1/16" thick	1.000	S.F.	.016	1.34	.87	2.21
Embossed	1.000	S.F.	.016	2.48	.87	3.35
Marbleized	1.000	S.F.	.016	2.48	.87	3.35
Plain	1.000	S.F.	.016	3.20	.87	4.07
.080" thick, embossed	1.000	S.F.	.016	1.62	.87	2.49
Marbleized	1.000	S.F.	.016	2.85	.87	3.72
Plain	1.000	S.F.	.016	2.65	.87	3.52
1/8" thick, marbleized	1.000	S.F.	.016	2.68	.87	3.55
Plain	1.000	S.F.	.016	1.71	.87	2.58
Vinyl tile, 12" x 12", .050" thick, minimum	1.000	S.F.	.016	4.08	.87	4.95
Maximum	1.000	S.F.	.016	5.70	.87	6.57
1/8" thick, minimum	1.000	S.F.	.016	7.70	.87	8.57
Maximum	1.000	S.F.	.016	3.60	.87	4.47
1/8" thick, solid colors	1.000	S.F.	.016	6.65	.87	7.52
Florentine pattern	1.000	S.F.	.016	7.10	.87	7.97
Marbleized or travertine pattern	1.000	S.F.	.016	6.85	.87	7.72
Vinyl sheet goods, backed, .070" thick, minimum	1.000	S.F.	.032	4.06	1.74	5.80
Maximum	1.000	S.F.	.040	4.77	2.17	6.94
.093" thick, minimum	1.000	S.F.	.035	4.53	1.89	6.42
Maximum	1.000	S.F.	.040	7.10	2.17	9.27
.125" thick, minimum	1.000	S.F.	.035	4.26	1.89	6.15
Maximum	1.000	S.F.	.040	8.25	2.17	10.42
Wood, oak, finished in place, 25/32" x 2-1/2" clear	1.000	S.F.	.074	4.74	3.96	8.70
Select	1.000	S.F.	.074	5.75	3.96	9.71
No. 1 common	1.000	S.F.	.074	5.60	3.96	9.56
Prefinished, oak, 2-1/2" wide	1.000	S.F.	.047	5.70	2.75	8.45
3-1/4" wide	1.000	S.F.	.043	6.20	2.53	8.73
Ranch plank, oak, random width	1.000	S.F.	.055	7.95	3.22	11.17
Parquet, 5/16" thick, finished in place, oak, minimum	1.000	S.F.	.077	6.95	4.13	11.08
Maximum	1.000	S.F.	.107	11.75	5.90	17.65
Teak, minimum	1.000	S.F.	.077	7.95	4.13	12.08
Maximum	1.000	S.F.	.107	12.75	5.90	18.65
Sleepers, treated, 16" O.C., 1" x 2"	1.000	S.F.	.007	.32	.40	.72
1" x 3"	1.000	S.F.	.008	.52	.47	.99
2" x 4"	1.000	S.F.	.011	.63	.62	1.25
2" x 6"	1.000	S.F.	.012	.99	.72	1.71
Subfloor, plywood, 1/2" thick	1.000	S.F.	.011	.69	.62	1.31
5/8" thick	1.000	S.F.	.012	.86	.69	1.55
3/4" thick	1.000	S.F.	.013	1.03	.75	1.78
Ceramic tile, color group 2, 1" x 1"	1.000	S.F.	.087	7.05	4.23	11.28
2" x 2" or 2" x 1"	1.000	S.F.	.084	7.30	4.07	11.37
Color group 1, 8" x 8"	1.000	S.F.	.064	5.75	2.58	8.33
12" x 12"	1.000	S.F.	.049	6.40	2.67	9.07
16" x 16"	1.000	S.F.	.029	8.25	2.76	11.01

System Description	QUAN.	UNIT	LABOR HOURS	COST EACH		
				MAT.	INST.	TOTAL
7 RISERS, OAK TREADS, BOX STAIRS						
Treads, oak, 1-1/4" x 10" wide, 3' long	6.000	Ea.	2.667	666	156	822
Risers, 3/4" thick, beech	7.000	Ea.	.672	198.45	39.27	237.72
30" primed pine balusters	12.000	Ea.	1.000	48.84	58.44	107.28
Newels, 3" wide, plain, paint grade, square	2.000	Ea.	2.286	116	134	250
Handrails, oak laminated	7.000	L.F.	.933	294	54.60	348.60
Stringers, 2" x 10", 3 each	21.000	L.F.	.306	9.24	17.85	27.09
TOTAL		Ea.	7.864	1,332.53	460.16	1,792.69
14 RISERS, OAK TREADS, BOX STAIRS						
Treads, oak, 1-1/4" x 10" wide, 3' long	13.000	Ea.	5.778	1,443	338	1,781
Risers, 3/4" thick, beech	14.000	Ea.	1.344	396.90	78.54	475.44
30" primed pine balusters	26.000	Ea.	2.167	105.82	126.62	232.44
Newels, 3" wide, plain, paint grade, square	2.000	Ea.	2.286	116	134	250
Handrails, oak, laminated	14.000	L.F.	1.867	588	109.20	697.20
Stair stringers, 2" x 10"	42.000	L.F.	5.169	63.42	302.40	365.82
TOTAL		Ea.	18.611	2,713.14	1,088.76	3,801.90
14 RISERS, PINE TREADS, BOX STAIRS						
Treads, pine, 9-1/2" x 3/4" thick	13.000	Ea.	5.778	228.80	338	566.80
Risers, 3/4" thick, pine	14.000	Ea.	1.344	150.36	78.54	228.90
30" primed pine balusters	26.000	Ea.	2.167	105.82	126.62	232.44
Newels, 3" wide, plain, paint grade, square	2.000	Ea.	2.286	116	134	250
Handrails, oak, laminated	14.000	L.F.	1.867	588	109.20	697.20
Stair stringers, 2" x 10"	42.000	L.F.	5.169	63.42	302.40	365.82
TOTAL		Ea.	18.611	1,252.40	1,088.76	2,341.16

Description	QUAN.	UNIT	LABOR HOURS	COST EACH		
				MAT.	INST.	TOTAL

Stairway Price Sheet	QUAN.	UNIT	LABOR HOURS	COST EACH		
				MAT.	INST.	TOTAL
Treads, oak, 1-1/16" x 9-1/2", 3' long, 7 riser stair	6.000	Ea.	2.667	665	156	821
14 riser stair	13.000	Ea.	5.778	1,450	340	1,790
1-1/16" x 11-1/2", 3' long, 7 riser stair	6.000	Ea.	2.667	720	156	876
14 riser stair	13.000	Ea.	5.778	1,550	340	1,890
Pine, 3/4" x 9-1/2", 3' long, 7 riser stair	6.000	Ea.	2.667	106	156	262
14 riser stair	13.000	Ea.	5.778	229	340	569
3/4" x 11-1/4", 3' long, 7 riser stair	6.000	Ea.	2.667	113	156	269
14 riser stair	13.000	Ea.	5.778	245	340	585
Risers, oak, 3/4" x 7-1/2" high, 7 riser stair	7.000	Ea.	2.625	150	39.50	189.50
14 riser stair	14.000	Ea.	5.250	300	78.50	378.50
Beech, 3/4" x 7-1/2" high, 7 riser stair	7.000	Ea.	2.625	198	39.50	237.50
14 riser stair	14.000	Ea.	5.250	395	78.50	473.50
Baluster, turned, 30" high, primed pine, 7 riser stair	12.000	Ea.	3.429	49	58.50	107.50
14 riser stair	26.000	Ea.	7.428	106	127	233
30" birch, 7 riser stair	12.000	Ea.	3.429	44.50	53	97.50
14 riser stair	26.000	Ea.	7.428	96	115	211
42" pine, 7 riser stair	12.000	Ea.	3.556	65	58.50	123.50
14 riser stair	26.000	Ea.	7.704	140	127	267
42" birch, 7 riser stair	12.000	Ea.	3.556	65	58.50	123.50
14 riser stair	26.000	Ea.	7.704	140	127	267
Newels, 3-1/4" wide, starting, 7 riser stair	2.000	Ea.	2.286	116	134	250
14 riser stair	2.000	Ea.	2.286	116	134	250
Landing, 7 riser stair	2.000	Ea.	3.200	145	187	332
14 riser stair	2.000	Ea.	3.200	145	187	332
Handrails, oak, laminated, 7 riser stair	7.000	L.F.	.933	294	54.50	348.50
14 riser stair	14.000	L.F.	1.867	590	109	699
Stringers, fir, 2" x 10" 7 riser stair	21.000	L.F.	2.585	31.50	151	182.50
14 riser stair	42.000	L.F.	5.169	63.50	300	363.50
2" x 12", 7 riser stair	21.000	L.F.	2.585	40.50	151	191.50
14 riser stair	42.000	L.F.	5.169	81	300	381

Special Stairways	QUAN.	UNIT	LABOR HOURS	COST EACH		
				MAT.	INST.	TOTAL
Basement stairs, open risers	1.000	Flight	4.000	850	234	1,084
Spiral stairs, oak, 4'-6" diameter, prefabricated, 9' high	1.000	Flight	10.667	3,650	625	4,275
Aluminum, 5'-0" diameter stock unit	1.000	Flight	9.956	8,200	745	8,945
Custom unit	1.000	Flight	9.956	14,400	745	15,145
Cast iron, 4'-0" diameter, minimum	1.000	Flight	9.956	10,200	745	10,945
Maximum	1.000	Flight	17.920	17,900	1,350	19,250
Steel, industrial, pre-erected, 3'-6" wide, bar rail	1.000	Flight	7.724	10,200	825	11,025
Picket rail	1.000	Flight	7.724	11,400	825	12,225

Soffit Drywall — Soffit Framing — Top Cabinets — Counter Top — Bottom Cabinets

System Description	QUAN.	UNIT	LABOR HOURS	COST PER L.F.		
				MAT.	INST.	TOTAL
KITCHEN, ECONOMY GRADE						
Top cabinets, economy grade	1.000	L.F.	.171	69.12	9.92	79.04
Bottom cabinets, economy grade	1.000	L.F.	.256	103.68	14.88	118.56
Square edge, plastic face countertop	1.000	L.F.	.267	37	15.60	52.60
Blocking, wood, 2" x 4"	1.000	L.F.	.032	.45	1.87	2.32
Soffit, framing, wood, 2" x 4"	4.000	L.F.	.071	1.80	4.16	5.96
Soffit drywall	2.000	S.F.	.047	.88	2.78	3.66
Drywall painting	2.000	S.F.	.013	.12	.78	.90
TOTAL		L.F.	.857	213.05	49.99	263.04
AVERAGE GRADE						
Top cabinets, average grade	1.000	L.F.	.213	86.40	12.40	98.80
Bottom cabinets, average grade	1.000	L.F.	.320	129.60	18.60	148.20
Solid surface countertop, solid color	1.000	L.F.	.800	87.50	47	134.50
Blocking, wood, 2" x 4"	1.000	L.F.	.032	.45	1.87	2.32
Soffit framing, wood, 2" x 4"	4.000	L.F.	.071	1.80	4.16	5.96
Soffit drywall	2.000	S.F.	.047	.88	2.78	3.66
Drywall painting	2.000	S.F.	.013	.12	.78	.90
TOTAL		L.F.	1.496	306.75	87.59	394.34
CUSTOM GRADE						
Top cabinets, custom grade	1.000	L.F.	.256	188	15	203
Bottom cabinets, custom grade	1.000	L.F.	.384	282	22.50	304.50
Solid surface countertop, premium patterned color	1.000	L.F.	1.067	154	62.50	216.50
Blocking, wood, 2" x 4"	1.000	L.F.	.032	.45	1.87	2.32
Soffit framing, wood, 2" x 4"	4.000	L.F.	.071	1.80	4.16	5.96
Soffit drywall	2.000	S.F.	.047	.88	2.78	3.66
Drywall painting	2.000	S.F.	.013	.12	.78	.90
TOTAL		L.F.	1.870	627.25	109.59	736.84

Description	QUAN.	UNIT	LABOR HOURS	COST PER L.F.		
				MAT.	INST.	TOTAL

Kitchen Price Sheet	QUAN.	UNIT	LABOR HOURS	COST PER L.F.		
				MAT.	INST.	TOTAL
Top cabinets, economy grade	1.000	L.F.	.171	69	9.90	78.90
Average grade	1.000	L.F.	.213	86.50	12.40	98.90
Custom grade	1.000	L.F.	.256	188	15	203
Bottom cabinets, economy grade	1.000	L.F.	.256	104	14.90	118.90
Average grade	1.000	L.F.	.320	130	18.60	148.60
Custom grade	1.000	L.F.	.384	282	22.50	304.50
Counter top, laminated plastic, 7/8" thick, no splash	1.000	L.F.	.267	36.50	15.60	52.10
With backsplash	1.000	L.F.	.267	34	15.60	49.60
1-1/4" thick, no splash	1.000	L.F.	.286	42.50	16.70	59.20
With backsplash	1.000	L.F.	.286	47.50	16.70	64.20
Post formed, laminated plastic	1.000	L.F.	.267	11.40	15.60	27
Ceramic tile, with backsplash		L.F.	.427	19.25	9.35	28.60
Marble, with backsplash, minimum	1.000	L.F.	.471	48	27.50	75.50
Maximum	1.000	L.F.	.615	120	36	156
Maple, solid laminated, no backsplash	1.000	L.F.	.286	86.50	16.70	103.20
With backsplash	1.000	L.F.	.286	103	16.70	119.70
Solid Surface, with backsplash, minimum	1.000	L.F.	.842	97.50	49	146.50
Maximum	1.000	L.F.	1.067	154	62.50	216.50
Blocking, wood, 2" x 4"	1.000	L.F.	.032	.45	1.87	2.32
2" x 6"	1.000	L.F.	.036	.69	2.11	2.80
2" x 8"	1.000	L.F.	.040	.96	2.34	3.30
Soffit framing, wood, 2" x 3"	4.000	L.F.	.064	1.72	3.76	5.48
2" x 4"	4.000	L.F.	.071	1.80	4.16	5.96
Soffit, drywall, painted	2.000	S.F.	.060	1	3.56	4.56
Paneling, standard	2.000	S.F.	.064	3.24	3.74	6.98
Deluxe	2.000	S.F.	.091	2.80	5.35	8.15
Sinks, porcelain on cast iron, single bowl, 21" x 24"	1.000	Ea.	10.334	625	610	1,235
21" x 30"	1.000	Ea.	10.334	905	610	1,515
Double bowl, 20" x 32"	1.000	Ea.	10.810	705	635	1,340
Stainless steel, single bowl, 16" x 20"	1.000	Ea.	10.334	965	610	1,575
22" x 25"	1.000	Ea.	10.334	1,050	610	1,660
Double bowl, 20" x 32"	1.000	Ea.	10.810	870	635	1,505

Appliance Price Sheet	QUAN.	UNIT	LABOR HOURS	COST PER L.F.		
				MAT.	INST.	TOTAL
Range, free standing, minimum	1.000	Ea.	3.600	610	203	813
Maximum	1.000	Ea.	6.000	2,250	310	2,560
Built-in, minimum	1.000	Ea.	3.333	1,075	220	1,295
Maximum	1.000	Ea.	10.000	1,900	600	2,500
Counter top range, 4-burner, minimum	1.000	Ea.	3.333	455	220	675
Maximum	1.000	Ea.	4.667	2,025	310	2,335
Compactor, built-in, minimum	1.000	Ea.	2.215	780	134	914
Maximum	1.000	Ea.	3.282	1,300	197	1,497
Dishwasher, built-in, minimum	1.000	Ea.	6.735	555	440	995
Maximum	1.000	Ea.	9.235	815	600	1,415
Garbage disposer, minimum	1.000	Ea.	2.810	201	184	385
Maximum	1.000	Ea.	2.810	365	184	549
Microwave oven, minimum	1.000	Ea.	2.615	153	173	326
Maximum	1.000	Ea.	4.615	545	305	850
Range hood, ducted, minimum	1.000	Ea.	4.658	128	283	411
Maximum	1.000	Ea.	5.991	1,050	365	1,415
Ductless, minimum	1.000	Ea.	2.615	140	161	301
Maximum	1.000	Ea.	3.948	1,075	241	1,316
Refrigerator, 16 cu.ft., minimum	1.000	Ea.	2.000	705	89	794
Maximum	1.000	Ea.	3.200	1,125	142	1,267
16 cu.ft. with icemaker, minimum	1.000	Ea.	4.210	940	225	1,165
Maximum	1.000	Ea.	5.410	1,375	278	1,653
19 cu.ft., minimum	1.000	Ea.	2.667	590	119	709
Maximum	1.000	Ea.	4.667	1,025	208	1,233
19 cu.ft. with icemaker, minimum	1.000	Ea.	5.143	830	267	1,097
Maximum	1.000	Ea.	7.143	1,275	355	1,630
Sinks, porcelain on cast iron single bowl, 21" x 24"	1.000	Ea.	10.334	625	610	1,235
21" x 30"	1.000	Ea.	10.334	905	610	1,515
Double bowl, 20" x 32"	1.000	Ea.	10.810	705	635	1,340
Stainless steel, single bowl 16" x 20"	1.000	Ea.	10.334	965	610	1,575
22" x 25"	1.000	Ea.	10.334	1,050	610	1,660
Double bowl, 20" x 32"	1.000	Ea.	10.810	870	635	1,505
Water heater, electric, 30 gallon	1.000	Ea.	3.636	1,200	237	1,437
40 gallon	1.000	Ea.	4.000	1,275	261	1,536
Gas, 30 gallon	1.000	Ea.	4.000	2,125	261	2,386
75 gallon	1.000	Ea.	5.333	3,225	350	3,575
Wall, packaged terminal heater/air conditioner cabinet, wall sleeve, louver, electric heat, thermostat, manual changeover, 208V						
6000 BTUH cooling, 8800 BTU heating	1.000	Ea.	2.667	950	163	1,113
9000 BTUH cooling, 13,900 BTU heating	1.000	Ea.	3.200	1,400	195	1,595
12,000 BTUH cooling, 13,900 BTU heating	1.000	Ea.	4.000	1,500	244	1,744
15,000 BTUH cooling, 13,900 BTU heating	1.000	Ea.	5.333	1,750	325	2,075

System Description	QUAN.	UNIT	LABOR HOURS	COST EACH		
				MAT.	INST.	TOTAL
Curtain rods, stainless, 1" diameter, 3' long	1.000	Ea.	.615	30.50	36	66.50
5' long	1.000	Ea.	.615	30.50	36	66.50
Grab bar, 1" diameter, 12" long	1.000	Ea.	.283	28	16.60	44.60
36" long	1.000	Ea.	.340	32.50	20	52.50
1-1/4" diameter, 12" long	1.000	Ea.	.333	33	19.50	52.50
36" long	1.000	Ea.	.400	38.50	23.50	62
1-1/2" diameter, 12" long	1.000	Ea.	.383	38	22.50	60.50
36" long	1.000	Ea.	.460	44.50	27	71.50
Mirror, 18" x 24"	1.000	Ea.	.400	52	23.50	75.50
72" x 24"	1.000	Ea.	1.333	310	78	388
Medicine chest with mirror, 18" x 24"	1.000	Ea.	.400	212	23.50	235.50
36" x 24"	1.000	Ea.	.600	320	35.50	355.50
Toilet tissue dispenser, surface mounted, minimum	1.000	Ea.	.267	22	15.60	37.60
Maximum	1.000	Ea.	.400	33	23.50	56.50
Flush mounted, minimum	1.000	Ea.	.293	24	17.15	41.15
Maximum	1.000	Ea.	.427	35	25	60
Towel bar, 18" long, minimum	1.000	Ea.	.278	39	16.40	55.40
Maximum	1.000	Ea.	.348	49	20.50	69.50
24" long, minimum	1.000	Ea.	.313	44	18.45	62.45
Maximum	1.000	Ea.	.383	54	22.50	76.50
36" long, minimum	1.000	Ea.	.381	67.50	22.50	90
Maximum	1.000	Ea.	.419	74.50	25	99.50

Chimney — Mantle — Facing Brick — Firebox — Hearth — Cleanout

Damper

Foundation

Footing

System Description	QUAN.	UNIT	LABOR HOURS	COST EACH		
				MAT.	INST.	TOTAL
MASONRY FIREPLACE						
Footing, 8" thick, concrete, 4' x 7'	.700	C.Y.	2.800	140	156.18	296.18
Foundation, concrete block, 32" x 60" x 4' deep	1.000	Ea.	5.275	202.80	286.80	489.60
Fireplace, brick firebox, 30" x 29" opening	1.000	Ea.	40.000	630	2,125	2,755
Damper, cast iron, 30" opening	1.000	Ea.	1.333	137	78	215
Facing brick, standard size brick, 6' x 5'	30.000	S.F.	5.217	143.10	283.50	426.60
Hearth, standard size brick, 3' x 6'	1.000	Ea.	8.000	234	425	659
Chimney, standard size brick, 8" x 12" flue, one story house	12.000	V.L.F.	12.000	516	642	1,158
Mantle, 4" x 8", wood	6.000	L.F.	1.333	57.60	78	135.60
Cleanout, cast iron, 8" x 8"	1.000	Ea.	.667	52	39	91
TOTAL		Ea.	76.625	2,112.50	4,113.48	6,225.98

The costs in this system are on a cost each basis.

Description	QUAN.	UNIT	LABOR HOURS	COST EACH		
				MAT.	INST.	TOTAL

Masonry Fireplace Price Sheet

	QUAN.	UNIT	LABOR HOURS	COST EACH MAT.	COST EACH INST.	COST EACH TOTAL
Footing 8" thick, 3' x 6'	.440	C.Y.	1.326	88	98	186
4' x 7'	.700	C.Y.	2.110	140	156	296
5' x 8'	1.000	C.Y.	3.014	200	223	423
1' thick, 3' x 6'	.670	C.Y.	2.020	134	150	284
4' x 7'	1.030	C.Y.	3.105	206	230	436
5' x 8'	1.480	C.Y.	4.461	296	330	626
Foundation-concrete block, 24" x 48", 4' deep	1.000	Ea.	4.267	162	229	391
8' deep	1.000	Ea.	8.533	325	460	785
24" x 60", 4' deep	1.000	Ea.	4.978	189	268	457
8' deep	1.000	Ea.	9.956	380	535	915
32" x 48", 4' deep	1.000	Ea.	4.711	179	253	432
8' deep	1.000	Ea.	9.422	360	505	865
32" x 60", 4' deep	1.000	Ea.	5.333	203	287	490
8' deep	1.000	Ea.	10.845	410	585	995
32" x 72", 4' deep	1.000	Ea.	6.133	233	330	563
8' deep	1.000	Ea.	12.267	465	660	1,125
Fireplace, brick firebox 30" x 29" opening	1.000	Ea.	40.000	630	2,125	2,755
48" x 30" opening	1.000	Ea.	60.000	945	3,200	4,145
Steel fire box with registers, 25" opening	1.000	Ea.	26.667	1,175	1,425	2,600
48" opening	1.000	Ea.	44.000	1,950	2,350	4,300
Damper, cast iron, 30" opening	1.000	Ea.	1.333	137	78	215
36" opening	1.000	Ea.	1.556	160	91	251
Steel, 30" opening	1.000	Ea.	1.333	131	78	209
36" opening	1.000	Ea.	1.556	153	91	244
Facing for fireplace, standard size brick, 6' x 5'	30.000	S.F.	5.217	143	284	427
7' x 5'	35.000	S.F.	6.087	167	330	497
8' x 6'	48.000	S.F.	8.348	229	455	684
Fieldstone, 6' x 5'	30.000	S.F.	5.217	435	284	719
7' x 5'	35.000	S.F.	6.087	510	330	840
8' x 6'	48.000	S.F.	8.348	700	455	1,155
Sheetrock on metal, studs, 6' x 5'	30.000	S.F.	.980	26.50	57.50	84
7' x 5'	35.000	S.F.	1.143	31	67	98
8' x 6'	48.000	S.F.	1.568	42	91.50	133.50
Hearth, standard size brick, 3' x 6'	1.000	Ea.	8.000	234	425	659
3' x 7'	1.000	Ea.	9.280	271	495	766
3' x 8'	1.000	Ea.	10.640	310	565	875
Stone, 3' x 6'	1.000	Ea.	8.000	243	425	668
3' x 7'	1.000	Ea.	9.280	282	495	777
3' x 8'	1.000	Ea.	10.640	325	565	890
Chimney, standard size brick, 8" x 12" flue, one story house	12.000	V.L.F.	12.000	515	640	1,155
Two story house	20.000	V.L.F.	20.000	860	1,075	1,935
Mantle wood, beams, 4" x 8"	6.000	L.F.	1.333	57.50	78	135.50
4" x 10"	6.000	L.F.	1.371	68	80	148
Ornate, prefabricated, 6' x 3'-6" opening, minimum	1.000	Ea.	1.600	495	93.50	588.50
Maximum	1.000	Ea.	1.600	660	93.50	753.50
Cleanout, door and frame, cast iron, 8" x 8"	1.000	Ea.	.667	52	39	91
12" x 12"	1.000	Ea.	.800	98	47	145

For customer support on your Residential Costs with RSMeans Data, call 800.448.8182.

239

Chimney, Flue, Fittings & Framing

Framing

Mantle

Facing Brick

Prefabricated Fireplace

Hearth

System Description	QUAN.	UNIT	LABOR HOURS	MAT.	INST.	TOTAL
PREFABRICATED FIREPLACE						
Prefabricated fireplace, metal, painted	1.000	Ea.	6.154	1,675	360	2,035
Framing, 2" x 4" studs, 6' x 5'	35.000	L.F.	.509	15.40	29.75	45.15
Fire resistant gypsum drywall, unfinished	40.000	S.F.	.320	16.40	18.80	35.20
Drywall finishing adder	40.000	S.F.	.320	2	18.80	20.80
Facing, brick, standard size brick, 6' x 5'	30.000	S.F.	5.217	143.10	283.50	426.60
Hearth, standard size brick, 3' x 6'	1.000	Ea.	8.000	234	425	659
Chimney, one story house, framing, 2" x 4" studs	80.000	L.F.	1.164	35.20	68	103.20
Sheathing, plywood, 5/8" thick	32.000	S.F.	.758	94.08	44.48	138.56
Flue, 10" metal, insulated pipe	12.000	V.L.F.	4.000	570	230.40	800.40
Fittings, ceiling support	1.000	Ea.	.667	156	38.50	194.50
Fittings, joist shield	1.000	Ea.	.727	770	42	812
Fittings, roof flashing	1.000	Ea.	.667	440	38.50	478.50
Mantle beam, wood, 4" x 8"	6.000	L.F.	1.333	57.60	78	135.60
TOTAL		Ea.	29.836	4,208.78	1,675.73	5,884.51

The costs in this system are on a cost each basis.

Description	QUAN.	UNIT	LABOR HOURS	MAT.	INST.	TOTAL

Prefabricated Fireplace Price Sheet

	QUAN.	UNIT	LABOR HOURS	COST EACH		
				MAT.	INST.	TOTAL
Prefabricated fireplace, minimum	1.000	Ea.	6.154	1,675	360	2,035
Average	1.000	Ea.	8.000	1,925	470	2,395
Maximum	1.000	Ea.	8.889	3,500	520	4,020
Framing, 2" x 4" studs, fireplace, 6' x 5'	35.000	L.F.	.509	15.40	30	45.40
7' x 5'	40.000	L.F.	.582	17.60	34	51.60
8' x 6'	45.000	L.F.	.655	19.80	38.50	58.30
Sheetrock, 1/2" thick, fireplace, 6' x 5'	40.000	S.F.	.640	18.40	37.50	55.90
7' x 5'	45.000	S.F.	.720	20.50	42.50	63
8' x 6'	50.000	S.F.	.800	23	47	70
Facing for fireplace, brick, 6' x 5'	30.000	S.F.	5.217	143	284	427
7' x 5'	35.000	S.F.	6.087	167	330	497
8' x 6'	48.000	S.F.	8.348	229	455	684
Fieldstone, 6' x 5'	30.000	S.F.	5.217	420	284	704
7' x 5'	35.000	S.F.	6.087	490	330	820
8' x 6'	48.000	S.F.	8.348	675	455	1,130
Hearth, standard size brick, 3' x 6'	1.000	Ea.	8.000	234	425	659
3' x 7'	1.000	Ea.	9.280	271	495	766
3' x 8'	1.000	Ea.	10.640	310	565	875
Stone, 3' x 6'	1.000	Ea.	8.000	243	425	668
3' x 7'	1.000	Ea.	9.280	282	495	777
3' x 8'	1.000	Ea.	10.640	325	565	890
Chimney, framing, 2" x 4", one story house	80.000	L.F.	1.164	35	68	103
Two story house	120.000	L.F.	1.746	53	102	155
Sheathing, plywood, 5/8" thick	32.000	S.F.	.758	94	44.50	138.50
Stucco on plywood	32.000	S.F.	1.125	57	64.50	121.50
Flue, 10" metal pipe, insulated, one story house	12.000	V.L.F.	4.000	570	230	800
Two story house	20.000	V.L.F.	6.667	950	385	1,335
Fittings, ceiling support	1.000	Ea.	.667	156	38.50	194.50
Fittings joist sheild, one story house	1.000	Ea.	.667	770	42	812
Two story house	2.000	Ea.	1.333	1,550	84	1,634
Fittings roof flashing	1.000	Ea.	.667	440	38.50	478.50
Mantle, wood beam, 4" x 8"	6.000	L.F.	1.333	57.50	78	135.50
4" x 10"	6.000	L.F.	1.371	68	80	148
Ornate prefabricated, 6' x 3'-6" opening, minimum	1.000	Ea.	1.600	495	93.50	588.50
Maximum	1.000	Ea.	1.600	660	93.50	753.50

System Description	QUAN.	UNIT	LABOR HOURS	COST EACH		
				MAT.	INST.	TOTAL
Economy, lean-to, shell only, not including 2' stub wall, fndtn, flrs, heat						
4' x 16'	1.000	Ea.	26.212	2,675	1,525	4,200
4' x 24'	1.000	Ea.	30.259	3,075	1,775	4,850
6' x 10'	1.000	Ea.	16.552	1,925	965	2,890
6' x 16'	1.000	Ea.	23.034	2,675	1,350	4,025
6' x 24'	1.000	Ea.	29.793	3,450	1,750	5,200
8' x 10'	1.000	Ea.	22.069	2,550	1,300	3,850
8' x 16'	1.000	Ea.	38.400	4,450	2,250	6,700
8' x 24'	1.000	Ea.	49.655	5,750	2,900	8,650
Free standing, 8' x 8'	1.000	Ea.	17.356	1,750	1,025	2,775
8' x 16'	1.000	Ea.	30.211	3,075	1,775	4,850
8' x 24'	1.000	Ea.	39.051	3,950	2,275	6,225
10' x 10'	1.000	Ea.	18.824	4,350	1,100	5,450
10' x 16'	1.000	Ea.	24.095	5,575	1,400	6,975
10' x 24'	1.000	Ea.	31.624	7,300	1,850	9,150
14' x 10'	1.000	Ea.	20.741	7,075	1,200	8,275
14' x 16'	1.000	Ea.	24.889	8,475	1,450	9,925
14' x 24'	1.000	Ea.	33.349	11,400	1,950	13,350
Standard,lean-to,shell only,not incl.2'stub wall, fndtn,flrs, heat 4'x10'	1.000	Ea.	28.235	2,875	1,650	4,525
4' x 16'	1.000	Ea.	39.341	4,025	2,300	6,325
4' x 24'	1.000	Ea.	45.412	4,625	2,650	7,275
6' x 10'	1.000	Ea.	24.827	2,875	1,450	4,325
6' x 16'	1.000	Ea.	34.538	4,000	2,025	6,025
6' x 24'	1.000	Ea.	44.689	5,175	2,600	7,775
8' x 10'	1.000	Ea.	33.103	3,850	1,925	5,775
8' x 16'	1.000	Ea.	57.600	6,675	3,350	10,025
8' x 24'	1.000	Ea.	74.482	8,650	4,350	13,000
Free standing, 8' x 8'	1.000	Ea.	26.034	2,650	1,525	4,175
8' x 16'	1.000	Ea.	45.316	4,600	2,650	7,250
8' x 24'	1.000	Ea.	58.577	5,950	3,425	9,375
10' x 10'	1.000	Ea.	28.236	6,525	1,650	8,175
10' x 16'	1.000	Ea.	36.142	8,350	2,100	10,450
10' x 24'	1.000	Ea.	47.436	11,000	2,775	13,775
14' x 10'	1.000	Ea.	31.112	10,600	1,825	12,425
14' x 16'	1.000	Ea.	37.334	12,700	2,175	14,875
14' x 24'	1.000	Ea.	50.030	17,100	2,925	20,025
Deluxe,lean-to,shell only,not incl.2'stub wall, fndtn, flrs or heat, 4'x10'	1.000	Ea.	20.645	4,650	1,200	5,850
4' x 16'	1.000	Ea.	33.032	7,425	1,925	9,350
4' x 24'	1.000	Ea.	49.548	11,100	2,875	13,975
6' x 10'	1.000	Ea.	30.968	6,950	1,800	8,750
6' x 16'	1.000	Ea.	49.548	11,100	2,875	13,975
6' x 24'	1.000	Ea.	74.323	16,700	4,325	21,025
8' x 10'	1.000	Ea.	41.290	9,275	2,400	11,675
8' x 16'	1.000	Ea.	66.065	14,800	3,850	18,650
8' x 24'	1.000	Ea.	99.097	22,300	5,750	28,050
Freestanding, 8' x 8'	1.000	Ea.	18.618	6,050	1,100	7,150
8' x 16'	1.000	Ea.	37.236	12,100	2,175	14,275
8' x 24'	1.000	Ea.	55.855	18,100	3,275	21,375
10' x 10'	1.000	Ea.	29.091	9,450	1,700	11,150
10' x 16'	1.000	Ea.	46.546	15,100	2,725	17,825
10' x 24'	1.000	Ea.	69.818	22,700	4,075	26,775
14' x 10'	1.000	Ea.	40.727	13,200	2,375	15,575
14' x 16'	1.000	Ea.	65.164	21,200	3,800	25,000
14' x 24'	1.000	Ea.	97.746	31,800	5,700	37,500

System Description	QUAN.	UNIT	LABOR HOURS	COST EACH		
				MAT.	INST.	TOTAL
Swimming pools, vinyl lined, metal sides, sand bottom, 12' x 28'	1.000	Ea.	50.177	7,800	3,100	10,900
12' x 32'	1.000	Ea.	55.366	8,600	3,450	12,050
12' x 36'	1.000	Ea.	60.061	9,325	3,725	13,050
16' x 32'	1.000	Ea.	66.798	10,400	4,150	14,550
16' x 36'	1.000	Ea.	71.190	11,100	4,425	15,525
16' x 40'	1.000	Ea.	74.703	11,600	4,650	16,250
20' x 36'	1.000	Ea.	77.860	12,100	4,825	16,925
20' x 40'	1.000	Ea.	82.135	12,800	5,100	17,900
20' x 44'	1.000	Ea.	90.348	14,000	5,600	19,600
24' x 40'	1.000	Ea.	98.562	15,300	6,125	21,425
24' x 44'	1.000	Ea.	108.418	16,800	6,750	23,550
24' x 48'	1.000	Ea.	118.274	18,400	7,350	25,750
Vinyl lined, concrete sides, 12' x 28'	1.000	Ea.	79.447	12,300	4,925	17,225
12' x 32'	1.000	Ea.	88.818	13,800	5,525	19,325
12' x 36'	1.000	Ea.	97.656	15,200	6,075	21,275
16' x 32'	1.000	Ea.	111.393	17,300	6,925	24,225
16' x 36'	1.000	Ea.	121.354	18,900	7,550	26,450
16' x 40'	1.000	Ea.	130.445	20,300	8,125	28,425
28' x 36'	1.000	Ea.	140.585	21,800	8,750	30,550
20' x 40'	1.000	Ea.	149.336	23,200	9,275	32,475
20' x 44'	1.000	Ea.	164.270	25,500	10,200	35,700
24' x 40'	1.000	Ea.	179.203	27,800	11,100	38,900
24' x 44'	1.000	Ea.	197.124	30,600	12,300	42,900
24' x 48'	1.000	Ea.	215.044	33,400	13,400	46,800
Gunite, bottom and sides, 12' x 28'	1.000	Ea.	129.767	18,000	8,050	26,050
12' x 32'	1.000	Ea.	142.164	19,700	8,850	28,550
12' x 36'	1.000	Ea.	153.028	21,200	9,525	30,725
16' x 32'	1.000	Ea.	167.743	23,200	10,400	33,600
16' x 36'	1.000	Ea.	176.421	24,400	11,000	35,400
16' x 40'	1.000	Ea.	182.368	25,300	11,400	36,700
20' x 36'	1.000	Ea.	187.949	26,000	11,700	37,700
20' x 40'	1.000	Ea.	179.200	34,400	11,100	45,500
20' x 44'	1.000	Ea.	197.120	37,800	12,300	50,100
24' x 40'	1.000	Ea.	215.040	41,300	13,400	54,700
24' x 44'	1.000	Ea.	273.244	37,900	17,000	54,900
24' x 48'	1.000	Ea.	298.077	41,300	18,600	59,900

System Description	QUAN.	UNIT	LABOR HOURS	COST PER S.F.		
				MAT.	INST.	TOTAL
8′ X 12′ DECK, PRESSURE TREATED LUMBER, JOISTS 16″ O.C.						
4″ x 4″ Posts	.500	L.F.	.021	.76	1.20	1.96
Ledger, bolted 4′ O.C.	.125	L.F.	.005	.21	.30	.51
Joists, 2″ x 10″, 16″ O.C.	1.080	L.F.	.019	1.70	1.12	2.82
5/4″ x 6″ decking	1.000	S.F.	.025	2.26	1.46	3.72
2″ x 12″ stair stringers	.375	L.F.	.046	.71	2.70	3.41
5/4″ x 6″ stair treads	.500	L.F.	.050	.53	2.93	3.46
4′ x 4″ handrail posts	.210	L.F.	.009	.32	.50	.82
2″ x 6″ handrail cap	.520	L.F.	.014	.47	.81	1.28
2″ x 4″ baluster support	1.040	L.F.	.028	.61	1.62	2.23
2″ x 2″ balusters	3.850	L.F.	.093	1.54	5.47	7.01
Post footings	.042	Ea.	.134	1.22	6.93	8.15
Concrete step	.010	Ea.	.016	.81	.93	1.74
Joist hangers	.210	Ea.	.010	.32	.59	.91
TOTAL		S.F.	.470	11.46	26.56	38.02
12′ X 16′ DECK, PRESSURE TREATED LUMBER, JOISTS 24″ O.C.						
4″ x 4″ Posts	.312	L.F.	.013	.47	.75	1.22
Ledger, bolted 4′ O.C.	.083	L.F.	.003	.11	.20	.31
Joists, 2″ x 8″, 16″ O.C.	.810	L.F.	.014	1.27	.84	2.11
5/4″ x 6″ decking	1.000	S.F.	.025	2.26	1.46	3.72
2″ x 12″ stair stringers	.188	L.F.	.023	.36	1.35	1.71
5/4″ x 6″ stair treads	.250	L.F.	.025	1.33	1.46	2.79
4″ x 4″ handrail posts	.125	L.F.	.005	.19	.30	.49
2″ x 6″ handrail cap	.323	L.F.	.009	.29	.50	.79
2″ x 4″ baluster support	.650	L.F.	.017	.38	1.01	1.39
2″ x 2″ balusters	2.440	L.F.	.059	.98	3.46	4.44
Post footings	.026	Ea.	.083	.75	4.29	5.04
Concrete step	.005	Ea.	.008	.41	.47	.88
Joist hangers	.135	Ea.	.007	.20	.38	.58
Deck support girder	.083	L.F.	.002	.26	.14	.40
TOTAL		S.F.	.293	9.26	16.61	25.87

The costs in this system are on a square foot basis.

System Description	QUAN.	UNIT	LABOR HOURS	COST PER S.F.		
				MAT.	INST.	TOTAL
12' X 24' DECK, REDWOOD OR CEDAR, JOISTS 16" O.C.						
4" x 4" redwood posts	.291	L.F.	.012	2.05	.70	2.75
Redwood joists, 2" x 8", 16" O.C.	.001	M.B.F.	.010	5.50	.59	6.09
5/4" x 6" redwood decking	1.000	S.F.	.025	5.25	1.46	6.71
Stair stringers	.125	L.F.	.015	.24	.90	1.14
Stringer trim	.083	L.F.	.003	.44	.19	.63
Stair treads	.135	S.F.	.003	.71	.20	.91
Handrail supports	.083	L.F.	.003	.59	.20	.79
Handrail cap	.152	L.F.	.004	1.25	.24	1.49
Baluster supports	.416	L.F.	.011	3.43	.65	4.08
Balusters	1.875	L.F.	.050	2.42	2.93	5.35
Post footings	.024	Ea.	.077	.70	3.96	4.66
Concrete step	.003	Ea.	.005	.24	.28	.52
Joist hangers	.132	Ea.	.006	.20	.37	.57
Deck support girder		M.B.F.	.003	1.50	.16	1.66
TOTAL		S.F.	.227	24.52	12.83	37.35

The costs in this system are on a square foot basis.

Wood Deck Price Sheet	QUAN.	UNIT	LABOR HOURS	COST PER S.F.		
				MAT.	INST.	TOTAL
Decking, treated lumber, 1" x 4"	3.430	L.F.	.031	8.90	5.85	14.75
2" x 4"	3.430	L.F.	.033	6.75	5.35	12.10
2" x 6"	2.200	L.F.	.041	4.27	3.21	7.48
5/4" x 6"	2.200	L.F.	.027	4.97	3.21	8.18
Redwood or cedar, 1" x 4"	3.430	L.F.	.035	7.65	5.85	13.50
2" x 4"	3.430	L.F.	.036	15.05	5.35	20.40
2" x 6"	2.200	L.F.	.028	18.05	3.21	21.26
5/4" x 6"	2.200	L.F.	.027	11.65	3.21	14.86
Joists for deck, treated lumber, 2" x 8", 16" O.C.	1.000	L.F.	.015	1.19	.85	2.04
24" O.C.	.750	L.F.	.012	.89	.64	1.53
2" x 10", 16" O.C.	1.000	L.F.	.018	1.57	1.04	2.61
24" O.C.	.750	L.F.	.014	1.18	.78	1.96
Redwood or cedar, 2" x 8", 16" O.C.	1.000	L.F.	.015	5	.85	5.85
24" O.C.	.750	L.F.	.012	3.75	.64	4.39
2" x 10", 16" O.C.	1.000	L.F.	.018	8.35	1.04	9.39
24" O.C.	.750	L.F.	.014	6.25	.78	7.03
Girder for joists, treated lumber, 2" x 10", 8' x 12' deck	.250	L.F.	.002	.39	.21	.60
12' x 16' deck	.167	L.F.	.001	.26	.14	.40
12' x 24' deck	.167	L.F.	.001	.26	.14	.40
Redwood or cedar, 2" x 10", 8' x 12' deck	.250	L.F.	.002	2.09	.26	2.35
12' x 16' deck	.167	L.F.	.001	1.39	.17	1.56
12' x 24' deck	.167	L.F.	.001	1.39	.17	1.56
Posts, 4" x 4", including concrete footing, 8' x 12' deck	.500	L.F.	.022	1.95	7.95	9.90
12' x 16' deck	.312	L.F.	.017	1.22	5.05	6.27
12' x 24' deck	.291	L.F.	.017	1.14	4.66	5.80
Stairs 2" x 10" stringers, treated lumber, 8' x 12' deck	1.000	Set	.020	1.52	4.70	6.22
12' x 16' deck	1.000	Set	.012	.76	2.35	3.11
12' x 24' deck	1.000	Set	.008	.53	1.65	2.18
Redwood or cedar, 8' x 12' deck	1.000	Set	.040	3.90	4.70	8.60
12' x 16' deck	1.000	Set	.020	1.95	2.35	4.30
12' x 24' deck	1.000	Set	.012	1.37	1.65	3.02
Railings 2" x 4", treated lumber, 8' x 12' deck	.520	L.F.	.026	2.62	7.90	10.52
12' x 16' deck	.323	L.F.	.017	1.65	4.97	6.62
12' x 24' deck	.210	L.F.	.014	1.19	3.65	4.84
Redwood or cedar, 8' x 12' deck	1.000	L.F.	.009	10.60	8.40	19

Wood Deck Price Sheet

	QUAN.	UNIT	LABOR HOURS	COST PER S.F.		
				MAT.	INST.	TOTAL
12' x 16' deck	.670	L.F.	.006	6.60	5.30	11.90
12' x 24' deck	.540	L.F.	.005	4.70	3.92	8.62
Alternative decking, wood/plastic composite, 5/4" x 6"	2.200	L.F.	.055	8.25	3.21	11.46
1" x 4" square edge fir	3.430	L.F.	.100	9	5.85	14.85
1" x 4" tongue and groove fir	3.430	L.F.	.122	5.75	7.15	12.90
1" x 4" mahogany	3.430	L.F.	.100	8.15	5.85	14
5/4" x 6" PVC	2.200	L.F.	.064	9.45	3.74	13.19

Lavatory

Vanity Top

Piping

Vanity Base Cabinet

Water Closet

System Description	QUAN.	UNIT	LABOR HOURS	COST EACH		
				MAT.	INST.	TOTAL
LAVATORY INSTALLED WITH VANITY, PLUMBING IN 2 WALLS						
Water closet, floor mounted, 2 piece, close coupled, white	1.000	Ea.	3.019	214	177	391
Rough-in, vent, 2″ diameter DWV piping	1.000	Ea.	.955	92	56	148
Waste, 4″ diameter DWV piping	1.000	Ea.	.828	115.50	48.60	164.10
Supply, 1/2″ diameter type "L" copper supply piping	1.000	Ea.	.593	23.34	38.70	62.04
Lavatory, 20″ x 18″, P.E. cast iron white	1.000	Ea.	2.500	350	147	497
Rough-in, vent, 1-1/2″ diameter DWV piping	1.000	Ea.	.901	88	53	141
Waste, 2″ diameter DWV piping	1.000	Ea.	.955	92	56	148
Supply, 1/2″ diameter type "L" copper supply piping	1.000	Ea.	.988	38.90	64.50	103.40
Piping, supply, 1/2″ diameter type "L" copper supply piping	10.000	L.F.	.988	38.90	64.50	103.40
Waste, 4″ diameter DWV piping	7.000	L.F.	1.931	269.50	113.40	382.90
Vent, 2″ diameter DWV piping	12.000	L.F.	2.866	276	168	444
Vanity base cabinet, 2 door, 30″ wide	1.000	Ea.	1.000	445	58.50	503.50
Vanity top, plastic & laminated, square edge	2.670	L.F.	.712	117.48	41.65	159.13
TOTAL		Ea.	18.236	2,160.62	1,086.85	3,247.47
LAVATORY WITH WALL-HUNG LAVATORY, PLUMBING IN 2 WALLS						
Water closet, floor mounted, 2 piece close coupled, white	1.000	Ea.	3.019	214	177	391
Rough-in, vent, 2″ diameter DWV piping	1.000	Ea.	.955	92	56	148
Waste, 4″ diameter DWV piping	1.000	Ea.	.828	115.50	48.60	164.10
Supply, 1/2″ diameter type "L" copper supply piping	1.000	Ea.	.593	23.34	38.70	62.04
Lavatory, 20″ x 18″, P.E. cast iron, wall hung, white	1.000	Ea.	2.000	294	117	411
Rough-in, vent, 1-1/2″ diameter DWV piping	1.000	Ea.	.901	88	53	141
Waste, 2″ diameter DWV piping	1.000	Ea.	.955	92	56	148
Supply, 1/2″ diameter type "L" copper supply piping	1.000	Ea.	.988	38.90	64.50	103.40
Piping, supply, 1/2″ diameter type "L" copper supply piping	10.000	L.F.	.988	38.90	64.50	103.40
Waste, 4″ diameter DWV piping	7.000	L.F.	1.931	269.50	113.40	382.90
Vent, 2″ diameter DWV piping	12.000	L.F.	2.866	276	168	444
Carrier, steel for studs, no arms	1.000	Ea.	1.143	106	74.50	180.50
TOTAL		Ea.	17.167	1,648.14	1,031.20	2,679.34

Description	QUAN.	UNIT	LABOR HOURS	COST EACH		
				MAT.	INST.	TOTAL

Two Fixture Lavatory Price Sheet

	QUAN.	UNIT	LABOR HOURS	COST EACH MAT.	COST EACH INST.	COST EACH TOTAL
Water closet, close coupled standard 2 piece, white	1.000	Ea.	3.019	214	177	391
Color	1.000	Ea.	3.019	385	177	562
One piece elongated bowl, white	1.000	Ea.	3.019	670	177	847
Color	1.000	Ea.	3.019	885	177	1,062
Low profile, one piece elongated bowl, white	1.000	Ea.	3.019	675	177	852
Color	1.000	Ea.	3.019	885	177	1,062
Rough-in for water closet						
1/2" copper supply, 4" cast iron waste, 2" cast iron vent	1.000	Ea.	2.376	231	143	374
4" PVC waste, 2" PVC vent	1.000	Ea.	2.678	119	161	280
4" copper waste , 2" copper vent	1.000	Ea.	2.520	243	157	400
3" cast iron waste, 1-1/2" cast iron vent	1.000	Ea.	2.244	177	136	313
3" PVC waste, 1-1/2" PVC vent	1.000	Ea.	2.388	111	150	261
3" copper waste, 1-1/2" copper vent	1.000	Ea.	2.524	212	152	364
1/2" PVC supply, 4" PVC waste, 2" PVC vent	1.000	Ea.	2.974	142	180	322
3" PVC waste, 1-1/2" PVC vent	1.000	Ea.	2.684	134	169	303
1/2" steel supply, 4" cast iron waste, 2" cast iron vent	1.000	Ea.	2.545	247	154	401
4" cast iron waste, 2" steel vent	1.000	Ea.	2.590	215	157	372
4" PVC waste, 2" PVC vent	1.000	Ea.	2.847	135	172	307
Lavatory, vanity top mounted, P.E. on cast iron 20" x 18" white	1.000	Ea.	2.500	350	147	497
Color	1.000	Ea.	2.500	510	147	657
Steel, enameled 10" x 17" white	1.000	Ea.	2.759	166	162	328
Color	1.000	Ea.	2.500	170	147	317
Vitreous china 20" x 16", white	1.000	Ea.	2.963	262	174	436
Color	1.000	Ea.	2.963	262	174	436
Wall hung, P.E. on cast iron, 20" x 18", white	1.000	Ea.	2.000	294	117	411
Color	1.000	Ea.	2.000	305	117	422
Vitreous china 19" x 17", white	1.000	Ea.	2.286	164	134	298
Color	1.000	Ea.	2.286	186	134	320
Rough-in supply waste and vent for lavatory						
1/2" copper supply, 2" cast iron waste, 1-1/2" cast iron vent	1.000	Ea.	2.844	219	174	393
2" PVC waste, 1-1/2" PVC vent	1.000	Ea.	2.962	163	186	349
2" copper waste, 1-1/2" copper vent	1.000	Ea.	2.308	170	151	321
1-1/2" PVC waste, 1-1/4" PVC vent	1.000	Ea.	2.639	162	172	334
1-1/2" copper waste, 1-1/4" copper vent	1.000	Ea.	2.114	148	138	286
1/2" PVC supply, 2" PVC waste, 1-1/2" PVC vent	1.000	Ea.	3.456	201	218	419
1-1/2" PVC waste, 1-1/4" PVC vent	1.000	Ea.	3.133	200	204	404
1/2" steel supply, 2" cast iron waste, 1-1/2" cast iron vent	1.000	Ea.	3.126	246	192	438
2" cast iron waste, 2" steel vent	1.000	Ea.	3.225	217	198	415
2" PVC waste, 1-1/2" PVC vent	1.000	Ea.	3.244	189	205	394
1-1/2" PVC waste, 1-1/4" PVC vent	1.000	Ea.	2.921	189	191	380
Piping, supply, 1/2" copper, type "L"	10.000	L.F.	.988	39	64.50	103.50
1/2" steel	10.000	L.F.	1.270	65.50	83	148.50
1/2" PVC	10.000	L.F.	1.482	77	96.50	173.50
Waste, 4" cast iron	7.000	L.F.	1.931	270	113	383
4" copper	7.000	L.F.	2.800	345	165	510
4" PVC	7.000	L.F.	2.333	77.50	137	214.50
Vent, 2" cast iron	12.000	L.F.	2.866	276	168	444
2" copper	12.000	L.F.	2.182	218	142	360
2" PVC	12.000	L.F.	3.254	188	191	379
2" steel	12.000	Ea.	3.000	179	176	355
Vanity base cabinet, 2 door, 24" x 30"	1.000	Ea.	1.000	445	58.50	503.50
24" x 36"	1.000	Ea.	1.200	435	70	505
Vanity top, laminated plastic, square edge 25" x 32"	2.670	L.F.	.712	117	41.50	158.50
25" x 38"	3.170	L.F.	.845	139	49.50	188.50
Post formed, laminated plastic, 25" x 32"	2.670	L.F.	.712	30.50	41.50	72
25" x 38"	3.170	L.F.	.845	36	49.50	85.50
Cultured marble, 25" x 32" with bowl	1.000	Ea.	2.500	210	147	357
25" x 38" with bowl	1.000	Ea.	2.500	244	147	391
Carrier for lavatory, steel for studs	1.000	Ea.	1.143	106	74.50	180.50
Wood 2" x 8" blocking	1.330	L.F.	.053	1.28	3.11	4.39

System Description	QUAN.	UNIT	LABOR HOURS	COST EACH		
				MAT.	INST.	TOTAL
BATHROOM INSTALLED WITH VANITY						
Water closet, floor mounted, 2 piece, close coupled, white	1.000	Ea.	3.019	214	177	391
Rough-in, waste, 4" diameter DWV piping	1.000	Ea.	.828	115.50	48.60	164.10
Vent, 2" diameter DWV piping	1.000	Ea.	.955	92	56	148
Supply, 1/2" diameter type "L" copper supply piping	1.000	Ea.	.593	23.34	38.70	62.04
Lavatory, 20" x 18", P.E. cast iron with accessories, white	1.000	Ea.	2.500	350	147	497
Rough-in, supply, 1/2" diameter type "L" copper supply piping	1.000	Ea.	.988	38.90	64.50	103.40
Waste, 1-1/2" diameter DWV piping	1.000	Ea.	1.803	176	106	282
Bathtub, P.E. cast iron, 5' long with accessories, white	1.000	Ea.	3.636	1,250	213	1,463
Rough-in, waste, 4" diameter DWV piping	1.000	Ea.	.828	115.50	48.60	164.10
Vent, 1-1/2" diameter DWV piping	1.000	Ea.	.593	58.60	38.60	97.20
Supply, 1/2" diameter type "L" copper supply piping	1.000	Ea.	.988	38.90	64.50	103.40
Piping, supply, 1/2" diameter type "L" copper supply piping	20.000	L.F.	1.975	77.80	129	206.80
Waste, 4" diameter DWV piping	9.000	L.F.	2.483	346.50	145.80	492.30
Vent, 2" diameter DWV piping	6.000	L.F.	1.500	89.70	88.20	177.90
Vanity base cabinet, 2 door, 30" wide	1.000	Ea.	1.000	445	58.50	503.50
Vanity top, plastic laminated square edge	2.670	L.F.	.712	98.79	41.65	140.44
TOTAL		Ea.	24.401	3,530.53	1,465.65	4,996.18
BATHROOM WITH WALL HUNG LAVATORY						
Water closet, floor mounted, 2 piece, close coupled, white	1.000	Ea.	3.019	214	177	391
Rough-in, vent, 2" diameter DWV piping	1.000	Ea.	.955	92	56	148
Waste, 4" diameter DWV piping	1.000	Ea.	.828	115.50	48.60	164.10
Supply, 1/2" diameter type "L" copper supply piping	1.000	Ea.	.593	23.34	38.70	62.04
Lavatory, 20" x 18" P.E. cast iron, wall hung, white	1.000	Ea.	2.000	294	117	411
Rough-in, waste, 1-1/2" diameter DWV piping	1.000	Ea.	1.803	176	106	282
Supply, 1/2" diameter type "L" copper supply piping	1.000	Ea.	.988	38.90	64.50	103.40
Bathtub, P.E. cast iron, 5' long with accessories, white	1.000	Ea.	3.636	1,250	213	1,463
Rough-in, waste, 4" diameter DWV piping	1.000	Ea.	.828	115.50	48.60	164.10
Supply, 1/2" diameter type "L" copper supply piping	1.000	Ea.	.988	38.90	64.50	103.40
Vent, 1-1/2" diameter DWV piping	1.000	Ea.	1.482	146.50	96.50	243
Piping, supply, 1/2" diameter type "L" copper supply piping	20.000	L.F.	1.975	77.80	129	206.80
Waste, 4" diameter DWV piping	9.000	L.F.	2.483	346.50	145.80	492.30
Vent, 2" diameter DWV piping	6.000	L.F.	1.500	89.70	88.20	177.90
Carrier, steel, for studs, no arms	1.000	Ea.	1.143	106	74.50	180.50
TOTAL		Ea.	24.221	3,124.64	1,467.90	4,592.54

The costs in this system are a cost each basis, all necessary piping is included.

Three Fixture Bathroom Price Sheet	QUAN.	UNIT	LABOR HOURS	COST EACH MAT.	COST EACH INST.	COST EACH TOTAL
Water closet, close coupled standard 2 piece, white	1.000	Ea.	3.019	214	177	391
Color	1.000	Ea.	3.019	385	177	562
One piece, elongated bowl, white	1.000	Ea.	3.019	670	177	847
Color	1.000	Ea.	3.019	885	177	1,062
Low profile, one piece elongated bowl, white	1.000	Ea.	3.019	675	177	852
Color	1.000	Ea.	3.019	885	177	1,062
Rough-in, for water closet						
1/2" copper supply, 4" cast iron waste, 2" cast iron vent	1.000	Ea.	2.376	231	143	374
4" PVC/DWV waste, 2" PVC vent	1.000	Ea.	2.678	119	161	280
4" copper waste, 2" copper vent	1.000	Ea.	2.520	243	157	400
3" cast iron waste, 1-1/2" cast iron vent	1.000	Ea.	2.244	177	136	313
3" PVC waste, 1-1/2" PVC vent	1.000	Ea.	2.388	111	150	261
3" copper waste, 1-1/2" copper vent	1.000	Ea.	2.014	163	126	289
1/2" PVC supply, 4" PVC waste, 2" PVC vent	1.000	Ea.	2.974	142	180	322
3" PVC waste, 1-1/2" PVC supply	1.000	Ea.	2.684	134	169	303
1/2" steel supply, 4" cast iron waste, 2" cast iron vent	1.000	Ea.	2.545	247	154	401
4" cast iron waste, 2" steel vent	1.000	Ea.	2.590	215	157	372
4" PVC waste, 2" PVC vent	1.000	Ea.	2.847	135	172	307
Lavatory, wall hung, P.E. cast iron 20" x 18", white	1.000	Ea.	2.000	294	117	411
Color	1.000	Ea.	2.000	305	117	422
Vitreous china 19" x 17", white	1.000	Ea.	2.286	164	134	298
Color	1.000	Ea.	2.286	186	134	320
Lavatory, for vanity top, P.E. cast iron 20" x 18"", white	1.000	Ea.	2.500	350	147	497
Color	1.000	Ea.	2.500	510	147	657
Steel, enameled 20" x 17", white	1.000	Ea.	2.759	166	162	328
Color	1.000	Ea.	2.500	170	147	317
Vitreous china 20" x 16", white	1.000	Ea.	2.963	262	174	436
Color	1.000	Ea.	2.963	262	174	436
Rough-in, for lavatory						
1/2" copper supply, 1-1/2" C.I. waste, 1-1/2" C.I. vent	1.000	Ea.	2.791	215	171	386
1-1/2" PVC waste, 1-1/4" PVC vent	1.000	Ea.	2.639	162	172	334
1/2" steel supply, 1-1/4" cast iron waste, 1-1/4" steel vent	1.000	Ea.	2.890	180	178	358
1-1/4" PVC waste, 1-1/4" PVC vent	1.000	Ea.	2.794	190	182	372
1/2" PVC supply, 1-1/2" PVC waste, 1-1/2" PVC vent	1.000	Ea.	3.260	199	213	412
Bathtub, P.E. cast iron, 5' long corner with fittings, white	1.000	Ea.	3.636	1,250	213	1,463
Color	1.000	Ea.	3.636	1,575	213	1,788
Rough-in, for bathtub						
1/2" copper supply, 4" cast iron waste, 1-1/2" copper vent	1.000	Ea.	2.409	213	152	365
4" PVC waste, 1-1/2" PVC vent	1.000	Ea.	2.877	133	181	314
1/2" steel supply, 4" cast iron waste, 1-1/2" steel vent	1.000	Ea.	2.898	211	179	390
4" PVC waste, 1-1/2" PVC vent	1.000	Ea.	3.159	160	200	360
1/2" PVC supply, 4" PVC waste, 1-1/2" PVC vent	1.000	Ea.	3.371	171	213	384
Piping, supply 1/2" copper	20.000	L.F.	1.975	78	129	207
1/2" steel	20.000	L.F.	2.540	131	166	297
1/2" PVC	20.000	L.F.	2.963	154	193	347
Piping, waste, 4" cast iron no hub	9.000	L.F.	2.483	345	146	491
4" PVC/DWV	9.000	L.F.	3.000	100	176	276
4" copper/DWV	9.000	L.F.	3.600	440	212	652
Piping, vent 2" cast iron no hub	6.000	L.F.	1.433	138	84	222
2" copper/DWV	6.000	L.F.	1.091	109	71	180
2" PVC/DWV	6.000	L.F.	1.627	94	95.50	189.50
2" steel, galvanized	6.000	L.F.	1.500	89.50	88	177.50
Vanity base cabinet, 2 door, 24" x 30"	1.000	Ea.	1.000	445	58.50	503.50
24" x 36"	1.000	Ea.	1.200	435	70	505
Vanity top, laminated plastic square edge 25" x 32"	2.670	L.F.	.712	99	41.50	140.50
25" x 38"	3.160	L.F.	.843	117	49.50	166.50
Cultured marble, 25" x 32", with bowl	1.000	Ea.	2.500	210	147	357
25" x 38", with bowl	1.000	Ea.	2.500	244	147	391
Carrier, for lavatory, steel for studs, no arms	1.000	Ea.	1.143	106	74.50	180.50
Wood, 2" x 8" blocking	1.300	L.F.	.052	1.25	3.04	4.29

System Description	QUAN.	UNIT	LABOR HOURS	COST EACH		
				MAT.	INST.	TOTAL
BATHROOM WITH LAVATORY INSTALLED IN VANITY						
Water closet, floor mounted, 2 piece, close coupled, white	1.000	Ea.	3.019	214	177	391
Rough-in, waste, 4" diameter DWV piping	1.000	Ea.	.828	115.50	48.60	164.10
Vent, 2" diameter DWV piping	1.000	Ea.	.955	92	56	148
Supply, 1/2" diameter type "L" copper supply piping	1.000	Ea.	.593	23.34	38.70	62.04
Lavatory, 20" x 18", P.E. cast iron with accessories, white	1.000	Ea.	2.500	350	147	497
Rough-in, waste, 1-1/2" diameter DWV piping	1.000	Ea.	1.803	176	106	282
Supply, 1/2" diameter type "L" copper supply piping	1.000	Ea.	.988	38.90	64.50	103.40
Bathtub, P.E. cast iron 5' long with accessories, white	1.000	Ea.	3.636	1,250	213	1,463
Rough-in, waste, 4" diameter DWV piping	1.000	Ea.	.828	115.50	48.60	164.10
Vent, 1-1/2" diameter DWV piping	1.000	Ea.	.593	58.60	38.60	97.20
Supply, 1/2" diameter type "L" copper supply piping	1.000	Ea.	.988	38.90	64.50	103.40
Piping, supply, 1/2" diameter type "L" copper supply piping	10.000	L.F.	.988	38.90	64.50	103.40
Waste, 4" diameter DWV piping	6.000	L.F.	1.655	231	97.20	328.20
Vent, 2" diameter DWV piping	6.000	L.F.	1.500	89.70	88.20	177.90
Vanity base cabinet, 2 door, 30" wide	1.000	Ea.	1.000	445	58.50	503.50
Vanity top, plastic laminated square edge	2.670	L.F.	.712	98.79	41.65	140.44
TOTAL		Ea.	22.586	3,376.13	1,352.55	4,728.68
BATHROOM WITH WALL HUNG LAVATORY						
Water closet, floor mounted, 2 piece, close coupled, white	1.000	Ea.	3.019	214	177	391
Rough-in, vent, 2" diameter DWV piping	1.000	Ea.	.955	92	56	148
Waste, 4" diameter DWV piping	1.000	Ea.	.828	115.50	48.60	164.10
Supply, 1/2" diameter type "L" copper supply piping	1.000	Ea.	.593	23.34	38.70	62.04
Lavatory, 20" x 18" P.E. cast iron, wall hung, white	1.000	Ea.	2.000	294	117	411
Rough-in, waste, 1-1/2" diameter DWV piping	1.000	Ea.	1.803	176	106	282
Supply, 1/2" diameter type "L" copper supply piping	1.000	Ea.	.988	38.90	64.50	103.40
Bathtub, P.E. cast iron, 5' long with accessories, white	1.000	Ea.	3.636	1,250	213	1,463
Rough-in, waste, 4" diameter DWV piping	1.000	Ea.	.828	115.50	48.60	164.10
Supply, 1/2" diameter type "L" copper supply piping	1.000	Ea.	.988	38.90	64.50	103.40
Vent, 1-1/2" diameter DWV piping	1.000	Ea.	.593	58.60	38.60	97.20
Piping, supply, 1/2" diameter type "L" copper supply piping	10.000	L.F.	.988	38.90	64.50	103.40
Waste, 4" diameter DWV piping	6.000	L.F.	1.655	231	97.20	328.20
Vent, 2" diameter DWV piping	6.000	L.F.	1.500	89.70	88.20	177.90
Carrier, steel, for studs, no arms	1.000	Ea.	1.143	106	74.50	180.50
TOTAL		Ea.	21.517	2,882.34	1,296.90	4,179.24

The costs in this system are on a cost each basis. All necessary piping is included.

Three Fixture Bathroom Price Sheet	QUAN.	UNIT	LABOR HOURS	COST EACH		
				MAT.	INST.	TOTAL
Water closet, close coupled standard 2 piece, white	1.000	Ea.	3.019	214	177	391
Color	1.000	Ea.	3.019	385	177	562
One piece elongated bowl, white	1.000	Ea.	3.019	670	177	847
Color	1.000	Ea.	3.019	885	177	1,062
Low profile, one piece elongated bowl, white	1.000	Ea.	3.019	675	177	852
Color	1.000	Ea.	3.019	885	177	1,062
Rough-in for water closet						
1/2" copper supply, 4" cast iron waste, 2" cast iron vent	1.000	Ea.	2.376	231	143	374
4" PVC/DWV waste, 2" PVC vent	1.000	Ea.	2.678	119	161	280
4" carrier waste, 2" copper vent	1.000	Ea.	2.520	243	157	400
3" cast iron waste, 1-1/2" cast iron vent	1.000	Ea.	2.244	177	136	313
3" PVC waste, 1-1/2" PVC vent	1.000	Ea.	2.388	111	150	261
3" copper waste, 1-1/2" copper vent	1.000	Ea.	2.014	163	126	289
1/2" PVC supply, 4" PVC waste, 2" PVC vent	1.000	Ea.	2.974	142	180	322
3" PVC waste, 1-1/2" PVC supply	1.000	Ea.	2.684	134	169	303
1/2" steel supply, 4" cast iron waste, 2" cast iron vent	1.000	Ea.	2.545	247	154	401
4" cast iron waste, 2" steel vent	1.000	Ea.	2.590	215	157	372
4" PVC waste, 2" PVC vent	1.000	Ea.	2.847	135	172	307
Lavatory, wall hung, PE cast iron 20" x 18", white	1.000	Ea.	2.000	294	117	411
Color	1.000	Ea.	2.000	305	117	422
Vitreous china 19" x 17", white	1.000	Ea.	2.286	164	134	298
Color	1.000	Ea.	2.286	186	134	320
Lavatory, for vanity top, PE cast iron 20" x 18", white	1.000	Ea.	2.500	350	147	497
Color	1.000	Ea.	2.500	510	147	657
Steel enameled 20" x 17", white	1.000	Ea.	2.759	166	162	328
Color	1.000	Ea.	2.500	170	147	317
Vitreous china 20" x 16", white	1.000	Ea.	2.963	262	174	436
Color	1.000	Ea.	2.963	262	174	436
Rough-in for lavatory						
1/2" copper supply, 1-1/2" cast iron waste, 1-1/2" cast iron vent	1.000	Ea.	2.791	215	171	386
1-1/2" PVC waste, 1-1/4" PVC vent	1.000	Ea.	2.639	162	172	334
1/2" steel supply, 1-1/4" cast iron waste, 1-1/4" steel vent	1.000	Ea.	2.890	180	178	358
1-1/4" PVC waste, 1-1/4" PVC vent	1.000	Ea.	2.794	190	182	372
1/2" PVC supply, 1-1/2" PVC waste, 1-1/2" PVC vent	1.000	Ea.	3.260	199	213	412
Bathtub, PE cast iron, 5' long corner with fittings, white	1.000	Ea.	3.636	1,250	213	1,463
Color	1.000	Ea.	3.636	1,575	213	1,788
Rough-in for bathtub						
1/2" copper supply, 4" cast iron waste, 1-1/2" copper vent	1.000	Ea.	2.409	213	152	365
4" PVC waste, 1/2" PVC vent	1.000	Ea.	2.877	133	181	314
1/2" steel supply, 4" cast iron waste, 1-1/2" steel vent	1.000	Ea.	2.898	211	179	390
4" PVC waste, 1-1/2" PVC vent	1.000	Ea.	3.159	160	200	360
1/2" PVC supply, 4" PVC waste, 1-1/2" PVC vent	1.000	Ea.	3.371	171	213	384
Piping supply, 1/2" copper	10.000	L.F.	.988	39	64.50	103.50
1/2" steel	10.000	L.F.	1.270	65.50	83	148.50
1/2" PVC	10.000	L.F.	1.482	77	96.50	173.50
Piping waste, 4" cast iron no hub	6.000	L.F.	1.655	231	97	328
4" PVC/DWV	6.000	L.F.	2.000	66.50	117	183.50
4" copper/DWV	6.000	L.F.	2.400	294	141	435
Piping vent 2" cast iron no hub	6.000	L.F.	1.433	138	84	222
2" copper/DWV	6.000	L.F.	1.091	109	71	180
2" PVC/DWV	6.000	L.F.	1.627	94	95.50	189.50
2" steel, galvanized	6.000	L.F.	1.500	89.50	88	177.50
Vanity base cabinet, 2 door, 24" x 30"	1.000	Ea.	1.000	445	58.50	503.50
24" x 36"	1.000	Ea.	1.200	435	70	505
Vanity top, laminated plastic square edge 25" x 32"	2.670	L.F.	.712	99	41.50	140.50
25" x 38"	3.160	L.F.	.843	117	49.50	166.50
Cultured marble, 25" x 32", with bowl	1.000	Ea.	2.500	210	147	357
25" x 38", with bowl	1.000	Ea.	2.500	244	147	391
Carrier, for lavatory, steel for studs, no arms	1.000	Ea.	1.143	106	74.50	180.50
Wood, 2" x 8" blocking	1.300	L.F.	.052	1.25	3.04	4.29

System Description	QUAN.	UNIT	LABOR HOURS	COST EACH		
				MAT.	INST.	TOTAL
BATHROOM WITH LAVATORY INSTALLED IN VANITY						
Water closet, floor mounted, 2 piece, close coupled, white	1.000	Ea.	3.019	214	177	391
Rough-in, vent, 2" diameter DWV piping	1.000	Ea.	.955	92	56	148
Waste, 4" diameter DWV piping	1.000	Ea.	.828	115.50	48.60	164.10
Supply, 1/2" diameter type "L" copper supply piping	1.000	Ea.	.593	23.34	38.70	62.04
Lavatory, 20" x 18", PE cast iron with accessories, white	1.000	Ea.	2.500	350	147	497
Rough-in, vent, 1-1/2" diameter DWV piping	1.000	Ea.	1.803	176	106	282
Supply, 1/2" diameter type "L" copper supply piping	1.000	Ea.	.988	38.90	64.50	103.40
Bathtub, P.E. cast iron, 5' long with accessories, white	1.000	Ea.	3.636	1,250	213	1,463
Rough-in, waste, 4" diameter DWV piping	1.000	Ea.	.828	115.50	48.60	164.10
Supply, 1/2" diameter type "L" copper supply piping	1.000	Ea.	.988	38.90	64.50	103.40
Vent, 1-1/2" diameter DWV piping	1.000	Ea.	.593	58.60	38.60	97.20
Piping, supply, 1/2" diameter type "L" copper supply piping	32.000	L.F.	3.161	124.48	206.40	330.88
Waste, 4" diameter DWV piping	12.000	L.F.	3.310	462	194.40	656.40
Vent, 2" diameter DWV piping	6.000	L.F.	1.500	89.70	88.20	177.90
Vanity base cabinet, 2 door, 30" wide	1.000	Ea.	1.000	445	58.50	503.50
Vanity top, plastic laminated square edge	2.670	L.F.	.712	98.79	41.65	140.44
TOTAL		Ea.	26.414	3,692.71	1,591.65	5,284.36
BATHROOM WITH WALL HUNG LAVATORY						
Water closet, floor mounted, 2 piece, close coupled, white	1.000	Ea.	3.019	214	177	391
Rough-in, vent, 2" diameter DWV piping	1.000	Ea.	.955	92	56	148
Waste, 4" diameter DWV piping	1.000	Ea.	.828	115.50	48.60	164.10
Supply, 1/2" diameter type "L" copper supply piping	1.000	Ea.	.593	23.34	38.70	62.04
Lavatory, 20" x 18" P.E. cast iron, wall hung, white	1.000	Ea.	2.000	294	117	411
Rough-in, waste, 1-1/2" diameter DWV piping	1.000	Ea.	1.803	176	106	282
Supply, 1/2" diameter type "L" copper supply piping	1.000	Ea.	.988	38.90	64.50	103.40
Bathtub, P.E. cast iron, 5' long with accessories, white	1.000	Ea.	3.636	1,250	213	1,463
Rough-in, waste, 4" diameter DWV piping	1.000	Ea.	.828	115.50	48.60	164.10
Supply, 1/2" diameter type "L" copper supply piping	1.000	Ea.	.988	38.90	64.50	103.40
Vent, 1-1/2" diameter DWV piping	1.000	Ea.	.593	58.60	38.60	97.20
Piping, supply, 1/2" diameter type "L" copper supply piping	32.000	L.F.	3.161	124.48	206.40	330.88
Waste, 4" diameter DWV piping	12.000	L.F.	3.310	462	194.40	656.40
Vent, 2" diameter DWV piping	6.000	L.F.	1.500	89.70	88.20	177.90
Carrier steel, for studs, no arms	1.000	Ea.	1.143	106	74.50	180.50
TOTAL		Ea.	25.345	3,198.92	1,536	4,734.92

The costs in this system are on a cost each basis. All necessary piping is included.

Three Fixture Bathroom Price Sheet	QUAN.	UNIT	LABOR HOURS	COST EACH MAT.	COST EACH INST.	COST EACH TOTAL
Water closet, close coupled, standard 2 piece, white	1.000	Ea.	3.019	214	177	391
Color	1.000	Ea.	3.019	385	177	562
One piece, elongated bowl, white	1.000	Ea.	3.019	670	177	847
Color	1.000	Ea.	3.019	885	177	1,062
Low profile, one piece, elongated bowl, white	1.000	Ea.	3.019	675	177	852
Color	1.000	Ea.	3.019	885	177	1,062
Rough-in, for water closet						
1/2" copper supply, 4" cast iron waste, 2" cast iron vent	1.000	Ea.	2.376	231	143	374
4" PVC/DWV waste, 2" PVC vent	1.000	Ea.	2.678	119	161	280
4" copper waste, 2" copper vent	1.000	Ea.	2.520	243	157	400
3" cast iron waste, 1-1/2" cast iron vent	1.000	Ea.	2.244	177	136	313
3" PVC waste, 1-1/2" PVC vent	1.000	Ea.	2.388	111	150	261
3" copper waste, 1-1/2" copper vent	1.000	Ea.	2.014	163	126	289
1/2" PVC supply, 4" PVC waste, 2" PVC vent	1.000	Ea.	2.974	142	180	322
3" PVC waste, 1-1/2" PVC supply	1.000	Ea.	2.684	134	169	303
1/2" steel supply, 4" cast iron waste, 2" cast iron vent	1.000	Ea.	2.545	247	154	401
4" cast iron waste, 2" steel vent	1.000	Ea.	2.590	215	157	372
4" PVC waste, 2" PVC vent	1.000	Ea.	2.847	135	172	307
Lavatory wall hung, P.E. cast iron, 20" x 18", white	1.000	Ea.	2.000	294	117	411
Color	1.000	Ea.	2.000	305	117	422
Vitreous china, 19" x 17", white	1.000	Ea.	2.286	164	134	298
Color	1.000	Ea.	2.286	186	134	320
Lavatory, for vanity top, P.E., cast iron, 20" x 18", white	1.000	Ea.	2.500	350	147	497
Color	1.000	Ea.	2.500	510	147	657
Steel, enameled, 20" x 17", white	1.000	Ea.	2.759	166	162	328
Color	1.000	Ea.	2.500	170	147	317
Vitreous china, 20" x 16", white	1.000	Ea.	2.963	262	174	436
Color	1.000	Ea.	2.963	262	174	436
Rough-in, for lavatory						
1/2" copper supply, 1-1/2" C.I. waste, 1-1/2" C.I. vent	1.000	Ea.	2.791	215	171	386
1-1/2" PVC waste, 1-1/4" PVC vent	1.000	Ea.	2.639	162	172	334
1/2" steel supply, 1-1/4" cast iron waste, 1-1/4" steel vent	1.000	Ea.	2.890	180	178	358
1-1/4" PVC waste, 1-1/4" PVC vent	1.000	Ea.	2.794	190	182	372
1/2" PVC supply, 1-1/2" PVC waste, 1-1/2" PVC vent	1.000	Ea.	3.260	199	213	412
Bathtub, P.E. cast iron, 5' long corner with fittings, white	1.000	Ea.	3.636	1,250	213	1,463
Color	1.000	Ea.	3.636	1,575	213	1,788
Rough-in, for bathtub						
1/2" copper supply, 4" cast iron waste, 1-1/2" copper vent	1.000	Ea.	2.409	213	152	365
4" PVC waste, 1/2" PVC vent	1.000	Ea.	2.877	133	181	314
1/2" steel supply, 4" cast iron waste, 1-1/2" steel vent	1.000	Ea.	2.898	211	179	390
4" PVC waste, 1-1/2" PVC vent	1.000	Ea.	3.159	160	200	360
1/2" PVC supply, 4" PVC waste, 1-1/2" PVC vent	1.000	Ea.	3.371	171	213	384
Piping, supply, 1/2" copper	32.000	L.F.	3.161	124	206	330
1/2" steel	32.000	L.F.	4.063	210	266	476
1/2" PVC	32.000	L.F.	4.741	246	310	556
Piping, waste, 4" cast iron no hub	12.000	L.F.	3.310	460	194	654
4" PVC/DWV	12.000	L.F.	4.000	133	235	368
4" copper/DWV	12.000	L.F.	4.800	590	282	872
Piping, vent, 2" cast iron no hub	6.000	L.F.	1.433	138	84	222
2" copper/DWV	6.000	L.F.	1.091	109	71	180
2" PVC/DWV	6.000	L.F.	1.627	94	95.50	189.50
2" steel, galvanized	6.000	L.F.	1.500	89.50	88	177.50
Vanity base cabinet, 2 door, 24" x 30"	1.000	Ea.	1.000	445	58.50	503.50
24" x 36"	1.000	Ea.	1.200	435	70	505
Vanity top, laminated plastic square edge, 25" x 32"	2.670	L.F.	.712	99	41.50	140.50
25" x 38"	3.160	L.F.	.843	117	49.50	166.50
Cultured marble, 25" x 32", with bowl	1.000	Ea.	2.500	210	147	357
25" x 38", with bowl	1.000	Ea.	2.500	244	147	391
Carrier, for lavatory, steel for studs, no arms	1.000	Ea.	1.143	106	74.50	180.50
Wood, 2" x 8" blocking	1.300	L.F.	.052	1.25	3.04	4.29

Corner Bathtub

Lavatory

Vanity Top

Water Closet

Vanity Base Cabinet

System Description	QUAN.	UNIT	LABOR HOURS	COST EACH		
				MAT.	INST.	TOTAL
BATHROOM WITH LAVATORY INSTALLED IN VANITY						
Water closet, floor mounted, 2 piece, close coupled, white	1.000	Ea.	3.019	214	177	391
Rough-in, vent, 2" diameter DWV piping	1.000	Ea.	.955	92	56	148
Waste, 4" diameter DWV piping	1.000	Ea.	.828	115.50	48.60	164.10
Supply, 1/2" diameter type "L" copper supply piping	1.000	Ea.	.593	23.34	38.70	62.04
Lavatory, 20" x 18", P.E. cast iron with fittings, white	1.000	Ea.	2.500	350	147	497
Rough-in, waste, 1-1/2" diameter DWV piping	1.000	Ea.	1.803	176	106	282
Supply, 1/2" diameter type "L" copper supply piping	1.000	Ea.	.988	38.90	64.50	103.40
Bathtub, P.E. cast iron, corner with fittings, white	1.000	Ea.	3.636	2,950	213	3,163
Rough-in, waste, 4" diameter DWV piping	1.000	Ea.	.828	115.50	48.60	164.10
Supply, 1/2" diameter type "L" copper supply piping	1.000	Ea.	.988	38.90	64.50	103.40
Vent, 1-1/2" diameter DWV piping	1.000	Ea.	.593	58.60	38.60	97.20
Piping, supply, 1/2" diameter type "L" copper supply piping	32.000	L.F.	3.161	124.48	206.40	330.88
Waste, 4" diameter DWV piping	12.000	L.F.	3.310	462	194.40	656.40
Vent, 2" diameter DWV piping	6.000	L.F.	1.500	89.70	88.20	177.90
Vanity base cabinet, 2 door, 30" wide	1.000	Ea.	1.000	445	58.50	503.50
Vanity top, plastic laminated, square edge	2.670	L.F.	.712	117.48	41.65	159.13
TOTAL		Ea.	26.414	5,411.40	1,591.65	7,003.05
BATHROOM WITH WALL HUNG LAVATORY						
Water closet, floor mounted, 2 piece, close coupled, white	1.000	Ea.	3.019	214	177	391
Rough-in, vent, 2" diameter DWV piping	1.000	Ea.	.955	92	56	148
Waste, 4" diameter DWV piping	1.000	Ea.	.828	115.50	48.60	164.10
Supply, 1/2" diameter type "L" copper supply piping	1.000	Ea.	.593	23.34	38.70	62.04
Lavatory, 20" x 18", P.E. cast iron, with fittings, white	1.000	Ea.	2.000	294	117	411
Rough-in, waste, 1-1/2" diameter DWV piping	1.000	Ea.	1.803	176	106	282
Supply, 1/2" diameter type "L" copper supply piping	1.000	Ea.	.988	38.90	64.50	103.40
Bathtub, P.E. cast iron, corner, with fittings, white	1.000	Ea.	3.636	2,950	213	3,163
Rough-in, waste, 4" diameter DWV piping	1.000	Ea.	.828	115.50	48.60	164.10
Supply, 1/2" diameter type "L" copper supply piping	1.000	Ea.	.988	38.90	64.50	103.40
Vent, 1-1/2" diameter DWV piping	1.000	Ea.	.593	58.60	38.60	97.20
Piping, supply, 1/2" diameter type "L" copper supply piping	32.000	L.F.	3.161	124.48	206.40	330.88
Waste, 4" diameter DWV piping	12.000	L.F.	3.310	462	194.40	656.40
Vent, 2" diameter DWV piping	6.000	L.F.	1.500	89.70	88.20	177.90
Carrier, steel, for studs, no arms	1.000	Ea.	1.143	106	74.50	180.50
TOTAL		Ea.	25.345	4,898.92	1,536	6,434.92

The costs in this system are on a cost each basis. All necessary piping is included.

Three Fixture Bathroom Price Sheet	QUAN.	UNIT	LABOR HOURS	COST EACH		
				MAT.	INST.	TOTAL
Water closet, close coupled, standard 2 piece, white	1.000	Ea.	3.019	214	177	391
Color	1.000	Ea.	3.019	385	177	562
One piece elongated bowl, white	1.000	Ea.	3.019	670	177	847
Color	1.000	Ea.	3.019	885	177	1,062
Low profile, one piece elongated bowl, white	1.000	Ea.	3.019	675	177	852
Color	1.000	Ea.	3.019	885	177	1,062
Rough-in, for water closet						
1/2" copper supply, 4" cast iron waste, 2" cast iron vent	1.000	Ea.	2.376	231	143	374
4" PVC/DWV waste, 2" PVC vent	1.000	Ea.	2.678	119	161	280
4" copper waste, 2" copper vent	1.000	Ea.	2.520	243	157	400
3" cast iron waste, 1-1/2" cast iron vent	1.000	Ea.	2.244	177	136	313
3" PVC waste, 1-1/2" PVC vent	1.000	Ea.	2.388	111	150	261
3" copper waste, 1-1/2" copper vent	1.000	Ea.	2.014	163	126	289
1/2" PVC supply, 4" PVC waste, 2" PVC vent	1.000	Ea.	2.974	142	180	322
3" PVC waste, 1-1/2" PVC supply	1.000	Ea.	2.684	134	169	303
1/2" steel supply, 4" cast iron waste, 2" cast iron vent	1.000	Ea.	2.545	247	154	401
4" cast iron waste, 2" steel vent	1.000	Ea.	2.590	215	157	372
4" PVC waste, 2" PVC vent	1.000	Ea.	2.847	135	172	307
Lavatory, wall hung P.E. cast iron 20" x 18", white	1.000	Ea.	2.000	294	117	411
Color	1.000	Ea.	2.000	305	117	422
Vitreous china 19" x 17", white	1.000	Ea.	2.286	164	134	298
Color	1.000	Ea.	2.286	186	134	320
Lavatory, for vanity top, P.E., cast iron, 20" x 18", white	1.000	Ea.	2.500	350	147	497
Color	1.000	Ea.	2.500	510	147	657
Steel enameled 20" x 17", white	1.000	Ea.	2.759	166	162	328
Color	1.000	Ea.	2.500	170	147	317
Vitreous china 20" x 16", white	1.000	Ea.	2.963	262	174	436
Color	1.000	Ea.	2.963	262	174	436
Rough-in, for lavatory						
1/2" copper supply, 1-1/2" cast iron waste, 1-1/2" cast iron vent	1.000	Ea.	2.791	215	171	386
1-1/2" PVC waste, 1-1/4" PVC vent	1.000	Ea.	2.639	162	172	334
1/2" steel supply, 1-1/4" cast iron waste, 1-1/4" steel vent	1.000	Ea.	2.890	180	178	358
1-1/4" PVC waste, 1-1/4" PVC vent	1.000	Ea.	2.794	190	182	372
1/2" PVC supply, 1-1/2" PVC waste, 1-1/2" PVC vent	1.000	Ea.	3.260	199	213	412
Bathtub, P.E. cast iron, corner with fittings, white	1.000	Ea.	3.636	2,950	213	3,163
Color	1.000	Ea.	4.000	3,400	235	3,635
Rough-in, for bathtub						
1/2" copper supply, 4" cast iron waste, 1-1/2" copper vent	1.000	Ea.	2.409	213	152	365
4" PVC waste, 1-1/2" PVC vent	1.000	Ea.	2.877	133	181	314
1/2" steel supply, 4" cast iron waste, 1-1/2" steel vent	1.000	Ea.	2.898	211	179	390
4" PVC waste, 1-1/2" PVC vent	1.000	Ea.	3.159	160	200	360
1/2" PVC supply, 4" PVC waste, 1-1/2" PVC vent	1.000	Ea.	3.371	171	213	384
Piping, supply, 1/2" copper	32.000	L.F.	3.161	124	206	330
1/2" steel	32.000	L.F.	4.063	210	266	476
1/2" PVC	32.000	L.F.	4.741	246	310	556
Piping, waste, 4" cast iron, no hub	12.000	L.F.	3.310	460	194	654
4" PVC/DWV	12.000	L.F.	4.000	133	235	368
4" copper/DWV	12.000	L.F.	4.800	590	282	872
Piping, vent 2" cast iron, no hub	6.000	L.F.	1.433	138	84	222
2" copper/DWV	6.000	L.F.	1.091	109	71	180
2" PVC/DWV	6.000	L.F.	1.627	94	95.50	189.50
2" steel, galvanized	6.000	L.F.	1.500	89.50	88	177.50
Vanity base cabinet, 2 door, 24" x 30"	1.000	Ea.	1.000	445	58.50	503.50
24" x 36"	1.000	Ea.	1.200	435	70	505
Vanity top, laminated plastic square edge 25" x 32"	2.670	L.F.	.712	117	41.50	158.50
25" x 38"	3.160	L.F.	.843	139	49.50	188.50
Cultured marble, 25" x 32", with bowl	1.000	Ea.	2.500	210	147	357
25" x 38", with bowl	1.000	Ea.	2.500	244	147	391
Carrier, for lavatory, steel for studs, no arms	1.000	Ea.	1.143	106	74.50	180.50
Wood, 2" x 8" blocking	1.300	L.F.	.053	1.28	3.11	4.39

Lavatory

Vanity Top

Vanity Base
Cabinet

Shower

Water Closet

System Description	QUAN.	UNIT	LABOR HOURS	COST EACH		
				MAT.	INST.	TOTAL
BATHROOM WITH SHOWER, LAVATORY INSTALLED IN VANITY						
Water closet, floor mounted, 2 piece, close coupled, white	1.000	Ea.	3.019	214	177	391
Rough-in, vent, 2" diameter DWV piping	1.000	Ea.	.955	92	56	148
Waste, 4" diameter DWV piping	1.000	Ea.	.828	115.50	48.60	164.10
Supply, 1/2" diameter type "L" copper supply piping	1.000	Ea.	.593	23.34	38.70	62.04
Lavatory, 20" x 18" P.E. cast iron with fittings, white	1.000	Ea.	2.500	350	147	497
Rough-in, waste, 1-1/2" diameter DWV piping	1.000	Ea.	1.803	176	106	282
Supply, 1/2" diameter type "L" copper supply piping	1.000	Ea.	.988	38.90	64.50	103.40
Shower, steel enameled, stone base, corner, white	1.000	Ea.	3.200	1,300	188	1,488
Shower mixing valve	1.000	Ea.	1.333	145	87	232
Shower door	1.000	Ea.	1.000	455	64	519
Rough-in, vent, 1-1/2" diameter DWV piping	1.000	Ea.	.225	22	13.25	35.25
Waste, 2" diameter DWV piping	1.000	Ea.	1.433	138	84	222
Supply, 1/2" diameter type "L" copper supply piping	1.000	Ea.	1.580	62.24	103.20	165.44
Piping, supply, 1/2" diameter type "L" copper supply piping	36.000	L.F.	4.148	163.38	270.90	434.28
Waste, 4" diameter DWV piping	7.000	L.F.	2.759	385	162	547
Vent, 2" diameter DWV piping	6.000	L.F.	2.250	134.55	132.30	266.85
Vanity base 2 door, 30" wide	1.000	Ea.	1.000	445	58.50	503.50
Vanity top, plastic laminated, square edge	2.170	L.F.	.712	90.78	41.65	132.43
TOTAL		Ea.	30.326	4,350.69	1,842.60	6,193.29
BATHROOM WITH SHOWER, WALL HUNG LAVATORY						
Water closet, floor mounted, close coupled	1.000	Ea.	3.019	214	177	391
Rough-in, vent, 2" diameter DWV piping	1.000	Ea.	.955	92	56	148
Waste, 4" diameter DWV piping	1.000	Ea.	.828	115.50	48.60	164.10
Supply, 1/2" diameter type "L" copper supply piping	1.000	Ea.	.593	23.34	38.70	62.04
Lavatory, 20" x 18" P.E. cast iron with fittings, white	1.000	Ea.	2.000	294	117	411
Rough-in, waste, 1-1/2" diameter DWV piping	1.000	Ea.	1.803	176	106	282
Supply, 1/2" diameter type "L" copper supply piping	1.000	Ea.	.988	38.90	64.50	103.40
Shower, steel enameled, stone base, white	1.000	Ea.	3.200	1,300	188	1,488
Mixing valve	1.000	Ea.	1.333	145	87	232
Shower door	1.000	Ea.	1.000	455	64	519
Rough-in, vent, 1-1/2" diameter DWV piping	1.000	Ea.	.225	22	13.25	35.25
Waste, 2" diameter DWV piping	1.000	Ea.	1.433	138	84	222
Supply, 1/2" diameter type "L" copper supply piping	1.000	Ea.	1.580	62.24	103.20	165.44
Piping, supply, 1/2" diameter type "L" copper supply piping	36.000	L.F.	4.148	163.38	270.90	434.28
Waste, 4" diameter DWV piping	7.000	L.F.	2.759	385	162	547
Vent, 2" diameter DWV piping	6.000	L.F.	2.250	134.55	132.30	266.85
Carrier, steel, for studs, no arms	1.000	Ea.	1.143	106	74.50	180.50
TOTAL		Ea.	29.257	3,864.91	1,786.95	5,651.86

The costs in this system are on a cost each basis. All necessary piping
is included.

Three Fixture Bathroom Price Sheet

	QUAN.	UNIT	LABOR HOURS	COST EACH MAT.	COST EACH INST.	COST EACH TOTAL
Water closet, close coupled, standard 2 piece, white	1.000	Ea.	3.019	214	177	391
Color	1.000	Ea.	3.019	385	177	562
One piece elongated bowl, white	1.000	Ea.	3.019	670	177	847
Color	1.000	Ea.	3.019	885	177	1,062
Low profile, one piece elongated bowl, white	1.000	Ea.	3.019	675	177	852
Color	1.000	Ea.	3.019	885	177	1,062
Rough-in, for water closet						
1/2" copper supply, 4" cast iron waste, 2" cast iron vent	1.000	Ea.	2.376	231	143	374
4" PVC/DWV waste, 2" PVC vent	1.000	Ea.	2.678	119	161	280
4" copper waste, 2" copper vent	1.000	Ea.	2.520	243	157	400
3" cast iron waste, 1-1/2" cast iron vent	1.000	Ea.	2.244	177	136	313
3" PVC waste, 1-1/2" PVC vent	1.000	Ea.	2.388	111	150	261
3" copper waste, 1-1/2" copper vent	1.000	Ea.	2.014	163	126	289
1/2" PVC supply, 4" PVC waste, 2" PVC vent	1.000	Ea.	2.974	142	180	322
3" PVC waste, 1-1/2" PVC supply	1.000	Ea.	2.684	134	169	303
1/2" steel supply, 4" cast iron waste, 2" cast iron vent	1.000	Ea.	2.545	247	154	401
4" cast iron waste, 2" steel vent	1.000	Ea.	2.590	215	157	372
4" PVC waste, 2" PVC vent	1.000	Ea.	2.847	135	172	307
Lavatory, wall hung, P.E. cast iron 20" x 18", white	1.000	Ea.	2.000	294	117	411
Color	1.000	Ea.	2.000	305	117	422
Vitreous china 19" x 17", white	1.000	Ea.	2.286	164	134	298
Color	1.000	Ea.	2.286	186	134	320
Lavatory, for vanity top, P.E. cast iron 20" x 18", white	1.000	Ea.	2.500	350	147	497
Color	1.000	Ea.	2.500	510	147	657
Steel enameled 20" x 17", white	1.000	Ea.	2.759	166	162	328
Color	1.000	Ea.	2.500	170	147	317
Vitreous china 20" x 16", white	1.000	Ea.	2.963	262	174	436
Color	1.000	Ea.	2.963	262	174	436
Rough-in, for lavatory						
1/2" copper supply, 1-1/2" cast iron waste, 1-1/2" cast iron vent	1.000	Ea.	2.791	215	171	386
1-1/2" PVC waste, 1-1/2" PVC vent	1.000	Ea.	2.639	162	172	334
1/2" steel supply, 1-1/4" cast iron waste, 1-1/4" steel vent	1.000	Ea.	2.890	180	178	358
1-1/4" PVC waste, 1-1/4" PVC vent	1.000	Ea.	2.921	189	191	380
1/2" PVC supply, 1-1/2" PVC waste, 1-1/2" PVC vent	1.000	Ea.	3.260	199	213	412
Shower, steel enameled stone base, 32" x 32", white	1.000	Ea.	8.000	1,300	188	1,488
Color	1.000	Ea.	7.822	1,975	172	2,147
36" x 36" white	1.000	Ea.	8.889	1,625	196	1,821
Color	1.000	Ea.	8.889	2,250	196	2,446
Rough-in, for shower						
1/2" copper supply, 4" cast iron waste, 1-1/2" copper vent	1.000	Ea.	3.238	222	200	422
4" PVC waste, 1-1/2" PVC vent	1.000	Ea.	3.429	171	213	384
1/2" steel supply, 4" cast iron waste, 1-1/2" steel vent	1.000	Ea.	3.665	250	229	479
4" PVC waste, 1-1/2" PVC vent	1.000	Ea.	3.881	214	243	457
1/2" PVC supply, 4" PVC waste, 1-1/2" PVC vent	1.000	Ea.	4.219	232	264	496
Piping, supply, 1/2" copper	36.000	L.F.	4.148	163	271	434
1/2" steel	36.000	L.F.	5.333	275	350	625
1/2" PVC	36.000	L.F.	6.222	325	405	730
Piping, waste, 4" cast iron no hub	7.000	L.F.	2.759	385	162	547
4" PVC/DWV	7.000	L.F.	3.333	111	196	307
4" copper/DWV	7.000	L.F.	4.000	490	235	725
Piping, vent, 2" cast iron no hub	6.000	L.F.	2.149	207	126	333
2" copper/DWV	6.000	L.F.	1.636	163	107	270
2" PVC/DWV	6.000	L.F.	2.441	141	143	284
2" steel, galvanized	6.000	L.F.	2.250	135	132	267
Vanity base cabinet, 2 door, 24" x 30"	1.000	Ea.	1.000	445	58.50	503.50
24" x 36"	1.000	Ea.	1.200	435	70	505
Vanity top, laminated plastic square edge, 25" x 32"	2.170	L.F.	.712	91	41.50	132.50
25" x 38"	2.670	L.F.	.845	108	49.50	157.50
Carrier, for lavatory, steel for studs, no arms	1.000	Ea.	1.143	106	74.50	180.50
Wood, 2" x 8" blocking	1.300	L.F.	.052	1.25	3.04	4.29

Shower

Water Closet

Lavatory

Vanity Top

Vanity Base Cabinet

System Description	QUAN.	UNIT	LABOR HOURS	COST EACH		
				MAT.	INST.	TOTAL
BATHROOM WITH LAVATORY INSTALLED IN VANITY						
Water closet, floor mounted, 2 piece, close coupled, white	1.000	Ea.	3.019	214	177	391
Rough-in, vent, 2" diameter DWV piping	1.000	Ea.	.955	92	56	148
Waste, 4" diameter DWV piping	1.000	Ea.	.828	115.50	48.60	164.10
Supply, 1/2" diameter type "L" copper supply piping	1.000	Ea.	.593	23.34	38.70	62.04
Lavatory, 20" x 18", P.E. cast iron with fittings, white	1.000	Ea.	2.500	350	147	497
Rough-in, waste, 1-1/2" diameter DWV piping	1.000	Ea.	1.803	176	106	282
Supply, 1/2" diameter type "L" copper supply piping	1.000	Ea.	.988	38.90	64.50	103.40
Shower, steel enameled, stone base, corner, white	1.000	Ea.	3.200	1,300	188	1,488
Mixing valve	1.000	Ea.	1.333	145	87	232
Shower door	1.000	Ea.	1.000	455	64	519
Rough-in, vent, 1-1/2" diameter DWV piping	1.000	Ea.	.225	22	13.25	35.25
Waste, 2" diameter DWV piping	1.000	Ea.	1.433	138	84	222
Supply, 1/2" diameter type "L" copper supply piping	1.000	Ea.	1.580	62.24	103.20	165.44
Piping, supply, 1/2" diameter type "L" copper supply piping	36.000	L.F.	3.556	140.04	232.20	372.24
Waste, 4" diameter DWV piping	7.000	L.F.	1.931	269.50	113.40	382.90
Vent, 2" diameter DWV piping	6.000	L.F.	1.500	89.70	88.20	177.90
Vanity base, 2 door, 30" wide	1.000	Ea.	1.000	445	58.50	503.50
Vanity top, plastic laminated, square edge	2.670	L.F.	.712	98.79	41.65	140.44
TOTAL		Ea.	28.156	4,175.01	1,711.20	5,886.21
BATHROOM, WITH WALL HUNG LAVATORY						
Water closet, floor mounted, 2 piece, close coupled, white	1.000	Ea.	3.019	214	177	391
Rough-in, vent, 2" diameter DWV piping	1.000	Ea.	.955	92	56	148
Waste, 4" diameter DWV piping	1.000	Ea.	.828	115.50	48.60	164.10
Supply, 1/2" diameter type "L" copper supply piping	1.000	Ea.	.593	23.34	38.70	62.04
Lavatory, wall hung, 20" x 18" P.E. cast iron with fittings, white	1.000	Ea.	2.000	294	117	411
Rough-in, waste, 1-1/2" diameter DWV piping	1.000	Ea.	1.803	176	106	282
Supply, 1/2" diameter type "L" copper supply piping	1.000	Ea.	.988	38.90	64.50	103.40
Shower, steel enameled, stone base, corner, white	1.000	Ea.	3.200	1,300	188	1,488
Mixing valve	1.000	Ea.	1.333	145	87	232
Shower door	1.000	Ea.	1.000	455	64	519
Rough-in, waste, 1-1/2" diameter DWV piping	1.000	Ea.	.225	22	13.25	35.25
Waste, 2" diameter DWV piping	1.000	Ea.	1.433	138	84	222
Supply, 1/2" diameter type "L" copper supply piping	1.000	Ea.	1.580	62.24	103.20	165.44
Piping, supply, 1/2" diameter type "L" copper supply piping	36.000	L.F.	3.556	140.04	232.20	372.24
Waste, 4" diameter DWV piping	7.000	L.F.	1.931	269.50	113.40	382.90
Vent, 2" diameter DWV piping	6.000	L.F.	1.500	89.70	88.20	177.90
Carrier, steel, for studs, no arms	1.000	Ea.	1.143	106	74.50	180.50
TOTAL		Ea.	27.087	3,681.22	1,655.55	5,336.77

The costs in this system are on a cost each basis. All necessary piping is included.

Three Fixture Bathroom Price Sheet

Three Fixture Bathroom Price Sheet	QUAN.	UNIT	LABOR HOURS	COST EACH		
				MAT.	INST.	TOTAL
Water closet, close coupled, standard 2 piece, white	1.000	Ea.	3.019	214	177	391
Color	1.000	Ea.	3.019	385	177	562
One piece elongated bowl, white	1.000	Ea.	3.019	670	177	847
Color	1.000	Ea.	3.019	885	177	1,062
Low profile one piece elongated bowl, white	1.000	Ea.	3.019	675	177	852
Color	1.000	Ea.	3.623	885	177	1,062
Rough-in, for water closet						
1/2" copper supply, 4" cast iron waste, 2" cast iron vent	1.000	Ea.	2.376	231	143	374
4" P.V.C./DWV waste, 2" PVC vent	1.000	Ea.	2.678	119	161	280
4" copper waste, 2" copper vent	1.000	Ea.	2.520	243	157	400
3" cast iron waste, 1-1/2" cast iron vent	1.000	Ea.	2.244	177	136	313
3" PVC waste, 1-1/2" PVC vent	1.000	Ea.	2.388	111	150	261
3" copper waste, 1-1/2" copper vent	1.000	Ea.	2.014	163	126	289
1/2" P.V.C. supply, 4" P.V.C. waste, 2" P.V.C. vent	1.000	Ea.	2.974	142	180	322
3" P.V.C. waste, 1-1/2" P.V.C. vent	1.000	Ea.	2.684	134	169	303
1/2" steel supply, 4" cast iron waste, 2" cast iron vent	1.000	Ea.	2.545	247	154	401
4" cast iron waste, 2" steel vent	1.000	Ea.	2.590	215	157	372
4" P.V.C. waste, 2" P.V.C. vent	1.000	Ea.	2.847	135	172	307
Lavatory, wall hung P.E. cast iron 20" x 18", white	1.000	Ea.	2.000	294	117	411
Color	1.000	Ea.	2.000	305	117	422
Vitreous china 19" x 17", white	1.000	Ea.	2.286	164	134	298
Color	1.000	Ea.	2.286	186	134	320
Lavatory, for vanity top P.E. cast iron 20" x 18", white	1.000	Ea.	2.500	350	147	497
Color	1.000	Ea.	2.500	510	147	657
Steel enameled 20" x 17", white	1.000	Ea.	2.759	166	162	328
Color	1.000	Ea.	2.500	170	147	317
Vitreous china 20" x 16", white	1.000	Ea.	2.963	262	174	436
Color	1.000	Ea.	2.963	262	174	436
Rough-in, for lavatory						
1/2" copper supply, 1-1/2" cast iron waste, 1-1/2" cast iron vent	1.000	Ea.	2.791	215	171	386
1-1/2" P.V.C. waste, 1-1/2" P.V.C. vent	1.000	Ea.	2.639	162	172	334
1/2" steel supply, 1-1/2" cast iron waste, 1-1/4" steel vent	1.000	Ea.	2.890	180	178	358
1-1/2" P.V.C. waste, 1-1/4" P.V.C. vent	1.000	Ea.	2.921	189	191	380
1/2" P.V.C. supply, 1-1/2" P.V.C. waste, 1-1/2" P.V.C. vent	1.000	Ea.	3.260	199	213	412
Shower, steel enameled stone base, 32" x 32", white	1.000	Ea.	8.000	1,300	188	1,488
Color	1.000	Ea.	7.822	1,975	172	2,147
36" x 36", white	1.000	Ea.	8.889	1,625	196	1,821
Color	1.000	Ea.	8.889	2,250	196	2,446
Rough-in, for shower						
1/2" copper supply, 2" cast iron waste, 1-1/2" copper vent	1.000	Ea.	3.161	215	197	412
2" P.V.C. waste, 1-1/2" P.V.C. vent	1.000	Ea.	3.429	171	213	384
1/2" steel supply, 2" cast iron waste, 1-1/2" steel vent	1.000	Ea.	3.887	345	242	587
2" P.V.C. waste, 1-1/2" P.V.C. vent	1.000	Ea.	3.881	214	243	457
1/2" P.V.C. supply, 2" P.V.C. waste, 1-1/2" P.V.C. vent	1.000	Ea.	4.219	232	264	496
Piping, supply, 1/2" copper	36.000	L.F.	3.556	140	232	372
1/2" steel	36.000	L.F.	4.571	236	299	535
1/2" P.V.C.	36.000	L.F.	5.333	277	345	622
Waste, 4" cast iron, no hub	7.000	L.F.	1.931	270	113	383
4" P.V.C./DWV	7.000	L.F.	2.333	77.50	137	214.50
4" copper/DWV	7.000	L.F.	2.800	345	165	510
Vent, 2" cast iron, no hub	6.000	L.F.	1.091	109	71	180
2" copper/DWV	6.000	L.F.	1.091	109	71	180
2" P.V.C./DWV	6.000	L.F.	1.627	94	95.50	189.50
2" steel, galvanized	6.000	L.F.	1.500	89.50	88	177.50
Vanity base cabinet, 2 door, 24" x 30"	1.000	Ea.	1.000	445	58.50	503.50
24" x 36"	1.000	Ea.	1.200	435	70	505
Vanity top, laminated plastic square edge, 25" x 32"	2.670	L.F.	.712	99	41.50	140.50
25" x 38"	3.170	L.F.	.845	117	49.50	166.50
Carrier, for lavatory, steel, for studs, no arms	1.000	Ea.	1.143	106	74.50	180.50
Wood, 2" x 8" blocking	1.300	L.F.	.052	1.25	3.04	4.29

System Description	QUAN.	UNIT	LABOR HOURS	COST EACH		
				MAT.	INST.	TOTAL
BATHROOM WITH LAVATORY INSTALLED IN VANITY						
Water closet, floor mounted, 2 piece, close coupled, white	1.000	Ea.	3.019	214	177	391
Rough-in, vent, 2" diameter DWV piping	1.000	Ea.	.955	92	56	148
Waste, 4" diameter DWV piping	1.000	Ea.	.828	115.50	48.60	164.10
Supply, 1/2" diameter type "L" copper supply piping	1.000	Ea.	.593	23.34	38.70	62.04
Lavatory, 20" x 18" P.E. cast iron with fittings, white	1.000	Ea.	2.500	350	147	497
Shower, steel, enameled, stone base, corner, white	1.000	Ea.	3.333	1,925	196	2,121
Mixing valve	1.000	Ea.	1.333	145	87	232
Shower door	1.000	Ea.	1.000	455	64	519
Rough-in, waste, 1-1/2" diameter DWV piping	2.000	Ea.	4.507	440	265	705
Supply, 1/2" diameter type "L" copper supply piping	2.000	Ea.	3.161	124.48	206.40	330.88
Bathtub, P.E. cast iron, 5' long with fittings, white	1.000	Ea.	3.636	1,250	213	1,463
Rough-in, waste, 4" diameter DWV piping	1.000	Ea.	.828	115.50	48.60	164.10
Supply, 1/2" diameter type "L" copper supply piping	1.000	Ea.	.988	38.90	64.50	103.40
Vent, 1-1/2" diameter DWV piping	1.000	Ea.	.593	58.60	38.60	97.20
Piping, supply, 1/2" diameter type "L" copper supply piping	42.000	L.F.	4.148	163.38	270.90	434.28
Waste, 4" diameter DWV piping	10.000	L.F.	2.759	385	162	547
Vent, 2" diameter DWV piping	13.000	L.F.	3.250	194.35	191.10	385.45
Vanity base, 2 doors, 30" wide	1.000	Ea.	1.000	445	58.50	503.50
Vanity top, plastic laminated, square edge	2.670	L.F.	.712	98.79	41.65	140.44
TOTAL		Ea.	39.143	6,633.84	2,374.55	9,008.39
BATHROOM WITH WALL HUNG LAVATORY						
Water closet, floor mounted, 2 piece, close coupled, white	1.000	Ea.	3.019	214	177	391
Rough-in, vent, 2" diameter DWV piping	1.000	Ea.	.955	92	56	148
Waste, 4" diameter DWV piping	1.000	Ea.	.828	115.50	48.60	164.10
Supply, 1/2" diameter type "L" copper supply piping	1.000	Ea.	.593	23.34	38.70	62.04
Lavatory, 20" x 18" P.E. cast iron with fittings, white	1.000	Ea.	2.000	294	117	411
Shower, steel enameled, stone base, corner , white	1.000	Ea.	3.333	1,925	196	2,121
Mixing valve	1.000	Ea.	1.333	145	87	232
Shower door	1.000	Ea.	1.000	455	64	519
Rough-in, waste, 1-1/2" diameter DWV piping	2.000	Ea.	4.507	440	265	705
Supply, 1/2" diameter type "L" copper supply piping	2.000	Ea.	3.161	124.48	206.40	330.88
Bathtub, P.E. cast iron, 5' long with fittings, white	1.000	Ea.	3.636	1,250	213	1,463
Rough-in, waste, 4" diameter DWV piping	1.000	Ea.	.828	115.50	48.60	164.10
Supply, 1/2" diameter type "L" copper supply piping	1.000	Ea.	.988	38.90	64.50	103.40
Vent, 1-1/2" diameter copper DWV piping	1.000	Ea.	.593	58.60	38.60	97.20
Piping, supply, 1/2" diameter type "L" copper supply piping	42.000	L.F.	4.148	163.38	270.90	434.28
Waste, 4" diameter DWV piping	10.000	L.F.	2.759	385	162	547
Vent, 2" diameter DWV piping	13.000	L.F.	3.250	194.35	191.10	385.45
Carrier, steel, for studs, no arms	1.000	Ea.	1.143	106	74.50	180.50
TOTAL		Ea.	38.074	6,140.05	2,318.90	8,458.95

The costs in this system are on a cost each basis. All necessary piping is included.

Four Fixture Bathroom Price Sheet

Description	QUAN.	UNIT	LABOR HOURS	MAT.	INST.	TOTAL
Water closet, close coupled, standard 2 piece, white	1.000	Ea.	3.019	214	177	391
Color	1.000	Ea.	3.019	385	177	562
One piece elongated bowl, white	1.000	Ea.	3.019	670	177	847
Color	1.000	Ea.	3.019	885	177	1,062
Low profile, one piece elongated bowl, white	1.000	Ea.	3.019	675	177	852
Color	1.000	Ea.	3.019	885	177	1,062
1/2" copper supply, 4" cast iron waste, 2" cast iron vent	1.000	Ea.	2.376	231	143	374
4" PVC/DWV waste, 2" PVC vent	1.000	Ea.	2.678	119	161	280
4" copper waste, 2" copper vent	1.000	Ea.	2.520	243	157	400
3" cast iron waste, 1-1/2" cast iron vent	1.000	Ea.	2.244	177	136	313
3" P.V.C. waste, 1-1/2" P.V.C. vent	1.000	Ea.	2.388	111	150	261
3" copper waste, 1-1/2" copper vent	1.000	Ea.	2.014	163	126	289
1/2" P.V.C. supply, 4" P.V.C. waste, 2" P.V.C. vent	1.000	Ea.	2.974	142	180	322
3" P.V.C. waste, 1-1/2" P.V.C. vent	1.000	Ea.	2.684	134	169	303
1/2" steel supply, 4" cast iron waste, 2" cast iron vent	1.000	Ea.	2.545	247	154	401
4" cast iron waste, 2" steel vent	1.000	Ea.	2.590	215	157	372
4" P.V.C. waste, 2" P.V.C. vent	1.000	Ea.	2.847	135	172	307
Lavatory, wall hung P.E. cast iron 20" x 18", white	1.000	Ea.	2.000	294	117	411
Color	1.000	Ea.	2.000	305	117	422
Vitreous china 19" x 17", white	1.000	Ea.	2.286	164	134	298
Color	1.000	Ea.	2.286	186	134	320
Lavatory for vanity top, P.E. cast iron 20" x 18", white	1.000	Ea.	2.500	350	147	497
Color	1.000	Ea.	2.500	510	147	657
Steel enameled, 20" x 17", white	1.000	Ea.	2.759	166	162	328
Color	1.000	Ea.	2.500	170	147	317
Vitreous china 20" x 16", white	1.000	Ea.	2.963	262	174	436
Color	1.000	Ea.	2.963	262	174	436
Shower, steel enameled stone base, 36" square, white	1.000	Ea.	8.889	1,925	196	2,121
Color	1.000	Ea.	8.889	1,975	196	2,171
Rough-in, for lavatory or shower						
1/2" copper supply, 1-1/2" cast iron waste, 1-1/2" cast iron vent	1.000	Ea.	3.834	282	236	518
1-1/2" P.V.C. waste, 1-1/4" P.V.C. vent	1.000	Ea.	3.675	216	240	456
1/2" steel supply, 1-1/4" cast iron waste, 1-1/4" steel vent	1.000	Ea.	4.103	263	255	518
1-1/4" P.V.C. waste, 1-1/4" P.V.C. vent	1.000	Ea.	3.937	260	257	517
1/2" P.V.C. supply, 1-1/2" P.V.C. waste, 1-1/2" P.V.C. vent	1.000	Ea.	4.592	276	299	575
Bathtub, P.E. cast iron, 5' long with fittings, white	1.000	Ea.	3.636	1,250	213	1,463
Color	1.000	Ea.	3.636	1,575	213	1,788
Steel, enameled 5' long with fittings, white	1.000	Ea.	2.909	550	171	721
Color	1.000	Ea.	2.909	550	171	721
Rough-in, for bathtub						
1/2" copper supply, 4" cast iron waste, 1-1/2" copper vent	1.000	Ea.	2.409	213	152	365
4" P.V.C. waste, 1-1/2" P.V.C. vent	1.000	Ea.	2.877	133	181	314
1/2" steel supply, 4" cast iron waste, 1-1/2" steel vent	1.000	Ea.	2.898	211	179	390
4" P.V.C. waste, 1-1/2" P.V.C. vent	1.000	Ea.	3.159	160	200	360
1/2" P.V.C. supply, 4" P.V.C. waste, 1-1/2" P.V.C. vent	1.000	Ea.	3.371	171	213	384
Piping, supply, 1/2" copper	42.000	L.F.	4.148	163	271	434
1/2" steel	42.000	L.F.	5.333	275	350	625
1/2" P.V.C.	42.000	L.F.	6.222	325	405	730
Waste, 4" cast iron, no hub	10.000	L.F.	2.759	385	162	547
4" P.V.C./DWV	10.000	L.F.	3.333	111	196	307
4" copper/DWV	10.000	Ea.	4.000	490	235	725
Vent 2" cast iron, no hub	13.000	L.F.	3.105	299	182	481
2" copper/DWV	13.000	L.F.	2.364	236	154	390
2" P.V.C./DWV	13.000	L.F.	3.525	203	207	410
2" steel, galvanized	13.000	L.F.	3.250	194	191	385
Vanity base cabinet, 2 doors, 30" wide	1.000	Ea.	1.000	445	58.50	503.50
Vanity top, plastic laminated, square edge	2.670	L.F.	.712	99	41.50	140.50
Carrier, steel for studs, no arms	1.000	Ea.	1.143	106	74.50	180.50
Wood, 2" x 8" blocking	1.300	L.F.	.052	1.25	3.04	4.29

System Description	QUAN.	UNIT	LABOR HOURS	COST EACH MAT.	COST EACH INST.	COST EACH TOTAL
BATHROOM WITH LAVATORY INSTALLED IN VANITY						
Water closet, floor mounted, 2 piece, close coupled, white	1.000	Ea.	3.019	214	177	391
Rough-in, vent, 2″ diameter DWV piping	1.000	Ea.	.955	92	56	148
Waste, 4″ diameter DWV piping	1.000	Ea.	.828	115.50	48.60	164.10
Supply, 1/2″ diameter type "L" copper supply piping	1.000	Ea.	.593	23.34	38.70	62.04
Lavatory, 20″ x 18″ P.E. cast iron with fittings, white	1.000	Ea.	2.500	350	147	497
Shower, steel, enameled, stone base, corner, white	1.000	Ea.	3.333	1,925	196	2,121
Mixing valve	1.000	Ea.	1.333	145	87	232
Shower door	1.000	Ea.	1.000	455	64	519
Rough-in, waste, 1-1/2″ diameter DWV piping	2.000	Ea.	4.507	440	265	705
Supply, 1/2″ diameter type "L" copper supply piping	2.000	Ea.	3.161	124.48	206.40	330.88
Bathtub, P.E. cast iron, 5′ long with fittings, white	1.000	Ea.	3.636	1,250	213	1,463
Rough-in, waste, 4″ diameter DWV piping	1.000	Ea.	.828	115.50	48.60	164.10
Supply, 1/2″ diameter type "L" copper supply piping	1.000	Ea.	.988	38.90	64.50	103.40
Vent, 1-1/2″ diameter DWV piping	1.000	Ea.	.593	58.60	38.60	97.20
Piping, supply, 1/2″ diameter type "L" copper supply piping	42.000	L.F.	4.939	194.50	322.50	517
Waste, 4″ diameter DWV piping	10.000	L.F.	4.138	577.50	243	820.50
Vent, 2″ diameter DWV piping	13.000	L.F.	4.500	269.10	264.60	533.70
Vanity base, 2 doors, 30″ wide	1.000	Ea.	1.000	445	58.50	503.50
Vanity top, plastic laminated, square edge	2.670	L.F.	.712	90.78	41.65	132.43
TOTAL		Ea.	42.563	6,924.20	2,580.65	9,504.85
BATHROOM WITH WALL HUNG LAVATORY						
Water closet, floor mounted, 2 piece, close coupled, white	1.000	Ea.	3.019	214	177	391
Rough-in, vent, 2″ diameter DWV piping	1.000	Ea.	.955	92	56	148
Waste, 4″ diameter DWV piping	1.000	Ea.	.828	115.50	48.60	164.10
Supply, 1/2″ diameter type "L" copper supply piping	1.000	Ea.	.593	23.34	38.70	62.04
Lavatory, 20″ x 18″ P.E. cast iron with fittings, white	1.000	Ea.	2.000	294	117	411
Shower, steel enameled, stone base, corner, white	1.000	Ea.	3.333	1,925	196	2,121
Mixing valve	1.000	Ea.	1.333	145	87	232
Shower door	1.000	Ea.	1.000	455	64	519
Rough-in, waste, 1-1/2″ diameter DWV piping	2.000	Ea.	4.507	440	265	705
Supply, 1/2″ diameter type "L" copper supply piping	2.000	Ea.	3.161	124.48	206.40	330.88
Bathtub, P.E. cast iron, 5′ long with fittings, white	1.000	Ea.	3.636	1,250	213	1,463
Rough-in, waste, 4″ diameter DWV piping	1.000	Ea.	.828	115.50	48.60	164.10
Supply, 1/2″ diameter type "L" copper supply piping	1.000	Ea.	.988	38.90	64.50	103.40
Vent, 1-1/2″ diameter DWV piping	1.000	Ea.	.593	58.60	38.60	97.20
Piping, supply, 1/2″ diameter type "L" copper supply piping	42.000	L.F.	4.939	194.50	322.50	517
Waste, 4″ diameter DWV piping	10.000	L.F.	4.138	577.50	243	820.50
Vent, 2″ diameter DWV piping	13.000	L.F.	4.500	269.10	264.60	533.70
Carrier, steel for studs, no arms	1.000	Ea.	1.143	106	74.50	180.50
TOTAL		Ea.	41.494	6,438.42	2,525	8,963.42

The costs in this system are on a cost each basis. All necessary piping is included.

Four Fixture Bathroom Price Sheet	QUAN.	UNIT	LABOR HOURS	COST EACH		
				MAT.	INST.	TOTAL
Water closet, close coupled, standard 2 piece, white	1.000	Ea.	3.019	214	177	391
Color	1.000	Ea.	3.019	385	177	562
One piece, elongated bowl, white	1.000	Ea.	3.019	670	177	847
Color	1.000	Ea.	3.019	885	177	1,062
Low profile, one piece elongated bowl, white	1.000	Ea.	3.019	675	177	852
Color	1.000	Ea.	3.019	885	177	1,062
Rough-in, for water closet						
1/2" copper supply, 4" cast iron waste, 2" cast iron vent	1.000	Ea.	2.376	231	143	374
4" PVC/DWV waste, 2" PVC vent	1.000	Ea.	2.678	119	161	280
4" copper waste, 2" copper vent	1.000	Ea.	2.520	243	157	400
3" cast iron waste, 1-1/2" cast iron vent	1.000	Ea.	2.244	177	136	313
3" PVC waste, 1-1/2" PVC vent	1.000	Ea.	2.388	111	150	261
3" PVC waste, 1-1/2" PVC vent	1.000	Ea.	2.014	163	126	289
1/2" PVC supply, 4" PVC waste, 2" PVC vent	1.000	Ea.	2.974	142	180	322
3" PVC waste, 1-1/2" PVC vent	1.000	Ea.	2.684	134	169	303
1/2" steel supply, 4" cast iron waste, 2" cast iron vent	1.000	Ea.	2.545	247	154	401
4" cast iron waste, 2" steel vent	1.000	Ea.	2.590	215	157	372
4" PVC waste, 2" PVC vent	1.000	Ea.	2.847	135	172	307
Lavatory wall hung, P.E. cast iron 20" x 18", white	1.000	Ea.	2.000	294	117	411
Color	1.000	Ea.	2.000	305	117	422
Vitreous china 19" x 17", white	1.000	Ea.	2.286	164	134	298
Color	1.000	Ea.	2.286	186	134	320
Lavatory for vanity top, P.E. cast iron, 20" x 18", white	1.000	Ea.	2.500	350	147	497
Color	1.000	Ea.	2.500	510	147	657
Steel, enameled 20" x 17", white	1.000	Ea.	2.759	166	162	328
Color	1.000	Ea.	2.500	170	147	317
Vitreous china 20" x 16", white	1.000	Ea.	2.963	262	174	436
Color	1.000	Ea.	2.963	262	174	436
Shower, steel enameled, stone base 36" square, white	1.000	Ea.	8.889	1,925	196	2,121
Color	1.000	Ea.	8.889	1,975	196	2,171
Rough-in, for lavatory and shower						
1/2" copper supply, 1-1/2" cast iron waste, 1-1/2" cast iron vent	1.000	Ea.	7.668	565	470	1,035
1-1/2" PVC waste, 1-1/4" PVC vent	1.000	Ea.	7.352	430	480	910
1/2" steel supply, 1-1/4" cast iron waste, 1-1/4" steel vent	1.000	Ea.	8.205	525	510	1,035
1-1/4" PVC waste, 1-1/4" PVC vent	1.000	Ea.	7.873	520	515	1,035
1/2" PVC supply, 1-1/2" PVC waste, 1-1/2" PVC vent	1.000	Ea.	9.185	550	600	1,150
Bathtub, P.E. cast iron, 5' long with fittings, white	1.000	Ea.	3.636	1,250	213	1,463
Color	1.000	Ea.	3.636	1,575	213	1,788
Steel enameled, 5' long with fittings, white	1.000	Ea.	2.909	550	171	721
Color	1.000	Ea.	2.909	550	171	721
Rough-in, for bathtub						
1/2" copper supply, 4" cast iron waste, 1-1/2" copper vent	1.000	Ea.	2.409	213	152	365
4" PVC waste, 1-1/2" PVC vent	1.000	Ea.	2.877	133	181	314
1/2" steel supply, 4" cast iron waste, 1-1/2" steel vent	1.000	Ea.	2.898	211	179	390
4" PVC waste, 1-1/2" PVC vent	1.000	Ea.	3.159	160	200	360
1/2" PVC supply, 4" PVC waste, 1-1/2" PVC vent	1.000	Ea.	3.371	171	213	384
Piping supply, 1/2" copper	42.000	L.F.	4.148	163	271	434
1/2" steel	42.000	L.F.	5.333	275	350	625
1/2" PVC	42.000	L.F.	6.222	325	405	730
Piping, waste, 4" cast iron, no hub	10.000	L.F.	3.586	500	211	711
4" PVC/DWV	10.000	L.F.	4.333	144	254	398
4" copper/DWV	10.000	L.F.	5.200	635	305	940
Piping, vent, 2" cast iron, no hub	13.000	L.F.	3.105	299	182	481
2" copper/DWV	13.000	L.F.	2.364	236	154	390
2" PVC/DWV	13.000	L.F.	3.525	203	207	410
2" steel, galvanized	13.000	L.F.	3.250	194	191	385
Vanity base cabinet, 2 doors, 30" wide	1.000	Ea.	1.000	445	58.50	503.50
Vanity top, plastic laminated, square edge	3.160	L.F.	.843	117	49.50	166.50
Carrier, steel, for studs, no arms	1.000	Ea.	1.143	106	74.50	180.50
Wood, 2" x 8" blocking	1.300	L.F.	.052	1.25	3.04	4.29

Shower

Vanity Top

Water Closet

Bathtub

Cabinet

System Description	QUAN.	UNIT	LABOR HOURS	COST EACH		
				MAT.	INST.	TOTAL
BATHROOM WITH SHOWER, BATHTUB, LAVATORIES IN VANITY						
Water closet, floor mounted, 1 piece, white	1.000	Ea.	3.019	675	177	852
Rough-in, vent, 2" diameter DWV piping	1.000	Ea.	.955	92	56	148
Waste, 4" diameter DWV piping	1.000	Ea.	.828	115.50	48.60	164.10
Supply, 1/2" diameter type "L" copper supply piping	1.000	Ea.	.593	23.34	38.70	62.04
Lavatory, 20" x 16", vitreous china oval, with fittings, white	2.000	Ea.	5.926	524	348	872
Shower, steel enameled, stone base, corner, white	1.000	Ea.	3.333	1,925	196	2,121
Mixing valve	1.000	Ea.	1.333	145	87	232
Shower door	1.000	Ea.	1.000	455	64	519
Rough-in, waste, 1-1/2" diameter DWV piping	3.000	Ea.	5.408	528	318	846
Supply, 1/2" diameter type "L" copper supply piping	3.000	Ea.	2.963	116.70	193.50	310.20
Bathtub, P.E. cast iron, 5' long with fittings, white	1.000	Ea.	3.636	1,250	213	1,463
Rough-in, waste, 4" diameter DWV piping	1.000	Ea.	1.103	154	64.80	218.80
Supply, 1/2" diameter type "L" copper supply piping	1.000	Ea.	.988	38.90	64.50	103.40
Vent, 1-1/2" diameter copper DWV piping	1.000	Ea.	.593	58.60	38.60	97.20
Piping, supply, 1/2" diameter type "L" copper supply piping	42.000	L.F.	4.148	163.38	270.90	434.28
Waste, 4" diameter DWV piping	10.000	L.F.	2.759	385	162	547
Vent, 2" diameter DWV piping	13.000	L.F.	3.250	194.35	191.10	385.45
Vanity base, 2 door, 24" x 48"	1.000	Ea.	1.400	570	82	652
Vanity top, plastic laminated, square edge	4.170	L.F.	1.112	154.29	65.05	219.34
TOTAL		Ea.	44.347	7,568.06	2,678.75	10,246.81

The costs in this system are on a cost each basis. All necessary piping is included.

Description	QUAN.	UNIT	LABOR HOURS	COST EACH		
				MAT.	INST.	TOTAL

Five Fixture Bathroom Price Sheet

Description	QUAN.	UNIT	LABOR HOURS	MAT.	INST.	TOTAL
Water closet, close coupled, standard 2 piece, white	1.000	Ea.	3.019	214	177	391
Color	1.000	Ea.	3.019	385	177	562
One piece elongated bowl, white	1.000	Ea.	3.019	670	177	847
Color	1.000	Ea.	3.019	885	177	1,062
Low profile, one piece elongated bowl, white	1.000	Ea.	3.019	675	177	852
Color	1.000	Ea.	3.019	885	177	1,062
Rough-in, supply, waste and vent for water closet						
1/2" copper supply, 4" cast iron waste, 2" cast iron vent	1.000	Ea.	2.376	231	143	374
4" P.V.C./DWV waste, 2" P.V.C. vent	1.000	Ea.	2.678	119	161	280
4" copper waste, 2" copper vent	1.000	Ea.	2.520	243	157	400
3" cast iron waste, 1-1/2" cast iron vent	1.000	Ea.	2.244	177	136	313
3" P.V.C. waste, 1-1/2" P.V.C. vent	1.000	Ea.	2.388	111	150	261
3" copper waste, 1-1/2" copper vent	1.000	Ea.	2.014	163	126	289
1/2" P.V.C. supply, 4" P.V.C. waste, 2" P.V.C. vent	1.000	Ea.	2.974	142	180	322
3" P.V.C. waste, 1-1/2" P.V.C. supply	1.000	Ea.	2.684	134	169	303
1/2" steel supply, 4" cast iron waste, 2" cast iron vent	1.000	Ea.	2.545	247	154	401
4" cast iron waste, 2" steel vent	1.000	Ea.	2.590	215	157	372
4" P.V.C. waste, 2" P.V.C. vent	1.000	Ea.	2.847	135	172	307
Lavatory, wall hung, P.E. cast iron 20" x 18", white	2.000	Ea.	4.000	590	234	824
Color	2.000	Ea.	4.000	610	234	844
Vitreous china, 19" x 17", white	2.000	Ea.	4.571	330	268	598
Color	2.000	Ea.	4.571	370	268	638
Lavatory, for vanity top, P.E. cast iron, 20" x 18", white	2.000	Ea.	5.000	700	294	994
Color	2.000	Ea.	5.000	1,025	294	1,319
Steel enameled 20" x 17", white	2.000	Ea.	5.517	330	325	655
Color	2.000	Ea.	5.000	340	294	634
Vitreous china 20" x 16", white	2.000	Ea.	5.926	525	350	875
Color	2.000	Ea.	5.926	525	350	875
Shower, steel enameled, stone base 36" square, white	1.000	Ea.	8.889	1,925	196	2,121
Color	1.000	Ea.	8.889	1,975	196	2,171
Rough-in, for lavatory or shower						
1/2" copper supply, 1-1/2" cast iron waste, 1-1/2" cast iron vent	3.000	Ea.	8.371	645	510	1,155
1-1/2" P.V.C. waste, 1-1/4" P.V.C. vent	3.000	Ea.	7.916	485	515	1,000
1/2" steel supply, 1-1/4" cast iron waste, 1-1/4" steel vent	3.000	Ea.	8.670	540	535	1,075
1-1/4" P.V.C. waste, 1-1/4" P.V.C. vent	3.000	Ea.	8.381	570	545	1,115
1/2" P.V.C. supply, 1-1/2" P.V.C. waste, 1-1/2" P.V.C. vent	3.000	Ea.	9.778	595	640	1,235
Bathtub, P.E. cast iron 5' long with fittings, white	1.000	Ea.	3.636	1,250	213	1,463
Color	1.000	Ea.	3.636	1,575	213	1,788
Steel, enameled 5' long with fittings, white	1.000	Ea.	2.909	550	171	721
Color	1.000	Ea.	2.909	550	171	721
Rough-in, for bathtub						
1/2" copper supply, 4" cast iron waste, 1-1/2" copper vent	1.000	Ea.	2.684	252	168	420
4" P.V.C. waste, 1-1/2" P.V.C. vent	1.000	Ea.	3.210	144	201	345
1/2" steel supply, 4" cast iron waste, 1-1/2" steel vent	1.000	Ea.	3.173	249	195	444
4" P.V.C. waste, 1-1/2" P.V.C. vent	1.000	Ea.	3.492	171	219	390
1/2" P.V.C. supply, 4" P.V.C. waste, 1-1/2" P.V.C. vent	1.000	Ea.	3.704	182	233	415
Piping, supply, 1/2" copper	42.000	L.F.	4.148	163	271	434
1/2" steel	42.000	L.F.	5.333	275	350	625
1/2" P.V.C.	42.000	L.F.	6.222	325	405	730
Piping, waste, 4" cast iron, no hub	10.000	L.F.	2.759	385	162	547
4" P.V.C./DWV	10.000	L.F.	3.333	111	196	307
4" copper/DWV	10.000	L.F.	4.000	490	235	725
Piping, vent, 2" cast iron, no hub	13.000	L.F.	3.105	299	182	481
2" copper/DWV	13.000	L.F.	2.364	236	154	390
2" P.V.C./DWV	13.000	L.F.	3.525	203	207	410
2" steel, galvanized	13.000	L.F.	3.250	194	191	385
Vanity base cabinet, 2 doors, 24" x 48"	1.000	Ea.	1.400	570	82	652
Vanity top, plastic laminated, square edge	4.170	L.F.	1.112	154	65	219
Carrier, steel, for studs, no arms	1.000	Ea.	1.143	106	74.50	180.50
Wood, 2" x 8" blocking	1.300	L.F.	.052	1.25	3.04	4.29

System Description	QUAN.	UNIT	LABOR HOURS	COST PER SYSTEM		
				MAT.	INST.	TOTAL
HEATING ONLY, GAS FIRED HOT AIR, ONE ZONE, 1200 S.F. BUILDING						
Furnace, gas, up flow	1.000	Ea.	5.000	760	288	1,048
Intermittent pilot	1.000	Ea.		249		249
Supply duct, rigid fiberglass	176.000	S.F.	12.068	154.88	721.60	876.48
Return duct, sheet metal, galvanized	158.000	Lb.	16.137	99.54	963.80	1,063.34
Lateral ducts, 6″ flexible fiberglass	144.000	L.F.	8.862	492.48	509.76	1,002.24
Register, elbows	12.000	Ea.	6.400	195	366	561
Floor registers, enameled steel	12.000	Ea.	3.000	167.40	192	359.40
Floor grille, return air	2.000	Ea.	.727	62	47	109
Thermostat	1.000	Ea.	1.000	56	68	124
Plenum	1.000	Ea.	1.000	101	57.50	158.50
TOTAL		System	54.194	2,337.30	3,213.66	5,550.96
HEATING/COOLING, GAS FIRED FORCED AIR, ONE ZONE, 1200 S.F. BUILDING						
Furnace, including plenum, compressor, coil	1.000	Ea.	14.720	6,026	846.40	6,872.40
Intermittent pilot	1.000	Ea.		249		249
Supply duct, rigid fiberglass	176.000	S.F.	12.068	154.88	721.60	876.48
Return duct, sheet metal, galvanized	158.000	Lb.	16.137	99.54	963.80	1,063.34
Lateral duct, 6″ flexible fiberglass	144.000	L.F.	8.862	492.48	509.76	1,002.24
Register elbows	12.000	Ea.	6.400	195	366	561
Floor registers, enameled steel	12.000	Ea.	3.000	167.40	192	359.40
Floor grille return air	2.000	Ea.	.727	62	47	109
Thermostat	1.000	Ea.	1.000	56	68	124
Refrigeration piping, 25 ft. (pre-charged)	1.000	Ea.		310		310
TOTAL		System	62.914	7,812.30	3,714.56	11,526.86

The costs in these systems are based on complete system basis. For larger buildings use the price sheet on the opposite page.

Description	QUAN.	UNIT	LABOR HOURS	COST PER SYSTEM		
				MAT.	INST.	TOTAL

Gas Heating/Cooling Price Sheet	QUAN.	UNIT	LABOR HOURS	COST EACH MAT.	COST EACH INST.	COST EACH TOTAL
Furnace, heating only, 100 MBH, area to 1200 S.F.	1.000	Ea.	5.000	760	288	1,048
120 MBH, area to 1500 S.F.	1.000	Ea.	5.000	760	288	1,048
160 MBH, area to 2000 S.F.	1.000	Ea.	5.714	1,500	330	1,830
200 MBH, area to 2400 S.F.	1.000	Ea.	6.154	3,375	355	3,730
Heating/cooling, 100 MBH heat, 36 MBH cool, to 1200 S.F.	1.000	Ea.	16.000	6,550	920	7,470
120 MBH heat, 42 MBH cool, to 1500 S.F.	1.000	Ea.	18.462	7,000	1,100	8,100
144 MBH heat, 47 MBH cool, to 2000 S.F.	1.000	Ea.	20.000	8,075	1,200	9,275
200 MBH heat, 60 MBH cool, to 2400 S.F.	1.000	Ea.	34.286	8,475	2,050	10,525
Intermittent pilot, 100 MBH furnace	1.000	Ea.		249		249
200 MBH furnace	1.000	Ea.		249		249
Supply duct, rectangular, area to 1200 S.F., rigid fiberglass	176.000	S.F.	12.068	155	720	875
Sheet metal insulated	228.000	Lb.	31.331	1,025	3,225	4,250
Area to 1500 S.F., rigid fiberglass	176.000	S.F.	12.068	155	720	875
Sheet metal insulated	228.000	Lb.	31.331	1,025	3,225	4,250
Area to 2400 S.F., rigid fiberglass	205.000	S.F.	14.057	180	840	1,020
Sheet metal insulated	271.000	Lb.	37.048	1,200	3,775	4,975
Round flexible, insulated 6″ diameter, to 1200 S.F.	156.000	L.F.	9.600	535	550	1,085
To 1500 S.F.	184.000	L.F.	11.323	630	650	1,280
8″ diameter, to 2000 S.F.	269.000	L.F.	23.911	1,125	1,375	2,500
To 2400 S.F.	248.000	L.F.	22.045	1,025	1,275	2,300
Return duct, sheet metal galvanized, to 1500 S.F.	158.000	Lb.	16.137	99.50	965	1,064.50
To 2400 S.F.	191.000	Lb.	19.507	120	1,175	1,295
Lateral ducts, flexible round 6″ insulated, to 1200 S.F.	144.000	L.F.	8.862	490	510	1,000
To 1500 S.F.	172.000	L.F.	10.585	590	610	1,200
To 2000 S.F.	261.000	L.F.	16.062	895	925	1,820
To 2400 S.F.	300.000	L.F.	18.462	1,025	1,050	2,075
Spiral steel insulated, to 1200 S.F.	144.000	L.F.	20.067	1,600	3,175	4,775
To 1500 S.F.	172.000	L.F.	23.952	1,900	3,775	5,675
To 2000 S.F.	261.000	L.F.	36.352	2,875	5,725	8,600
To 2400 S.F.	300.000	L.F.	41.825	3,300	6,600	9,900
Rectangular sheet metal galvanized insulated, to 1200 S.F.	228.000	Lb.	39.056	1,875	4,975	6,850
To 1500 S.F.	344.000	Lb.	53.966	2,275	6,375	8,650
To 2000 S.F.	522.000	Lb.	81.926	3,450	9,700	13,150
To 2400 S.F.	600.000	Lb.	94.189	3,975	11,100	15,075
Register elbows, to 1500 S.F.	12.000	Ea.	6.400	195	365	560
To 2400 S.F.	14.000	Ea.	7.460	228	425	653
Floor registers, enameled steel w/damper, to 1500 S.F.	12.000	Ea.	3.000	167	192	359
To 2400 S.F.	14.000	Ea.	4.308	230	276	506
Return air grille, area to 1500 S.F. 12″ x 12″	2.000	Ea.	.727	62	47	109
Area to 2400 S.F. 8″ x 16″	2.000	Ea.	.444	40.50	28.50	69
Area to 2400 S.F. 8″ x 16″	2.000	Ea.	.727	62	47	109
16″ x 16″	1.000	Ea.	.364	39.50	23.50	63
Thermostat, manual, 1 set back	1.000	Ea.	1.000	56	68	124
Electric, timed, 1 set back	1.000	Ea.	1.000	84.50	68	152.50
2 set back	1.000	Ea.	1.000	268	68	336
Plenum, heating only, 100 M.B.H.	1.000	Ea.	1.000	101	57.50	158.50
120 MBH	1.000	Ea.	1.000	101	57.50	158.50
160 MBH	1.000	Ea.	1.000	101	57.50	158.50
200 MBH	1.000	Ea.	1.000	101	57.50	158.50
Refrigeration piping, 3/8″	25.000	L.F.		31.50		31.50
3/4″	25.000	L.F.		69.50		69.50
7/8″	25.000	L.F.		81		81
Refrigerant piping, 25 ft. (precharged)	1.000	Ea.		310		310
Diffusers, ceiling, 6″ diameter, to 1500 S.F.	10.000	Ea.	4.444	121	285	406
To 2400 S.F.	12.000	Ea.	6.000	155	385	540
Floor, aluminum, adjustable, 2-1/4″ x 12″ to 1500 S.F.	12.000	Ea.	3.000	113	192	305
To 2400 S.F.	14.000	Ea.	3.500	132	224	356
Side wall, aluminum, adjustable, 8″ x 4″, to 1500 S.F.	12.000	Ea.	3.000	230	192	422
5″ x 10″ to 2400 S.F.	12.000	Ea.	3.692	305	236	541

System Description	QUAN.	UNIT	LABOR HOURS	COST PER SYSTEM		
				MAT.	INST.	TOTAL
HEATING ONLY, OIL FIRED HOT AIR, ONE ZONE, 1200 S.F. BUILDING						
Furnace, oil fired, atomizing gun type burner	1.000	Ea.	4.571	2,800	263	3,063
3/8" diameter copper supply pipe	1.000	Ea.	2.759	100.20	180	280.20
Shut off valve	1.000	Ea.	.333	14	21.50	35.50
Oil tank, 275 gallon, on legs	1.000	Ea.	3.200	565	195	760
Supply duct, rigid fiberglass	176.000	S.F.	12.068	154.88	721.60	876.48
Return duct, sheet metal, galvanized	158.000	Lb.	16.137	99.54	963.80	1,063.34
Lateral ducts, 6" flexible fiberglass	144.000	L.F.	8.862	492.48	509.76	1,002.24
Register elbows	12.000	Ea.	6.400	195	366	561
Floor register, enameled steel	12.000	Ea.	3.000	167.40	192	359.40
Floor grille, return air	2.000	Ea.	.727	62	47	109
Thermostat	1.000	Ea.	1.000	56	68	124
TOTAL		System	59.057	4,706.50	3,527.66	8,234.16
HEATING/COOLING, OIL FIRED, FORCED AIR, ONE ZONE, 1200 S.F. BUILDING						
Furnace, including plenum, compressor, coil	1.000	Ea.	16.000	7,000	920	7,920
3/8" diameter copper supply pipe	1.000	Ea.	2.759	100.20	180	280.20
Shut off valve	1.000	Ea.	.333	14	21.50	35.50
Oil tank, 275 gallon on legs	1.000	Ea.	3.200	565	195	760
Supply duct, rigid fiberglass	176.000	S.F.	12.068	154.88	721.60	876.48
Return duct, sheet metal, galvanized	158.000	Lb.	16.137	99.54	963.80	1,063.34
Lateral ducts, 6" flexible fiberglass	144.000	L.F.	8.862	492.48	509.76	1,002.24
Register elbows	12.000	Ea.	6.400	195	366	561
Floor registers, enameled steel	12.000	Ea.	3.000	167.40	192	359.40
Floor grille, return air	2.000	Ea.	.727	62	47	109
Refrigeration piping (precharged)	25.000	L.F.		310		310
TOTAL		System	69.486	9,160.50	4,116.66	13,277.16

Description	QUAN.	UNIT	LABOR HOURS	COST PER SYSTEM		
				MAT.	INST.	TOTAL

Oil Fired Heating/Cooling Price Sheet	QUAN.	UNIT	LABOR HOURS	COST EACH MAT.	COST EACH INST.	COST EACH TOTAL
Furnace, heating, 95.2 MBH, area to 1200 S.F.	1.000	Ea.	4.706	2,800	271	3,071
123.2 MBH, area to 1500 S.F.	1.000	Ea.	5.000	2,825	288	3,113
151.2 MBH, area to 2000 S.F.	1.000	Ea.	5.333	3,025	305	3,330
200 MBH, area to 2400 S.F.	1.000	Ea.	6.154	3,750	355	4,105
Heating/cooling, 95.2 MBH heat, 36 MBH cool, to 1200 S.F.	1.000	Ea.	16.000	7,000	920	7,920
112 MBH heat, 42 MBH cool, to 1500 S.F.	1.000	Ea.	24.000	10,500	1,375	11,875
151 MBH heat, 47 MBH cool, to 2000 S.F.	1.000	Ea.	20.800	9,100	1,200	10,300
184.8 MBH heat, 60 MBH cool, to 2400 S.F.	1.000	Ea.	24.000	4,325	1,425	5,750
Oil piping to furnace, 3/8" dia., copper	1.000	Ea.	3.412	254	220	474
Oil tank, on legs above ground, 275 gallons	1.000	Ea.	3.200	565	195	760
550 gallons	1.000	Ea.	5.926	4,550	360	4,910
Below ground, 275 gallons	1.000	Ea.	3.200	565	195	760
550 gallons	1.000	Ea.	5.926	4,550	360	4,910
1000 gallons	1.000	Ea.	6.400	7,450	390	7,840
Supply duct, rectangular, area to 1200 S.F., rigid fiberglass	176.000	S.F.	12.068	155	720	875
Sheet metal, insulated	228.000	Lb.	31.331	1,025	3,225	4,250
Area to 1500 S.F., rigid fiberglass	176.000	S.F.	12.068	155	720	875
Sheet metal, insulated	228.000	Lb.	31.331	1,025	3,225	4,250
Area to 2400 S.F., rigid fiberglass	205.000	S.F.	14.057	180	840	1,020
Sheet metal, insulated	271.000	Lb.	37.048	1,200	3,775	4,975
Round flexible, insulated, 6" diameter to 1200 S.F.	156.000	L.F.	9.600	535	550	1,085
To 1500 S.F.	184.000	L.F.	11.323	630	650	1,280
8" diameter to 2000 S.F.	269.000	L.F.	23.911	1,125	1,375	2,500
To 2400 S.F.	269.000	L.F.	22.045	1,025	1,275	2,300
Return duct, sheet metal galvanized, to 1500 S.F.	158.000	Lb.	16.137	99.50	965	1,064.50
To 2400 S.F.	191.000	Lb.	19.507	120	1,175	1,295
Lateral ducts, flexible round, 6", insulated to 1200 S.F.	144.000	L.F.	8.862	490	510	1,000
To 1500 S.F.	172.000	L.F.	10.585	590	610	1,200
To 2000 S.F.	261.000	L.F.	16.062	895	925	1,820
To 2400 S.F.	300.000	L.F.	18.462	1,025	1,050	2,075
Spiral steel, insulated to 1200 S.F.	144.000	L.F.	20.067	1,600	3,175	4,775
To 1500 S.F.	172.000	L.F.	23.952	1,900	3,775	5,675
To 2000 S.F.	261.000	L.F.	36.352	2,875	5,725	8,600
To 2400 S.F.	300.000	L.F.	41.825	3,300	6,600	9,900
Rectangular sheet metal galvanized insulated, to 1200 S.F.	288.000	Lb.	45.183	1,900	5,350	7,250
To 1500 S.F.	344.000	Lb.	53.966	2,275	6,375	8,650
To 2000 S.F.	522.000	Lb.	81.926	3,450	9,700	13,150
To 2400 S.F.	600.000	Lb.	94.189	3,975	11,100	15,075
Register elbows, to 1500 S.F.	12.000	Ea.	6.400	195	365	560
To 2400 S.F.	14.000	Ea.	7.470	228	425	653
Floor registers, enameled steel w/damper, to 1500 S.F.	12.000	Ea.	3.000	167	192	359
To 2400 S.F.	14.000	Ea.	4.308	230	276	506
Return air grille, area to 1500 S.F., 12" x 12"	2.000	Ea.	.727	62	47	109
12" x 24"	1.000	Ea.	.444	40.50	28.50	69
Area to 2400 S.F., 8" x 16"	2.000	Ea.	.727	62	47	109
16" x 16"	1.000	Ea.	.364	39.50	23.50	63
Thermostat, manual, 1 set back	1.000	Ea.	1.000	56	68	124
Electric, timed, 1 set back	1.000	Ea.	1.000	84.50	68	152.50
2 set back	1.000	Ea.	1.000	268	68	336
Refrigeration piping, 3/8"	25.000	L.F.		31.50		31.50
3/4"	25.000	L.F.		69.50		69.50
Diffusers, ceiling, 6" diameter, to 1500 S.F.	10.000	Ea.	4.444	121	285	406
To 2400 S.F.	12.000	Ea.	6.000	155	385	540
Floor, aluminum, adjustable, 2-1/4" x 12" to 1500 S.F.	12.000	Ea.	3.000	113	192	305
To 2400 S.F.	14.000	Ea.	3.500	132	224	356
Side wall, aluminum, adjustable, 8" x 4", to 1500 S.F.	12.000	Ea.	3.000	230	192	422
5" x 10" to 2400 S.F.	12.000	Ea.	3.692	305	236	541

For customer support on your Residential Costs with RSMeans Data, call 800.448.8182.

271

System Description	QUAN.	UNIT	LABOR HOURS	COST EACH		
				MAT.	INST.	TOTAL
OIL FIRED HOT WATER HEATING SYSTEM, AREA TO 1200 S.F.						
Boiler package, oil fired, 97 MBH, area to 1200 S.F. building	1.000	Ea.	15.000	2,075	880	2,955
3/8" diameter copper supply pipe	1.000	Ea.	2.759	100.20	180	280.20
Shut off valve	1.000	Ea.	.333	14	21.50	35.50
Oil tank, 275 gallon, with black iron filler pipe	1.000	Ea.	3.200	565	195	760
Supply piping, 3/4" copper tubing	176.000	L.F.	18.526	950.40	1,205.60	2,156
Supply fittings, copper 3/4"	36.000	Ea.	15.158	109.08	990	1,099.08
Supply valves, 3/4"	2.000	Ea.	.800	296	52	348
Baseboard radiation, 3/4"	106.000	L.F.	35.333	752.60	2,173	2,925.60
Zone valve	1.000	Ea.	.400	164	27	191
TOTAL		Ea.	91.509	5,026.28	5,724.10	10,750.38
OIL FIRED HOT WATER HEATING SYSTEM, AREA TO 2400 S.F.						
Boiler package, oil fired, 225 MBH, area to 2400 S.F. building	1.000	Ea.	25.105	4,325	1,475	5,800
3/8" diameter copper supply pipe	1.000	Ea.	2.759	100.20	180	280.20
Shut off valve	1.000	Ea.	.333	14	21.50	35.50
Oil tank, 550 gallon, with black iron pipe filler pipe	1.000	Ea.	5.926	4,550	360	4,910
Supply piping, 3/4" copper tubing	228.000	L.F.	23.999	1,231.20	1,561.80	2,793
Supply fittings, copper	46.000	Ea.	19.368	139.38	1,265	1,404.38
Supply valves	2.000	Ea.	.800	296	52	348
Baseboard radiation	212.000	L.F.	70.666	1,505.20	4,346	5,851.20
Zone valve	1.000	Ea.	.400	164	27	191
TOTAL		Ea.	149.356	12,324.98	9,288.30	21,613.28

The costs in this system are on a cost each basis. The costs represent total cost for the system based on a gross square foot of plan area.

Description	QUAN.	UNIT	LABOR HOURS	COST EACH		
				MAT.	INST.	TOTAL

Hot Water Heating Price Sheet

Hot Water Heating Price Sheet	QUAN.	UNIT	LABOR HOURS	COST EACH		
				MAT.	INST.	TOTAL
Boiler, oil fired, 97 MBH, area to 1200 S.F.	1.000	Ea.	15.000	2,075	880	2,955
118 MBH, area to 1500 S.F.	1.000	Ea.	16.506	2,200	970	3,170
161 MBH, area to 2000 S.F.	1.000	Ea.	18.405	2,700	1,075	3,775
215 MBH, area to 2400 S.F.	1.000	Ea.	19.704	3,975	2,300	6,275
Oil piping, (valve & filter), 3/8" copper	1.000	Ea.	3.289	114	202	316
1/4" copper	1.000	Ea.	3.242	135	210	345
Oil tank, filler pipe and cap on legs, 275 gallon	1.000	Ea.	3.200	565	195	760
550 gallon	1.000	Ea.	5.926	4,550	360	4,910
Buried underground, 275 gallon	1.000	Ea.	3.200	565	195	760
550 gallon	1.000	Ea.	5.926	4,550	360	4,910
1000 gallon	1.000	Ea.	6.400	7,450	390	7,840
Supply piping copper, area to 1200 S.F., 1/2" tubing	176.000	L.F.	17.384	685	1,125	1,810
3/4" tubing	176.000	L.F.	18.526	950	1,200	2,150
Area to 1500 S.F., 1/2" tubing	186.000	L.F.	18.371	725	1,200	1,925
3/4" tubing	186.000	L.F.	19.578	1,000	1,275	2,275
Area to 2000 S.F., 1/2" tubing	204.000	L.F.	20.149	795	1,325	2,120
3/4" tubing	204.000	L.F.	21.473	1,100	1,400	2,500
Area to 2400 S.F., 1/2" tubing	228.000	L.F.	22.520	885	1,475	2,360
3/4" tubing	228.000	L.F.	23.999	1,225	1,550	2,775
Supply pipe fittings copper, area to 1200 S.F., 1/2"	36.000	Ea.	14.400	48.50	935	983.50
3/4"	36.000	Ea.	15.158	109	990	1,099
Area to 1500 S.F., 1/2"	40.000	Ea.	16.000	54	1,050	1,104
3/4"	40.000	Ea.	16.842	121	1,100	1,221
Area to 2000 S.F., 1/2"	44.000	Ea.	17.600	59.50	1,150	1,209.50
3/4"	44.000	Ea.	18.526	133	1,200	1,333
Area to 2400, S.F., 1/2"	46.000	Ea.	18.400	62	1,200	1,262
3/4"	46.000	Ea.	19.368	139	1,275	1,414
Supply valves, 1/2" pipe size	2.000	Ea.	.667	222	43	265
3/4"	2.000	Ea.	.800	296	52	348
Baseboard radiation, area to 1200 S.F., 1/2" tubing	106.000	L.F.	28.267	1,325	1,725	3,050
3/4" tubing	106.000	L.F.	35.333	755	2,175	2,930
Area to 1500 S.F., 1/2" tubing	134.000	L.F.	35.734	1,675	2,175	3,850
3/4" tubing	134.000	L.F.	44.666	950	2,750	3,700
Area to 2000 S.F., 1/2" tubing	178.000	L.F.	47.467	2,225	2,900	5,125
3/4" tubing	178.000	L.F.	59.333	1,275	3,650	4,925
Area to 2400 S.F., 1/2" tubing	212.000	L.F.	56.534	2,650	3,450	6,100
3/4" tubing	212.000	L.F.	70.666	1,500	4,350	5,850
Zone valves, 1/2" tubing	1.000	Ea.	.400	164	27	191
3/4" tubing	1.000	Ea.	.400	171	27	198

For customer support on your Residential Costs with RSMeans Data, call 800.448.8182.

273

System Description	QUAN.	UNIT	LABOR HOURS	COST EACH		
				MAT.	INST.	TOTAL
ROOFTOP HEATING/COOLING UNIT, AREA TO 2000 S.F.						
Rooftop unit, single zone, electric cool, gas heat, to 2000 S.F.	1.000	Ea.	28.521	4,800	1,750	6,550
Gas piping	34.500	L.F.	5.207	174.23	339.83	514.06
Duct, supply and return, galvanized steel	38.000	Lb.	3.881	23.94	231.80	255.74
Insulation, ductwork	33.000	S.F.	6.286	164.67	343.20	507.87
Lateral duct, flexible duct 12" diameter, insulated	72.000	L.F.	11.520	417.60	662.40	1,080
Diffusers	4.000	Ea.	4.571	1,196	292	1,488
Return registers	1.000	Ea.	.727	98	46.50	144.50
TOTAL		Ea.	60.713	6,874.44	3,665.73	10,540.17
ROOFTOP HEATING/COOLING UNIT, AREA TO 5000 S.F.						
Rooftop unit, single zone, electric cool, gas heat, to 5000 S.F.	1.000	Ea.	42.032	14,400	2,475	16,875
Gas piping	86.250	L.F.	13.019	435.56	849.56	1,285.12
Duct supply and return, galvanized steel	95.000	Lb.	9.702	59.85	579.50	639.35
Insulation, ductwork	82.000	S.F.	15.619	409.18	852.80	1,261.98
Lateral duct, flexible duct, 12" diameter, insulated	180.000	L.F.	28.800	1,044	1,656	2,700
Diffusers	10.000	Ea.	11.429	2,990	730	3,720
Return registers	3.000	Ea.	2.182	294	139.50	433.50
TOTAL		Ea.	122.783	19,632.59	7,282.36	26,914.95

Description	QUAN.	UNIT	LABOR HOURS	COST EACH		
				MAT.	INST.	TOTAL

Rooftop Price Sheet	QUAN.	UNIT	LABOR HOURS	COST EACH		
				MAT.	INST.	TOTAL
Rooftop unit, single zone, electric cool, gas heat to 2000 S.F.	1.000	Ea.	28.521	4,800	1,750	6,550
Area to 3000 S.F.	1.000	Ea.	35.982	10,100	2,125	12,225
Area to 5000 S.F.	1.000	Ea.	42.032	14,400	2,475	16,875
Area to 10000 S.F.	1.000	Ea.	68.376	39,300	4,175	43,475
Gas piping, area 2000 through 4000 S.F.	34.500	L.F.	5.207	174	340	514
Area 5000 to 10000 S.F.	86.250	L.F.	13.019	435	850	1,285
Duct, supply and return, galvanized steel, to 2000 S.F.	38.000	Lb.	3.881	24	232	256
Area to 3000 S.F.	57.000	Lb.	5.821	36	350	386
Area to 5000 S.F.	95.000	Lb.	9.702	60	580	640
Area to 10000 S.F.	190.000	Lb.	19.405	120	1,150	1,270
Rigid fiberglass, area to 2000 S.F.	33.000	S.F.	2.263	29	135	164
Area to 3000 S.F.	49.000	S.F.	3.360	43	201	244
Area to 5000 S.F.	82.000	S.F.	5.623	72	335	407
Area to 10000 S.F.	164.000	S.F.	11.245	144	670	814
Insulation, supply and return, blanket type, area to 2000 S.F.	33.000	S.F.	1.508	165	345	510
Area to 3000 S.F.	49.000	S.F.	2.240	245	510	755
Area to 5000 S.F.	82.000	S.F.	3.748	410	855	1,265
Area to 10000 S.F.	164.000	S.F.	7.496	820	1,700	2,520
Lateral ducts, flexible round, 12" insulated, to 2000 S.F.	72.000	L.F.	11.520	420	660	1,080
Area to 3000 S.F.	108.000	L.F.	17.280	625	995	1,620
Area to 5000 S.F.	180.000	L.F.	28.800	1,050	1,650	2,700
Area to 10000 S.F.	360.000	L.F.	57.600	2,100	3,300	5,400
Rectangular, galvanized steel, to 2000 S.F.	239.000	Lb.	24.409	151	1,450	1,601
Area to 3000 S.F.	360.000	Lb.	36.767	227	2,200	2,427
Area to 5000 S.F.	599.000	Lb.	61.176	375	3,650	4,025
Area to 10000 S.F.	998.000	Lb.	101.926	630	6,100	6,730
Diffusers, ceiling, 1 to 4 way blow, 24" x 24", to 2000 S.F.	4.000	Ea.	4.571	1,200	292	1,492
Area to 3000 S.F.	6.000	Ea.	6.857	1,800	440	2,240
Area to 5000 S.F.	10.000	Ea.	11.429	3,000	730	3,730
Area to 10000 S.F.	20.000	Ea.	22.857	5,975	1,450	7,425
Return grilles, 24" x 24", to 2000 S.F.	1.000	Ea.	.727	98	46.50	144.50
Area to 3000 S.F.	2.000	Ea.	1.455	196	93	289
Area to 5000 S.F.	3.000	Ea.	2.182	294	140	434
Area to 10000 S.F.	5.000	Ea.	3.636	490	233	723

For customer support on your Residential Costs with RSMeans Data, call 800.448.8182.

275

Weather Cap

Service Entrance Cable

Meter Socket

Panelboard, Including Breakers

Ground Cable

Ground Rod with Clamp

System Description	QUAN.	UNIT	LABOR HOURS	COST EACH		
				MAT.	INST.	TOTAL
100 AMP SERVICE						
Weather cap	1.000	Ea.	.667	8.90	44	52.90
Service entrance cable	10.000	L.F.	.762	38.10	50	88.10
Meter socket	1.000	Ea.	2.500	47.50	165	212.50
Ground rod with clamp	1.000	Ea.	1.455	22	96	118
Ground cable	5.000	L.F.	.250	7.35	16.45	23.80
Panel board, 12 circuit	1.000	Ea.	6.667	234	440	674
TOTAL		Ea.	12.301	357.85	811.45	1,169.30
200 AMP SERVICE						
Weather cap	1.000	Ea.	1.000	23	66	89
Service entrance cable	10.000	L.F.	1.143	36	75.50	111.50
Meter socket	1.000	Ea.	4.211	101	277	378
Ground rod with clamp	1.000	Ea.	1.818	42.50	120	162.50
Ground cable	10.000	L.F.	.500	14.70	32.90	47.60
3/4" EMT	5.000	L.F.	.308	5.40	20.25	25.65
Panel board, 24 circuit	1.000	Ea.	12.308	335	730	1,065
TOTAL		Ea.	21.288	557.60	1,321.65	1,879.25
400 AMP SERVICE						
Weather cap	1.000	Ea.	2.963	166	195	361
Service entrance cable	180.000	L.F.	5.760	680.40	379.80	1,060.20
Meter socket	1.000	Ea.	4.211	101	277	378
Ground rod with clamp	1.000	Ea.	2.000	56	132	188
Ground cable	20.000	L.F.	.485	48	32	80
3/4" Greenfield	20.000	L.F.	1.000	8	65.80	73.80
Current transformer cabinet	1.000	Ea.	6.154	209	405	614
Panel board, 42 circuit	1.000	Ea.	33.333	4,425	2,200	6,625
TOTAL		Ea.	55.906	5,693.40	3,686.60	9,380

Thermostat ⟶

Electric Baseboard ⟶

System Description	QUAN.	UNIT	LABOR HOURS	COST EACH		
				MAT.	INST.	TOTAL
4' BASEBOARD HEATER						
Electric baseboard heater, 4' long	1.000	Ea.	1.194	38.50	78.50	117
Thermostat, integral	1.000	Ea.	.500	29.50	33	62.50
Romex, 12-3 with ground	40.000	L.F.	1.600	20.40	105.20	125.60
Panel board breaker, 20 Amp	1.000	Ea.	.300	27.75	19.80	47.55
TOTAL		Ea.	3.594	116.15	236.50	352.65
6' BASEBOARD HEATER						
Electric baseboard heater, 6' long	1.000	Ea.	1.600	54	105	159
Thermostat, integral	1.000	Ea.	.500	29.50	33	62.50
Romex, 12-3 with ground	40.000	L.F.	1.600	20.40	105.20	125.60
Panel board breaker, 20 Amp	1.000	Ea.	.400	37	26.40	63.40
TOTAL		Ea.	4.100	140.90	269.60	410.50
8' BASEBOARD HEATER						
Electric baseboard heater, 8' long	1.000	Ea.	2.000	65.50	132	197.50
Thermostat, integral	1.000	Ea.	.500	29.50	33	62.50
Romex, 12-3 with ground	40.000	L.F.	1.600	20.40	105.20	125.60
Panel board breaker, 20 Amp	1.000	Ea.	.500	46.25	33	79.25
TOTAL		Ea.	4.600	161.65	303.20	464.85
10' BASEBOARD HEATER						
Electric baseboard heater, 10' long	1.000	Ea.	2.424	202	160	362
Thermostat, integral	1.000	Ea.	.500	29.50	33	62.50
Romex, 12-3 with ground	40.000	L.F.	1.600	20.40	105.20	125.60
Panel board breaker, 20 Amp	1.000	Ea.	.750	69.38	49.50	118.88
TOTAL		Ea.	5.274	321.28	347.70	668.98

The costs in this system are on a cost each basis and include all
necessary conduit fittings.

Description	QUAN.	UNIT	LABOR HOURS	COST EACH		
				MAT.	INST.	TOTAL

System Description	QUAN.	UNIT	LABOR HOURS	COST EACH		
				MAT.	INST.	TOTAL
Air conditioning receptacles						
Using non-metallic sheathed cable	1.000	Ea.	.800	21.50	52.50	74
Using BX cable	1.000	Ea.	.964	28	63.50	91.50
Using EMT conduit	1.000	Ea.	1.194	41.50	78.50	120
Disposal wiring						
Using non-metallic sheathed cable	1.000	Ea.	.889	26.50	58.50	85
Using BX cable	1.000	Ea.	1.067	32.50	70	102.50
Using EMT conduit	1.000	Ea.	1.333	47.50	88	135.50
Dryer circuit						
Using non-metallic sheathed cable	1.000	Ea.	1.455	35.50	96	131.50
Using BX cable	1.000	Ea.	1.739	42	115	157
Using EMT conduit	1.000	Ea.	2.162	53	142	195
Duplex receptacles						
Using non-metallic sheathed cable	1.000	Ea.	.615	21.50	40.50	62
Using BX cable	1.000	Ea.	.741	28	49	77
Using EMT conduit	1.000	Ea.	.920	41.50	60.50	102
Exhaust fan wiring						
Using non-metallic sheathed cable	1.000	Ea.	.800	16.20	52.50	68.70
Using BX cable	1.000	Ea.	.964	23	63.50	86.50
Using EMT conduit	1.000	Ea.	1.194	36.50	78.50	115
Furnace circuit & switch						
Using non-metallic sheathed cable	1.000	Ea.	1.333	30	88	118
Using BX cable	1.000	Ea.	1.600	39.50	105	144.50
Using EMT conduit	1.000	Ea.	2.000	49	132	181
Ground fault						
Using non-metallic sheathed cable	1.000	Ea.	1.000	59.50	66	125.50
Using BX cable	1.000	Ea.	1.212	68.50	80	148.50
Using EMT conduit	1.000	Ea.	1.481	83	97.50	180.50
Heater circuits						
Using non-metallic sheathed cable	1.000	Ea.	1.000	21	66	87
Using BX cable	1.000	Ea.	1.212	26.50	80	106.50
Using EMT conduit	1.000	Ea.	1.481	39	97.50	136.50
Lighting wiring						
Using non-metallic sheathed cable	1.000	Ea.	.500	21.50	33	54.50
Using BX cable	1.000	Ea.	.602	26	39.50	65.50
Using EMT conduit	1.000	Ea.	.748	37.50	49	86.50
Range circuits						
Using non-metallic sheathed cable	1.000	Ea.	2.000	80.50	132	212.50
Using BX cable	1.000	Ea.	2.424	113	160	273
Using EMT conduit	1.000	Ea.	2.963	95	195	290
Switches, single pole						
Using non-metallic sheathed cable	1.000	Ea.	.500	16.20	33	49.20
Using BX cable	1.000	Ea.	.602	23	39.50	62.50
Using EMT conduit	1.000	Ea.	.748	36.50	49	85.50
Switches, 3-way						
Using non-metallic sheathed cable	1.000	Ea.	.667	19.45	44	63.45
Using BX cable	1.000	Ea.	.800	25.50	52.50	78
Using EMT conduit	1.000	Ea.	1.333	46	88	134
Water heater						
Using non-metallic sheathed cable	1.000	Ea.	1.600	28	105	133
Using BX cable	1.000	Ea.	1.905	40	125	165
Using EMT conduit	1.000	Ea.	2.353	44.50	155	199.50
Weatherproof receptacle						
Using non-metallic sheathed cable	1.000	Ea.	1.333	123	88	211
Using BX cable	1.000	Ea.	1.600	129	105	234
Using EMT conduit	1.000	Ea.	2.000	142	132	274

System Description	QUAN.	UNIT	LABOR HOURS	COST EACH		
				MAT.	INST.	TOTAL
Fluorescent strip, 4' long, 1 light, average	1.000	Ea.	.941	34	62	96
Deluxe	1.000	Ea.	1.129	41	74.50	115.50
2 lights, average	1.000	Ea.	1.000	47.50	66	113.50
Deluxe	1.000	Ea.	1.200	57	79	136
8' long, 1 light, average	1.000	Ea.	1.194	60.50	78.50	139
Deluxe	1.000	Ea.	1.433	72.50	94	166.50
2 lights, average	1.000	Ea.	1.290	73	85	158
Deluxe	1.000	Ea.	1.548	87.50	102	189.50
Surface mounted, 4' x 1', economy	1.000	Ea.	.914	57.50	60.50	118
Average	1.000	Ea.	1.143	72	75.50	147.50
Deluxe	1.000	Ea.	1.371	86.50	90.50	177
4' x 2', economy	1.000	Ea.	1.208	75	79.50	154.50
Average	1.000	Ea.	1.509	93.50	99.50	193
Deluxe	1.000	Ea.	1.811	112	119	231
Recessed, 4' x 1', 2 lamps, economy	1.000	Ea.	1.123	45	74	119
Average	1.000	Ea.	1.404	56.50	92.50	149
Deluxe	1.000	Ea.	1.684	68	111	179
4' x 2', 4 lamps, economy	1.000	Ea.	1.362	55	89.50	144.50
Average	1.000	Ea.	1.702	68.50	112	180.50
Deluxe	1.000	Ea.	2.043	82	134	216
Incandescent, exterior, 150W, single spot	1.000	Ea.	.500	35	33	68
Double spot	1.000	Ea.	1.167	97	77	174
Recessed, 100W, economy	1.000	Ea.	.800	57	53	110
Average	1.000	Ea.	1.000	71	66	137
Deluxe	1.000	Ea.	1.200	85	79	164
150W, economy	1.000	Ea.	.800	92	53	145
Average	1.000	Ea.	1.000	115	66	181
Deluxe	1.000	Ea.	1.200	138	79	217
Surface mounted, 60W, economy	1.000	Ea.	.800	72	52.50	124.50
Average	1.000	Ea.	1.000	80	66	146
Deluxe	1.000	Ea.	1.194	113	78.50	191.50
Metal halide, recessed 2' x 2' 250W	1.000	Ea.	2.500	281	165	446
2' x 2', 400W	1.000	Ea.	2.759	405	182	587
Surface mounted, 2' x 2', 250W	1.000	Ea.	2.963	380	195	575
2' x 2', 400W	1.000	Ea.	3.333	450	220	670
High bay, single, unit, 400W	1.000	Ea.	3.478	455	229	684
Twin unit, 400W	1.000	Ea.	5.000	910	330	1,240
Low bay, 250W	1.000	Ea.	2.500	400	165	565

Unit Price Section

Table of Contents

Table of Contents (cont.)

How RSMeans Unit Price Data Works

All RSMeans unit price data is organized in the same way.

03 30 Cast-In-Place Concrete

03 30 53 – Miscellaneous Cast-In-Place Concrete

① 03 30 53.40 Concrete In Place	Crew	Daily Output	Labor-Hours	Unit	Material	2017 Bare Costs Labor	Equipment ⑨	Total	Total Incl O&P
		⑤	⑥	⑦	⑧			⑩	⑪
0010 **CONCRETE IN PLACE** ④									
0020 Including forms (4 uses), Grade 60 rebar, concrete (Portland cement									
0050 Type I), placement and finishing unless otherwise indicated									
0500 Chimney foundations (5000 psi), over 5 C.Y.	C-14C	32.22	3.476	C.Y.	167	115	.87	282.87	380
0510 (3500 psi), under 5 C.Y. ③	"	23.71	4.724	"	193	157	1.18	351.18	475
3540 Equipment pad (3000 psi), 3' x 3' x 6" thick	C-14H	45	1.067	Ea.	49	36.50	.63	86.13	116
② 3550 4' x 4' x 6" thick		30	1.600		73.50	55	.94	129.44	174
3560 5' x 5' x 8" thick		18	2.667		131	92	1.57	224.57	299
3570 6' x 6' x 8" thick		14	3.429		177	118	2.02	297.02	395
3580 8' x 8' x 10" thick		8	6		380	207	3.54	590.54	770
3590 10' x 10' x 12" thick		5	9.600		655	330	5.65	990.65	1,275
3800 Footings (3000 psi), spread under 1 C.Y.	C-14C	28	4	C.Y.	181	133	1	315	425
3825 1 C.Y. to 5 C.Y.		43	2.605		218	86.50	.65	305.15	385
3850 Over 5 C.Y.		75	1.493		201	49.50	.37	250.87	305

It is important to understand the structure of RSMeans Unit Price data, so that you can find information easily and use it correctly.

① Line Numbers

Line Numbers consist of 12 characters, which identify a unique location in the database for each task. The first 6 or 8 digits conform to the Construction Specifications Institute MasterFormat® 2014. The remainder of the digits are a further breakdown in order to arrange items in understandable groups of similar tasks. Line numbers are consistent across all of our publications, so a line number in any of our products will always refer to the same item of work.

② Descriptions

Descriptions are shown in a hierarchical structure to make them readable. In order to read a complete description, read up through the indents to the top of the section. Include everything that is above and to the left that is not contradicted by information below. For instance, the complete description for line 03 30 53.40 3550 is "Concrete in place, including forms (4 uses), Grade 60 rebar, concrete (Portland cement Type 1), placement and finishing unless otherwise indicated; Equipment pad (3000 psi), 4' x 4' x 6" thick."

③ RSMeans Data

When using **RSMeans data**, it is important to read through an entire section to ensure that you use the data that most closely matches your work. Note that sometimes there is additional information shown in the section that may improve your price. There are frequently lines that further describe, add to, or adjust data for specific situations.

④ Reference Information

Gordian's RSMeans engineers have created **reference** information to assist you in your estimate. **If** there is information that applies to a section, it will be indicated at the start of the section.

⑤ Crews

Crews include labor and/or equipment necessary to accomplish each task. In this case, Crew C-14H is used. Gordian's RSMeans staff selects a crew to represent the workers and equipment that are typically used for that task. In this case, Crew C-14H consists of one carpenter foreman (outside), two carpenters, one rodman, one laborer, one cement finisher, and one gas engine vibrator. Details of all crews can be found in the reference section.

Crews - Residential

Crew No.	Bare Costs		Incl. Subs O&P		Cost Per Labor-Hour	
Crew C-14H	Hr.	Daily	Hr.	Daily	Bare Costs	Incl. O&P
1 Carpenter Foreman (outside)	$36.95	$295.60	$61.80	$494.40	$34.44	$57.40
2 Carpenters	34.95	559.20	58.45	935.20		
1 Rodman (reinf.)	38.55	308.40	64.80	518.40		
1 Laborer	26.60	212.80	44.50	356.00		
1 Cement Finisher	34.65	277.20	56.40	451.20		
1 Gas Engine Vibrator		28.25		31.07	0.59	0.65
48 L.H., Daily Totals		$1681.45		$2786.28	$35.03	$58.05

⑥ Daily Output

The **Daily Output** is the amount of work that the crew can do in a normal 8-hour workday, including mobilization, layout, movement of materials, and cleanup. In this case, crew C-14H can install thirty 4' x 4' x 6" thick concrete pads in a day. Daily output is variable and based on many factors, including the size of the job, location, and environmental conditions. RSMeans data represents work done in daylight (or adequate lighting) and temperate conditions.

⑦ Labor-Hours

The figure in the **Labor-Hours** column is the amount of labor required to perform one unit of work—in this case the amount of labor required to construct one 4' x 4' equipment pad. This figure is calculated by dividing the number of hours of labor in the crew by the daily output (48 labor hours divided by 30 pads = 1.6 hours of labor per pad). Multiply 1.600 times 60 to see the value in minutes: 60 x 1.6 = 96

minutes. Note: the labor-hour figure is not dependent on the crew size. A change in crew size will result in a corresponding change in daily output, but the labor-hours per unit of work will not change.

⑧ Unit of Measure

All RSMeans unit cost data includes the typical **Unit of Measure** used for estimating that item. For concrete-in-place the typical unit is cubic yards (C.Y.) or each (Ea.). For installing broadloom carpet it is square yard, and for gypsum board it is square foot. The estimator needs to take special care that the unit in the data matches the unit in the take-off. Unit conversions may be found in the Reference Section.

⑨ Bare Costs

Bare Costs are the costs of materials, labor, and equipment that the installing contractor pays. They represent the cost, in U.S. dollars, for one unit of work. They do not include any markups for profit or labor burden.

⑩ Bare Total

The **Total column** represents the total bare cost for the installing contractor, in U.S. dollars. In this case, the sum of $73.50 for material + $55.00 for labor + $.94 for equipment is $129.44.

⑪ Total Incl O&P

The **Total Incl O&P column** is the total cost, including overhead and profit, that the installing contractor will charge the customer. This represents the cost of materials plus 10% profit, the cost of labor plus labor burden and 10% profit, and the cost of equipment plus 10% profit. It does not include the general contractor's overhead and profit. Note: See the inside back cover of the printed product or the reference section of the electronic product for details of how the labor burden is calculated.

National Average

The RSMeans data in our print publications represents a "national average" cost. This data should be modified to the project location using the City Cost Indexes or Location Factors tables found in the Reference Section. Use the location factors to adjust estimate totals if the project covers multiple trades. Use the city cost indexes (CCI) for single trade projects or projects where a more detailed analysis is required. All figures in the two tables are derived from the same research. The last row of data in the CCI, the weighted average, is the same as the numbers reported for each location in the location factor table.

How RSMeans Unit Price Data Works (Continued)

	Project Name: Pre-Engineered Steel Building			Architect: As Shown				
Location:	Anywhere, USA						01/01/17	RESI
Line Number	Description	Qty	Unit	Material	Labor	Equipment	SubContract	Estimate Total
03 30 53.40 3940	Strip footing, 12" x 24", reinforced	34	C.Y.	$5,304.00	$2,635.00	$19.72	$0.00	
03 30 53.40 3950	Strip footing, 12" x 36", reinforced	15	C.Y.	$2,250.00	$930.00	$7.05	$0.00	
03 11 13.65 3000	Concrete slab edge forms	500	L.F.	$170.00	$820.00	$0.00	$0.00	
03 22 11.10 0200	Welded wire fabric reinforcing	150	C.S.F.	$2,820.00	$2,985.00	$0.00	$0.00	
03 31 13.35 0300	Ready mix concrete, 4000 psi for slab on grade	278	C.Y.	$34,750.00	$0.00	$0.00	$0.00	
03 31 13.70 4300	Place, strike off & consolidate concrete slab	278	C.Y.	$0.00	$3,433.30	$141.78	$0.00	
03 35 13.30 0250	Machine float & trowel concrete slab	15,000	S.F.	$0.00	$6,750.00	$450.00	$0.00	
03 15 16.20 0140	Cut control joints in concrete slab	950	L.F.	$47.50	$294.50	$85.50	$0.00	
03 39 23.13 0300	Sprayed concrete curing membrane	150	C.S.F.	$1,905.00	$672.00	$0.00	$0.00	
Division 03	**Subtotal**			**$47,246.50**	**$18,519.80**	**$704.05**	**$0.00**	**$66,470.35**
08 36 13.10 2650	Manual 10' x 10' steel sectional overhead door	8	Ea.	$10,000.00	$2,480.00	$0.00	$0.00	
08 36 13.10 2860	Insulation and steel back panel for OH door	800	S.F.	$3,800.00	$0.00	$0.00	$0.00	
Division 08	**Subtotal**			**$13,800.00**	**$2,480.00**	**$0.00**	**$0.00**	**$16,280.00**
13 34 19.50 1100	Pre-Engineered Steel Building, 100' x 150' x 24'	15,000	SF Flr.	$0.00	$0.00	$0.00	$315,000.00	
13 34 19.50 6050	Framing for PESB door opening, 3' x 7'	4	Opng.	$0.00	$0.00	$0.00	$1,920.00	
13 34 19.50 6100	Framing for PESB door opening, 10' x 10'	8	Opng.	$0.00	$0.00	$0.00	$8,200.00	
13 34 19.50 6200	Framing for PESB window opening, 4' x 3'	6	Opng.	$0.00	$0.00	$0.00	$2,910.00	
13 34 19.50 5750	PESB door, 3' x 7', single leaf	4	Opng.	$2,460.00	$492.00	$0.00	$0.00	
13 34 19.50 7750	PESB sliding window, 4' x 3' with screen	6	Opng.	$2,490.00	$285.00	$66.00	$0.00	
13 34 19.50 6550	PESB gutter, eave type, 26 ga., painted	300	L.F.	$2,190.00	$579.00	$0.00	$0.00	
13 34 19.50 8650	PESB roof vent, 12" wide x 10' long	15	Ea.	$547.50	$2,310.00	$0.00	$0.00	
13 34 19.50 6900	PESB insulation, vinyl faced, 4" thick	27,400	S.F.	$12,878.00	$6,576.00	$0.00	$0.00	
Division 13	**Subtotal**			**$20,565.50**	**$10,242.00**	**$66.00**	**$328,030.00**	**$358,903.50**
			Subtotal	$81,612.00	$31,241.80	$770.05	$328,030.00	$441,653.85
Division 01	**General Requirements @ 7%**			5,712.84	2,186.93	53.90	22,962.10	
			Estimate Subtotal	$87,324.84	$33,428.73	$823.95	$350,992.10	$441,653.85
			Sales Tax @ 5%	4,366.24		41.20	8,774.80	
			Subtotal A	91,691.08	33,428.73	865.15	359,766.90	
			GC O & P	9,169.11	22,698.10	86.52	35,976.69	
			Subtotal B	100,860.19	56,126.83	951.67	395,743.59	$553,682.28
			Contingency @ 5%					27,684.11
			Subtotal C					$581,366.39
			Bond @ $12/1000 +10% O&P					7,674.04
			Subtotal D					$589,040.43
			Location Adjustment Factor		102.30			13,547.93
			Grand Total					**$602,588.36**

This estimate is based on an interactive spreadsheet. A copy of this spreadsheet is located at
www.RSMeans.com/2017samples. You are free to download it and adjust it to your methodology.

Sample Estimate

This sample demonstrates the elements of an estimate, including a tally of the RSMeans data lines and a summary of the markups on a contractor's work to arrive at a total cost to the owner. The Location Factor with RSMeans data is added at the bottom of the estimate to adjust the cost of the work to a specific location.

---

1 Work Performed

The body of the estimate shows the RSMeans data selected, including the line number, a brief description of each item, its take-off unit and quantity, and the bare costs of materials, labor, and equipment. This estimate also includes a column titled "SubContract." This data is taken from the column "Total Incl O&P" and represents the total that a subcontractor would charge a general contractor for the work, including the sub's markup for overhead and profit.

2 Division 1, General Requirements

This is the first division numerically but the last division estimated. Division 1 includes project-wide needs provided by the general contractor. These requirements vary by project but may include temporary facilities and utilities, security, testing, project cleanup, etc. For small projects a percentage can be used, typically between 5% and 15% of project cost. For large projects the costs may be itemized and priced individually.

3 Sales Tax

If the work is subject to state or local sales taxes, the amount must be added to the estimate. Sales tax may be added to material costs, equipment costs, and subcontracted work. In this case, sales tax was added in all three categories. It was assumed that approximately half the subcontracted work would be material cost, so the tax was applied to 50% of the subcontract total.

4 GC O&P

This entry represents the general contractor's markup on material, labor, equipment, and subcontractor costs. Our standard markup on materials, equipment, and subcontracted work is 10%. In this estimate, the markup on the labor performed by the GC's workers uses "Skilled Workers Average" shown in Column F on the table "Installing Contractor's Overhead & Profit," which can be found on the inside-back cover of the printed product or in the Reference Section of the electronic product.

5 Contingency

A factor for contingency may be added to any estimate to represent the cost of unknowns that may occur between the time that the estimate is performed and the time the project is constructed. The amount of the allowance will depend on the stage of design at which the estimate is done and the contractor's assessment of the risk involved. Refer to section 01 21 16.50 for contingency allowances.

6 Bonds

Bond costs should be added to the estimate. The figures here represent a typical performance bond, ensuring the owner that if the general contractor does not complete the obligations in the construction contract the bonding company will pay the cost for completion of the work.

7 Location Adjustment

RSMeans published data is based on national average costs. If necessary, adjust the total cost of the project using a location factor from the "Location Factor" table or the "City Cost Index" table. Use location factors if the work is general, covering multiple trades. If the work is by a single trade (e.g., masonry) use the more specific data found in the "City Cost Indexes."

Estimating Tips
01 20 00 Price and Payment Procedures

- Allowances that should be added to estimates to cover contingencies and job conditions that are not included in the national average material and labor costs are shown in Section 01 21.

- When estimating historic preservation projects (depending on the condition of the existing structure and the owner's requirements), a 15%–20% contingency or allowance is recommended, regardless of the stage of the drawings.

01 30 00 Administrative Requirements

- Before determining a final cost estimate, it is a good practice to review all the items listed in Subdivisions 01 31 and 01 32 to make final adjustments for items that may need customizing to specific job conditions.

- Requirements for initial and periodic submittals can represent a significant cost to the General Requirements of a job. Thoroughly check the submittal specifications when estimating a project to determine any costs that should be included.

01 40 00 Quality Requirements

- All projects will require some degree of quality control. This cost is not included in the unit cost of construction listed in each division. Depending upon the terms of the contract, the various costs of inspection and testing can be the responsibility of either the owner or the contractor. Be sure to include the required costs in your estimate.

01 50 00 Temporary Facilities and Controls

- Barricades, access roads, safety nets, scaffolding, security, and many more requirements for the execution of a safe project are elements of direct cost. These costs can easily be overlooked when preparing an estimate. When looking through the major classifications of this subdivision, determine which items apply to each division in your estimate.

- Construction equipment rental costs can be found in the Reference Section in Section 01 54 33. Operators' wages are not included in equipment rental costs.

- Equipment mobilization and demobilization costs are not included in equipment rental costs and must be considered separately.

- The cost of small tools provided by the installing contractor for his workers is covered in the "Overhead" column on the "Installing Contractor's Overhead and Profit" table that lists labor trades, base rates, and markups and, therefore, is included in the "Total Incl. O&P" cost of any unit price line item.

01 70 00 Execution and Closeout Requirements

- When preparing an estimate, thoroughly read the specifications to determine the requirements for Contract Closeout. Final cleaning, record documentation, operation and maintenance data, warranties and bonds, and spare parts and maintenance materials can all be elements of cost for the completion of a contract. Do not overlook these in your estimate.

Reference Numbers

Reference numbers are shown at the beginning of some major classifications. These numbers refer to related items in the Reference Section. The reference information may be an estimating procedure, an alternate pricing method, or technical information.

Note: Not all subdivisions listed here necessarily appear. ∎

Did you know?

Our online estimating solution gives you the same access to RSMeans' data with 24/7 access:

- Quickly locate costs in the searchable database.

- Build cost lists, estimates, and reports in minutes.

- Adjust costs to any location in the U.S. and Canada with the click of a button.

Start your free trial today at
www.RSMeansOnline.com

01 11 Summary of Work

01 11 31 – Professional Consultants

01 11 31.10 Architectural Fees		Crew	Daily Output	Labor-Hours	Unit	Material	2017 Bare Costs Labor	Equipment	Total	Total Incl O&P
0010	**ARCHITECTURAL FEES** R011110-10									
0020	For new construction									
0060	Minimum				Project				4.90%	4.90%
0090	Maximum								16%	16%
0100	For alteration work, to $500,000, add to new construction fee								50%	50%
0150	Over $500,000, add to new construction fee								25%	25%

01 11 31.20 Construction Management Fees										
0010	**CONSTRUCTION MANAGEMENT FEES**									
0060	For work to $100,000				Project				10%	10%
0070	To $250,000								9%	9%
0090	To $1,000,000								6%	6%

01 11 31.75 Renderings										
0010	**RENDERINGS** Color, matted, 20" x 30", eye level,									
0050	Average				Ea.	3,100			3,100	3,400

01 21 Allowances

01 21 16 – Contingency Allowances

01 21 16.50 Contingencies

		Crew	Daily Output	Labor-Hours	Unit	Material	Labor	Equipment	Total	Total Incl O&P
0010	**CONTINGENCIES**, Add to estimate									
0020	Conceptual stage				Project				20%	20%
0150	Final working drawing stage				"				3%	3%

01 21 55 – Job Conditions Allowance

01 21 55.50 Job Conditions

		Crew	Daily Output	Labor-Hours	Unit	Material	Labor	Equipment	Total	Total Incl O&P
0010	**JOB CONDITIONS** Modifications to applicable									
8000	Remove and reset contents of small room	1 Clab	6.50	1.231	Room		32.50		32.50	55
8010	Average room		4.70	1.702			45.50		45.50	75.50
8020	Large room		3.50	2.286			61		61	102
8030	Extra large room		2.40	3.333			88.50		88.50	148

01 21 63 – Taxes

01 21 63.10 Taxes

		Crew	Daily Output	Labor-Hours	Unit	Material	Labor	Equipment	Total	Total Incl O&P
0010	**TAXES** R012909-80									
0020	Sales tax, State, average				%	5.08%				
0050	Maximum R012909-85					7.50%				
0200	Social Security, on first $118,500 of wages						7.65%			
0300	Unemployment, combined Federal and State, minimum						.60%			
0350	Average						9.60%			
0400	Maximum						12%			

01 31 Project Management and Coordination

01 31 13 – Project Coordination

01 31 13.30 Insurance

		Crew	Daily Output	Labor-Hours	Unit	Material	2017 Bare Costs Labor	Equipment	Total	Total Incl O&P
0010	**INSURANCE** R013113-40									
0020	Builders risk, standard, minimum				Job				.24%	.24%
0050	Maximum R013113-60								.64%	.64%
0200	All-risk type, minimum								.25%	.25%
0250	Maximum								.62%	.62%
0400	Contractor's equipment floater, minimum				Value				.50%	.50%
0450	Maximum				"				1.50%	1.50%
0600	Public liability, average				Job				2.02%	2.02%
0800	Workers' compensation & employer's liability, average									
0850	by trade, carpentry, general				Payroll		13.93%			
0900	Clerical						.46%			
0950	Concrete						12.44%			
1000	Electrical						5.52%			
1050	Excavation						9.03%			
1100	Glazing						12.91%			
1150	Insulation						11.13%			
1200	Lathing						8.67%			
1250	Masonry						13.73%			
1300	Painting & decorating						11.68%			
1350	Pile driving						14.53%			
1400	Plastering						10.73%			
1450	Plumbing						6.94%			
1500	Roofing						30.73%			
1550	Sheet metal work (HVAC)						8.82%			
1600	Steel erection, structural						27.45%			
1650	Tile work, interior ceramic						8.85%			
1700	Waterproofing, brush or hand caulking						7.01%			
1800	Wrecking						20.85%			
2000	Range of 35 trades in 50 states, excl. wrecking & clerical, min.						1.41%			
2100	Average						12.25%			
2200	Maximum						108.79%			

01 41 Regulatory Requirements

01 41 26 – Permit Requirements

01 41 26.50 Permits

		Crew	Daily Output	Labor-Hours	Unit	Material	Labor	Equipment	Total	Total Incl O&P
0010	**PERMITS**									
0020	Rule of thumb, most cities, minimum				Job				.50%	.50%
0100	Maximum				"				2%	2%

01 54 Construction Aids

01 54 16 – Temporary Hoists

01 54 16.50 Weekly Forklift Crew

		Crew	Daily Output	Labor-Hours	Unit	Material	Labor	Equipment	Total	Total Incl O&P
0010	**WEEKLY FORKLIFT CREW**									
0100	All-terrain forklift, 45' lift, 35' reach, 9000 lb. capacity	A-3P	.20	40	Week		1,400	2,600	4,000	5,200

For customer support on your Residential Costs with RSMeans Data, call 800.448.8182.

293

01 54 Construction Aids

01 54 19 – Temporary Cranes

01 54 19.50 Daily Crane Crews		Crew	Daily Output	Labor-Hours	Unit	Material	2017 Bare Costs Labor	Equipment	Total	Total Incl O&P
0010	**DAILY CRANE CREWS** for small jobs, portal to portal									
0100	12-ton truck-mounted hydraulic crane	A-3H	1	8	Day		298	770	1,068	1,350
0900	If crane is needed on a Saturday, Sunday or Holiday									
0910	At time-and-a-half, add				Day		50%			
0920	At double time, add				"		100%			

01 54 23 – Temporary Scaffolding and Platforms

01 54 23.60 Pump Staging

		Crew	Daily Output	Labor-Hours	Unit	Material	Labor	Equipment	Total	Total Incl O&P
0010	**PUMP STAGING**, Aluminum									
1300	System in place, 50' working height, per use based on 50 uses	2 Carp	84.80	.189	C.S.F.	6.95	6.60		13.55	18.70
1400	100 uses	R015423-20		84.80	.189		3.49	6.60	10.09	14.90
1500	150 uses			84.80	.189		2.34	6.60	8.94	13.60

01 54 23.70 Scaffolding

		Crew	Daily Output	Labor-Hours	Unit	Material	Labor	Equipment	Total	Total Incl O&P
0010	**SCAFFOLDING**	R015423-10								
0015	Steel tube, regular, no plank, labor only to erect & dismantle									
0091	Building exterior, wall face, 1 to 5 stories, 6'-4" x 5' frames	3 Clab	8	3	C.S.F.		80		80	134
0201	6 to 12 stories	4 Clab	8	4			106		106	178
0310	13 to 20 stories	5 Carp	8	5			175		175	292
0461	Building interior, walls face area, up to 16' high	3 Clab	12	2			53		53	89
0561	16' to 40' high		10	2.400			64		64	107
0801	Building interior floor area, up to 30' high		150	.160	C.C.F.		4.26		4.26	7.10
0901	Over 30' high	4 Clab	160	.200	"		5.30		5.30	8.90
0906	Complete system for face of walls, no plank, material only rent/mo				C.S.F.	35			35	38.50
0908	Interior spaces, no plank, material only rent/mo				C.C.F.	4.28			4.28	4.71
0910	Steel tubular, heavy duty shoring, buy									
0920	Frames 5' high 2' wide				Ea.	88			88	97
0925	5' high 4' wide					101			101	111
0930	6' high 2' wide					102			102	112
0935	6' high 4' wide					117			117	129
0940	Accessories									
0945	Cross braces				Ea.	17			17	18.70
0950	U-head, 8" x 8"					21			21	23
0955	J-head, 4" x 8"					15.20			15.20	16.70
0960	Base plate, 8" x 8"					17			17	18.70
0965	Leveling jack					36			36	39.50
1000	Steel tubular, regular, buy									
1100	Frames 3' high 5' wide				Ea.	89			89	97.50
1150	5' high 5' wide					94.50			94.50	104
1200	6'-4" high 5' wide					140			140	154
1350	7'-6" high 6' wide					170			170	187
1500	Accessories, cross braces					16.50			16.50	18.15
1550	Guardrail post					17.60			17.60	19.35
1600	Guardrail 7' section					8			8	8.80
1650	Screw jacks & plates					21.50			21.50	24
1700	Sidearm brackets					28			28	30.50
1750	8" casters					31			31	34
1800	Plank 2" x 10" x 16'-0"					59.50			59.50	65.50
1900	Stairway section					275			275	305
1910	Stairway starter bar					32			32	35
1920	Stairway inside handrail					53			53	58
1930	Stairway outside handrail					86			86	94.50
1940	Walk-thru frame guardrail					41.50			41.50	46

01 54 Construction Aids

01 54 23 – Temporary Scaffolding and Platforms

01 54 23.70 Scaffolding

		Crew	Daily Output	Labor-Hours	Unit	Material	2017 Bare Costs Labor	Equipment	Total	Total Incl O&P
2000	Steel tubular, regular, rent/mo.									
2100	Frames 3' high 5' wide				Ea.	5			5	5.50
2150	5' high 5' wide					5			5	5.50
2200	6'-4" high 5' wide					5.40			5.40	5.95
2250	7'-6" high 6' wide					10			10	11
2500	Accessories, cross braces					1			1	1.10
2550	Guardrail post					1			1	1.10
2600	Guardrail 7' section					1			1	1.10
2650	Screw jacks & plates					2			2	2.20
2700	Sidearm brackets					2			2	2.20
2750	8" casters					8			8	8.80
2800	Outrigger for rolling tower					3			3	3.30
2850	Plank 2" x 10" x 16'-0"					10			10	11
2900	Stairway section					33			33	36.50
2940	Walk-thru frame guardrail				▼	2.50			2.50	2.75
3000	Steel tubular, heavy duty shoring, rent/mo.									
3250	5' high 2' & 4' wide				Ea.	8.50			8.50	9.35
3300	6' high 2' & 4' wide					8.50			8.50	9.35
3500	Accessories, cross braces					1			1	1.10
3600	U-head, 8" x 8"					2.50			2.50	2.75
3650	J-head, 4" x 8"					2.50			2.50	2.75
3700	Base plate, 8" x 8"					1			1	1.10
3750	Leveling jack					2.50			2.50	2.75
5700	Planks, 2" x 10" x 16'-0", labor only to erect & remove to 50' H	3 Carp	72	.333			11.65		11.65	19.50
5800	Over 50' high	4 Carp	80	.400	▼		14		14	23.50

01 54 23.80 Staging Aids

		Crew	Daily Output	Labor-Hours	Unit	Material	2017 Bare Costs Labor	Equipment	Total	Total Incl O&P
0010	**STAGING AIDS** and fall protection equipment									
0100	Sidewall staging bracket, tubular, buy				Ea.	52.50			52.50	57.50
0110	Cost each per day, based on 250 days use				Day	.21			.21	.23
0200	Guard post, buy				Ea.	54.50			54.50	60
0210	Cost each per day, based on 250 days use				Day	.22			.22	.24
0300	End guard chains, buy per pair				Pair	40			40	44
0310	Cost per set per day, based on 250 days use				Day	.21			.21	.23
1010	Cost each per day, based on 250 days use				"	.04			.04	.04
1100	Wood bracket, buy				Ea.	23			23	25.50
1110	Cost each per day, based on 250 days use				Day	.09			.09	.10
2010	Cost per pair per day, based on 250 days use				"	.50			.50	.56
2100	Steel siderail jack, buy per pair				Pair	97.50			97.50	107
2110	Cost per pair per day, based on 250 days use				Day	.39			.39	.43
3010	Cost each per day, based on 250 days use				"	.24			.24	.26
3100	Aluminum scaffolding plank, 20" wide x 24' long, buy				Ea.	790			790	870
3110	Cost each per day, based on 250 days use				Day	3.16			3.16	3.48
4010	Cost each per day, based on 250 days use				"	.73			.73	.80
4100	Rope for safety line, 5/8" x 100' nylon, buy				Ea.	58			58	64
4110	Cost each per day, based on 250 days use				Day	.23			.23	.26
4200	Permanent U-Bolt roof anchor, buy				Ea.	35.50			35.50	39.50
4300	Temporary (one use) roof ridge anchor, buy				"	32			32	35.50
5000	Installation (setup and removal) of staging aids									
5010	Sidewall staging bracket	2 Carp	64	.250	Ea.		8.75		8.75	14.60
5020	Guard post with 2 wood rails	"	64	.250			8.75		8.75	14.60
5030	End guard chains, set	1 Carp	64	.125			4.37		4.37	7.30
5100	Roof shingling bracket	▼	96	.083	▼		2.91		2.91	4.87

For customer support on your Residential Costs with RSMeans Data, call 800.448.8182.

295

01 54 Construction Aids

01 54 23 – Temporary Scaffolding and Platforms

01 54 23.80 Staging Aids		Crew	Daily Output	Labor-Hours	Unit	Material	2017 Bare Costs Labor	2017 Bare Costs Equipment	Total	Total Incl O&P
5200	Ladder jack	1 Carp	64	.125	Ea.		4.37		4.37	7.30
5300	Wood plank, 2" x 10" x 16'	2 Carp	80	.200			7		7	11.70
5310	Aluminum scaffold plank, 20" x 24'	"	40	.400			14		14	23.50
5410	Safety rope	1 Carp	40	.200			7		7	11.70
5420	Permanent U-Bolt roof anchor (install only)	2 Carp	40	.400			14		14	23.50
5430	Temporary roof ridge anchor (install only)	1 Carp	64	.125			4.37		4.37	7.30

01 54 36 – Equipment Mobilization

01 54 36.50 Mobilization		Crew	Daily Output	Labor-Hours	Unit	Material	2017 Bare Costs Labor	2017 Bare Costs Equipment	Total	Total Incl O&P
0010	**MOBILIZATION** (Use line item again for demobilization) R015436-50									
0015	Up to 25 mi. haul dist. (50 mi. RT for mob/demob crew)									
1200	Small equipment, placed in rear of, or towed by pickup truck	A-3A	4	2	Ea.		70.50	35	105.50	155
1300	Equipment hauled on 3-ton capacity towed trailer	A-3Q	2.67	3			106	61.50	167.50	243
1400	20-ton capacity	B-34U	2	8			270	232	502	700
1500	40-ton capacity	B-34N	2	8			275	365	640	860
1700	Crane, truck-mounted, up to 75 ton (driver only)	1 Eqhv	4	2			74.50		74.50	123
2500	For each additional 5 miles haul distance, add						10%	10%		
3000	For large pieces of equipment, allow for assembly/knockdown									
3100	For mob/demob of micro-tunneling equip, see Section 33 05 23.19									

01 56 Temporary Barriers and Enclosures

01 56 13 – Temporary Air Barriers

01 56 13.60 Tarpaulins		Crew	Daily Output	Labor-Hours	Unit	Material	2017 Bare Costs Labor	2017 Bare Costs Equipment	Total	Total Incl O&P
0010	**TARPAULINS**									
0020	Cotton duck, 10 oz. to 13.13 oz. per S.Y., 6' x 8'				S.F.	.88			.88	.97
0050	30' x 30'					.59			.59	.65
0200	Reinforced polyethylene 3 mils thick, white					.04			.04	.04
0300	4 mils thick, white, clear or black					.12			.12	.13
0730	Polyester reinforced w/integral fastening system, 11 mils thick					.22			.22	.24

01 56 16 – Temporary Dust Barriers

01 56 16.10 Dust Barriers, Temporary		Crew	Daily Output	Labor-Hours	Unit	Material	2017 Bare Costs Labor	2017 Bare Costs Equipment	Total	Total Incl O&P
0010	**DUST BARRIERS, TEMPORARY**									
0020	Spring loaded telescoping pole & head, to 12', erect and dismantle	1 Clab	240	.033	Ea.		.89		.89	1.48
0025	Cost per day (based upon 250 days)				Day	.26			.26	.29
0030	To 21', erect and dismantle	1 Clab	240	.033	Ea.		.89		.89	1.48
0035	Cost per day (based upon 250 days)				Day	.58			.58	.63
0040	Accessories, caution tape reel, erect and dismantle	1 Clab	480	.017	Ea.		.44		.44	.74
0045	Cost per day (based upon 250 days)				Day	.37			.37	.40
0060	Foam rail and connector, erect and dismantle	1 Clab	240	.033	Ea.		.89		.89	1.48
0065	Cost per day (based upon 250 days)				Day	.12			.12	.13
0070	Caution tape	1 Clab	384	.021	C.L.F.	3.13	.55		3.68	4.37
0080	Zipper, standard duty		60	.133	Ea.	8	3.55		11.55	14.75
0090	Heavy duty		48	.167	"	9.75	4.43		14.18	18.15
0100	Polyethylene sheet, 4 mil		37	.216	Sq.	2.58	5.75		8.33	12.45
0110	6 mil		37	.216	"	3.73	5.75		9.48	13.70
1000	Dust partition, 6 mil polyethylene, 1" x 3" frame	2 Carp	2000	.008	S.F.	.31	.28		.59	.81
1080	2" x 4" frame	"	2000	.008	"	.34	.28		.62	.84

01 66 Product Storage and Handling Requirements

01 66 19 – Material Handling

01 66 19.10 Material Handling	Crew	Daily Output	Labor-Hours	Unit	Material	2017 Bare Costs Labor	Equipment	Total	Total Incl O&P
0010 **MATERIAL HANDLING**									
0020 Above 2nd story, via stairs, per CY of material per floor	2 Clab	145	.110	C.Y.		2.94		2.94	4.91
0030 Via elevator, per CY of material		240	.067			1.77		1.77	2.97
0050 Distances greater than 200', per CY of material per each addl 200'		300	.053			1.42		1.42	2.37

01 71 Examination and Preparation

01 71 23 – Field Engineering

01 71 23.13 Construction Layout

	Crew	Daily Output	Labor-Hours	Unit	Material	2017 Bare Costs Labor	Equipment	Total	Total Incl O&P
0010 **CONSTRUCTION LAYOUT**									
1100 Crew for layout of building, trenching or pipe laying, 2 person crew	A-6	1	16	Day		560	41.50	601.50	975
1200 3 person crew	A-7	1	24	"		890	41.50	931.50	1,525

01 74 Cleaning and Waste Management

01 74 13 – Progress Cleaning

01 74 13.20 Cleaning Up

	Crew	Daily Output	Labor-Hours	Unit	Material	2017 Bare Costs Labor	Equipment	Total	Total Incl O&P
0010 **CLEANING UP**									
0020 After job completion, allow, minimum				Job				.30%	.30%
0040 Maximum				"				1%	1%

01 76 Protecting Installed Construction

01 76 13 – Temporary Protection of Installed Construction

01 76 13.20 Temporary Protection

	Crew	Daily Output	Labor-Hours	Unit	Material	2017 Bare Costs Labor	Equipment	Total	Total Incl O&P
0010 **TEMPORARY PROTECTION**									
0020 Flooring, 1/8" tempered hardboard, taped seams	2 Carp	1500	.011	S.F.	.45	.37		.82	1.12
0030 Peel away carpet protection	1 Clab	3200	.003	"	.13	.07		.20	.25

For customer support on your Residential Costs with RSMeans Data, call 800.448.8182.

297

Division Notes

	CREW	DAILY OUTPUT	LABOR-HOURS	UNIT	BARE COSTS				TOTAL INCL O&P
					MAT.	LABOR	EQUIP.	TOTAL	

Estimating Tips
02 30 00 Subsurface Investigation
In preparing estimates on structures involving earthwork or foundations, all information concerning soil characteristics should be obtained. Look particularly for hazardous waste, evidence of prior dumping of debris, and previous stream beds.

02 40 00 Demolition and Structure Moving
The costs shown for selective demolition do not include rubbish handling or disposal. These items should be estimated separately using RSMeans data or other sources.

- Historic preservation often requires that the contractor remove materials from the existing structure, rehab them, and replace them. The estimator must be aware of any related measures and precautions that must be taken when doing selective demolition and cutting and patching. Requirements may include special handling and storage, as well as security.

- In addition to Subdivision 02 41 00, you can find selective demolition items in each division. Example: Roofing demolition is in Division 7.
- Absent of any other specific reference, an approximate demolish-in-place cost can be obtained by halving the new-install labor cost. To remove for reuse, allow the entire new-install labor figure.

02 40 00 Building Deconstruction
This section provides costs for the careful dismantling and recycling of most low-rise building materials.

02 50 00 Containment of Hazardous Waste
This section addresses on-site hazardous waste disposal costs.

02 80 00 Hazardous Material Disposal/Remediation
This subdivision includes information on hazardous waste handling, asbestos remediation, lead remediation, and mold remediation. See reference numbers R028213-20 and R028319-60 for further guidance in using these unit price lines.

02 90 00 Monitoring Chemical Sampling, Testing Analysis
This section provides costs for on-site sampling and testing hazardous waste.

Reference Numbers
Reference numbers are shown at the beginning of some major classifications. These numbers refer to related items in the Reference Section. The reference information may be an estimating procedure, an alternate pricing method, or technical information.

Note: Not all subdivisions listed here necessarily appear. ■

Did you know?
Our online estimating solution gives you the same access to RSMeans' data with 24/7 access:

- Quickly locate costs in the searchable database.
- Build cost lists, estimates, and reports in minutes.
- Adjust costs to any location in the U.S. and Canada with the click of a button.

Start your free trial today at
www.RSMeansOnline.com

02 21 Surveys

02 21 13 – Site Surveys

02 21 13.09 Topographical Surveys	Crew	Daily Output	Labor-Hours	Unit	Material	2017 Bare Costs Labor	2017 Bare Costs Equipment	Total	Total Incl O&P
0010 **TOPOGRAPHICAL SURVEYS**									
0020 Topographical surveying, conventional, minimum	A-7	3.30	7.273	Acre	19.35	269	12.60	300.95	485
0100 Maximum	A-8	.60	53.333	"	58	1,925	69.50	2,052.50	3,375

02 21 13.13 Boundary and Survey Markers

	Crew	Daily Output	Labor-Hours	Unit	Material	Labor	Equipment	Total	Total Incl O&P
0010 **BOUNDARY AND SURVEY MARKERS**									
0300 Lot location and lines, large quantities, minimum	A-7	2	12	Acre	34	445	21	500	800
0320 Average	"	1.25	19.200		53	710	33	796	1,275
0400 Small quantities, maximum	A-8	1	32	↓	72.50	1,150	41.50	1,264	2,050
0600 Monuments, 3' long	A-7	10	2.400	Ea.	40	89	4.15	133.15	197
0800 Property lines, perimeter, cleared land	"	1000	.024	L.F.	.06	.89	.04	.99	1.60
0900 Wooded land	A-8	875	.037	"	.08	1.33	.05	1.46	2.35

02 32 Geotechnical Investigations

02 32 13 – Subsurface Drilling and Sampling

02 32 13.10 Boring and Exploratory Drilling

	Crew	Daily Output	Labor-Hours	Unit	Material	Labor	Equipment	Total	Total Incl O&P
0010 **BORING AND EXPLORATORY DRILLING**									
0020 Borings, initial field stake out & determination of elevations	A-6	1	16	Day		560	41.50	601.50	975
0100 Drawings showing boring details				Total		335		335	425
0200 Report and recommendations from P.E.						775		775	970
0300 Mobilization and demobilization	B-55	4	4	↓		117	263	380	485
0350 For over 100 miles, per added mile		450	.036	Mile		1.04	2.34	3.38	4.29
0600 Auger holes in earth, no samples, 2-1/2" diameter		78.60	.204	L.F.		5.95	13.40	19.35	24.50
0800 Cased borings in earth, with samples, 2-1/2" diameter		55.50	.288	"	11	8.40	18.95	38.35	47
1400 Borings, earth, drill rig and crew with truck mounted auger	↓	1	16	Day		465	1,050	1,515	1,925
1500 For inner city borings add, minimum								10%	10%
1510 Maximum								20%	20%

02 41 Demolition

02 41 13 – Selective Site Demolition

02 41 13.17 Demolish, Remove Pavement and Curb

		Crew	Daily Output	Labor-Hours	Unit	Material	Labor	Equipment	Total	Total Incl O&P
0010 **DEMOLISH, REMOVE PAVEMENT AND CURB**	R024119-10									
5010 Pavement removal, bituminous roads, up to 3" thick		B-38	690	.035	S.Y.		1.03	.79	1.82	2.58
5050 4" to 6" thick			420	.057			1.68	1.31	2.99	4.24
5100 Bituminous driveways			640	.038			1.11	.86	1.97	2.78
5200 Concrete to 6" thick, hydraulic hammer, mesh reinforced			255	.094			2.77	2.15	4.92	7
5300 Rod reinforced		↓	200	.120	↓		3.54	2.74	6.28	8.90
5600 With hand held air equipment, bituminous, to 6" thick		B-39	1900	.025	S.F.		.68	.11	.79	1.26
5700 Concrete to 6" thick, no reinforcing			1600	.030			.81	.13	.94	1.50
5800 Mesh reinforced			1400	.034			.92	.15	1.07	1.71
5900 Rod reinforced		↓	765	.063	↓		1.69	.28	1.97	3.14
6000 Curbs, concrete, plain		B-6	360	.067	L.F.		1.96	1.02	2.98	4.39
6100 Reinforced			275	.087			2.57	1.33	3.90	5.75
6200 Granite			360	.067			1.96	1.02	2.98	4.39
6300 Bituminous		↓	528	.045	↓		1.34	.69	2.03	2.99

02 41 13.23 Utility Line Removal

	Crew	Daily Output	Labor-Hours	Unit	Material	Labor	Equipment	Total	Total Incl O&P
0010 **UTILITY LINE REMOVAL**									
0015 No hauling, abandon catch basin or manhole	B-6	7	3.429	Ea.		101	52.50	153.50	226
0020 Remove existing catch basin or manhole, masonry		4	6			177	91.50	268.50	395
0030 Catch basin or manhole frames and covers, stored	↓	13	1.846			54.50	28	82.50	122

02 41 Demolition

02 41 13 – Selective Site Demolition

02 41 13.23 Utility Line Removal	Crew	Daily Output	Labor-Hours	Unit	Material	2017 Bare Costs Labor	Equipment	Total	Total Incl O&P
0040	Remove and reset	B-6	7	3.429	Ea.		101	52.50	153.50	226
2900	Pipe removal, sewer/water, no excavation, 12" diameter	↓	175	.137	L.F.		4.04	2.09	6.13	9.05
2930	15"-18" diameter	B-12Z	150	.160			4.83	10.25	15.08	19.30
2960	21"-24" diameter	"	120	.200	↓		6.05	12.80	18.85	24

02 41 13.30 Minor Site Demolition

		Crew	Daily Output	Labor-Hours	Unit	Material	Labor	Equipment	Total	Total Incl O&P
0010	**MINOR SITE DEMOLITION** R024119-10									
1000	Masonry walls, block, solid	B-5	1800	.022	C.F.		.64	.83	1.47	1.98
1200	Brick, solid		900	.044			1.29	1.66	2.95	3.98
1400	Stone, with mortar		900	.044			1.29	1.66	2.95	3.98
1500	Dry set	↓	1500	.027	↓		.77	1	1.77	2.39
4000	Sidewalk removal, bituminous, 2" thick	B-6	350	.069	S.Y.		2.02	1.05	3.07	4.51
4010	2-1/2" thick		325	.074			2.18	1.13	3.31	4.86
4050	Brick, set in mortar		185	.130			3.82	1.98	5.80	8.55
4100	Concrete, plain, 4"		160	.150			4.42	2.29	6.71	9.85
4110	Plain, 5"		140	.171			5.05	2.62	7.67	11.30
4120	Plain, 6"		120	.200			5.90	3.05	8.95	13.15
4200	Mesh reinforced, concrete, 4"		150	.160			4.72	2.44	7.16	10.55
4210	5" thick		131	.183			5.40	2.80	8.20	12.05
4220	6" thick	↓	112	.214	↓		6.30	3.27	9.57	14.10
4300	Slab on grade removal, plain	B-5	45	.889	C.Y.		25.50	33	58.50	79.50
4310	Mesh reinforced		33	1.212			35	45.50	80.50	109
4320	Rod reinforced	↓	25	1.600			46.50	60	106.50	143
4400	For congested sites or small quantities, add up to								200%	200%
4450	For disposal on site, add	B-11A	232	.069			2.17	5.95	8.12	10.15
4500	To 5 miles, add	B-34D	76	.105	↓		3.41	9.25	12.66	15.75

02 41 13.60 Selective Demolition Fencing

		Crew	Daily Output	Labor-Hours	Unit	Material	Labor	Equipment	Total	Total Incl O&P
0010	**SELECTIVE DEMOLITION FENCING** R024119-10									
1600	Fencing, barbed wire, 3 strand	2 Clab	430	.037	L.F.		.99		.99	1.66
1650	5 strand	"	280	.057			1.52		1.52	2.54
1700	Chain link, posts & fabric, 8' to 10' high, remove only	B-6	445	.054	↓		1.59	.82	2.41	3.55

02 41 16 – Structure Demolition

02 41 16.13 Building Demolition

		Crew	Daily Output	Labor-Hours	Unit	Material	Labor	Equipment	Total	Total Incl O&P
0010	**BUILDING DEMOLITION** Large urban projects, incl. 20 mi. haul R024119-10									
0500	Small bldgs, or single bldgs, no salvage included, steel	B-3	14800	.003	C.F.		.10	.17	.27	.35
0600	Concrete	"	11300	.004	"		.13	.23	.36	.47
0605	Concrete, plain	B-5	33	1.212	C.Y.		35	45.50	80.50	109
0610	Reinforced		25	1.600			46.50	60	106.50	143
0615	Concrete walls		34	1.176			34	44	78	106
0620	Elevated slabs	↓	26	1.538	↓		44.50	57.50	102	138
0650	Masonry	B-3	14800	.003	C.F.		.10	.17	.27	.35
0700	Wood		14800	.003	"		.10	.17	.27	.35
1000	Demoliton single family house, one story, wood 1600 S.F.		1	48	Ea.		1,475	2,575	4,050	5,250
1020	3200 S.F.		.50	96			2,925	5,125	8,050	10,500
1200	Demoliton two family house, two story, wood 2400 S.F.		.67	71.964			2,200	3,850	6,050	7,875
1220	4200 S.F.		.38	128			3,900	6,850	10,750	14,000
1300	Demoliton three family house, three story, wood 3200 S.F.		.50	96			2,925	5,125	8,050	10,500
1320	5400 S.F.	↓	.30	160	↓		4,875	8,550	13,425	17,500

For customer support on your Residential Costs with RSMeans Data, call 800.448.8182.

301

02 41 Demolition

02 41 16 – Structure Demolition

02 41 16.17 Building Demolition Footings and Foundations	Crew	Daily Output	Labor-Hours	Unit	Material	2017 Bare Costs Labor	Equipment	Total	Total Incl O&P
0010 **BUILDING DEMOLITION FOOTINGS AND FOUNDATIONS** R024119-10									
0200 Floors, concrete slab on grade,									
0240 4" thick, plain concrete	B-13L	5000	.003	S.F.		.12	.40	.52	.64
0280 Reinforced, wire mesh		4000	.004			.15	.50	.65	.80
0300 Rods		4500	.004			.13	.45	.58	.71
0400 6" thick, plain concrete		4000	.004			.15	.50	.65	.80
0420 Reinforced, wire mesh		3200	.005			.19	.63	.82	1
0440 Rods		3600	.004			.17	.56	.73	.89
1000 Footings, concrete, 1' thick, 2' wide		300	.053	L.F.		1.99	6.70	8.69	10.70
1080 1'-6" thick, 2' wide		250	.064			2.39	8.05	10.44	12.80
1120 3' wide		200	.080			2.98	10.10	13.08	16.05
1200 Average reinforcing, add								10%	10%
2000 Walls, block, 4" thick	B-13L	8000	.002	S.F.		.07	.25	.32	.40
2040 6" thick		6000	.003			.10	.34	.44	.53
2080 8" thick		4000	.004			.15	.50	.65	.80
2100 12" thick		3000	.005			.20	.67	.87	1.07
2400 Concrete, plain concrete, 6" thick		4000	.004			.15	.50	.65	.80
2420 8" thick		3500	.005			.17	.58	.75	.91
2440 10" thick		3000	.005			.20	.67	.87	1.07
2500 12" thick		2500	.006			.24	.81	1.05	1.28
2600 For average reinforcing, add								10%	10%
4000 For congested sites or small quantities, add up to								200%	200%
4200 Add for disposal, on site	B-11A	232	.069	C.Y.		2.17	5.95	8.12	10.15
4250 To five miles	B-30	220	.109	"		3.68	10.25	13.93	17.30

02 41 19 – Selective Demolition

02 41 19.13 Selective Building Demolition

0010 **SELECTIVE BUILDING DEMOLITION**									
0020 Costs related to selective demolition of specific building components									
0025 are included under Common Work Results (XX 05)									
0030 in the component's appropriate division.									

02 41 19.16 Selective Demolition, Cutout

0010 **SELECTIVE DEMOLITION, CUTOUT** R024119-10									
0020 Concrete, elev. slab, light reinforcement, under 6 C.F.	B-9	65	.615	C.F.		16.60	3.28	19.88	31.50
0050 Light reinforcing, over 6 C.F.		75	.533	"		14.40	2.84	17.24	27
0200 Slab on grade to 6" thick, not reinforced, under 8 S.F.		85	.471	S.F.		12.70	2.51	15.21	24.50
0250 8 – 16 S.F.		175	.229	"		6.15	1.22	7.37	11.65
0255 For over 16 S.F. see Line 02 41 16.17 0400									
0600 Walls, not reinforced, under 6 C.F.	B-9	60	.667	C.F.		18	3.55	21.55	34
0650 6 – 12 C.F.	"	80	.500	"		13.50	2.67	16.17	25.50
0655 For over 12 C.F. see Line 02 41 16.17 2500									
1000 Concrete, elevated slab, bar reinforced, under 6 C.F.	B-9	45	.889	C.F.		24	4.74	28.74	45
1050 Bar reinforced, over 6 C.F.		50	.800	"		21.50	4.26	25.76	40.50
1200 Slab on grade to 6" thick, bar reinforced, under 8 S.F.		75	.533	S.F.		14.40	2.84	17.24	27
1250 8 – 16 S.F.		150	.267	"		7.20	1.42	8.62	13.60
1255 For over 16 S.F. see Line 02 41 16.17 0440									
1400 Walls, bar reinforced, under 6 C.F.	B-9	50	.800	C.F.		21.50	4.26	25.76	40.50
1450 6 – 12 C.F.	"	70	.571	"		15.45	3.05	18.50	29.50
1455 For over 12 C.F. see Lines 02 41 16.17 2500 and 2600									
2000 Brick, to 4 S.F. opening, not including toothing									
2040 4" thick	B-9	30	1.333	Ea.		36	7.10	43.10	68
2060 8" thick		18	2.222			60	11.85	71.85	113

02 41 Demolition

02 41 19 – Selective Demolition

02 41 19.16 Selective Demolition, Cutout

		Crew	Daily Output	Labor-Hours	Unit	Material	2017 Bare Costs Labor	2017 Bare Costs Equipment	Total	Total Incl O&P
2080	12" thick	B-9	10	4	Ea.		108	21.50	129.50	205
2400	Concrete block, to 4 S.F. opening, 2" thick		35	1.143			31	6.10	37.10	58
2420	4" thick		30	1.333			36	7.10	43.10	68
2440	8" thick		27	1.481			40	7.90	47.90	75.50
2460	12" thick		24	1.667			45	8.90	53.90	85.50
2600	Gypsum block, to 4 S.F. opening, 2" thick		80	.500			13.50	2.67	16.17	25.50
2620	4" thick		70	.571			15.45	3.05	18.50	29.50
2640	8" thick		55	.727			19.65	3.88	23.53	37.50
2800	Terra cotta, to 4 S.F. opening, 4" thick		70	.571			15.45	3.05	18.50	29.50
2840	8" thick		65	.615			16.60	3.28	19.88	31.50
2880	12" thick	↓	50	.800	↓		21.50	4.26	25.76	40.50
3000	Toothing masonry cutouts, brick, soft old mortar	1 Brhe	40	.200	V.L.F.		5.75		5.75	9.65
3100	Hard mortar		30	.267			7.65		7.65	12.85
3200	Block, soft old mortar		70	.114			3.28		3.28	5.50
3400	Hard mortar	↓	50	.160	↓		4.59		4.59	7.70
6000	Walls, interior, not including re-framing,									
6010	openings to 5 S.F.									
6100	Drywall to 5/8" thick	1 Clab	24	.333	Ea.		8.85		8.85	14.85
6200	Paneling to 3/4" thick		20	.400			10.65		10.65	17.80
6300	Plaster, on gypsum lath		20	.400			10.65		10.65	17.80
6340	On wire lath	↓	14	.571			15.20		15.20	25.50
7000	Wood frame, not including re-framing, openings to 5 S.F.									
7200	Floors, sheathing and flooring to 2" thick	1 Clab	5	1.600	Ea.		42.50		42.50	71
7310	Roofs, sheathing to 1" thick, not including roofing		6	1.333			35.50		35.50	59.50
7410	Walls, sheathing to 1" thick, not including siding	↓	7	1.143	↓		30.50		30.50	51

02 41 19.19 Selective Demolition

		Crew	Daily Output	Labor-Hours	Unit	Material	2017 Bare Costs Labor	2017 Bare Costs Equipment	Total	Total Incl O&P
0010	**SELECTIVE DEMOLITION**, Rubbish Handling R024119-10									
0020	The following are to be added to the demolition prices									
0600	Dumpster, weekly rental, 1 dump/week, 6 C.Y. capacity (2 Tons)				Week	415			415	455
0700	10 C.Y. capacity (3 Tons)					480			480	530
0725	20 C.Y. capacity (5 Tons) R024119-20					565			565	625
0800	30 C.Y. capacity (7 Tons)					730			730	800
0840	40 C.Y. capacity (10 Tons)				↓	775			775	850
2000	Load, haul, dump and return, 0 – 50' haul, hand carried	2 Clab	24	.667	C.Y.		17.75		17.75	29.50
2005	Wheeled		37	.432			11.50		11.50	19.25
2040	0 – 100' haul, hand carried		16.50	.970			26		26	43
2045	Wheeled	↓	25	.640			17		17	28.50
2050	Forklift	A-3R	25	.320			11.25	6.85	18.10	26
2080	Haul and return, add per each extra 100' haul, hand carried	2 Clab	35.50	.451			12		12	20
2085	Wheeled		54	.296			7.90		7.90	13.20
2120	For travel in elevators, up to 10 floors, add		140	.114			3.04		3.04	5.10
2130	0 – 50' haul, incl. up to 5 riser stairs, hand carried		23	.696			18.50		18.50	31
2135	Wheeled		35	.457			12.15		12.15	20.50
2140	6 – 10 riser stairs, hand carried		22	.727			19.35		19.35	32.50
2145	Wheeled		34	.471			12.50		12.50	21
2150	11 – 20 riser stairs, hand carried		20	.800			21.50		21.50	35.50
2155	Wheeled		31	.516			13.75		13.75	23
2160	21 – 40 riser stairs, hand carried		16	1			26.50		26.50	44.50
2165	Wheeled		24	.667			17.75		17.75	29.50
2170	0 – 100' haul, incl. 5 riser stairs, hand carried		15	1.067			28.50		28.50	47.50
2175	Wheeled		23	.696			18.50		18.50	31
2180	6 – 10 riser stairs, hand carried		14	1.143			30.50		30.50	51

02 41 Demolition

02 41 19 – Selective Demolition

02 41 19.19 Selective Demolition

	02 41 19.19 Selective Demolition	Crew	Daily Output	Labor-Hours	Unit	Material	2017 Bare Costs Labor	Equipment	Total	Total Incl O&P
2185	Wheeled	2 Clab	21	.762	C.Y.		20.50		20.50	34
2190	11 – 20 riser stairs, hand carried		12	1.333			35.50		35.50	59.50
2195	Wheeled		18	.889			23.50		23.50	39.50
2200	21 – 40 riser stairs, hand carried		8	2			53		53	89
2205	Wheeled		12	1.333			35.50		35.50	59.50
2210	Haul and return, add per each extra 100' haul, hand carried		35.50	.451			12		12	20
2215	Wheeled		54	.296			7.90		7.90	13.20
2220	For each additional flight of stairs, up to 5 risers, add		550	.029	Flight		.77		.77	1.29
2225	6 – 10 risers, add		275	.058			1.55		1.55	2.59
2230	11 – 20 risers, add		138	.116			3.08		3.08	5.15
2235	21 – 40 risers, add		69	.232			6.15		6.15	10.30
3000	Loading & trucking, including 2 mile haul, chute loaded	B-16	45	.711	C.Y.		20.50	14.30	34.80	49.50
3040	Hand loading truck, 50' haul	"	48	.667			19.05	13.40	32.45	46.50
3080	Machine loading truck	B-17	120	.267			8.05	6.30	14.35	20.50
5000	Haul, per mile, up to 8 C.Y. truck	B-34B	1165	.007			.22	.55	.77	.98
5100	Over 8 C.Y. truck	"	1550	.005			.17	.41	.58	.74

02 41 19.20 Selective Demolition, Dump Charges

	02 41 19.20 Selective Demolition, Dump Charges	Crew	Daily Output	Labor-Hours	Unit	Material	2017 Bare Costs Labor	Equipment	Total	Total Incl O&P
0010	**SELECTIVE DEMOLITION, DUMP CHARGES** R024119-10									
0020	Dump charges, typical urban city, tipping fees only									
0100	Building construction materials				Ton	74			74	81
0200	Trees, brush, lumber					63			63	69.50
0300	Rubbish only					63			63	69.50
0500	Reclamation station, usual charge					74			74	81

02 41 19.21 Selective Demolition, Gutting

	02 41 19.21 Selective Demolition, Gutting	Crew	Daily Output	Labor-Hours	Unit	Material	2017 Bare Costs Labor	Equipment	Total	Total Incl O&P
0010	**SELECTIVE DEMOLITION, GUTTING** R024119-10									
0020	Building interior, including disposal, dumpster fees not included									
0500	Residential building									
0560	Minimum	B-16	400	.080	SF Flr.		2.28	1.61	3.89	5.55
0580	Maximum	"	360	.089	"		2.54	1.78	4.32	6.20
0900	Commercial building									
1000	Minimum	B-16	350	.091	SF Flr.		2.61	1.84	4.45	6.35
1020	Maximum	"	250	.128	"		3.65	2.57	6.22	8.95

02 83 Lead Remediation

02 83 19 – Lead-Based Paint Remediation

02 83 19.22 Preparation of Lead Containment Area

	02 83 19.22 Preparation of Lead Containment Area	Crew	Daily Output	Labor-Hours	Unit	Material	2017 Bare Costs Labor	Equipment	Total	Total Incl O&P
0010	**PREPARATION OF LEAD CONTAINMENT AREA**									
0020	Lead abatement work area, test kit, per swab	1 Skwk	16	.500	Ea.	3.12	17.90		21.02	33.50
0025	For dust barriers see Section 01 56 16.10									
0050	Caution sign	1 Skwk	48	.167	Ea.	8.65	5.95		14.60	19.50
0100	Pre-cleaning, HEPA vacuum and wet wipe, floor and wall surfaces	3 Skwk	5000	.005	S.F.	.01	.17		.18	.31
0105	Ceiling, 6' - 11' high		4100	.006		.08	.21		.29	.43
0108	12' - 15' high		3550	.007		.07	.24		.31	.49
0115	Over 15' high		3000	.008		.09	.29		.38	.58
0500	Cover surfaces with polyethylene sheeting									
0550	Floors, each layer, 6 mil	3 Skwk	8000	.003	S.F.	.04	.11		.15	.22
0560	Walls, each layer, 6 mil	"	6000	.004	"	.04	.14		.18	.28
0570	For heights above 14', add						20%			
2400	Post abatement cleaning of protective sheeting, HEPA vacuum & wet wipe	3 Skwk	5000	.005	S.F.	.01	.17		.18	.31
2450	Doff, bag and seal protective sheeting		12000	.002		.01	.07		.08	.13

02 83 Lead Remediation

02 83 19 – Lead-Based Paint Remediation

02 83 19.22 Preparation of Lead Containment Area

		Crew	Daily Output	Labor-Hours	Unit	Material	2017 Bare Costs Labor	2017 Bare Costs Equipment	Total	Total Incl O&P
2500	Post abatement cleaning, HEPA vacuum & wet wipe	3 Skwk	5000	.005	S.F.	.01	.17		.18	.31

02 83 19.23 Encapsulation of Lead-Based Paint

		Crew	Daily Output	Labor-Hours	Unit	Material	2017 Bare Costs Labor	2017 Bare Costs Equipment	Total	Total Incl O&P
0010	**ENCAPSULATION OF LEAD-BASED PAINT**									
0020	Interior, brushwork, trim, under 6"	1 Pord	240	.033	L.F.	2.32	.97		3.29	4.16
0030	6" to 12" wide		180	.044		3.03	1.30		4.33	5.45
0040	Balustrades		300	.027		2.02	.78		2.80	3.51
0050	Pipe to 4" diameter		500	.016		1.21	.47		1.68	2.10
0060	To 8" diameter		375	.021		1.52	.62		2.14	2.70
0070	To 12" diameter		250	.032		2.22	.93		3.15	3.98
0080	To 16" diameter		170	.047		3.33	1.37		4.70	5.95
0090	Cabinets, ornate design		200	.040	S.F.	3.03	1.17		4.20	5.25
0100	Simple design		250	.032	"	2.32	.93		3.25	4.09
0110	Doors, 3' x 7', both sides, incl. frame & trim									
0120	Flush	1 Pord	6	1.333	Ea.	28.50	39		67.50	95.50
0130	French, 10 – 15 lite		3	2.667		6.05	78		84.05	136
0140	Panel		4	2		35.50	58.50		94	136
0150	Louvered		2.75	2.909		32.50	85		117.50	176
0160	Windows, per interior side, per 15 S.F.									
0170	1 to 6 lite	1 Pord	14	.571	Ea.	20	16.70		36.70	49.50
0180	7 to 10 lite		7.50	1.067		22	31		53	76
0190	12 lite		5.75	1.391		30.50	40.50		71	101
0200	Radiators		8	1		70.50	29		99.50	126
0210	Grilles, vents		275	.029	S.F.	2.02	.85		2.87	3.62
0220	Walls, roller, drywall or plaster		1000	.008		.61	.23		.84	1.06
0230	With spunbonded reinforcing fabric		720	.011		.71	.32		1.03	1.32
0240	Wood		800	.010		.71	.29		1	1.26
0250	Ceilings, roller, drywall or plaster		900	.009		.71	.26		.97	1.21
0260	Wood		700	.011		.81	.33		1.14	1.44
0270	Exterior, brushwork, gutters and downspouts		300	.027	L.F.	1.92	.78		2.70	3.40
0280	Columns		400	.020	S.F.	1.41	.58		1.99	2.51
0290	Spray, siding		600	.013	"	1.01	.39		1.40	1.75
0300	Miscellaneous									
0310	Electrical conduit, brushwork, to 2" diameter	1 Pord	500	.016	L.F.	1.21	.47		1.68	2.10
0320	Brick, block or concrete, spray		500	.016	S.F.	1.21	.47		1.68	2.10
0330	Steel, flat surfaces and tanks to 12"		500	.016		1.21	.47		1.68	2.10
0340	Beams, brushwork		400	.020		1.41	.58		1.99	2.51
0350	Trusses		400	.020		1.41	.58		1.99	2.51

02 83 19.26 Removal of Lead-Based Paint

		Crew	Daily Output	Labor-Hours	Unit	Material	2017 Bare Costs Labor	2017 Bare Costs Equipment	Total	Total Incl O&P
0010	**REMOVAL OF LEAD-BASED PAINT**									
0011	By chemicals, per application									
0050	Baseboard, to 6" wide	1 Pord	64	.125	L.F.	.80	3.65		4.45	6.95
0070	To 12" wide		32	.250	"	1.47	7.30		8.77	13.65
0200	Balustrades, one side		28	.286	S.F.	1.50	8.35		9.85	15.40
1400	Cabinets, simple design		32	.250		1.37	7.30		8.67	13.55
1420	Ornate design		25	.320		1.60	9.35		10.95	17.15
1600	Cornice, simple design		60	.133		1.60	3.89		5.49	8.20
1620	Ornate design		20	.400		5.55	11.70		17.25	25.50
2800	Doors, one side, flush		84	.095		1.73	2.78		4.51	6.50
2820	Two panel		80	.100		1.37	2.92		4.29	6.35
2840	Four panel		45	.178		1.43	5.20		6.63	10.10
2880	For trim, one side, add		64	.125	L.F.	.77	3.65		4.42	6.90
3000	Fence, picket, one side		30	.267	S.F.	1.37	7.80		9.17	14.35

For customer support on your Residential Costs with RSMeans Data, call 800.448.8182.

305

02 83 Lead Remediation

02 83 19 – Lead-Based Paint Remediation

02 83 19.26 Removal of Lead-Based Paint

		Crew	Daily Output	Labor-Hours	Unit	Material	2017 Bare Costs Labor	Equipment	Total	Total Incl O&P
3200	Grilles, one side, simple design	1 Pord	30	.267	S.F.	1.37	7.80		9.17	14.35
3220	Ornate design		25	.320	↓	1.47	9.35		10.82	17
3240	Handrails		90	.089	L.F.	1.37	2.60		3.97	5.80
4400	Pipes, to 4" diameter		90	.089		1.73	2.60		4.33	6.20
4420	To 8" diameter		50	.160		3.47	4.67		8.14	11.50
4440	To 12" diameter		36	.222		5.20	6.50		11.70	16.40
4460	To 16" diameter		20	.400	↓	6.95	11.70		18.65	27
4500	For hangers, add		40	.200	Ea.	2.53	5.85		8.38	12.45
4800	Siding		90	.089	S.F.	1.31	2.60		3.91	5.70
5000	Trusses, open		55	.145	SF Face	2.02	4.25		6.27	9.20
6200	Windows, one side only, double hung, 1/1 light, 24" x 48" high		4	2	Ea.	24	58.50		82.50	123
6220	30" x 60" high		3	2.667		32.50	78		110.50	165
6240	36" x 72" high		2.50	3.200		38.50	93.50		132	196
6280	40" x 80" high		2	4		47.50	117		164.50	245
6400	Colonial window, 6/6 light, 24" x 48" high		2	4		47.50	117		164.50	245
6420	30" x 60" high		1.50	5.333		62.50	156		218.50	325
6440	36" x 72" high		1	8		94	234		328	490
6480	40" x 80" high		1	8		94	234		328	490
6600	8/8 light, 24" x 48" high		2	4		47.50	117		164.50	245
6620	40" x 80" high		1	8		94	234		328	490
6800	12/12 light, 24" x 48" high		1	8		94	234		328	490
6820	40" x 80" high	↓	.75	10.667	↓	126	310		436	655
6840	Window frame & trim items, included in pricing above									

02 85 Mold Remediation

02 85 33 – Removal and Disposal of Materials with Mold

02 85 33.50 Demolition in Mold Contaminated Area

		Crew	Daily Output	Labor-Hours	Unit	Material	2017 Bare Costs Labor	Equipment	Total	Total Incl O&P
0010	**DEMOLITION IN MOLD CONTAMINATED AREA**									
0200	Ceiling, including suspension system, plaster and lath	A-9	2100	.030	S.F.	.09	1.09		1.18	1.95
0210	Finished plaster, leaving wire lath		585	.109		.31	3.92		4.23	7
0220	Suspended acoustical tile		3500	.018		.05	.66		.71	1.17
0230	Concealed tile grid system		3000	.021		.06	.76		.82	1.37
0240	Metal pan grid system		1500	.043		.12	1.53		1.65	2.72
0250	Gypsum board		2500	.026		.07	.92		.99	1.64
0255	Plywood		2500	.026	↓	.07	.92		.99	1.64
0260	Lighting fixtures up to 2' x 4'	↓	72	.889	Ea.	2.55	32		34.55	57
0400	Partitions, non load bearing									
0410	Plaster, lath, and studs	A-9	690	.093	S.F.	.91	3.33		4.24	6.65
0450	Gypsum board and studs		1390	.046		.13	1.65		1.78	2.95
0465	Carpet & pad		1390	.046	↓	.13	1.65		1.78	2.95
0600	Pipe insulation, air cell type, up to 4" diameter pipe		900	.071	L.F.	.20	2.55		2.75	4.54
0610	4" to 8" diameter pipe		800	.080		.23	2.87		3.10	5.10
0620	10" to 12" diameter pipe		700	.091		.26	3.28		3.54	5.85
0630	14" to 16" diameter pipe		550	.116	↓	.33	4.17		4.50	7.40
0650	Over 16" diameter pipe	↓	650	.098	S.F.	.28	3.53		3.81	6.30
9000	For type B (supplied air) respirator equipment, add				%				10%	10%

Estimating Tips
General

- Carefully check all the plans and specifications. Concrete often appears on drawings other than structural drawings, including mechanical and electrical drawings for equipment pads. The cost of cutting and patching is often difficult to estimate. See Subdivision 03 81 for Concrete Cutting, Subdivision 02 41 19.16 for Cutout Demolition, Subdivision 03 05 05.10 for Concrete Demolition, and Subdivision 02 41 19.19 for Rubbish Handling (handling, loading, and hauling of debris).

- Always obtain concrete prices from suppliers near the job site. A volume discount can often be negotiated, depending upon competition in the area. Remember to add for waste, particularly for slabs and footings on grade.

03 10 00 Concrete Forming and Accessories

- A primary cost for concrete construction is forming. Most jobs today are constructed with prefabricated forms. The selection of the forms best suited for the job and the total square feet of forms required for efficient concrete forming and placing are key elements in estimating concrete construction. Enough forms must be available for erection to make efficient use of the concrete placing equipment and crew.

- Concrete accessories for forming and placing depend upon the systems used. Study the plans and specifications to ensure that all special accessory requirements have been included in the cost estimate, such as anchor bolts, inserts, and hangers.

- Included within costs for forms-in-place are all necessary bracing and shoring.

03 20 00 Concrete Reinforcing

- Ascertain that the reinforcing steel supplier has included all accessories, cutting, bending, and an allowance for lapping, splicing, and waste. A good rule of thumb is 10% for lapping, splicing, and waste. Also, 10% waste should be allowed for welded wire fabric.

- The unit price items in the subdivisions for Reinforcing In Place, Glass Fiber Reinforcing, and Welded Wire Fabric include the labor to install accessories such as beam and slab bolsters, high chairs, and bar ties and tie wire. The material cost for these accessories is not included; they may be obtained from the Accessories Subdivisions.

03 30 00 Cast-In-Place Concrete

- When estimating structural concrete, pay particular attention to requirements for concrete additives, curing methods, and surface treatments. Special consideration for climate, hot or cold, must be included in your estimate. Be sure to include requirements for concrete placing equipment and concrete finishing.

- For accurate concrete estimating, the estimator must consider each of the following major components individually: forms, reinforcing steel, ready-mix concrete, placement of the concrete, and finishing of the top surface. For faster estimating, Subdivision 03 30 53.40 for Concrete-In-Place can be used; here, various items of concrete work are presented that include the costs of all five major components (unless specifically stated otherwise).

03 40 00 Precast Concrete
03 50 00 Cast Decks and Underlayment

- The cost of hauling precast concrete structural members is often an important factor. For this reason, it is important to get a quote from the nearest supplier. It may become economically feasible to set up precasting beds on the site if the hauling costs are prohibitive.

Reference Numbers

Reference numbers are shown at the beginning of some major classifications. These numbers refer to related items in the Reference Section. The reference information may be an estimating procedure, an alternate pricing method, or technical information.

Note: Not all subdivisions listed here necessarily appear. ■

03 01 Maintenance of Concrete

03 01 30 – Maintenance of Cast-In-Place Concrete

03 01 30.64 Floor Patching

		Crew	Daily Output	Labor-Hours	Unit	Material	2017 Bare Costs Labor	2017 Bare Costs Equipment	Total	Total Incl O&P
0010	**FLOOR PATCHING**									
0012	Floor patching, 1/4" thick, small areas, regular	1 Cefi	170	.047	S.F.	3.16	1.63		4.79	6.15
0100	Epoxy	"	100	.080	"	7.60	2.77		10.37	12.85

03 05 Common Work Results for Concrete

03 05 13 – Basic Concrete Materials

03 05 13.85 Winter Protection

		Crew	Daily Output	Labor-Hours	Unit	Material	2017 Bare Costs Labor	2017 Bare Costs Equipment	Total	Total Incl O&P
0010	**WINTER PROTECTION**									
0012	For heated ready mix, add				C.Y.	4.45			4.45	4.90
0100	Temporary heat to protect concrete, 24 hours	2 Clab	50	.320	M.S.F.	200	8.50		208.50	234
0200	Temporary shelter for slab on grade, wood frame/polyethylene sheeting									
0201	Build or remove, light framing for short spans	2 Carp	10	1.600	M.S.F.	300	56		356	425
0210	Large framing for long spans	"	3	5.333	"	395	186		581	740
0710	Electrically heated pads, 15 watts/S.F., 20 uses				S.F.	.56			.56	.61

03 11 Concrete Forming

03 11 13 – Structural Cast-In-Place Concrete Forming

03 11 13.25 Forms In Place, Columns

			Crew	Daily Output	Labor-Hours	Unit	Material	2017 Bare Costs Labor	2017 Bare Costs Equipment	Total	Total Incl O&P
0010	**FORMS IN PLACE, COLUMNS**										
1500	Round fiber tube, recycled paper, 1 use, 8" diameter	G	C-1	155	.206	L.F.	1.91	6.35		8.26	12.75
1550	10" diameter	G		155	.206		2.56	6.35		8.91	13.45
1600	12" diameter	G		150	.213		3.05	6.55		9.60	14.35
1650	14" diameter	G		145	.221		4.26	6.80		11.06	16.10
1700	16" diameter	G		140	.229		5.25	7.05		12.30	17.60
1720	18" diameter	G		140	.229		6.15	7.05		13.20	18.60
5000	Job-built plywood, 8" x 8" columns, 1 use			165	.194	SFCA	2.44	5.95		8.39	12.70
5500	12" x 12" columns, 1 use			180	.178	"	2.37	5.45		7.82	11.75
7400	Steel framed plywood, based on 50 uses of purchased										
7420	forms, and 4 uses of bracing lumber										
7500	8" x 8" column		C-1	340	.094	SFCA	2.17	2.90		5.07	7.25
7550	10" x 10"			350	.091		1.89	2.81		4.70	6.80
7600	12" x 12"			370	.086		1.61	2.66		4.27	6.25

03 11 13.45 Forms In Place, Footings

		Crew	Daily Output	Labor-Hours	Unit	Material	2017 Bare Costs Labor	2017 Bare Costs Equipment	Total	Total Incl O&P
0010	**FORMS IN PLACE, FOOTINGS**									
0020	Continuous wall, plywood, 1 use	C-1	375	.085	SFCA	6.85	2.62		9.47	11.90
0150	4 use	"	485	.066	"	2.23	2.03		4.26	5.85
1500	Keyway, 4 use, tapered wood, 2" x 4"	1 Carp	530	.015	L.F.	.22	.53		.75	1.12
1550	2" x 6"	"	500	.016	"	.31	.56		.87	1.28
5000	Spread footings, job-built lumber, 1 use	C-1	305	.105	SFCA	2.20	3.23		5.43	7.80
5150	4 use	"	414	.077	"	.72	2.38		3.10	4.78

03 11 13.50 Forms In Place, Grade Beam

		Crew	Daily Output	Labor-Hours	Unit	Material	2017 Bare Costs Labor	2017 Bare Costs Equipment	Total	Total Incl O&P
0010	**FORMS IN PLACE, GRADE BEAM**									
0020	Job-built plywood, 1 use	C-2	530	.091	SFCA	3.10	2.82		5.92	8.15
0150	4 use	"	605	.079	"	1.01	2.47		3.48	5.25

03 11 13.65 Forms In Place, Slab On Grade

			Crew	Daily Output	Labor-Hours	Unit	Material	2017 Bare Costs Labor	2017 Bare Costs Equipment	Total	Total Incl O&P
0010	**FORMS IN PLACE, SLAB ON GRADE**										
1000	Bulkhead forms w/keyway, wood, 6" high, 1 use		C-1	510	.063	L.F.	1.01	1.93		2.94	4.35
1400	Bulkhead form for slab, 4-1/2" high, exp metal, incl keyway & stakes	G		1200	.027		.93	.82		1.75	2.40

03 11 Concrete Forming

03 11 13 – Structural Cast-In-Place Concrete Forming

03 11 13.65 Forms In Place, Slab On Grade

		Crew	Daily Output	Labor-Hours	Unit	Material	2017 Bare Costs Labor	Equipment	Total	Total Incl O&P
1410	5-1/2" high [G]	C-1	1100	.029	L.F.	1.17	.89		2.06	2.79
1420	7-1/2" high [G]		960	.033		1.31	1.03		2.34	3.16
1430	9-1/2" high [G]		840	.038	↓	1.43	1.17		2.60	3.54
2000	Curb forms, wood, 6" to 12" high, on grade, 1 use		215	.149	SFCA	2.62	4.58		7.20	10.60
2150	4 use		275	.116	"	.85	3.58		4.43	6.95
3000	Edge forms, wood, 4 use, on grade, to 6" high		600	.053	L.F.	.34	1.64		1.98	3.12
3050	7" to 12" high		435	.074	SFCA	.82	2.26		3.08	4.70
4000	For slab blockouts, to 12" high, 1 use		200	.160	L.F.	.80	4.92		5.72	9.15
4100	Plastic (extruded), to 6" high, multiple use, on grade		800	.040	"	6.65	1.23		7.88	9.40
8760	Void form, corrugated fiberboard, 4" x 12", 4' long [G]		3000	.011	S.F.	3.14	.33		3.47	4
8770	6" x 12", 4' long	↓	3000	.011		3.75	.33		4.08	4.68
8780	1/4" thick hardboard protective cover for void form	2 Carp	1500	.011	↓	.63	.37		1	1.31

03 11 13.85 Forms In Place, Walls

		Crew	Daily Output	Labor-Hours	Unit	Material	2017 Bare Costs Labor	Equipment	Total	Total Incl O&P
0010	**FORMS IN PLACE, WALLS**									
0100	Box out for wall openings, to 16" thick, to 10 S.F.	C-2	24	2	Ea.	26.50	62		88.50	133
0150	Over 10 S.F. (use perimeter)	"	280	.171	L.F.	2.27	5.35		7.62	11.45
0250	Brick shelf, 4" w, add to wall forms, use wall area above shelf									
0260	1 use	C-2	240	.200	SFCA	2.44	6.20		8.64	13.15
0350	4 use	↓	300	.160	"	.97	4.97		5.94	9.40
0500	Bulkhead, wood with keyway, 1 use, 2 piece	↓	265	.181	L.F.	2.13	5.65		7.78	11.80
0600	Bulkhead forms with keyway, 1 piece expanded metal, 8" wall [G]	C-1	1000	.032		1.31	.98		2.29	3.09
0610	10" wall [G]	"	800	.040	↓	1.43	1.23		2.66	3.63
2000	Wall, job-built plywood, to 8' high, 1 use	C-2	370	.130	SFCA	2.56	4.03		6.59	9.55
2050	2 use		435	.110		1.64	3.43		5.07	7.55
2100	3 use		495	.097		1.19	3.01		4.20	6.35
2150	4 use		505	.095		.97	2.96		3.93	6.05
2400	Over 8' to 16' high, 1 use		280	.171		2.85	5.35		8.20	12.10
2450	2 use		345	.139		1.33	4.33		5.66	8.70
2500	3 use		375	.128		.95	3.98		4.93	7.75
2550	4 use	↓	395	.122	↓	.78	3.78		4.56	7.20
7800	Modular prefabricated plywood, based on 20 uses of purchased									
7820	forms, and 4 uses of bracing lumber									
7860	To 8' high	C-2	800	.060	SFCA	.94	1.87		2.81	4.17
8060	Over 8' to 16' high	"	600	.080	"	1	2.49		3.49	5.25

03 11 19 – Insulating Concrete Forming

03 11 19.10 Insulating Forms, Left In Place

		Crew	Daily Output	Labor-Hours	Unit	Material	2017 Bare Costs Labor	Equipment	Total	Total Incl O&P
0010	**INSULATING FORMS, LEFT IN PLACE**									
0020	S.F. is for exterior face, but includes forms for both faces (total R22)									
2000	4" wall, straight block, 16" x 48" (5.33 S.F.) [G]	2 Carp	90	.178	Ea.	20.50	6.20		26.70	33
2010	90 corner block, exterior 16" x 38" x 22" (6.67 S.F.) [G]		75	.213		24.50	7.45		31.95	39.50
2020	45 corner block, exterior 16" x 34" x 18" (5.78 S.F.) [G]		75	.213		24	7.45		31.45	39
2100	6" wall, straight block, 16" x 48" (5.33 S.F.) [G]		90	.178		21	6.20		27.20	33.50
2110	90 corner block, exterior 16" x 32" x 24" (6.22 S.F.) [G]		75	.213		27	7.45		34.45	42
2120	45 corner block, exterior 16" x 26" x 18" (4.89 S.F.) [G]		75	.213		23.50	7.45		30.95	38.50
2130	Brick ledge block, 16" x 48" (5.33 S.F.) [G]		80	.200		26	7		33	40
2140	Taper top block, 16" x 48" (5.33 S.F.) [G]		80	.200		24.50	7		31.50	38.50
2200	8" wall, straight block, 16" x 48" (5.33 S.F.) [G]		90	.178		22	6.20		28.20	35
2210	90 corner block, exterior 16" x 34" x 26" (6.67 S.F.) [G]		75	.213		29.50	7.45		36.95	45
2220	45 corner block, exterior 16" x 28" x 20" (5.33 S.F.) [G]		75	.213		24.50	7.45		31.95	39.50
2230	Brick ledge block, 16" x 48" (5.33 S.F.) [G]		80	.200		27.50	7		34.50	41.50
2240	Taper top block, 16" x 48" (5.33 S.F.) [G]	↓	80	.200	↓	25.50	7		32.50	39.50

03 11 Concrete Forming

03 11 23 – Permanent Stair Forming

03 11 23.75 Forms In Place, Stairs		Crew	Daily Output	Labor-Hours	Unit	Material	2017 Bare Costs Labor	Equipment	Total	Total Incl O&P
0010	**FORMS IN PLACE, STAIRS**									
0015	(Slant length x width), 1 use	C-2	165	.291	S.F.	5.90	9.05		14.95	21.50
0150	4 use		190	.253		2.08	7.85		9.93	15.50
2000	Stairs, cast on sloping ground (length x width), 1 use		220	.218		2.28	6.80		9.08	13.90
2025	2 use		232	.207		1.26	6.45		7.71	12.20
2050	3 use		244	.197		.91	6.10		7.01	11.25
2100	4 use		256	.188		.74	5.85		6.59	10.60

03 15 Concrete Accessories

03 15 05 – Concrete Forming Accessories

03 15 05.12 Chamfer Strips

		Crew	Daily Output	Labor-Hours	Unit	Material	Labor	Equipment	Total	Total Incl O&P
0010	**CHAMFER STRIPS**									
5000	Wood, 1/2" wide	1 Carp	535	.015	L.F.	.13	.52		.65	1.01
5200	3/4" wide		525	.015		.16	.53		.69	1.07
5400	1" wide		515	.016		.29	.54		.83	1.23

03 15 05.15 Column Form Accessories

			Crew	Daily Output	Labor-Hours	Unit	Material	Labor	Equipment	Total	Total Incl O&P
0010	**COLUMN FORM ACCESSORIES**										
1000	Column clamps, adjustable to 24" x 24", buy	G				Set	160			160	176
1100	Rent per month	G				"	11.15			11.15	12.25

03 15 05.75 Sleeves and Chases

		Crew	Daily Output	Labor-Hours	Unit	Material	Labor	Equipment	Total	Total Incl O&P
0010	**SLEEVES AND CHASES**									
0100	Plastic, 1 use, 12" long, 2" diameter	1 Carp	100	.080	Ea.	1.62	2.80		4.42	6.45
0150	4" diameter		90	.089		4.54	3.11		7.65	10.20
0200	6" diameter		75	.107		7.80	3.73		11.53	14.80

03 15 05.80 Snap Ties

			Crew	Daily Output	Labor-Hours	Unit	Material	Labor	Equipment	Total	Total Incl O&P
0010	**SNAP TIES**, 8-1/4" L&W (Lumber and wedge)										
0100	2250 lb., w/flat washer, 8" wall	G				C	93			93	102
0150	10" wall	G					135			135	149
0200	12" wall	G					140			140	154
0500	With plastic cone, 8" wall	G					82			82	90
0550	10" wall	G					85			85	93.50
0600	12" wall	G					92			92	101

03 15 05.95 Wall and Foundation Form Accessories

			Crew	Daily Output	Labor-Hours	Unit	Material	Labor	Equipment	Total	Total Incl O&P
0010	**WALL AND FOUNDATION FORM ACCESSORIES**										
4000	Nail stakes, 3/4" diameter, 18" long	G				Ea.	3.40			3.40	3.74
4050	24" long	G					4.39			4.39	4.83
4200	30" long	G					5.65			5.65	6.20
4250	36" long	G					6.80			6.80	7.45

03 15 13 – Waterstops

03 15 13.50 Waterstops

		Crew	Daily Output	Labor-Hours	Unit	Material	Labor	Equipment	Total	Total Incl O&P
0010	**WATERSTOPS**, PVC and Rubber									
0020	PVC, ribbed 3/16" thick, 4" wide	1 Carp	155	.052	L.F.	1.36	1.80		3.16	4.52
0050	6" wide		145	.055		2.33	1.93		4.26	5.80
0500	With center bulb, 6" wide, 3/16" thick		135	.059		2.34	2.07		4.41	6.05
0550	3/8" thick		130	.062		4.27	2.15		6.42	8.30
0600	9" wide x 3/8" thick		125	.064		6.95	2.24		9.19	11.40

03 15 Concrete Accessories

03 15 16 – Concrete Construction Joints

03 15 16.20 Control Joints, Saw Cut

		Crew	Daily Output	Labor-Hours	Unit	Material	2017 Bare Costs Labor	Equipment	Total	Total Incl O&P
0010	**CONTROL JOINTS, SAW CUT**									
0100	Sawcut control joints in green concrete									
0120	1" depth	C-27	2000	.008	L.F.	.04	.28	.08	.40	.57
0140	1-1/2" depth		1800	.009		.05	.31	.09	.45	.65
0160	2" depth	↓	1600	.010	↓	.07	.35	.10	.52	.75
0180	Sawcut joint reservoir in cured concrete									
0182	3/8" wide x 3/4" deep, with single saw blade	C-27	1000	.016	L.F.	.05	.55	.15	.75	1.13
0184	1/2" wide x 1" deep, with double saw blades		900	.018		.10	.62	.17	.89	1.30
0186	3/4" wide x 1-1/2" deep, with double saw blades	↓	800	.020		.21	.69	.19	1.09	1.57
0190	Water blast joint to wash away laitance, 2 passes	C-29	2500	.003			.09	.03	.12	.17
0200	Air blast joint to blow out debris and air dry, 2 passes	C-28	2000	.004	↓		.14	.01	.15	.24
0300	For backer rod, see Section 07 91 23.10									
0340	For joint sealant, see Section 03 15 16.30 or 07 92 13.20									

03 15 16.30 Expansion Joints

				Crew	Daily Output	Labor-Hours	Unit	Material	2017 Bare Costs Labor	Equipment	Total	Total Incl O&P
0010	**EXPANSION JOINTS**											
0020	Keyed, cold, 24 ga., incl. stakes, 3-1/2" high	G	1 Carp	200	.040	L.F.	.87	1.40		2.27	3.30
0050	4-1/2" high	G		200	.040		.93	1.40		2.33	3.36
0100	5-1/2" high	G		195	.041		1.17	1.43		2.60	3.69
2000	Premolded, bituminous fiber, 1/2" x 6"			375	.021		.41	.75		1.16	1.70
2050	1" x 12"			300	.027		1.97	.93		2.90	3.73
2140	Concrete expansion joint, recycled paper and fiber, 1/2" x 6"	G		390	.021		.43	.72		1.15	1.68
2150	1/2" x 12"	G		360	.022		.87	.78		1.65	2.26
2500	Neoprene sponge, closed cell, 1/2" x 6"			375	.021		2.41	.75		3.16	3.90
2550	1" x 12"		↓	300	.027	↓	8.45	.93		9.38	10.80
5000	For installation in walls, add							75%			
5250	For installation in boxouts, add							25%			

03 15 19 – Cast-In Concrete Anchors

03 15 19.05 Anchor Bolt Accessories

		Crew	Daily Output	Labor-Hours	Unit	Material	2017 Bare Costs Labor	Equipment	Total	Total Incl O&P
0010	**ANCHOR BOLT ACCESSORIES**									
0015	For anchor bolts set in fresh concrete, see Section 03 15 19.10									
8150	Anchor bolt sleeve, plastic, 1" diam. bolts	1 Carp	60	.133	Ea.	12.95	4.66		17.61	22
8500	1-1/2" diameter		28	.286		19.20	10		29.20	37.50
8600	2" diameter		24	.333		19.45	11.65		31.10	41
8650	3" diameter	↓	20	.400	↓	35.50	14		49.50	62.50

03 15 19.10 Anchor Bolts

				Crew	Daily Output	Labor-Hours	Unit	Material	2017 Bare Costs Labor	Equipment	Total	Total Incl O&P
0010	**ANCHOR BOLTS**											
0015	Made from recycled materials											
0025	Single bolts installed in fresh concrete, no templates											
0030	Hooked w/nut and washer, 1/2" diameter, 8" long	G	1 Carp	132	.061	Ea.	1.38	2.12		3.50	5.05
0040	12" long	G		131	.061		1.53	2.13		3.66	5.25
0070	3/4" diameter, 8" long	G		127	.063		4.12	2.20		6.32	8.20
0080	12" long	G	↓	125	.064	↓	5.15	2.24		7.39	9.40

03 15 19.30 Inserts

				Crew	Daily Output	Labor-Hours	Unit	Material	2017 Bare Costs Labor	Equipment	Total	Total Incl O&P
0010	**INSERTS**											
1000	Inserts, slotted nut type for 3/4" bolts, 4" long	G	1 Carp	84	.095	Ea.	20	3.33		23.33	28
2100	6" long	G		84	.095		23	3.33		26.33	30.50
2150	8" long	G		84	.095		30.50	3.33		33.83	39
2200	Slotted, strap type, 4" long	G		84	.095		22	3.33		25.33	29.50
2300	8" long	G		84	.095		32.50	3.33		35.83	41.50
9950	For galvanized inserts, add							30%			

03 21 Reinforcement Bars

03 21 11 – Plain Steel Reinforcement Bars

03 21 11.60 Reinforcing In Place		Crew	Daily Output	Labor-Hours	Unit	Material	2017 Bare Costs Labor	Equipment	Total	Total Incl O&P
0010	**REINFORCING IN PLACE**, 50-60 ton lots, A615 Grade 60									
0020	Includes labor, but not material cost, to install accessories									
0030	Made from recycled materials									
0502	Footings, #4 to #7	G	4 Rodm	4200	.008	Lb.	.47	.29		.76	1.01
0550	#8 to #18	G		3.60	8.889	Ton	940	345		1,285	1,600
0602	Slab on grade, #3 to #7	G		4200	.008	Lb.	.47	.29		.76	1.01
0702	Walls, #3 to #7	G		6000	.005	"	.47	.21		.68	.87
0750	#8 to #18	G	↓	4	8	Ton	940	310		1,250	1,550
0900	For other than 50 – 60 ton lots									
1000	Under 10 ton job, #3 to #7, add						25%	10%		
1010	#8 to #18, add						20%	10%		
1050	10 – 50 ton job, #3 to #7, add						10%			
1060	#8 to #18, add						5%			
1100	60 – 100 ton job, #3 to #7, deduct						5%			
1110	#8 to #18, deduct						10%			
1150	Over 100 ton job, #3 to #7, deduct						10%			
1160	#8 to #18, deduct						15%			
2400	Dowels, 2 feet long, deformed, #3	G	2 Rodm	520	.031	Ea.	.39	1.19		1.58	2.42
2410	#4	G		480	.033		.69	1.28		1.97	2.92
2420	#5	G		435	.037		1.08	1.42		2.50	3.57
2430	#6	G	↓	360	.044	↓	1.55	1.71		3.26	4.59
2600	Dowel sleeves for CIP concrete, 2-part system									
2610	Sleeve base, plastic, for 5/8" smooth dowel sleeve, fasten to edge form		1 Rodm	200	.040	Ea.	.53	1.54		2.07	3.17
2615	Sleeve, plastic, 12" long, for 5/8" smooth dowel, snap onto base			400	.020		1.33	.77		2.10	2.76
2620	Sleeve base, for 3/4" smooth dowel sleeve			175	.046		.53	1.76		2.29	3.54
2625	Sleeve, 12" long, for 3/4" smooth dowel			350	.023		1.21	.88		2.09	2.81
2630	Sleeve base, for 1" smooth dowel sleeve			150	.053		.68	2.06		2.74	4.21
2635	Sleeve, 12" long, for 1" smooth dowel		↓	300	.027		1.42	1.03		2.45	3.29
2700	Dowel caps, visual warning only, plastic, #3 to #8		2 Rodm	800	.020		.29	.77		1.06	1.62
2720	#8 to #18			750	.021		.74	.82		1.56	2.20
2750	Impalement protective, plastic, #4 to #9		↓	800	.020	↓	1.62	.77		2.39	3.08

03 22 Fabric and Grid Reinforcing

03 22 11 – Plain Welded Wire Fabric Reinforcing

03 22 11.10 Welded Wire Fabric

		Crew	Daily Output	Labor-Hours	Unit	Material	2017 Bare Costs Labor	Equipment	Total	Total Incl O&P
0011	**WELDED WIRE FABRIC**, 6 x 6 - W1.4 x W1.4 (10 x 10)	G	2 Rodm	3500	.005	S.F.	.14	.18		.32	.46
0301	6 x 6 - W2.9 x W2.9 (6 x 6) 42 lb. per C.S.F.	G		2900	.006		.24	.21		.45	.63
0501	4 x 4 - W1.4 x W1.4 (10 x 10) 31 lb. per C.S.F.	G	↓	3100	.005	↓	.22	.20		.42	.57
0750	Rolls									
0901	2 x 2 - #12 galv. for gunite reinforcing	G	2 Rodm	650	.025	S.F.	.67	.95		1.62	2.34

03 22 13 – Galvanized Welded Wire Fabric Reinforcing

03 22 13.10 Galvanized Welded Wire Fabric

		Crew	Daily Output	Labor-Hours	Unit	Material	2017 Bare Costs Labor	Equipment	Total	Total Incl O&P
0010	**GALVANIZED WELDED WIRE FABRIC**									
0100	Add to plain welded wire pricing for galvanized welded wire					Lb.	.23			.23	.25

03 22 16 – Epoxy-Coated Welded Wire Fabric Reinforcing

03 22 16.10 Epoxy-Coated Welded Wire Fabric

		Crew	Daily Output	Labor-Hours	Unit	Material	2017 Bare Costs Labor	Equipment	Total	Total Incl O&P
0010	**EPOXY-COATED WELDED WIRE FABRIC**									
0100	Add to plain welded wire pricing for epoxy-coated welded wire					Lb.	.39			.39	.42

03 23 05 – Prestressing Tendons

03 23 05.50 Prestressing Steel

		Crew	Daily Output	Labor-Hours	Unit	Material	2017 Bare Costs Labor	2017 Bare Costs Equipment	Total	Total Incl O&P
0010	**PRESTRESSING STEEL**									
3000	Slabs on grade, 0.5-inch diam. non-bonded strands, HDPE sheathed,									
3050	attached dead-end anchors, loose stressing-end anchors									
3100	25' x 30' slab, strands @ 36" O.C., placing	2 Rodm	2940	.005	S.F.	.63	.21		.84	1.04
3105	Stressing	C-4A	3750	.004			.16	.01	.17	.29
3110	42" O.C., placing	2 Rodm	3200	.005		.56	.19		.75	.93
3115	Stressing	C-4A	4040	.004			.15	.01	.16	.27
3120	48" O.C., placing	2 Rodm	3510	.005		.49	.18		.67	.83
3125	Stressing	C-4A	4390	.004			.14	.01	.15	.25
3150	25' x 40' slab, strands @ 36" O.C., placing	2 Rodm	3370	.005		.61	.18		.79	.98
3155	Stressing	C-4A	4360	.004			.14	.01	.15	.25
3160	42" O.C., placing	2 Rodm	3760	.004		.52	.16		.68	.86
3165	Stressing	C-4A	4820	.003			.13	.01	.14	.23
3170	48" O.C., placing	2 Rodm	4090	.004		.47	.15		.62	.76
3175	Stressing	C-4A	5190	.003			.12	.01	.13	.21
3200	30' x 30' slab, strands @ 36" O.C., placing	2 Rodm	3260	.005		.60	.19		.79	.98
3205	Stressing	C-4A	4190	.004			.15	.01	.16	.26
3210	42" O.C., placing	2 Rodm	3530	.005		.54	.17		.71	.89
3215	Stressing	C-4A	4500	.004			.14	.01	.15	.24
3220	48" O.C., placing	2 Rodm	3840	.004		.48	.16		.64	.80
3225	Stressing	C-4A	4850	.003			.13	.01	.14	.22
3230	30' x 40' slab, strands @ 36" O.C., placing	2 Rodm	3780	.004		.58	.16		.74	.91
3235	Stressing	C-4A	4920	.003			.13	.01	.14	.22
3240	42" O.C., placing	2 Rodm	4190	.004		.51	.15		.66	.81
3245	Stressing	C-4A	5410	.003			.11	.01	.12	.20
3250	48" O.C., placing	2 Rodm	4520	.004		.46	.14		.60	.74
3255	Stressing	C-4A	5790	.003			.11	.01	.12	.19
3260	30' x 50' slab, strands @ 36" O.C., placing	2 Rodm	4300	.004		.55	.14		.69	.85
3265	Stressing	C-4A	5650	.003			.11	.01	.12	.19
3270	42" O.C., placing	2 Rodm	4720	.003		.49	.13		.62	.76
3275	Stressing	C-4A	6150	.003			.10	.01	.11	.18
3280	48" O.C., placing	2 Rodm	5240	.003		.43	.12		.55	.67
3285	Stressing	C-4A	6760	.002	▼		.09	.01	.10	.16

03 24 Fibrous Reinforcing

03 24 05 – Reinforcing Fibers

03 24 05.30 Synthetic Fibers

		Crew	Daily Output	Labor-Hours	Unit	Material	Labor	Equipment	Total	Total Incl O&P
0010	**SYNTHETIC FIBERS**									
0100	Synthetic fibers, add to concrete				Lb.	4.40			4.40	4.84
0110	1-1/2 lb. per C.Y.				C.Y.	6.80			6.80	7.50

03 24 05.70 Steel Fibers

			Crew	Daily Output	Labor-Hours	Unit	Material	Labor	Equipment	Total	Total Incl O&P
0010	**STEEL FIBERS**										
0140	ASTM A850, Type V, continuously deformed, 1-1/2" long x 0.045" diam.										
0150	Add to price of ready mix concrete	G				Lb.	1.13			1.13	1.24
0205	Alternate pricing, dosing at 5 lb. per C.Y., add to price of RMC	G				C.Y.	5.65			5.65	6.20
0210	10 lb. per C.Y.	G					11.30			11.30	12.45
0215	15 lb. per C.Y.	G					16.95			16.95	18.65
0220	20 lb. per C.Y.	G					22.50			22.50	25
0225	25 lb. per C.Y.	G					28.50			28.50	31
0230	30 lb. per C.Y.	G					34			34	37.50
0235	35 lb. per C.Y.	G					39.50			39.50	43.50

For customer support on your Residential Costs with RSMeans Data, call 800.448.8182.

313

03 24 Fibrous Reinforcing

03 24 05 – Reinforcing Fibers

03 24 05.70 Steel Fibers		Crew	Daily Output	Labor-Hours	Unit	Material	2017 Bare Costs Labor	Equipment	Total	Total Incl O&P
0240	40 lb. per C.Y.	G			C.Y.	45			45	49.50
0250	50 lb. per C.Y.	G				56.50			56.50	62
0275	75 lb. per C.Y.	G				85			85	93
0300	100 lb. per C.Y.	G				113			113	124

03 30 Cast-In-Place Concrete

03 30 53 – Miscellaneous Cast-In-Place Concrete

03 30 53.40 Concrete In Place

		Crew	Daily Output	Labor-Hours	Unit	Material	2017 Bare Costs Labor	Equipment	Total	Total Incl O&P
0010	**CONCRETE IN PLACE**									
0020	Including forms (4 uses), Grade 60 rebar, concrete (Portland cement									
0050	Type I), placement and finishing unless otherwise indicated									
0500	Chimney foundations (5000 psi), over 5 C.Y.	C-14C	32.22	3.476	C.Y.	167	115	.87	282.87	380
0510	(3500 psi), under 5 C.Y.	"	23.71	4.724	"	193	157	1.18	351.18	475
3540	Equipment pad (3000 psi), 3' x 3' x 6" thick	C-14H	45	1.067	Ea.	49	36.50	.63	86.13	116
3550	4' x 4' x 6" thick		30	1.600		73.50	55	.94	129.44	174
3560	5' x 5' x 8" thick		18	2.667		131	92	1.57	224.57	299
3570	6' x 6' x 8" thick		14	3.429		177	118	2.02	297.02	395
3580	8' x 8' x 10" thick		8	6		380	207	3.54	590.54	770
3590	10' x 10' x 12" thick		5	9.600		655	330	5.65	990.65	1,275
3800	Footings (3000 psi), spread under 1 C.Y.	C-14C	28	4	C.Y.	181	133	1	315	425
3825	1 C.Y. to 5 C.Y.		43	2.605		218	86.50	.65	305.15	385
3850	Over 5 C.Y.		75	1.493		201	49.50	.37	250.87	305
3900	Footings, strip (3000 psi), 18" x 9", unreinforced	C-14L	40	2.400		143	77.50	.70	221.20	287
3920	18" x 9", reinforced	C-14C	35	3.200		165	106	.80	271.80	360
3925	20" x 10", unreinforced	C-14L	45	2.133		139	69	.62	208.62	269
3930	20" x 10", reinforced	C-14C	40	2.800		157	93	.70	250.70	330
3935	24" x 12", unreinforced	C-14L	55	1.745		137	56.50	.51	194.01	246
3940	24" x 12", reinforced	C-14C	48	2.333		156	77.50	.58	234.08	300
3945	36" x 12", unreinforced	C-14L	70	1.371		133	44.50	.40	177.90	220
3950	36" x 12", reinforced	C-14C	60	1.867		150	62	.47	212.47	270
4000	Foundation mat (3000 psi), under 10 C.Y.		38.67	2.896		218	96	.72	314.72	400
4050	Over 20 C.Y.		56.40	1.986		193	66	.50	259.50	325
4520	Handicap access ramp (4000 psi), railing both sides, 3' wide	C-14H	14.58	3.292	L.F.	330	113	1.94	444.94	555
4525	5' wide		12.22	3.928		340	135	2.32	477.32	605
4530	With 6" curb and rails both sides, 3' wide		8.55	5.614		340	193	3.31	536.31	700
4535	5' wide		7.31	6.566		345	226	3.87	574.87	760
4650	Slab on grade (3500 psi), not including finish, 4" thick	C-14E	60.75	1.449	C.Y.	142	49.50	.46	191.96	239
4700	6" thick	"	92	.957	"	137	32.50	.31	169.81	206
4701	Thickened slab edge (3500 psi), for slab on grade poured									
4702	monolithically with slab; depth is in addition to slab thickness;									
4703	formed vertical outside edge, earthen bottom and inside slope									
4705	8" deep x 8" wide bottom, unreinforced	C-14L	2190	.044	L.F.	3.85	1.42	.01	5.28	6.60
4710	8" x 8", reinforced	C-14C	1670	.067		6.05	2.23	.02	8.30	10.40
4715	12" deep x 12" wide bottom, unreinforced	C-14L	1800	.053		7.90	1.72	.02	9.64	11.60
4720	12" x 12", reinforced	C-14C	1310	.086		11.95	2.84	.02	14.81	17.90
4725	16" deep x 16" wide bottom, unreinforced	C-14L	1440	.067		13.45	2.15	.02	15.62	18.40
4730	16" x 16", reinforced	C-14C	1120	.100		18.25	3.32	.03	21.60	25.50
4735	20" deep x 20" wide bottom, unreinforced	C-14L	1150	.083		20.50	2.70	.02	23.22	27
4740	20" x 20", reinforced	C-14C	920	.122		26.50	4.04	.03	30.57	36
4745	24" deep x 24" wide bottom, unreinforced	C-14L	930	.103		29	3.34	.03	32.37	37.50
4750	24" x 24", reinforced	C-14C	740	.151		37	5	.04	42.04	49

03 30 Cast-In-Place Concrete

03 30 53 – Miscellaneous Cast-In-Place Concrete

03 30 53.40 Concrete In Place

		Crew	Daily Output	Labor-Hours	Unit	Material	2017 Bare Costs Labor	Equipment	Total	Total Incl O&P
4751	Slab on grade (3500 psi), incl. troweled finish, not incl. forms									
4760	or reinforcing, over 10,000 S.F., 4" thick	C-14F	3425	.021	S.F.	1.58	.68	.01	2.27	2.85
4820	6" thick	"	3350	.021	"	2.30	.69	.01	3	3.67
5000	Slab on grade (3000 psi), incl. broom finish, not incl. forms									
5001	or reinforcing, 4" thick	C-14G	2873	.019	S.F.	1.53	.61	.01	2.15	2.71
5010	6" thick		2590	.022		2.40	.68	.01	3.09	3.77
5020	8" thick		2320	.024		3.13	.76	.01	3.90	4.70
6800	Stairs (3500 psi), not including safety treads, free standing, 3'-6" wide	C-14H	83	.578	LF Nose	6	19.90	.34	26.24	40
6850	Cast on ground		125	.384	"	5.05	13.25	.23	18.53	28
7000	Stair landings, free standing		200	.240	S.F.	4.82	8.25	.14	13.21	19.25
7050	Cast on ground		475	.101	"	3.85	3.48	.06	7.39	10.10

03 31 Structural Concrete

03 31 13 – Heavyweight Structural Concrete

03 31 13.25 Concrete, Hand Mix

		Crew	Daily Output	Labor-Hours	Unit	Material	2017 Bare Costs Labor	Equipment	Total	Total Incl O&P
0010	**CONCRETE, HAND MIX** for small quantities or remote areas									
0050	Includes bulk local aggregate, bulk sand, bagged Portland									
0060	cement (Type I) and water, using gas powered cement mixer									
0125	2500 psi	C-30	135	.059	C.F.	3.69	1.58	1.22	6.49	8.05
0130	3000 psi		135	.059		3.96	1.58	1.22	6.76	8.35
0135	3500 psi		135	.059		4.11	1.58	1.22	6.91	8.50
0140	4000 psi		135	.059		4.30	1.58	1.22	7.10	8.70
0145	4500 psi		135	.059		4.50	1.58	1.22	7.30	8.95
0150	5000 psi		135	.059		4.80	1.58	1.22	7.60	9.30
0300	Using pre-bagged dry mix and wheelbarrow (80-lb. bag = 0.6 C.F.)									
0340	4000 psi	1 Clab	48	.167	C.F.	6.50	4.43		10.93	14.55

03 31 13.30 Concrete, Volumetric Site-Mixed

		Crew	Daily Output	Labor-Hours	Unit	Material	2017 Bare Costs Labor	Equipment	Total	Total Incl O&P
0010	**CONCRETE, VOLUMETRIC SITE-MIXED**									
0015	Mixed on-site in volumetric truck									
0020	Includes local aggregate, sand, Portland cement (Type I) and water									
0025	Excludes all additives and treatments									
0100	3000 psi, 1 C.Y. mixed and discharged				C.Y.	194			194	214
0110	2 C.Y.					148			148	163
0120	3 C.Y.					132			132	145
0130	4 C.Y.					119			119	131
0140	5 C.Y.					111			111	122
0200	For truck holding/waiting time past first 2 on-site hours, add				Hr.	88			88	97
0210	For trip charge beyond first 20 miles, each way, add				Mile	3.50			3.50	3.85
0220	For each additional increase of 500 psi, add				Ea.	4.17			4.17	4.59

03 31 13.35 Heavyweight Concrete, Ready Mix

		Crew	Daily Output	Labor-Hours	Unit	Material	2017 Bare Costs Labor	Equipment	Total	Total Incl O&P
0010	**HEAVYWEIGHT CONCRETE, READY MIX**, delivered									
0012	Includes local aggregate, sand, Portland cement (Type I) and water									
0015	Excludes all additives and treatments									
0020	2000 psi				C.Y.	112			112	124
0100	2500 psi					116			116	127
0150	3000 psi					118			118	130
0200	3500 psi					121			121	133
0300	4000 psi					125			125	137
0350	4500 psi					128			128	141
0400	5000 psi					131			131	144

03 31 Structural Concrete

03 31 13 – Heavyweight Structural Concrete

03 31 13.35 Heavyweight Concrete, Ready Mix

		Crew	Daily Output	Labor-Hours	Unit	Material	2017 Bare Costs Labor	2017 Bare Costs Equipment	Total	Total Incl O&P
0411	6000 psi				C.Y.	135			135	148
0412	8000 psi					142			142	156
0413	10,000 psi					149			149	164
0414	12,000 psi					156			156	172
1000	For high early strength (Portland cement Type III), add					10%				
1300	For winter concrete (hot water), add					4.45			4.45	4.90
1410	For mid-range water reducer, add					3.33			3.33	3.66
1420	For high-range water reducer/superplasticizer, add					6			6	6.60
1430	For retarder, add					3.23			3.23	3.55
1440	For non-Chloride accelerator, add					5.70			5.70	6.25
1450	For Chloride accelerator, per 1%, add					3			3	3.30
1460	For fiber reinforcing, synthetic (1 lb./C.Y.), add					6.70			6.70	7.35
1500	For Saturday delivery, add					8.50			8.50	9.35
1510	For truck holding/waiting time past 1st hour per load, add				Hr.	96.50			96.50	106
1520	For short load (less than 4 C.Y.), add per load				Ea.	74.50			74.50	82
2000	For all lightweight aggregate, add				C.Y.	45%				

03 31 13.70 Placing Concrete

		Crew	Daily Output	Labor-Hours	Unit	Material	2017 Bare Costs Labor	2017 Bare Costs Equipment	Total	Total Incl O&P
0010	**PLACING CONCRETE**									
0020	Includes labor and equipment to place, level (strike off) and consolidate									
1900	Footings, continuous, shallow, direct chute	C-6	120	.400	C.Y.		11.30	.47	11.77	19.30
1950	Pumped	C-20	150	.427			12.40	5.75	18.15	27
2000	With crane and bucket	C-7	90	.800			23.50	12.85	36.35	53
2400	Footings, spread, under 1 C.Y., direct chute	C-6	55	.873			24.50	1.03	25.53	42
2600	Over 5 C.Y., direct chute		120	.400			11.30	.47	11.77	19.30
2900	Foundation mats, over 20 C.Y., direct chute		350	.137			3.88	.16	4.04	6.65
4300	Slab on grade, up to 6" thick, direct chute		110	.436			12.35	.51	12.86	21
4350	Pumped	C-20	130	.492			14.30	6.65	20.95	31.50
4400	With crane and bucket	C-7	110	.655			19.30	10.50	29.80	43.50
4900	Walls, 8" thick, direct chute	C-6	90	.533			15.10	.63	15.73	25.50
4950	Pumped	C-20	100	.640			18.60	8.65	27.25	40.50
5000	With crane and bucket	C-7	80	.900			26.50	14.45	40.95	60
5050	12" thick, direct chute	C-6	100	.480			13.55	.57	14.12	23
5100	Pumped	C-20	110	.582			16.90	7.85	24.75	36.50
5200	With crane and bucket	C-7	90	.800			23.50	12.85	36.35	53
5600	Wheeled concrete dumping, add to placing costs above									
5610	Walking cart, 50' haul, add	C-18	32	.281	C.Y.		7.55	1.81	9.36	14.60
5620	150' haul, add		24	.375			10.05	2.42	12.47	19.50
5700	250' haul, add		18	.500			13.40	3.22	16.62	26
5800	Riding cart, 50' haul, add	C-19	80	.113			3.02	1.21	4.23	6.40
5810	150' haul, add		60	.150			4.02	1.61	5.63	8.50
5900	250' haul, add		45	.200			5.35	2.15	7.50	11.30

03 35 Concrete Finishing

03 35 13 – High-Tolerance Concrete Floor Finishing

03 35 13.30 Finishing Floors, High Tolerance	Crew	Daily Output	Labor-Hours	Unit	Material	2017 Bare Costs Labor	Equipment	Total	Total Incl O&P
0010 **FINISHING FLOORS, HIGH TOLERANCE**									
0012 Finishing of fresh concrete flatwork requires that concrete									
0013 first be placed, struck off & consolidated									
0015 Basic finishing for various unspecified flatwork									
0100 Bull float only	C-10	4000	.006	S.F.		.19		.19	.31
0125 Bull float & manual float		2000	.012			.38		.38	.63
0150 Bull float, manual float, & broom finish, w/edging & joints		1850	.013			.41		.41	.68
0200 Bull float, manual float & manual steel trowel	▼	1265	.019	▼		.61		.61	.99
0210 For specified Random Access Floors in ACI Classes 1, 2, 3 and 4 to achieve									
0215 Composite Overall Floor Flatness and Levelness values up to FF35/FL25									
0250 Bull float, machine float & machine trowel (walk-behind)	C-10C	1715	.014	S.F.		.45	.03	.48	.76
0300 Power screed, bull float, machine float & trowel (walk-behind)	C-10D	2400	.010			.32	.05	.37	.57
0350 Power screed, bull float, machine float & trowel (ride-on)	C-10E	4000	.006	▼		.19	.06	.25	.38

03 35 23 – Exposed Aggregate Concrete Finishing

03 35 23.30 Finishing Floors, Exposed Aggregate	Crew	Daily Output	Labor-Hours	Unit	Material	2017 Bare Costs Labor	Equipment	Total	Total Incl O&P
0010 **FINISHING FLOORS, EXPOSED AGGREGATE**									
1600 Exposed local aggregate finish, seeded on fresh concrete, 3 lb. per S.F.	1 Cefi	625	.013	S.F.	.20	.44		.64	.94
1650 4 lb. per S.F.	"	465	.017	"	.33	.60		.93	1.34

03 35 29 – Tooled Concrete Finishing

03 35 29.30 Finishing Floors, Tooled	Crew	Daily Output	Labor-Hours	Unit	Material	2017 Bare Costs Labor	Equipment	Total	Total Incl O&P
0010 **FINISHING FLOORS, TOOLED**									
4400 Stair finish, fresh concrete, float finish	1 Cefi	275	.029	S.F.		1.01		1.01	1.64
4500 Steel trowel finish	"	200	.040	"		1.39		1.39	2.26

03 35 29.60 Finishing Walls	Crew	Daily Output	Labor-Hours	Unit	Material	2017 Bare Costs Labor	Equipment	Total	Total Incl O&P
0010 **FINISHING WALLS**									
0020 Break ties and patch voids	1 Cefi	540	.015	S.F.	.04	.51		.55	.89
0050 Burlap rub with grout	"	450	.018		.04	.62		.66	1.05
0300 Bush hammer, green concrete	B-39	1000	.048			1.29	.21	1.50	2.39
0350 Cured concrete	"	650	.074			1.99	.33	2.32	3.69
0500 Acid etch	1 Cefi	575	.014	▼	.14	.48		.62	.93
0850 Grind form fins flush	1 Clab	700	.011	L.F.		.30		.30	.51

03 35 33 – Stamped Concrete Finishing

03 35 33.50 Slab Texture Stamping	Crew	Daily Output	Labor-Hours	Unit	Material	2017 Bare Costs Labor	Equipment	Total	Total Incl O&P
0010 **SLAB TEXTURE STAMPING**									
0050 Stamping requires that concrete first be placed, struck off, consolidated,									
0060 bull floated and free of bleed water. Decorative stamping tasks include:									
0100 Step 1 - first application of dry shake colored hardener	1 Cefi	6400	.001	S.F.	.43	.04		.47	.54
0110 Step 2 - bull float		6400	.001			.04		.04	.07
0130 Step 3 - second application of dry shake colored hardener	▼	6400	.001		.21	.04		.25	.30
0140 Step 4 - bull float, manual float & steel trowel	3 Cefi	1280	.019			.65		.65	1.06
0150 Step 5 - application of dry shake colored release agent	1 Cefi	6400	.001		.10	.04		.14	.18
0160 Step 6 - place, tamp & remove mats	3 Cefi	2400	.010		.88	.35		1.23	1.53
0170 Step 7 - touch up edges, mat joints & simulated grout lines	1 Cefi	1280	.006			.22		.22	.35
0300 Alternate stamping estimating method includes all tasks above	4 Cefi	800	.040		1.62	1.39		3.01	4.04
0400 Step 8 - pressure wash @ 3000 psi after 24 hours	1 Cefi	1600	.005			.17		.17	.28
0500 Step 9 - roll 2 coats cure/seal compound when dry	"	800	.010	▼	.63	.35		.98	1.25

03 39 Concrete Curing

03 39 13 – Water Concrete Curing

03 39 13.50 Water Curing	Crew	Daily Output	Labor-Hours	Unit	Material	2017 Bare Costs Labor	Equipment	Total	Total Incl O&P
0011 **WATER CURING**									
0020 With burlap, 4 uses assumed, 7.5 oz.	2 Clab	5500	.003	S.F.	.15	.08		.23	.29
0101 10 oz.	"	5500	.003	"	.27	.08		.35	.42

03 39 23 – Membrane Concrete Curing

03 39 23.13 Chemical Compound Membrane Concrete Curing

	Crew	Daily Output	Labor-Hours	Unit	Material	Labor	Equipment	Total	Total Incl O&P
0010 **CHEMICAL COMPOUND MEMBRANE CONCRETE CURING**									
0301 Sprayed membrane curing compound	2 Clab	9500	.002	S.F.	.13	.04		.17	.21

03 39 23.23 Sheet Membrane Concrete Curing

	Crew	Daily Output	Labor-Hours	Unit	Material	Labor	Equipment	Total	Total Incl O&P
0010 **SHEET MEMBRANE CONCRETE CURING**									
0201 Curing blanket, burlap/poly, 2-ply	2 Clab	7000	.002	S.F.	.27	.06		.33	.39

03 41 Precast Structural Concrete

03 41 23 – Precast Concrete Stairs

03 41 23.50 Precast Stairs

	Crew	Daily Output	Labor-Hours	Unit	Material	Labor	Equipment	Total	Total Incl O&P
0010 **PRECAST STAIRS**									
0020 Precast concrete treads on steel stringers, 3' wide	C-12	75	.640	Riser	151	22	7.65	180.65	211
0300 Front entrance, 5' wide with 48" platform, 2 risers		16	3	Flight	575	103	36	714	840
0350 5 risers		12	4		910	137	47.50	1,094.50	1,275
0500 6' wide, 2 risers		15	3.200		635	110	38	783	925
0550 5 risers		11	4.364		1,000	150	52	1,202	1,400
0700 7' wide, 2 risers		14	3.429		810	118	41	969	1,125
1200 Basement entrance stairwell, 6 steps, incl. steel bulkhead door	B-51	22	2.182		1,700	60.50	9.90	1,770.40	1,975
1250 14 steps	"	11	4.364		2,850	121	19.75	2,990.75	3,350

03 48 Precast Concrete Specialties

03 48 43 – Precast Concrete Trim

03 48 43.40 Precast Lintels

	Crew	Daily Output	Labor-Hours	Unit	Material	Labor	Equipment	Total	Total Incl O&P
0010 **PRECAST LINTELS**, smooth gray, prestressed, stock units only									
0800 4" wide, 8" high, x 4' long	D-10	28	1.143	Ea.	30	39.50	15.55	85.05	116
0850 8' long		24	1.333		75	46	18.15	139.15	179
1000 6" wide, 8" high, x 4' long		26	1.231		44	42.50	16.75	103.25	138
1050 10' long		22	1.455		110	50	19.80	179.80	227

03 48 43.90 Precast Window Sills

	Crew	Daily Output	Labor-Hours	Unit	Material	Labor	Equipment	Total	Total Incl O&P
0010 **PRECAST WINDOW SILLS**									
0600 Precast concrete, 4" tapers to 3", 9" wide	D-1	70	.229	L.F.	17.40	7.25		24.65	31.50
0650 11" wide	"	60	.267	"	28.50	8.45		36.95	45

03 54 Cast Underlayment

03 54 13 – Gypsum Cement Underlayment

03 54 13.50 Poured Gypsum Underlayment		Crew	Daily Output	Labor-Hours	Unit	Material	2017 Bare Costs Labor	Equipment	Total	Total Incl O&P
0010	**POURED GYPSUM UNDERLAYMENT**									
0400	Underlayment, gypsum based, self-leveling 2500 psi, pumped, 1/2" thick	C-8	24000	.002	S.F.	.38	.07	.03	.48	.58
0500	3/4" thick		20000	.003		.57	.09	.04	.70	.81
0600	1" thick		16000	.004		.76	.11	.05	.92	1.07
1400	Hand placed, 1/2" thick	C-18	450	.020		.38	.54	.13	1.05	1.46
1500	3/4" thick	"	300	.030		.57	.80	.19	1.56	2.19

03 63 Epoxy Grouting

03 63 05 – Grouting of Dowels and Fasteners

03 63 05.10 Epoxy Only

		Crew	Daily Output	Labor-Hours	Unit	Material	2017 Bare Costs Labor	Equipment	Total	Total Incl O&P
0010	**EPOXY ONLY**									
1500	Chemical anchoring, epoxy cartridge, excludes layout, drilling, fastener									
1530	For fastener 3/4" diam. x 6" embedment	2 Skwk	72	.222	Ea.	5.15	7.95		13.10	19
1535	1" diam. x 8" embedment		66	.242		7.75	8.65		16.40	23
1540	1-1/4" diam. x 10" embedment		60	.267		15.45	9.55		25	33
1545	1-3/4" diam. x 12" embedment		54	.296		26	10.60		36.60	46.50
1550	14" embedment		48	.333		31	11.90		42.90	54
1555	2" diam. x 12" embedment		42	.381		41	13.60		54.60	68.50
1560	18" embedment		32	.500		51.50	17.90		69.40	86.50

03 82 Concrete Boring

03 82 16 – Concrete Drilling

03 82 16.10 Concrete Impact Drilling

		Crew	Daily Output	Labor-Hours	Unit	Material	2017 Bare Costs Labor	Equipment	Total	Total Incl O&P
0010	**CONCRETE IMPACT DRILLING**									
0020	Includes bit cost, layout and set-up time, no anchors									
0050	Up to 4" deep in concrete/brick floors/walls									
0100	Holes, 1/4" diameter	1 Carp	75	.107	Ea.	.07	3.73		3.80	6.35
0150	For each additional inch of depth in same hole, add		430	.019		.02	.65		.67	1.11
0200	3/8" diameter		63	.127		.06	4.44		4.50	7.45
0250	For each additional inch of depth in same hole, add		340	.024		.01	.82		.83	1.40
0300	1/2" diameter		50	.160		.06	5.60		5.66	9.40
0350	For each additional inch of depth in same hole, add		250	.032		.02	1.12		1.14	1.89
0400	5/8" diameter		48	.167		.10	5.85		5.95	9.85
0450	For each additional inch of depth in same hole, add		240	.033		.03	1.16		1.19	1.98
0500	3/4" diameter		45	.178		.13	6.20		6.33	10.55
0550	For each additional inch of depth in same hole, add		220	.036		.03	1.27		1.30	2.17
0600	7/8" diameter		43	.186		.18	6.50		6.68	11.05
0650	For each additional inch of depth in same hole, add		210	.038		.04	1.33		1.37	2.28
0700	1" diameter		40	.200		.16	7		7.16	11.85
0750	For each additional inch of depth in same hole, add		190	.042		.04	1.47		1.51	2.50
0800	1-1/4" diameter		38	.211		.29	7.35		7.64	12.60
0850	For each additional inch of depth in same hole, add		180	.044		.07	1.55		1.62	2.68
0900	1-1/2" diameter		35	.229		.44	8		8.44	13.85
0950	For each additional inch of depth in same hole, add		165	.048		.11	1.69		1.80	2.95
1000	For ceiling installations, add						40%			

Division Notes

	CREW	DAILY OUTPUT	LABOR-HOURS	UNIT	BARE COSTS				TOTAL INCL O&P
					MAT.	LABOR	EQUIP.	TOTAL	

Estimating Tips
04 05 00 Common Work Results for Masonry

- The terms mortar and grout are often used interchangeably—and incorrectly. Mortar is used to bed masonry units, seal the entry of air and moisture, provide architectural appearance, and allow for size variations in the units. Grout is used primarily in reinforced masonry construction and to bond the masonry to the reinforcing steel. Common mortar types are M (2500 psi), S (1800 psi), N (750 psi), and O (350 psi), and they conform to ASTM C270. Grout is either fine or coarse and conforms to ASTM C476, and in-place strengths generally exceed 2500 psi. Mortar and grout are different components of masonry construction and are placed by entirely different methods. An estimator should be aware of their unique uses and costs.

- Mortar is included in all assembled masonry line items. The mortar cost, part of the assembled masonry material cost, includes all ingredients, all labor, and all equipment required. Please see reference number R040513-10.

- Waste, specifically the loss/droppings of mortar and the breakage of brick and block, is included in all unit cost lines that include mortar and masonry units in this division. A factor of 25% is added for mortar and 3% for brick and concrete masonry units.

- Scaffolding or staging is not included in any of the Division 4 costs. Refer to Subdivision 01 54 23 for scaffolding and staging costs.

04 20 00 Unit Masonry

- The most common types of unit masonry are brick and concrete masonry. The major classifications of brick are building brick (ASTM C62), facing brick (ASTM C216), glazed brick, fire brick, and pavers. Many varieties of texture and appearance can exist within these classifications, and the estimator would be wise to check local custom and availability within the project area. For repair and remodeling jobs, matching the existing brick may be the most important criteria.

- Brick and concrete block are priced by the piece and then converted into a price per square foot of wall. Openings less than two square feet are generally ignored by the estimator because any savings in units used are offset by the cutting and trimming required.

- It is often difficult and expensive to find and purchase small lots of historic brick. Costs can vary widely. Many design issues affect costs, selection of mortar mix, and repairs or replacement of masonry materials. Cleaning techniques must be reflected in the estimate.

- All masonry walls, whether interior or exterior, require bracing. The cost of bracing walls during construction should be included by the estimator, and this bracing must remain in place until permanent bracing is complete. Permanent bracing of masonry walls is accomplished by masonry itself, in the form of pilasters or abutting wall corners, or by anchoring the walls to the structural frame. Accessories in the form of anchors, anchor slots, and ties are used, but their supply and installation can be by different trades. For instance, anchor slots on spandrel beams and columns are supplied and welded in place by the steel fabricator, but the ties from the slots into the masonry are installed by the bricklayer. Regardless of the installation method, the estimator must be certain that these accessories are accounted for in pricing.

Reference Numbers

Reference numbers are shown at the beginning of some major classifications. These numbers refer to related items in the Reference Section. The reference information may be an estimating procedure, an alternate pricing method, or technical information.

Note: Not all subdivisions listed here necessarily appear. ∎

04 01 Maintenance of Masonry

04 01 20 – Maintenance of Unit Masonry

04 01 20.20 Pointing Masonry

		Crew	Daily Output	Labor-Hours	Unit	Material	2017 Bare Costs Labor	Equipment	Total	Total Incl O&P
0010	**POINTING MASONRY**									
0300	Cut and repoint brick, hard mortar, running bond	1 Bric	80	.100	S.F.	.56	3.49		4.05	6.45
0320	Common bond		77	.104		.56	3.62		4.18	6.70
0360	Flemish bond		70	.114		.59	3.98		4.57	7.35
0400	English bond		65	.123		.59	4.29		4.88	7.85
0600	Soft old mortar, running bond		100	.080		.56	2.79		3.35	5.30
0620	Common bond		96	.083		.56	2.90		3.46	5.50
0640	Flemish bond		90	.089		.59	3.10		3.69	5.85
0680	English bond		82	.098		.59	3.40		3.99	6.35
0700	Stonework, hard mortar		140	.057	L.F.	.75	1.99		2.74	4.16
0720	Soft old mortar		160	.050	"	.75	1.74		2.49	3.75
1000	Repoint, mask and grout method, running bond		95	.084	S.F.	.75	2.93		3.68	5.75
1020	Common bond		90	.089		.75	3.10		3.85	6
1040	Flemish bond		86	.093		.79	3.24		4.03	6.30
1060	English bond		77	.104		.79	3.62		4.41	6.95
2000	Scrub coat, sand grout on walls, thin mix, brushed		120	.067		3.27	2.32		5.59	7.50
2020	Troweled		98	.082		4.56	2.84		7.40	9.80

04 01 20.30 Pointing CMU

		Crew	Daily Output	Labor-Hours	Unit	Material	2017 Bare Costs Labor	Equipment	Total	Total Incl O&P
0010	**POINTING CMU**									
0300	Cut and repoint block, hard mortar, running bond	1 Bric	190	.042	S.F.	.23	1.47		1.70	2.71
0310	Stacked bond		200	.040		.23	1.39		1.62	2.59
0600	Soft old mortar, running bond		230	.035		.23	1.21		1.44	2.28
0610	Stacked bond		245	.033		.23	1.14		1.37	2.16

04 01 30 – Unit Masonry Cleaning

04 01 30.60 Brick Washing

			Crew	Daily Output	Labor-Hours	Unit	Material	2017 Bare Costs Labor	Equipment	Total	Total Incl O&P
0010	**BRICK WASHING**	R040130-10									
0012	Acid cleanser, smooth brick surface		1 Bric	560	.014	S.F.	.05	.50		.55	.89
0050	Rough brick			400	.020		.06	.70		.76	1.24
0060	Stone, acid wash			600	.013		.08	.46		.54	.87
1000	Muriatic acid, price per gallon in 5 gallon lots					Gal.	9.70			9.70	10.70

04 05 Common Work Results for Masonry

04 05 05 – Selective Demolition for Masonry

04 05 05.10 Selective Demolition

			Crew	Daily Output	Labor-Hours	Unit	Material	2017 Bare Costs Labor	Equipment	Total	Total Incl O&P
0010	**SELECTIVE DEMOLITION**	R024119-10									
0200	Bond beams, 8" block with #4 bar		2 Clab	32	.500	L.F.		13.30		13.30	22.50
0300	Concrete block walls, unreinforced, 2" thick			1200	.013	S.F.		.35		.35	.59
0310	4" thick			1150	.014			.37		.37	.62
0320	6" thick			1100	.015			.39		.39	.65
0330	8" thick			1050	.015			.41		.41	.68
0340	10" thick			1000	.016			.43		.43	.71
0360	12" thick			950	.017			.45		.45	.75
0380	Reinforced alternate courses, 2" thick			1130	.014			.38		.38	.63
0390	4" thick			1080	.015			.39		.39	.66
0400	6" thick			1035	.015			.41		.41	.69
0410	8" thick			990	.016			.43		.43	.72
0420	10" thick			940	.017			.45		.45	.76
0430	12" thick			890	.018			.48		.48	.80
0440	Reinforced alternate courses & vertically 48" OC, 4" thick			900	.018			.47		.47	.79
0450	6" thick			850	.019			.50		.50	.84

04 05 Common Work Results for Masonry

04 05 05 – Selective Demolition for Masonry

04 05 05.10 Selective Demolition	Crew	Daily Output	Labor-Hours	Unit	Material	2017 Bare Costs Labor	Equipment	Total	Total Incl O&P
0460	8" thick	2 Clab	800	.020	S.F.		.53		.53	.89
0480	10" thick		750	.021			.57		.57	.95
0490	12" thick		700	.023			.61		.61	1.02
1000	Chimney, 16" x 16", soft old mortar	1 Clab	55	.145	C.F.		3.87		3.87	6.45
1020	Hard mortar		40	.200			5.30		5.30	8.90
1030	16" x 20", soft old mortar		55	.145			3.87		3.87	6.45
1040	Hard mortar		40	.200			5.30		5.30	8.90
1050	16" x 24", soft old mortar		55	.145			3.87		3.87	6.45
1060	Hard mortar		40	.200			5.30		5.30	8.90
1080	20" x 20", soft old mortar		55	.145			3.87		3.87	6.45
1100	Hard mortar		40	.200			5.30		5.30	8.90
1110	20" x 24", soft old mortar		55	.145			3.87		3.87	6.45
1120	Hard mortar		40	.200			5.30		5.30	8.90
1140	20" x 32", soft old mortar		55	.145			3.87		3.87	6.45
1160	Hard mortar		40	.200			5.30		5.30	8.90
1200	48" x 48", soft old mortar		55	.145			3.87		3.87	6.45
1220	Hard mortar		40	.200			5.30		5.30	8.90
1250	Metal, high temp steel jacket, 24" diameter	E-2	130	.369	V.L.F.		14.30	12.85	27.15	39.50
1260	60" diameter	"	60	.800			31	28	59	85.50
1280	Flue lining, up to 12" x 12"	1 Clab	200	.040			1.06		1.06	1.78
1282	Up to 24" x 24"		150	.053			1.42		1.42	2.37
2000	Columns, 8" x 8", soft old mortar		48	.167			4.43		4.43	7.40
2020	Hard mortar		40	.200			5.30		5.30	8.90
2060	16" x 16", soft old mortar		16	.500			13.30		13.30	22.50
2100	Hard mortar		14	.571			15.20		15.20	25.50
2140	24" x 24", soft old mortar		8	1			26.50		26.50	44.50
2160	Hard mortar		6	1.333			35.50		35.50	59.50
2200	36" x 36", soft old mortar		4	2			53		53	89
2220	Hard mortar		3	2.667			71		71	119
2230	Alternate pricing method, soft old mortar		30	.267	C.F.		7.10		7.10	11.85
2240	Hard mortar		23	.348	"		9.25		9.25	15.50
3000	Copings, precast or masonry, to 8" wide									
3020	Soft old mortar	1 Clab	180	.044	L.F.		1.18		1.18	1.98
3040	Hard mortar	"	160	.050	"		1.33		1.33	2.23
3100	To 12" wide									
3120	Soft old mortar	1 Clab	160	.050	L.F.		1.33		1.33	2.23
3140	Hard mortar	"	140	.057	"		1.52		1.52	2.54
4000	Fireplace, brick, 30" x 24" opening									
4020	Soft old mortar	1 Clab	2	4	Ea.		106		106	178
4040	Hard mortar		1.25	6.400			170		170	285
4100	Stone, soft old mortar		1.50	5.333			142		142	237
4120	Hard mortar		1	8			213		213	355
5000	Veneers, brick, soft old mortar		140	.057	S.F.		1.52		1.52	2.54
5020	Hard mortar		125	.064			1.70		1.70	2.85
5050	Glass block, up to 4" thick		500	.016			.43		.43	.71
5100	Granite and marble, 2" thick		180	.044			1.18		1.18	1.98
5120	4" thick		170	.047			1.25		1.25	2.09
5140	Stone, 4" thick		180	.044			1.18		1.18	1.98
5160	8" thick		175	.046			1.22		1.22	2.03
5400	Alternate pricing method, stone, 4" thick		60	.133	C.F.		3.55		3.55	5.95
5420	8" thick		85	.094	"		2.50		2.50	4.19

For customer support on your Residential Costs with RSMeans Data, call 800.448.8182.

323

04 05 Common Work Results for Masonry

04 05 13 – Masonry Mortaring

04 05 13.10 Cement

		Crew	Daily Output	Labor-Hours	Unit	Material	2017 Bare Costs Labor	Equipment	Total	Total Incl O&P
0010	**CEMENT** R040513-10									
0100	Masonry, 70 lb. bag, T.L. lots				Bag	13.55			13.55	14.90
0150	L.T.L. lots					14.35			14.35	15.80
0200	White, 70 lb. bag, T.L. lots					17.70			17.70	19.50
0250	L.T.L. lots					17.75			17.75	19.55

04 05 16 – Masonry Grouting

04 05 16.30 Grouting

		Crew	Daily Output	Labor-Hours	Unit	Material	2017 Bare Costs Labor	Equipment	Total	Total Incl O&P
0010	**GROUTING**									
0011	Bond beams & lintels, 8" deep, 6" thick, 0.15 C.F. per L.F.	D-4	1480	.027	L.F.	.70	.80	.09	1.59	2.21
0020	8" thick, 0.2 C.F. per L.F.		1400	.029		1.13	.84	.09	2.06	2.75
0050	10" thick, 0.25 C.F. per L.F.		1200	.033		1.17	.98	.11	2.26	3.06
0060	12" thick, 0.3 C.F. per L.F.		1040	.038		1.40	1.14	.13	2.67	3.58
0200	Concrete block cores, solid, 4" thk., by hand, 0.067 C.F.per S.F. of wall	D-8	1100	.036	S.F.	.31	1.18		1.49	2.32
0210	6" thick, pumped, 0.175 C.F. per S.F.	D-4	720	.056		.82	1.64	.18	2.64	3.85
0250	8" thick, pumped, 0.258 C.F. per S.F.		680	.059		1.21	1.74	.20	3.15	4.45
0300	10" thick, pumped, 0.340 C.F. per S.F.		660	.061		1.59	1.79	.20	3.58	4.97
0350	12" thick, pumped, 0.422 C.F. per S.F.		640	.063		1.97	1.84	.21	4.02	5.50

04 05 19 – Masonry Anchorage and Reinforcing

04 05 19.05 Anchor Bolts

		Crew	Daily Output	Labor-Hours	Unit	Material	2017 Bare Costs Labor	Equipment	Total	Total Incl O&P
0010	**ANCHOR BOLTS**									
0015	Installed in fresh grout in CMU bond beams or filled cores, no templates									
0020	Hooked, with nut and washer, 1/2" diam., 8" long	1 Bric	132	.061	Ea.	1.38	2.11		3.49	5.05
0030	12" long		131	.061		1.53	2.13		3.66	5.25
0040	5/8" diameter, 8" long		129	.062		3.35	2.16		5.51	7.30
0050	12" long		127	.063		4.12	2.20		6.32	8.20
0060	3/4" diameter, 8" long		127	.063		4.12	2.20		6.32	8.20
0070	12" long		125	.064		5.15	2.23		7.38	9.40

04 05 19.16 Masonry Anchors

		Crew	Daily Output	Labor-Hours	Unit	Material	2017 Bare Costs Labor	Equipment	Total	Total Incl O&P
0010	**MASONRY ANCHORS**									
0020	For brick veneer, galv., corrugated, 7/8" x 7", 22 Ga.	1 Bric	10.50	.762	C	15.35	26.50		41.85	61.50
0100	24 Ga.		10.50	.762		9.90	26.50		36.40	55.50
0150	16 Ga.		10.50	.762		29	26.50		55.50	76.50
0200	Buck anchors, galv., corrugated, 16 ga., 2" bend, 8" x 2"		10.50	.762		59	26.50		85.50	110
0250	8" x 3"		10.50	.762		61.50	26.50		88	112
0660	Cavity wall, Z-type, galvanized, 6" long, 1/8" diam.		10.50	.762		25.50	26.50		52	72.50
0670	3/16" diameter		10.50	.762		31	26.50		57.50	78.50
0680	1/4" diameter		10.50	.762		39	26.50		65.50	87.50
0850	8" long, 3/16" diameter		10.50	.762		26	26.50		52.50	73
0855	1/4" diameter		10.50	.762		47	26.50		73.50	96
1000	Rectangular type, galvanized, 1/4" diameter, 2" x 6"		10.50	.762		73	26.50		99.50	125
1050	4" x 6"		10.50	.762		88.50	26.50		115	142
1100	3/16" diameter, 2" x 6"		10.50	.762		45.50	26.50		72	94.50
1150	4" x 6"		10.50	.762		52	26.50		78.50	102
1500	Rigid partition anchors, plain, 8" long, 1" x 1/8"		10.50	.762		230	26.50		256.50	298
1550	1" x 1/4"		10.50	.762		271	26.50		297.50	345
1580	1-1/2" x 1/8"		10.50	.762		253	26.50		279.50	325
1600	1-1/2" x 1/4"		10.50	.762		315	26.50		341.50	395
1650	2" x 1/8"		10.50	.762		299	26.50		325.50	375
1700	2" x 1/4"		10.50	.762		395	26.50		421.50	480

04 05 Common Work Results for Masonry

04 05 19 – Masonry Anchorage and Reinforcing

04 05 19.26 Masonry Reinforcing Bars		Crew	Daily Output	Labor-Hours	Unit	Material	2017 Bare Costs Labor	Equipment	Total	Total Incl O&P
0010	**MASONRY REINFORCING BARS**	R040519-50								
0015	Steel bars A615, placed horiz., #3 & #4 bars	1 Bric	450	.018	Lb.	.47	.62		1.09	1.56
0050	Placed vertical, #3 & #4 bars		350	.023		.47	.80		1.27	1.86
0060	#5 & #6 bars		650	.012		.47	.43		.90	1.24
0200	Joint reinforcing, regular truss, to 6" wide, mill std galvanized		30	.267	C.L.F.	22.50	9.30		31.80	40.50
0250	12" wide		20	.400		26.50	13.95		40.45	52.50
0400	Cavity truss with drip section, to 6" wide		30	.267		22	9.30		31.30	39.50
0450	12" wide		20	.400		25.50	13.95		39.45	51.50

04 21 Clay Unit Masonry

04 21 13 – Brick Masonry

04 21 13.13 Brick Veneer Masonry

		Crew	Daily Output	Labor-Hours	Unit	Material	2017 Bare Costs Labor	Equipment	Total	Total Incl O&P
0010	**BRICK VENEER MASONRY**, T.L. lots, excl. scaff., grout & reinforcing									
0015	Material costs incl. 3% brick and 25% mortar waste	R042110-10								
2000	Standard, sel. common, 4" x 2-2/3" x 8" (6.75/S.F.)	R042110-20 D-8	230	.174	S.F.	4.34	5.65		9.99	14.20
2020	Red, 4" x 2-2/3" x 8", running bond		220	.182		4.15	5.90		10.05	14.45
2050	Full header every 6th course (7.88/S.F.)	R042110-50	185	.216		4.83	7		11.83	17.05
2100	English, full header every 2nd course (10.13/S.F.)		140	.286		6.20	9.25		15.45	22.50
2150	Flemish, alternate header every course (9.00/S.F.)		150	.267		5.50	8.65		14.15	20.50
2200	Flemish, alt. header every 6th course (7.13/S.F.)		205	.195		4.38	6.30		10.68	15.40
2250	Full headers throughout (13.50/S.F.)		105	.381		8.25	12.35		20.60	29.50
2300	Rowlock course (13.50/S.F.)		100	.400		8.25	12.95		21.20	30.50
2350	Rowlock stretcher (4.50/S.F.)		310	.129		2.79	4.18		6.97	10.05
2400	Soldier course (6.75/S.F.)		200	.200		4.15	6.50		10.65	15.40
2450	Sailor course (4.50/S.F.)		290	.138		2.79	4.47		7.26	10.55
2600	Buff or gray face, running bond (6.75/S.F.)		220	.182		4.38	5.90		10.28	14.70
2700	Glazed face brick, running bond		210	.190		12.95	6.15		19.10	24.50
2750	Full header every 6th course (7.88/S.F.)		170	.235		15.15	7.60		22.75	29.50
3000	Jumbo, 6" x 4" x 12" running bond (3.00/S.F.)		435	.092		5.15	2.98		8.13	10.70
3050	Norman, 4" x 2-2/3" x 12" running bond (4.5/S.F.)		320	.125		6.40	4.05		10.45	13.85
3100	Norwegian, 4" x 3-1/5" x 12" (3.75/S.F.)		375	.107		5.70	3.46		9.16	12.05
3150	Economy, 4" x 4" x 8" (4.50/S.F.)		310	.129		4.49	4.18		8.67	11.95
3200	Engineer, 4" x 3-1/5" x 8" (5.63/S.F.)		260	.154		3.98	4.98		8.96	12.75
3250	Roman, 4" x 2" x 12" (6.00/S.F.)		250	.160		7.20	5.20		12.40	16.60
3300	S.C.R., 6" x 2-2/3" x 12" (4.50/S.F.)		310	.129		6.20	4.18		10.38	13.85
3350	Utility, 4" x 4" x 12" (3.00/S.F.)		360	.111		5.10	3.60		8.70	11.65
3360	For less than truck load lots, add					.10%				
3400	For cavity wall construction, add						15%			
3450	For stacked bond, add						10%			
3500	For interior veneer construction, add						15%			
3550	For curved walls, add						30%			

04 21 13.14 Thin Brick Veneer

		Crew	Daily Output	Labor-Hours	Unit	Material	2017 Bare Costs Labor	Equipment	Total	Total Incl O&P
0010	**THIN BRICK VENEER**									
0015	Material costs incl. 3% brick and 25% mortar waste									
0020	On & incl. metal panel support sys, modular, 2-2/3" x 5/8" x 8", red	D-7	92	.174	S.F.	9.35	5.20		14.55	18.65
0100	Closure, 4" x 5/8" x 8"		110	.145		9.10	4.33		13.43	17.05
0110	Norman, 2-2/3" x 5/8" x 12"		110	.145		9.15	4.33		13.48	17.10
0120	Utility, 4" x 5/8" x 12"		125	.128		8.85	3.81		12.66	15.95
0130	Emperor, 4" x 3/4" x 16"		175	.091		10	2.72		12.72	15.40
0140	Super emperor, 8" x 3/4" x 16"		195	.082		10.30	2.45		12.75	15.30

04 21 Clay Unit Masonry

04 21 13 – Brick Masonry

04 21 13.14 Thin Brick Veneer

		Crew	Daily Output	Labor-Hours	Unit	Material	2017 Bare Costs Labor	Equipment	Total	Total Incl O&P
0150	For L shaped corners with 4" return, add				L.F.	9.25			9.25	10.20
0200	On masonry/plaster back-up, modular, 2-2/3" x 5/8" x 8", red	D-7	137	.117	S.F.	4.36	3.48		7.84	10.45
0210	Closure, 4" x 5/8" x 8"		165	.097		4.12	2.89		7.01	9.20
0220	Norman, 2-2/3" x 5/8" x 12"		165	.097		4.16	2.89		7.05	9.25
0230	Utility, 4" x 5/8" x 12"		185	.086		3.88	2.58		6.46	8.45
0240	Emperor, 4" x 3/4" x 16"		260	.062		5	1.83		6.83	8.50
0250	Super emperor, 8" x 3/4" x 16"		285	.056		5.35	1.67		7.02	8.55
0260	For L shaped corners with 4" return, add				L.F.	9.25			9.25	10.20
0270	For embedment into pre-cast concrete panels, add				S.F.	14.40			14.40	15.85

04 21 13.15 Chimney

		Crew	Daily Output	Labor-Hours	Unit	Material	2017 Bare Costs Labor	Equipment	Total	Total Incl O&P
0010	**CHIMNEY**, excludes foundation, scaffolding, grout and reinforcing									
0100	Brick, 16" x 16", 8" flue	D-1	18.20	.879	V.L.F.	25	28		53	74.50
0150	16" x 20" with one 8" x 12" flue		16	1		39	32		71	96.50
0200	16" x 24" with two 8" x 8" flues		14	1.143		57	36.50		93.50	124
0250	20" x 20" with one 12" x 12" flue		13.70	1.168		46.50	37		83.50	114
0300	20" x 24" with two 8" x 12" flues		12	1.333		65	42.50		107.50	143
0350	20" x 32" with two 12" x 12" flues		10	1.600		82.50	51		133.50	176

04 21 13.18 Columns

		Crew	Daily Output	Labor-Hours	Unit	Material	2017 Bare Costs Labor	Equipment	Total	Total Incl O&P
0010	**COLUMNS**, solid, excludes scaffolding, grout and reinforcing									
0050	Brick, 8" x 8", 9 brick per V.L.F.	D-1	56	.286	V.L.F.	5.30	9.10		14.40	21
0100	12" x 8", 13.5 brick per V.L.F.		37	.432		7.90	13.75		21.65	31.50
0200	12" x 12", 20 brick per V.L.F.		25	.640		11.75	20.50		32.25	47
0300	16" x 12", 27 brick per V.L.F.		19	.842		15.85	27		42.85	62.50
0400	16" x 16", 36 brick per V.L.F.		14	1.143		21	36.50		57.50	84.50
0500	20" x 16", 45 brick per V.L.F.		11	1.455		26.50	46		72.50	107
0600	20" x 20", 56 brick per V.L.F.		9	1.778		33	56.50		89.50	131
0700	24" x 20", 68 brick per V.L.F.		7	2.286		40	72.50		112.50	166
0800	24" x 24", 81 brick per V.L.F.		6	2.667		47.50	85		132.50	195
1000	36" x 36", 182 brick per V.L.F.		3	5.333		107	169		276	400

04 21 13.30 Oversized Brick

		Crew	Daily Output	Labor-Hours	Unit	Material	2017 Bare Costs Labor	Equipment	Total	Total Incl O&P
0010	**OVERSIZED BRICK**, excludes scaffolding, grout and reinforcing									
0100	Veneer, 4" x 2.25" x 16"	D-8	387	.103	S.F.	5.30	3.35		8.65	11.45
0102	8" x 2.25" x 16", multicell		265	.151		16.65	4.89		21.54	26.50
0105	4" x 2.75" x 16"		412	.097		5.50	3.14		8.64	11.35
0107	8" x 2.75" x 16", multicell		295	.136		16.70	4.39		21.09	26
0110	4" x 4" x 16"		460	.087		3.61	2.82		6.43	8.70
0120	4" x 8" x 16"		533	.075		4.25	2.43		6.68	8.75
0122	4" x 8" x 16" multicell		327	.122		15.65	3.96		19.61	24
0125	Loadbearing, 6" x 4" x 16", grouted and reinforced		387	.103		10.75	3.35		14.10	17.40
0130	8" x 4" x 16", grouted and reinforced		327	.122		11.80	3.96		15.76	19.60
0132	10" x 4" x 16", grouted and reinforced		327	.122		24	3.96		27.96	32.50
0135	6" x 8" x 16", grouted and reinforced		440	.091		13.95	2.94		16.89	20.50
0140	8" x 8" x 16", grouted and reinforced		400	.100		14.90	3.24		18.14	22
0145	Curtainwall/reinforced veneer, 6" x 4" x 16"		387	.103		15.35	3.35		18.70	22.50
0150	8" x 4" x 16"		327	.122		18.70	3.96		22.66	27
0152	10" x 4" x 16"		327	.122		26.50	3.96		30.46	35.50
0155	6" x 8" x 16"		440	.091		19.05	2.94		21.99	26
0160	8" x 8" x 16"		400	.100		26.50	3.24		29.74	35
0200	For 1 to 3 slots in face, add					15%				
0210	For 4 to 7 slots in face, add					25%				
0220	For bond beams, add					20%				
0230	For bullnose shapes, add					20%				

04 21 Clay Unit Masonry

04 21 13 – Brick Masonry

04 21 13.30 Oversized Brick

		Crew	Daily Output	Labor-Hours	Unit	Material	2017 Bare Costs Labor	2017 Bare Costs Equipment	Total	Total Incl O&P
0240	For open end knockout, add				S.F.	10%				
0250	For white or gray color group, add					10%				
0260	For 135 degree corner, add					250%				

04 21 13.32 Brick Veneer Masonry

		Crew	Daily Output	Labor-Hours	Unit	Material	Labor	Equipment	Total	Total Incl O&P
0010	**BRICK VENEER MASONRY**, for residential installations									
0020	Residential brick veneer, queen size	D-14	337	.095	S.F.	2.71	3.16		5.87	8.30
0030	Modular size	"	270	.119	"	4.10	3.95		8.05	11.15

04 21 13.35 Common Building Brick

		Crew	Daily Output	Labor-Hours	Unit	Material	Labor	Equipment	Total	Total Incl O&P
0010	**COMMON BUILDING BRICK**, C62, TL lots, material only	R042110-20								
0020	Standard				M	500			500	550
0050	Select				"	520			520	570

04 21 13.45 Face Brick

		Crew	Daily Output	Labor-Hours	Unit	Material	Labor	Equipment	Total	Total Incl O&P
0010	**FACE BRICK** Material Only, C216, TL lots	R042110-20								
0300	Standard modular, 4" x 2-2/3" x 8"				M	490			490	540
2170	For less than truck load lots, add					15			15	16.50
2180	For buff or gray brick, add					16			16	17.60

04 22 Concrete Unit Masonry

04 22 10 – Concrete Masonry Units

04 22 10.11 Autoclave Aerated Concrete Block

			Crew	Daily Output	Labor-Hours	Unit	Material	Labor	Equipment	Total	Total Incl O&P
0010	**AUTOCLAVE AERATED CONCRETE BLOCK**, excl. scaffolding, grout & reinforcing										
0050	Solid, 4" x 8" x 24", incl. mortar	G	D-8	600	.067	S.F.	1.62	2.16		3.78	5.40
0060	6" x 8" x 24"	G		600	.067		2.44	2.16		4.60	6.30
0070	8" x 8" x 24"	G		575	.070		3.26	2.25		5.51	7.35
0080	10" x 8" x 24"	G		575	.070		3.98	2.25		6.23	8.15
0090	12" x 8" x 24"	G		550	.073		4.88	2.36		7.24	9.30

04 22 10.14 Concrete Block, Back-Up

		Crew	Daily Output	Labor-Hours	Unit	Material	Labor	Equipment	Total	Total Incl O&P
0010	**CONCRETE BLOCK, BACK-UP**, C90, 2000 psi R042210-20									
0020	Normal weight, 8" x 16" units, tooled joint 1 side									
0050	Not-reinforced, 2000 psi, 2" thick	D-8	475	.084	S.F.	1.56	2.73		4.29	6.30
0200	4" thick		460	.087		1.88	2.82		4.70	6.80
0300	6" thick		440	.091		2.45	2.94		5.39	7.65
0350	8" thick		400	.100		2.62	3.24		5.86	8.35
0400	10" thick		330	.121		3.10	3.93		7.03	10
0450	12" thick	D-9	310	.155		4.27	4.92		9.19	12.95
1000	Reinforced, alternate courses, 4" thick	D-8	450	.089		2.05	2.88		4.93	7.10
1100	6" thick		430	.093		2.62	3.01		5.63	7.95
1150	8" thick		395	.101		2.82	3.28		6.10	8.60
1200	10" thick		320	.125		3.26	4.05		7.31	10.40
1250	12" thick	D-9	300	.160		4.44	5.10		9.54	13.45

04 22 10.16 Concrete Block, Bond Beam

		Crew	Daily Output	Labor-Hours	Unit	Material	Labor	Equipment	Total	Total Incl O&P
0010	**CONCRETE BLOCK, BOND BEAM**, C90, 2000 psi									
0020	Not including grout or reinforcing									
0125	Regular block, 6" thick	D-8	584	.068	L.F.	2.69	2.22		4.91	6.70
0130	8" high, 8" thick	"	565	.071		2.80	2.29		5.09	6.95
0150	12" thick	D-9	510	.094		3.97	2.99		6.96	9.35
0525	Lightweight, 6" thick	D-8	592	.068		2.92	2.19		5.11	6.90

04 22 Concrete Unit Masonry

04 22 10 – Concrete Masonry Units

04 22 10.19 Concrete Block, Insulation Inserts	Crew	Daily Output	Labor-Hours	Unit	Material	2017 Bare Costs Labor	Equipment	Total	Total Incl O&P
0010 **CONCRETE BLOCK, INSULATION INSERTS**									
0100 Styrofoam, plant installed, add to block prices									
0200 8" x 16" units, 6" thick				S.F.	1.22			1.22	1.34
0250 8" thick					1.37			1.37	1.51
0300 10" thick					1.42			1.42	1.56
0350 12" thick					1.57			1.57	1.73
0500 8" x 8" units, 8" thick					1.22			1.22	1.34
0550 12" thick					1.42			1.42	1.56

04 22 10.23 Concrete Block, Decorative	Crew	Daily Output	Labor-Hours	Unit	Material	2017 Bare Costs Labor	Equipment	Total	Total Incl O&P
0010 **CONCRETE BLOCK, DECORATIVE**, C90, 2000 psi									
5000 Split rib profile units, 1" deep ribs, 8 ribs									
5100 8" x 16" x 4" thick	D-8	345	.116	S.F.	3.96	3.76		7.72	10.65
5150 6" thick		325	.123		4.49	3.99		8.48	11.65
5200 8" thick		300	.133		5.05	4.32		9.37	12.85
5250 12" thick	D-9	275	.175		5.90	5.55		11.45	15.80
5400 For special deeper colors, 4" thick, add					1.32			1.32	1.45
5450 12" thick, add					1.38			1.38	1.52
5600 For white, 4" thick, add					1.32			1.32	1.45
5650 6" thick, add					1.34			1.34	1.48
5700 8" thick, add					1.39			1.39	1.53
5750 12" thick, add					1.44			1.44	1.58

04 22 10.24 Concrete Block, Exterior	Crew	Daily Output	Labor-Hours	Unit	Material	2017 Bare Costs Labor	Equipment	Total	Total Incl O&P
0010 **CONCRETE BLOCK, EXTERIOR**, C90, 2000 psi									
0020 Reinforced alt courses, tooled joints 2 sides									
0100 Normal weight, 8" x 16" x 6" thick	D-8	395	.101	S.F.	2.40	3.28		5.68	8.15
0200 8" thick		360	.111		3.71	3.60		7.31	10.15
0250 10" thick		290	.138		4.30	4.47		8.77	12.25
0300 12" thick	D-9	250	.192		5	6.10		11.10	15.75

04 22 10.26 Concrete Block Foundation Wall	Crew	Daily Output	Labor-Hours	Unit	Material	2017 Bare Costs Labor	Equipment	Total	Total Incl O&P
0010 **CONCRETE BLOCK FOUNDATION WALL**, C90/C145									
0050 Normal-weight, cut joints, horiz joint reinf, no vert reinf.									
0200 Hollow, 8" x 16" x 6" thick	D-8	455	.088	S.F.	3.07	2.85		5.92	8.15
0250 8" thick		425	.094		3.29	3.05		6.34	8.70
0300 10" thick		350	.114		3.77	3.70		7.47	10.35
0350 12" thick	D-9	300	.160		4.97	5.10		10.07	14
0500 Solid, 8" x 16" block, 6" thick	D-8	440	.091		3.13	2.94		6.07	8.40
0550 8" thick	"	415	.096		4.37	3.12		7.49	10.05
0600 12" thick	D-9	350	.137		6.25	4.36		10.61	14.20

04 22 10.32 Concrete Block, Lintels	Crew	Daily Output	Labor-Hours	Unit	Material	2017 Bare Costs Labor	Equipment	Total	Total Incl O&P
0010 **CONCRETE BLOCK, LINTELS**, C90, normal weight									
0100 Including grout and horizontal reinforcing									
0200 8" x 8" x 8", 1 #4 bar	D-4	300	.133	L.F.	3.88	3.93	.44	8.25	11.35
0250 2 #4 bars		295	.136		4.09	4	.45	8.54	11.70
0400 8" x 16" x 8", 1 #4 bar		275	.145		3.95	4.29	.48	8.72	12.10
0450 2 #4 bars		270	.148		4.17	4.37	.49	9.03	12.45
1000 12" x 8" x 8", 1 #4 bar		275	.145		5.30	4.29	.48	10.07	13.60
1100 2 #4 bars		270	.148		5.55	4.37	.49	10.41	14
1150 2 #5 bars		270	.148		5.75	4.37	.49	10.61	14.25
1200 2 #6 bars		265	.151		6.05	4.45	.50	11	14.65
1500 12" x 16" x 8", 1 #4 bar		250	.160		6	4.72	.53	11.25	15.05
1600 2 #3 bars		245	.163		6	4.82	.54	11.36	15.30

04 22 Concrete Unit Masonry

04 22 10 – Concrete Masonry Units

04 22 10.32 Concrete Block, Lintels

		Crew	Daily Output	Labor-Hours	Unit	Material	2017 Bare Costs Labor	Equipment	Total	Total Incl O&P
1650	2 #4 bars	D-4	245	.163	L.F.	6.20	4.82	.54	11.56	15.50
1700	2 #5 bars	↓	240	.167	↓	6.40	4.92	.55	11.87	15.90

04 22 10.33 Lintel Block

		Crew	Daily Output	Labor-Hours	Unit	Material	Labor	Equipment	Total	Total Incl O&P
0010	**LINTEL BLOCK**									
3481	Lintel block 6" x 8" x 8"	D-1	300	.053	Ea.	1.32	1.69		3.01	4.29
3501	6" x 16" x 8"		275	.058		2.10	1.85		3.95	5.40
3521	8" x 8" x 8"		275	.058		1.20	1.85		3.05	4.42
3561	8" x 16" x 8"	↓	250	.064	↓	2.10	2.03		4.13	5.70

04 22 10.34 Concrete Block, Partitions

		Crew	Daily Output	Labor-Hours	Unit	Material	Labor	Equipment	Total	Total Incl O&P
0010	**CONCRETE BLOCK, PARTITIONS**, excludes scaffolding									
1000	Lightweight block, tooled joints, 2 sides, hollow									
1100	Not reinforced, 8" x 16" x 4" thick	D-8	440	.091	S.F.	1.90	2.94		4.84	7.05
1150	6" thick		410	.098		2.69	3.16		5.85	8.25
1200	8" thick		385	.104		3.28	3.37		6.65	9.25
1250	10" thick	↓	370	.108		3.98	3.50		7.48	10.30
1300	12" thick	D-9	350	.137	↓	4.19	4.36		8.55	11.90
4000	Regular block, tooled joints, 2 sides, hollow									
4100	Not reinforced, 8" x 16" x 4" thick	D-8	430	.093	S.F.	1.79	3.01		4.80	7
4150	6" thick		400	.100		2.35	3.24		5.59	8.05
4200	8" thick		375	.107		2.52	3.46		5.98	8.55
4250	10" thick	↓	360	.111		3	3.60		6.60	9.35
4300	12" thick	D-9	340	.141	↓	4.18	4.49		8.67	12.15

04 23 Glass Unit Masonry

04 23 13 – Vertical Glass Unit Masonry

04 23 13.10 Glass Block

		Crew	Daily Output	Labor-Hours	Unit	Material	Labor	Equipment	Total	Total Incl O&P
0010	**GLASS BLOCK**									
0100	Plain, 4" thick, under 1,000 S.F., 6" x 6"	D-8	115	.348	S.F.	28.50	11.25		39.75	50.50
0150	8" x 8"		160	.250		16.05	8.10		24.15	31.50
0160	end block		160	.250		60.50	8.10		68.60	80
0170	90 deg corner		160	.250		56	8.10		64.10	75
0180	45 deg corner		160	.250		46	8.10		54.10	64
0200	12" x 12"		175	.229		24	7.40		31.40	39
0210	4" x 8"		160	.250		28.50	8.10		36.60	45
0220	6" x 8"	↓	160	.250	↓	21	8.10		29.10	36.50
0700	For solar reflective blocks, add					100%				
1000	Thinline, plain, 3-1/8" thick, under 1,000 S.F., 6" x 6"	D-8	115	.348	S.F.	23	11.25		34.25	44
1050	8" x 8"		160	.250		12.75	8.10		20.85	27.50
1400	For cleaning block after installation (both sides), add	↓	1000	.040	↓	.16	1.30		1.46	2.35

329

For customer support on your Residential Costs with RSMeans Data, call 800.448.8182.

04 24 Adobe Unit Masonry

04 24 16 – Manufactured Adobe Unit Masonry

04 24 16.06 Adobe Brick

04 24 16.06 Adobe Brick	Crew	Daily Output	Labor-Hours	Unit	Material	2017 Bare Costs Labor	Equipment	Total	Total Incl O&P
0010 **ADOBE BRICK**, Semi-stabilized, with cement mortar									
0060　Brick, 10" x 4" x 14", 2.6/S.F.　G	D-8	560	.071	S.F.	4.80	2.31		7.11	9.20
0080　　12" x 4" x 16", 2.3/S.F.　G		580	.069		7.05	2.23		9.28	11.50
0100　　10" x 4" x 16", 2.3/S.F.　G		590	.068		6.55	2.20		8.75	10.95
0120　　8" x 4" x 16", 2.3/S.F.　G		560	.071		5	2.31		7.31	9.40
0140　　4" x 4" x 16", 2.3/S.F.　G		540	.074		4.89	2.40		7.29	9.45
0160　　6" x 4" x 16", 2.3/S.F.　G		540	.074		4.54	2.40		6.94	9.05
0180　　4" x 4" x 12", 3.0/S.F.　G		520	.077		5.25	2.49		7.74	10
0200　　8" x 4" x 12", 3.0/S.F.　G	▼	520	.077	▼	4.35	2.49		6.84	8.95

04 27 Multiple-Wythe Unit Masonry

04 27 10 – Multiple-Wythe Masonry

04 27 10.10 Cornices

	Crew	Daily Output	Labor-Hours	Unit	Material	Labor	Equipment	Total	Total Incl O&P
0010 **CORNICES**									
0110　Face bricks, 12 brick/S.F.	D-1	30	.533	SF Face	5.85	16.95		22.80	35
0150　　15 brick/S.F.	"	23	.696	"	7	22		29	44.50

04 27 10.30 Brick Walls

	Crew	Daily Output	Labor-Hours	Unit	Material	Labor	Equipment	Total	Total Incl O&P
0010 **BRICK WALLS**, including mortar, excludes scaffolding									
0800　Face brick, 4" thick wall, 6.75 brick/S.F.	D-8	215	.186	S.F.	4.07	6.05		10.12	14.60
0850　Common brick, 4" thick wall, 6.75 brick/S.F.		240	.167		4.14	5.40		9.54	13.60
0900　　8" thick, 13.50 brick/S.F.		135	.296		8.55	9.60		18.15	25.50
1000　　12" thick, 20.25 brick/S.F.		95	.421		12.90	13.65		26.55	37
1050　　16" thick, 27.00 brick/S.F.		75	.533		17.45	17.25		34.70	48
1200　Reinforced, face brick, 4" thick wall, 6.75 brick/S.F.		210	.190		4.23	6.15		10.38	15
1220　Common brick, 4" thick wall, 6.75 brick/S.F.		235	.170		4.30	5.50		9.80	13.95
1250　　8" thick, 13.50 brick/S.F.		130	.308		8.90	9.95		18.85	26.50
1300　　12" thick, 20.25 brick/S.F.		90	.444		13.40	14.40		27.80	38.50
1350　　16" thick, 27.00 brick/S.F.	▼	70	.571	▼	18.10	18.50		36.60	51

04 27 10.40 Steps

	Crew	Daily Output	Labor-Hours	Unit	Material	Labor	Equipment	Total	Total Incl O&P
0010 **STEPS**									
0012　Entry steps, select common brick	D-1	.30	53.333	M	520	1,700		2,220	3,425

04 41 Dry-Placed Stone

04 41 10 – Dry Placed Stone

04 41 10.10 Rough Stone Wall

	Crew	Daily Output	Labor-Hours	Unit	Material	Labor	Equipment	Total	Total Incl O&P
0011 **ROUGH STONE WALL**, Dry									
0012　Dry laid (no mortar), under 18" thick　G	D-1	60	.267	C.F.	13	8.45		21.45	28.50
0100　Random fieldstone, under 18" thick　G	D-12	60	.533		13	16.95		29.95	43
0150　　Over 18" thick　G	"	63	.508		15.60	16.15		31.75	44
0500　Field stone veneer　G	D-8	120	.333	S.F.	12.70	10.80		23.50	32
0510　Valley stone veneer　G		120	.333		12.70	10.80		23.50	32
0520　River stone veneer　G	▼	120	.333	▼	12.70	10.80		23.50	32
0600　Rubble stone walls, in mortar bed, up to 18" thick　G	D-11	75	.320	C.F.	15.70	10.50		26.20	35

For customer support on your Residential Costs with RSMeans Data, call 800.448.8182.

04 43 10 – Masonry with Natural and Processed Stone

04 43 10.45 Granite

		Crew	Daily Output	Labor-Hours	Unit	Material	2017 Bare Costs Labor	Equipment	Total	Total Incl O&P
0010	**GRANITE**, cut to size									
2500	Steps, copings, etc., finished on more than one surface									
2550	Low price, gray, light gray, etc.	D-10	50	.640	C.F.	94	22	8.70	124.70	150
2575	Medium price, pink, brown, etc.		50	.640		122	22	8.70	152.70	181
2600	High price, red, black, etc.	↓	50	.640	↓	150	22	8.70	180.70	212
2800	Pavers, 4" x 4" x 4" blocks, split face and joints									
2850	Low price, gray, light gray, etc.	D-11	80	.300	S.F.	13.30	9.85		23.15	31
2875	Medium price, pinks, browns, etc.		80	.300		21.50	9.85		31.35	40
2900	High price, red, black, etc.	↓	80	.300	↓	29.50	9.85		39.35	49
5000	Reclaimed or antique									
5010	Treads, up to 12" wide	D-10	100	.320	L.F.	42.50	11	4.36	57.86	70
5020	Up to 18" wide		100	.320		38.50	11	4.36	53.86	65.50
5030	Capstone, size varies		50	.640		30.50	22	8.70	61.20	80
5040	Posts	↓	30	1.067	V.L.F.	30.50	36.50	14.50	81.50	111

04 43 10.55 Limestone

		Crew	Daily Output	Labor-Hours	Unit	Material	2017 Bare Costs Labor	Equipment	Total	Total Incl O&P
0010	**LIMESTONE**, cut to size									
0020	Veneer facing panels									
0500	Texture finish, light stick, 4-1/2" thick, 5' x 12'	D-4	300	.133	S.F.	20.50	3.93	.44	24.87	29.50
0750	5" thick, 5' x 14' panels	D-10	275	.116		21.50	4.01	1.58	27.09	32.50
1000	Sugarcube finish, 2" thick, 3' x 5' panels		275	.116		29	4.01	1.58	34.59	40.50
1050	3" thick, 4' x 9' panels		275	.116		25.50	4.01	1.58	31.09	37
1200	4" thick, 5' x 11' panels		275	.116		31.50	4.01	1.58	37.09	43
1400	Sugarcube, textured finish, 4-1/2" thick, 5' x 12'		275	.116		32.50	4.01	1.58	38.09	44.50
1450	5" thick, 5' x 14' panels		275	.116	↓	34	4.01	1.58	39.59	45.50
2000	Coping, sugarcube finish, top & 2 sides		30	1.067	C.F.	68.50	36.50	14.50	119.50	153
2100	Sills, lintels, jambs, trim, stops, sugarcube finish, simple		20	1.600		68.50	55	22	145.50	192
2150	Detailed		20	1.600	↓	68.50	55	22	145.50	192
2300	Steps, extra hard, 14" wide, 6" rise	↓	50	.640	L.F.	25.50	22	8.70	56.20	74.50
3000	Quoins, plain finish, 6" x 12" x 12"	D-12	25	1.280	Ea.	41	40.50		81.50	114
3050	6" x 16" x 24"	"	25	1.280	"	55	40.50		95.50	129

04 43 10.60 Marble

		Crew	Daily Output	Labor-Hours	Unit	Material	2017 Bare Costs Labor	Equipment	Total	Total Incl O&P
0011	**MARBLE**, ashlar, split face, +/- 4" thick, random									
0040	Lengths 1' to 4' & heights 2" to 7-1/2", average	D-8	175	.229	S.F.	18.30	7.40		25.70	32.50
0100	Base, polished, 3/4" or 7/8" thick, polished, 6" high	D-10	65	.492	L.F.	12	16.95	6.70	35.65	49
1000	Facing, polished finish, cut to size, 3/4" to 7/8" thick									
1050	Carrara or equal	D-10	130	.246	S.F.	22.50	8.45	3.35	34.30	43
1100	Arabescato or equal	"	130	.246	"	39.50	8.45	3.35	51.30	61.50
2200	Window sills, 6" x 3/4" thick	D-1	85	.188	L.F.	11.10	6		17.10	22.50
2500	Flooring, polished tiles, 12" x 12" x 3/8" thick									
2510	Thin set, Giallo Solare or equal	D-11	90	.267	S.F.	17.50	8.75		26.25	34
2600	Sky Blue or equal		90	.267		16	8.75		24.75	32.50
2700	Mortar bed, Giallo Solare or equal		65	.369		17.50	12.10		29.60	40
2740	Sky Blue or equal	↓	65	.369		16	12.10		28.10	38
2780	Travertine, 3/8" thick, Sierra or equal	D-10	130	.246		9.40	8.45	3.35	21.20	28
2790	Silver or equal	"	130	.246	↓	26	8.45	3.35	37.80	46.50
3500	Thresholds, 3' long, 7/8" thick, 4" to 5" wide, plain	D-12	24	1.333	Ea.	35.50	42.50		78	110
3550	Beveled	"	24	1.333	"	71.50	42.50		114	150
3700	Window stools, polished, 7/8" thick, 5" wide	↓	85	.376	L.F.	21.50	11.95		33.45	44

04 43 10.75 Sandstone or Brownstone

		Crew	Daily Output	Labor-Hours	Unit	Material	2017 Bare Costs Labor	Equipment	Total	Total Incl O&P
0011	**SANDSTONE OR BROWNSTONE**									
0100	Sawed face veneer, 2-1/2" thick, to 2' x 4' panels	D-10	130	.246	S.F.	20	8.45	3.35	31.80	40
0150	4" thick, to 3'-6" x 8' panels	↓	100	.320		20	11	4.36	35.36	45

For customer support on your Residential Costs with RSMeans Data, call 800.448.8182.

331

04 43 Stone Masonry

04 43 10 - Masonry with Natural and Processed Stone

04 43 10.75 Sandstone or Brownstone		Crew	Daily Output	Labor-Hours	Unit	Material	2017 Bare Costs Labor	Equipment	Total	Total Incl O&P
0300	Split face, random sizes	D-10	100	.320	S.F.	13.40	11	4.36	28.76	38
0350	Cut stone trim (limestone)									
0360	Ribbon stone, 4" thick, 5' pieces	D-8	120	.333	Ea.	160	10.80		170.80	194
0370	Cove stone, 4" thick, 5' pieces		105	.381		161	12.35		173.35	198
0380	Cornice stone, 10" to 12" wide		90	.444		199	14.40		213.40	243
0390	Band stone, 4" thick, 5' pieces		145	.276		109	8.95		117.95	135
0410	Window and door trim, 3" to 4" wide		160	.250		93.50	8.10		101.60	117
0420	Key stone, 18" long		60	.667		93.50	21.50		115	139

04 43 10.80 Slate										
0010	**SLATE**									
3100	Stair landings, 1" thick, black, clear	D-1	65	.246	S.F.	21	7.80		28.80	36.50
3200	Ribbon	"	65	.246	"	23.50	7.80		31.30	38.50
3500	Stair treads, sand finish, 1" thick x 12" wide									
3600	3 L.F. to 6 L.F.	D-10	120	.267	L.F.	25	9.20	3.63	37.83	47
3700	Ribbon, sand finish, 1" thick x 12" wide									
3750	To 6 L.F.	D-10	120	.267	L.F.	21	9.20	3.63	33.83	43

04 43 10.85 Window Sill										
0010	**WINDOW SILL**									
0020	Bluestone, thermal top, 10" wide, 1-1/2" thick	D-1	85	.188	S.F.	9.60	6		15.60	20.50
0050	2" thick		75	.213	"	9.60	6.80		16.40	22
0100	Cut stone, 5" x 8" plain		48	.333	L.F.	12.55	10.60		23.15	31.50
0200	Face brick on edge, brick, 8" wide		80	.200		5.45	6.35		11.80	16.65
0400	Marble, 9" wide, 1" thick		85	.188		8.95	6		14.95	19.90
0900	Slate, colored, unfading, honed, 12" wide, 1" thick		85	.188		8.95	6		14.95	19.85
0950	2" thick		70	.229		8.95	7.25		16.20	22

04 51 Flue Liner Masonry

04 51 10 - Clay Flue Lining

04 51 10.10 Flue Lining										
0010	**FLUE LINING**, including mortar									
0020	Clay, 8" x 8"	D-1	125	.128	V.L.F.	5.85	4.07		9.92	13.25
0100	8" x 12"		103	.155		8.45	4.94		13.39	17.60
0200	12" x 12"		93	.172		11	5.45		16.45	21.50
0300	12" x 18"		84	.190		22.50	6.05		28.55	35
0400	18" x 18"		75	.213		29	6.80		35.80	43.50
0500	20" x 20"		66	.242		43.50	7.70		51.20	60.50
0600	24" x 24"		56	.286		55.50	9.10		64.60	76.50
1000	Round, 18" diameter		66	.242		39.50	7.70		47.20	56.50
1100	24" diameter		47	.340		76	10.80		86.80	102

04 57 Masonry Fireplaces

04 57 10 – Brick or Stone Fireplaces

04 57 10.10 Fireplace		Crew	Daily Output	Labor-Hours	Unit	Material	2017 Bare Costs Labor	Equipment	Total	Total Incl O&P
0010	**FIREPLACE**									
0100	Brick fireplace, not incl. foundations or chimneys									
0110	30" x 29" opening, incl. chamber, plain brickwork	D-1	.40	40	Ea.	570	1,275		1,845	2,750
0200	Fireplace box only (110 brick)	"	2	8	"	162	254		416	605
0300	For elaborate brickwork and details, add					35%	35%			
0400	For hearth, brick & stone, add	D-1	2	8	Ea.	213	254		467	660
0410	For steel, damper, cleanouts, add		4	4		17.55	127		144.55	232
0600	Plain brickwork, incl. metal circulator		.50	32		900	1,025		1,925	2,700
0800	Face brick only, standard size, 8" x 2-2/3" x 4"		.30	53.333	M	600	1,700		2,300	3,500
0900	Stone fireplace, fieldstone, add				SF Face	8.95			8.95	9.80
1000	Cut stone, add				"	8.40			8.40	9.25

04 72 Cast Stone Masonry

04 72 10 – Cast Stone Masonry Features

04 72 10.10 Coping

		Crew	Daily Output	Labor-Hours	Unit	Material	2017 Bare Costs Labor	Equipment	Total	Total Incl O&P
0010	**COPING**, stock units									
0050	Precast concrete, 10" wide, 4" tapers to 3-1/2", 8" wall	D-1	75	.213	L.F.	20.50	6.80		27.30	34.50
0100	12" wide, 3-1/2" tapers to 3", 10" wall		70	.229		22.50	7.25		29.75	36.50
0110	14" wide, 4" tapers to 3-1/2", 12" wall		65	.246		25.50	7.80		33.30	41
0150	16" wide, 4" tapers to 3-1/2", 14" wall		60	.267		27.50	8.45		35.95	44.50
0300	Limestone for 12" wall, 4" thick		90	.178		14.80	5.65		20.45	26
0350	6" thick		80	.200		22	6.35		28.35	35
0500	Marble, to 4" thick, no wash, 9" wide		90	.178		12.90	5.65		18.55	23.50
0550	12" wide		80	.200		18	6.35		24.35	30.50
0700	Terra cotta, 9" wide		90	.178		6.45	5.65		12.10	16.60
0750	12" wide		80	.200		8.80	6.35		15.15	20.50
0800	Aluminum, for 12" wall		80	.200		9	6.35		15.35	20.50

04 72 20 – Cultured Stone Veneer

04 72 20.10 Cultured Stone Veneer Components

		Crew	Daily Output	Labor-Hours	Unit	Material	2017 Bare Costs Labor	Equipment	Total	Total Incl O&P
0010	**CULTURED STONE VENEER COMPONENTS**									
0110	On wood frame and sheathing substrate, random sized cobbles, corner stones	D-8	70	.571	V.L.F.	10.40	18.50		28.90	42.50
0120	Field stones		140	.286	S.F.	7.55	9.25		16.80	24
0130	Random sized flats, corner stones		70	.571	V.L.F.	10.70	18.50		29.20	43
0140	Field stones		140	.286	S.F.	8.90	9.25		18.15	25.50
0150	Horizontal lined ledgestones, corner stones		75	.533	V.L.F.	10.40	17.25		27.65	40.50
0160	Field stones		150	.267	S.F.	7.55	8.65		16.20	23
0170	Random shaped flats, corner stones		65	.615	V.L.F.	10.40	19.95		30.35	45
0180	Field stones		150	.267	S.F.	7.55	8.65		16.20	23
0190	Random shaped/textured face, corner stones		65	.615	V.L.F.	10.40	19.95		30.35	45
0200	Field stones		130	.308	S.F.	7.55	9.95		17.50	25
0210	Random shaped river rock, corner stones		65	.615	V.L.F.	10.40	19.95		30.35	45
0220	Field stones		130	.308	S.F.	7.55	9.95		17.50	25
0240	On concrete or CMU substrate, random sized cobbles, corner stones		70	.571	V.L.F.	9.75	18.50		28.25	41.50
0250	Field stones		140	.286	S.F.	7.20	9.25		16.45	23.50
0260	Random sized flats, corner stones		70	.571	V.L.F.	10.05	18.50		28.55	42
0270	Field stones		140	.286	S.F.	8.55	9.25		17.80	25
0280	Horizontal lined ledgestones, corner stones		75	.533	V.L.F.	9.75	17.25		27	39.50
0290	Field stones		150	.267	S.F.	7.20	8.65		15.85	22.50
0300	Random shaped flats, corner stones		70	.571	V.L.F.	9.75	18.50		28.25	41.50
0310	Field stones		140	.286	S.F.	7.20	9.25		16.45	23.50

333

04 72 Cast Stone Masonry

04 72 20 – Cultured Stone Veneer

04 72 20.10 Cultured Stone Veneer Components	Crew	Daily Output	Labor-Hours	Unit	Material	2017 Bare Costs Labor	Equipment	Total	Total Incl O&P
0320	Random shaped/textured face, corner stones	D-8	65	.615	V.L.F.	9.75	19.95		29.70	44
0330	Field stones		130	.308	S.F.	7.20	9.95		17.15	24.50
0340	Random shaped river rock, corner stones		65	.615	V.L.F.	9.75	19.95		29.70	44
0350	Field stones		130	.308	S.F.	7.20	9.95		17.15	24.50
0360	Cultured stone veneer, #15 felt weather resistant barrier	1 Clab	3700	.002	Sq.	5.30	.06		5.36	5.95
0390	Water table or window sill, 18" long	1 Bric	80	.100	Ea.	10	3.49		13.49	16.85

334

Estimating Tips

05 05 00 Common Work Results for Metals

- Nuts, bolts, washers, connection angles, and plates can add a significant amount to both the tonnage of a structural steel job and the estimated cost. As a rule of thumb, add 10% to the total weight to account for these accessories.

- Type 2 steel construction, commonly referred to as "simple construction," consists generally of field-bolted connections with lateral bracing supplied by other elements of the building, such as masonry walls or x-bracing. The estimator should be aware, however, that shop connections may be accomplished by welding or bolting. The method may be particular to the fabrication shop and may have an impact on the estimated cost.

05 10 00 Structural Steel

- Steel items can be obtained from two sources: a fabrication shop or a metals service center. Fabrication shops can fabricate items under more controlled conditions than crews in the field can. They are also more efficient and can produce items more economically. Metal service centers serve as a source of long mill shapes to both fabrication shops and contractors.

- Most line items in this structural steel subdivision, and most items in 05 50 00 Metal Fabrications, are indicated as being shop fabricated. The bare material cost for these shop fabricated items is the "Invoice Cost" from the shop and includes the mill base price of steel plus mill extras, transportation to the shop, shop drawings and detailing where warranted, shop fabrication and handling, sandblasting and a shop coat of primer paint, all necessary structural bolts, and delivery to the job site. The bare labor cost and bare equipment cost for these shop fabricated items are for field installation or erection.

- Line items in Subdivision 05 12 23.40 Lightweight Framing, and other items scattered in Division 5, are indicated as being field fabricated. The bare material cost for these field fabricated items is the "Invoice Cost" from the metals service center and includes the mill base price of steel plus mill extras, transportation to the metals service center, material handling, and delivery of long lengths of mill shapes to the job site. Material costs for structural bolts and welding rods should be added to the estimate. The bare labor cost and bare equipment cost for these items are for both field fabrication and field installation or erection, and include time for cutting, welding, and drilling in the fabricated metal items. Drilling into concrete and fasteners to fasten field fabricated items to other work are not included and should be added to the estimate.

05 20 00 Steel Joist Framing

- In any given project the total weight of open web steel joists is determined by the loads to be supported and the design. However, economies can be realized in minimizing the amount of labor used to place the joists. This is done by maximizing the joist spacing, and therefore minimizing the number of joists required to be installed on the job. Certain spacings and locations may be required by the design, but in other cases maximizing the spacing and keeping it as uniform as possible will keep the costs down.

05 30 00 Steel Decking

- The takeoff and estimating of a metal deck involves more than the area of the floor or roof and the type of deck specified or shown on the drawings. Many different sizes and types of openings may exist. Small openings

for individual pipes or conduits may be drilled after the floor/roof is installed, but larger openings may require special deck lengths as well as reinforcing or structural support. The estimator should determine who will be supplying this reinforcing. Additionally, some deck terminations are part of the deck package, such as screed angles and pour stops, and others will be part of the steel contract, such as angles attached to structural members and cast-in-place angles and plates. The estimator must ensure that all pieces are accounted for in the complete estimate.

05 50 00 Metal Fabrications

- The most economical steel stairs are those that use common materials, standard details, and most importantly, a uniform and relatively simple method of field assembly. Commonly available A36/A992 channels and plates are very good choices for the main stringers of the stairs, as are angles and tees for the carrier members. Risers and treads are usually made by specialty shops, and it is most economical to use a typical detail in as many places as possible. The stairs should be pre-assembled and shipped directly to the site. The field connections should be simple and straightforward enough to be accomplished efficiently, and with minimum equipment and labor.

Reference Numbers

Reference numbers are shown at the beginning of some major classifications. These numbers refer to related items in the Reference Section. The reference information may be an estimating procedure, an alternate pricing method, or technical information.

Note: Not all subdivisions listed here necessarily appear. ∎

Did you know?

Our online estimating solution gives you the same access to RSMeans' data with 24/7 access:

- Quickly locate costs in the searchable database.
- Build cost lists, estimates, and reports in minutes.
- Adjust costs to any location in the U.S. and Canada with the click of a button.

Start your free trial today at
www.RSMeansOnline.com

05 05 Common Work Results for Metals

05 05 19 – Post-Installed Concrete Anchors

05 05 19.10 Chemical Anchors

		Crew	Daily Output	Labor-Hours	Unit	Material	2017 Bare Costs Labor	Equipment	Total	Total Incl O&P
0010	**CHEMICAL ANCHORS**									
0020	Includes layout & drilling									
1430	Chemical anchor, w/rod & epoxy cartridge, 3/4" diam. x 9-1/2" long	B-89A	27	.593	Ea.	9.80	18.50	4.24	32.54	46.50
1435	1" diameter x 11-3/4" long		24	.667		18.25	21	4.77	44.02	60.50
1440	1-1/4" diameter x 14" long		21	.762		37	24	5.45	66.45	87
1445	1-3/4" diameter x 15" long		20	.800		65	25	5.75	95.75	120
1450	18" long		17	.941		78	29.50	6.75	114.25	142
1455	2" diameter x 18" long		16	1		103	31	7.15	141.15	173
1460	24" long	▼	15	1.067	▼	134	33.50	7.65	175.15	211

05 05 19.20 Expansion Anchors

			Crew	Daily Output	Labor-Hours	Unit	Material	2017 Bare Costs Labor	Equipment	Total	Total Incl O&P
0010	**EXPANSION ANCHORS**										
0100	Anchors for concrete, brick or stone, no layout and drilling										
0200	Expansion shields, zinc, 1/4" diameter, 1-5/16" long, single	G	1 Carp	90	.089	Ea.	.45	3.11		3.56	5.70
0300	1-3/8" long, double	G		85	.094		.55	3.29		3.84	6.10
0400	3/8" diameter, 1-1/2" long, single	G		85	.094		.68	3.29		3.97	6.25
0500	2" long, double	G		80	.100		1.22	3.50		4.72	7.20
0600	1/2" diameter, 2-1/16" long, single	G		80	.100		1.25	3.50		4.75	7.25
0700	2-1/2" long, double	G		75	.107		2.35	3.73		6.08	8.85
0800	5/8" diameter, 2-5/8" long, single	G		75	.107		2.16	3.73		5.89	8.65
0900	2-3/4" long, double	G		70	.114		3.31	3.99		7.30	10.35
1000	3/4" diameter, 2-3/4" long, single	G		70	.114		3.27	3.99		7.26	10.30
1100	3-15/16" long, double	G	▼	65	.123	▼	6.15	4.30		10.45	14
2100	Hollow wall anchors for gypsum wall board, plaster or tile										
2500	3/16" diameter, short	G	1 Carp	150	.053	Ea.	.47	1.86		2.33	3.64
3000	Toggle bolts, bright steel, 1/8" diameter, 2" long	G		85	.094		.22	3.29		3.51	5.75
3100	4" long	G		80	.100		.27	3.50		3.77	6.15
3200	3/16" diameter, 3" long	G		80	.100		.29	3.50		3.79	6.15
3300	6" long	G		75	.107		.38	3.73		4.11	6.65
3400	1/4" diameter, 3" long	G		75	.107		.36	3.73		4.09	6.65
3500	6" long	G		70	.114		.54	3.99		4.53	7.30
3600	3/8" diameter, 3" long	G		70	.114		.96	3.99		4.95	7.75
3700	6" long	G		60	.133		1.38	4.66		6.04	9.30
3800	1/2" diameter, 4" long	G		60	.133		1.94	4.66		6.60	9.95
3900	6" long	G	▼	50	.160	▼	2.48	5.60		8.08	12.10
4000	Nailing anchors										
4100	Nylon nailing anchor, 1/4" diameter, 1" long		1 Carp	3.20	2.500	C	22	87.50		109.50	170
4200	1-1/2" long			2.80	2.857		26	100		126	196
4300	2" long			2.40	3.333		30.50	117		147.50	229
4400	Metal nailing anchor, 1/4" diameter, 1" long	G		3.20	2.500		20.50	87.50		108	169
4500	1-1/2" long	G		2.80	2.857		26	100		126	196
4600	2" long	G	▼	2.40	3.333	▼	31.50	117		148.50	230
5000	Screw anchors for concrete, masonry,										
5100	stone & tile, no layout or drilling included										
5700	Lag screw shields, 1/4" diameter, short	G	1 Carp	90	.089	Ea.	.37	3.11		3.48	5.60
5800	Long	G		85	.094		.43	3.29		3.72	5.95
5900	3/8" diameter, short	G		85	.094		.72	3.29		4.01	6.30
6000	Long	G		80	.100		.95	3.50		4.45	6.90
6100	1/2" diameter, short	G		80	.100		1.06	3.50		4.56	7
6200	Long	G		75	.107		1.35	3.73		5.08	7.75
6300	5/8" diameter, short	G		70	.114		1.64	3.99		5.63	8.50
6400	Long	G		65	.123		2.05	4.30		6.35	9.45
6600	Lead, #6 & #8, 3/4" long	G		260	.031		.20	1.08		1.28	2.02

336

05 05 Common Work Results for Metals

05 05 19 – Post-Installed Concrete Anchors

05 05 19.20 Expansion Anchors

		Crew	Daily Output	Labor-Hours	Unit	Material	2017 Bare Costs Labor	Equipment	Total	Total Incl O&P
6700	#10 - #14, 1-1/2" long [G]	1 Carp	200	.040	Ea.	.41	1.40		1.81	2.79
6800	#16 & #18, 1-1/2" long [G]		160	.050		.43	1.75		2.18	3.39
6900	Plastic, #6 & #8, 3/4" long		260	.031		.04	1.08		1.12	1.84
7000	#8 & #10, 7/8" long		240	.033		.04	1.16		1.20	1.99
7100	#10 & #12, 1" long		220	.036		.05	1.27		1.32	2.19
7200	#14 & #16, 1-1/2" long		160	.050		.08	1.75		1.83	3.01
8950	Self-drilling concrete screw, hex washer head, 3/16" diam. x 1-3/4" long [G]		300	.027		.21	.93		1.14	1.79
8960	2-1/4" long [G]		250	.032		.25	1.12		1.37	2.15
8970	Phillips flat head, 3/16" diam. x 1-3/4" long [G]		300	.027		.21	.93		1.14	1.79
8980	2-1/4" long [G]		250	.032		.24	1.12		1.36	2.13

05 05 21 – Fastening Methods for Metal

05 05 21.15 Drilling Steel

		Crew	Daily Output	Labor-Hours	Unit	Material	2017 Bare Costs Labor	Equipment	Total	Total Incl O&P
0010	**DRILLING STEEL**									
1910	Drilling & layout for steel, up to 1/4" deep, no anchor									
1920	Holes, 1/4" diameter	1 Sswk	112	.071	Ea.	.10	2.75		2.85	5.10
1925	For each additional 1/4" depth, add		336	.024		.10	.92		1.02	1.77
1930	3/8" diameter		104	.077		.09	2.97		3.06	5.45
1935	For each additional 1/4" depth, add		312	.026		.09	.99		1.08	1.89
1940	1/2" diameter		96	.083		.11	3.21		3.32	5.95
1945	For each additional 1/4" depth, add		288	.028		.11	1.07		1.18	2.06
1950	5/8" diameter		88	.091		.16	3.50		3.66	6.55
1955	For each additional 1/4" depth, add		264	.030		.16	1.17		1.33	2.29
1960	3/4" diameter		80	.100		.20	3.86		4.06	7.15
1965	For each additional 1/4" depth, add		240	.033		.20	1.28		1.48	2.54
1970	7/8" diameter		72	.111		.26	4.28		4.54	8.05
1975	For each additional 1/4" depth, add		216	.037		.26	1.43		1.69	2.87
1980	1" diameter		64	.125		.23	4.82		5.05	8.95
1985	For each additional 1/4" depth, add		192	.042		.23	1.61		1.84	3.15
1990	For drilling up, add						40%			

05 05 23 – Metal Fastenings

05 05 23.10 Bolts and Hex Nuts

		Crew	Daily Output	Labor-Hours	Unit	Material	2017 Bare Costs Labor	Equipment	Total	Total Incl O&P
0010	**BOLTS & HEX NUTS**, Steel, A307									
0100	1/4" diameter, 1/2" long [G]	1 Sswk	140	.057	Ea.	.06	2.20		2.26	4.05
0200	1" long [G]		140	.057		.07	2.20		2.27	4.06
0300	2" long [G]		130	.062		.10	2.37		2.47	4.40
0400	3" long [G]		130	.062		.15	2.37		2.52	4.46
0500	4" long [G]		120	.067		.17	2.57		2.74	4.82
0600	3/8" diameter, 1" long [G]		130	.062		.14	2.37		2.51	4.45
0700	2" long [G]		130	.062		.18	2.37		2.55	4.49
0800	3" long [G]		120	.067		.24	2.57		2.81	4.90
0900	4" long [G]		120	.067		.30	2.57		2.87	4.97
1000	5" long [G]		115	.070		.38	2.68		3.06	5.25
1100	1/2" diameter, 1-1/2" long [G]		120	.067		.40	2.57		2.97	5.10
1200	2" long [G]		120	.067		.46	2.57		3.03	5.15
1300	4" long [G]		115	.070		.75	2.68		3.43	5.70
1400	6" long [G]		110	.073		1.05	2.80		3.85	6.20
1500	8" long [G]		105	.076		1.38	2.94		4.32	6.80
1600	5/8" diameter, 1-1/2" long [G]		120	.067		.85	2.57		3.42	5.60
1700	2" long [G]		120	.067		.94	2.57		3.51	5.65
1800	4" long [G]		115	.070		1.34	2.68		4.02	6.35
1900	6" long [G]		110	.073		1.72	2.80		4.52	6.95
2000	8" long [G]		105	.076		2.55	2.94		5.49	8.10

For customer support on your Residential Costs with RSMeans Data, call 800.448.8182.

337

05 05 23.10 Bolts and Hex Nuts

			Crew	Daily Output	Labor-Hours	Unit	Material	2017 Bare Costs Labor	Equipment	Total	Total Incl O&P
2100	10" long	G	1 Sswk	100	.080	Ea.	3.20	3.08		6.28	9.05
2200	3/4" diameter, 2" long	G		120	.067		1.15	2.57		3.72	5.90
2300	4" long	G		110	.073		1.65	2.80		4.45	6.85
2400	6" long	G		105	.076		2.12	2.94		5.06	7.65
2500	8" long	G		95	.084		3.20	3.25		6.45	9.35
2600	10" long	G		85	.094		4.20	3.63		7.83	11.15
2700	12" long	G		80	.100		4.92	3.86		8.78	12.35
2800	1" diameter, 3" long	G		105	.076		2.67	2.94		5.61	8.25
2900	6" long	G		90	.089		3.92	3.43		7.35	10.50
3000	12" long	G		75	.107		7.05	4.11		11.16	15.25
3100	For galvanized, add						75%				
3200	For stainless, add						350%				

05 05 23.30 Lag Screws

			Crew	Daily Output	Labor-Hours	Unit	Material	2017 Bare Costs Labor	Equipment	Total	Total Incl O&P
0010	**LAG SCREWS**										
0020	Steel, 1/4" diameter, 2" long	G	1 Carp	200	.040	Ea.	.11	1.40		1.51	2.46
0100	3/8" diameter, 3" long	G		150	.053		.34	1.86		2.20	3.49
0200	1/2" diameter, 3" long	G		130	.062		.70	2.15		2.85	4.37
0300	5/8" diameter, 3" long	G		120	.067		1.20	2.33		3.53	5.20

05 05 23.50 Powder Actuated Tools and Fasteners

			Crew	Daily Output	Labor-Hours	Unit	Material	2017 Bare Costs Labor	Equipment	Total	Total Incl O&P
0010	**POWDER ACTUATED TOOLS & FASTENERS**										
0020	Stud driver, .22 caliber, single shot					Ea.	151			151	166
0100	.27 caliber, semi automatic, strip					"	460			460	505
0300	Powder load, single shot, .22 cal, power level 2, brown					C	5.60			5.60	6.20
0400	Strip, .27 cal, power level 4, red						8.10			8.10	8.90
0600	Drive pin, .300 x 3/4" long	G	1 Carp	4.80	1.667		4.36	58.50		62.86	102
0700	.300 x 3" long with washer	G	"	4	2		13.30	70		83.30	132

05 05 23.55 Rivets

			Crew	Daily Output	Labor-Hours	Unit	Material	2017 Bare Costs Labor	Equipment	Total	Total Incl O&P
0010	**RIVETS**										
0100	Aluminum rivet & mandrel, 1/2" grip length x 1/8" diameter	G	1 Carp	4.80	1.667	C	8.80	58.50		67.30	107
0200	3/16" diameter	G		4	2		12.95	70		82.95	131
0300	Aluminum rivet, steel mandrel, 1/8" diameter	G		4.80	1.667		10.35	58.50		68.85	109
0400	3/16" diameter	G		4	2		16.60	70		86.60	135
0500	Copper rivet, steel mandrel, 1/8" diameter	G		4.80	1.667		9.95	58.50		68.45	108
0800	Stainless rivet & mandrel, 1/8" diameter	G		4.80	1.667		28	58.50		86.50	128
0900	3/16" diameter	G		4	2		44	70		114	166
1000	Stainless rivet, steel mandrel, 1/8" diameter	G		4.80	1.667		16	58.50		74.50	115
1100	3/16" diameter	G		4	2		26	70		96	146
1200	Steel rivet and mandrel, 1/8" diameter	G		4.80	1.667		8.55	58.50		67.05	107
1300	3/16" diameter	G		4	2		13.70	70		83.70	132
1400	Hand riveting tool, standard					Ea.	76.50			76.50	84
1500	Deluxe						395			395	435
1600	Power riveting tool, standard						505			505	555
1700	Deluxe						1,650			1,650	1,825

05 12 Structural Steel Framing

05 12 23 – Structural Steel for Buildings

05 12 23.10 Ceiling Supports		Crew	Daily Output	Labor-Hours	Unit	Material	2017 Bare Costs Labor	Equipment	Total	Total Incl O&P
0010	**CEILING SUPPORTS**									
1000	Entrance door/folding partition supports, shop fabricated	G E-4	60	.533	L.F.	26	21	2.17	49.17	69
1100	Linear accelerator door supports	G	14	2.286		119	89.50	9.30	217.80	300
1200	Lintels or shelf angles, hung, exterior hot dipped galv.	G	267	.120		17.90	4.68	.49	23.07	28.50
1250	Two coats primer paint instead of galv.	G	267	.120		15.50	4.68	.49	20.67	26
1400	Monitor support, ceiling hung, expansion bolted	G	4	8	Ea.	415	310	32.50	757.50	1,050
1450	Hung from pre-set inserts	G	6	5.333		445	208	21.50	674.50	890
1600	Motor supports for overhead doors	G	4	8		211	310	32.50	553.50	835
1700	Partition support for heavy folding partitions, without pocket	G	24	1.333	L.F.	59.50	52	5.40	116.90	165
1750	Supports at pocket only	G	12	2.667		119	104	10.85	233.85	330
2000	Rolling grilles & fire door supports	G	34	.941		51	37	3.82	91.82	127
2100	Spider-leg light supports, expansion bolted to ceiling slab	G	8	4	Ea.	170	156	16.25	342.25	485
2150	Hung from pre-set inserts	G	12	2.667	"	183	104	10.85	297.85	400
2400	Toilet partition support	G	36	.889	L.F.	59.50	34.50	3.61	97.61	132
2500	X-ray travel gantry support	G	12	2.667	"	204	104	10.85	318.85	425

05 12 23.15 Columns, Lightweight

		Crew	Daily Output	Labor-Hours	Unit	Material	Labor	Equipment	Total	Total Incl O&P
0010	**COLUMNS, LIGHTWEIGHT**									
8000	Lally columns, to 8', 3-1/2" diameter	2 Carp	24	.667	Ea.	44	23.50		67.50	87.50
8080	4" diameter	"	20	.800	"	54	28		82	107

05 12 23.17 Columns, Structural

		Crew	Daily Output	Labor-Hours	Unit	Material	Labor	Equipment	Total	Total Incl O&P
0010	**COLUMNS, STRUCTURAL**									
0015	Made from recycled materials									
0020	Shop fab'd for 100-ton, 1-2 story project, bolted connections									
0800	Steel, concrete filled, extra strong pipe, 3-1/2" diameter	E-2	660	.073	L.F.	43.50	2.81	2.53	48.84	55.50
0830	4" diameter		780	.062		48	2.38	2.14	52.52	59.50
0890	5" diameter		1020	.047		57.50	1.82	1.64	60.96	68
0930	6" diameter		1200	.040		76	1.55	1.39	78.94	88
0940	8" diameter		1100	.044		76	1.69	1.52	79.21	88
1100	For galvanizing, add				Lb.	.25			.25	.27
1300	For web ties, angles, etc., add per added lb.	1 Sswk	945	.008		1.31	.33		1.64	2.03
1500	Steel pipe, extra strong, no concrete, 3" to 5" diameter	G E-2	16000	.003		1.31	.12	.10	1.53	1.76
1600	6" to 12" diameter	G	14000	.003		1.31	.13	.12	1.56	1.81
5100	Structural tubing, rect., 5" to 6" wide, light section	G	8000	.006		1.31	.23	.21	1.75	2.08
5200	Heavy section	G	12000	.004		1.31	.15	.14	1.60	1.87
8090	For projects 75 to 99 tons, add				%	10%				
8092	50 to 74 tons, add					20%				
8094	25 to 49 tons, add					30%	10%			
8096	10 to 24 tons, add					50%	25%			
8098	2 to 9 tons, add					75%	50%			
8099	Less than 2 tons, add					100%	100%			

05 12 23.45 Lintels

		Crew	Daily Output	Labor-Hours	Unit	Material	Labor	Equipment	Total	Total Incl O&P
0010	**LINTELS**									
0015	Made from recycled materials									
0020	Plain steel angles, shop fabricated, under 500 lb.	G 1 Bric	550	.015	Lb.	1.01	.51		1.52	1.96
0100	500 to 1000 lb.	G	640	.013	"	.98	.44		1.42	1.81
2000	Steel angles, 3-1/2" x 3", 1/4" thick, 2'-6" long	G	47	.170	Ea.	14.15	5.95		20.10	25.50
2100	4'-6" long	G	26	.308		25.50	10.70		36.20	46
2600	4" x 3-1/2", 1/4" thick, 5'-0" long	G	21	.381		32.50	13.30		45.80	58.50
2700	9'-0" long	G	12	.667		58.50	23		81.50	104

For customer support on your Residential Costs with RSMeans Data, call 800.448.8182.

339

05 12 Structural Steel Framing

05 12 23 – Structural Steel for Buildings

05 12 23.65 Plates

		Crew	Daily Output	Labor-Hours	Unit	Material	2017 Bare Costs Labor	Equipment	Total	Total Incl O&P
0010	**PLATES**									
0015	Made from recycled materials									
0020	For connections & stiffener plates, shop fabricated									
0050	1/8" thick (5.1 lb./S.F.)	G			S.F.	6.70			6.70	7.35
0100	1/4" thick (10.2 lb./S.F.)	G				13.35			13.35	14.70
0300	3/8" thick (15.3 lb./S.F.)	G				20			20	22
0400	1/2" thick (20.4 lb./S.F.)	G				26.50			26.50	29.50
0450	3/4" thick (30.6 lb./S.F.)	G				40			40	44
0500	1" thick (40.8 lb./S.F.)	G			↓	53.50			53.50	59
2000	Steel plate, warehouse prices, no shop fabrication									
2100	1/4" thick (10.2 lb./S.F.)	G			S.F.	6.05			6.05	6.65

05 12 23.79 Structural Steel

		Crew	Daily Output	Labor-Hours	Unit	Material	2017 Bare Costs Labor	Equipment	Total	Total Incl O&P
0010	**STRUCTURAL STEEL**									
0020	Shop fab'd for 100-ton, 1-2 story project, bolted conn's.									
0050	Beams, W 6 x 9	G	E-2	720	.067	L.F.	14.15	2.58	2.32	19.05	22.50
0100	W 8 x 10	G		720	.067		15.75	2.58	2.32	20.65	24.50
0200	Columns, W 6 x 15	G		540	.089		25.50	3.44	3.09	32.03	37.50
0250	W 8 x 31	G	↓	540	.089	↓	53	3.44	3.09	59.53	67.50
7990	For projects 75 to 99 tons, add					All	10%				
7992	50 to 75 tons, add						20%				
7994	25 to 49 tons, add						30%	10%			
7996	10 to 24 tons, add						50%	25%			
7998	2 to 9 tons, add						75%	50%			
7999	Less than 2 tons, add						100%	100%			

05 31 Steel Decking

05 31 23 – Steel Roof Decking

05 31 23.50 Roof Decking

		Crew	Daily Output	Labor-Hours	Unit	Material	2017 Bare Costs Labor	Equipment	Total	Total Incl O&P
0010	**ROOF DECKING**									
0015	Made from recycled materials									
2100	Open type, 1-1/2" deep, Type B, wide rib, galv., 22 ga., under 50 sq.	G	E-4	4500	.007	S.F.	2.32	.28	.03	2.63	3.08
2600	20 ga., under 50 squares	G		3865	.008		2.70	.32	.03	3.05	3.59
2900	18 ga., under 50 squares	G		3800	.008		3.49	.33	.03	3.85	4.47
3050	16 ga., under 50 squares	G	↓	3700	.009	↓	4.71	.34	.04	5.09	5.85

05 31 33 – Steel Form Decking

05 31 33.50 Form Decking

		Crew	Daily Output	Labor-Hours	Unit	Material	2017 Bare Costs Labor	Equipment	Total	Total Incl O&P
0010	**FORM DECKING**									
0015	Made from recycled materials									
6100	Slab form, steel, 28 ga., 9/16" deep, Type UFS, uncoated	G	E-4	4000	.008	S.F.	1.74	.31	.03	2.08	2.51
6200	Galvanized	G		4000	.008		1.54	.31	.03	1.88	2.29
6220	24 ga., 1" deep, Type UF1X, uncoated	G		3900	.008		1.67	.32	.03	2.02	2.46
6240	Galvanized	G		3900	.008		1.97	.32	.03	2.32	2.79
6300	24 ga., 1-5/16" deep, Type UFX, uncoated	G		3800	.008		1.78	.33	.03	2.14	2.58
6400	Galvanized	G		3800	.008		2.09	.33	.03	2.45	2.93
6500	22 ga., 1-5/16" deep, uncoated	G		3700	.009		2.25	.34	.04	2.63	3.13
6600	Galvanized	G		3700	.009		2.30	.34	.04	2.68	3.18
6700	22 ga., 2" deep, uncoated	G		3600	.009		2.93	.35	.04	3.32	3.89
6800	Galvanized	G	↓	3600	.009	↓	2.87	.35	.04	3.26	3.83

05 41 Structural Metal Stud Framing

05 41 13 – Load-Bearing Metal Stud Framing

05 41 13.05 Bracing

		Crew	Daily Output	Labor-Hours	Unit	Material	2017 Bare Costs Labor	Equipment	Total	Total Incl O&P
0010	**BRACING**, shear wall X-bracing, per 10' x 10' bay, one face									
0015	Made of recycled materials									
0120	Metal strap, 20 ga. x 4" wide	G	2 Carp	18	.889	Ea.	18.90	31		49.90	73
0130	6" wide	G		18	.889		31.50	31		62.50	86.50
0160	18 ga. x 4" wide	G		16	1		33	35		68	94.50
0170	6" wide	G		16	1		48.50	35		83.50	112
0410	Continuous strap bracing, per horizontal row on both faces									
0420	Metal strap, 20 ga. x 2" wide, studs 12" O.C.	G	1 Carp	7	1.143	C.L.F.	57	40		97	130
0430	16" O.C.	G		8	1		57	35		92	122
0440	24" O.C.	G		10	.800		57	28		85	110
0450	18 ga. x 2" wide, studs 12" O.C.	G		6	1.333		79	46.50		125.50	165
0460	16" O.C.	G		7	1.143		79	40		119	154
0470	24" O.C.	G		8	1		79	35		114	146

05 41 13.10 Bridging

		Crew	Daily Output	Labor-Hours	Unit	Material	2017 Bare Costs Labor	Equipment	Total	Total Incl O&P
0010	**BRIDGING**, solid between studs w/1-1/4" leg track, per stud bay									
0015	Made from recycled materials									
0200	Studs 12" O.C., 18 ga. x 2-1/2" wide	G	1 Carp	125	.064	Ea.	.95	2.24		3.19	4.79
0210	3-5/8" wide	G		120	.067		1.16	2.33		3.49	5.15
0220	4" wide	G		120	.067		1.22	2.33		3.55	5.25
0230	6" wide	G		115	.070		1.60	2.43		4.03	5.85
0240	8" wide	G		110	.073		1.97	2.54		4.51	6.40
0300	16 ga. x 2-1/2" wide	G		115	.070		1.21	2.43		3.64	5.40
0310	3-5/8" wide	G		110	.073		1.47	2.54		4.01	5.85
0320	4" wide	G		110	.073		1.57	2.54		4.11	6
0330	6" wide	G		105	.076		2.01	2.66		4.67	6.65
0340	8" wide	G		100	.080		2.51	2.80		5.31	7.45
1200	Studs 16" O.C., 18 ga. x 2-1/2" wide	G		125	.064		1.22	2.24		3.46	5.10
1210	3-5/8" wide	G		120	.067		1.49	2.33		3.82	5.55
1220	4" wide	G		120	.067		1.57	2.33		3.90	5.60
1230	6" wide	G		115	.070		2.05	2.43		4.48	6.30
1240	8" wide	G		110	.073		2.52	2.54		5.06	7.05
1300	16 ga. x 2-1/2" wide	G		115	.070		1.55	2.43		3.98	5.80
1310	3-5/8" wide	G		110	.073		1.88	2.54		4.42	6.30
1320	4" wide	G		110	.073		2.01	2.54		4.55	6.45
1330	6" wide	G		105	.076		2.57	2.66		5.23	7.30
1340	8" wide	G		100	.080		3.22	2.80		6.02	8.20
2200	Studs 24" O.C., 18 ga. x 2-1/2" wide	G		125	.064		1.77	2.24		4.01	5.70
2210	3-5/8" wide	G		120	.067		2.15	2.33		4.48	6.25
2220	4" wide	G		120	.067		2.27	2.33		4.60	6.40
2230	6" wide	G		115	.070		2.96	2.43		5.39	7.35
2240	8" wide	G		110	.073		3.65	2.54		6.19	8.25
2300	16 ga. x 2-1/2" wide	G		115	.070		2.24	2.43		4.67	6.55
2310	3-5/8" wide	G		110	.073		2.72	2.54		5.26	7.25
2320	4" wide	G		110	.073		2.91	2.54		5.45	7.45
2330	6" wide	G		105	.076		3.72	2.66		6.38	8.55
2340	8" wide	G		100	.080		4.65	2.80		7.45	9.80
3000	Continuous bridging, per row									
3100	16 ga. x 1-1/2" channel thru studs 12" O.C.	G	1 Carp	6	1.333	C.L.F.	51.50	46.50		98	135
3110	16" O.C.	G		7	1.143		51.50	40		91.50	124
3120	24" O.C.	G		8.80	.909		51.50	32		83.50	110
4100	2" x 2" angle x 18 ga., studs 12" O.C.	G		7	1.143		80.50	40		120.50	156
4110	16" O.C.	G		9	.889		80.50	31		111.50	141

05 41 Structural Metal Stud Framing

05 41 13 – Load-Bearing Metal Stud Framing

05 41 13.10 Bridging

		Crew	Daily Output	Labor-Hours	Unit	Material	2017 Bare Costs Labor	Equipment	Total	Total Incl O&P
4120	24" O.C.	G 1 Carp	12	.667	C.L.F.	80.50	23.50		104	128
4200	16 ga., studs 12" O.C.	G	5	1.600		101	56		157	205
4210	16" O.C.	G	7	1.143		101	40		141	178
4220	24" O.C.	G	10	.800		101	28		129	158

05 41 13.25 Framing, Boxed Headers/Beams

		Crew	Daily Output	Labor-Hours	Unit	Material	2017 Bare Costs Labor	Equipment	Total	Total Incl O&P
0010	**FRAMING, BOXED HEADERS/BEAMS**									
0015	Made from recycled materials									
0200	Double, 18 ga. x 6" deep	G 2 Carp	220	.073	L.F.	5.50	2.54		8.04	10.30
0210	8" deep	G	210	.076		6.05	2.66		8.71	11.10
0220	10" deep	G	200	.080		7.40	2.80		10.20	12.85
0230	12" deep	G	190	.084		8.05	2.94		10.99	13.75
0300	16 ga. x 8" deep	G	180	.089		7	3.11		10.11	12.90
0310	10" deep	G	170	.094		8.45	3.29		11.74	14.65
0320	12" deep	G	160	.100		9.15	3.50		12.65	15.95
0400	14 ga. x 10" deep	G	140	.114		9.75	3.99		13.74	17.40
0410	12" deep	G	130	.123		10.65	4.30		14.95	18.95
1210	Triple, 18 ga. x 8" deep	G	170	.094		8.75	3.29		12.04	15.15
1220	10" deep	G	165	.097		10.60	3.39		13.99	17.30
1230	12" deep	G	160	.100		11.60	3.50		15.10	18.60
1300	16 ga. x 8" deep	G	145	.110		10.15	3.86		14.01	17.60
1310	10" deep	G	140	.114		12.15	3.99		16.14	20
1320	12" deep	G	135	.119		13.25	4.14		17.39	21.50
1400	14 ga. x 10" deep	G	115	.139		13.25	4.86		18.11	23
1410	12" deep	G	110	.145		14.65	5.10		19.75	24.50

05 41 13.30 Framing, Stud Walls

		Crew	Daily Output	Labor-Hours	Unit	Material	2017 Bare Costs Labor	Equipment	Total	Total Incl O&P
0010	**FRAMING, STUD WALLS** w/top & bottom track, no openings,									
0020	Headers, beams, bridging or bracing									
0025	Made from recycled materials									
4100	8' high walls, 18 ga. x 2-1/2" wide, studs 12" O.C.	G 2 Carp	54	.296	L.F.	9.15	10.35		19.50	27.50
4110	16" O.C.	G	77	.208		7.35	7.25		14.60	20
4120	24" O.C.	G	107	.150		5.50	5.25		10.75	14.80
4130	3-5/8" wide, studs 12" O.C.	G	53	.302		10.85	10.55		21.40	29.50
4140	16" O.C.	G	76	.211		8.70	7.35		16.05	22
4150	24" O.C.	G	105	.152		6.55	5.35		11.90	16.10
4160	4" wide, studs 12" O.C.	G	52	.308		11.30	10.75		22.05	30.50
4170	16" O.C.	G	74	.216		9.05	7.55		16.60	22.50
4180	24" O.C.	G	103	.155		6.80	5.45		12.25	16.60
4190	6" wide, studs 12" O.C.	G	51	.314		14.40	10.95		25.35	34
4200	16" O.C.	G	73	.219		11.55	7.65		19.20	25.50
4210	24" O.C.	G	101	.158		8.70	5.55		14.25	18.85
4220	8" wide, studs 12" O.C.	G	50	.320		17.45	11.20		28.65	38
4230	16" O.C.	G	72	.222		14	7.75		21.75	28.50
4240	24" O.C.	G	100	.160		10.60	5.60		16.20	21
4300	16 ga. x 2-1/2" wide, studs 12" O.C.	G	47	.340		10.85	11.90		22.75	32
4310	16" O.C.	G	68	.235		8.60	8.20		16.80	23
4320	24" O.C.	G	94	.170		6.35	5.95		12.30	16.90
4330	3-5/8" wide, studs 12" O.C.	G	46	.348		12.95	12.15		25.10	34.50
4340	16" O.C.	G	66	.242		10.25	8.45		18.70	25.50
4350	24" O.C.	G	92	.174		7.55	6.10		13.65	18.45
4360	4" wide, studs 12" O.C.	G	45	.356		13.55	12.45		26	36
4370	16" O.C.	G	65	.246		10.75	8.60		19.35	26
4380	24" O.C.	G	90	.178		7.95	6.20		14.15	19.10

05 41 13 – Load-Bearing Metal Stud Framing

05 41 13.30 Framing, Stud Walls		Crew	Daily Output	Labor-Hours	Unit	Material	2017 Bare Costs Labor	Equipment	Total	Total Incl O&P
4390	6" wide, studs 12" O.C.	G	2 Carp	44	.364	L.F.	17.05	12.70		29.75	40.50
4400	16" O.C.	G		64	.250		13.55	8.75		22.30	29.50
4410	24" O.C.	G		88	.182		10.05	6.35		16.40	21.50
4420	8" wide, studs 12" O.C.	G		43	.372		21	13		34	45
4430	16" O.C.	G		63	.254		16.60	8.90		25.50	33
4440	24" O.C.	G		86	.186		12.30	6.50		18.80	24.50
5100	10' high walls, 18 ga. x 2-1/2" wide, studs 12" O.C.	G		54	.296		11	10.35		21.35	29.50
5110	16" O.C.	G		77	.208		8.70	7.25		15.95	22
5120	24" O.C.	G		107	.150		6.40	5.25		11.65	15.80
5130	3-5/8" wide, studs 12" O.C.	G		53	.302		13	10.55		23.55	32
5140	16" O.C.	G		76	.211		10.30	7.35		17.65	23.50
5150	24" O.C.	G		105	.152		7.60	5.35		12.95	17.25
5160	4" wide, studs 12" O.C.	G		52	.308		13.55	10.75		24.30	33
5170	16" O.C.	G		74	.216		10.75	7.55		18.30	24.50
5180	24" O.C.	G		103	.155		7.95	5.45		13.40	17.80
5190	6" wide, studs 12" O.C.	G		51	.314		17.25	10.95		28.20	37.50
5200	16" O.C.	G		73	.219		13.70	7.65		21.35	28
5210	24" O.C.	G		101	.158		10.15	5.55		15.70	20.50
5220	8" wide, studs 12" O.C.	G		50	.320		21	11.20		32.20	41.50
5230	16" O.C.	G		72	.222		16.55	7.75		24.30	31.50
5240	24" O.C.	G		100	.160		12.30	5.60		17.90	23
5300	16 ga. x 2-1/2" wide, studs 12" O.C.	G		47	.340		13.10	11.90		25	34.50
5310	16" O.C.	G		68	.235		10.30	8.20		18.50	25
5320	24" O.C.	G		94	.170		7.45	5.95		13.40	18.15
5330	3-5/8" wide, studs 12" O.C.	G		46	.348		15.60	12.15		27.75	37.50
5340	16" O.C.	G		66	.242		12.25	8.45		20.70	27.50
5350	24" O.C.	G		92	.174		8.90	6.10		15	19.95
5360	4" wide, studs 12" O.C.	G		45	.356		16.35	12.45		28.80	39
5370	16" O.C.	G		65	.246		12.85	8.60		21.45	28.50
5380	24" O.C.	G		90	.178		9.35	6.20		15.55	20.50
5390	6" wide, studs 12" O.C.	G		44	.364		20.50	12.70		33.20	44
5400	16" O.C.	G		64	.250		16.15	8.75		24.90	32.50
5410	24" O.C.	G		88	.182		11.80	6.35		18.15	23.50
5420	8" wide, studs 12" O.C.	G		43	.372		25	13		38	49.50
5430	16" O.C.	G		63	.254		19.80	8.90		28.70	37
5440	24" O.C.	G		86	.186		14.45	6.50		20.95	27
6190	12' high walls, 18 ga. x 6" wide, studs 12" O.C.	G		41	.390		20	13.65		33.65	45
6200	16" O.C.	G		58	.276		15.80	9.65		25.45	33.50
6210	24" O.C.	G		81	.198		11.55	6.90		18.45	24.50
6220	8" wide, studs 12" O.C.	G		40	.400		24.50	14		38.50	50
6230	16" O.C.	G		57	.281		19.15	9.80		28.95	37.50
6240	24" O.C.	G		80	.200		14	7		21	27
6390	16 ga. x 6" wide, studs 12" O.C.	G		35	.457		24	16		40	53
6400	16" O.C.	G		51	.314		18.80	10.95		29.75	39
6410	24" O.C.	G		70	.229		13.55	8		21.55	28.50
6420	8" wide, studs 12" O.C.	G		34	.471		29.50	16.45		45.95	60
6430	16" O.C.	G		50	.320		23	11.20		34.20	44
6440	24" O.C.	G		69	.232		16.60	8.10		24.70	32
6530	14 ga. x 3-5/8" wide, studs 12" O.C.	G		34	.471		22.50	16.45		38.95	52.50
6540	16" O.C.	G		48	.333		17.75	11.65		29.40	39
6550	24" O.C.	G		65	.246		12.75	8.60		21.35	28.50
6560	4" wide, studs 12" O.C.	G		33	.485		24	16.95		40.95	55
6570	16" O.C.	G		47	.340		18.75	11.90		30.65	40.50

For customer support on your Residential Costs with RSMeans Data, call 800.448.8182.

343

05 41 Structural Metal Stud Framing

05 41 13 – Load-Bearing Metal Stud Framing

05 41 13.30 Framing, Stud Walls

			Crew	Daily Output	Labor-Hours	Unit	Material	2017 Bare Costs Labor	Equipment	Total	Total Incl O&P
6580	24" O.C.	G	2 Carp	64	.250	L.F.	13.50	8.75		22.25	29.50
6730	12 ga. x 3-5/8" wide, studs 12" O.C.	G		31	.516		31.50	18.05		49.55	64.50
6740	16" O.C.	G		43	.372		24.50	13		37.50	48.50
6750	24" O.C.	G		59	.271		17.15	9.50		26.65	34.50
6760	4" wide, studs 12" O.C.	G		30	.533		33.50	18.65		52.15	68
6770	16" O.C.	G		42	.381		26	13.30		39.30	51
6780	24" O.C.	G		58	.276		18.30	9.65		27.95	36
7390	16' high walls, 16 ga. x 6" wide, studs 12" O.C.	G		33	.485		31	16.95		47.95	62.50
7400	16" O.C.	G		48	.333		24	11.65		35.65	46
7410	24" O.C.	G		67	.239		17.05	8.35		25.40	32.50
7420	8" wide, studs 12" O.C.	G		32	.500		38	17.50		55.50	71
7430	16" O.C.	G		47	.340		29.50	11.90		41.40	52.50
7440	24" O.C.	G		66	.242		21	8.45		29.45	37
7560	14 ga. x 4" wide, studs 12" O.C.	G		31	.516		31	18.05		49.05	64
7570	16" O.C.	G		45	.356		24	12.45		36.45	47.50
7580	24" O.C.	G		61	.262		17	9.15		26.15	34
7590	6" wide, studs 12" O.C.	G		30	.533		39	18.65		57.65	74
7600	16" O.C.	G		44	.364		30	12.70		42.70	54.50
7610	24" O.C.	G		60	.267		21.50	9.30		30.80	39
7760	12 ga. x 4" wide, studs 12" O.C.	G		29	.552		44	19.30		63.30	80.50
7770	16" O.C.	G		40	.400		33.50	14		47.50	60.50
7780	24" O.C.	G		55	.291		23.50	10.15		33.65	42.50
7790	6" wide, studs 12" O.C.	G		28	.571		55.50	19.95		75.45	94.50
7800	16" O.C.	G		39	.410		42.50	14.35		56.85	70.50
7810	24" O.C.	G		54	.296		29.50	10.35		39.85	50
8590	20' high walls, 14 ga. x 6" wide, studs 12" O.C.	G		29	.552		48	19.30		67.30	85
8600	16" O.C.	G		42	.381		37	13.30		50.30	63
8610	24" O.C.	G		57	.281		26	9.80		35.80	45
8620	8" wide, studs 12" O.C.	G		28	.571		52	19.95		71.95	90.50
8630	16" O.C.	G		41	.390		40	13.65		53.65	67
8640	24" O.C.	G		56	.286		28.50	10		38.50	47.50
8790	12 ga. x 6" wide, studs 12" O.C.	G		27	.593		68	20.50		88.50	110
8800	16" O.C.	G		37	.432		52	15.10		67.10	83
8810	24" O.C.	G		51	.314		36	10.95		46.95	58
8820	8" wide, studs 12" O.C.	G		26	.615		82.50	21.50		104	127
8830	16" O.C.	G		36	.444		63	15.55		78.55	95.50
8840	24" O.C.	G		50	.320		43.50	11.20		54.70	66.50

05 42 Cold-Formed Metal Joist Framing

05 42 13 – Cold-Formed Metal Floor Joist Framing

05 42 13.05 Bracing

			Crew	Daily Output	Labor-Hours	Unit	Material	2017 Bare Costs Labor	Equipment	Total	Total Incl O&P
0010	**BRACING**, continuous, per row, top & bottom										
0015	Made from recycled materials										
0120	Flat strap, 20 ga. x 2" wide, joists at 12" O.C.	G	1 Carp	4.67	1.713	C.L.F.	60	60		120	166
0130	16" O.C.	G		5.33	1.501		57.50	52.50		110	151
0140	24" O.C.	G		6.66	1.201		55.50	42		97.50	131
0150	18 ga. x 2" wide, joists at 12" O.C.	G		4	2		78.50	70		148.50	204
0160	16" O.C.	G		4.67	1.713		77	60		137	185
0170	24" O.C.	G		5.33	1.501		75.50	52.50		128	171

05 42 13 – Cold-Formed Metal Floor Joist Framing

05 42 13.10 Bridging		Crew	Daily Output	Labor-Hours	Unit	Material	2017 Bare Costs Labor	Equipment	Total	Total Incl O&P
0010	**BRIDGING**, solid between joists w/1-1/4" leg track, per joist bay									
0015	Made from recycled materials									
0230	Joists 12" O.C., 18 ga. track x 6" wide	G	1 Carp	80	.100	Ea.	1.60	3.50		5.10	7.60
0240	8" wide	G		75	.107		1.97	3.73		5.70	8.40
0250	10" wide	G		70	.114		2.46	3.99		6.45	9.40
0260	12" wide	G		65	.123		2.78	4.30		7.08	10.25
0330	16 ga. track x 6" wide	G		70	.114		2.01	3.99		6	8.90
0340	8" wide	G		65	.123		2.51	4.30		6.81	9.95
0350	10" wide	G		60	.133		3.10	4.66		7.76	11.20
0360	12" wide	G		55	.145		3.58	5.10		8.68	12.45
0440	14 ga. track x 8" wide	G		60	.133		3.13	4.66		7.79	11.25
0450	10" wide	G		55	.145		3.89	5.10		8.99	12.80
0460	12" wide	G		50	.160		4.49	5.60		10.09	14.30
0550	12 ga. track x 10" wide	G		45	.178		5.70	6.20		11.90	16.65
0560	12" wide	G		40	.200		5.80	7		12.80	18.10
1230	16" O.C., 18 ga. track x 6" wide	G		80	.100		2.05	3.50		5.55	8.10
1240	8" wide	G		75	.107		2.52	3.73		6.25	9.05
1250	10" wide	G		70	.114		3.15	3.99		7.14	10.15
1260	12" wide	G		65	.123		3.56	4.30		7.86	11.10
1330	16 ga. track x 6" wide	G		70	.114		2.57	3.99		6.56	9.55
1340	8" wide	G		65	.123		3.22	4.30		7.52	10.75
1350	10" wide	G		60	.133		3.98	4.66		8.64	12.15
1360	12" wide	G		55	.145		4.59	5.10		9.69	13.55
1440	14 ga. track x 8" wide	G		60	.133		4.01	4.66		8.67	12.20
1450	10" wide	G		55	.145		4.98	5.10		10.08	14
1460	12" wide	G		50	.160		5.75	5.60		11.35	15.70
1550	12 ga. track x 10" wide	G		45	.178		7.30	6.20		13.50	18.40
1560	12" wide	G		40	.200		7.45	7		14.45	19.90
2230	24" O.C., 18 ga. track x 6" wide	G		80	.100		2.96	3.50		6.46	9.10
2240	8" wide	G		75	.107		3.65	3.73		7.38	10.25
2250	10" wide	G		70	.114		4.56	3.99		8.55	11.70
2260	12" wide	G		65	.123		5.15	4.30		9.45	12.85
2330	16 ga. track x 6" wide	G		70	.114		3.72	3.99		7.71	10.80
2340	8" wide	G		65	.123		4.65	4.30		8.95	12.30
2350	10" wide	G		60	.133		5.75	4.66		10.41	14.15
2360	12" wide	G		55	.145		6.65	5.10		11.75	15.80
2440	14 ga. track x 8" wide	G		60	.133		5.80	4.66		10.46	14.20
2450	10" wide	G		55	.145		7.20	5.10		12.30	16.45
2460	12" wide	G		50	.160		8.35	5.60		13.95	18.50
2550	12 ga. track x 10" wide	G		45	.178		10.55	6.20		16.75	22
2560	12" wide	G		40	.200		10.80	7		17.80	23.50

05 42 13.25 Framing, Band Joist

05 42 13.25 Framing, Band Joist		Crew	Daily Output	Labor-Hours	Unit	Material	2017 Bare Costs Labor	Equipment	Total	Total Incl O&P
0010	**FRAMING, BAND JOIST** (track) fastened to bearing wall										
0015	Made from recycled materials										
0220	18 ga. track x 6" deep	G	2 Carp	1000	.016	L.F.	1.30	.56		1.86	2.37
0230	8" deep	G		920	.017		1.61	.61		2.22	2.79
0240	10" deep	G		860	.019		2.01	.65		2.66	3.30
0320	16 ga. track x 6" deep	G		900	.018		1.64	.62		2.26	2.84
0330	8" deep	G		840	.019		2.05	.67		2.72	3.36
0340	10" deep	G		780	.021		2.53	.72		3.25	3.98
0350	12" deep	G		740	.022		2.92	.76		3.68	4.47
0430	14 ga. track x 8" deep	G		750	.021		2.55	.75		3.30	4.06

05 42 Cold-Formed Metal Joist Framing

05 42 13 – Cold-Formed Metal Floor Joist Framing

05 42 13.25 Framing, Band Joist

			Crew	Daily Output	Labor-Hours	Unit	Material	2017 Bare Costs Labor	Equipment	Total	Total Incl O&P
0440	10" deep	G	2 Carp	720	.022	L.F.	3.17	.78		3.95	4.79
0450	12" deep	G		700	.023		3.66	.80		4.46	5.35
0540	12 ga. track x 10" deep	G		670	.024		4.64	.83		5.47	6.50
0550	12" deep	G		650	.025		4.75	.86		5.61	6.65

05 42 13.30 Framing, Boxed Headers/Beams

			Crew	Daily Output	Labor-Hours	Unit	Material	2017 Bare Costs Labor	Equipment	Total	Total Incl O&P
0010	**FRAMING, BOXED HEADERS/BEAMS**										
0015	Made from recycled materials										
0200	Double, 18 ga. x 6" deep	G	2 Carp	220	.073	L.F.	5.50	2.54		8.04	10.30
0210	8" deep	G		210	.076		6.05	2.66		8.71	11.10
0220	10" deep	G		200	.080		7.40	2.80		10.20	12.85
0230	12" deep	G		190	.084		8.05	2.94		10.99	13.75
0300	16 ga. x 8" deep	G		180	.089		7	3.11		10.11	12.90
0310	10" deep	G		170	.094		8.45	3.29		11.74	14.75
0320	12" deep	G		160	.100		9.15	3.50		12.65	15.95
0400	14 ga. x 10" deep	G		140	.114		9.75	3.99		13.74	17.40
0410	12" deep	G		130	.123		10.65	4.30		14.95	18.95
0500	12 ga. x 10" deep	G		110	.145		12.85	5.10		17.95	22.50
0510	12" deep	G		100	.160		14.15	5.60		19.75	25
1210	Triple, 18 ga. x 8" deep	G		170	.094		8.75	3.29		12.04	15.15
1220	10" deep	G		165	.097		10.60	3.39		13.99	17.30
1230	12" deep	G		160	.100		11.60	3.50		15.10	18.60
1300	16 ga. x 8" deep	G		145	.110		10.15	3.86		14.01	17.60
1310	10" deep	G		140	.114		12.15	3.99		16.14	20
1320	12" deep	G		135	.119		13.25	4.14		17.39	21.50
1400	14 ga. x 10" deep	G		115	.139		14.10	4.86		18.96	23.50
1410	12" deep	G		110	.145		15.50	5.10		20.60	25.50
1500	12 ga. x 10" deep	G		90	.178		18.75	6.20		24.95	31
1510	12" deep	G		85	.188		21	6.60		27.60	34

05 42 13.40 Framing, Joists

			Crew	Daily Output	Labor-Hours	Unit	Material	2017 Bare Costs Labor	Equipment	Total	Total Incl O&P
0010	**FRAMING, JOISTS**, no band joists (track), web stiffeners, headers,										
0020	Beams, bridging or bracing										
0025	Made from recycled materials										
0030	Joists (2" flange) and fasteners, materials only										
0220	18 ga. x 6" deep	G				L.F.	1.69			1.69	1.86
0230	8" deep	G					1.98			1.98	2.18
0240	10" deep	G					2.34			2.34	2.58
0320	16 ga. x 6" deep	G					2.07			2.07	2.28
0330	8" deep	G					2.47			2.47	2.71
0340	10" deep	G					2.89			2.89	3.18
0350	12" deep	G					3.28			3.28	3.60
0430	14 ga. x 8" deep	G					3.10			3.10	3.41
0440	10" deep	G					3.57			3.57	3.93
0450	12" deep	G					4.06			4.06	4.47
0540	12 ga. x 10" deep	G					5.20			5.20	5.70
0550	12" deep	G					5.90			5.90	6.50
1010	Installation of joists to band joists, beams & headers, labor only										
1220	18 ga. x 6" deep		2 Carp	110	.145	Ea.		5.10		5.10	8.50
1230	8" deep			90	.178			6.20		6.20	10.40
1240	10" deep			80	.200			7		7	11.70
1320	16 ga. x 6" deep			95	.168			5.90		5.90	9.85
1330	8" deep			70	.229			8		8	13.35
1340	10" deep			60	.267			9.30		9.30	15.60

05 42 Cold-Formed Metal Joist Framing

05 42 13 – Cold-Formed Metal Floor Joist Framing

05 42 13.40 Framing, Joists

		Crew	Daily Output	Labor-Hours	Unit	Material	2017 Bare Costs Labor	Equipment	Total	Total Incl O&P
1350	12" deep	2 Carp	55	.291	Ea.		10.15		10.15	17
1430	14 ga. x 8" deep		65	.246			8.60		8.60	14.40
1440	10" deep		45	.356			12.45		12.45	21
1450	12" deep		35	.457			16		16	26.50
1540	12 ga. x 10" deep		40	.400			14		14	23.50
1550	12" deep		30	.533			18.65		18.65	31

05 42 13.45 Framing, Web Stiffeners

			Crew	Daily Output	Labor-Hours	Unit	Material	2017 Bare Costs Labor	Equipment	Total	Total Incl O&P
0010	**FRAMING, WEB STIFFENERS** at joist bearing, fabricated from										
0020	Stud piece (1-5/8" flange) to stiffen joist (2" flange)										
0025	Made from recycled materials										
2120	For 6" deep joist, with 18 ga. x 2-1/2" stud	G	1 Carp	120	.067	Ea.	.92	2.33		3.25	4.91
2130	3-5/8" stud	G		110	.073		1.08	2.54		3.62	5.45
2140	4" stud	G		105	.076		1.12	2.66		3.78	5.70
2150	6" stud	G		100	.080		1.42	2.80		4.22	6.25
2160	8" stud	G		95	.084		1.71	2.94		4.65	6.80
2220	8" deep joist, with 2-1/2" stud	G		120	.067		1.23	2.33		3.56	5.25
2230	3-5/8" stud	G		110	.073		1.45	2.54		3.99	5.85
2240	4" stud	G		105	.076		1.50	2.66		4.16	6.10
2250	6" stud	G		100	.080		1.90	2.80		4.70	6.75
2260	8" stud	G		95	.084		2.29	2.94		5.23	7.45
2320	10" deep joist, with 2-1/2" stud	G		110	.073		1.53	2.54		4.07	5.95
2330	3-5/8" stud	G		100	.080		1.79	2.80		4.59	6.65
2340	4" stud	G		95	.084		1.86	2.94		4.80	6.95
2350	6" stud	G		90	.089		2.36	3.11		5.47	7.80
2360	8" stud	G		85	.094		2.84	3.29		6.13	8.60
2420	12" deep joist, with 2-1/2" stud	G		110	.073		1.84	2.54		4.38	6.25
2430	3-5/8" stud	G		100	.080		2.16	2.80		4.96	7.05
2440	4" stud	G		95	.084		2.24	2.94		5.18	7.40
2450	6" stud	G		90	.089		2.84	3.11		5.95	8.30
2460	8" stud	G		85	.094		3.42	3.29		6.71	9.25
3130	For 6" deep joist, with 16 ga. x 3-5/8" stud	G		100	.080		1.34	2.80		4.14	6.15
3140	4" stud	G		95	.084		1.40	2.94		4.34	6.45
3150	6" stud	G		90	.089		1.75	3.11		4.86	7.15
3160	8" stud	G		85	.094		2.14	3.29		5.43	7.85
3230	8" deep joist, with 3-5/8" stud	G		100	.080		1.80	2.80		4.60	6.65
3240	4" stud	G		95	.084		1.88	2.94		4.82	7
3250	6" stud	G		90	.089		2.35	3.11		5.46	7.80
3260	8" stud	G		85	.094		2.87	3.29		6.16	8.65
3330	10" deep joist, with 3-5/8" stud	G		85	.094		2.22	3.29		5.51	7.95
3340	4" stud	G		80	.100		2.32	3.50		5.82	8.40
3350	6" stud	G		75	.107		2.91	3.73		6.64	9.45
3360	8" stud	G		70	.114		3.55	3.99		7.54	10.60
3430	12" deep joist, with 3-5/8" stud	G		85	.094		2.68	3.29		5.97	8.45
3440	4" stud	G		80	.100		2.80	3.50		6.30	8.95
3450	6" stud	G		75	.107		3.50	3.73		7.23	10.10
3460	8" stud	G		70	.114		4.28	3.99		8.27	11.40
4230	For 8" deep joist, with 14 ga. x 3-5/8" stud	G		90	.089		2.22	3.11		5.33	7.65
4240	4" stud	G		85	.094		2.35	3.29		5.64	8.10
4250	6" stud	G		80	.100		2.95	3.50		6.45	9.10
4260	8" stud	G		75	.107		3.15	3.73		6.88	9.70
4330	10" deep joist, with 3-5/8" stud	G		75	.107		2.76	3.73		6.49	9.30
4340	4" stud	G		70	.114		2.91	3.99		6.90	9.90

05 42 Cold-Formed Metal Joist Framing

05 42 13 – Cold-Formed Metal Floor Joist Framing

05 42 13.45 Framing, Web Stiffeners

			Crew	Daily Output	Labor-Hours	Unit	Material	2017 Bare Costs Labor	Equipment	Total	Total Incl O&P
4350	6" stud	G	1 Carp	65	.123	Ea.	3.65	4.30		7.95	11.20
4360	8" stud	G		60	.133		3.90	4.66		8.56	12.10
4430	12" deep joist, with 3-5/8" stud	G		75	.107		3.32	3.73		7.05	9.90
4440	4" stud	G		70	.114		3.50	3.99		7.49	10.55
4450	6" stud	G		65	.123		4.40	4.30		8.70	12.05
4460	8" stud	G		60	.133		4.70	4.66		9.36	12.95
5330	For 10" deep joist, with 12 ga. x 3-5/8" stud	G		65	.123		3.97	4.30		8.27	11.55
5340	4" stud	G		60	.133		4.23	4.66		8.89	12.10
5350	6" stud	G		55	.145		5.35	5.10		10.45	14.40
5360	8" stud	G		50	.160		6.45	5.60		12.05	16.45
5430	12" deep joist, with 3-5/8" stud	G		65	.123		4.78	4.30		9.08	12.45
5440	4" stud	G		60	.133		5.10	4.66		9.76	13.40
5450	6" stud	G		55	.145		6.45	5.10		11.55	15.60
5460	8" stud	G		50	.160		7.80	5.60		13.40	17.90

05 42 23 – Cold-Formed Metal Roof Joist Framing

05 42 23.05 Framing, Bracing

			Crew	Daily Output	Labor-Hours	Unit	Material	2017 Bare Costs Labor	Equipment	Total	Total Incl O&P
0010	**FRAMING, BRACING**										
0015	Made from recycled materials										
0020	Continuous bracing, per row										
0100	16 ga. x 1-1/2" channel thru rafters/trusses @ 16" O.C.	G	1 Carp	4.50	1.778	C.L.F.	51.50	62		113.50	161
0120	24" O.C.	G		6	1.333		51.50	46.50		98	135
0300	2" x 2" angle x 18 ga., rafters/trusses @ 16" O.C.	G		6	1.333		80.50	46.50		127	167
0320	24" O.C.	G		8	1		80.50	35		115.50	147
0400	16 ga., rafters/trusses @ 16" O.C.	G		4.50	1.778		101	62		163	215
0420	24" O.C.	G		6.50	1.231		101	43		144	183

05 42 23.10 Framing, Bridging

			Crew	Daily Output	Labor-Hours	Unit	Material	2017 Bare Costs Labor	Equipment	Total	Total Incl O&P
0010	**FRAMING, BRIDGING**										
0015	Made from recycled materials										
0020	Solid, between rafters w/1-1/4" leg track, per rafter bay										
1200	Rafters 16" O.C., 18 ga. x 4" deep	G	1 Carp	60	.133	Ea.	1.57	4.66		6.23	9.50
1210	6" deep	G		57	.140		2.05	4.91		6.96	10.45
1220	8" deep	G		55	.145		2.52	5.10		7.62	11.30
1230	10" deep	G		52	.154		3.15	5.40		8.55	12.45
1240	12" deep	G		50	.160		3.56	5.60		9.16	13.25
2200	24" O.C., 18 ga. x 4" deep	G		60	.133		2.27	4.66		6.93	10.30
2210	6" deep	G		57	.140		2.96	4.91		7.87	11.45
2220	8" deep	G		55	.145		3.65	5.10		8.75	12.50
2230	10" deep	G		52	.154		4.56	5.40		9.96	14
2240	12" deep	G		50	.160		5.15	5.60		10.75	15

05 42 23.50 Framing, Parapets

			Crew	Daily Output	Labor-Hours	Unit	Material	2017 Bare Costs Labor	Equipment	Total	Total Incl O&P
0010	**FRAMING, PARAPETS**										
0015	Made from recycled materials										
0100	3' high installed on 1st story, 18 ga. x 4" wide studs, 12" O.C.	G	2 Carp	100	.160	L.F.	5.70	5.60		11.30	15.60
0110	16" O.C.	G		150	.107		4.85	3.73		8.58	11.60
0120	24" O.C.	G		200	.080		4.01	2.80		6.81	9.10
0200	6" wide studs, 12" O.C.	G		100	.160		7.30	5.60		12.90	17.40
0210	16" O.C.	G		150	.107		6.25	3.73		9.98	13.10
0220	24" O.C.	G		200	.080		5.15	2.80		7.95	10.40
1100	Installed on 2nd story, 18 ga. x 4" wide studs, 12" O.C.	G		95	.168		5.70	5.90		11.60	16.10
1110	16" O.C.	G		145	.110		4.85	3.86		8.71	11.80
1120	24" O.C.	G		190	.084		4.01	2.94		6.95	9.35
1200	6" wide studs, 12" O.C.	G		95	.168		7.30	5.90		13.20	17.90

05 42 Cold-Formed Metal Joist Framing

05 42 23 - Cold-Formed Metal Roof Joist Framing

05 42 23.50 Framing, Parapets

		Crew	Daily Output	Labor-Hours	Unit	Material	2017 Bare Costs Labor	Equipment	Total	Total Incl O&P
1210	16" O.C.	[G] 2 Carp	145	.110	L.F.	6.25	3.86		10.11	13.30
1220	24" O.C.	[G]	190	.084		5.15	2.94		8.09	10.60
2100	Installed on gable, 18 ga. x 4" wide studs, 12" O.C.	[G]	85	.188		5.70	6.60		12.30	17.25
2110	16" O.C.	[G]	130	.123		4.85	4.30		9.15	12.55
2120	24" O.C.	[G]	170	.094		4.01	3.29		7.30	9.90
2200	6" wide studs, 12" O.C.	[G]	85	.188		7.30	6.60		13.90	19.05
2210	16" O.C.	[G]	130	.123		6.25	4.30		10.55	14.05
2220	24" O.C.	[G]	170	.094		5.15	3.29		8.44	11.20

05 42 23.60 Framing, Roof Rafters

		Crew	Daily Output	Labor-Hours	Unit	Material	2017 Bare Costs Labor	Equipment	Total	Total Incl O&P
0010	**FRAMING, ROOF RAFTERS**									
0015	Made from recycled materials									
0100	Boxed ridge beam, double, 18 ga. x 6" deep	[G] 2 Carp	160	.100	L.F.	5.50	3.50		9	11.90
0110	8" deep	[G]	150	.107		6.05	3.73		9.78	12.90
0120	10" deep	[G]	140	.114		7.40	3.99		11.39	14.85
0130	12" deep	[G]	130	.123		8.05	4.30		12.35	16.05
0200	16 ga. x 6" deep	[G]	150	.107		6.20	3.73		9.93	13.10
0210	8" deep	[G]	140	.114		7	3.99		10.99	14.40
0220	10" deep	[G]	130	.123		8.45	4.30		12.75	16.45
0230	12" deep	[G]	120	.133		9.15	4.66		13.81	17.90
1100	Rafters, 2" flange, material only, 18 ga. x 6" deep	[G]				1.69			1.69	1.86
1110	8" deep	[G]				1.98			1.98	2.18
1120	10" deep	[G]				2.34			2.34	2.58
1130	12" deep	[G]				2.70			2.70	2.97
1200	16 ga. x 6" deep	[G]				2.07			2.07	2.28
1210	8" deep	[G]				2.47			2.47	2.71
1220	10" deep	[G]				2.89			2.89	3.18
1230	12" deep	[G]				3.28			3.28	3.60
2100	Installation only, ordinary rafter to 4:12 pitch, 18 ga. x 6" deep	2 Carp	35	.457	Ea.		16		16	26.50
2110	8" deep		30	.533			18.65		18.65	31
2120	10" deep		25	.640			22.50		22.50	37.50
2130	12" deep		20	.800			28		28	47
2200	16 ga. x 6" deep		30	.533			18.65		18.65	31
2210	8" deep		25	.640			22.50		22.50	37.50
2220	10" deep		20	.800			28		28	47
2230	12" deep		15	1.067			37.50		37.50	62.50
8100	Add to labor, ordinary rafters on steep roofs						25%			
8110	Dormers & complex roofs						50%			
8200	Hip & valley rafters to 4:12 pitch						25%			
8210	Steep roofs						50%			
8220	Dormers & complex roofs						75%			
8300	Hip & valley jack rafters to 4:12 pitch						50%			
8310	Steep roofs						75%			
8320	Dormers & complex roofs						100%			

05 42 23.70 Framing, Soffits and Canopies

		Crew	Daily Output	Labor-Hours	Unit	Material	2017 Bare Costs Labor	Equipment	Total	Total Incl O&P
0010	**FRAMING, SOFFITS & CANOPIES**									
0015	Made from recycled materials									
0130	Continuous ledger track @ wall, studs @ 16" O.C., 18 ga. x 4" wide	[G] 2 Carp	535	.030	L.F.	1.05	1.05		2.10	2.90
0140	6" wide	[G]	500	.032		1.36	1.12		2.48	3.37
0150	8" wide	[G]	465	.034		1.68	1.20		2.88	3.86
0160	10" wide	[G]	430	.037		2.10	1.30		3.40	4.48
0230	Studs @ 24" O.C., 18 ga. x 4" wide	[G]	800	.020		1	.70		1.70	2.27
0240	6" wide	[G]	750	.021		1.30	.75		2.05	2.68

05 42 Cold-Formed Metal Joist Framing

05 42 23 – Cold-Formed Metal Roof Joist Framing

05 42 23.70 Framing, Soffits and Canopies

			Crew	Daily Output	Labor-Hours	Unit	Material	2017 Bare Costs Labor	Equipment	Total	Total Incl O&P
0250	8" wide	G	2 Carp	700	.023	L.F.	1.61	.80		2.41	3.11
0260	10" wide	G	↓	650	.025	↓	2.01	.86		2.87	3.65
1000	Horizontal soffit and canopy members, material only										
1030	1-5/8" flange studs, 18 ga. x 4" deep	G				L.F.	1.34			1.34	1.48
1040	6" deep	G					1.70			1.70	1.87
1050	8" deep	G					2.05			2.05	2.26
1140	2" flange joists, 18 ga. x 6" deep	G					1.93			1.93	2.13
1150	8" deep	G					2.27			2.27	2.49
1160	10" deep	G				↓	2.68			2.68	2.94
4030	Installation only, 18 ga., 1-5/8" flange x 4" deep		2 Carp	130	.123	Ea.		4.30		4.30	7.20
4040	6" deep			110	.145			5.10		5.10	8.50
4050	8" deep			90	.178			6.20		6.20	10.40
4140	2" flange, 18 ga. x 6" deep			110	.145			5.10		5.10	8.50
4150	8" deep			90	.178			6.20		6.20	10.40
4160	10" deep		↓	80	.200			7		7	11.70
6010	Clips to attach fascia to rafter tails, 2" x 2" x 18 ga. angle	G	1 Carp	120	.067		.95	2.33		3.28	4.94
6020	16 ga. angle	G	"	100	.080	↓	1.20	2.80		4	6

05 44 Cold-Formed Metal Trusses

05 44 13 – Cold-Formed Metal Roof Trusses

05 44 13.60 Framing, Roof Trusses

			Crew	Daily Output	Labor-Hours	Unit	Material	2017 Bare Costs Labor	Equipment	Total	Total Incl O&P
0010	**FRAMING, ROOF TRUSSES**										
0015	Made from recycled materials										
0020	Fabrication of trusses on ground, Fink (W) or King Post, to 4:12 pitch										
0120	18 ga. x 4" chords, 16' span	G	2 Carp	12	1.333	Ea.	62.50	46.50		109	147
0130	20' span	G		11	1.455		78.50	51		129.50	171
0140	24' span	G		11	1.455		94	51		145	188
0150	28' span	G		10	1.600		110	56		166	215
0160	32' span	G		10	1.600		125	56		181	232
0250	6" chords, 28' span	G		9	1.778		139	62		201	257
0260	32' span	G		9	1.778		159	62		221	279
0270	36' span	G		8	2		179	70		249	315
0280	40' span	G		8	2		199	70		269	335
1120	5:12 to 8:12 pitch, 18 ga. x 4" chords, 16' span	G		10	1.600		71.50	56		127.50	173
1130	20' span	G		9	1.778		89.50	62		151.50	203
1140	24' span	G		9	1.778		108	62		170	222
1150	28' span	G		8	2		125	70		195	255
1160	32' span	G		8	2		143	70		213	275
1250	6" chords, 28' span	G		7	2.286		159	80		239	310
1260	32' span	G		7	2.286		182	80		262	335
1270	36' span	G		6	2.667		204	93		297	380
1280	40' span	G		6	2.667		227	93		320	405
2120	9:12 to 12:12 pitch, 18 ga. x 4" chords, 16' span	G		8	2		89.50	70		159.50	216
2130	20' span	G		7	2.286		112	80		192	257
2140	24' span	G		7	2.286		134	80		214	282
2150	28' span	G		6	2.667		157	93		250	330
2160	32' span	G		6	2.667		179	93		272	355
2250	6" chords, 28' span	G		5	3.200		199	112		311	405
2260	32' span	G		5	3.200		227	112		339	435
2270	36' span	G		4	4		256	140		396	515
2280	40' span	G	↓	4	4		284	140		424	545

05 44 Cold-Formed Metal Trusses

05 44 13 – Cold-Formed Metal Roof Trusses

05 44 13.60 Framing, Roof Trusses	Crew	Daily Output	Labor-Hours	Unit	Material	2017 Bare Costs Labor	Equipment	Total	Total Incl O&P
5120	Erection only of roof trusses, to 4:12 pitch, 16' span	F-6	48	.833	Ea.		26.50	11.95	38.45	57.50
5130	20' span		46	.870			28	12.45	40.45	60
5140	24' span		44	.909			29	13	42	63
5150	28' span		42	.952			30.50	13.65	44.15	66
5160	32' span		40	1			32	14.30	46.30	69.50
5170	36' span		38	1.053			34	15.05	49.05	73
5180	40' span		36	1.111			35.50	15.90	51.40	77
5220	5:12 to 8:12 pitch, 16' span		42	.952			30.50	13.65	44.15	66
5230	20' span		40	1			32	14.30	46.30	69.50
5240	24' span		38	1.053			34	15.05	49.05	73
5250	28' span		36	1.111			35.50	15.90	51.40	77
5260	32' span		34	1.176			37.50	16.85	54.35	81.50
5270	36' span		32	1.250			40	17.90	57.90	86.50
5280	40' span		30	1.333			43	19.10	62.10	92.50
5320	9:12 to 12:12 pitch, 16' span		36	1.111			35.50	15.90	51.40	77
5330	20' span		34	1.176			37.50	16.85	54.35	81.50
5340	24' span		32	1.250			40	17.90	57.90	86.50
5350	28' span		30	1.333			43	19.10	62.10	92.50
5360	32' span		28	1.429			46	20.50	66.50	99
5370	36' span		26	1.538			49.50	22	71.50	107
5380	40' span		24	1.667			53.50	24	77.50	116

05 51 Metal Stairs

05 51 13 – Metal Pan Stairs

05 51 13.50 Pan Stairs

		Crew	Daily Output	Labor-Hours	Unit	Material	Labor	Equipment	Total	Total Incl O&P
0010	PAN STAIRS, shop fabricated, steel stringers									
0015	Made from recycled materials									
1700	Pre-erected, steel pan tread, 3'-6" wide, 2 line pipe rail	G	E-2	87	.552	Riser	660	21.50	19.20	700.70	785
1800	With flat bar picket rail	G	"	87	.552	"	740	21.50	19.20	780.70	875

05 51 23 – Metal Fire Escapes

05 51 23.50 Fire Escape Stairs

		Crew	Daily Output	Labor-Hours	Unit	Material	Labor	Equipment	Total	Total Incl O&P
0010	FIRE ESCAPE STAIRS, portable										
0100	Portable ladder					Ea.	112			112	123

05 52 Metal Railings

05 52 13 – Pipe and Tube Railings

05 52 13.50 Railings, Pipe

			Crew	Daily Output	Labor-Hours	Unit	Material	Labor	Equipment	Total	Total Incl O&P
0010	RAILINGS, PIPE, shop fab'd, 3'-6" high, posts @ 5' O.C.										
0015	Made from recycled materials										
0020	Aluminum, 2 rail, satin finish, 1-1/4" diameter	G	E-4	160	.200	L.F.	52	7.80	.81	60.61	72
0030	Clear anodized	G		160	.200		64	7.80	.81	72.61	85.50
0040	Dark anodized	G		160	.200		71	7.80	.81	79.61	93
0080	1-1/2" diameter, satin finish	G		160	.200		61	7.80	.81	69.61	82
0090	Clear anodized	G		160	.200		68.50	7.80	.81	77.11	90.50
0100	Dark anodized	G		160	.200		75.50	7.80	.81	84.11	98
0140	Aluminum, 3 rail, 1-1/4" diam., satin finish	G		137	.234		67.50	9.10	.95	77.55	92
0150	Clear anodized	G		137	.234		84	9.10	.95	94.05	110
0160	Dark anodized	G		137	.234		92.50	9.10	.95	102.55	120
0200	1-1/2" diameter, satin finish	G		137	.234		80	9.10	.95	90.05	106

05 52 Metal Railings

05 52 13 – Pipe and Tube Railings

05 52 13.50 Railings, Pipe		Crew	Daily Output	Labor-Hours	Unit	Material	2017 Bare Costs Labor	Equipment	Total	Total Incl O&P
0210	Clear anodized	G E-4	137	.234	L.F.	91.50	9.10	.95	101.55	119
0220	Dark anodized	G	137	.234		100	9.10	.95	110.05	128
0500	Steel, 2 rail, on stairs, primed, 1-1/4" diameter	G	160	.200		26	7.80	.81	34.61	43.50
0520	1-1/2" diameter	G	160	.200		28	7.80	.81	36.61	46
0540	Galvanized, 1-1/4" diameter	G	160	.200		35	7.80	.81	43.61	53.50
0560	1-1/2" diameter	G	160	.200		39.50	7.80	.81	48.11	58.50
0580	Steel, 3 rail, primed, 1-1/4" diameter	G	137	.234		38.50	9.10	.95	48.55	60
0600	1-1/2" diameter	G	137	.234		40.50	9.10	.95	50.55	62
0620	Galvanized, 1-1/4" diameter	G	137	.234		54	9.10	.95	64.05	77
0640	1-1/2" diameter	G	137	.234		62.50	9.10	.95	72.55	86.50
0700	Stainless steel, 2 rail, 1-1/4" diam. #4 finish	G	137	.234		114	9.10	.95	124.05	143
0720	High polish	G	137	.234		184	9.10	.95	194.05	220
0740	Mirror polish	G	137	.234		230	9.10	.95	240.05	271
0760	Stainless steel, 3 rail, 1-1/2" diam., #4 finish	G	120	.267		171	10.40	1.08	182.48	208
0770	High polish	G	120	.267		284	10.40	1.08	295.48	330
0780	Mirror finish	G	120	.267		345	10.40	1.08	356.48	400
0900	Wall rail, alum. pipe, 1-1/4" diam., satin finish	G	213	.150		25	5.85	.61	31.46	39
0905	Clear anodized	G	213	.150		31	5.85	.61	37.46	45.50
0910	Dark anodized	G	213	.150		37	5.85	.61	43.46	52
0915	1-1/2" diameter, satin finish	G	213	.150		28	5.85	.61	34.46	42.50
0920	Clear anodized	G	213	.150		35	5.85	.61	41.46	50
0925	Dark anodized	G	213	.150		43.50	5.85	.61	49.96	59.50
0930	Steel pipe, 1-1/4" diameter, primed	G	213	.150		15.50	5.85	.61	21.96	28.50
0935	Galvanized	G	213	.150		22.50	5.85	.61	28.96	36.50
0940	1-1/2" diameter	G	176	.182		16	7.10	.74	23.84	31.50
0945	Galvanized	G	213	.150		22.50	5.85	.61	28.96	36.50
0955	Stainless steel pipe, 1-1/2" diam., #4 finish	G	107	.299		91	11.70	1.21	103.91	122
0960	High polish	G	107	.299		185	11.70	1.21	197.91	226
0965	Mirror polish	G	107	.299		219	11.70	1.21	231.91	263
2000	2-line pipe rail (1-1/2" T&B) with 1/2" pickets @ 4-1/2" O.C.,									
2005	attached handrail on brackets									
2010	42" high aluminum, satin finish, straight & level	G E-4	120	.267	L.F.	266	10.40	1.08	277.48	315
2050	42" high steel, primed, straight & level	G "	120	.267		131	10.40	1.08	142.48	164
4000	For curved and level rails, add						10%	10%		
4100	For sloped rails for stairs, add						30%	30%		

05 58 Formed Metal Fabrications

05 58 25 – Formed Lamp Posts

05 58 25.40 Lamp Posts

0010	LAMP POSTS									
0020	Aluminum, 7' high, stock units, post only	G 1 Carp	16	.500	Ea.	87	17.50		104.50	125
0100	Mild steel, plain	G "	16	.500	"	74.50	17.50		92	111

05 71 Decorative Metal Stairs

05 71 13 – Fabricated Metal Spiral Stairs

05 71 13.50 Spiral Stairs

		Crew	Daily Output	Labor-Hours	Unit	Material	2017 Bare Costs Labor	2017 Bare Costs Equipment	Total	Total Incl O&P
0010	**SPIRAL STAIRS**									
1805	Shop fabricated, custom ordered									
1810	Aluminum, 5'-0" diameter, plain units	G	E-4	45	.711	Riser	530	28	2.89	560.89	640
1820	Fancy units	G		45	.711		925	28	2.89	955.89	1,075
1900	Cast iron, 4'-0" diameter, plain units	G		45	.711		665	28	2.89	695.89	785
1920	Fancy units	G		25	1.280		1,150	50	5.20	1,205.20	1,375
3100	Spiral stair kits, 12 stacking risers to fit exact floor height									
3110	Steel, flat metal treads, primed, 3'-6" diameter	G	2 Carp	1.60	10	Flight	1,300	350		1,650	2,000
3120	4'-0" diameter	G		1.45	11.034		1,475	385		1,860	2,250
3130	4'-6" diameter	G		1.35	11.852		1,625	415		2,040	2,500
3140	5'-0" diameter	G		1.25	12.800		1,775	445		2,220	2,725
3310	Checkered plate tread, primed, 3'-6" diameter	G		1.45	11.034		1,550	385		1,935	2,350
3320	4'-0" diameter	G		1.35	11.852		1,725	415		2,140	2,600
3330	4'-6" diameter	G		1.25	12.800		1,900	445		2,345	2,825
3340	5'-0" diameter	G		1.15	13.913		2,075	485		2,560	3,100
3510	Red oak covers on flat metal treads, 3'-6" diameter			1.35	11.852		2,350	415		2,765	3,300
3520	4'-0" diameter			1.25	12.800		2,800	445		3,245	3,825
3530	4'-6" diameter			1.15	13.913		3,025	485		3,510	4,150
3540	5'-0" diameter			1.05	15.238		3,250	535		3,785	4,475

05 75 Decorative Formed Metal

05 75 13 – Columns

05 75 13.10 Aluminum Columns

		Crew	Daily Output	Labor-Hours	Unit	Material	2017 Bare Costs Labor	2017 Bare Costs Equipment	Total	Total Incl O&P
0010	**ALUMINUM COLUMNS**									
0015	Made from recycled materials									
0020	Aluminum, extruded, stock units, no cap or base, 6" diameter	G	E-4	240	.133	L.F.	12.50	5.20	.54	18.24	23.50
0100	8" diameter	G	"	170	.188	"	15.95	7.35	.76	24.06	31.50
0410	Caps and bases, plain, 6" diameter	G				Set	24.50			24.50	27
0420	8" diameter	G				"	30			30	33
0500	For square columns, add to column prices above					L.F.	50%				
0700	Residential, flat, 8' high, plain	G	E-4	20	1.600	Ea.	97.50	62.50	6.50	166.50	227
0720	Fancy	G		20	1.600		190	62.50	6.50	259	330
0740	Corner type, plain	G		20	1.600		168	62.50	6.50	237	305
0760	Fancy	G		20	1.600		330	62.50	6.50	399	485

05 75 13.20 Columns, Ornamental

		Crew	Daily Output	Labor-Hours	Unit	Material	2017 Bare Costs Labor	2017 Bare Costs Equipment	Total	Total Incl O&P
0010	**COLUMNS, ORNAMENTAL**, shop fabricated									
6400	Mild steel, flat, 9" wide, stock units, painted, plain	G	E-4	160	.200	V.L.F.	9.15	7.80	.81	17.76	25
6450	Fancy	G		160	.200		17.75	7.80	.81	26.36	34.50
6500	Corner columns, painted, plain	G		160	.200		15.75	7.80	.81	24.36	32.50
6550	Fancy	G		160	.200		31	7.80	.81	39.61	49.50

For customer support on your Residential Costs with RSMeans Data, call 800.448.8182.

353

Division Notes

	CREW	DAILY OUTPUT	LABOR-HOURS	UNIT	BARE COSTS				TOTAL INCL O&P
					MAT.	LABOR	EQUIP.	TOTAL	

Estimating Tips
06 05 00 Common Work Results for Wood, Plastics, and Composites

- Common to any wood-framed structure are the accessory connector items such as screws, nails, adhesives, hangers, connector plates, straps, angles, and hold-downs. For typical wood-framed buildings, such as residential projects, the aggregate total for these items can be significant, especially in areas where seismic loading is a concern. For floor and wall framing, the material cost is based on 10 to 25 lbs. of accessory connectors per MBF. Hold-downs, hangers, and other connectors should be taken off by the piece.

  Included with material costs are fasteners for a normal installation. Gordian's RSMeans engineers use manufacturers' recommendations, written specifications, and/or standard construction practice for the sizing and spacing of fasteners. Prices for various fasteners are shown for informational purposes only. Adjustments should be made if unusual fastening conditions exist.

06 10 00 Carpentry

- Lumber is a traded commodity and therefore sensitive to supply and demand in the marketplace. Even with "budgetary" estimating of wood-framed projects, it is advisable to call local suppliers for the latest market pricing.

- The common quantity unit for wood-framed projects is "thousand board feet" (MBF). A board foot is a volume of wood—1" x 1' x 1' or 144 cubic inches. Board-foot quantities are generally calculated using nominal material dimensions— dressed sizes are ignored. Board foot per lineal foot of any stick of lumber can be calculated by dividing the nominal cross-sectional area by 12. As an example, 2,000 lineal feet of 2 x 12 equates to 4 MBF by dividing the nominal area, 2 x 12, by 12, which equals 2, and multiplying by 2,000 to give 4,000 board feet. This simple rule applies to all nominal dimensioned lumber.

- Waste is an issue of concern at the quantity takeoff for any area of construction. Framing lumber is sold in even foot lengths, i.e., 8', 10', 12', 14', 16' and depending on spans, wall heights, and the grade of lumber, waste is inevitable. A rule of thumb for lumber waste is 5%–10% depending on material quality and the complexity of the framing.

- Wood in various forms and shapes is used in many projects, even where the main structural framing is steel, concrete, or masonry. Plywood as a back-up partition material and 2x boards used as blocking and cant strips around roof edges are two common examples. The estimator should ensure that the costs of all wood materials are included in the final estimate.

06 20 00 Finish Carpentry

- It is necessary to consider the grade of workmanship when estimating labor costs for erecting millwork and an interior finish. In practice, there are three grades: premium, custom, and economy. The RSMeans daily output for base and case moldings is in the range of 200 to 250 L.F. per carpenter per day. This is appropriate for most average custom-grade projects. For premium projects, an adjustment to productivity of 25%–50% should be made, depending on the complexity of the job.

Reference Numbers

Reference numbers are shown at the beginning of some major classifications. These numbers refer to related items in the Reference Section. The reference information may be an estimating procedure, an alternate pricing method, or technical information.

Note: Not all subdivisions listed here necessarily appear. ■

Did you know?

Our online estimating solution gives you the same access to RSMeans' data with 24/7 access:

- Quickly locate costs in the searchable database.
- Build cost lists, estimates, and reports in minutes.
- Adjust costs to any location in the U.S. and Canada with the click of a button.

Start your free trial today at
www.RSMeansOnline.com

06 05 05.10 Selective Demolition Wood Framing	Crew	Daily Output	Labor-Hours	Unit	Material	2017 Bare Costs Labor	Equipment	Total	Total Incl O&P
0010 **SELECTIVE DEMOLITION WOOD FRAMING** R024119-10									
0100 Timber connector, nailed, small	1 Clab	96	.083	Ea.		2.22		2.22	3.71
0110 Medium		60	.133			3.55		3.55	5.95
0120 Large		48	.167			4.43		4.43	7.40
0130 Bolted, small		48	.167			4.43		4.43	7.40
0140 Medium		32	.250			6.65		6.65	11.15
0150 Large		24	.333			8.85		8.85	14.85
2958 Beams, 2" x 6"	2 Clab	1100	.015	L.F.		.39		.39	.65
2960 2" x 8"		825	.019			.52		.52	.86
2965 2" x 10"		665	.024			.64		.64	1.07
2970 2" x 12"		550	.029			.77		.77	1.29
2972 2" x 14"		470	.034			.91		.91	1.51
2975 4" x 8"	B-1	413	.058			1.58		1.58	2.65
2980 4" x 10"		330	.073			1.98		1.98	3.32
2985 4" x 12"		275	.087			2.38		2.38	3.98
3000 6" x 8"		275	.087			2.38		2.38	3.98
3040 6" x 10"		220	.109			2.97		2.97	4.97
3080 6" x 12"		185	.130			3.54		3.54	5.90
3120 8" x 12"		140	.171			4.67		4.67	7.80
3160 10" x 12"		110	.218			5.95		5.95	9.95
3162 Alternate pricing method		1.10	21.818	M.B.F.		595		595	995
3170 Blocking, in 16" OC wall framing, 2" x 4"	1 Clab	600	.013	L.F.		.35		.35	.59
3172 2" x 6"		400	.020			.53		.53	.89
3174 In 24" OC wall framing, 2" x 4"		600	.013			.35		.35	.59
3176 2" x 6"		400	.020			.53		.53	.89
3178 Alt method, wood blocking removal from wood framing		.40	20	M.B.F.		530		530	890
3179 Wood blocking removal from steel framing		.36	22.222	"		590		590	990
3180 Bracing, let in, 1" x 3", studs 16" OC		1050	.008	L.F.		.20		.20	.34
3181 Studs 24" OC		1080	.007			.20		.20	.33
3182 1" x 4", studs 16" OC		1050	.008			.20		.20	.34
3183 Studs 24" OC		1080	.007			.20		.20	.33
3184 1" x 6", studs 16" OC		1050	.008			.20		.20	.34
3185 Studs 24" OC		1080	.007			.20		.20	.33
3186 2" x 3", studs 16" OC		800	.010			.27		.27	.45
3187 Studs 24" OC		830	.010			.26		.26	.43
3188 2" x 4", studs 16" OC		800	.010			.27		.27	.45
3189 Studs 24" OC		830	.010			.26		.26	.43
3190 2" x 6", studs 16" OC		800	.010			.27		.27	.45
3191 Studs 24" OC		830	.010			.26		.26	.43
3192 2" x 8", studs 16" OC		800	.010			.27		.27	.45
3193 Studs 24" OC		830	.010			.26		.26	.43
3194 "T" shaped metal bracing, studs at 16" OC		1060	.008			.20		.20	.34
3195 Studs at 24" OC		1200	.007			.18		.18	.30
3196 Metal straps, studs at 16" OC		1200	.007			.18		.18	.30
3197 Studs at 24" OC		1240	.006			.17		.17	.29
3200 Columns, round, 8' to 14' tall		40	.200	Ea.		5.30		5.30	8.90
3202 Dimensional lumber sizes	2 Clab	1.10	14.545	M.B.F.		385		385	645
3250 Blocking, between joists	1 Clab	320	.025	Ea.		.67		.67	1.11
3252 Bridging, metal strap, between joists		320	.025	Pr.		.67		.67	1.11
3254 Wood, between joists		320	.025	"		.67		.67	1.11
3260 Door buck, studs, header & access., 8' high 2" x 4" wall, 3' wide		32	.250	Ea.		6.65		6.65	11.15
3261 4' wide		32	.250			6.65		6.65	11.15
3262 5' wide		32	.250			6.65		6.65	11.15

356

For customer support on your Residential Costs with RSMeans Data, call 800.448.8182.

06 05 05.10 Selective Demolition Wood Framing		Crew	Daily Output	Labor-Hours	Unit	Material	2017 Bare Costs Labor	Equipment	Total	Total Incl O&P
3263	6' wide	1 Clab	32	.250	Ea.		6.65		6.65	11.15
3264	8' wide		30	.267			7.10		7.10	11.85
3265	10' wide		30	.267			7.10		7.10	11.85
3266	12' wide		30	.267			7.10		7.10	11.85
3267	2" x 6" wall, 3' wide		32	.250			6.65		6.65	11.15
3268	4' wide		32	.250			6.65		6.65	11.15
3269	5' wide		32	.250			6.65		6.65	11.15
3270	6' wide		32	.250			6.65		6.65	11.15
3271	8' wide		30	.267			7.10		7.10	11.85
3272	10' wide		30	.267			7.10		7.10	11.85
3273	12' wide		30	.267			7.10		7.10	11.85
3274	Window buck, studs, header & access., 8' high 2" x 4" wall, 2' wide		24	.333			8.85		8.85	14.85
3275	3' wide		24	.333			8.85		8.85	14.85
3276	4' wide		24	.333			8.85		8.85	14.85
3277	5' wide		24	.333			8.85		8.85	14.85
3278	6' wide		24	.333			8.85		8.85	14.85
3279	7' wide		24	.333			8.85		8.85	14.85
3280	8' wide		22	.364			9.65		9.65	16.20
3281	10' wide		22	.364			9.65		9.65	16.20
3282	12' wide		22	.364			9.65		9.65	16.20
3283	2" x 6" wall, 2' wide		24	.333			8.85		8.85	14.85
3284	3' wide		24	.333			8.85		8.85	14.85
3285	4' wide		24	.333			8.85		8.85	14.85
3286	5' wide		24	.333			8.85		8.85	14.85
3287	6' wide		24	.333			8.85		8.85	14.85
3288	7' wide		24	.333			8.85		8.85	14.85
3289	8' wide		22	.364			9.65		9.65	16.20
3290	10' wide		22	.364			9.65		9.65	16.20
3291	12' wide		22	.364			9.65		9.65	16.20
3360	Deck or porch decking		825	.010	L.F.		.26		.26	.43
3400	Fascia boards, 1" x 6"		500	.016			.43		.43	.71
3440	1" x 8"		450	.018			.47		.47	.79
3480	1" x 10"		400	.020			.53		.53	.89
3490	2" x 6"		450	.018			.47		.47	.79
3500	2" x 8"		400	.020			.53		.53	.89
3510	2" x 10"		350	.023			.61		.61	1.02
3610	Furring, on wood walls or ceiling		4000	.002	S.F.		.05		.05	.09
3620	On masonry or concrete walls or ceiling		1200	.007	"		.18		.18	.30
3800	Headers over openings, 2 @ 2" x 6"		110	.073	L.F.		1.93		1.93	3.24
3840	2 @ 2" x 8"		100	.080			2.13		2.13	3.56
3880	2 @ 2" x 10"		90	.089			2.36		2.36	3.96
3885	Alternate pricing method		.26	30.651	M.B.F.		815		815	1,375
3920	Joists, 1" x 4"		1250	.006	L.F.		.17		.17	.28
3930	1" x 6"		1135	.007			.19		.19	.31
3940	1" x 8"		1000	.008			.21		.21	.36
3950	1" x 10"		895	.009			.24		.24	.40
3960	1" x 12"		765	.010			.28		.28	.47
4200	2" x 4"	2 Clab	1000	.016			.43		.43	.71
4230	2" x 6"		970	.016			.44		.44	.73
4240	2" x 8"		940	.017			.45		.45	.76
4250	2" x 10"		910	.018			.47		.47	.78
4280	2" x 12"		880	.018			.48		.48	.81
4281	2" x 14"		850	.019			.50		.50	.84

06 05 05.10 Selective Demolition Wood Framing		Crew	Daily Output	Labor-Hours	Unit	Material	2017 Bare Costs Labor	Equipment	Total	Total Incl O&P
4282	Composite joists, 9-1/2"	2 Clab	960	.017	L.F.		.44		.44	.74
4283	11-7/8"		930	.017			.46		.46	.77
4284	14"		897	.018			.47		.47	.79
4285	16"		865	.019			.49		.49	.82
4290	Wood joists, alternate pricing method		1.50	10.667	M.B.F.		284		284	475
4500	Open web joist, 12" deep		500	.032	L.F.		.85		.85	1.42
4505	14" deep		475	.034			.90		.90	1.50
4510	16" deep		450	.036			.95		.95	1.58
4520	18" deep		425	.038			1		1	1.68
4530	24" deep		400	.040			1.06		1.06	1.78
4550	Ledger strips, 1" x 2"	1 Clab	1200	.007			.18		.18	.30
4560	1" x 3"		1200	.007			.18		.18	.30
4570	1" x 4"		1200	.007			.18		.18	.30
4580	2" x 2"		1100	.007			.19		.19	.32
4590	2" x 4"		1000	.008			.21		.21	.36
4600	2" x 6"		1000	.008			.21		.21	.36
4601	2" x 8" or 2" x 10"		800	.010			.27		.27	.45
4602	4" x 6"		600	.013			.35		.35	.59
4604	4" x 8"		450	.018			.47		.47	.79
5400	Posts, 4" x 4"	2 Clab	800	.020			.53		.53	.89
5405	4" x 6"		550	.029			.77		.77	1.29
5410	4" x 8"		440	.036			.97		.97	1.62
5425	4" x 10"		390	.041			1.09		1.09	1.83
5430	4" x 12"		350	.046			1.22		1.22	2.03
5440	6" x 6"		400	.040			1.06		1.06	1.78
5445	6" x 8"		350	.046			1.22		1.22	2.03
5450	6" x 10"		320	.050			1.33		1.33	2.23
5455	6" x 12"		290	.055			1.47		1.47	2.46
5480	8" x 8"		300	.053			1.42		1.42	2.37
5500	10" x 10"		240	.067			1.77		1.77	2.97
5660	Tongue and groove floor planks		2	8	M.B.F.		213		213	355
5682	Rafters, ordinary, 16" OC, 2" x 4"		880	.018	S.F.		.48		.48	.81
5683	2" x 6"		840	.019			.51		.51	.85
5684	2" x 8"		820	.020			.52		.52	.87
5685	2" x 10"		820	.020			.52		.52	.87
5686	2" x 12"		810	.020			.53		.53	.88
5687	24" OC, 2" x 4"		1170	.014			.36		.36	.61
5688	2" x 6"		1117	.014			.38		.38	.64
5689	2" x 8"		1091	.015			.39		.39	.65
5690	2" x 10"		1091	.015			.39		.39	.65
5691	2" x 12"		1077	.015			.40		.40	.66
5795	Rafters, ordinary, 2" x 4" (alternate method)		862	.019	L.F.		.49		.49	.83
5800	2" x 6" (alternate method)		850	.019			.50		.50	.84
5840	2" x 8" (alternate method)		837	.019			.51		.51	.85
5855	2" x 10" (alternate method)		825	.019			.52		.52	.86
5865	2" x 12" (alternate method)		812	.020			.52		.52	.88
5870	Sill plate, 2" x 4"	1 Clab	1170	.007			.18		.18	.30
5871	2" x 6"		780	.010			.27		.27	.46
5872	2" x 8"		586	.014			.36		.36	.61
5873	Alternate pricing method		.78	10.256	M.B.F.		273		273	455
5885	Ridge board, 1" x 4"	2 Clab	900	.018	L.F.		.47		.47	.79
5886	1" x 6"		875	.018			.49		.49	.81
5887	1" x 8"		850	.019			.50		.50	.84

06 05 05 – Selective Demolition for Wood, Plastics, and Composites

06 05 05.10 Selective Demolition Wood Framing	Crew	Daily Output	Labor-Hours	Unit	Material	2017 Bare Costs Labor	2017 Bare Costs Equipment	Total	Total Incl O&P
5888	1" x 10"	2 Clab	825	.019	L.F.		.52		.52	.86
5889	1" x 12"		800	.020			.53		.53	.89
5890	2" x 4"		900	.018			.47		.47	.79
5892	2" x 6"		875	.018			.49		.49	.81
5894	2" x 8"		850	.019			.50		.50	.84
5896	2" x 10"		825	.019			.52		.52	.86
5898	2" x 12"		800	.020			.53		.53	.89
6050	Rafter tie, 1" x 4"		1250	.013			.34		.34	.57
6052	1" x 6"		1135	.014			.38		.38	.63
6054	2" x 4"		1000	.016			.43		.43	.71
6056	2" x 6"		970	.016			.44		.44	.73
6070	Sleepers, on concrete, 1" x 2"	1 Clab	4700	.002			.05		.05	.08
6075	1" x 3"		4000	.002			.05		.05	.09
6080	2" x 4"		3000	.003			.07		.07	.12
6085	2" x 6"		2600	.003			.08		.08	.14
6086	Sheathing from roof, 5/16"	2 Clab	1600	.010	S.F.		.27		.27	.45
6088	3/8"		1525	.010			.28		.28	.47
6090	1/2"		1400	.011			.30		.30	.51
6092	5/8"		1300	.012			.33		.33	.55
6094	3/4"		1200	.013			.35		.35	.59
6096	Board sheathing from roof		1400	.011			.30		.30	.51
6100	Sheathing, from walls, 1/4"		1200	.013			.35		.35	.59
6110	5/16"		1175	.014			.36		.36	.61
6120	3/8"		1150	.014			.37		.37	.62
6130	1/2"		1125	.014			.38		.38	.63
6140	5/8"		1100	.015			.39		.39	.65
6150	3/4"		1075	.015			.40		.40	.66
6152	Board sheathing from walls		1500	.011			.28		.28	.47
6158	Subfloor/roof deck, with boards		2200	.007			.19		.19	.32
6159	Subfloor/roof deck, with tongue & groove boards		2000	.008			.21		.21	.36
6160	Plywood, 1/2" thick		768	.021			.55		.55	.93
6162	5/8" thick		760	.021			.56		.56	.94
6164	3/4" thick		750	.021			.57		.57	.95
6165	1-1/8" thick		720	.022			.59		.59	.99
6166	Underlayment, particle board, 3/8" thick	1 Clab	780	.010			.27		.27	.46
6168	1/2" thick		768	.010			.28		.28	.46
6170	5/8" thick		760	.011			.28		.28	.47
6172	3/4" thick		750	.011			.28		.28	.47
6200	Stairs and stringers, straight run	2 Clab	40	.400	Riser		10.65		10.65	17.80
6240	With platforms, winders or curves	"	26	.615	"		16.35		16.35	27.50
6300	Components, tread	1 Clab	110	.073	Ea.		1.93		1.93	3.24
6320	Riser		80	.100	"		2.66		2.66	4.45
6390	Stringer, 2" x 10"		260	.031	L.F.		.82		.82	1.37
6400	2" x 12"		260	.031			.82		.82	1.37
6410	3" x 10"		250	.032			.85		.85	1.42
6420	3" x 12"		250	.032			.85		.85	1.42
6590	Wood studs, 2" x 3"	2 Clab	3076	.005			.14		.14	.23
6600	2" x 4"		2000	.008			.21		.21	.36
6640	2" x 6"		1600	.010			.27		.27	.45
6720	Wall framing, including studs, plates and blocking, 2" x 4"	1 Clab	600	.013	S.F.		.35		.35	.59
6740	2" x 6"		480	.017	"		.44		.44	.74
6750	Headers, 2" x 4"		1125	.007	L.F.		.19		.19	.32
6755	2" x 6"		1125	.007			.19		.19	.32

For customer support on your Residential Costs with RSMeans Data, call 800.448.8182.

359

06 05 05 – Selective Demolition for Wood, Plastics, and Composites

06 05 05.10 Selective Demolition Wood Framing

		Crew	Daily Output	Labor-Hours	Unit	Material	2017 Bare Costs Labor	Equipment	Total	Total Incl O&P
6760	2" x 8"	1 Clab	1050	.008	L.F.		.20		.20	.34
6765	2" x 10"		1050	.008			.20		.20	.34
6770	2" x 12"		1000	.008			.21		.21	.36
6780	4" x 10"		525	.015			.41		.41	.68
6785	4" x 12"		500	.016			.43		.43	.71
6790	6" x 8"		560	.014			.38		.38	.64
6795	6" x 10"		525	.015			.41		.41	.68
6797	6" x 12"		500	.016			.43		.43	.71
7000	Trusses									
7050	12' span	2 Clab	74	.216	Ea.		5.75		5.75	9.60
7150	24' span	F-3	66	.606			19.45	8.70	28.15	42
7200	26' span		64	.625			20	8.95	28.95	43.50
7250	28' span		62	.645			20.50	9.25	29.75	44.50
7300	30' span		58	.690			22	9.90	31.90	48
7350	32' span		56	.714			23	10.25	33.25	50
7400	34' span		54	.741			24	10.60	34.60	51.50
7450	36' span		52	.769			24.50	11	35.50	53.50
8000	Soffit, T & G wood	1 Clab	520	.015	S.F.		.41		.41	.68
8010	Hardboard, vinyl or aluminum	"	640	.013			.33		.33	.56
8030	Plywood	2 Carp	315	.051			1.78		1.78	2.97
9500	See Section 02 41 19.19 for rubbish handling									

06 05 05.20 Selective Demolition Millwork and Trim

		Crew	Daily Output	Labor-Hours	Unit	Material	2017 Bare Costs Labor	Equipment	Total	Total Incl O&P
0010	**SELECTIVE DEMOLITION MILLWORK AND TRIM** R024119-10									
1000	Cabinets, wood, base cabinets, per L.F.	2 Clab	80	.200	L.F.		5.30		5.30	8.90
1020	Wall cabinets, per L.F.	"	80	.200	"		5.30		5.30	8.90
1060	Remove and reset, base cabinets	2 Carp	18	.889	Ea.		31		31	52
1070	Wall cabinets		20	.800			28		28	47
1072	Oven cabinet, 7' high		11	1.455			51		51	85
1074	Cabinet door, up to 2' high	1 Clab	66	.121			3.22		3.22	5.40
1076	2' - 4' high	"	46	.174			4.63		4.63	7.75
1100	Steel, painted, base cabinets	2 Clab	60	.267	L.F.		7.10		7.10	11.85
1120	Wall cabinets		60	.267	"		7.10		7.10	11.85
1200	Casework, large area		320	.050	S.F.		1.33		1.33	2.23
1220	Selective		200	.080	"		2.13		2.13	3.56
1500	Counter top, straight runs		200	.080	L.F.		2.13		2.13	3.56
1510	L, U or C shapes		120	.133	"		3.55		3.55	5.95
2000	Paneling, 4' x 8' sheets		2000	.008	S.F.		.21		.21	.36
2100	Boards, 1" x 4"		700	.023			.61		.61	1.02
2120	1" x 6"		750	.021			.57		.57	.95
2140	1" x 8"		800	.020			.53		.53	.89
3000	Trim, baseboard, to 6" wide		1200	.013	L.F.		.35		.35	.59
3040	Greater than 6" and up to 12" wide		1000	.016			.43		.43	.71
3080	Remove and reset, minimum	2 Carp	400	.040			1.40		1.40	2.34
3090	Maximum	"	300	.053			1.86		1.86	3.12
3100	Ceiling trim	2 Clab	1000	.016			.43		.43	.71
3120	Chair rail		1200	.013			.35		.35	.59
3140	Railings with balusters		240	.067			1.77		1.77	2.97
3160	Wainscoting		700	.023	S.F.		.61		.61	1.02
4000	Curtain rod	1 Clab	80	.100	L.F.		2.66		2.66	4.45

06 05 23 – Wood, Plastic, and Composite Fastenings

06 05 23.10 Nails

		Crew	Daily Output	Labor-Hours	Unit	Material	2017 Bare Costs Labor	Equipment	Total	Total Incl O&P
0010	**NAILS**, material only, based upon 50# box purchase									
0020	Copper nails, plain				Lb.	11			11	12.10
0400	Stainless steel, plain					8.45			8.45	9.25
0500	Box, 3d to 20d, bright					1.49			1.49	1.64
0520	Galvanized					2.08			2.08	2.29
0600	Common, 3d to 60d, plain					1.25			1.25	1.38
0700	Galvanized					2.08			2.08	2.29
0800	Aluminum					9.90			9.90	10.85
1000	Annular or spiral thread, 4d to 60d, plain					2.79			2.79	3.07
1200	Galvanized					3.13			3.13	3.44
1400	Drywall nails, plain					1.48			1.48	1.63
1600	Galvanized					1.91			1.91	2.10
1800	Finish nails, 4d to 10d, plain					1.29			1.29	1.42
2000	Galvanized					2.07			2.07	2.28
2100	Aluminum					6.80			6.80	7.50
2300	Flooring nails, hardened steel, 2d to 10d, plain					3.53			3.53	3.88
2400	Galvanized					4.32			4.32	4.75
2500	Gypsum lath nails, 1-1/8", 13 ga. flathead, blued					2.53			2.53	2.78
2600	Masonry nails, hardened steel, 3/4" to 3" long, plain					2.22			2.22	2.44
2700	Galvanized					3.60			3.60	3.96
2900	Roofing nails, threaded, galvanized					2.32			2.32	2.55
3100	Aluminum					6.15			6.15	6.75
3300	Compressed lead head, threaded, galvanized					2.90			2.90	3.19
3600	Siding nails, plain shank, galvanized					2.20			2.20	2.42
3800	Aluminum					5.85			5.85	6.45
5000	Add to prices above for cement coating					.15			.15	.17
5200	Zinc or tin plating					.20			.20	.22
5500	Vinyl coated sinkers, 8d to 16d					2.56			2.56	2.82

06 05 23.50 Wood Screws

		Crew	Daily Output	Labor-Hours	Unit	Material	2017 Bare Costs Labor	Equipment	Total	Total Incl O&P
0010	**WOOD SCREWS**									
0020	#8, 1" long, steel				C	4.28			4.28	4.71
0100	Brass					10.75			10.75	11.80
0200	#8, 2" long, steel					5.65			5.65	6.20
0300	Brass					18.85			18.85	20.50
0400	#10, 1" long, steel					4.72			4.72	5.20
0500	Brass					14.50			14.50	15.95
0600	#10, 2" long, steel					6.85			6.85	7.50
0700	Brass					23.50			23.50	25.50
0800	#10, 3" long, steel					10.05			10.05	11.05
1000	#12, 2" long, steel					8.80			8.80	9.70
1100	Brass					31			31	34
1500	#12, 3" long, steel					11.30			11.30	12.40
2000	#12, 4" long, steel					19.70			19.70	21.50

06 05 23.60 Timber Connectors

		Crew	Daily Output	Labor-Hours	Unit	Material	2017 Bare Costs Labor	Equipment	Total	Total Incl O&P
0010	**TIMBER CONNECTORS**									
0020	Add up cost of each part for total cost of connection									
0100	Connector plates, steel, with bolts, straight	2 Carp	75	.213	Ea.	27.50	7.45		34.95	43
0110	Tee, 7 ga.		50	.320		35	11.20		46.20	57
0120	T-Strap, 14 ga., 12" x 8" x 2"		50	.320		35	11.20		46.20	57
0150	Anchor plates, 7 ga., 9" x 7"		75	.213		27.50	7.45		34.95	43
0200	Bolts, machine, sq. hd. with nut & washer, 1/2" diameter, 4" long	1 Carp	140	.057		.75	2		2.75	4.17
0300	7-1/2" long		130	.062		1.37	2.15		3.52	5.10

For customer support on your Residential Costs with RSMeans Data, call 800.448.8182.

361

06 05 23.60 Timber Connectors		Crew	Daily Output	Labor-Hours	Unit	Material	2017 Bare Costs Labor	Equipment	Total	Total Incl O&P
0500	3/4" diameter, 7-1/2" long	1 Carp	130	.062	Ea.	3.20	2.15		5.35	7.10
0610	Machine bolts, w/nut, washer, 3/4" diam., 15" L, HD's & beam hangers		95	.084		5.95	2.94		8.89	11.45
0720	Machine bolts, sq. hd. w/nut & wash		150	.053	Lb.	3.68	1.86		5.54	7.15
0800	Drilling bolt holes in timber, 1/2" diameter		450	.018	Inch		.62		.62	1.04
0900	1" diameter		350	.023	"		.80		.80	1.34
1100	Framing anchor, angle, 3" x 3" x 1-1/2", 12 ga		175	.046	Ea.	2.56	1.60		4.16	5.50
1150	Framing anchors, 18 ga., 4-1/2" x 2-3/4"		175	.046		2.56	1.60		4.16	5.50
1160	Framing anchors, 18 ga., 4-1/2" x 3"		175	.046		2.56	1.60		4.16	5.50
1170	Clip anchors plates, 18 ga., 12" x 1-1/8"		175	.046		2.56	1.60		4.16	5.50
1250	Holdowns, 3 ga. base, 10 ga. body		8	1		26	35		61	87.50
1260	Holdowns, 7 ga. 11-1/16" x 3-1/4"		8	1		26	35		61	87.50
1270	Holdowns, 7 ga. 14-3/8" x 3-1/8"		8	1		26	35		61	87.50
1275	Holdowns, 12 ga. 8" x 2-1/2"		8	1		26	35		61	87.50
1300	Joist and beam hangers, 18 ga. galv., for 2" x 4" joist		175	.046		.80	1.60		2.40	3.55
1400	2" x 6" to 2" x 10" joist		165	.048		1.36	1.69		3.05	4.33
1600	16 ga. galv., 3" x 6" to 3" x 10" joist		160	.050		3.02	1.75		4.77	6.25
1700	3" x 10" to 3" x 14" joist		160	.050		4.88	1.75		6.63	8.25
1800	4" x 6" to 4" x 10" joist		155	.052		3.08	1.80		4.88	6.40
1900	4" x 10" to 4" x 14" joist		155	.052		5.30	1.80		7.10	8.85
2000	Two-2" x 6" to two-2" x 10" joists		150	.053		4	1.86		5.86	7.50
2100	Two-2" x 10" to two-2" x 14" joists		150	.053		4.48	1.86		6.34	8.05
2300	3/16" thick, 6" x 8" joist		145	.055		65	1.93		66.93	74.50
2400	6" x 10" joist		140	.057		67.50	2		69.50	78
2500	6" x 12" joist		135	.059		64.50	2.07		66.57	74.50
2700	1/4" thick, 6" x 14" joist		130	.062		67	2.15		69.15	77
2900	Plywood clips, extruded aluminum H clip, for 3/4" panels					.22			.22	.24
3000	Galvanized 18 ga. back-up clip					.18			.18	.20
3200	Post framing, 16 ga. galv. for 4" x 4" base, 2 piece	1 Carp	130	.062		14.50	2.15		16.65	19.55
3300	Cap		130	.062		22.50	2.15		24.65	28.50
3500	Rafter anchors, 18 ga. galv., 1-1/2" wide, 5-1/4" long		145	.055		.48	1.93		2.41	3.75
3600	10-3/4" long		145	.055		1.43	1.93		3.36	4.79
3800	Shear plates, 2-5/8" diameter		120	.067		2.44	2.33		4.77	6.60
3900	4" diameter		115	.070		5.70	2.43		8.13	10.35
4000	Sill anchors, embedded in concrete or block, 25-1/2" long		115	.070		12.70	2.43		15.13	18.00
4100	Spike grids, 3" x 6"		120	.067		.96	2.33		3.29	4.96
4400	Split rings, 2-1/2" diameter		120	.067		2.02	2.33		4.35	6.10
4500	4" diameter		110	.073		2.98	2.54		5.52	7.55
4550	Tie plate, 20 ga., 7" x 3-1/8"		110	.073		2.98	2.54		5.52	7.55
4560	5" x 4-1/8"		110	.073		2.98	2.54		5.52	7.55
4575	Twist straps, 18 ga., 12" x 1-1/4"		110	.073		2.98	2.54		5.52	7.55
4580	16" x 1-1/4"		110	.073		2.98	2.54		5.52	7.55
4600	Strap ties, 20 ga., 2-1/16" wide, 12-13/16" long		180	.044		.87	1.55		2.42	3.56
4700	16 ga., 1-3/8" wide, 12" long		180	.044		.87	1.55		2.42	3.56
4800	1-1/4" wide, 21-5/8" long		160	.050		2.88	1.75		4.63	6.10
5000	Toothed rings, 2-5/8" or 4" diameter		90	.089		2.05	3.11		5.16	7.45
5200	Truss plates, nailed, 20 ga., up to 32' span		17	.471	Truss	12.85	16.45		29.30	41.50
5400	Washers, 2" x 2" x 1/8"				Ea.	.38			.38	.42
5500	3" x 3" x 3/16"				"	1.14			1.14	1.25
6000	Angles and gussets, painted									
6012	7 ga., 3-1/4" x 3-1/4" x 2-1/2" long	1 Carp	1.90	4.211	C	1,075	147		1,222	1,425
6014	3-1/4" x 3-1/4" x 5" long		1.90	4.211		2,100	147		2,247	2,550
6016	3-1/4" x 3-1/4" x 7-1/2" long		1.85	4.324		3,975	151		4,126	4,600
6018	5-3/4" x 5-3/4" x 2-1/2" long		1.85	4.324		2,550	151		2,701	3,075

06 05 Common Work Results for Wood, Plastics, and Composites

06 05 23 – Wood, Plastic, and Composite Fastenings

06 05 23.60 Timber Connectors		Crew	Daily Output	Labor-Hours	Unit	Material	Labor	Equipment	Total	Total Incl O&P
6020	5-3/4" x 5-3/4" x 5" long	1 Carp	1.85	4.324	C	4,075	151		4,226	4,725
6022	5-3/4" x 5-3/4" x 7-1/2" long		1.80	4.444		6,000	155		6,155	6,875
6024	3 ga., 4-1/4" x 4-1/4" x 3" long		1.85	4.324		2,725	151		2,876	3,225
6026	4-1/4" x 4-1/4" x 6" long		1.85	4.324		5,850	151		6,001	6,675
6028	4-1/4" x 4-1/4" x 9" long		1.80	4.444		6,575	155		6,730	7,475
6030	7-1/4" x 7-1/4" x 3" long		1.80	4.444		4,700	155		4,855	5,425
6032	7-1/4" x 7-1/4" x 6" long		1.80	4.444		6,350	155		6,505	7,225
6034	7-1/4" x 7-1/4" x 9" long		1.75	4.571		14,200	160		14,360	15,900
6036	Gussets									
6038	7 ga., 8-1/8" x 8-1/8" x 2-3/4" long	1 Carp	1.80	4.444	C	4,850	155		5,005	5,575
6040	3 ga., 9-3/4" x 9-3/4" x 3-1/4" long	"	1.80	4.444	"	7,275	155		7,430	8,250
6101	Beam hangers, polymer painted									
6102	Bolted, 3 ga. (W x H x L)									
6104	3-1/4" x 9" x 12" top flange	1 Carp	1	8	C	19,100	280		19,380	21,500
6106	5-1/4" x 9" x 12" top flange		1	8		20,000	280		20,280	22,500
6108	5-1/4" x 11" x 11-3/4" top flange		1	8		20,800	280		21,080	23,300
6110	6-7/8" x 9" x 12" top flange		1	8		20,600	280		20,880	23,200
6112	6-7/8" x 11" x 13-1/2" top flange		1	8		24,300	280		24,580	27,300
6114	8-7/8" x 11" x 15-1/2" top flange		1	8		23,600	280		23,880	26,400
6116	Nailed, 3 ga. (W x H x L)									
6118	3-1/4" x 10-1/2" x 10" top flange	1 Carp	1.80	4.444	C	20,500	155		20,655	22,900
6120	3-1/4" x 10-1/2" x 12" top flange		1.80	4.444		21,400	155		21,555	23,900
6122	5-1/4" x 9-1/2" x 10" top flange		1.80	4.444		22,300	155		22,455	24,900
6124	5-1/4" x 9-1/2" x 12" top flange		1.80	4.444		22,900	155		23,055	25,500
6128	6-7/8" x 8-1/2" x 12" top flange		1.80	4.444		20,600	155		20,755	23,000
6134	Saddle hangers, glu-lam (W x H x L)									
6136	3-1/4" x 10-1/2" x 5-1/4" x 6" saddle	1 Carp	.50	16	C	15,600	560		16,160	18,100
6138	3-1/4" x 10-1/2" x 6-7/8" x 6" saddle		.50	16		16,600	560		17,160	19,100
6140	3-1/4" x 10-1/2" x 8-7/8" x 6" saddle		.50	16		17,400	560		17,960	20,000
6142	3-1/4" x 19-1/2" x 5-1/4" x 10-1/8" saddle		.40	20		17,400	700		18,100	20,400
6144	3-1/4" x 19-1/2" x 6-7/8" x 10-1/8" saddle		.40	20		16,800	700		17,500	19,700
6146	3-1/4" x 19-1/2" x 8-7/8" x 10-1/8" saddle		.40	20		17,400	700		18,100	20,300
6148	5-1/4" x 9-1/2" x 5-1/4" x 12" saddle		.50	16		18,400	560		18,960	21,100
6150	5-1/4" x 9-1/2" x 6-7/8" x 9" saddle		.50	16		20,400	560		20,960	23,300
6152	5-1/4" x 10-1/2" x spec x 12" saddle		.50	16		22,000	560		22,560	25,100
6154	5-1/4" x 18" x 5-1/4" x 12-1/8" saddle		.40	20		18,700	700		19,400	21,800
6156	5-1/4" x 18" x 6-7/8" x 12-1/8" saddle		.40	20		20,600	700		21,300	23,900
6158	5-1/4" x 18" x spec x 12-1/8" saddle		.40	20		22,400	700		23,100	25,900
6160	6-7/8" x 8-1/2" x 6-7/8" x 12" saddle		.50	16		22,000	560		22,560	25,100
6162	6-7/8" x 8-1/2" x 8-7/8" x 12" saddle		.50	16		22,800	560		23,360	26,000
6164	6-7/8" x 10-1/2" x spec x 12" saddle		.50	16		21,900	560		22,460	25,000
6166	6-7/8" x 18" x 6-7/8" x 13-3/4" saddle		.40	20		21,800	700		22,500	25,200
6168	6-7/8" x 18" x 8-7/8" x 13-3/4" saddle		.40	20		23,500	700		24,200	27,000
6170	6-7/8" x 18" x spec x 13-3/4" saddle		.40	20		24,400	700		25,100	28,000
6172	8-7/8" x 18" x spec x 15-3/4" saddle		.40	20		38,300	700		39,000	43,400
6201	Beam and purlin hangers, galvanized, 12 ga.									
6202	Purlin or joist size, 3" x 8"	1 Carp	1.70	4.706	C	2,025	164		2,189	2,500
6204	3" x 10"		1.70	4.706		2,250	164		2,414	2,750
6206	3" x 12"		1.65	4.848		2,525	169		2,694	3,050
6208	3" x 14"		1.65	4.848		2,675	169		2,844	3,225
6210	3" x 16"		1.65	4.848		2,850	169		3,019	3,400
6212	4" x 8"		1.65	4.848		2,025	169		2,194	2,500
6214	4" x 10"		1.65	4.848		2,250	169		2,419	2,750

06 05 23.60 Timber Connectors		Crew	Daily Output	Labor-Hours	Unit	Material	2017 Bare Costs Labor	Equipment	Total	Total Incl O&P
6216	4" x 12"	1 Carp	1.60	5	C	2,675	175		2,850	3,225
6218	4" x 14"		1.60	5		2,800	175		2,975	3,375
6220	4" x 16"		1.60	5		2,975	175		3,150	3,575
6222	6" x 8"		1.60	5		2,700	175		2,875	3,250
6224	6" x 10"		1.55	5.161		2,725	180		2,905	3,300
6226	6" x 12"		1.55	5.161		4,675	180		4,855	5,425
6228	6" x 14"		1.50	5.333		4,950	186		5,136	5,750
6230	6" x 16"	▼	1.50	5.333	▼	5,275	186		5,461	6,100
6250	Beam seats									
6252	Beam size, 5-1/4" wide									
6254	5" x 7" x 1/4"	1 Carp	1.80	4.444	C	7,950	155		8,105	9,000
6256	6" x 7" x 3/8"		1.80	4.444		8,725	155		8,880	9,850
6258	7" x 7" x 3/8"		1.80	4.444		9,400	155		9,555	10,600
6260	8" x 7" x 3/8"	▼	1.80	4.444	▼	11,100	155		11,255	12,500
6262	Beam size, 6-7/8" wide									
6264	5" x 9" x 1/4"	1 Carp	1.80	4.444	C	9,425	155		9,580	10,700
6266	6" x 9" x 3/8"		1.80	4.444		12,400	155		12,555	13,900
6268	7" x 9" x 3/8"		1.80	4.444		12,200	155		12,355	13,700
6270	8" x 9" x 3/8"	▼	1.80	4.444	▼	14,500	155		14,655	16,200
6272	Special beams, over 6-7/8" wide									
6274	5" x 10" x 3/8"	1 Carp	1.80	4.444	C	12,500	155		12,655	14,100
6276	6" x 10" x 3/8"		1.80	4.444		14,700	155		14,855	16,500
6278	7" x 10" x 3/8"		1.80	4.444		15,500	155		15,655	17,300
6280	8" x 10" x 3/8"		1.75	4.571		15,900	160		16,060	17,800
6282	5-1/4" x 12" x 5/16"		1.75	4.571		12,300	160		12,460	13,800
6284	6-1/2" x 12" x 3/8"		1.75	4.571		20,400	160		20,560	22,700
6286	5-1/4" x 16" x 5/16"		1.70	4.706		18,100	164		18,264	20,200
6288	6-1/2" x 16" x 3/8"		1.70	4.706		24,200	164		24,364	27,000
6290	5-1/4" x 20" x 5/16"		1.70	4.706		22,000	164		22,164	24,500
6292	6-1/2" x 20" x 3/8"	▼	1.65	4.848	▼	28,600	169		28,769	31,800
6300	Column bases									
6302	4 x 4, 16 ga.	1 Carp	1.80	4.444	C	775	155		930	1,125
6306	7 ga.		1.80	4.444		2,900	155		3,055	3,425
6308	4 x 6, 16 ga.		1.80	4.444		1,750	155		1,905	2,175
6312	7 ga.		1.80	4.444		2,850	155		3,005	3,375
6314	6 x 6, 16 ga.		1.75	4.571		2,300	160		2,460	2,800
6318	7 ga.		1.75	4.571		3,650	160		3,810	4,275
6320	6 x 8, 7 ga.		1.70	4.706		3,150	164		3,314	3,750
6322	6 x 10, 7 ga.		1.70	4.706		3,400	164		3,564	4,000
6324	6 x 12, 7 ga.		1.70	4.706		3,675	164		3,839	4,325
6326	8 x 8, 7 ga.		1.65	4.848		6,200	169		6,369	7,100
6330	8 x 10, 7 ga.		1.65	4.848		7,225	169		7,394	8,225
6332	8 x 12, 7 ga.		1.60	5		7,850	175		8,025	8,925
6334	10 x 10, 3 ga.		1.60	5		8,000	175		8,175	9,125
6336	10 x 12, 3 ga.		1.60	5		9,200	175		9,375	10,400
6338	12 x 12, 3 ga.	▼	1.55	5.161	▼	10,000	180		10,180	11,300
6350	Column caps, painted, 3 ga.									
6352	3-1/4" x 3-5/8"	1 Carp	1.80	4.444	C	10,400	155		10,555	11,700
6354	3-1/4" x 5-1/2"		1.80	4.444		10,400	155		10,555	11,700
6356	3-5/8" x 3-5/8"		1.80	4.444		8,475	155		8,630	9,575
6358	3-5/8" x 5-1/2"		1.80	4.444		8,475	155		8,630	9,575
6360	5-1/4" x 5-1/2"		1.75	4.571		10,200	160		10,360	11,500
6362	5-1/4" x 7-1/2"		1.75	4.571		10,900	160		11,060	12,300

06 05 23.60 Timber Connectors		Crew	Daily Output	Labor-Hours	Unit	Material	2017 Bare Costs Labor	Equipment	Total	Total Incl O&P
6364	5-1/2" x 3-5/8"	1 Carp	1.75	4.571	C	10,200	160		10,360	11,500
6366	5-1/2" x 5-1/2"		1.75	4.571		10,200	160		10,360	11,500
6368	5-1/2" x 7-1/2"		1.70	4.706		11,700	164		11,864	13,200
6370	6-7/8" x 5-1/2"		1.70	4.706		12,200	164		12,364	13,800
6372	6-7/8" x 6-7/8"		1.70	4.706		12,200	164		12,364	13,800
6374	6-7/8" x 7-1/2"		1.70	4.706		12,200	164		12,364	13,800
6376	7-1/2" x 5-1/2"		1.65	4.848		12,800	169		12,969	14,400
6378	7-1/2" x 7-1/2"		1.65	4.848		12,800	169		12,969	14,400
6380	8-7/8" x 5-1/2"		1.60	5		13,500	175		13,675	15,200
6382	8-7/8" x 7-1/2"		1.60	5		13,500	175		13,675	15,200
6384	9-1/2" x 5-1/2"		1.60	5		18,300	175		18,475	20,400
6400	Floor tie anchors, polymer paint									
6402	10 ga., 3" x 37-1/2"	1 Carp	1.80	4.444	C	4,875	155		5,030	5,600
6404	3-1/2" x 45-1/2"		1.75	4.571		5,100	160		5,260	5,875
6406	3 ga., 3-1/2" x 56"		1.70	4.706		8,975	164		9,139	10,200
6410	Girder hangers									
6412	6" wall thickness, 4" x 6"	1 Carp	1.80	4.444	C	2,725	155		2,880	3,250
6414	4" x 8"		1.80	4.444		3,050	155		3,205	3,600
6416	8" wall thickness, 4" x 6"		1.80	4.444		3,050	155		3,205	3,600
6418	4" x 8"		1.80	4.444		3,050	155		3,205	3,600
6420	Hinge connections, polymer painted									
6422	3/4" thick top plate									
6424	5-1/4" x 12" w/5" x 5" top	1 Carp	1	8	C	35,800	280		36,080	39,900
6426	5-1/4" x 15" w/6" x 6" top		.80	10		38,100	350		38,450	42,500
6428	5-1/4" x 18" w/7" x 7" top		.70	11.429		40,100	400		40,500	44,800
6430	5-1/4" x 26" w/9" x 9" top		.60	13.333		42,600	465		43,065	47,700
6432	1" thick top plate									
6434	6-7/8" x 14" w/5" x 5" top	1 Carp	.80	10	C	43,700	350		44,050	48,600
6436	6-7/8" x 17" w/6" x 6" top		.80	10		48,600	350		48,950	54,000
6438	6-7/8" x 21" w/7" x 7" top		.70	11.429		53,000	400		53,400	59,000
6440	6-7/8" x 31" w/9" x 9" top		.60	13.333		58,000	465		58,465	64,500
6442	1-1/4" thick top plate									
6444	8-7/8" x 16" w/5" x 5" top	1 Carp	.60	13.333	C	54,500	465		54,965	61,000
6446	8-7/8" x 21" w/6" x 6" top		.50	16		60,000	560		60,560	67,000
6448	8-7/8" x 26" w/7" x 7" top		.40	20		68,000	700		68,700	75,500
6450	8-7/8" x 39" w/9" x 9" top		.30	26.667		84,500	930		85,430	94,500
6460	Holddowns									
6462	Embedded along edge									
6464	26" long, 12 ga.	1 Carp	.90	8.889	C	1,175	310		1,485	1,825
6466	35" long, 12 ga.		.85	9.412		1,625	330		1,955	2,350
6468	35" long, 10 ga.		.85	9.412		1,700	330		2,030	2,425
6470	Embedded away from edge									
6472	Medium duty, 12 ga.									
6474	18-1/2" long	1 Carp	.95	8.421	C	825	294		1,119	1,400
6476	23-3/4" long		.90	8.889		960	310		1,270	1,575
6478	28" long		.85	9.412		980	330		1,310	1,625
6480	35" long		.85	9.412		1,350	330		1,680	2,025
6482	Heavy duty, 10 ga.									
6484	28" long	1 Carp	.85	9.412	C	1,750	330		2,080	2,475
6486	35" long	"	.85	9.412	"	1,900	330		2,230	2,650
6490	Surface mounted (W x H)									
6492	2-1/2" x 5-3/4", 7 ga.	1 Carp	1	8	C	2,025	280		2,305	2,725
6494	2-1/2" x 8", 12 ga.		1	8		1,225	280		1,505	1,825

For customer support on your Residential Costs with RSMeans Data, call 800.448.8182.

365

06 05 23.60 Timber Connectors		Crew	Daily Output	Labor-Hours	Unit	Material	2017 Bare Costs Labor	Equipment	Total	Total Incl O&P
6496	2-7/8" x 6-3/8", 7 ga.	1 Carp	1	8	C	4,775	280		5,055	5,725
6498	2-7/8" x 12-1/2", 3 ga.		1	8		4,500	280		4,780	5,425
6500	3-3/16" x 9-3/8", 10 ga.		1	8		3,000	280		3,280	3,775
6502	3-1/2" x 11-5/8", 3 ga.		1	8		5,550	280		5,830	6,575
6504	3-1/2" x 14-3/4", 3 ga.		1	8		7,075	280		7,355	8,275
6506	3-1/2" x 16-1/2", 3 ga.		1	8		8,450	280		8,730	9,775
6508	3-1/2" x 20-1/2", 3 ga.		.90	8.889		9,200	310		9,510	10,600
6510	3-1/2" x 24-1/2", 3 ga.		.90	8.889		11,000	310		11,310	12,600
6512	4-1/4" x 20-3/4", 3 ga.		.90	8.889		7,625	310		7,935	8,925
6520	Joist hangers									
6522	Sloped, field adjustable, 18 ga.									
6524	2" x 6"	1 Carp	1.65	4.848	C	545	169		714	885
6526	2" x 8"		1.65	4.848		985	169		1,154	1,350
6528	2" x 10" and up		1.65	4.848		1,425	169		1,594	1,825
6530	3" x 10" and up		1.60	5		1,175	175		1,350	1,600
6532	4" x 10" and up		1.55	5.161		1,350	180		1,530	1,775
6536	Skewed 45°, 16 ga.									
6538	2" x 4"	1 Carp	1.75	4.571	C	1,075	160		1,235	1,450
6540	2" x 6" or 2" x 8"		1.65	4.848		980	169		1,149	1,350
6542	2" x 10" or 2" x 12"		1.65	4.848		1,025	169		1,194	1,400
6544	2" x 14" or 2" x 16"		1.60	5		1,825	175		2,000	2,300
6546	(2) 2" x 6" or (2) 2" x 8"		1.60	5		1,650	175		1,825	2,100
6548	(2) 2" x 10" or (2) 2" x 12"		1.55	5.161		1,750	180		1,930	2,225
6550	(2) 2" x 14" or (2) 2" x 16"		1.50	5.333		2,775	186		2,961	3,350
6552	4" x 6" or 4" x 8"		1.60	5		1,375	175		1,550	1,800
6554	4" x 10" or 4" x 12"		1.55	5.161		1,600	180		1,780	2,075
6556	4" x 14" or 4" x 16"		1.55	5.161		2,475	180		2,655	3,025
6560	Skewed 45°, 14 ga.									
6562	(2) 2" x 6" or (2) 2" x 8"	1 Carp	1.60	5	C	1,900	175		2,075	2,375
6564	(2) 2" x 10" or (2) 2" x 12"		1.55	5.161		2,625	180		2,805	3,175
6566	(2) 2" x 14" or (2) 2" x 16"		1.50	5.333		3,850	186		4,036	4,525
6568	4" x 6" or 4" x 8"		1.60	5		2,075	175		2,250	2,600
6570	4" x 10" or 4" x 12"		1.55	5.161		2,375	180		2,555	2,900
6572	4" x 14" or 4" x 16"		1.55	5.161		3,175	180		3,355	3,800
6590	Joist hangers, heavy duty 12 ga., galvanized									
6592	2" x 4"	1 Carp	1.75	4.571	C	1,275	160		1,435	1,675
6594	2" x 6"		1.65	4.848		1,400	169		1,569	1,800
6595	2" x 6", 16 ga.		1.65	4.848		1,325	169		1,494	1,725
6596	2" x 8"		1.65	4.848		2,100	169		2,269	2,600
6597	2" x 8", 16 ga.		1.65	4.848		2,000	169		2,169	2,475
6598	2" x 10"		1.65	4.848		2,175	169		2,344	2,650
6600	2" x 12"		1.65	4.848		2,650	169		2,819	3,200
6602	2" x 14"		1.65	4.848		2,775	169		2,944	3,325
6604	2" x 16"		1.65	4.848		2,925	169		3,094	3,500
6606	3" x 4"		1.65	4.848		1,775	169		1,944	2,225
6608	3" x 6"		1.65	4.848		2,375	169		2,544	2,875
6610	3" x 8"		1.65	4.848		2,400	169		2,569	2,925
6612	3" x 10"		1.60	5		2,775	175		2,950	3,350
6614	3" x 12"		1.60	5		3,325	175		3,500	3,975
6616	3" x 14"		1.60	5		3,900	175		4,075	4,600
6618	3" x 16"		1.60	5		4,300	175		4,475	5,050
6620	(2) 2" x 4"		1.75	4.571		2,075	160		2,235	2,550
6622	(2) 2" x 6"		1.60	5		2,500	175		2,675	3,025

06 05 23 – Wood, Plastic, and Composite Fastenings

06 05 23.60 Timber Connectors		Crew	Daily Output	Labor-Hours	Unit	Material	2017 Bare Costs Labor	Equipment	Total	Total Incl O&P
6624	(2) 2" x 8"	1 Carp	1.60	5	C	2,550	175		2,725	3,100
6626	(2) 2" x 10"		1.55	5.161		2,750	180		2,930	3,325
6628	(2) 2" x 12"		1.55	5.161		3,525	180		3,705	4,175
6630	(2) 2" x 14"		1.50	5.333		3,550	186		3,736	4,225
6632	(2) 2" x 16"		1.50	5.333		3,600	186		3,786	4,250
6634	4" x 4"		1.65	4.848		1,500	169		1,669	1,925
6636	4" x 6"		1.60	5		1,650	175		1,825	2,125
6638	4" x 8"		1.60	5		1,900	175		2,075	2,400
6640	4" x 10"		1.55	5.161		2,350	180		2,530	2,875
6642	4" x 12"		1.55	5.161		2,500	180		2,680	3,025
6644	4" x 14"		1.55	5.161		2,975	180		3,155	3,575
6646	4" x 16"		1.55	5.161		3,275	180		3,455	3,900
6648	(3) 2" x 10"		1.50	5.333		3,600	186		3,786	4,275
6650	(3) 2" x 12"		1.50	5.333		4,025	186		4,211	4,725
6652	(3) 2" x 14"		1.45	5.517		4,325	193		4,518	5,075
6654	(3) 2" x 16"		1.45	5.517		4,400	193		4,593	5,150
6656	6" x 6"		1.60	5		1,950	175		2,125	2,425
6658	6" x 8"		1.60	5		2,000	175		2,175	2,500
6660	6" x 10"		1.55	5.161		2,400	180		2,580	2,925
6662	6" x 12"		1.55	5.161		2,725	180		2,905	3,300
6664	6" x 14"		1.50	5.333		3,425	186		3,611	4,050
6666	6" x 16"		1.50	5.333		4,025	186		4,211	4,725
6690	Knee braces, galvanized, 12 ga.									
6692	Beam depth, 10" x 15" x 5' long	1 Carp	1.80	4.444	C	5,225	155		5,380	6,000
6694	15" x 22-1/2" x 7' long		1.70	4.706		6,000	164		6,164	6,875
6696	22-1/2" x 28-1/2" x 8' long		1.60	5		6,450	175		6,625	7,375
6698	28-1/2" x 36" x 10' long		1.55	5.161		6,725	180		6,905	7,700
6700	36" x 42" x 12' long		1.50	5.333		7,425	186		7,611	8,450
6710	Mudsill anchors									
6714	2" x 4" or 3" x 4"	1 Carp	115	.070	C	1,425	2.43		1,427.43	1,550
6716	2" x 6" or 3" x 6"		115	.070		1,425	2.43		1,427.43	1,550
6718	Block wall, 13-1/4" long		115	.070		85	2.43		87.43	97.50
6720	21-1/4" long		115	.070		126	2.43		128.43	143
6730	Post bases, 12 ga. galvanized									
6732	Adjustable, 3-9/16" x 3-9/16"	1 Carp	1.30	6.154	C	1,075	215		1,290	1,525
6734	3-9/16" x 5-1/2"		1.30	6.154		2,025	215		2,240	2,575
6736	4" x 4"		1.30	6.154		930	215		1,145	1,375
6738	4" x 6"		1.30	6.154		2,700	215		2,915	3,325
6740	5-1/2" x 5-1/2"		1.30	6.154		3,325	215		3,540	4,000
6742	6" x 6"		1.30	6.154		3,325	215		3,540	4,000
6744	Elevated, 3-9/16" x 3-1/4"		1.30	6.154		1,150	215		1,365	1,625
6746	5-1/2" x 3-5/16"		1.30	6.154		1,650	215		1,865	2,150
6748	5-1/2" x 5"		1.30	6.154		2,450	215		2,665	3,050
6750	Regular, 3-9/16" x 3-3/8"		1.30	6.154		880	215		1,095	1,325
6752	4" x 3-3/8"		1.30	6.154		1,250	215		1,465	1,725
6754	18 ga., 5-1/4" x 3-1/8"		1.30	6.154		1,300	215		1,515	1,775
6755	5-1/2" x 3-3/8"		1.30	6.154		1,300	215		1,515	1,775
6756	5-1/2" x 5-3/8"		1.30	6.154		1,875	215		2,090	2,400
6758	6" x 3-3/8"		1.30	6.154		2,250	215		2,465	2,825
6760	6" x 5-3/8"		1.30	6.154		2,500	215		2,715	3,100
6762	Post combination cap/bases									
6764	3-9/16" x 3-9/16"	1 Carp	1.20	6.667	C	460	233		693	895
6766	3-9/16" x 5-1/2"		1.20	6.667		1,050	233		1,283	1,550

For customer support on your Residential Costs with RSMeans Data, call 800.448.8182.

367

06 05 23.60 Timber Connectors	Crew	Daily Output	Labor-Hours	Unit	Material	2017 Bare Costs Labor	Equipment	Total	Total Incl O&P
6768	4" x 4"	1 Carp	1.20	6.667	C	2,075	233		2,308	2,700
6770	5-1/2" x 5-1/2"		1.20	6.667		1,150	233		1,383	1,675
6772	6" x 6"		1.20	6.667		4,150	233		4,383	4,975
6774	7-1/2" x 7-1/2"		1.20	6.667		4,550	233		4,783	5,425
6776	8" x 8"		1.20	6.667		4,725	233		4,958	5,600
6790	Post-beam connection caps									
6792	Beam size 3-9/16"									
6794	12 ga. post, 4" x 4"	1 Carp	1	8	C	2,900	280		3,180	3,650
6796	4" x 6"		1	8		3,850	280		4,130	4,725
6798	4" x 8"		1	8		5,700	280		5,980	6,725
6800	16 ga. post, 4" x 4"		1	8		1,200	280		1,480	1,775
6802	4" x 6"		1	8		2,000	280		2,280	2,650
6804	4" x 8"		1	8		3,350	280		3,630	4,150
6805	18 ga. post, 2-7/8" x 3"		1	8		3,350	280		3,630	4,150
6806	Beam size 5-1/2"									
6808	12 ga. post, 6" x 4"	1 Carp	1	8	C	3,350	280		3,630	4,150
6810	6" x 6"		1	8		5,450	280		5,730	6,475
6812	6" x 8"		1	8		3,750	280		4,030	4,600
6816	16 ga. post, 6" x 4"		1	8		1,875	280		2,155	2,550
6818	6" x 6"		1	8		2,000	280		2,280	2,650
6820	Beam size 7-1/2"									
6822	12 ga. post, 8" x 4"	1 Carp	1	8	C	4,775	280		5,055	5,725
6824	8" x 6"		1	8		5,025	280		5,305	6,000
6826	8" x 8"		1	8		7,550	280		7,830	8,775
6840	Purlin anchors, embedded									
6842	Heavy duty, 10 ga.									
6844	Straight, 28" long	1 Carp	1.60	5	C	1,425	175		1,600	1,875
6846	35" long		1.50	5.333		1,775	186		1,961	2,250
6848	Twisted, 28" long		1.60	5		1,425	175		1,600	1,875
6850	35" long		1.50	5.333		1,775	186		1,961	2,250
6852	Regular duty, 12 ga.									
6854	Straight, 18-1/2" long	1 Carp	1.80	4.444	C	820	155		975	1,150
6856	23-3/4" long		1.70	4.706		1,025	164		1,189	1,400
6858	29" long		1.60	5		1,050	175		1,225	1,450
6860	35" long		1.50	5.333		1,450	186		1,636	1,900
6862	Twisted, 18" long		1.80	4.444		820	155		975	1,150
6866	28" long		1.60	5		980	175		1,155	1,375
6868	35" long		1.50	5.333		1,450	186		1,636	1,900
6870	Straight, plastic coated									
6872	23-1/2" long	1 Carp	1.60	5	C	2,025	175		2,200	2,525
6874	26-7/8" long		1.60	5		2,375	175		2,550	2,900
6876	32-1/2" long		1.50	5.333		2,525	186		2,711	3,075
6878	35-7/8" long		1.50	5.333		2,625	186		2,811	3,200
6890	Purlin hangers, painted									
6892	12 ga., 2" x 6"	1 Carp	1.80	4.444	C	1,850	155		2,005	2,300
6894	2" x 8"		1.80	4.444		2,025	155		2,180	2,475
6896	2" x 10"		1.80	4.444		2,175	155		2,330	2,650
6898	2" x 12"		1.75	4.571		2,325	160		2,485	2,850
6900	2" x 14"		1.75	4.571		2,500	160		2,660	3,025
6902	2" x 16"		1.75	4.571		2,650	160		2,810	3,200
6904	3" x 6"		1.70	4.706		1,875	164		2,039	2,325
6906	3" x 8"		1.70	4.706		2,025	164		2,189	2,500
6908	3" x 10"		1.70	4.706		2,175	164		2,339	2,675

06 05 Common Work Results for Wood, Plastics, and Composites

06 05 23 – Wood, Plastic, and Composite Fastenings

06 05 23.60 Timber Connectors	Crew	Daily Output	Labor-Hours	Unit	Material	2017 Bare Costs Labor	Equipment	Total	Total Incl O&P
6910	3" x 12"	1 Carp	1.65	4.848	C	2,500	169		2,669	3,025
6912	3" x 14"		1.65	4.848		2,675	169		2,844	3,200
6914	3" x 16"		1.65	4.848		2,825	169		2,994	3,375
6916	4" x 6"		1.65	4.848		1,875	169		2,044	2,325
6918	4" x 8"		1.65	4.848		2,025	169		2,194	2,500
6920	4" x 10"		1.65	4.848		2,200	169		2,369	2,675
6922	4" x 12"		1.60	5		2,600	175		2,775	3,150
6924	4" x 14"		1.60	5		2,750	175		2,925	3,325
6926	4" x 16"		1.60	5		2,925	175		3,100	3,500
6928	6" x 6"		1.60	5		2,475	175		2,650	3,025
6930	6" x 8"		1.60	5		2,625	175		2,800	3,175
6932	6" x 10"		1.55	5.161		2,675	180		2,855	3,250
6934	double 2" x 6"		1.70	4.706		2,025	164		2,189	2,500
6936	double 2" x 8"		1.70	4.706		2,175	164		2,339	2,675
6938	double 2" x 10"		1.70	4.706		2,350	164		2,514	2,850
6940	double 2" x 12"		1.65	4.848		2,500	169		2,669	3,025
6942	double 2" x 14"		1.65	4.848		2,675	169		2,844	3,200
6944	double 2" x 16"		1.65	4.848		2,825	169		2,994	3,375
6960	11 ga., 4" x 6"		1.65	4.848		3,700	169		3,869	4,350
6962	4" x 8"		1.65	4.848		3,975	169		4,144	4,650
6964	4" x 10"		1.65	4.848		4,250	169		4,419	4,950
6966	6" x 6"		1.60	5		3,750	175		3,925	4,425
6968	6" x 8"		1.60	5		4,025	175		4,200	4,725
6970	6" x 10"		1.55	5.161		4,300	180		4,480	5,025
6972	6" x 12"		1.55	5.161		4,575	180		4,755	5,325
6974	6" x 14"		1.55	5.161		4,850	180		5,030	5,625
6976	6" x 16"		1.50	5.333		5,125	186		5,311	5,950
6978	7 ga., 8" x 6"		1.60	5		4,075	175		4,250	4,775
6980	8" x 8"		1.60	5		4,350	175		4,525	5,075
6982	8" x 10"		1.55	5.161		4,625	180		4,805	5,375
6984	8" x 12"		1.55	5.161		4,900	180		5,080	5,700
6986	8" x 14"		1.50	5.333		5,175	186		5,361	6,000
6988	8" x 16"		1.50	5.333		5,450	186		5,636	6,300
7000	Strap connectors, galvanized									
7002	12 ga., 2-1/16" x 36"	1 Carp	1.55	5.161	C	1,175	180		1,355	1,600
7004	2-1/16" x 47"		1.50	5.333		1,625	186		1,811	2,100
7005	10 ga., 2-1/16" x 72"		1.50	5.333		1,725	186		1,911	2,200
7006	7 ga., 2-1/16" x 34"		1.55	5.161		2,900	180		3,080	3,500
7008	2-1/16" x 45"		1.50	5.333		3,825	186		4,011	4,500
7010	3 ga., 3" x 32"		1.55	5.161		4,925	180		5,105	5,725
7012	3" x 41"		1.55	5.161		5,125	180		5,305	5,925
7014	3" x 50"		1.50	5.333		7,825	186		8,011	8,900
7016	3" x 59"		1.50	5.333		9,475	186		9,661	10,700
7018	3-1/2" x 68"		1.45	5.517		9,650	193		9,843	10,900
7030	Tension ties									
7032	19-1/8" long, 16 ga., 3/4" anchor bolt	1 Carp	1.80	4.444	C	1,350	155		1,505	1,725
7034	20" long, 12 ga., 1/2" anchor bolt		1.80	4.444		1,750	155		1,905	2,175
7036	20" long, 12 ga., 3/4" anchor bolt		1.80	4.444		1,750	155		1,905	2,175
7038	27-3/4" long, 12 ga., 3/4" anchor bolt		1.75	4.571		3,100	160		3,260	3,700
7050	Truss connectors, galvanized									
7052	Adjustable hanger									
7054	18 ga., 2" x 6"	1 Carp	1.65	4.848	C	530	169		699	865
7056	4" x 6"		1.65	4.848		695	169		864	1,050

For customer support on your Residential Costs with RSMeans Data, call 800.448.8182.

369

06 05 23 – Wood, Plastic, and Composite Fastenings

06 05 23.60 Timber Connectors

		Crew	Daily Output	Labor-Hours	Unit	Material	2017 Bare Costs Labor	Equipment	Total	Total Incl O&P
7058	16 ga., 4" x 10"	1 Carp	1.60	5	C	1,025	175		1,200	1,425
7060	(2) 2" x 10"	↓	1.60	5	↓	1,025	175		1,200	1,425
7062	Connectors to plate									
7064	16 ga., 2" x 4" plate	1 Carp	1.80	4.444	C	520	155		675	830
7066	2" x 6" plate	"	1.80	4.444	"	670	155		825	1,000
7068	Hip jack connector									
7070	14 ga.	1 Carp	1.50	5.333	C	3,225	186		3,411	3,850

06 05 23.80 Metal Bracing

		Crew	Daily Output	Labor-Hours	Unit	Material	2017 Bare Costs Labor	Equipment	Total	Total Incl O&P
0010	**METAL BRACING**									
0302	Let-in, "T" shaped, 22 ga. galv. steel, studs at 16" O.C.	1 Carp	580	.014	L.F.	.83	.48		1.31	1.72
0402	Studs at 24" O.C.		600	.013		.83	.47		1.30	1.69
0502	Steel straps, 16 ga. galv. steel, studs at 16" O.C.		600	.013		1.07	.47		1.54	1.96
0602	Studs at 24" O.C.	↓	620	.013	↓	1.07	.45		1.52	1.93

06 11 Wood Framing

06 11 10 – Framing with Dimensional, Engineered or Composite Lumber

06 11 10.01 Forest Stewardship Council Certification

		Crew	Daily Output	Labor-Hours	Unit	Material	2017 Bare Costs Labor	Equipment	Total	Total Incl O&P
0010	**FOREST STEWARDSHIP COUNCIL CERTIFICATION**									
0020	For Forest Stewardship Council (FSC) cert dimension lumber, add [G]					65%				

06 11 10.02 Blocking

		Crew	Daily Output	Labor-Hours	Unit	Material	2017 Bare Costs Labor	Equipment	Total	Total Incl O&P
0010	**BLOCKING**									
1790	Bolted to concrete									
1798	Ledger board, 2" x 4"	1 Carp	180	.044	L.F.	5.15	1.55		6.70	8.25
1800	2" x 6"		160	.050		5.15	1.75		6.90	8.55
1810	4" x 6"		140	.057		8.90	2		10.90	13.15
1820	4" x 8"	↓	120	.067	↓	9.35	2.33		11.68	14.15
1950	Miscellaneous, to wood construction									
2000	2" x 4"	1 Carp	250	.032	L.F.	.41	1.12		1.53	2.32
2005	Pneumatic nailed		305	.026		.41	.92		1.33	1.98
2050	2" x 6"		222	.036		.63	1.26		1.89	2.80
2055	Pneumatic nailed		271	.030		.63	1.03		1.66	2.43
2100	2" x 8"		200	.040		.87	1.40		2.27	3.30
2105	Pneumatic nailed		244	.033		.88	1.15		2.03	2.89
2150	2" x 10"		178	.045		1.38	1.57		2.95	4.14
2155	Pneumatic nailed		217	.037		1.39	1.29		2.68	3.68
2200	2" x 12"		151	.053		1.75	1.85		3.60	5.05
2205	Pneumatic nailed	↓	185	.043	↓	1.76	1.51		3.27	4.47
2300	To steel construction									
2320	2" x 4"	1 Carp	208	.038	L.F.	.41	1.34		1.75	2.70
2340	2" x 6"		180	.044		.63	1.55		2.18	3.29
2360	2" x 8"		158	.051		.87	1.77		2.64	3.92
2380	2" x 10"		136	.059		1.38	2.06		3.44	4.96
2400	2" x 12"	↓	109	.073	↓	1.75	2.57		4.32	6.20

06 11 10.04 Wood Bracing

		Crew	Daily Output	Labor-Hours	Unit	Material	2017 Bare Costs Labor	Equipment	Total	Total Incl O&P
0010	**WOOD BRACING**									
0012	Let-in, with 1" x 6" boards, studs @ 16" O.C.	1 Carp	150	.053	L.F.	.76	1.86		2.62	3.95
0202	Studs @ 24" O.C.	"	230	.035	"	.76	1.22		1.98	2.86

06 11 10 – Framing with Dimensional, Engineered or Composite Lumber

06 11 10.06 Bridging

		Crew	Daily Output	Labor-Hours	Unit	Material	2017 Bare Costs Labor	Equipment	Total	Total Incl O&P
0010	**BRIDGING**									
0012	Wood, for joists 16" O.C., 1" x 3"	1 Carp	130	.062	Pr.	.68	2.15		2.83	4.34
0017	Pneumatic nailed		170	.047		.73	1.64		2.37	3.56
0102	2" x 3" bridging		130	.062		.68	2.15		2.83	4.35
0107	Pneumatic nailed		170	.047		.70	1.64		2.34	3.52
0302	Steel, galvanized, 18 ga., for 2" x 10" joists at 12" O.C.		130	.062		1.98	2.15		4.13	5.80
0352	16" O.C.		135	.059		1.86	2.07		3.93	5.50
0402	24" O.C.		140	.057		1.94	2		3.94	5.45
0602	For 2" x 14" joists at 16" O.C.		130	.062		1.40	2.15		3.55	5.15
0902	Compression type, 16" O.C., 2" x 8" joists		200	.040		.94	1.40		2.34	3.38
1002	2" x 12" joists		200	.040		.94	1.40		2.34	3.38

06 11 10.10 Beam and Girder Framing

		Crew	Daily Output	Labor-Hours	Unit	Material	2017 Bare Costs Labor	Equipment	Total	Total Incl O&P
0010	**BEAM AND GIRDER FRAMING** R061110-30									
1000	Single, 2" x 6"	2 Carp	700	.023	L.F.	.63	.80		1.43	2.03
1005	Pneumatic nailed		812	.020		.63	.69		1.32	1.85
1020	2" x 8"		650	.025		.87	.86		1.73	2.40
1025	Pneumatic nailed		754	.021		.88	.74		1.62	2.21
1040	2" x 10"		600	.027		1.38	.93		2.31	3.07
1045	Pneumatic nailed		696	.023		1.39	.80		2.19	2.86
1060	2" x 12"		550	.029		1.75	1.02		2.77	3.63
1065	Pneumatic nailed		638	.025		1.76	.88		2.64	3.41
1080	2" x 14"		500	.032		2.21	1.12		3.33	4.30
1085	Pneumatic nailed		580	.028		2.22	.96		3.18	4.05
1100	3" x 8"		550	.029		2.80	1.02		3.82	4.78
1120	3" x 10"		500	.032		3.53	1.12		4.65	5.75
1140	3" x 12"		450	.036		4.24	1.24		5.48	6.75
1160	3" x 14"		400	.040		4.94	1.40		6.34	7.80
1170	4" x 6"	F-3	1100	.036		2.99	1.17	.52	4.68	5.80
1180	4" x 8"		1000	.040		3.40	1.28	.57	5.25	6.50
1200	4" x 10"		950	.042		4.84	1.35	.60	6.79	8.25
1220	4" x 12"		900	.044		5.35	1.42	.64	7.41	9
1240	4" x 14"		850	.047		6.25	1.51	.67	8.43	10.15
1250	6" x 8"		525	.076		7.70	2.44	1.09	11.23	13.80
1260	6" x 10"		500	.080		6.75	2.56	1.15	10.46	12.95
1290	8" x 12"		300	.133		16.15	4.27	1.91	22.33	27
2000	Double, 2" x 6"	2 Carp	625	.026		1.26	.89		2.15	2.88
2005	Pneumatic nailed		725	.022		1.27	.77		2.04	2.68
2020	2" x 8"		575	.028		1.75	.97		2.72	3.55
2025	Pneumatic nailed		667	.024		1.76	.84		2.60	3.33
2040	2" x 10"		550	.029		2.75	1.02		3.77	4.73
2045	Pneumatic nailed		638	.025		2.77	.88		3.65	4.52
2060	2" x 12"		525	.030		3.50	1.07		4.57	5.65
2065	Pneumatic nailed		610	.026		3.52	.92		4.44	5.40
2080	2" x 14"		475	.034		4.42	1.18		5.60	6.85
2085	Pneumatic nailed		551	.029		4.45	1.01		5.46	6.60
3000	Triple, 2" x 6"		550	.029		1.88	1.02		2.90	3.77
3005	Pneumatic nailed		638	.025		1.90	.88		2.78	3.56
3020	2" x 8"		525	.030		2.62	1.07		3.69	4.66
3025	Pneumatic nailed		609	.026		2.64	.92		3.56	4.44
3040	2" x 10"		500	.032		4.13	1.12		5.25	6.40
3045	Pneumatic nailed		580	.028		4.16	.96		5.12	6.20
3060	2" x 12"		475	.034		5.25	1.18		6.43	7.75

For customer support on your Residential Costs with RSMeans Data, call 800.448.8182.

371

06 11 Wood Framing

06 11 10 – Framing with Dimensional, Engineered or Composite Lumber

06 11 10.10 Beam and Girder Framing	Crew	Daily Output	Labor-Hours	Unit	Material	2017 Bare Costs Labor	Equipment	Total	Total Incl O&P
3065	Pneumatic nailed	2 Carp	551	.029	L.F.	5.30	1.01		6.31	7.50
3080	2" x 14"		450	.036		7.25	1.24		8.49	10.10
3085	Pneumatic nailed		522	.031		6.65	1.07		7.72	9.15

06 11 10.12 Ceiling Framing

		Crew	Daily Output	Labor-Hours	Unit	Material	Labor	Equipment	Total	Total Incl O&P
0010	**CEILING FRAMING**									
6000	Suspended, 2" x 3"	2 Carp	1000	.016	L.F.	.39	.56		.95	1.37
6050	2" x 4"		900	.018		.41	.62		1.03	1.49
6100	2" x 6"		800	.020		.63	.70		1.33	1.86
6150	2" x 8"		650	.025		.87	.86		1.73	2.40

06 11 10.14 Posts and Columns

		Crew	Daily Output	Labor-Hours	Unit	Material	Labor	Equipment	Total	Total Incl O&P
0010	**POSTS AND COLUMNS**									
0100	4" x 4"	2 Carp	390	.041	L.F.	1.79	1.43		3.22	4.36
0150	4" x 6"		275	.058		2.99	2.03		5.02	6.70
0200	4" x 8"		220	.073		3.40	2.54		5.94	8
0250	6" x 6"		215	.074		5.20	2.60		7.80	10.10
0300	6" x 8"		175	.091		7.70	3.20		10.90	13.85
0350	6" x 10"		150	.107		6.75	3.73		10.48	13.65

06 11 10.18 Joist Framing

		Crew	Daily Output	Labor-Hours	Unit	Material	Labor	Equipment	Total	Total Incl O&P
0010	**JOIST FRAMING**									
2000	Joists, 2" x 4"	2 Carp	1250	.013	L.F.	.41	.45		.86	1.20
2005	Pneumatic nailed		1438	.011		.41	.39		.80	1.10
2100	2" x 6"		1250	.013		.63	.45		1.08	1.44
2105	Pneumatic nailed		1438	.011		.63	.39		1.02	1.35
2150	2" x 8"		1100	.015		.87	.51		1.38	1.81
2155	Pneumatic nailed		1265	.013		.88	.44		1.32	1.71
2200	2" x 10"		900	.018		1.38	.62		2	2.55
2205	Pneumatic nailed		1035	.015		1.39	.54		1.93	2.42
2250	2" x 12"		875	.018		1.75	.64		2.39	3
2255	Pneumatic nailed		1006	.016		1.76	.56		2.32	2.87
2300	2" x 14"		770	.021		2.21	.73		2.94	3.64
2305	Pneumatic nailed		886	.018		2.22	.63		2.85	3.50
2350	3" x 6"		925	.017		1.95	.60		2.55	3.15
2400	3" x 10"		780	.021		3.53	.72		4.25	5.10
2450	3" x 12"		600	.027		4.24	.93		5.17	6.20
2500	4" x 6"		800	.020		2.99	.70		3.69	4.46
2550	4" x 10"		600	.027		4.84	.93		5.77	6.90
2600	4" x 12"		450	.036		5.35	1.24		6.59	8
2605	Sister joist, 2" x 6"		800	.020		.63	.70		1.33	1.86
2606	Pneumatic nailed		960	.017		.63	.58		1.21	1.67
3000	Composite wood joist 9-1/2" deep		.90	17.778	M.L.F.	1,675	620		2,295	2,900
3010	11-1/2" deep		.88	18.182		1,900	635		2,535	3,175
3020	14" deep		.82	19.512		2,275	680		2,955	3,650
3030	16" deep		.78	20.513		3,650	715		4,365	5,200
4000	Open web joist 12" deep		.88	18.182		3,600	635		4,235	5,025
4002	Per linear foot		880	.018	L.F.	3.60	.64		4.24	5
4004	Treated, per linear foot		880	.018	"	4.46	.64		5.10	5.95
4010	14" deep		.82	19.512	M.L.F.	3,650	680		4,330	5,150
4012	Per linear foot		820	.020	L.F.	3.64	.68		4.32	5.15
4014	Treated, per linear foot		820	.020	"	4.65	.68		5.33	6.25
4020	16" deep		.78	20.513	M.L.F.	3,900	715		4,615	5,500
4022	Per linear foot		780	.021	L.F.	3.90	.72		4.62	5.50
4024	Treated, per linear foot		780	.021	"	5.05	.72		5.77	6.75

06 11 Wood Framing

06 11 10 − Framing with Dimensional, Engineered or Composite Lumber

06 11 10.18 Joist Framing

		Crew	Daily Output	Labor-Hours	Unit	Material	2017 Bare Costs Labor	Equipment	Total	Total Incl O&P
4030	18" deep	2 Carp	.74	21.622	M.L.F.	3,800	755		4,555	5,450
4032	Per linear foot		740	.022	L.F.	3.80	.76		4.56	5.45
4034	Treated, per linear foot		740	.022	"	5.10	.76		5.86	6.85
6000	Composite rim joist, 1-1/4" x 9-1/2"		.90	17.778	M.L.F.	1,900	620		2,520	3,125
6010	1-1/4" x 11-1/2"		.88	18.182		2,300	635		2,935	3,625
6020	1-1/4" x 14-1/2"		.82	19.512		2,700	680		3,380	4,125
6030	1-1/4" x 16-1/2"		.78	20.513		2,925	715		3,640	4,425

06 11 10.24 Miscellaneous Framing

		Crew	Daily Output	Labor-Hours	Unit	Material	2017 Bare Costs Labor	Equipment	Total	Total Incl O&P
0010	**MISCELLANEOUS FRAMING**									
2000	Firestops, 2" x 4"	2 Carp	780	.021	L.F.	.41	.72		1.13	1.65
2005	Pneumatic nailed		952	.017		.41	.59		1	1.43
2100	2" x 6"		600	.027		.63	.93		1.56	2.25
2105	Pneumatic nailed		732	.022		.63	.76		1.39	1.98
5000	Nailers, treated, wood construction, 2" x 4"		800	.020		.53	.70		1.23	1.75
5005	Pneumatic nailed		960	.017		.53	.58		1.11	1.55
5100	2" x 6"		750	.021		.81	.75		1.56	2.14
5105	Pneumatic nailed		900	.018		.82	.62		1.44	1.94
5120	2" x 8"		700	.023		1.06	.80		1.86	2.50
5125	Pneumatic nailed		840	.019		1.06	.67		1.73	2.28
5200	Steel construction, 2" x 4"		750	.021		.53	.75		1.28	1.83
5220	2" x 6"		700	.023		.81	.80		1.61	2.24
5240	2" x 8"		650	.025		1.06	.86		1.92	2.61
7000	Rough bucks, treated, for doors or windows, 2" x 6"		400	.040		.81	1.40		2.21	3.23
7005	Pneumatic nailed		480	.033		.82	1.16		1.98	2.85
7100	2" x 8"		380	.042		1.06	1.47		2.53	3.62
7105	Pneumatic nailed		456	.035		1.06	1.23		2.29	3.22
8000	Stair stringers, 2" x 10"		130	.123		1.38	4.30		5.68	8.70
8100	2" x 12"		130	.123		1.75	4.30		6.05	9.15
8150	3" x 10"		125	.128		3.53	4.47		8	11.40
8200	3" x 12"		125	.128		4.24	4.47		8.71	12.15
8870	Laminated structural lumber, 1-1/4" x 11-1/2"		130	.123		2.31	4.30		6.61	9.75
8880	1-1/4" x 14-1/2"		130	.123		2.67	4.30		6.97	10.15

06 11 10.26 Partitions

		Crew	Daily Output	Labor-Hours	Unit	Material	2017 Bare Costs Labor	Equipment	Total	Total Incl O&P
0010	**PARTITIONS**									
0020	Single bottom and double top plate, no waste, std. & better lumber									
0180	2" x 4" studs, 8' high, studs 12" O.C.	2 Carp	80	.200	L.F.	4.49	7		11.49	16.65
0185	12" O.C., pneumatic nailed		96	.167		4.53	5.85		10.38	14.75
0200	16" O.C.		100	.160		3.68	5.60		9.28	13.40
0205	16" O.C., pneumatic nailed		120	.133		3.71	4.66		8.37	11.90
0300	24" O.C.		125	.128		2.86	4.47		7.33	10.65
0305	24" O.C., pneumatic nailed		150	.107		2.88	3.73		6.61	9.40
0380	10' high, studs 12" O.C.		80	.200		5.30	7		12.30	17.55
0385	12" O.C., pneumatic nailed		96	.167		5.35	5.85		11.20	15.65
0400	16" O.C.		100	.160		4.29	5.60		9.89	14.05
0405	16" O.C., pneumatic nailed		120	.133		4.33	4.66		8.99	12.55
0500	24" O.C.		125	.128		3.27	4.47		7.74	11.10
0505	24" O.C., pneumatic nailed		150	.107		3.30	3.73		7.03	9.90
0580	12' high, studs 12" O.C.		65	.246		6.15	8.60		14.75	21
0585	12" O.C., pneumatic nailed		78	.205		6.20	7.15		13.35	18.80
0600	16" O.C.		80	.200		4.90	7		11.90	17.10
0605	16" O.C., pneumatic nailed		96	.167		4.94	5.85		10.79	15.20
0700	24" O.C.		100	.160		3.68	5.60		9.28	13.40

06 11 10.26 Partitions

		Crew	Daily Output	Labor-Hours	Unit	Material	2017 Bare Costs Labor	Equipment	Total	Total Incl O&P
0705	24" O.C., pneumatic nailed	2 Carp	120	.133	L.F.	3.71	4.66		8.37	11.90
0780	2" x 6" studs, 8' high, studs 12" O.C.		70	.229		6.90	8		14.90	21
0785	12" O.C., pneumatic nailed		84	.190		6.95	6.65		13.60	18.80
0800	16" O.C.		90	.178		5.65	6.20		11.85	16.60
0805	16" O.C., pneumatic nailed		108	.148		5.70	5.20		10.90	14.90
0900	24" O.C.		115	.139		4.40	4.86		9.26	13
0905	24" O.C., pneumatic nailed		138	.116		4.43	4.05		8.48	11.65
0980	10' high, studs 12" O.C.		70	.229		8.15	8		16.15	22.50
0985	12" O.C., pneumatic nailed		84	.190		8.25	6.65		14.90	20
1000	16" O.C.		90	.178		6.60	6.20		12.80	17.65
1005	16" O.C., pneumatic nailed		108	.148		6.65	5.20		11.85	15.95
1100	24" O.C.		115	.139		5	4.86		9.86	13.70
1105	24" O.C., pneumatic nailed		138	.116		5.05	4.05		9.10	12.35
1180	12' high, studs 12" O.C.		55	.291		9.40	10.15		19.55	27.50
1185	12" O.C., pneumatic nailed		66	.242		9.50	8.45		17.95	24.50
1200	16" O.C.		70	.229		7.55	8		15.55	21.50
1205	16" O.C., pneumatic nailed		84	.190		7.60	6.65		14.25	19.50
1300	24" O.C.		90	.178		5.65	6.20		11.85	16.60
1305	24" O.C., pneumatic nailed		108	.148		5.70	5.20		10.90	14.90
1400	For horizontal blocking, 2" x 4", add		600	.027		.41	.93		1.34	2.01
1500	2" x 6", add		600	.027		.63	.93		1.56	2.25
1600	For openings, add	▼	250	.064	▼		2.24		2.24	3.74
1702	Headers for above openings, material only, add				B.F.	.72			.72	.80

06 11 10.28 Porch or Deck Framing

		Crew	Daily Output	Labor-Hours	Unit	Material	2017 Bare Costs Labor	Equipment	Total	Total Incl O&P
0010	**PORCH OR DECK FRAMING**									
0100	Treated lumber, posts or columns, 4" x 4"	2 Carp	390	.041	L.F.	1.37	1.43		2.80	3.91
0110	4" x 6"		275	.058		2.06	2.03		4.09	5.65
0120	4" x 8"		220	.073		3.84	2.54		6.38	8.50
0130	Girder, single, 4" x 4"		675	.024		1.37	.83		2.20	2.90
0140	4" x 6"		600	.027		2.06	.93		2.99	3.82
0150	4" x 8"		525	.030		3.84	1.07		4.91	6
0160	Double, 2" x 4"		625	.026		1.08	.89		1.97	2.69
0170	2" x 6"		600	.027		1.67	.93		2.60	3.39
0180	2" x 8"		575	.028		2.17	.97		3.14	4.02
0190	2" x 10"		550	.029		2.86	1.02		3.88	4.84
0200	2" x 12"		525	.030		4.06	1.07		5.13	6.25
0210	Triple, 2" x 4"		575	.028		1.62	.97		2.59	3.42
0220	2" x 6"		550	.029		2.50	1.02		3.52	4.45
0230	2" x 8"		525	.030		3.26	1.07		4.33	5.35
0240	2" x 10"		500	.032		4.29	1.12		5.41	6.60
0250	2" x 12"		475	.034		6.10	1.18		7.28	8.65
0260	Ledger, bolted 4' O.C., 2" x 4"		400	.040		.70	1.40		2.10	3.11
0270	2" x 6"		395	.041		.98	1.42		2.40	3.45
0280	2" x 8"		390	.041		1.22	1.43		2.65	3.74
0290	2" x 10"		385	.042		1.55	1.45		3	4.14
0300	2" x 12"		380	.042		2.14	1.47		3.61	4.81
0310	Joists, 2" x 4"		1250	.013		.54	.45		.99	1.35
0320	2" x 6"		1250	.013		.83	.45		1.28	1.67
0330	2" x 8"		1100	.015		1.09	.51		1.60	2.04
0340	2" x 10"		900	.018		1.43	.62		2.05	2.61
0350	2" x 12"		875	.018		1.71	.64		2.35	2.96
0360	Railings and trim, 1" x 4"	1 Carp	300	.027	▼	.50	.93		1.43	2.11

06 11 10 – Framing with Dimensional, Engineered or Composite Lumber

06 11 10.28 Porch or Deck Framing	Crew	Daily Output	Labor-Hours	Unit	Material	2017 Bare Costs Labor	Equipment	Total	Total Incl O&P
0370	2" x 2"	1 Carp	300	.027	L.F.	.36	.93		1.29	1.95
0380	2" x 4"		300	.027		.53	.93		1.46	2.15
0390	2" x 6"		300	.027		.82	.93		1.75	2.46
0400	Decking, 1" x 4"		275	.029	S.F.	2.37	1.02		3.39	4.30
0410	2" x 4"		300	.027		1.79	.93		2.72	3.53
0420	2" x 6"		320	.025		1.77	.87		2.64	3.40
0430	5/4" x 6"		320	.025		2.06	.87		2.93	3.72
0440	Balusters, square, 2" x 2"	2 Carp	660	.024	L.F.	.36	.85		1.21	1.82
0450	Turned, 2" x 2"		420	.038		.48	1.33		1.81	2.75
0460	Stair stringer, 2" x 10"		130	.123		1.43	4.30		5.73	8.75
0470	2" x 12"		130	.123		1.71	4.30		6.01	9.10
0480	Stair treads, 1" x 4"		140	.114		2.37	3.99		6.36	9.30
0490	2" x 4"		140	.114		.54	3.99		4.53	7.30
0500	2" x 6"		160	.100		.81	3.50		4.31	6.75
0510	5/4" x 6"		160	.100		.96	3.50		4.46	6.90
0520	Turned handrail post, 4" x 4"		64	.250	Ea.	32.50	8.75		41.25	50.50
0530	Lattice panel, 4' x 8', 1/2"		1600	.010	S.F.	.82	.35		1.17	1.48
0535	3/4"		1600	.010	"	1.22	.35		1.57	1.92
0540	Cedar, posts or columns, 4" x 4"		390	.041	L.F.	4.02	1.43		5.45	6.80
0550	4" x 6"		275	.058		7.30	2.03		9.33	11.40
0560	4" x 8"		220	.073		10.45	2.54		12.99	15.70
0800	Decking, 1" x 4"		550	.029		2.02	1.02		3.04	3.93
0810	2" x 4"		600	.027		3.99	.93		4.92	5.95
0820	2" x 6"		640	.025		7.45	.87		8.32	9.65
0830	5/4" x 6"		640	.025		4.80	.87		5.67	6.75
0840	Railings and trim, 1" x 4"		600	.027		2.02	.93		2.95	3.79
0860	2" x 4"		600	.027		3.99	.93		4.92	5.95
0870	2" x 6"		600	.027		7.45	.93		8.38	9.75
0920	Stair treads, 1" x 4"		140	.114		2.02	3.99		6.01	8.95
0930	2" x 4"		140	.114		3.99	3.99		7.98	11.10
0940	2" x 6"		160	.100		7.45	3.50		10.95	14.05
0950	5/4" x 6"		160	.100		4.80	3.50		8.30	11.15
0980	Redwood, posts or columns, 4" x 4"		390	.041		6.45	1.43		7.88	9.45
0990	4" x 6"		275	.058		12.60	2.03		14.63	17.25
1000	4" x 8"		220	.073		23.50	2.54		26.04	30.50
1240	Decking, 1" x 4"	1 Carp	275	.029	S.F.	3.97	1.02		4.99	6.05
1260	2" x 6"		340	.024		7.50	.82		8.32	9.65
1270	5/4" x 6"		320	.025		4.77	.87		5.64	6.70
1280	Railings and trim, 1" x 4"	2 Carp	600	.027	L.F.	1.17	.93		2.10	2.85
1310	2" x 6"		600	.027		7.50	.93		8.43	9.80
1420	Alternative decking, wood/plastic composite, 5/4" x 6" G		640	.025		3.42	.87		4.29	5.20
1440	1" x 4" square edge fir		550	.029		2.38	1.02		3.40	4.32
1450	1" x 4" tongue and groove fir		450	.036		1.52	1.24		2.76	3.75
1460	1" x 4" mahogany		550	.029		2.16	1.02		3.18	4.08
1462	5/4" x 6" PVC		550	.029		3.91	1.02		4.93	6
1465	Framing, porch or deck, alt deck fastening, screws, add	1 Carp	240	.033	S.F.		1.16		1.16	1.95
1470	Accessories, joist hangers, 2" x 4"		160	.050	Ea.	.80	1.75		2.55	3.80
1480	2" x 6" through 2" x 12"		150	.053		1.36	1.86		3.22	4.62
1530	Post footing, incl excav, backfill, tube form & concrete, 4' deep, 8" dia	F-7	12	2.667		13.55	82		95.55	152
1540	10" diameter		11	2.909		19.70	89.50		109.20	172
1550	12" diameter		10	3.200		26.50	98.50		125	194

For customer support on your Residential Costs with RSMeans Data, call 800.448.8182.

375

06 11 Wood Framing

06 11 10 - Framing with Dimensional, Engineered or Composite Lumber

06 11 10.30 Roof Framing	Crew	Daily Output	Labor-Hours	Unit	Material	2017 Bare Costs Labor	Equipment	Total	Total Incl O&P
0010 **ROOF FRAMING**									
1900 Rough fascia, 2" x 6"	2 Carp	250	.064	L.F.	.63	2.24		2.87	4.43
2000 2" x 8"		225	.071		.87	2.49		3.36	5.10
2100 2" x 10"		180	.089		1.38	3.11		4.49	6.70
5002 Rafters, to 4 in 12 pitch, 2" x 6", ordinary		1000	.016		.63	.56		1.19	1.63
5021 On steep roofs		800	.020		.63	.70		1.33	1.86
5041 On dormers or complex roofs		590	.027		.63	.95		1.58	2.28
5062 2" x 8", ordinary		950	.017		.87	.59		1.46	1.94
5081 On steep roofs		750	.021		.87	.75		1.62	2.21
5101 On dormers or complex roofs		540	.030		.87	1.04		1.91	2.69
5122 2" x 10", ordinary		630	.025		1.38	.89		2.27	2.99
5141 On steep roofs		495	.032		1.38	1.13		2.51	3.40
5161 On dormers or complex roofs		425	.038		1.38	1.32		2.70	3.71
5182 2" x 12", ordinary		575	.028		1.75	.97		2.72	3.56
5201 On steep roofs		455	.035		1.75	1.23		2.98	3.99
5221 On dormers or complex roofs		395	.041		1.75	1.42		3.17	4.30
5250 Composite rafter, 9-1/2" deep		575	.028		1.69	.97		2.66	3.49
5260 11-1/2" deep		575	.028		1.91	.97		2.88	3.73
5301 Hip and valley rafters, 2" x 6", ordinary		760	.021		.63	.74		1.37	1.92
5321 On steep roofs		585	.027		.63	.96		1.59	2.29
5341 On dormers or complex roofs		510	.031		.63	1.10		1.73	2.52
5361 2" x 8", ordinary		720	.022		.87	.78		1.65	2.26
5381 On steep roofs		545	.029		.87	1.03		1.90	2.68
5401 On dormers or complex roofs		470	.034		.87	1.19		2.06	2.95
5421 2" x 10", ordinary		570	.028		1.38	.98		2.36	3.15
5441 On steep roofs		440	.036		1.38	1.27		2.65	3.64
5461 On dormers or complex roofs		380	.042		1.38	1.47		2.85	3.97
5481 2" x 12", ordinary		525	.030		1.75	1.07		2.82	3.71
5501 On steep roofs		410	.039		1.75	1.36		3.11	4.21
5521 On dormers or complex roofs		355	.045		1.75	1.58		3.33	4.56
5541 Hip and valley jacks, 2" x 6", ordinary		600	.027		.63	.93		1.56	2.25
5561 On steep roofs		475	.034		.63	1.18		1.81	2.66
5581 On dormers or complex roofs		410	.039		.63	1.36		1.99	2.97
5601 2" x 8", ordinary		490	.033		.87	1.14		2.01	2.87
5621 On steep roofs		385	.042		.87	1.45		2.32	3.39
5641 On dormers or complex roofs		335	.048		.87	1.67		2.54	3.75
5661 2" x 10", ordinary		450	.036		1.38	1.24		2.62	3.59
5681 On steep roofs		350	.046		1.38	1.60		2.98	4.18
5701 On dormers or complex roofs		305	.052		1.38	1.83		3.21	4.58
5721 2" x 12", ordinary		375	.043		1.75	1.49		3.24	4.42
5741 On steep roofs		295	.054		1.75	1.90		3.65	5.10
5762 On dormers or complex roofs		255	.063		1.75	2.19		3.94	5.60
5781 Rafter tie, 1" x 4", #3		800	.020		.49	.70		1.19	1.71
5791 2" x 4", #3		800	.020		.41	.70		1.11	1.62
5801 Ridge board, #2 or better, 1" x 6"		600	.027		.76	.93		1.69	2.39
5821 1" x 8"		550	.029		1.26	1.02		2.28	3.09
5841 1" x 10"		500	.032		1.64	1.12		2.76	3.67
5861 2" x 6"		500	.032		.63	1.12		1.75	2.56
5881 2" x 8"		450	.036		.87	1.24		2.11	3.04
5901 2" x 10"		400	.040		1.38	1.40		2.78	3.85
5921 Roof cants, split, 4" x 4"		650	.025		1.79	.86		2.65	3.40
5941 6" x 6"		600	.027		5.20	.93		6.13	7.30

06 11 Wood Framing

06 11 10 – Framing with Dimensional, Engineered or Composite Lumber

06 11 10.30 Roof Framing

		Crew	Daily Output	Labor-Hours	Unit	Material	2017 Bare Costs Labor	Equipment	Total	Total Incl O&P
5961	Roof curbs, untreated, 2" x 6"	2 Carp	520	.031	L.F.	.63	1.08		1.71	2.49
5981	2" x 12"		400	.040		1.75	1.40		3.15	4.27
6001	Sister rafters, 2" x 6"		800	.020		.63	.70		1.33	1.86
6021	2" x 8"		640	.025		.86	.87		1.73	2.41
6041	2" x 10"		535	.030		1.38	1.05		2.43	3.26
6061	2" x 12"		455	.035		1.75	1.23		2.98	3.99

06 11 10.32 Sill and Ledger Framing

		Crew	Daily Output	Labor-Hours	Unit	Material	2017 Bare Costs Labor	Equipment	Total	Total Incl O&P
0010	**SILL AND LEDGER FRAMING**									
0020	Extruded polystyrene sill sealer, 5-1/2" wide	1 Carp	1600	.005	L.F.	.14	.17		.31	.44
2002	Ledgers, nailed, 2" x 4"	2 Carp	755	.021		.41	.74		1.15	1.69
2052	2" x 6"		600	.027		.63	.93		1.56	2.25
2102	Bolted, not including bolts, 3" x 6"		325	.049		1.93	1.72		3.65	5
2152	3" x 12"		233	.069		4.21	2.40		6.61	8.65
2602	Mud sills, redwood, construction grade, 2" x 4"		895	.018		2.26	.62		2.88	3.54
2622	2" x 6"		780	.021		3.40	.72		4.12	4.94
4002	Sills, 2" x 4"		600	.027		.40	.93		1.33	2
4052	2" x 6"		550	.029		.62	1.02		1.64	2.38
4082	2" x 8"		500	.032		.86	1.12		1.98	2.82
4101	2" x 10"		450	.036		1.36	1.24		2.60	3.57
4121	2" x 12"		400	.040		1.73	1.40		3.13	4.24
4202	Treated, 2" x 4"		550	.029		.52	1.02		1.54	2.27
4222	2" x 6"		500	.032		.80	1.12		1.92	2.75
4242	2" x 8"		450	.036		1.04	1.24		2.28	3.23
4261	2" x 10"		400	.040		1.38	1.40		2.78	3.85
4281	2" x 12"		350	.046		1.97	1.60		3.57	4.83
4402	4" x 4"		450	.036		1.33	1.24		2.57	3.55
4422	4" x 6"		350	.046		2	1.60		3.60	4.86
4462	4" x 8"		300	.053		3.76	1.86		5.62	7.25
4480	4" x 10"		260	.062		4.80	2.15		6.95	8.90

06 11 10.34 Sleepers

		Crew	Daily Output	Labor-Hours	Unit	Material	2017 Bare Costs Labor	Equipment	Total	Total Incl O&P
0010	**SLEEPERS**									
0100	On concrete, treated, 1" x 2"	2 Carp	2350	.007	L.F.	.29	.24		.53	.72
0150	1" x 3"		2000	.008		.47	.28		.75	.99
0200	2" x 4"		1500	.011		.57	.37		.94	1.25
0250	2" x 6"		1300	.012		.90	.43		1.33	1.71

06 11 10.36 Soffit and Canopy Framing

		Crew	Daily Output	Labor-Hours	Unit	Material	2017 Bare Costs Labor	Equipment	Total	Total Incl O&P
0010	**SOFFIT AND CANOPY FRAMING**									
1002	Canopy or soffit framing, 1" x 4"	2 Carp	900	.018	L.F.	.49	.62		1.11	1.58
1021	1" x 6"		850	.019		.76	.66		1.42	1.93
1042	1" x 8"		750	.021		1.26	.75		2.01	2.64
1102	2" x 4"		620	.026		.41	.90		1.31	1.96
1121	2" x 6"		560	.029		.63	1		1.63	2.36
1142	2" x 8"		500	.032		.87	1.12		1.99	2.83
1202	3" x 4"		500	.032		1.17	1.12		2.29	3.16
1221	3" x 6"		400	.040		1.95	1.40		3.35	4.48
1242	3" x 10"		300	.053		3.53	1.86		5.39	7

06 11 10.38 Treated Lumber Framing Material

		Crew	Daily Output	Labor-Hours	Unit	Material	2017 Bare Costs Labor	Equipment	Total	Total Incl O&P
0010	**TREATED LUMBER FRAMING MATERIAL**									
0100	2" x 4"				M.B.F.	780			780	860
0110	2" x 6"					805			805	885
0120	2" x 8"					785			785	860
0130	2" x 10"					825			825	910

For customer support on your Residential Costs with RSMeans Data, call 800.448.8182.

06 11 10 – Framing with Dimensional, Engineered or Composite Lumber

06 11 10.38 Treated Lumber Framing Material	Crew	Daily Output	Labor-Hours	Unit	Material	2017 Bare Costs Labor	Equipment	Total	Total Incl O&P
0140	2" x 12"				M.B.F.	985			985	1,075
0200	4" x 4"					1,000			1,000	1,100
0210	4" x 6"					1,000			1,000	1,100
0220	4" x 8"					1,400			1,400	1,550

06 11 10.40 Wall Framing

	06 11 10.40 Wall Framing	Crew	Daily Output	Labor-Hours	Unit	Material	2017 Bare Costs Labor	Equipment	Total	Total Incl O&P
0010	**WALL FRAMING** R061110-30									
0100	Door buck, studs, header, access, 8' H, 2" x 4" wall, 3' W	1 Carp	32	.250	Ea.	17.15	8.75		25.90	33.50
0110	4' wide		32	.250		18.40	8.75		27.15	34.50
0120	5' wide		32	.250		22	8.75		30.75	39
0130	6' wide		32	.250		24	8.75		32.75	41
0140	8' wide		30	.267		35.50	9.30		44.80	54.50
0150	10' wide		30	.267		48.50	9.30		57.80	69
0160	12' wide		30	.267		67	9.30		76.30	89
0170	2" x 6" wall, 3' wide		32	.250		24	8.75		32.75	41
0180	4' wide		32	.250		25.50	8.75		34.25	42.50
0190	5' wide		32	.250		29	8.75		37.75	46.50
0200	6' wide		32	.250		31	8.75		39.75	48.50
0210	8' wide		30	.267		42.50	9.30		51.80	62.50
0220	10' wide		30	.267		56	9.30		65.30	77
0230	12' wide		30	.267		74	9.30		83.30	97
0240	Window buck, studs, header & access, 8' high 2" x 4" wall, 2' wide		24	.333		18.20	11.65		29.85	39.50
0250	3' wide		24	.333		21	11.65		32.65	43
0260	4' wide		24	.333		23.50	11.65		35.15	45
0270	5' wide		24	.333		27	11.65		38.65	49.50
0280	6' wide		24	.333		30	11.65		41.65	52.50
0290	7' wide		24	.333		40	11.65		51.65	63.50
0300	8' wide		22	.364		44	12.70		56.70	70
0310	10' wide		22	.364		58.50	12.70		71.20	86
0320	12' wide		22	.364		79	12.70		91.70	109
0330	2" x 6" wall, 2' wide		24	.333		27	11.65		38.65	49
0340	3' wide		24	.333		30	11.65		41.65	52.50
0350	4' wide		24	.333		32.50	11.65		44.15	55.50
0360	5' wide		24	.333		37	11.65		48.65	60
0370	6' wide		24	.333		40.50	11.65		52.15	64
0380	7' wide		24	.333		51	11.65		62.65	76
0390	8' wide		22	.364		56	12.70		68.70	83
0400	10' wide		22	.364		71	12.70		83.70	99.50
0410	12' wide		22	.364		93	12.70		105.70	124
2002	Headers over openings, 2" x 6"	2 Carp	360	.044	L.F.	.63	1.55		2.18	3.29
2007	2" x 6", pneumatic nailed		432	.037		.63	1.29		1.92	2.87
2052	2" x 8"		340	.047		.87	1.64		2.51	3.71
2057	2" x 8", pneumatic nailed		408	.039		.88	1.37		2.25	3.26
2101	2" x 10"		320	.050		1.38	1.75		3.13	4.43
2106	2" x 10", pneumatic nailed		384	.042		1.39	1.46		2.85	3.96
2152	2" x 12"		300	.053		1.75	1.86		3.61	5.05
2157	2" x 12", pneumatic nailed		360	.044		1.76	1.55		3.31	4.54
2180	4" x 8"		260	.062		3.40	2.15		5.55	7.35
2185	4" x 8", pneumatic nailed		312	.051		3.42	1.79		5.21	6.75
2191	4" x 10"		240	.067		4.84	2.33		7.17	9.25
2196	4" x 10", pneumatic nailed		288	.056		4.86	1.94		6.80	8.60
2202	4" x 12"		190	.084		5.35	2.94		8.29	10.80
2207	4" x 12", pneumatic nailed		228	.070		5.40	2.45		7.85	10

06 11 Wood Framing

06 11 10 – Framing with Dimensional, Engineered or Composite Lumber

06 11 10.40 Wall Framing	Crew	Daily Output	Labor-Hours	Unit	Material	2017 Bare Costs Labor	Equipment	Total	Total Incl O&P
2241	6" x 10"	2 Carp	165	.097	L.F.	6.75	3.39		10.14	13.05
2246	6" x 10", pneumatic nailed		198	.081		6.75	2.82		9.57	12.15
2251	6" x 12"		140	.114		8.45	3.99		12.44	16
2256	6" x 12", pneumatic nailed		168	.095		8.50	3.33		11.83	14.90
5002	Plates, untreated, 2" x 3"		850	.019		.39	.66		1.05	1.53
5007	2" x 3", pneumatic nailed		1020	.016		.40	.55		.95	1.36
5022	2" x 4"		800	.020		.41	.70		1.11	1.62
5027	2" x 4", pneumatic nailed		960	.017		.41	.58		.99	1.42
5041	2" x 6"		750	.021		.63	.75		1.38	1.94
5045	2" x 6", pneumatic nailed		900	.018		.63	.62		1.25	1.74
5061	Treated, 2" x 3"		850	.019		.48	.66		1.14	1.63
5066	2" x 3", treated, pneumatic nailed		1020	.016		.49	.55		1.04	1.46
5081	2" x 4"		800	.020		.53	.70		1.23	1.75
5086	2" x 4", treated, pneumatic nailed		960	.017		.53	.58		1.11	1.55
5101	2" x 6"		750	.021		.81	.75		1.56	2.14
5106	2" x 6", treated, pneumatic nailed		900	.018		.82	.62		1.44	1.94
5122	Studs, 8' high wall, 2" x 3"		1200	.013		.39	.47		.86	1.21
5127	2" x 3", pneumatic nailed		1440	.011		.40	.39		.79	1.09
5142	2" x 4"		1100	.015		.40	.51		.91	1.29
5147	2" x 4", pneumatic nailed		1320	.012		.41	.42		.83	1.16
5162	2" x 6"		1000	.016		.63	.56		1.19	1.63
5167	2" x 6", pneumatic nailed		1200	.013		.63	.47		1.10	1.48
5182	3" x 4"		800	.020		1.17	.70		1.87	2.46
5187	3" x 4", pneumatic nailed		960	.017		1.18	.58		1.76	2.27
5201	Installed on second story, 2" x 3"		1170	.014		.39	.48		.87	1.23
5206	2" x 3", pneumatic nailed		1200	.013		.40	.47		.87	1.22
5221	2" x 4"		1015	.016		.41	.55		.96	1.37
5226	2" x 4", pneumatic nailed		1080	.015		.41	.52		.93	1.32
5241	2" x 6"		890	.018		.63	.63		1.26	1.74
5246	2" x 6", pneumatic nailed		1020	.016		.63	.55		1.18	1.62
5261	3" x 4"		800	.020		1.17	.70		1.87	2.46
5266	3" x 4", pneumatic nailed		960	.017		1.18	.58		1.76	2.27
5281	Installed on dormer or gable, 2" x 3"		1045	.015		.39	.54		.93	1.32
5286	2" x 3", pneumatic nailed		1254	.013		.40	.45		.85	1.19
5301	2" x 4"		905	.018		.41	.62		1.03	1.48
5306	2" x 4", pneumatic nailed		1086	.015		.41	.51		.92	1.31
5321	2" x 6"		800	.020		.63	.70		1.33	1.86
5326	2" x 6", pneumatic nailed		960	.017		.63	.58		1.21	1.67
5341	3" x 4"		700	.023		1.17	.80		1.97	2.63
5346	3" x 4", pneumatic nailed		840	.019		1.18	.67		1.85	2.41
5361	6' high wall, 2" x 3"		970	.016		.39	.58		.97	1.39
5366	2" x 3", pneumatic nailed		1164	.014		.40	.48		.88	1.24
5381	2" x 4"		850	.019		.41	.66		1.07	1.55
5386	2" x 4", pneumatic nailed		1020	.016		.41	.55		.96	1.37
5401	2" x 6"		740	.022		.63	.76		1.39	1.95
5406	2" x 6", pneumatic nailed		888	.018		.63	.63		1.26	1.75
5421	3" x 4"		600	.027		1.17	.93		2.10	2.85
5426	3" x 4", pneumatic nailed		720	.022		1.18	.78		1.96	2.60
5441	Installed on second story, 2" x 3"		950	.017		.40	.59		.99	1.42
5446	2" x 3", pneumatic nailed		1140	.014		.40	.49		.89	1.26
5461	2" x 4"		810	.020		.41	.69		1.10	1.60
5466	2" x 4", pneumatic nailed		972	.016		.41	.58		.99	1.41
5481	2" x 6"		700	.023		.63	.80		1.43	2.03

06 11 10.40 Wall Framing		Crew	Daily Output	Labor-Hours	Unit	Material	2017 Bare Costs Labor	Equipment	Total	Total Incl O&P
5486	2" x 6", pneumatic nailed	2 Carp	840	.019	L.F.	.63	.67		1.30	1.81
5501	3" x 4"		550	.029		1.17	1.02		2.19	2.99
5506	3" x 4", pneumatic nailed		660	.024		1.18	.85		2.03	2.72
5521	Installed on dormer or gable, 2" x 3"		850	.019		.39	.66		1.05	1.53
5526	2" x 3", pneumatic nailed		1020	.016		.40	.55		.95	1.36
5541	2" x 4"		720	.022		.41	.78		1.19	1.75
5546	2" x 4", pneumatic nailed		864	.019		.41	.65		1.06	1.53
5561	2" x 6"		620	.026		.63	.90		1.53	2.20
5566	2" x 6", pneumatic nailed		744	.022		.63	.75		1.38	1.96
5581	3" x 4"		480	.033		1.17	1.16		2.33	3.24
5586	3" x 4", pneumatic nailed		576	.028		1.18	.97		2.15	2.92
5601	3' high wall, 2" x 3"		740	.022		.39	.76		1.15	1.69
5606	2" x 3", pneumatic nailed		888	.018		.40	.63		1.03	1.49
5621	2" x 4"		640	.025		.41	.87		1.28	1.91
5626	2" x 4", pneumatic nailed		768	.021		.41	.73		1.14	1.67
5641	2" x 6"		550	.029		.63	1.02		1.65	2.39
5646	2" x 6", pneumatic nailed		660	.024		.63	.85		1.48	2.12
5661	3" x 4"		440	.036		1.17	1.27		2.44	3.42
5666	3" x 4", pneumatic nailed		528	.030		1.18	1.06		2.24	3.07
5681	Installed on second story, 2" x 3"		700	.023		.39	.80		1.19	1.77
5686	2" x 3", pneumatic nailed		840	.019		.40	.67		1.07	1.55
5701	2" x 4"		610	.026		.41	.92		1.33	1.98
5706	2" x 4", pneumatic nailed		732	.022		.41	.76		1.17	1.73
5721	2" x 6"		520	.031		.63	1.08		1.71	2.49
5726	2" x 6", pneumatic nailed		624	.026		.63	.90		1.53	2.20
5741	3" x 4"		430	.037		1.17	1.30		2.47	3.46
5746	3" x 4", pneumatic nailed		516	.031		1.18	1.08		2.26	3.11
5761	Installed on dormer or gable, 2" x 3"		625	.026		.39	.89		1.28	1.93
5766	2" x 3", pneumatic nailed		750	.021		.40	.75		1.15	1.69
5781	2" x 4"		545	.029		.41	1.03		1.44	2.17
5786	2" x 4", pneumatic nailed		654	.024		.41	.85		1.26	1.88
5801	2" x 6"		465	.034		.63	1.20		1.83	2.70
5806	2" x 6", pneumatic nailed		558	.029		.63	1		1.63	2.38
5821	3" x 4"		380	.042		1.17	1.47		2.64	3.75
5826	3" x 4", pneumatic nailed		456	.035		1.18	1.23		2.41	3.35
8250	For second story & above, add						5%			
8300	For dormer & gable, add						15%			

06 11 10.42 Furring

		Crew	Daily Output	Labor-Hours	Unit	Material	2017 Bare Costs Labor	Equipment	Total	Total Incl O&P
0010	**FURRING**									
0012	Wood strips, 1" x 2", on walls, on wood	1 Carp	550	.015	L.F.	.26	.51		.77	1.13
0015	On wood, pneumatic nailed		710	.011		.26	.39		.65	.94
0300	On masonry		495	.016		.28	.56		.84	1.25
0400	On concrete		260	.031		.28	1.08		1.36	2.11
0600	1" x 3", on walls, on wood		550	.015		.42	.51		.93	1.31
0605	On wood, pneumatic nailed		710	.011		.42	.39		.81	1.12
0700	On masonry		495	.016		.45	.56		1.01	1.43
0800	On concrete		260	.031		.45	1.08		1.53	2.29
0850	On ceilings, on wood		350	.023		.42	.80		1.22	1.80
0855	On wood, pneumatic nailed		450	.018		.42	.62		1.04	1.50
0900	On masonry		320	.025		.45	.87		1.32	1.95
0950	On concrete		210	.038		.45	1.33		1.78	2.72

06 11 Wood Framing

06 11 10 – Framing with Dimensional, Engineered or Composite Lumber

06 11 10.44 Grounds

		Crew	Daily Output	Labor-Hours	Unit	Material	2017 Bare Costs Labor	Equipment	Total	Total Incl O&P
0010	**GROUNDS**									
0020	For casework, 1" x 2" wood strips, on wood	1 Carp	330	.024	L.F.	.26	.85		1.11	1.70
0100	On masonry		285	.028		.28	.98		1.26	1.95
0200	On concrete		250	.032		.28	1.12		1.40	2.18
0400	For plaster, 3/4" deep, on wood		450	.018		.26	.62		.88	1.32
0500	On masonry		225	.036		.28	1.24		1.52	2.39
0600	On concrete		175	.046		.28	1.60		1.88	2.98
0700	On metal lath		200	.040		.28	1.40		1.68	2.65

06 12 Structural Panels

06 12 10 – Structural Insulated Panels

06 12 10.10 OSB Faced Panels

			Crew	Daily Output	Labor-Hours	Unit	Material	2017 Bare Costs Labor	Equipment	Total	Total Incl O&P
0010	**OSB FACED PANELS**										
0100	Structural insul. panels, 7/16" OSB both faces, EPS insul, 3-5/8" T	G	F-3	2075	.019	S.F.	3.65	.62	.28	4.55	5.35
0110	5-5/8" thick	G		1725	.023		4.10	.74	.33	5.17	6.10
0120	7-3/8" thick	G		1425	.028		4.45	.90	.40	5.75	6.85
0130	9-3/8" thick	G		1125	.036		4.75	1.14	.51	6.40	7.70
0140	7/16" OSB one face, EPS insul, 3-5/8" thick	G		2175	.018		3.75	.59	.26	4.60	5.40
0150	5-5/8" thick	G		1825	.022		4.35	.70	.31	5.36	6.30
0160	7-3/8" thick	G		1525	.026		4.85	.84	.38	6.07	7.15
0170	9-3/8" thick	G		1225	.033		5.35	1.05	.47	6.87	8.15
0190	7/16" OSB - 1/2" GWB faces, EPS insul, 3-5/8" T	G		2075	.019		3.45	.62	.28	4.35	5.15
0200	5-5/8" thick	G		1725	.023		4.10	.74	.33	5.17	6.10
0210	7-3/8" thick	G		1425	.028		4.65	.90	.40	5.95	7.05
0220	9-3/8" thick	G		1125	.036		5.25	1.14	.51	6.90	8.25
0240	7/16" OSB - 1/2" MRGWB faces, EPS insul, 3-5/8" T	G		2075	.019		3.55	.62	.28	4.45	5.25
0250	5-5/8" thick	G		1725	.023		4.25	.74	.33	5.32	6.30
0260	7-3/8" thick	G		1425	.028		4.65	.90	.40	5.95	7.05
0270	9-3/8" thick	G		1125	.036		5.35	1.14	.51	7	8.35
0300	For 1/2" GWB added to OSB skin, add	G					1.40			1.40	1.54
0310	For 1/2" MRGWB added to OSB skin, add	G					1.40			1.40	1.54
0320	For one T1-11 skin, add to OSB-OSB	G					1.95			1.95	2.15
0330	For one 19/32" CDX skin, add to OSB-OSB	G					1.50			1.50	1.65
0500	Structural insulated panel, 7/16" OSB both sides, straw core										
0510	4-3/8" T, walls (w/sill, splines, plates)	G	F-6	2400	.017	S.F.	7.55	.53	.24	8.32	9.45
0520	Floors (w/splines)	G		2400	.017		7.55	.53	.24	8.32	9.45
0530	Roof (w/splines)	G		2400	.017		7.55	.53	.24	8.32	9.45
0550	7-7/8" T, walls (w/sill, splines, plates)	G		2400	.017		11.40	.53	.24	12.17	13.70
0560	Floors (w/splines)	G		2400	.017		11.40	.53	.24	12.17	13.70
0570	Roof (w/splines)	G		2400	.017		11.40	.53	.24	12.17	13.70

06 12 19 – Composite Shearwall Panels

06 12 19.10 Steel and Wood Composite Shearwall Panels

		Crew	Daily Output	Labor-Hours	Unit	Material	2017 Bare Costs Labor	Equipment	Total	Total Incl O&P
0010	**STEEL & WOOD COMPOSITE SHEARWALL PANELS**									
0020	Anchor bolts, 36" long (must be placed in wet concrete)	1 Carp	150	.053	Ea.	34.50	1.86		36.36	41
0030	On concrete, 2 x 4 & 2 x 6 walls, 7' - 10' high, 360 lb. shear, 12" wide	2 Carp	8	2		460	70		530	620
0040	715 lb. shear, 15" wide		8	2		510	70		580	675
0050	1860 lb. shear, 18" wide		8	2		525	70		595	695
0060	2780 lb. shear, 21" wide		8	2		560	70		630	730
0070	3790 lb. shear, 24" wide		8	2		640	70		710	815
0080	2 x 6 walls, 11' - 13' high, 1180 lb. shear, 18" wide		6	2.667		645	93		738	865

06 12 Structural Panels

06 12 19 – Composite Shearwall Panels

06 12 19.10 Steel and Wood Composite Shearwall Panels	Crew	Daily Output	Labor-Hours	Unit	Material	2017 Bare Costs Labor	Equipment	Total	Total Incl O&P
0090	1555 lb. shear, 21" wide	2 Carp	6	2.667	Ea.	720	93		813	945
0100	2280 lb. shear, 24" wide	↓	6	2.667	↓	805	93		898	1,050
0110	For installing above on wood floor frame, add									
0120	Coupler nuts, threaded rods, bolts, shear transfer plate kit	1 Carp	16	.500	Ea.	65	17.50		82.50	101
0130	Framing anchors, angle (2 required)	"	96	.083	"	2.56	2.91		5.47	7.70
0140	For blocking see Section 06 11 10.02									
0150	For installing above, first floor to second floor, wood floor frame, add									
0160	Add stack option to first floor wall panel				Ea.	71.50			71.50	78.50
0170	Threaded rods, bolts, shear transfer plate kit	1 Carp	16	.500		75	17.50		92.50	112
0180	Framing anchors, angle (2 required)	"	96	.083	↓	2.56	2.91		5.47	7.70
0190	For blocking see section 06 11 10.02									
0200	For installing stacked panels, balloon framing									
0210	Add stack option to first floor wall panel				Ea.	71.50			71.50	78.50
0220	Threaded rods, bolts kit	1 Carp	16	.500	"	45	17.50		62.50	78.50

06 13 Heavy Timber Construction

06 13 13 – Log Construction

06 13 13.10 Log Structures

		Crew	Daily Output	Labor-Hours	Unit	Material	2017 Bare Costs Labor	Equipment	Total	Total Incl O&P
0010	**LOG STRUCTURES**									
0020	Exterior walls, pine, D logs, with double T & G, 6" x 6"	2 Carp	500	.032	L.F.	4.97	1.12		6.09	7.30
0030	6" x 8"		375	.043		4.97	1.49		6.46	7.95
0040	8" x 6"		375	.043		4.97	1.49		6.46	7.95
0050	8" x 7"		322	.050		4.97	1.74		6.71	8.35
0060	Square/rectangular logs, with double T & G, 6" x 6"		500	.032		4.97	1.12		6.09	7.30
0070	6" x 8"		375	.043		4.97	1.49		6.46	7.95
0080	8" x 6"		375	.043		4.97	1.49		6.46	7.95
0090	8" x 7"		322	.050		4.97	1.74		6.71	8.35
0100	Round logs, with double T & G, 6" x 8"		375	.043		4.97	1.49		6.46	7.95
0110	8" x 7"		322	.050	↓	4.97	1.74		6.71	8.35
0120	Log siding, ship lapped, 2" x 6"		225	.071	S.F.	3.05	2.49		5.54	7.50
0130	2" x 8"		200	.080		2.56	2.80		5.36	7.50
0140	2" x 12"	↓	180	.089	↓	2.92	3.11		6.03	8.40
0150	Foam sealant strip, 3/8" x 3/8"	1 Carp	1920	.004	L.F.	.22	.15		.37	.48
0152	Chinking, 2" - 3" wide joint, 1/4" to 3/8" deep		600	.013		1.38	.47		1.85	2.30
0154	Caulking, 1/4" to 1/2" joint		900	.009		.50	.31		.81	1.07
0156	Backer rod, 1/4"	↓	900	.009	↓	.18	.31		.49	.72
0157	Penetrating wood preservative	1 Pord	2000	.004	S.F.	.15	.12		.27	.36
0158	Insect treatment	"	4000	.002	"	.36	.06		.42	.49
0160	Upper floor framing, pine, posts/columns, 4" x 6"	2 Carp	750	.021	L.F.	2.97	.75		3.72	4.52
0180	4" x 8"		562	.028		3.38	1		4.38	5.35
0190	6" x 6"		500	.032		5.20	1.12		6.32	7.55
0200	6" x 8"		375	.043		7.65	1.49		9.14	10.95
0210	8" x 8"		281	.057		9.25	1.99		11.24	13.50
0220	8" x 10"		225	.071		11.55	2.49		14.04	16.85
0230	Beams, 4" x 8"		562	.028		3.38	1		4.38	5.35
0240	4" x 10"		449	.036		4.81	1.25		6.06	7.40
0250	4" x 12"		375	.043		5.30	1.49		6.79	8.35
0260	6" x 8"		375	.043		7.65	1.49		9.14	10.95
0270	6" x 10"		300	.053		6.70	1.86		8.56	10.45
0280	6" x 12"		250	.064		8.40	2.24		10.64	13
0290	8" x 10"	↓	225	.071	↓	11.55	2.49		14.04	16.85

06 13 Heavy Timber Construction

06 13 13 – Log Construction

06 13 13.10 Log Structures

		Crew	Daily Output	Labor-Hours	Unit	Material	2017 Bare Costs Labor	Equipment	Total	Total Incl O&P
0300	8" x 12"	2 Carp	188	.085	L.F.	16.10	2.97		19.07	22.50
0310	Joists, 4" x 8"		562	.028		3.38	1		4.38	5.35
0320	4" x 10"		449	.036		4.81	1.25		6.06	7.40
0330	4" x 12"		375	.043		5.30	1.49		6.79	8.35
0340	6" x 8"		375	.043		7.65	1.49		9.14	10.95
0350	6" x 10"		300	.053		6.70	1.86		8.56	10.45
0360	6" x 12"		250	.064		8.40	2.24		10.64	13
0370	8" x 10"		225	.071		11.55	2.49		14.04	16.85
0380	8" x 12"		188	.085	▼	13.85	2.97		16.82	20
0390	Decking, 1" x 6" T & G		964	.017	S.F.	1.64	.58		2.22	2.77
0400	1" x 8" T & G		700	.023		1.49	.80		2.29	2.98
0410	2" x 6" T & G		482	.033	▼	3.51	1.16		4.67	5.80
0420	Gable end roof framing, rafters, 4" x 8"		562	.028	L.F.	3.38	1		4.38	5.35
0430	4" x 10"		449	.036		4.81	1.25		6.06	7.40
0450	4" x 12"		375	.043		5.30	1.49		6.79	8.35
0460	6" x 8"		375	.043		7.65	1.49		9.14	10.95
0470	6" x 10"		300	.053		6.70	1.86		8.56	10.45
0480	6" x 12"		250	.064		8.40	2.24		10.64	13
0490	8" x 10"		225	.071		11.55	2.49		14.04	16.85
0500	8" x 12"		188	.085		13.85	2.97		16.82	20
0510	Purlins, 4" x 8"		562	.028		3.38	1		4.38	5.35
0520	6" x 8"		375	.043	▼	7.65	1.49		9.14	10.95
0530	Roof decking, 1" x 6" T & G		640	.025	S.F.	1.64	.87		2.51	3.26
0540	1" x 8" T & G		430	.037		1.49	1.30		2.79	3.81
0550	2" x 6" T & G	▼	320	.050	▼	3.51	1.75		5.26	6.80

06 13 23 – Heavy Timber Framing

06 13 23.10 Heavy Framing

		Crew	Daily Output	Labor-Hours	Unit	Material	2017 Bare Costs Labor	Equipment	Total	Total Incl O&P
0010	**HEAVY FRAMING**									
0020	Beams, single 6" x 10"	2 Carp	1.10	14.545	M.B.F.	1,550	510		2,060	2,575
0100	Single 8" x 16"		1.20	13.333	"	1,925	465		2,390	2,900
0202	Built from 2" lumber, multiple 2" x 14"		900	.018	B.F.	.94	.62		1.56	2.07
0212	Built from 3" lumber, multiple 3" x 6"		700	.023		1.29	.80		2.09	2.76
0222	Multiple 3" x 8"		800	.020		1.39	.70		2.09	2.70
0232	Multiple 3" x 10"		900	.018		1.40	.62		2.02	2.58
0242	Multiple 3" x 12"		1000	.016		1.40	.56		1.96	2.48
0252	Built from 4" lumber, multiple 4" x 6"		800	.020		1.48	.70		2.18	2.80
0262	Multiple 4" x 8"		900	.018		1.27	.62		1.89	2.43
0272	Multiple 4" x 10"		1000	.016		1.44	.56		2	2.53
0282	Multiple 4" x 12"		1100	.015	▼	1.33	.51		1.84	2.31
0292	Columns, structural grade, 1500f, 4" x 4"		450	.036	L.F.	1.71	1.24		2.95	3.96
0302	6" x 6"		225	.071		4.37	2.49		6.86	8.95
0402	8" x 8"		240	.067		6.40	2.33		8.73	10.95
0502	10" x 10"		90	.178		13.50	6.20		19.70	25.50
0602	12" x 12"		70	.229	▼	18.55	8		26.55	34
0802	Floor planks, 2" thick, T & G, 2" x 6"		1050	.015	B.F.	1.61	.53		2.14	2.66
0902	2" x 10"		1100	.015		1.63	.51		2.14	2.64
1102	3" thick, 3" x 6"		1050	.015		1.62	.53		2.15	2.67
1202	3" x 10"		1100	.015		1.65	.51		2.16	2.67
1402	Girders, structural grade, 12" x 12"		800	.020		1.55	.70		2.25	2.87
1502	10" x 16"		1000	.016		2.55	.56		3.11	3.75
2302	Roof purlins, 4" thick, structural grade	▼	1050	.015	▼	1.27	.53		1.80	2.28

For customer support on your Residential Costs with RSMeans Data, call 800.448.8182.

383

06 15 Wood Decking

06 15 16 - Wood Roof Decking

06 15 16.10 Solid Wood Roof Decking

		Crew	Daily Output	Labor-Hours	Unit	Material	2017 Bare Costs Labor	Equipment	Total	Total Incl O&P
0010	**SOLID WOOD ROOF DECKING**									
0350	Cedar planks, 2" thick	2 Carp	350	.046	S.F.	6.50	1.60		8.10	9.75
0400	3" thick		320	.050		9.70	1.75		11.45	13.60
0500	4" thick		250	.064		12.95	2.24		15.19	18
0550	6" thick		200	.080		19.45	2.80		22.25	26
0650	Douglas fir, 2" thick		350	.046		2.55	1.60		4.15	5.50
0700	3" thick		320	.050		3.83	1.75		5.58	7.15
0800	4" thick		250	.064		5.10	2.24		7.34	9.35
0850	6" thick		200	.080		7.65	2.80		10.45	13.10
0950	Hemlock, 2" thick		350	.046		2.60	1.60		4.20	5.55
1000	3" thick		320	.050		3.89	1.75		5.64	7.20
1100	4" thick		250	.064		5.20	2.24		7.44	9.45
1150	6" thick		200	.080		7.80	2.80		10.60	13.25
1250	Western white spruce, 2" thick		350	.046		1.66	1.60		3.26	4.49
1300	3" thick		320	.050		2.49	1.75		4.24	5.65
1400	4" thick		250	.064		3.32	2.24		5.56	7.40
1450	6" thick		200	.080		4.97	2.80		7.77	10.15

06 15 23 - Laminated Wood Decking

06 15 23.10 Laminated Roof Deck

		Crew	Daily Output	Labor-Hours	Unit	Material	2017 Bare Costs Labor	Equipment	Total	Total Incl O&P
0010	**LAMINATED ROOF DECK**									
0020	Pine or hemlock, 3" thick	2 Carp	425	.038	S.F.	6.25	1.32		7.57	9.10
0100	4" thick		325	.049		8.15	1.72		9.87	11.85
0300	Cedar, 3" thick		425	.038		7.10	1.32		8.42	10
0400	4" thick		325	.049		9.50	1.72		11.22	13.35
0600	Fir, 3" thick		425	.038		5.55	1.32		6.87	8.30
0700	4" thick		325	.049		7.55	1.72		9.27	11.20

06 16 Sheathing

06 16 13 - Insulating Sheathing

06 16 13.10 Insulating Sheathing

			Crew	Daily Output	Labor-Hours	Unit	Material	2017 Bare Costs Labor	Equipment	Total	Total Incl O&P
0010	**INSULATING SHEATHING**										
0020	Expanded polystyrene, 1#/C.F. density, 3/4" thick, R2.89	G	2 Carp	1400	.011	S.F.	.35	.40		.75	1.06
0030	1" thick, R3.85	G		1300	.012		.42	.43		.85	1.18
0040	2" thick, R7.69	G		1200	.013		.68	.47		1.15	1.53
0050	Extruded polystyrene, 15 PSI compressive strength, 1" thick, R5	G		1300	.012		.77	.43		1.20	1.56
0060	2" thick, R10	G		1200	.013		.95	.47		1.42	1.83
0070	Polyisocyanurate, 2#/C.F. density, 3/4" thick	G		1400	.011		.58	.40		.98	1.31
0080	1" thick	G		1300	.012		.59	.43		1.02	1.37
0090	1-1/2" thick	G		1250	.013		.75	.45		1.20	1.57
0100	2" thick	G		1200	.013		.91	.47		1.38	1.78

06 16 23 - Subflooring

06 16 23.10 Subfloor

		Crew	Daily Output	Labor-Hours	Unit	Material	2017 Bare Costs Labor	Equipment	Total	Total Incl O&P
0010	**SUBFLOOR**									
0011	Plywood, CDX, 1/2" thick	2 Carp	1500	.011	SF Flr.	.63	.37		1	1.31
0015	Pneumatic nailed		1860	.009		.63	.30		.93	1.19
0102	5/8" thick		1350	.012		.78	.41		1.19	1.55
0107	Pneumatic nailed		1674	.010		.78	.33		1.11	1.42
0202	3/4" thick		1250	.013		.94	.45		1.39	1.78
0207	Pneumatic nailed		1550	.010		.94	.36		1.30	1.63
0302	1-1/8" thick, 2-4-1 including underlayment		1050	.015		2.10	.53		2.63	3.20

06 16 Sheathing

06 16 23 – Subflooring

06 16 23.10 Subfloor		Crew	Daily Output	Labor-Hours	Unit	Material	2017 Bare Costs Labor	Equipment	Total	Total Incl O&P
0440	With boards, 1" x 6", S4S, laid regular	2 Carp	900	.018	SF Flr.	1.64	.62		2.26	2.85
0452	1" x 8", laid regular		1000	.016		2.01	.56		2.57	3.15
0462	Laid diagonal		850	.019		2.01	.66		2.67	3.31
0502	1" x 10", laid regular		1100	.015		2.05	.51		2.56	3.11
0602	Laid diagonal		900	.018	↓	2.05	.62		2.67	3.30
1500	OSB, 5/8" thick		1330	.012	S.F.	.54	.42		.96	1.29
1600	3/4" thick	↓	1230	.013	"	.70	.45		1.15	1.53
8990	Subfloor adhesive, 3/8" bead	1 Carp	2300	.003	L.F.	.11	.12		.23	.32

06 16 26 – Underlayment

06 16 26.10 Wood Product Underlayment

06 16 26.10 Wood Product Underlayment		Crew	Daily Output	Labor-Hours	Unit	Material	2017 Bare Costs Labor	Equipment	Total	Total Incl O&P
0010	**WOOD PRODUCT UNDERLAYMENT**									
0015	Plywood, underlayment grade, 1/4" thick	2 Carp	1500	.011	S.F.	.95	.37		1.32	1.66
0018	Pneumatic nailed		1860	.009		.95	.30		1.25	1.54
0030	3/8" thick		1500	.011		1.05	.37		1.42	1.78
0070	Pneumatic nailed		1860	.009		1.05	.30		1.35	1.66
0102	1/2" thick		1450	.011		1.25	.39		1.64	2.02
0107	Pneumatic nailed		1798	.009		1.25	.31		1.56	1.90
0202	5/8" thick		1400	.011		1.38	.40		1.78	2.19
0207	Pneumatic nailed		1736	.009		1.38	.32		1.70	2.06
0302	3/4" thick		1300	.012		1.49	.43		1.92	2.36
0306	Pneumatic nailed		1612	.010		1.49	.35		1.84	2.22
0502	Particle board, 3/8" thick		1500	.011		.40	.37		.77	1.06
0507	Pneumatic nailed		1860	.009		.40	.30		.70	.94
0602	1/2" thick		1450	.011		.45	.39		.84	1.14
0607	Pneumatic nailed		1798	.009		.45	.31		.76	1.02
0802	5/8" thick		1400	.011		.54	.40		.94	1.26
0807	Pneumatic nailed		1736	.009		.54	.32		.86	1.13
0902	3/4" thick		1300	.012		.70	.43		1.13	1.49
0907	Pneumatic nailed		1612	.010		.70	.35		1.05	1.35
1100	Hardboard, underlayment grade, 4' x 4', .215" thick [G]	↓	1500	.011	↓	.63	.37		1	1.31

06 16 33 – Wood Board Sheathing

06 16 33.10 Board Sheathing

06 16 33.10 Board Sheathing		Crew	Daily Output	Labor-Hours	Unit	Material	2017 Bare Costs Labor	Equipment	Total	Total Incl O&P
0009	**BOARD SHEATHING**									
0010	Roof, 1" x 6" boards, laid horizontal	2 Carp	725	.022	S.F.	1.64	.77		2.41	3.10
0020	On steep roof		520	.031		1.64	1.08		2.72	3.61
0040	On dormers, hips, & valleys		480	.033		1.64	1.16		2.80	3.76
0050	Laid diagonal		650	.025		1.64	.86		2.50	3.25
0070	1" x 8" boards, laid horizontal		875	.018		2.01	.64		2.65	3.28
0080	On steep roof		635	.025		2.01	.88		2.89	3.68
0090	On dormers, hips, & valleys		580	.028		2.05	.96		3.01	3.87
0100	Laid diagonal		725	.022		2.01	.77		2.78	3.50
0110	Skip sheathing, 1" x 4", 7" OC	1 Carp	1200	.007		.61	.23		.84	1.07
0120	1" x 6", 9" OC		1450	.006		.75	.19		.94	1.15
0180	Tongue and groove sheathing/decking, 1" x 6"		1000	.008		1.80	.28		2.08	2.45
0190	2" x 6"	↓	1000	.008		3.86	.28		4.14	4.72
0200	Walls, 1" x 6" boards, laid regular	2 Carp	650	.025		1.64	.86		2.50	3.25
0210	Laid diagonal		585	.027		1.64	.96		2.60	3.41
0220	1" x 8" boards, laid regular		765	.021		2.01	.73		2.74	3.43
0230	Laid diagonal	↓	650	.025	↓	2.01	.86		2.87	3.65

For customer support on your Residential Costs with RSMeans Data, call 800.448.8182.

385

06 16 36.10 Sheathing		Crew	Daily Output	Labor-Hours	Unit	Material	2017 Bare Costs Labor	2017 Bare Costs Equipment	Total	Total Incl O&P
0010	**SHEATHING** R061636-20									
0012	Plywood on roofs, CDX									
0032	5/16" thick	2 Carp	1600	.010	S.F.	.59	.35		.94	1.23
0037	Pneumatic nailed		1952	.008		.59	.29		.88	1.13
0052	3/8" thick		1525	.010		.61	.37		.98	1.28
0057	Pneumatic nailed		1860	.009		.61	.30		.91	1.17
0102	1/2" thick		1400	.011		.63	.40		1.03	1.36
0103	Pneumatic nailed		1708	.009		.63	.33		.96	1.24
0202	5/8" thick		1300	.012		.78	.43		1.21	1.58
0207	Pneumatic nailed		1586	.010		.78	.35		1.13	1.45
0302	3/4" thick		1200	.013		.94	.47		1.41	1.81
0307	Pneumatic nailed		1464	.011		.94	.38		1.32	1.67
0502	Plywood on walls, with exterior CDX, 3/8" thick		1200	.013		.61	.47		1.08	1.45
0507	Pneumatic nailed		1488	.011		.61	.38		.99	1.30
0603	1/2" thick		1125	.014		.63	.50		1.13	1.52
0608	Pneumatic nailed		1395	.011		.63	.40		1.03	1.36
0702	5/8" thick		1050	.015		.78	.53		1.31	1.75
0707	Pneumatic nailed		1302	.012		.78	.43		1.21	1.58
0803	3/4" thick		975	.016		.94	.57		1.51	1.99
0808	Pneumatic nailed		1209	.013		.94	.46		1.40	1.80
1000	For shear wall construction, add						20%			
1200	For structural 1 exterior plywood, add				S.F.	10%				
3000	Wood fiber, regular, no vapor barrier, 1/2" thick	2 Carp	1200	.013		.64	.47		1.11	1.48
3100	5/8" thick		1200	.013		.70	.47		1.17	1.55
3300	No vapor barrier, in colors, 1/2" thick		1200	.013		.81	.47		1.28	1.67
3400	5/8" thick		1200	.013		.85	.47		1.32	1.72
3600	With vapor barrier one side, white, 1/2" thick		1200	.013		.60	.47		1.07	1.44
3700	Vapor barrier 2 sides, 1/2" thick		1200	.013		.84	.47		1.31	1.70
3800	Asphalt impregnated, 25/32" thick		1200	.013		.33	.47		.80	1.14
3850	Intermediate, 1/2" thick		1200	.013		.28	.47		.75	1.09
4500	Oriented strand board, on roof, 7/16" thick [G]		1460	.011		.38	.38		.76	1.06
4505	Pneumatic nailed [G]		1780	.009		.38	.31		.69	.95
4550	1/2" thick [G]		1400	.011		.38	.40		.78	1.09
4555	Pneumatic nailed [G]		1736	.009		.38	.32		.70	.96
4600	5/8" thick [G]		1300	.012		.58	.43		1.01	1.36
4605	Pneumatic nailed [G]		1586	.010		.58	.35		.93	1.23
4610	On walls, 7/16" thick [G]		1200	.013		.38	.47		.85	1.20
4615	Pneumatic nailed [G]		1488	.011		.38	.38		.76	1.05
4620	1/2" thick [G]		1195	.013		.38	.47		.85	1.20
4625	Pneumatic nailed [G]		1325	.012		.38	.42		.80	1.13
4630	5/8" thick [G]		1050	.015		.58	.53		1.11	1.53
4635	Pneumatic nailed [G]		1302	.012		.58	.43		1.01	1.36
4700	Oriented strand board, factory laminated W.R. barrier, on roof, 1/2" thick [G]		1400	.011		.71	.40		1.11	1.45
4705	Pneumatic nailed [G]		1736	.009		.71	.32		1.03	1.32
4720	5/8" thick [G]		1300	.012		.86	.43		1.29	1.67
4725	Pneumatic nailed [G]		1586	.010		.86	.35		1.21	1.54
4730	5/8" thick, T&G [G]		1150	.014		.86	.49		1.35	1.76
4735	Pneumatic nailed, T&G [G]		1400	.011		.86	.40		1.26	1.62
4740	On walls, 7/16" thick [G]		1200	.013		.61	.47		1.08	1.45
4745	Pneumatic nailed [G]		1488	.011		.61	.38		.99	1.30
4750	1/2" thick [G]		1195	.013		.71	.47		1.18	1.56
4755	Pneumatic nailed [G]		1325	.012		.71	.42		1.13	1.49

06 16 Sheathing

06 16 36 – Wood Panel Product Sheathing

06 16 36.10 Sheathing	Crew	Daily Output	Labor-Hours	Unit	Material	2017 Bare Costs Labor	Equipment	Total	Total Incl O&P
4800	Joint sealant tape, 3-1/2"	2 Carp	7600	.002	L.F.	.28	.07		.35	.43
4810	Joint sealant tape, 6"	↓	7600	.002	"	.41	.07		.48	.57

06 16 43 – Gypsum Sheathing

06 16 43.10 Gypsum Sheathing

		Crew	Daily Output	Labor-Hours	Unit	Material	Labor	Equipment	Total	Total Incl O&P
0010	**GYPSUM SHEATHING**									
0020	Gypsum, weatherproof, 1/2" thick	2 Carp	1125	.014	S.F.	.47	.50		.97	1.35
0040	With embedded glass mats	"	1100	.015	"	.70	.51		1.21	1.62

06 17 Shop-Fabricated Structural Wood

06 17 33 – Wood I-Joists

06 17 33.10 Wood and Composite I-Joists

		Crew	Daily Output	Labor-Hours	Unit	Material	Labor	Equipment	Total	Total Incl O&P
0010	**WOOD AND COMPOSITE I-JOISTS**									
0100	Plywood webs, incl. bridging & blocking, panels 24" O.C.									
1200	15' to 24' span, 50 psf live load	F-5	2400	.013	SF Flr.	1.90	.41		2.31	2.78
1300	55 psf live load		2250	.014		2.15	.44		2.59	3.10
1400	24' to 30' span, 45 psf live load		2600	.012		2.56	.38		2.94	3.46
1500	55 psf live load	↓	2400	.013	↓	4.12	.41		4.53	5.20

06 17 53 – Shop-Fabricated Wood Trusses

06 17 53.10 Roof Trusses

		Crew	Daily Output	Labor-Hours	Unit	Material	Labor	Equipment	Total	Total Incl O&P
0010	**ROOF TRUSSES**									
5000	Common wood, 2" x 4" metal plate connected, 24" O.C., 4/12 slope									
5010	1' overhang, 12' span	F-5	55	.582	Ea.	40.50	17.90		58.40	74.50
5050	20' span	F-6	62	.645		72	20.50	9.25	101.75	124
5100	24' span		60	.667		79	21.50	9.55	110.05	133
5150	26' span		57	.702		77	22.50	10.05	109.55	134
5200	28' span		53	.755		95	24	10.80	129.80	157
5240	30' span		51	.784		92.50	25	11.25	128.75	156
5250	32' span		50	.800		112	25.50	11.45	148.95	179
5280	34' span		48	.833		119	26.50	11.95	157.45	189
5350	8/12 pitch, 1' overhang, 20' span		57	.702		82	22.50	10.05	114.55	139
5400	24' span		55	.727		102	23.50	10.40	135.90	162
5450	26' span		52	.769		107	24.50	11	142.50	171
5500	28' span		49	.816		121	26	11.70	158.70	189
5550	32' span		45	.889		136	28.50	12.75	177.25	212
5600	36' span		41	.976		169	31.50	13.95	214.45	253
5650	38' span		40	1		189	32	14.30	235.30	277
5700	40' span	↓	40	1	↓	191	32	14.30	237.30	279

For customer support on your Residential Costs with RSMeans Data, call 800.448.8182.

387

06 18 Glued-Laminated Construction

06 18 13 – Glued-Laminated Beams

06 18 13.10 Laminated Beams

		Crew	Daily Output	Labor-Hours	Unit	Material	2017 Bare Costs Labor	Equipment	Total	Total Incl O&P
0010	**LAMINATED BEAMS**									
0050	3-1/2" x 18"	F-3	480	.083	L.F.	28	2.67	1.19	31.86	37
0100	5-1/4" x 11-7/8"		450	.089		27.50	2.85	1.27	31.62	36.50
0150	5-1/4" x 16"		360	.111		39	3.56	1.59	44.15	50.50
0200	5-1/4" x 18"		290	.138		42	4.42	1.98	48.40	55.50
0250	5-1/4" x 24"		220	.182		59	5.85	2.60	67.45	77.50
0300	7" x 11-7/8"		320	.125		41	4.01	1.79	46.80	53.50
0350	7" x 16"		260	.154		57	4.93	2.20	64.13	73
0400	7" x 18"	▼	210	.190		66	6.10	2.73	74.83	85.50
0500	For premium appearance, add to S.F. prices					5%				
0550	For industrial type, deduct					15%				
0600	For stain and varnish, add					5%				
0650	For 3/4" laminations, add				▼	25%				

06 18 13.20 Laminated Framing

		Crew	Daily Output	Labor-Hours	Unit	Material	2017 Bare Costs Labor	Equipment	Total	Total Incl O&P
0010	**LAMINATED FRAMING**									
0020	30 lb., short term live load, 15 lb. dead load									
0200	Straight roof beams, 20' clear span, beams 8' O.C.	F-3	2560	.016	SF Flr.	2.14	.50	.22	2.86	3.44
0300	Beams 16' O.C.		3200	.013		1.56	.40	.18	2.14	2.59
0500	40' clear span, beams 8' O.C.		3200	.013		4.06	.40	.18	4.64	5.35
0600	Beams 16' O.C.	▼	3840	.010		3.35	.33	.15	3.83	4.41
0800	60' clear span, beams 8' O.C.	F-4	2880	.014		6.95	.45	.37	7.77	8.80
0900	Beams 16' O.C.	"	3840	.010		5.20	.33	.28	5.81	6.55
1100	Tudor arches, 30' to 40' clear span, frames 8' O.C.	F-3	1680	.024		9.05	.76	.34	10.15	11.60
1200	Frames 16' O.C.	"	2240	.018		7.10	.57	.26	7.93	9.05
1400	50' to 60' clear span, frames 8' O.C.	F-4	2200	.018		9.75	.58	.49	10.82	12.25
1500	Frames 16' O.C.		2640	.015		8.30	.49	.41	9.20	10.40
1700	Radial arches, 60' clear span, frames 8' O.C.		1920	.021		9.15	.67	.56	10.38	11.80
1800	Frames 16' O.C.		2880	.014		7.25	.45	.37	8.07	9.10
2000	100' clear span, frames 8' O.C.		1600	.025		9.40	.80	.67	10.87	12.45
2100	Frames 16' O.C.		2400	.017		8.30	.53	.45	9.28	10.55
2300	120' clear span, frames 8' O.C.		1440	.028		12.50	.89	.75	14.14	16.05
2400	Frames 16' O.C.	▼	1920	.021		11.45	.67	.56	12.68	14.30
2600	Bowstring trusses, 20' O.C., 40' clear span	F-3	2400	.017		5.65	.53	.24	6.42	7.40
2700	60' clear span	F-4	3600	.011		5.10	.36	.30	5.76	6.55
2800	100' clear span		4000	.010		7.20	.32	.27	7.79	8.80
2900	120' clear span	▼	3600	.011		7.65	.36	.30	8.31	9.40
3100	For premium appearance, add to S.F. prices					5%				
3300	For industrial type, deduct					15%				
3500	For stain and varnish, add					5%				
3900	For 3/4" laminations, add to straight					25%				
4100	Add to curved				▼	15%				
4300	Alternate pricing method: (use nominal footage of									
4310	components). Straight beams, camber less than 6"	F-3	3.50	11.429	M.B.F.	3,000	365	164	3,529	4,100
4400	Columns, including hardware		2	20		3,225	640	286	4,151	4,950
4600	Curved members, radius over 32'		2.50	16		3,300	515	229	4,044	4,725
4700	Radius 10' to 32'	▼	3	13.333		3,275	425	191	3,891	4,525
4900	For complicated shapes, add maximum					100%				
5100	For pressure treating, add to straight					35%				
5200	Add to curved				▼	45%				
6000	Laminated veneer members, southern pine or western species									
6050	1-3/4" wide x 5-1/2" deep	2 Carp	480	.033	L.F.	3.24	1.16		4.40	5.50
6100	9-1/2" deep	↓	480	.033	↓	4.59	1.16		5.75	7

06 18 Glued-Laminated Construction

06 18 13 – Glued-Laminated Beams

06 18 13.20 Laminated Framing	Crew	Daily Output	Labor-Hours	Unit	Material	2017 Bare Costs Labor	Equipment	Total	Total Incl O&P
6150	14" deep	2 Carp	450	.036	L.F.	7.10	1.24		8.34	9.90
6200	18" deep	↓	450	.036	↓	9.90	1.24		11.14	13
6300	Parallel strand members, southern pine or western species									
6350	1-3/4" wide x 9-1/4" deep	2 Carp	480	.033	L.F.	4.81	1.16		5.97	7.25
6400	11-1/4" deep		450	.036		5.20	1.24		6.44	7.80
6450	14" deep		400	.040		7.80	1.40		9.20	10.95
6500	3-1/2" wide x 9-1/4" deep		480	.033		16.10	1.16		17.26	19.65
6550	11-1/4" deep		450	.036		19.90	1.24		21.14	24
6600	14" deep		400	.040		22.50	1.40		23.90	27
6650	7" wide x 9-1/4" deep		450	.036		33.50	1.24		34.74	39
6700	11-1/4" deep		420	.038		42	1.33		43.33	48.50
6750	14" deep	↓	400	.040	↓	50	1.40		51.40	57.50
8000	Straight beams									
8102	20' span									
8104	3-1/8" x 9"	F-3	30	1.333	Ea.	141	43	19.10	203.10	248
8106	X 10-1/2"		30	1.333		164	43	19.10	226.10	274
8108	X 12"		30	1.333		188	43	19.10	250.10	300
8110	X 13-1/2"		30	1.333		211	43	19.10	273.10	325
8112	X 15"		29	1.379		235	44	19.75	298.75	355
8114	5-1/8" x 10-1/2"		30	1.333		270	43	19.10	332.10	390
8116	X 12"		30	1.333		310	43	19.10	372.10	435
8118	X 13-1/2"		30	1.333		345	43	19.10	407.10	475
8120	X 15"		29	1.379		385	44	19.75	448.75	520
8122	X 16-1/2"		29	1.379		425	44	19.75	488.75	560
8124	X 18"		29	1.379		460	44	19.75	523.75	605
8126	X 19-1/2"		29	1.379		500	44	19.75	563.75	645
8128	X 21"		28	1.429		540	46	20.50	606.50	695
8130	X 22-1/2"		28	1.429		580	46	20.50	646.50	735
8132	X 24"		28	1.429		615	46	20.50	681.50	780
8134	6-3/4" x 12"		29	1.379		405	44	19.75	468.75	540
8136	X 13-1/2"		29	1.379		455	44	19.75	518.75	595
8138	X 15"		29	1.379		510	44	19.75	573.75	655
8140	X 16-1/2"		28	1.429		560	46	20.50	626.50	715
8142	X 18"		28	1.429		610	46	20.50	676.50	770
8144	X 19-1/2"		28	1.429		660	46	20.50	726.50	825
8146	X 21"		27	1.481		710	47.50	21	778.50	885
8148	X 22-1/2"		27	1.481		760	47.50	21	828.50	940
8150	X 24"		27	1.481		810	47.50	21	878.50	1,000
8152	X 25-1/2"		27	1.481		865	47.50	21	933.50	1,050
8154	X 27"		26	1.538		915	49.50	22	986.50	1,100
8156	X 28-1/2"		26	1.538		965	49.50	22	1,036.50	1,150
8158	X 30"	↓	26	1.538	↓	1,025	49.50	22	1,096.50	1,225
8200	30' span									
8250	3-1/8" x 9"	F-3	30	1.333	Ea.	211	43	19.10	273.10	325
8252	X 10-1/2"		30	1.333		247	43	19.10	309.10	365
8254	X 12"		30	1.333		282	43	19.10	344.10	405
8256	X 13-1/2"		30	1.333		315	43	19.10	377.10	445
8258	X 15"		29	1.379		350	44	19.75	413.75	485
8260	5-1/8" x 10-1/2"		30	1.333		405	43	19.10	467.10	540
8262	X 12"		30	1.333		460	43	19.10	522.10	605
8264	X 13-1/2"		30	1.333		520	43	19.10	582.10	665
8266	X 15"		29	1.379		580	44	19.75	643.75	730
8268	X 16-1/2"		29	1.379		635	44	19.75	698.75	795

06 18 13.20 Laminated Framing		Crew	Daily Output	Labor-Hours	Unit	Material	2017 Bare Costs Labor	Equipment	Total	Total Incl O&P
8270	X 18"	F-3	29	1.379	Ea.	695	44	19.75	758.75	860
8272	X 19-1/2"		29	1.379		750	44	19.75	813.75	920
8274	X 21"		28	1.429		810	46	20.50	876.50	990
8276	X 22-1/2"		28	1.429		865	46	20.50	931.50	1,050
8278	X 24"		28	1.429		925	46	20.50	991.50	1,125
8280	6-3/4" x 12"		29	1.379		610	44	19.75	673.75	765
8282	X 13-1/2"		29	1.379		685	44	19.75	748.75	850
8284	X 15"		29	1.379		760	44	19.75	823.75	930
8286	X 16-1/2"		28	1.429		835	46	20.50	901.50	1,025
8288	X 18"		28	1.429		915	46	20.50	981.50	1,100
8290	X 19-1/2"		28	1.429		990	46	20.50	1,056.50	1,200
8292	X 21"		27	1.481		1,075	47.50	21	1,143.50	1,275
8294	X 22-1/2"		27	1.481		1,150	47.50	21	1,218.50	1,350
8296	X 24"		27	1.481		1,225	47.50	21	1,293.50	1,450
8298	X 25-1/2"		27	1.481		1,300	47.50	21	1,368.50	1,525
8300	X 27"		26	1.538		1,375	49.50	22	1,446.50	1,600
8302	X 28-1/2"		26	1.538		1,450	49.50	22	1,521.50	1,700
8304	X 30"	▼	26	1.538	▼	1,525	49.50	22	1,596.50	1,775
8400	40' span									
8402	3-1/8" x 9"	F-3	30	1.333	Ea.	282	43	19.10	344.10	405
8404	X 10-1/2"		30	1.333		330	43	19.10	392.10	455
8406	X 12"		30	1.333		375	43	19.10	437.10	510
8408	X 13-1/2"		30	1.333		425	43	19.10	487.10	560
8410	X 15"		29	1.379		470	44	19.75	533.75	610
8412	5-1/8" x 10-1/2"		30	1.333		540	43	19.10	602.10	690
8414	X 12"		30	1.333		615	43	19.10	677.10	775
8416	X 13-1/2"		30	1.333		695	43	19.10	757.10	860
8418	X 15"		29	1.379		770	44	19.75	833.75	945
8420	X 16-1/2"		29	1.379		850	44	19.75	913.75	1,025
8422	X 18"		29	1.379		925	44	19.75	988.75	1,125
8424	X 19-1/2"		29	1.379		1,000	44	19.75	1,063.75	1,200
8426	X 21"		28	1.429		1,075	46	20.50	1,141.50	1,275
8428	X 22-1/2"		28	1.429		1,150	46	20.50	1,216.50	1,375
8430	X 24"		28	1.429		1,225	46	20.50	1,291.50	1,450
8432	6-3/4" x 12"		29	1.379		810	44	19.75	873.75	990
8434	X 13-1/2"		29	1.379		915	44	19.75	978.75	1,100
8436	X 15"		29	1.379		1,025	44	19.75	1,088.75	1,225
8438	X 16-1/2"		28	1.429		1,125	46	20.50	1,191.50	1,325
8440	X 18"		28	1.429		1,225	46	20.50	1,291.50	1,450
8442	X 19-1/2"		28	1.429		1,325	46	20.50	1,391.50	1,550
8444	X 21"		27	1.481		1,425	47.50	21	1,493.50	1,675
8446	X 22-1/2"		27	1.481		1,525	47.50	21	1,593.50	1,775
8448	X 24"		27	1.481		1,625	47.50	21	1,693.50	1,875
8450	X 25-1/2"		27	1.481		1,725	47.50	21	1,793.50	2,000
8452	X 27"		26	1.538		1,825	49.50	22	1,896.50	2,100
8454	X 28-1/2"		26	1.538		1,925	49.50	22	1,996.50	2,225
8456	X 30"	▼	26	1.538	▼	2,025	49.50	22	2,096.50	2,325

06 22 Millwork

06 22 13 – Standard Pattern Wood Trim

06 22 13.10 Millwork

		Crew	Daily Output	Labor-Hours	Unit	Material	2017 Bare Costs Labor	Equipment	Total	Total Incl O&P
0010	**MILLWORK**									
0020	Rule of thumb, milled material equals rough lumber cost x 3									
1020	1" x 12", custom birch				L.F.	4.70			4.70	5.15
1040	Cedar					6.95			6.95	7.65
1060	Oak					4.79			4.79	5.25
1080	Redwood					4.71			4.71	5.20
1100	Southern yellow pine					4.06			4.06	4.47
1120	Sugar pine					4.31			4.31	4.74
1140	Teak					32			32	35.50
1160	Walnut					7.50			7.50	8.25
1180	White pine					4.81			4.81	5.30

06 22 13.15 Moldings, Base

		Crew	Daily Output	Labor-Hours	Unit	Material	2017 Bare Costs Labor	Equipment	Total	Total Incl O&P
0010	**MOLDINGS, BASE**									
5100	Classic profile, 5/8" x 5-1/2", finger jointed and primed	1 Carp	250	.032	L.F.	1.49	1.12		2.61	3.51
5105	Poplar		240	.033		1.57	1.16		2.73	3.68
5110	Red oak		220	.036		2.41	1.27		3.68	4.78
5115	Maple		220	.036		3.64	1.27		4.91	6.15
5120	Cherry		220	.036		4.32	1.27		5.59	6.90
5125	3/4" x 7-1/2", finger jointed and primed		250	.032		1.89	1.12		3.01	3.95
5130	Poplar		240	.033		2.51	1.16		3.67	4.71
5135	Red oak		220	.036		3.50	1.27		4.77	6
5140	Maple		220	.036		4.84	1.27		6.11	7.45
5145	Cherry		220	.036		5.75	1.27		7.02	8.50
5150	Modern profile, 5/8" x 3-1/2", finger jointed and primed		250	.032		.91	1.12		2.03	2.87
5155	Poplar		240	.033		1	1.16		2.16	3.05
5160	Red oak		220	.036		1.65	1.27		2.92	3.94
5165	Maple		220	.036		2.55	1.27		3.82	4.93
5170	Cherry		220	.036		2.56	1.27		3.83	4.94
5175	Ogee profile, 7/16" x 3", finger jointed and primed		250	.032		.63	1.12		1.75	2.56
5180	Poplar		240	.033		.66	1.16		1.82	2.67
5185	Red oak		220	.036		.93	1.27		2.20	3.15
5200	9/16" x 3-1/2", finger jointed and primed		250	.032		.66	1.12		1.78	2.59
5205	Pine		240	.033		1.13	1.16		2.29	3.19
5210	Red oak		220	.036		2.80	1.27		4.07	5.20
5215	9/16" x 4-1/2", red oak		220	.036		4.19	1.27		5.46	6.75
5220	5/8" x 3-1/2", finger jointed and primed		250	.032		.91	1.12		2.03	2.87
5225	Poplar		240	.033		1	1.16		2.16	3.05
5230	Red oak		220	.036		1.65	1.27		2.92	3.94
5235	Maple		220	.036		2.55	1.27		3.82	4.93
5240	Cherry		220	.036		2.75	1.27		4.02	5.15
5245	5/8" x 4", finger jointed and primed		250	.032		1.17	1.12		2.29	3.16
5250	Poplar		240	.033		1.29	1.16		2.45	3.37
5255	Red oak		220	.036		1.85	1.27		3.12	4.16
5260	Maple		220	.036		2.85	1.27		4.12	5.25
5265	Cherry		220	.036		2.99	1.27		4.26	5.40
5270	Rectangular profile, oak, 3/8" x 1-1/4"		260	.031		1.29	1.08		2.37	3.22
5275	1/2" x 2-1/2"		255	.031		2.35	1.10		3.45	4.41
5280	1/2" x 3-1/2"		250	.032		2.78	1.12		3.90	4.93
5285	1" x 6"		240	.033		4.21	1.16		5.37	6.60
5290	1" x 8"		240	.033		5.80	1.16		6.96	8.35
5295	Pine, 3/8" x 1-3/4"		260	.031		.47	1.08		1.55	2.32
5300	7/16" x 2-1/2"		255	.031		.83	1.10		1.93	2.74

06 22 13 – Standard Pattern Wood Trim

06 22 13.15 Moldings, Base

		Crew	Daily Output	Labor-Hours	Unit	Material	2017 Bare Costs Labor	Equipment	Total	Total Incl O&P
5305	1" x 6"	1 Carp	240	.033	L.F.	.83	1.16		1.99	2.86
5310	1" x 8"		240	.033		1.06	1.16		2.22	3.11
5315	Shoe, 1/2" x 3/4", primed		260	.031		.49	1.08		1.57	2.34
5320	Pine		240	.033		.33	1.16		1.49	2.31
5325	Poplar		240	.033		.39	1.16		1.55	2.38
5330	Red oak		220	.036		.53	1.27		1.80	2.71
5335	Maple		220	.036		.70	1.27		1.97	2.90
5340	Cherry		220	.036		.80	1.27		2.07	3.01
5345	11/16" x 1-1/2", pine		240	.033		.70	1.16		1.86	2.72
5350	Caps, 11/16" x 1-3/8", pine		240	.033		.55	1.16		1.71	2.55
5355	3/4" x 1-3/4", finger jointed and primed		260	.031		.71	1.08		1.79	2.58
5360	Poplar		240	.033		1.01	1.16		2.17	3.06
5365	Red oak		220	.036		1.21	1.27		2.48	3.46
5370	Maple		220	.036		1.58	1.27		2.85	3.87
5375	Cherry		220	.036		3.29	1.27		4.56	5.75
5380	Combination base & shoe, 9/16" x 3-1/2" & 1/2" x 3/4", pine		125	.064		1.46	2.24		3.70	5.35
5385	Three piece oak, 6" high		80	.100		5.95	3.50		9.45	12.40
5390	Including 3/4" x 1" base shoe		70	.114		6.45	3.99		10.44	13.80
5395	Flooring cant strip, 3/4" x 3/4", pre-finished pine		260	.031		.51	1.08		1.59	2.36
5400	For pre-finished, stain and clear coat, add					.55			.55	.61
5405	Clear coat only, add					.45			.45	.50

06 22 13.30 Moldings, Casings

		Crew	Daily Output	Labor-Hours	Unit	Material	2017 Bare Costs Labor	Equipment	Total	Total Incl O&P
0010	**MOLDINGS, CASINGS**									
0085	Apron, 9/16" x 2-1/2", pine	1 Carp	250	.032	L.F.	1.63	1.12		2.75	3.66
0090	5/8" x 2-1/2", pine		250	.032		1.63	1.12		2.75	3.66
0110	5/8" x 3-1/2", pine		220	.036		1.86	1.27		3.13	4.17
0300	Band, 11/16" x 1-1/8", pine		270	.030		.75	1.04		1.79	2.55
0310	11/16" x 1-1/2", finger jointed and primed		270	.030		.76	1.04		1.80	2.56
0320	Pine		270	.030		.96	1.04		2	2.78
0330	11/16" x 1-3/4", finger jointed and primed		270	.030		.95	1.04		1.99	2.77
0350	Pine		270	.030		1.16	1.04		2.20	3
0355	Beaded, 3/4" x 3-1/2", finger jointed and primed		220	.036		1.11	1.27		2.38	3.35
0360	Poplar		220	.036		1.11	1.27		2.38	3.35
0365	Red oak		220	.036		1.65	1.27		2.92	3.94
0370	Maple		220	.036		2.55	1.27		3.82	4.93
0375	Cherry		220	.036		3.08	1.27		4.35	5.50
0380	3/4" x 4", finger jointed and primed		220	.036		1.20	1.27		2.47	3.45
0385	Poplar		220	.036		1.45	1.27		2.72	3.72
0390	Red oak		220	.036		2.02	1.27		3.29	4.35
0395	Maple		220	.036		2.65	1.27		3.92	5.05
0400	Cherry		220	.036		3.33	1.27		4.60	5.80
0405	3/4" x 5-1/2", finger jointed and primed		200	.040		1.27	1.40		2.67	3.74
0410	Poplar		200	.040		1.93	1.40		3.33	4.46
0415	Red oak		200	.040		2.84	1.40		4.24	5.45
0420	Maple		200	.040		3.73	1.40		5.13	6.45
0425	Cherry		200	.040		4.30	1.40		5.70	7.05
0430	Classic profile, 3/4" x 2-3/4", finger jointed and primed		250	.032		.82	1.12		1.94	2.77
0435	Poplar		250	.032		1	1.12		2.12	2.97
0440	Red oak		250	.032		1.46	1.12		2.58	3.47
0445	Maple		250	.032		2.09	1.12		3.21	4.17
0450	Cherry		250	.032		2.37	1.12		3.49	4.48
0455	Fluted, 3/4" x 3-1/2", poplar		220	.036		1.11	1.27		2.38	3.35

06 22 13 – Standard Pattern Wood Trim

06 22 13.30 Moldings, Casings		Crew	Daily Output	Labor-Hours	Unit	Material	2017 Bare Costs Labor	Equipment	Total	Total Incl O&P
0460	Red oak	1 Carp	220	.036	L.F.	1.65	1.27		2.92	3.94
0465	Maple		220	.036		2.55	1.27		3.82	4.93
0470	Cherry		220	.036		3.08	1.27		4.35	5.50
0475	3/4" x 4", poplar		220	.036		1.44	1.27		2.71	3.71
0480	Red oak		220	.036		2.03	1.27		3.30	4.36
0485	Maple		220	.036		2.65	1.27		3.92	5.05
0490	Cherry		220	.036		3.33	1.27		4.60	5.80
0495	3/4" x 5-1/2", poplar		200	.040		1.93	1.40		3.33	4.46
0500	Red oak		200	.040		2.84	1.40		4.24	5.45
0505	Maple		200	.040		3.73	1.40		5.13	6.45
0510	Cherry		200	.040		4.30	1.40		5.70	7.05
0515	3/4" x 7-1/2", poplar		190	.042		1.31	1.47		2.78	3.90
0520	Red oak		190	.042		3.93	1.47		5.40	6.80
0525	Maple		190	.042		5.65	1.47		7.12	8.65
0530	Cherry		190	.042		6.75	1.47		8.22	9.90
0535	3/4" x 9-1/2", poplar		180	.044		4.12	1.55		5.67	7.15
0540	Red oak		180	.044		6.55	1.55		8.10	9.80
0545	Maple		180	.044		9	1.55		10.55	12.50
0550	Cherry		180	.044		9.80	1.55		11.35	13.40
0555	Modern profile, 9/16" x 2-1/4", poplar		250	.032		.66	1.12		1.78	2.59
0560	Red oak		250	.032		.78	1.12		1.90	2.73
0565	11/16" x 2-1/2", finger jointed & primed		250	.032		.84	1.12		1.96	2.79
0570	Pine		250	.032		1.28	1.12		2.40	3.28
0575	3/4" x 2-1/2", poplar		250	.032		.88	1.12		2	2.84
0580	Red oak		250	.032		1.19	1.12		2.31	3.18
0585	Maple		250	.032		1.80	1.12		2.92	3.85
0590	Cherry		250	.032		2.27	1.12		3.39	4.37
0595	Mullion, 5/16" x 2", pine		270	.030		.86	1.04		1.90	2.67
0600	9/16" x 2-1/2", finger jointed and primed		250	.032		.98	1.12		2.10	2.95
0605	Pine		250	.032		1.28	1.12		2.40	3.28
0610	Red oak		250	.032		3.28	1.12		4.40	5.50
0615	1-1/16" x 3-3/4", red oak		220	.036		6.95	1.27		8.22	9.75
0620	Ogee, 7/16" x 2-1/2", poplar		250	.032		.57	1.12		1.69	2.50
0625	Red oak		250	.032		.78	1.12		1.90	2.73
0630	9/16" x 2-1/4", finger jointed and primed		250	.032		.53	1.12		1.65	2.45
0635	Poplar		250	.032		.57	1.12		1.69	2.50
0640	Red oak		250	.032		.78	1.12		1.90	2.73
0645	11/16" x 2-1/2", finger jointed and primed		250	.032		.72	1.12		1.84	2.66
0700	Pine		250	.032		1.41	1.12		2.53	3.42
0701	Red oak		250	.032		2.70	1.12		3.82	4.84
0730	11/16" x 3-1/2", finger jointed and primed		220	.036		1.20	1.27		2.47	3.45
0750	Pine		220	.036		1.72	1.27		2.99	4.02
0755	3/4" x 2-1/2", finger jointed and primed		250	.032		.85	1.12		1.97	2.80
0760	Poplar		250	.032		.88	1.12		2	2.84
0765	Red oak		250	.032		1.19	1.12		2.31	3.18
0770	Maple		250	.032		1.80	1.12		2.92	3.85
0775	Cherry		250	.032		2.27	1.12		3.39	4.37
0780	3/4" x 3-1/2", finger jointed and primed		220	.036		.94	1.27		2.21	3.16
0785	Poplar		220	.036		1.11	1.27		2.38	3.35
0790	Red oak		220	.036		1.65	1.27		2.92	3.94
0795	Maple		220	.036		2.55	1.27		3.82	4.93
0800	Cherry		220	.036		3.08	1.27		4.35	5.50
4700	Square profile, 1" x 1", teak		215	.037		2.39	1.30		3.69	4.80

06 22 13.30 Moldings, Casings		Crew	Daily Output	Labor-Hours	Unit	Material	2017 Bare Costs Labor	Equipment	Total	Total Incl O&P
4800	Rectangular profile, 1" x 3", teak	1 Carp	200	.040	L.F.	6.40	1.40		7.80	9.40

06 22 13.35 Moldings, Ceilings

		Crew	Daily Output	Labor-Hours	Unit	Material	2017 Bare Costs Labor	Equipment	Total	Total Incl O&P
0010	**MOLDINGS, CEILINGS**									
0600	Bed, 9/16" x 1-3/4", pine	1 Carp	270	.030	L.F.	1.06	1.04		2.10	2.89
0650	9/16" x 2", pine		270	.030		1.14	1.04		2.18	2.98
0710	9/16" x 1-3/4", oak		270	.030		2.35	1.04		3.39	4.31
1200	Cornice, 9/16" x 1-3/4", pine		270	.030		.96	1.04		2	2.78
1300	9/16" x 2-1/4", pine		265	.030		1.27	1.06		2.33	3.15
1350	Cove, 1/2" x 2-1/4", poplar		265	.030		1.02	1.06		2.08	2.88
1360	Red oak		265	.030		1.36	1.06		2.42	3.25
1370	Hard maple		265	.030		1.87	1.06		2.93	3.81
1380	Cherry		265	.030		2.28	1.06		3.34	4.26
2400	9/16" x 1-3/4", pine		270	.030		.97	1.04		2.01	2.80
2401	Oak		270	.030		1.26	1.04		2.30	3.11
2500	11/16" x 2-3/4", pine		265	.030		1.80	1.06		2.86	3.74
2510	Crown, 5/8" x 5/8", poplar		300	.027		.44	.93		1.37	2.04
2520	Red oak		300	.027		.52	.93		1.45	2.13
2530	Hard maple		300	.027		.70	.93		1.63	2.33
2540	Cherry		300	.027		.74	.93		1.67	2.37
2600	9/16" x 3-5/8", pine		250	.032		2.02	1.12		3.14	4.09
2700	11/16" x 4-1/4", pine		250	.032		2.85	1.12		3.97	5
2705	Oak		250	.032		6.30	1.12		7.42	8.80
2710	3/4" x 1-3/4", poplar		270	.030		.71	1.04		1.75	2.51
2720	Red oak		270	.030		1.05	1.04		2.09	2.88
2730	Hard maple		270	.030		1.39	1.04		2.43	3.26
2740	Cherry		270	.030		1.71	1.04		2.75	3.61
2750	3/4" x 2", poplar		270	.030		.94	1.04		1.98	2.76
2760	Red oak		270	.030		1.26	1.04		2.30	3.11
2770	Hard maple		270	.030		1.68	1.04		2.72	3.58
2780	Cherry		270	.030		1.88	1.04		2.92	3.80
2790	3/4" x 2-3/4", poplar		265	.030		1.02	1.06		2.08	2.88
2800	Red oak		265	.030		1.57	1.06		2.63	3.48
2810	Hard maple		265	.030		2.17	1.06		3.23	4.14
2820	Cherry		265	.030		2.40	1.06		3.46	4.40
2830	3/4" x 3-1/2", poplar		250	.032		1.30	1.12		2.42	3.30
2840	Red oak		250	.032		1.96	1.12		3.08	4.02
2850	Hard maple		250	.032		2.56	1.12		3.68	4.68
2860	Cherry		250	.032		3	1.12		4.12	5.15
2870	FJP poplar		250	.032		.92	1.12		2.04	2.88
2880	3/4" x 5", poplar		245	.033		1.93	1.14		3.07	4.03
2890	Red oak		245	.033		2.85	1.14		3.99	5.05
2900	Hard maple		245	.033		3.74	1.14		4.88	6
2910	Cherry		245	.033		4.32	1.14		5.46	6.65
2920	FJP poplar		245	.033		1.32	1.14		2.46	3.36
2930	3/4" x 6-1/4", poplar		240	.033		2.30	1.16		3.46	4.48
2940	Red oak		240	.033		3.47	1.16		4.63	5.75
2950	Hard maple		240	.033		4.53	1.16		5.69	6.95
2960	Cherry		240	.033		5.35	1.16		6.51	7.85
2970	7/8" x 8-3/4", poplar		220	.036		3.57	1.27		4.84	6.05
2980	Red oak		220	.036		4.76	1.27		6.03	7.40
2990	Hard maple		220	.036		6.80	1.27		8.07	9.60
3000	Cherry		220	.036		7.65	1.27		8.92	10.55

For customer support on your Residential Costs with RSMeans Data, call 800.448.8182.

06 22 13 – Standard Pattern Wood Trim

06 22 13.35 Moldings, Ceilings

		Crew	Daily Output	Labor-Hours	Unit	Material	2017 Bare Costs Labor	Equipment	Total	Total Incl O&P
3010	1" x 7-1/4", poplar	1 Carp	220	.036	L.F.	3.78	1.27		5.05	6.30
3020	Red oak		220	.036		5.90	1.27		7.17	8.60
3030	Hard maple		220	.036		8.15	1.27		9.42	11.10
3040	Cherry		220	.036		9.50	1.27		10.77	12.60
3050	1-1/16" x 4-1/4", poplar		250	.032		2.29	1.12		3.41	4.39
3060	Red oak		250	.032		2.69	1.12		3.81	4.83
3070	Hard maple		250	.032		3.56	1.12		4.68	5.80
3080	Cherry		250	.032		5.10	1.12		6.22	7.45
3090	Dentil crown, 3/4" x 5", poplar		250	.032		1.93	1.12		3.05	3.99
3100	Red oak		250	.032		2.85	1.12		3.97	5
3110	Hard maple		250	.032		3.74	1.12		4.86	6
3120	Cherry		250	.032		4.32	1.12		5.44	6.60
3130	Dentil piece for above, 1/2" x 1/2", poplar		300	.027		2.73	.93		3.66	4.56
3140	Red oak		300	.027		3.14	.93		4.07	5
3150	Hard maple		300	.027		3.57	.93		4.50	5.50
3160	Cherry		300	.027		3.89	.93		4.82	5.85

06 22 13.40 Moldings, Exterior

		Crew	Daily Output	Labor-Hours	Unit	Material	2017 Bare Costs Labor	Equipment	Total	Total Incl O&P
0010	**MOLDINGS, EXTERIOR**									
0100	Band board, cedar, rough sawn, 1" x 2"	1 Carp	300	.027	L.F.	.59	.93		1.52	2.21
0110	1" x 3"		300	.027		.88	.93		1.81	2.53
0120	1" x 4"		250	.032		1.18	1.12		2.30	3.16
0130	1" x 6"		250	.032		1.76	1.12		2.88	3.81
0140	1" x 8"		225	.036		2.35	1.24		3.59	4.67
0150	1" x 10"		225	.036		2.92	1.24		4.16	5.30
0160	1" x 12"		200	.040		3.51	1.40		4.91	6.20
0240	STK, 1" x 2"		300	.027		.54	.93		1.47	2.15
0250	1" x 3"		300	.027		.59	.93		1.52	2.21
0260	1" x 4"		250	.032		.66	1.12		1.78	2.60
0270	1" x 6"		250	.032		1.12	1.12		2.24	3.11
0280	1" x 8"		225	.036		1.71	1.24		2.95	3.96
0290	1" x 10"		225	.036		2.29	1.24		3.53	4.60
0300	1" x 12"		200	.040		3.69	1.40		5.09	6.40
0310	Pine, #2, 1" x 2"		300	.027		.27	.93		1.20	1.86
0320	1" x 3"		300	.027		.43	.93		1.36	2.03
0330	1" x 4"		250	.032		.52	1.12		1.64	2.45
0340	1" x 6"		250	.032		.79	1.12		1.91	2.74
0350	1" x 8"		225	.036		1.29	1.24		2.53	3.50
0360	1" x 10"		225	.036		1.68	1.24		2.92	3.93
0370	1" x 12"		200	.040		2.06	1.40		3.46	4.61
0380	D & better, 1" x 2"		300	.027		.44	.93		1.37	2.04
0390	1" x 3"		300	.027		.67	.93		1.60	2.29
0400	1" x 4"		250	.032		.89	1.12		2.01	2.85
0410	1" x 6"		250	.032		1.16	1.12		2.28	3.15
0420	1" x 8"		225	.036		1.62	1.24		2.86	3.87
0430	1" x 10"		225	.036		2.04	1.24		3.28	4.32
0440	1" x 12"		200	.040		2.64	1.40		4.04	5.25
0450	Redwood, clear all heart, 1" x 2"		300	.027		.64	.93		1.57	2.26
0460	1" x 3"		300	.027		.95	.93		1.88	2.60
0470	1" x 4"		250	.032		1.19	1.12		2.31	3.18
0480	1" x 6"		252	.032		1.78	1.11		2.89	3.82
0490	1" x 8"		225	.036		2.36	1.24		3.60	4.68
0500	1" x 10"		225	.036		3.97	1.24		5.21	6.45

For customer support on your Residential Costs with RSMeans Data, call 800.448.8182.

395

06 22 13.40 Moldings, Exterior		Crew	Daily Output	Labor-Hours	Unit	Material	2017 Bare Costs Labor	Equipment	Total	Total Incl O&P
0510	1" x 12"	1 Carp	200	.040	L.F.	4.76	1.40		6.16	7.60
0530	Corner board, cedar, rough sawn, 1" x 2"		225	.036		.59	1.24		1.83	2.73
0540	1" x 3"		225	.036		.88	1.24		2.12	3.05
0550	1" x 4"		200	.040		1.18	1.40		2.58	3.63
0560	1" x 6"		200	.040		1.76	1.40		3.16	4.28
0570	1" x 8"		200	.040		2.35	1.40		3.75	4.93
0580	1" x 10"		175	.046		2.92	1.60		4.52	5.90
0590	1" x 12"		175	.046		3.51	1.60		5.11	6.55
0670	STK, 1" x 2"		225	.036		.54	1.24		1.78	2.67
0680	1" x 3"		225	.036		.59	1.24		1.83	2.73
0690	1" x 4"		200	.040		.65	1.40		2.05	3.05
0700	1" x 6"		200	.040		1.12	1.40		2.52	3.58
0710	1" x 8"		200	.040		1.71	1.40		3.11	4.22
0720	1" x 10"		175	.046		2.29	1.60		3.89	5.20
0730	1" x 12"		175	.046		3.69	1.60		5.29	6.75
0740	Pine, #2, 1" x 2"		225	.036		.27	1.24		1.51	2.38
0750	1" x 3"		225	.036		.43	1.24		1.67	2.55
0760	1" x 4"		200	.040		.52	1.40		1.92	2.92
0770	1" x 6"		200	.040		.79	1.40		2.19	3.21
0780	1" x 8"		200	.040		1.29	1.40		2.69	3.76
0790	1" x 10"		175	.046		1.68	1.60		3.28	4.52
0800	1" x 12"		175	.046		2.06	1.60		3.66	4.94
0810	D & better, 1" x 2"		225	.036		.44	1.24		1.68	2.56
0820	1" x 3"		225	.036		.67	1.24		1.91	2.81
0830	1" x 4"		200	.040		.89	1.40		2.29	3.32
0840	1" x 6"		200	.040		1.16	1.40		2.56	3.62
0850	1" x 8"		200	.040		1.62	1.40		3.02	4.13
0860	1" x 10"		175	.046		2.04	1.60		3.64	4.91
0870	1" x 12"		175	.046		2.64	1.60		4.24	5.55
0880	Redwood, clear all heart, 1" x 2"		225	.036		.64	1.24		1.88	2.78
0890	1" x 3"		225	.036		.95	1.24		2.19	3.12
0900	1" x 4"		200	.040		1.19	1.40		2.59	3.65
0910	1" x 6"		200	.040		1.78	1.40		3.18	4.30
0920	1" x 8"		200	.040		2.36	1.40		3.76	4.94
0930	1" x 10"		175	.046		3.97	1.60		5.57	7.05
0940	1" x 12"		175	.046		4.76	1.60		6.36	7.90
0950	Cornice board, cedar, rough sawn, 1" x 2"		330	.024		.59	.85		1.44	2.07
0960	1" x 3"		290	.028		.88	.96		1.84	2.58
0970	1" x 4"		250	.032		1.18	1.12		2.30	3.16
0980	1" x 6"		250	.032		1.76	1.12		2.88	3.81
0990	1" x 8"		200	.040		2.35	1.40		3.75	4.93
1000	1" x 10"		180	.044		2.92	1.55		4.47	5.80
1010	1" x 12"		180	.044		3.51	1.55		5.06	6.45
1020	STK, 1" x 2"		330	.024		.54	.85		1.39	2.01
1030	1" x 3"		290	.028		.59	.96		1.55	2.26
1040	1" x 4"		250	.032		.66	1.12		1.78	2.60
1050	1" x 6"		250	.032		1.12	1.12		2.24	3.11
1060	1" x 8"		200	.040		1.71	1.40		3.11	4.22
1070	1" x 10"		180	.044		2.29	1.55		3.84	5.10
1080	1" x 12"		180	.044		3.69	1.55		5.24	6.65
1500	Pine, #2, 1" x 2"		330	.024		.27	.85		1.12	1.72
1510	1" x 3"		290	.028		.29	.96		1.25	1.93
1600	1" x 4"		250	.032		.52	1.12		1.64	2.45

06 22 Millwork

06 22 13 – Standard Pattern Wood Trim

06 22 13.40 Moldings, Exterior

		Crew	Daily Output	Labor-Hours	Unit	Material	2017 Bare Costs Labor	Equipment	Total	Total Incl O&P
1700	1" x 6"	1 Carp	250	.032	L.F.	.79	1.12		1.91	2.74
1800	1" x 8"		200	.040		1.29	1.40		2.69	3.76
1900	1" x 10"		180	.044		1.68	1.55		3.23	4.45
2000	1" x 12"		180	.044		2.06	1.55		3.61	4.87
2020	D & better, 1" x 2"		330	.024		.44	.85		1.29	1.90
2030	1" x 3"		290	.028		.67	.96		1.63	2.34
2040	1" x 4"		250	.032		.89	1.12		2.01	2.85
2050	1" x 6"		250	.032		1.16	1.12		2.28	3.15
2060	1" x 8"		200	.040		1.62	1.40		3.02	4.13
2070	1" x 10"		180	.044		2.04	1.55		3.59	4.84
2080	1" x 12"		180	.044		2.64	1.55		4.19	5.50
2090	Redwood, clear all heart, 1" x 2"		330	.024		.64	.85		1.49	2.12
2100	1" x 3"		290	.028		.95	.96		1.91	2.65
2110	1" x 4"		250	.032		1.19	1.12		2.31	3.18
2120	1" x 6"		250	.032		1.78	1.12		2.90	3.83
2130	1" x 8"		200	.040		2.36	1.40		3.76	4.94
2140	1" x 10"		180	.044		3.97	1.55		5.52	6.95
2150	1" x 12"		180	.044		4.76	1.55		6.31	7.85
2160	3 piece, 1" x 2", 1" x 4", 1" x 6", rough sawn cedar		80	.100		3.54	3.50		7.04	9.75
2180	STK cedar		80	.100		2.32	3.50		5.82	8.40
2200	#2 pine		80	.100		1.58	3.50		5.08	7.60
2210	D & better pine		80	.100		2.49	3.50		5.99	8.60
2220	Clear all heart redwood		80	.100		3.61	3.50		7.11	9.80
2230	1" x 8", 1" x 10", 1" x 12", rough sawn cedar		65	.123		8.75	4.30		13.05	16.80
2240	STK cedar		65	.123		7.65	4.30		11.95	15.65
2300	#2 pine		65	.123		4.99	4.30		9.29	12.70
2320	D & better pine		65	.123		6.25	4.30		10.55	14.10
2330	Clear all heart redwood		65	.123		11.05	4.30		15.35	19.35
2340	Door/window casing, cedar, rough sawn, 1" x 2"		275	.029		.59	1.02		1.61	2.35
2350	1" x 3"		275	.029		.88	1.02		1.90	2.67
2360	1" x 4"		250	.032		1.18	1.12		2.30	3.16
2370	1" x 6"		250	.032		1.76	1.12		2.88	3.81
2380	1" x 8"		230	.035		2.35	1.22		3.57	4.62
2390	1" x 10"		230	.035		2.92	1.22		4.14	5.25
2395	1" x 12"		210	.038		3.51	1.33		4.84	6.10
2410	STK, 1" x 2"		275	.029		.54	1.02		1.56	2.29
2420	1" x 3"		275	.029		.59	1.02		1.61	2.35
2430	1" x 4"		250	.032		.66	1.12		1.78	2.60
2440	1" x 6"		250	.032		1.12	1.12		2.24	3.11
2450	1" x 8"		230	.035		1.71	1.22		2.93	3.91
2460	1" x 10"		230	.035		2.29	1.22		3.51	4.55
2470	1" x 12"		210	.038		3.69	1.33		5.02	6.30
2550	Pine, #2, 1" x 2"		275	.029		.27	1.02		1.29	2
2560	1" x 3"		275	.029		.43	1.02		1.45	2.17
2570	1" x 4"		250	.032		.52	1.12		1.64	2.45
2580	1" x 6"		250	.032		.79	1.12		1.91	2.74
2590	1" x 8"		230	.035		1.29	1.22		2.51	3.45
2600	1" x 10"		230	.035		1.68	1.22		2.90	3.88
2610	1" x 12"		210	.038		2.06	1.33		3.39	4.50
2620	Pine, D & better, 1" x 2"		275	.029		.44	1.02		1.46	2.18
2630	1" x 3"		275	.029		.67	1.02		1.69	2.43
2640	1" x 4"		250	.032		.89	1.12		2.01	2.85
2650	1" x 6"		250	.032		1.16	1.12		2.28	3.15

06 22 13 – Standard Pattern Wood Trim

06 22 13.40 Moldings, Exterior		Crew	Daily Output	Labor-Hours	Unit	Material	2017 Bare Costs Labor	Equipment	Total	Total Incl O&P
2660	1" x 8"	1 Carp	230	.035	L.F.	1.62	1.22		2.84	3.82
2670	1" x 10"		230	.035		2.04	1.22		3.26	4.27
2680	1" x 12"		210	.038		2.64	1.33		3.97	5.15
2690	Redwood, clear all heart, 1" x 2"		275	.029		.64	1.02		1.66	2.40
2695	1" x 3"		275	.029		.95	1.02		1.97	2.74
2710	1" x 4"		250	.032		1.19	1.12		2.31	3.18
2715	1" x 6"		250	.032		1.78	1.12		2.90	3.83
2730	1" x 8"		230	.035		2.36	1.22		3.58	4.63
2740	1" x 10"		230	.035		3.97	1.22		5.19	6.40
2750	1" x 12"		210	.038		4.76	1.33		6.09	7.50
3500	Bellyband, pine, 11/16" x 4-1/4"		250	.032		3.23	1.12		4.35	5.45
3610	Brickmold, pine, 1-1/4" x 2"		200	.040		2.44	1.40		3.84	5
3620	FJP, 1-1/4" x 2"		200	.040		1.13	1.40		2.53	3.58
5100	Fascia, cedar, rough sawn, 1" x 2"		275	.029		.59	1.02		1.61	2.35
5110	1" x 3"		275	.029		.88	1.02		1.90	2.67
5120	1" x 4"		250	.032		1.18	1.12		2.30	3.16
5200	1" x 6"		250	.032		1.76	1.12		2.88	3.81
5300	1" x 8"		230	.035		2.35	1.22		3.57	4.62
5310	1" x 10"		230	.035		2.92	1.22		4.14	5.25
5320	1" x 12"		210	.038		3.51	1.33		4.84	6.10
5400	2" x 4"		220	.036		1.16	1.27		2.43	3.40
5500	2" x 6"		220	.036		1.74	1.27		3.01	4.04
5600	2" x 8"		200	.040		2.31	1.40		3.71	4.89
5700	2" x 10"		180	.044		2.88	1.55		4.43	5.75
5800	2" x 12"		170	.047		6.85	1.64		8.49	10.30
6120	STK, 1" x 2"		275	.029		.54	1.02		1.56	2.29
6130	1" x 3"		275	.029		.59	1.02		1.61	2.35
6140	1" x 4"		250	.032		.66	1.12		1.78	2.60
6150	1" x 6"		250	.032		1.12	1.12		2.24	3.11
6160	1" x 8"		230	.035		1.71	1.22		2.93	3.91
6170	1" x 10"		230	.035		2.29	1.22		3.51	4.55
6180	1" x 12"		210	.038		3.69	1.33		5.02	6.30
6185	2" x 2"		260	.031		.66	1.08		1.74	2.52
6190	Pine, #2, 1" x 2"		275	.029		.27	1.02		1.29	2
6200	1" x 3"		275	.029		.43	1.02		1.45	2.17
6210	1" x 4"		250	.032		.52	1.12		1.64	2.45
6220	1" x 6"		250	.032		.79	1.12		1.91	2.74
6230	1" x 8"		230	.035		1.29	1.22		2.51	3.45
6240	1" x 10"		230	.035		1.68	1.22		2.90	3.88
6250	1" x 12"		210	.038		2.06	1.33		3.39	4.50
6260	D & better, 1" x 2"		275	.029		.44	1.02		1.46	2.18
6270	1" x 3"		275	.029		.67	1.02		1.69	2.43
6280	1" x 4"		250	.032		.89	1.12		2.01	2.85
6290	1" x 6"		250	.032		1.16	1.12		2.28	3.15
6300	1" x 8"		230	.035		1.62	1.22		2.84	3.82
6310	1" x 10"		230	.035		2.04	1.22		3.26	4.27
6312	1" x 12"		210	.038		2.64	1.33		3.97	5.15
6330	Southern yellow, 1-1/4" x 5"		240	.033		2.60	1.16		3.76	4.81
6340	1-1/4" x 6"		240	.033		2.53	1.16		3.69	4.74
6350	1-1/4" x 8"		215	.037		3.13	1.30		4.43	5.60
6360	1-1/4" x 12"		190	.042		4.59	1.47		6.06	7.50
6370	Redwood, clear all heart, 1" x 2"		275	.029		.64	1.02		1.66	2.40
6380	1" x 3"		275	.029		1.19	1.02		2.21	3.01

398

06 22 13 – Standard Pattern Wood Trim

06 22 13.40 Moldings, Exterior	Crew	Daily Output	Labor-Hours	Unit	Material	2017 Bare Costs Labor	Equipment	Total	Total Incl O&P
6390	1" x 4"	1 Carp	250	.032	L.F.	1.19	1.12		2.31	3.18
6400	1" x 6"		250	.032		1.78	1.12		2.90	3.83
6410	1" x 8"		230	.035		2.36	1.22		3.58	4.63
6420	1" x 10"		230	.035		3.97	1.22		5.19	6.40
6430	1" x 12"		210	.038		4.76	1.33		6.09	7.50
6440	1-1/4" x 5"		240	.033		1.86	1.16		3.02	4
6450	1-1/4" x 6"		240	.033		2.23	1.16		3.39	4.40
6460	1-1/4" x 8"		215	.037		3.54	1.30		4.84	6.05
6470	1-1/4" x 12"		190	.042		7.15	1.47		8.62	10.30
6580	Frieze, cedar, rough sawn, 1" x 2"		275	.029		.59	1.02		1.61	2.35
6590	1" x 3"		275	.029		.88	1.02		1.90	2.67
6600	1" x 4"		250	.032		1.18	1.12		2.30	3.16
6610	1" x 6"		250	.032		1.76	1.12		2.88	3.81
6620	1" x 8"		250	.032		2.35	1.12		3.47	4.46
6630	1" x 10"		225	.036		2.92	1.24		4.16	5.30
6640	1" x 12"		200	.040		3.48	1.40		4.88	6.15
6650	STK, 1" x 2"		275	.029		.54	1.02		1.56	2.29
6660	1" x 3"		275	.029		.59	1.02		1.61	2.35
6670	1" x 4"		250	.032		.66	1.12		1.78	2.60
6680	1" x 6"		250	.032		1.12	1.12		2.24	3.11
6690	1" x 8"		250	.032		1.71	1.12		2.83	3.75
6700	1" x 10"		225	.036		2.29	1.24		3.53	4.60
6710	1" x 12"		200	.040		3.69	1.40		5.09	6.40
6790	Pine, #2, 1" x 2"		275	.029		.27	1.02		1.29	2
6800	1" x 3"		275	.029		.43	1.02		1.45	2.17
6810	1" x 4"		250	.032		.52	1.12		1.64	2.45
6820	1" x 6"		250	.032		.79	1.12		1.91	2.74
6830	1" x 8"		250	.032		1.29	1.12		2.41	3.29
6840	1" x 10"		225	.036		1.68	1.24		2.92	3.93
6850	1" x 12"		200	.040		2.06	1.40		3.46	4.61
6860	D & better, 1" x 2"		275	.029		.44	1.02		1.46	2.18
6870	1" x 3"		275	.029		.67	1.02		1.69	2.43
6880	1" x 4"		250	.032		.89	1.12		2.01	2.85
6890	1" x 6"		250	.032		1.16	1.12		2.28	3.15
6900	1" x 8"		250	.032		1.62	1.12		2.74	3.66
6910	1" x 10"		225	.036		2.04	1.24		3.28	4.32
6920	1" x 12"		200	.040		2.64	1.40		4.04	5.25
6930	Redwood, clear all heart, 1" x 2"		275	.029		.64	1.02		1.66	2.40
6940	1" x 3"		275	.029		.95	1.02		1.97	2.74
6950	1" x 4"		250	.032		1.19	1.12		2.31	3.18
6960	1" x 6"		250	.032		1.78	1.12		2.90	3.83
6970	1" x 8"		250	.032		2.36	1.12		3.48	4.47
6980	1" x 10"		225	.036		3.97	1.24		5.21	6.45
6990	1" x 12"		200	.040		4.76	1.40		6.16	7.60
7000	Grounds, 1" x 1", cedar, rough sawn		300	.027		.30	.93		1.23	1.89
7010	STK		300	.027		.33	.93		1.26	1.92
7020	Pine, #2		300	.027		.17	.93		1.10	1.75
7030	D & better		300	.027		.27	.93		1.20	1.86
7050	Redwood		300	.027		.39	.93		1.32	1.99
7060	Rake/verge board, cedar, rough sawn, 1" x 2"		225	.036		.59	1.24		1.83	2.73
7070	1" x 3"		225	.036		.88	1.24		2.12	3.05
7080	1" x 4"		200	.040		1.18	1.40		2.58	3.63
7090	1" x 6"		200	.040		1.76	1.40		3.16	4.28

06 22 13.40 Moldings, Exterior		Crew	Daily Output	Labor-Hours	Unit	Material	2017 Bare Costs Labor	2017 Bare Costs Equipment	Total	Total Incl O&P
7100	1" x 8"	1 Carp	190	.042	L.F.	2.35	1.47		3.82	5.05
7110	1" x 10"		190	.042		2.92	1.47		4.39	5.65
7120	1" x 12"		180	.044		3.51	1.55		5.06	6.45
7130	STK, 1" x 2"		225	.036		.54	1.24		1.78	2.67
7140	1" x 3"		225	.036		.59	1.24		1.83	2.73
7150	1" x 4"		200	.040		.66	1.40		2.06	3.07
7160	1" x 6"		200	.040		1.12	1.40		2.52	3.58
7170	1" x 8"		190	.042		1.71	1.47		3.18	4.34
7180	1" x 10"		190	.042		2.29	1.47		3.76	4.98
7190	1" x 12"		180	.044		3.69	1.55		5.24	6.65
7200	Pine, #2, 1" x 2"		225	.036		.27	1.24		1.51	2.38
7210	1" x 3"		225	.036		.43	1.24		1.67	2.55
7220	1" x 4"		200	.040		.52	1.40		1.92	2.92
7230	1" x 6"		200	.040		.79	1.40		2.19	3.21
7240	1" x 8"		190	.042		1.29	1.47		2.76	3.88
7250	1" x 10"		190	.042		1.68	1.47		3.15	4.31
7260	1" x 12"		180	.044		2.06	1.55		3.61	4.87
7340	D & better, 1" x 2"		225	.036		.44	1.24		1.68	2.56
7350	1" x 3"		225	.036		.67	1.24		1.91	2.81
7360	1" x 4"		200	.040		.89	1.40		2.29	3.32
7370	1" x 6"		200	.040		1.16	1.40		2.56	3.62
7380	1" x 8"		190	.042		1.62	1.47		3.09	4.25
7390	1" x 10"		190	.042		2.04	1.47		3.51	4.70
7400	1" x 12"		180	.044		2.64	1.55		4.19	5.50
7410	Redwood, clear all heart, 1" x 2"		225	.036		.64	1.24		1.88	2.78
7420	1" x 3"		225	.036		.95	1.24		2.19	3.12
7430	1" x 4"		200	.040		1.19	1.40		2.59	3.65
7440	1" x 6"		200	.040		1.78	1.40		3.18	4.30
7450	1" x 8"		190	.042		2.36	1.47		3.83	5.05
7460	1" x 10"		190	.042		3.97	1.47		5.44	6.85
7470	1" x 12"		180	.044		4.76	1.55		6.31	7.85
7480	2" x 4"		200	.040		2.29	1.40		3.69	4.86
7490	2" x 6"		182	.044		3.43	1.54		4.97	6.35
7500	2" x 8"		165	.048		4.56	1.69		6.25	7.85
7630	Soffit, cedar, rough sawn, 1" x 2"	2 Carp	440	.036		.59	1.27		1.86	2.78
7640	1" x 3"		440	.036		.88	1.27		2.15	3.10
7650	1" x 4"		420	.038		1.18	1.33		2.51	3.52
7660	1" x 6"		420	.038		1.76	1.33		3.09	4.17
7670	1" x 8"		420	.038		2.35	1.33		3.68	4.82
7680	1" x 10"		400	.040		2.92	1.40		4.32	5.55
7690	1" x 12"		400	.040		3.51	1.40		4.91	6.20
7700	STK, 1" x 2"		440	.036		.54	1.27		1.81	2.72
7710	1" x 3"		440	.036		.59	1.27		1.86	2.78
7720	1" x 4"		420	.038		.66	1.33		1.99	2.96
7730	1" x 6"		420	.038		1.12	1.33		2.45	3.47
7740	1" x 8"		420	.038		1.71	1.33		3.04	4.11
7750	1" x 10"		400	.040		2.29	1.40		3.69	4.86
7760	1" x 12"		400	.040		3.69	1.40		5.09	6.40
7770	Pine, #2, 1" x 2"		440	.036		.27	1.27		1.54	2.43
7780	1" x 3"		440	.036		.43	1.27		1.70	2.60
7790	1" x 4"		420	.038		.52	1.33		1.85	2.81
7800	1" x 6"		420	.038		.79	1.33		2.12	3.10
7810	1" x 8"		420	.038		1.29	1.33		2.62	3.65

06 22 Millwork

06 22 13 - Standard Pattern Wood Trim

06 22 13.40 Moldings, Exterior

		Crew	Daily Output	Labor-Hours	Unit	Material	2017 Bare Costs Labor	Equipment	Total	Total Incl O&P
7820	1" x 10"	2 Carp	400	.040	L.F.	1.68	1.40		3.08	4.19
7830	1" x 12"		400	.040		2.06	1.40		3.46	4.61
7840	D & better, 1" x 2"		440	.036		.44	1.27		1.71	2.61
7850	1" x 3"		440	.036		.67	1.27		1.94	2.86
7860	1" x 4"		420	.038		.89	1.33		2.22	3.21
7870	1" x 6"		420	.038		1.16	1.33		2.49	3.51
7880	1" x 8"		420	.038		1.62	1.33		2.95	4.02
7890	1" x 10"		400	.040		2.04	1.40		3.44	4.58
7900	1" x 12"		400	.040		2.64	1.40		4.04	5.25
7910	Redwood, clear all heart, 1" x 2"		440	.036		.64	1.27		1.91	2.83
7920	1" x 3"		440	.036		.95	1.27		2.22	3.17
7930	1" x 4"		420	.038		1.19	1.33		2.52	3.54
7940	1" x 6"		420	.038		1.78	1.33		3.11	4.19
7950	1" x 8"		420	.038		2.36	1.33		3.69	4.83
7960	1" x 10"		400	.040		3.97	1.40		5.37	6.70
7970	1" x 12"		400	.040		4.76	1.40		6.16	7.60
8050	Trim, crown molding, pine, 11/16" x 4-1/4"	1 Carp	250	.032		4.54	1.12		5.66	6.85
8060	Back band, 11/16" x 1-1/16"		250	.032		1	1.12		2.12	2.97
8070	Insect screen frame stock, 1-1/16" x 1-3/4"		395	.020		2.40	.71		3.11	3.82
8080	Dentils, 2-1/2" x 2-1/2" x 4", 6" O.C.		30	.267		1.31	9.30		10.61	17.05
8100	Fluted, 5-1/2"		165	.048		5.05	1.69		6.74	8.40
8110	Stucco bead, 1-3/8" x 1-5/8"		250	.032		2.51	1.12		3.63	4.63

06 22 13.45 Moldings, Trim

		Crew	Daily Output	Labor-Hours	Unit	Material	2017 Bare Costs Labor	Equipment	Total	Total Incl O&P
0010	**MOLDINGS, TRIM**									
0200	Astragal, stock pine, 11/16" x 1-3/4"	1 Carp	255	.031	L.F.	1.42	1.10		2.52	3.39
0250	1-5/16" x 2-3/16"		240	.033		2.10	1.16		3.26	4.26
0800	Chair rail, stock pine, 5/8" x 2-1/2"		270	.030		1.47	1.04		2.51	3.35
0900	5/8" x 3-1/2"		240	.033		2.30	1.16		3.46	4.48
1000	Closet pole, stock pine, 1-1/8" diameter		200	.040		1.11	1.40		2.51	3.56
1100	Fir, 1-5/8" diameter		200	.040		2.20	1.40		3.60	4.76
1150	Corner, inside, 5/16" x 1"		225	.036		.33	1.24		1.57	2.44
1160	Outside, 1-1/16" x 1-1/16"		240	.033		1.31	1.16		2.47	3.39
1161	1-5/16" x 1-5/16"		240	.033		1.55	1.16		2.71	3.66
3300	Half round, stock pine, 1/4" x 1/2"		270	.030		.24	1.04		1.28	1.99
3350	1/2" x 1"		255	.031		.73	1.10		1.83	2.63
3400	Handrail, fir, single piece, stock, hardware not included									
3450	1-1/2" x 1-3/4"	1 Carp	80	.100	L.F.	2.56	3.50		6.06	8.65
3470	Pine, 1-1/2" x 1-3/4"		80	.100		2.40	3.50		5.90	8.50
3500	1-1/2" x 2-1/2"		76	.105		2.46	3.68		6.14	8.85
3600	Lattice, stock pine, 1/4" x 1-1/8"		270	.030		.35	1.04		1.39	2.12
3700	1/4" x 1-3/4"		250	.032		.69	1.12		1.81	2.63
3800	Miscellaneous, custom, pine, 1" x 1"		270	.030		.40	1.04		1.44	2.17
3850	1" x 2"		265	.030		.80	1.06		1.86	2.64
3900	1" x 3"		240	.033		1.20	1.16		2.36	3.27
4100	Birch or oak, nominal 1" x 1"		240	.033		.39	1.16		1.55	2.38
4200	Nominal 1" x 3"		215	.037		1.18	1.30		2.48	3.46
4400	Walnut, nominal 1" x 1"		215	.037		.62	1.30		1.92	2.86
4500	Nominal 1" x 3"		200	.040		1.87	1.40		3.27	4.40
4700	Teak, nominal 1" x 1"		215	.037		2.69	1.30		3.99	5.10
4800	Nominal 1" x 3"		200	.040		8.05	1.40		9.45	11.20
4900	Quarter round, stock pine, 1/4" x 1/4"		275	.029		.24	1.02		1.26	1.96
4950	3/4" x 3/4"		255	.031		.50	1.10		1.60	2.38

06 22 Millwork

06 22 13 – Standard Pattern Wood Trim

06 22 13.45 Moldings, Trim

		Crew	Daily Output	Labor-Hours	Unit	Material	2017 Bare Costs Labor	2017 Bare Costs Equipment	Total	Total Incl O&P
5600	Wainscot moldings, 1-1/8" x 9/16", 2' high, minimum	1 Carp	76	.105	S.F.	12	3.68		15.68	19.35
5700	Maximum	↓	65	.123	"	16.40	4.30		20.70	25.50

06 22 13.50 Moldings, Window and Door

		Crew	Daily Output	Labor-Hours	Unit	Material	2017 Bare Costs Labor	2017 Bare Costs Equipment	Total	Total Incl O&P
0010	**MOLDINGS, WINDOW AND DOOR**									
2800	Door moldings, stock, decorative, 1-1/8" wide, plain	1 Carp	17	.471	Set	47.50	16.45		63.95	80
2900	Detailed		17	.471	"	91.50	16.45		107.95	129
2960	Clear pine door jamb, no stops, 11/16" x 4-9/16"		240	.033	L.F.	5.30	1.16		6.46	7.80
3150	Door trim set, 1 head and 2 sides, pine, 2-1/2" wide		12	.667	Opng.	24	23.50		47.50	65
3170	3-1/2" wide		11	.727	"	29	25.50		54.50	74.50
3250	Glass beads, stock pine, 3/8" x 1/2"		275	.029	L.F.	.33	1.02		1.35	2.06
3270	3/8" x 7/8"		270	.030		.42	1.04		1.46	2.19
4850	Parting bead, stock pine, 3/8" x 3/4"		275	.029		.44	1.02		1.46	2.18
4870	1/2" x 3/4"		255	.031		.42	1.10		1.52	2.29
5000	Stool caps, stock pine, 11/16" x 3-1/2"		200	.040		2.07	1.40		3.47	4.62
5100	1-1/16" x 3-1/4"		150	.053	↓	3.24	1.86		5.10	6.70
5300	Threshold, oak, 3' long, inside, 5/8" x 3-5/8"		32	.250	Ea.	6.50	8.75		15.25	22
5400	Outside, 1-1/2" x 7-5/8"	↓	16	.500	"	45	17.50		62.50	78.50
5900	Window trim sets, including casings, header, stops,									
5910	stool and apron, 2-1/2" wide, FJP	1 Carp	13	.615	Opng.	31.50	21.50		53	70.50
5950	Pine		10	.800		37	28		65	88
6000	Oak	↓	6	1.333		65.50	46.50		112	150

06 22 13.60 Moldings, Soffits

		Crew	Daily Output	Labor-Hours	Unit	Material	2017 Bare Costs Labor	2017 Bare Costs Equipment	Total	Total Incl O&P
0010	**MOLDINGS, SOFFITS**									
0200	Soffits, pine, 1" x 4"	2 Carp	420	.038	L.F.	.49	1.33		1.82	2.77
0210	1" x 6"		420	.038		.75	1.33		2.08	3.06
0220	1" x 8"		420	.038		1.25	1.33		2.58	3.61
0230	1" x 10"		400	.040		1.63	1.40		3.03	4.13
0240	1" x 12"		400	.040		2.01	1.40		3.41	4.55
0250	STK cedar, 1" x 4"		420	.038		.63	1.33		1.96	2.92
0260	1" x 6"		420	.038		1.09	1.33		2.42	3.43
0270	1" x 8"		420	.038		1.68	1.33		3.01	4.08
0280	1" x 10"		400	.040		2.24	1.40		3.64	4.80
0290	1" x 12"		400	.040	↓	3.64	1.40		5.04	6.35
1000	Exterior AC plywood, 1/4" thick		400	.040	S.F.	1.01	1.40		2.41	3.45
1050	3/8" thick		400	.040		1.05	1.40		2.45	3.50
1100	1/2" thick	↓	400	.040		1.25	1.40		2.65	3.72
1150	Polyvinyl chloride, white, solid	1 Carp	230	.035		2.15	1.22		3.37	4.40
1160	Perforated	"	230	.035	↓	2.15	1.22		3.37	4.40
1170	Accessories, "J" channel 5/8"	2 Carp	700	.023	L.F.	.49	.80		1.29	1.88

06 25 Prefinished Paneling

06 25 13 – Prefinished Hardboard Paneling

06 25 13.10 Paneling, Hardboard

			Crew	Daily Output	Labor-Hours	Unit	Material	2017 Bare Costs Labor	2017 Bare Costs Equipment	Total	Total Incl O&P
0010	**PANELING, HARDBOARD**										
0050	Not incl. furring or trim, hardboard, tempered, 1/8" thick	G	2 Carp	500	.032	S.F.	.45	1.12		1.57	2.37
0100	1/4" thick	G		500	.032		.64	1.12		1.76	2.57
0300	Tempered pegboard, 1/8" thick	G		500	.032		.44	1.12		1.56	2.35
0400	1/4" thick	G		500	.032		.70	1.12		1.82	2.64
0600	Untempered hardboard, natural finish, 1/8" thick	G		500	.032		.44	1.12		1.56	2.35
0700	1/4" thick	G		500	.032	↓	.53	1.12		1.65	2.45

06 25 Prefinished Paneling

06 25 13 – Prefinished Hardboard Paneling

06 25 13.10 Paneling, Hardboard

		Crew	Daily Output	Labor-Hours	Unit	Material	2017 Bare Costs Labor	Equipment	Total	Total Incl O&P
0900	Untempered pegboard, 1/8" thick	G 2 Carp	500	.032	S.F.	.48	1.12		1.60	2.40
1000	1/4" thick	G	500	.032		.48	1.12		1.60	2.40
1200	Plastic faced hardboard, 1/8" thick	G	500	.032		.62	1.12		1.74	2.55
1300	1/4" thick	G	500	.032		.84	1.12		1.96	2.79
1500	Plastic faced pegboard, 1/8" thick	G	500	.032		.62	1.12		1.74	2.55
1600	1/4" thick	G	500	.032		.80	1.12		1.92	2.75
1800	Wood grained, plain or grooved, 1/8" thick	G	500	.032		.65	1.12		1.77	2.59
1900	1/4" thick	G	425	.038	↓	1.42	1.32		2.74	3.76
2100	Moldings, wood grained MDF		500	.032	L.F.	.41	1.12		1.53	2.32
2200	Pine	↓	425	.038	"	1.40	1.32		2.72	3.74

06 25 16 – Prefinished Plywood Paneling

06 25 16.10 Paneling, Plywood

		Crew	Daily Output	Labor-Hours	Unit	Material	2017 Bare Costs Labor	Equipment	Total	Total Incl O&P
0010	**PANELING, PLYWOOD**									
2400	Plywood, prefinished, 1/4" thick, 4' x 8' sheets									
2410	with vertical grooves. Birch faced, economy	2 Carp	500	.032	S.F.	1.47	1.12		2.59	3.49
2420	Average		420	.038		1.20	1.33		2.53	3.55
2430	Custom		350	.046		1.27	1.60		2.87	4.07
2600	Mahogany, African		400	.040		2.45	1.40		3.85	5.05
2700	Philippine (Lauan)		500	.032		.65	1.12		1.77	2.59
2900	Oak		500	.032		1.34	1.12		2.46	3.34
3000	Cherry		400	.040		2	1.40		3.40	4.54
3200	Rosewood		320	.050		3.10	1.75		4.85	6.35
3400	Teak		400	.040		3.12	1.40		4.52	5.75
3600	Chestnut		375	.043		5.30	1.49		6.79	8.30
3800	Pecan		400	.040		2.50	1.40		3.90	5.10
3900	Walnut, average		500	.032		2.47	1.12		3.59	4.59
3950	Custom		400	.040		5.05	1.40		6.45	7.90
4000	Plywood, prefinished, 3/4" thick, stock grades, economy		320	.050		1.44	1.75		3.19	4.50
4100	Average		224	.071		4.93	2.50		7.43	9.60
4300	Architectural grade, custom		224	.071		5.40	2.50		7.90	10.10
4400	Luxury		160	.100		5.30	3.50		8.80	11.65
4600	Plywood, "A" face, birch, VC, 1/2" thick, natural		450	.036		1.85	1.24		3.09	4.12
4700	Select		450	.036		1.95	1.24		3.19	4.23
4900	Veneer core, 3/4" thick, natural		320	.050		2.25	1.75		4	5.40
5000	Select		320	.050		2.53	1.75		4.28	5.70
5200	Lumber core, 3/4" thick, natural		320	.050		3.14	1.75		4.89	6.35
5500	Plywood, knotty pine, 1/4" thick, A2 grade		450	.036		1.85	1.24		3.09	4.12
5600	A3 grade		450	.036		2.09	1.24		3.33	4.38
5800	3/4" thick, veneer core, A2 grade		320	.050		2.31	1.75		4.06	5.45
5900	A3 grade		320	.050		2.39	1.75		4.14	5.55
6100	Aromatic cedar, 1/4" thick, plywood		400	.040		2.25	1.40		3.65	4.82
6200	1/4" thick, particle board	↓	400	.040	↓	1.15	1.40		2.55	3.61

06 25 26 – Panel System

06 25 26.10 Panel Systems

		Crew	Daily Output	Labor-Hours	Unit	Material	2017 Bare Costs Labor	Equipment	Total	Total Incl O&P
0010	**PANEL SYSTEMS**									
0100	Raised panel, eng. wood core w/wood veneer, std., paint grade	2 Carp	300	.053	S.F.	12.15	1.86		14.01	16.45
0110	Oak veneer		300	.053		24	1.86		25.86	29.50
0120	Maple veneer		300	.053		30	1.86		31.86	36
0130	Cherry veneer		300	.053		37.50	1.86		39.36	44.50
0300	Class I fire rated, paint grade		300	.053		13.50	1.86		15.36	17.95
0310	Oak veneer		300	.053		30	1.86		31.86	36
0320	Maple veneer	↓	300	.053		41	1.86		42.86	48

For customer support on your Residential Costs with RSMeans Data, call 800.448.8182.

403

06 25 Prefinished Paneling

06 25 26 – Panel System

06 25 26.10 Panel Systems

06 25 26.10 Panel Systems	Crew	Daily Output	Labor-Hours	Unit	Material	2017 Bare Costs Labor	Equipment	Total	Total Incl O&P
0330	Cherry veneer	2 Carp	300	.053	S.F.	49	1.86		50.86	57
0510	Beadboard, 5/8" MDF, standard, primed		300	.053		9.35	1.86		11.21	13.40
0520	Oak veneer, unfinished		300	.053		14.70	1.86		16.56	19.25
0530	Maple veneer, unfinished		300	.053		15.80	1.86		17.66	20.50
0610	Rustic paneling, 5/8" MDF, standard, maple veneer, unfinished	↓	300	.053	↓	18.50	1.86		20.36	23.50

06 26 Board Paneling

06 26 13 – Profile Board Paneling

06 26 13.10 Paneling, Boards

06 26 13.10 Paneling, Boards	Crew	Daily Output	Labor-Hours	Unit	Material	2017 Bare Costs Labor	Equipment	Total	Total Incl O&P
0010	**PANELING, BOARDS**									
6400	Wood board paneling, 3/4" thick, knotty pine	2 Carp	300	.053	S.F.	2.05	1.86		3.91	5.40
6500	Rough sawn cedar		300	.053		3.30	1.86		5.16	6.75
6700	Redwood, clear, 1" x 4" boards		300	.053		4.96	1.86		6.82	8.55
6900	Aromatic cedar, closet lining, boards	↓	275	.058		2.42	2.03		4.45	6.05
8950	On ceiling, wood board, install	1 Carp	225	.036	↓	3.30	1.24		4.54	5.70

06 43 Wood Stairs and Railings

06 43 13 – Wood Stairs

06 43 13.20 Prefabricated Wood Stairs

06 43 13.20 Prefabricated Wood Stairs	Crew	Daily Output	Labor-Hours	Unit	Material	2017 Bare Costs Labor	Equipment	Total	Total Incl O&P
0010	**PREFABRICATED WOOD STAIRS**									
0100	Box stairs, prefabricated, 3'-0" wide									
0110	Oak treads, up to 14 risers	2 Carp	39	.410	Riser	92.50	14.35		106.85	126
0600	With pine treads for carpet, up to 14 risers	"	39	.410	"	59.50	14.35		73.85	89.50
1100	For 4' wide stairs, add				Flight	25%				
1550	Stairs, prefabricated stair handrail with balusters	1 Carp	30	.267	L.F.	82	9.30		91.30	106
1700	Basement stairs, prefabricated, pine treads									
1710	Pine risers, 3' wide, up to 14 risers	2 Carp	52	.308	Riser	59.50	10.75		70.25	83.50
4000	Residential, wood, oak treads, prefabricated		1.50	10.667	Flight	1,200	375		1,575	1,950
4200	Built in place	↓	.44	36.364	"	2,250	1,275		3,525	4,600
4400	Spiral, oak, 4'-6" diameter, unfinished, prefabricated,									
4500	incl. railing, 9' high	2 Carp	1.50	10.667	Flight	3,300	375		3,675	4,275

06 43 13.40 Wood Stair Parts

06 43 13.40 Wood Stair Parts	Crew	Daily Output	Labor-Hours	Unit	Material	2017 Bare Costs Labor	Equipment	Total	Total Incl O&P
0010	**WOOD STAIR PARTS**									
0020	Pin top balusters, 1-1/4", oak, 34"	1 Carp	96	.083	Ea.	5.20	2.91		8.11	10.55
0030	38"		96	.083		5.85	2.91		8.76	11.30
0040	42"		96	.083		6.35	2.91		9.26	11.85
0050	Poplar, 34"		96	.083		3.37	2.91		6.28	8.60
0060	38"		96	.083		3.99	2.91		6.90	9.25
0070	42"		96	.083		8.80	2.91		11.71	14.50
0080	Maple, 34"		96	.083		4.90	2.91		7.81	10.25
0090	38"		96	.083		5.60	2.91		8.51	11.05
0100	42"		96	.083		6.50	2.91		9.41	12
0130	Primed, 34"		96	.083		3.70	2.91		6.61	8.95
0140	38"		96	.083		4.25	2.91		7.16	9.55
0150	42"		96	.083		4.89	2.91		7.80	10.25
0180	Box top balusters, 1-1/4", oak, 34"		60	.133		8.95	4.66		13.61	17.65
0190	38"		60	.133		9.95	4.66		14.61	18.75
0200	42"		60	.133		10.95	4.66		15.61	19.85
0210	Poplar, 34"		60	.133		6.25	4.66		10.91	14.70

06 43 13.40 Wood Stair Parts	Crew	Daily Output	Labor-Hours	Unit	Material	2017 Bare Costs Labor	Equipment	Total	Total Incl O&P
0220	38"	1 Carp	60	.133	Ea.	6.95	4.66		11.61	15.45
0230	42"		60	.133		7.50	4.66		12.16	16.05
0240	Maple, 34"		60	.133		8.25	4.66		12.91	16.90
0250	38"		60	.133		9	4.66		13.66	17.70
0260	42"		60	.133		10	4.66		14.66	18.80
0290	Primed, 34"		60	.133		7	4.66		11.66	15.50
0300	38"		60	.133		8	4.66		12.66	16.60
0310	42"		60	.133		8.90	4.66		13.56	17.55
0340	Square balusters, cut from lineal stock, pine, 1-1/16" x 1-1/16"		180	.044	L.F.	1.50	1.55		3.05	4.25
0350	1-5/16" x 1-5/16"		180	.044		2.10	1.55		3.65	4.91
0360	1-5/8" x 1-5/8"		180	.044		3.30	1.55		4.85	6.25
0370	Turned newel, oak, 3-1/2" square, 48" high		8	1	Ea.	95	35		130	164
0380	62" high		8	1		101	35		136	170
0390	Poplar, 3-1/2" square, 48" high		8	1		52	35		87	116
0400	62" high		8	1		66	35		101	131
0410	Maple, 3-1/2" square, 48" high		8	1		65	35		100	130
0420	62" high		8	1		86	35		121	153
0430	Square newel, oak, 3-1/2" square, 48" high		8	1		59	35		94	124
0440	58" high		8	1		68.50	35		103.50	134
0450	Poplar, 3-1/2" square, 48" high		8	1		35.50	35		70.50	97.50
0460	58" high		8	1		43.50	35		78.50	107
0470	Maple, 3" square, 48" high		8	1		54	35		89	118
0480	58" high		8	1		68	35		103	134
0490	Railings, oak, economy		96	.083	L.F.	9.45	2.91		12.36	15.25
0500	Average		96	.083		13.50	2.91		16.41	19.70
0510	Custom		96	.083		17.95	2.91		20.86	24.50
0520	Maple, economy		96	.083		11.90	2.91		14.81	17.90
0530	Average		96	.083		13.50	2.91		16.41	19.70
0540	Custom		96	.083		18.55	2.91		21.46	25.50
0550	Oak, for bending rail, economy		48	.167		26	5.85		31.85	38.50
0560	Average		48	.167		28.50	5.85		34.35	41.50
0570	Custom		48	.167		32	5.85		37.85	45
0580	Maple, for bending rail, economy		48	.167		29.50	5.85		35.35	42.50
0590	Average		48	.167		30.50	5.85		36.35	43.50
0600	Custom		48	.167		33.50	5.85		39.35	47
0610	Risers, oak, 3/4" x 8", 36" long		80	.100	Ea.	13	3.50		16.50	20
0620	42" long		70	.114		15.15	3.99		19.14	23.50
0630	48" long		63	.127		17.30	4.44		21.74	26.50
0640	54" long		56	.143		19.50	4.99		24.49	30
0650	60" long		50	.160		21.50	5.60		27.10	33.50
0660	72" long		42	.190		26	6.65		32.65	39.50
0670	Poplar, 3/4" x 8", 36" long		80	.100		12.50	3.50		16	19.60
0680	42" long		71	.113		14.55	3.94		18.49	22.50
0690	48" long		63	.127		16.65	4.44		21.09	25.50
0700	54" long		56	.143		18.70	4.99		23.69	29
0710	60" long		50	.160		21	5.60		26.60	32.50
0720	72" long		42	.190		25	6.65		31.65	38.50
0730	Pine, 1" x 8", 36" long		80	.100		3.76	3.50		7.26	10
0740	42" long		70	.114		4.39	3.99		8.38	11.55
0750	48" long		63	.127		5	4.44		9.44	12.90
0760	54" long		56	.143		5.65	4.99		10.64	14.55
0770	60" long		50	.160		6.25	5.60		11.85	16.25
0780	72" long		42	.190		7.50	6.65		14.15	19.45

06 43 Wood Stairs and Railings

06 43 13 – Wood Stairs

06 43 13.40 Wood Stair Parts		Crew	Daily Output	Labor-Hours	Unit	Material	2017 Bare Costs Labor	Equipment	Total	Total Incl O&P
0790	Treads, oak, no returns, 1-1/32" x 11-1/2" x 36" long	1 Carp	32	.250	Ea.	29.50	8.75		38.25	47
0800	42" long		32	.250		34.50	8.75		43.25	52.50
0810	48" long		32	.250		39.50	8.75		48.25	57.50
0820	54" long		32	.250		44	8.75		52.75	63
0830	60" long		32	.250		49	8.75		57.75	68.50
0840	72" long		32	.250		59	8.75		67.75	79.50
0850	Mitred return one end, 1-1/32" x 11-1/2" x 36" long		24	.333		39	11.65		50.65	62.50
0860	42" long		24	.333		45.50	11.65		57.15	69.50
0870	48" long		24	.333		52	11.65		63.65	76.50
0880	54" long		24	.333		58.50	11.65		70.15	84
0890	60" long		24	.333		65	11.65		76.65	91
0900	72" long		24	.333		78	11.65		89.65	105
0910	Mitred return two ends, 1-1/32" x 11-1/2" x 36" long		12	.667		49	23.50		72.50	93
0920	42" long		12	.667		57	23.50		80.50	102
0930	48" long		12	.667		65.50	23.50		89	111
0940	54" long		12	.667		73.50	23.50		97	120
0950	60" long		12	.667		81.50	23.50		105	129
0960	72" long		12	.667		98	23.50		121.50	147
0970	Starting step, oak, 48", bullnose		8	1		172	35		207	248
0980	Double end bullnose		8	1		254	35		289	340
1030	Skirt board, pine, 1" x 10"		55	.145	L.F.	1.63	5.10		6.73	10.30
1040	1" x 12"		52	.154	"	2.01	5.40		7.41	11.20
1050	Oak landing tread, 1-1/16" thick		54	.148	S.F.	9	5.20		14.20	18.55
1060	Oak cove molding		96	.083	L.F.	1	2.91		3.91	5.95
1070	Oak stringer molding		96	.083	"	4	2.91		6.91	9.25
1090	Rail bolt, 5/16" x 3-1/2"		48	.167	Ea.	2.75	5.85		8.60	12.80
1100	5/16" x 4-1/2"		48	.167		2.75	5.85		8.60	12.80
1120	Newel post anchor		16	.500		13	17.50		30.50	43.50
1130	Tapered plug, 1/2"		240	.033		1	1.16		2.16	3.05
1140	1"		240	.033		.99	1.16		2.15	3.04

06 43 16 – Wood Railings

06 43 16.10 Wood Handrails and Railings

		Crew	Daily Output	Labor-Hours	Unit	Material	2017 Bare Costs Labor	Equipment	Total	Total Incl O&P
0010	**WOOD HANDRAILS AND RAILINGS**									
0020	Custom design, architectural grade, hardwood, plain	1 Carp	38	.211	L.F.	12.65	7.35		20	26
0100	Shaped		30	.267		63	9.30		72.30	85
0300	Stock interior railing with spindles 4" O.C., 4' long		40	.200		41	7		48	56.50
0400	8' long		48	.167		41	5.85		46.85	55

06 44 Ornamental Woodwork

06 44 19 – Wood Grilles

06 44 19.10 Grilles

		Crew	Daily Output	Labor-Hours	Unit	Material	2017 Bare Costs Labor	Equipment	Total	Total Incl O&P
0010	**GRILLES** and panels, hardwood, sanded									
0020	2' x 4' to 4' x 8', custom designs, unfinished, economy	1 Carp	38	.211	S.F.	62	7.35		69.35	80.50
0050	Average		30	.267		70	9.30		79.30	92.50
0100	Custom		19	.421		72	14.70		86.70	104

06 44 33 – Wood Mantels

06 44 33.10 Fireplace Mantels

		Crew	Daily Output	Labor-Hours	Unit	Material	2017 Bare Costs Labor	Equipment	Total	Total Incl O&P
0010	**FIREPLACE MANTELS**									
0015	6" molding, 6' x 3'-6" opening, plain, paint grade	1 Carp	5	1.600	Opng.	450	56		506	590
0100	Ornate, oak		5	1.600		600	56		656	755

06 44 Ornamental Woodwork

06 44 33 – Wood Mantels

06 44 33.10 Fireplace Mantels	Crew	Daily Output	Labor-Hours	Unit	Material	2017 Bare Costs Labor	Equipment	Total	Total Incl O&P
0300	Prefabricated pine, colonial type, stock, deluxe	1 Carp	2	4	Opng.	1,500	140		1,640	1,875
0400	Economy	↓	3	2.667	↓	705	93		798	930

06 44 33.20 Fireplace Mantel Beam

		Crew	Daily Output	Labor-Hours	Unit	Material	Labor	Equipment	Total	Total Incl O&P
0010	**FIREPLACE MANTEL BEAM**									
0020	Rough texture wood, 4" x 8"	1 Carp	36	.222	L.F.	8.75	7.75		16.50	22.50
0100	4" x 10"		35	.229	"	10.30	8		18.30	24.50
0300	Laminated hardwood, 2-1/4" x 10-1/2" wide, 6' long		5	1.600	Ea.	125	56		181	231
0400	8' long		5	1.600	"	145	56		201	253
0600	Brackets for above, rough sawn		12	.667	Pr.	12.05	23.50		35.55	52.50
0700	Laminated	↓	12	.667	"	17.20	23.50		40.70	58

06 44 39 – Wood Posts and Columns

06 44 39.10 Decorative Beams

		Crew	Daily Output	Labor-Hours	Unit	Material	Labor	Equipment	Total	Total Incl O&P
0010	**DECORATIVE BEAMS**									
0020	Rough sawn cedar, non-load bearing, 4" x 4"	2 Carp	180	.089	L.F.	1.35	3.11		4.46	6.70
0100	4" x 6"		170	.094		1.92	3.29		5.21	7.60
0200	4" x 8"		160	.100		2.52	3.50		6.02	8.60
0300	4" x 10"		150	.107		3.99	3.73		7.72	10.65
0400	4" x 12"		140	.114		5.05	3.99		9.04	12.25
0500	8" x 8"		130	.123		5.20	4.30		9.50	12.90
0600	Plastic beam, "hewn finish", 6" x 2"		240	.067		3.40	2.33		5.73	7.65
0601	6" x 4"	↓	220	.073	↓	3.75	2.54		6.29	8.40

06 44 39.20 Columns

		Crew	Daily Output	Labor-Hours	Unit	Material	Labor	Equipment	Total	Total Incl O&P
0010	**COLUMNS**									
0050	Aluminum, round colonial, 6" diameter	2 Carp	80	.200	V.L.F.	20	7		27	33.50
0100	8" diameter		62.25	.257		23	9		32	40
0200	10" diameter		55	.291		23	10.15		33.15	42.50
0250	Fir, stock units, hollow round, 6" diameter		80	.200		30	7		37	44.50
0300	8" diameter		80	.200		39	7		46	54.50
0350	10" diameter		70	.229		48	8		56	66.50
0360	12" diameter		65	.246		55.50	8.60		64.10	75.50
0400	Solid turned, to 8' high, 3-1/2" diameter		80	.200		9.90	7		16.90	22.50
0500	4-1/2" diameter		75	.213		12.10	7.45		19.55	26
0600	5-1/2" diameter		70	.229		16.35	8		24.35	31.50
0800	Square columns, built-up, 5" x 5"		65	.246		14.50	8.60		23.10	30.50
0900	Solid, 3-1/2" x 3-1/2"		130	.123		9.90	4.30		14.20	18.05
1600	Hemlock, tapered, T & G, 12" diam., 10' high		100	.160		40	5.60		45.60	53.50
1700	16' high		65	.246		74.50	8.60		83.10	96
1900	14" diameter, 10' high		100	.160		116	5.60		121.60	136
2000	18' high		65	.246		105	8.60		113.60	129
2200	18" diameter, 12' high		65	.246		168	8.60		176.60	199
2300	20' high		50	.320		120	11.20		131.20	151
2500	20" diameter, 14' high		40	.400		184	14		198	226
2600	20' high	↓	35	.457		173	16		189	218
2800	For flat pilasters, deduct				↓	33%				
3000	For splitting into halves, add				Ea.	110			110	121
4000	Rough sawn cedar posts, 4" x 4"	2 Carp	250	.064	V.L.F.	3.80	2.24		6.04	7.90
4100	4" x 6"		235	.068		6.80	2.38		9.18	11.50
4200	6" x 6"		220	.073		9.90	2.54		12.44	15.15
4300	8" x 8"	↓	200	.080	↓	20.50	2.80		23.30	27

06 48 Wood Frames

06 48 13 – Exterior Wood Door Frames

06 48 13.10 Exterior Wood Door Frames and Accessories	Crew	Daily Output	Labor-Hours	Unit	Material	2017 Bare Costs Labor	Equipment	Total	Total Incl O&P
0010 **EXTERIOR WOOD DOOR FRAMES AND ACCESSORIES**									
0400 Exterior frame, incl. ext. trim, pine, 5/4 x 4-9/16" deep	2 Carp	375	.043	L.F.	6.75	1.49		8.24	9.95
0420 5-3/16" deep		375	.043		8.30	1.49		9.79	11.60
0440 6-9/16" deep		375	.043		9.75	1.49		11.24	13.25
0600 Oak, 5/4 x 4-9/16" deep		350	.046		21	1.60		22.60	25.50
0620 5-3/16" deep		350	.046		23	1.60		24.60	28
0640 6-9/16" deep		350	.046		21.50	1.60		23.10	26
1000 Sills, 8/4 x 8" deep, oak, no horns		100	.160		6.65	5.60		12.25	16.65
1020 2" horns		100	.160		20.50	5.60		26.10	32
1040 3" horns		100	.160		20.50	5.60		26.10	32
1100 8/4 x 10" deep, oak, no horns		90	.178		6.40	6.20		12.60	17.45
1120 2" horns		90	.178		26.50	6.20		32.70	39.50
1140 3" horns		90	.178	↓	26.50	6.20		32.70	39.50
2000 Wood frame & trim, ext, colonial, 3' opng, fluted pilasters, flat head		22	.727	Ea.	515	25.50		540.50	610
2010 Dentil head		21	.762		590	26.50		616.50	690
2020 Ram's head		20	.800		695	28		723	810
2100 5'-4" opening, in-swing, fluted pilasters, flat head		17	.941		470	33		503	570
2120 Ram's head		15	1.067		1,400	37.50		1,437.50	1,625
2140 Out swing, fluted pilasters, flat head		17	.941		495	33		528	600
2160 Ram's head		15	1.067		1,575	37.50		1,612.50	1,800
2400 6'-0" opening, in-swing, fluted pilasters, flat head		16	1		495	35		530	605
2420 Ram's head		10	1.600		1,475	56		1,531	1,725
2460 Out-swing, fluted pilasters, flat head		16	1		500	35		535	610
2480 Ram's head		10	1.600	↓	1,475	56		1,531	1,725
2600 For two sidelights, flat head, add		30	.533	Opng.	230	18.65		248.65	284
2620 Ram's head, add		20	.800	"	850	28		878	980
2700 Custom birch frame, 3'-0" opening		16	1	Ea.	248	35		283	330
2750 6'-0" opening		16	1		370	35		405	465
2900 Exterior, modern, plain trim, 3' opng., in-swing, FJP		26	.615		47.50	21.50		69	88.50
2920 Fir		24	.667		56	23.50		79.50	101
2940 Oak	↓	22	.727	↓	65	25.50		90.50	114

06 48 16 – Interior Wood Door Frames

06 48 16.10 Interior Wood Door Jamb and Frames

06 48 16.10 Interior Wood Door Jamb and Frames	Crew	Daily Output	Labor-Hours	Unit	Material	2017 Bare Costs Labor	Equipment	Total	Total Incl O&P
0010 **INTERIOR WOOD DOOR JAMB AND FRAMES**									
3000 Interior frame, pine, 11/16" x 3-5/8" deep	2 Carp	375	.043	L.F.	4.50	1.49		5.99	7.45
3020 4-9/16" deep		375	.043		5.05	1.49		6.54	8.05
3040 5-3/16" deep		375	.043		4.66	1.49		6.15	7.65
3200 Oak, 11/16" x 3-5/8" deep		350	.046		10.25	1.60		11.85	13.95
3220 4-9/16" deep		350	.046		10.30	1.60		11.90	13.95
3240 5-3/16" deep		350	.046		14.95	1.60		16.55	19.10
3400 Walnut, 11/16" x 3-5/8" deep		350	.046		9.40	1.60		11	13
3420 4-9/16" deep		350	.046		9.90	1.60		11.50	13.55
3440 5-3/16" deep		350	.046	↓	10	1.60		11.60	13.65
3600 Pocket door frame		16	1	Ea.	82.50	35		117.50	149
3800 Threshold, oak, 5/8" x 3-5/8" deep		200	.080	L.F.	3.57	2.80		6.37	8.60
3820 4-5/8" deep		190	.084		4.03	2.94		6.97	9.35
3840 5-5/8" deep	↓	180	.089	↓	6.70	3.11		9.81	12.60

06 49 Wood Screens and Exterior Wood Shutters

06 49 19 – Exterior Wood Shutters

06 49 19.10 Shutters, Exterior	Crew	Daily Output	Labor-Hours	Unit	Material	2017 Bare Costs Labor	Equipment	Total	Total Incl O&P
0010 **SHUTTERS, EXTERIOR**									
0012 Aluminum, louvered, 1'-4" wide, 3'-0" long	1 Carp	10	.800	Pr.	201	28		229	269
0200 4'-0" long		10	.800		243	28		271	315
0300 5'-4" long		10	.800		287	28		315	360
0400 6'-8" long		9	.889		355	31		386	440
1000 Pine, louvered, primed, each 1'-2" wide, 3'-3" long		10	.800		215	28		243	283
1100 4'-7" long		10	.800		276	28		304	350
1250 Each 1'-4" wide, 3'-0" long		10	.800		224	28		252	294
1350 5'-3" long		10	.800		320	28		348	400
1500 Each 1'-6" wide, 3'-3" long		10	.800		255	28		283	325
1600 4'-7" long		10	.800		315	28		343	395
1620 Cedar, louvered, 1'-2" wide, 5'-7" long		10	.800		325	28		353	405
1630 Each 1'-4" wide, 2'-2" long		10	.800		176	28		204	241
1640 3'-0" long		10	.800		224	28		252	293
1650 3'-3" long		10	.800		234	28		262	305
1660 3'-11" long		10	.800		270	28		298	345
1670 4'-3" long		10	.800		294	28		322	370
1680 5'-3" long		10	.800		310	28		338	385
1690 5'-11" long		10	.800		350	28		378	430
1700 Door blinds, 6'-9" long, each 1'-3" wide		9	.889		385	31		416	475
1710 1'-6" wide		9	.889		440	31		471	535
1720 Cedar, solid raised panel, each 1'-4" wide, 3'-3" long		10	.800		330	28		358	410
1730 3'-11" long		10	.800		375	28		403	460
1740 4'-3" long		10	.800		390	28		418	470
1750 4'-7" long		10	.800		395	28		423	480
1760 4'-11" long		10	.800		430	28		458	515
1770 5'-11" long		10	.800		530	28		558	625
1800 Door blinds, 6'-9" long, each 1'-3" wide		9	.889		535	31		566	640
1900 1'-6" wide		9	.889		630	31		661	745
2500 Polystyrene, solid raised panel, each 1'-4" wide, 3'-3" long		10	.800		76	28		104	131
2600 3'-11" long		10	.800		93	28		121	149
2700 4'-7" long		10	.800		105	28		133	163
2800 5'-3" long		10	.800		120	28		148	179
2900 6'-8" long		9	.889		149	31		180	216
4500 Polystyrene, louvered, each 1'-2" wide, 3'-3" long		10	.800		36	28		64	86.50
4600 4'-7" long		10	.800		48.50	28		76.50	100
4750 5'-3" long		10	.800		59	28		87	112
4850 6'-8" long		9	.889		65.50	31		96.50	124
6000 Vinyl, louvered, each 1'-2" x 4'-7" long		10	.800		64	28		92	118
6200 Each 1'-4" x 6'-8" long		9	.889		83.50	31		114.50	144
8000 PVC exterior rolling shutters									
8100 including crank control	1 Carp	8	1	Ea.	565	35		600	680
8500 Insulative - 6' x 6'-8" stock unit	"	8	1	"	805	35		840	945

For customer support on your Residential Costs with RSMeans Data, call 800.448.8182.

409

06 51 Structural Plastic Shapes and Plates

06 51 13 – Plastic Lumber

06 51 13.10 Recycled Plastic Lumber

		Crew	Daily Output	Labor-Hours	Unit	Material	2017 Bare Costs Labor	Equipment	Total	Total Incl O&P
0010	**RECYCLED PLASTIC LUMBER**									
4000	Sheeting, recycled plastic, black or white, 4' x 8' x 1/8" Ⓖ	2 Carp	1100	.015	S.F.	1.10	.51		1.61	2.06
4010	4' x 8' x 3/16" Ⓖ		1100	.015		1.70	.51		2.21	2.72
4020	4' x 8' x 1/4" Ⓖ		950	.017		1.96	.59		2.55	3.14
4030	4' x 8' x 3/8" Ⓖ		950	.017		3.40	.59		3.99	4.72
4040	4' x 8' x 1/2" Ⓖ		900	.018		4.45	.62		5.07	5.95
4050	4' x 8' x 5/8" Ⓖ		900	.018		6.70	.62		7.32	8.45
4060	4' x 8' x 3/4" Ⓖ		850	.019		8.40	.66		9.06	10.35
4070	Add for colors Ⓖ				Ea.	5%				
8500	100% recycled plastic, var colors, NLB, 2" x 2" Ⓖ				L.F.	1.91			1.91	2.10
8510	2" x 4" Ⓖ					3.95			3.95	4.35
8520	2" x 6" Ⓖ					6.20			6.20	6.80
8530	2" x 8" Ⓖ					8.50			8.50	9.35
8540	2" x 10" Ⓖ					12.40			12.40	13.60
8550	5/4" x 4" Ⓖ					4			4	4.40
8560	5/4" x 6" Ⓖ					5.70			5.70	6.25
8570	1" x 6" Ⓖ					3.11			3.11	3.42
8580	1/2" x 8" Ⓖ					3.83			3.83	4.21
8590	2" x 10" T & G Ⓖ					12.20			12.20	13.40
8600	3" x 10" T & G Ⓖ					18			18	19.80
8610	Add for premium colors Ⓖ					20%				

06 51 13.12 Structural Plastic Lumber

		Crew	Daily Output	Labor-Hours	Unit	Material	2017 Bare Costs Labor	Equipment	Total	Total Incl O&P
0010	**STRUCTURAL PLASTIC LUMBER**									
1320	Plastic lumber, posts or columns, 4" x 4"	2 Carp	390	.041	L.F.	10.30	1.43		11.73	13.75
1325	4" x 6"		275	.058		13.30	2.03		15.33	18
1330	4" x 8"		220	.073		19.55	2.54		22.09	26
1340	Girder, single, 4" x 4"		675	.024		10.30	.83		11.13	12.75
1345	4" x 6"		600	.027		13.30	.93		14.23	16.15
1350	4" x 8"		525	.030		19.55	1.07		20.62	23.50
1352	Double, 2" x 4"		625	.026		9.50	.89		10.39	11.95
1354	2" x 6"		600	.027		12.85	.93		13.78	15.70
1356	2" x 8"		575	.028		16.80	.97		17.77	20
1358	2" x 10"		550	.029		20.50	1.02		21.52	24
1360	2" x 12"		525	.030		25	1.07		26.07	29.50
1362	Triple, 2" x 4"		575	.028		14.25	.97		15.22	17.35
1364	2" x 6"		550	.029		19.30	1.02		20.32	22.50
1366	2" x 8"		525	.030		25	1.07		26.07	30
1368	2" x 10"		500	.032		31	1.12		32.12	36
1370	2" x 12"		475	.034		37.50	1.18		38.68	43
1372	Ledger, bolted 4' O.C., 2" x 4"		400	.040		4.91	1.40		6.31	7.75
1374	2" x 6"		550	.029		6.50	1.02		7.52	8.85
1376	2" x 8"		390	.041		8.55	1.43		9.98	11.80
1378	2" x 10"		385	.042		10.40	1.45		11.85	13.85
1380	2" x 12"		380	.042		12.60	1.47		14.07	16.30
1382	Joists, 2" x 4"		1250	.013		4.75	.45		5.20	6
1384	2" x 6"		1250	.013		6.45	.45		6.90	7.80
1386	2" x 8"		1100	.015		8.40	.51		8.91	10.10
1388	2" x 10"		500	.032		10.35	1.12		11.47	13.25
1390	2" x 12"		875	.018		12.45	.64		13.09	14.75
1392	Railings and trim, 5/4" x 4"	1 Carp	300	.027		4.15	.93		5.08	6.15
1394	2" x 2"		300	.027		2.47	.93		3.40	4.28
1396	2" x 4"		300	.027		4.73	.93		5.66	6.75

06 51 Structural Plastic Shapes and Plates

06 51 13 – Plastic Lumber

06 51 13.12 Structural Plastic Lumber		Crew	Daily Output	Labor-Hours	Unit	Material	2017 Bare Costs Labor	Equipment	Total	Total Incl O&P
1398	2" x 6"	1 Carp	300	.027	L.F.	6.40	.93		7.33	8.60

06 63 Plastic Railings

06 63 10 – Plastic (PVC) Railings

06 63 10.10 Plastic Railings

		Crew	Daily Output	Labor-Hours	Unit	Material	Labor	Equipment	Total	Total Incl O&P
0010	**PLASTIC RAILINGS**									
0100	Horizontal PVC handrail with balusters, 3-1/2" wide, 36" high	1 Carp	96	.083	L.F.	26.50	2.91		29.41	34
0150	42" high		96	.083		30	2.91		32.91	38
0200	Angled PVC handrail with balusters, 3-1/2" wide, 36" high		72	.111		31	3.88		34.88	40.50
0250	42" high		72	.111		33.50	3.88		37.38	43.50
0300	Post sleeve for 4 x 4 post		96	.083		13.55	2.91		16.46	19.75
0400	Post cap for 4 x 4 post, flat profile		48	.167	Ea.	13.90	5.85		19.75	25
0450	Newel post style profile		48	.167		25	5.85		30.85	37.50
0500	Raised corbeled profile		48	.167		37	5.85		42.85	50.50
0550	Post base trim for 4 x 4 post		96	.083		19.20	2.91		22.11	26

06 65 Plastic Trim

06 65 10 – PVC Trim

06 65 10.10 PVC Trim, Exterior

		Crew	Daily Output	Labor-Hours	Unit	Material	Labor	Equipment	Total	Total Incl O&P
0010	**PVC TRIM, EXTERIOR**									
0100	Cornerboards, 5/4" x 6" x 6"	1 Carp	240	.033	L.F.	7.20	1.16		8.36	9.90
0110	Door/window casing, 1" x 4"		200	.040		1.39	1.40		2.79	3.87
0120	1" x 6"		200	.040		2.06	1.40		3.46	4.61
0130	1" x 8"		195	.041		2.72	1.43		4.15	5.40
0140	1" x 10"		195	.041		3.44	1.43		4.87	6.20
0150	1" x 12"		190	.042		4.22	1.47		5.69	7.10
0160	5/4" x 4"		195	.041		2.05	1.43		3.48	4.66
0170	5/4" x 6"		195	.041		3.02	1.43		4.45	5.70
0180	5/4" x 8"		190	.042		3.99	1.47		5.46	6.85
0190	5/4" x 10"		190	.042		5.10	1.47		6.57	8.05
0200	5/4" x 12"		185	.043		5.35	1.51		6.86	8.45
0210	Fascia, 1" x 4"		250	.032		1.39	1.12		2.51	3.40
0220	1" x 6"		250	.032		2.06	1.12		3.18	4.14
0230	1" x 8"		225	.036		2.72	1.24		3.96	5.05
0240	1" x 10"		225	.036		3.44	1.24		4.68	5.85
0250	1" x 12"		200	.040		4.22	1.40		5.62	7
0260	5/4" x 4"		240	.033		2.05	1.16		3.21	4.21
0270	5/4" x 6"		240	.033		3.02	1.16		4.18	5.25
0280	5/4" x 8"		215	.037		3.99	1.30		5.29	6.55
0290	5/4" x 10"		215	.037		5.10	1.30		6.40	7.75
0300	5/4" x 12"		190	.042		5.35	1.47		6.82	8.35
0310	Frieze, 1" x 4"		250	.032		1.39	1.12		2.51	3.40
0320	1" x 6"		250	.032		2.06	1.12		3.18	4.14
0330	1" x 8"		225	.036		2.72	1.24		3.96	5.05
0340	1" x 10"		225	.036		3.44	1.24		4.68	5.85
0350	1" x 12"		200	.040		4.22	1.40		5.62	7
0360	5/4" x 4"		240	.033		2.05	1.16		3.21	4.21
0370	5/4" x 6"		240	.033		3.02	1.16		4.18	5.25
0380	5/4" x 8"		215	.037		3.99	1.30		5.29	6.55

For customer support on your Residential Costs with RSMeans Data, call 800.448.8182.

411

06 65 Plastic Trim

06 65 10 – PVC Trim

06 65 10.10 PVC Trim, Exterior	Crew	Daily Output	Labor-Hours	Unit	Material	2017 Bare Costs Labor	Equipment	Total	Total Incl O&P
0390	5/4" x 10"	1 Carp	215	.037	L.F.	5.10	1.30		6.40	7.75
0400	5/4" x 12"		190	.042		5.35	1.47		6.82	8.35
0410	Rake, 1" x 4"		200	.040		1.39	1.40		2.79	3.87
0420	1" x 6"		200	.040		2.06	1.40		3.46	4.61
0430	1" x 8"		190	.042		2.72	1.47		4.19	5.45
0440	1" x 10"		190	.042		3.44	1.47		4.91	6.25
0450	1" x 12"		180	.044		4.22	1.55		5.77	7.25
0460	5/4" x 4"		195	.041		2.05	1.43		3.48	4.66
0470	5/4" x 6"		195	.041		3.02	1.43		4.45	5.70
0480	5/4" x 8"		185	.043		3.99	1.51		5.50	6.90
0490	5/4" x 10"		185	.043		5.10	1.51		6.61	8.15
0500	5/4" x 12"		175	.046		5.35	1.60		6.95	8.55
0510	Rake trim, 1" x 4"		225	.036		1.39	1.24		2.63	3.61
0520	1" x 6"		225	.036		2.06	1.24		3.30	4.35
0560	5/4" x 4"		220	.036		2.05	1.27		3.32	4.39
0570	5/4" x 6"	▼	220	.036		3.02	1.27		4.29	5.45
0610	Soffit, 1" x 4"	2 Carp	420	.038		1.39	1.33		2.72	3.76
0620	1" x 6"		420	.038		2.06	1.33		3.39	4.50
0630	1" x 8"		420	.038		2.72	1.33		4.05	5.20
0640	1" x 10"		400	.040		3.44	1.40		4.84	6.10
0650	1" x 12"		400	.040		4.22	1.40		5.62	7
0660	5/4" x 4"		410	.039		2.05	1.36		3.41	4.54
0670	5/4" x 6"		410	.039		3.02	1.36		4.38	5.60
0680	5/4" x 8"		410	.039		3.99	1.36		5.35	6.65
0690	5/4" x 10"		390	.041		5.10	1.43		6.53	8
0700	5/4" x 12"	▼	390	.041	▼	5.35	1.43		6.78	8.30

06 80 Composite Fabrications

06 80 10 – Composite Decking

06 80 10.10 Woodgrained Composite Decking

		Crew	Daily Output	Labor-Hours	Unit	Material	2017 Bare Costs Labor	Equipment	Total	Total Incl O&P
0010	**WOODGRAINED COMPOSITE DECKING**									
0100	Woodgrained composite decking, 1" x 6"	2 Carp	640	.025	L.F.	3.72	.87		4.59	5.55
0110	Grooved edge		660	.024		3.87	.85		4.72	5.70
0120	2" x 6"		640	.025		3.81	.87		4.68	5.65
0130	Encased, 1" x 6"		640	.025		3.81	.87		4.68	5.65
0140	Grooved edge		660	.024		3.96	.85		4.81	5.80
0150	2" x 6"	▼	640	.025	▼	5.35	.87		6.22	7.30

06 81 Composite Railings

06 81 10 – Encased Railings

06 81 10.10 Encased Composite Railings

		Crew	Daily Output	Labor-Hours	Unit	Material	2017 Bare Costs Labor	Equipment	Total	Total Incl O&P
0010	**ENCASED COMPOSITE RAILINGS**									
0100	Encased composite railing, 6' long, 36" high, incl. balusters	1 Carp	16	.500	Ea.	169	17.50		186.50	215
0110	42" high, incl. balusters		16	.500		190	17.50		207.50	238
0120	8' long, 36" high, incl. balusters		12	.667		169	23.50		192.50	225
0130	42" high, incl. balusters		12	.667		189	23.50		212.50	247
0140	Accessories, post sleeve, 4" x 4", 39" long		32	.250		25	8.75		33.75	42
0150	96" long		24	.333		95	11.65		106.65	124
0160	6" x 6", 39" long	▼	32	.250	▼	52.50	8.75		61.25	72

For customer support on your Residential Costs with RSMeans Data, call 800.448.8182.

06 81 Composite Railings

06 81 10 - Encased Railings

06 81 10.10 Encased Composite Railings	Crew	Daily Output	Labor-Hours	Unit	Material	2017 Bare Costs Labor	Equipment	Total	Total Incl O&P
0170	96" long	1 Carp	24	.333	Ea.	149	11.65		160.65	184
0180	Accessories, post skirt, 4" x 4"		96	.083		4.34	2.91		7.25	9.65
0190	6" x 6"		96	.083		5.30	2.91		8.21	10.65
0200	Post cap, 4" x 4", flat		48	.167		6.65	5.85		12.50	17.05
0210	Pyramid		48	.167		6.65	5.85		12.50	17.05
0220	Post cap, 6" x 6", flat		48	.167		10.80	5.85		16.65	21.50
0230	Pyramid		48	.167		10.95	5.85		16.80	22

Division Notes

	CREW	DAILY OUTPUT	LABOR-HOURS	UNIT	BARE COSTS				TOTAL INCL O&P
					MAT.	LABOR	EQUIP.	TOTAL	

Estimating Tips
07 10 00 Dampproofing and Waterproofing

- Be sure of the job specifications before pricing this subdivision. The difference in cost between waterproofing and dampproofing can be great. Waterproofing will hold back standing water. Dampproofing prevents the transmission of water vapor. Also included in this section are vapor retarding membranes.

07 20 00 Thermal Protection

- Insulation and fireproofing products are measured by area, thickness, volume or R-value. Specifications may give only what the specific R-value should be in a certain situation. The estimator may need to choose the type of insulation to meet that R-value.

07 30 00 Steep Slope Roofing
07 40 00 Roofing and Siding Panels

- Many roofing and siding products are bought and sold by the square. One square is equal to an area that measures 100 square feet.

  This simple change in unit of measure could create a large error if the estimator is not observant. Accessories necessary for a complete installation must be figured into any calculations for both material and labor.

07 50 00 Membrane Roofing
07 60 00 Flashing and Sheet Metal
07 70 00 Roofing and Wall Specialties and Accessories

- The items in these subdivisions compose a roofing system. No one component completes the installation, and all must be estimated. Built-up or single-ply membrane roofing systems are made up of many products and installation trades. Wood blocking at roof perimeters or penetrations, parapet coverings, reglets, roof drains, gutters, downspouts, sheet metal flashing, skylights, smoke vents, and roof hatches all need to be considered along with the roofing material. Several different installation trades will need to work together on the roofing system. Inherent difficulties in the scheduling and coordination of various trades must be accounted for when estimating labor costs.

07 90 00 Joint Protection

- To complete the weather-tight shell, the sealants and caulkings must be estimated. Where different materials meet—at expansion joints, at flashing penetrations, and at hundreds of other locations throughout a construction project—caulking and sealants provide another line of defense against water penetration. Often, an entire system is based on the proper location and placement of caulking or sealants. The detailed drawings that are included as part of a set of architectural plans show typical locations for these materials. When caulking or sealants are shown at typical locations, this means the estimator must include them for all the locations where this detail is applicable. Be careful to keep different types of sealants separate, and remember to consider backer rods and primers if necessary.

Reference Numbers

Reference numbers are shown at the beginning of some major classifications. These numbers refer to related items in the Reference Section. The reference information may be an estimating procedure, an alternate pricing method, or technical information.

Note: Not all subdivisions listed here necessarily appear. ■

Did you know?

Our online estimating solution gives you the same access to RSMeans' data with 24/7 access:

- Quickly locate costs in the searchable database.
- Build cost lists, estimates, and reports in minutes.
- Adjust costs to any location in the U.S. and Canada with the click of a button.

Start your free trial today at
www.RSMeansOnline.com

07 01 50 – Maintenance of Membrane Roofing

07 01 50.10 Roof Coatings	Crew	Daily Output	Labor-Hours	Unit	Material	2017 Bare Costs Labor	2017 Bare Costs Equipment	Total	Total Incl O&P
0010 **ROOF COATINGS**									
0012 Asphalt, brush grade, material only				Gal.	9			9	9.90
0800 Glass fibered roof & patching cement, 5 gallon					8.65			8.65	9.50
1100 Roof patch & flashing cement, 5 gallon					8.75			8.75	9.60

07 05 Common Work Results for Thermal and Moisture Protection

07 05 05 – Selective Demolition for Thermal and Moisture Protection

07 05 05.10 Selective Demo., Thermal and Moist. Protection

		Crew	Daily Output	Labor-Hours	Unit	Material	2017 Bare Costs Labor	2017 Bare Costs Equipment	Total	Total Incl O&P
0010	**SELECTIVE DEMO., THERMAL AND MOISTURE PROTECTION**									
0020	Caulking/sealant, to 1" x 1" joint R024119-10	1 Clab	600	.013	L.F.		.35		.35	.59
0120	Downspouts, including hangers		350	.023	"		.61		.61	1.02
0220	Flashing, sheet metal		290	.028	S.F.		.73		.73	1.23
0420	Gutters, aluminum or wood, edge hung		240	.033	L.F.		.89		.89	1.48
0520	Built-in		100	.080	"		2.13		2.13	3.56
0620	Insulation, air/vapor barrier		3500	.002	S.F.		.06		.06	.10
0670	Batts or blankets		1400	.006	C.F.		.15		.15	.25
0720	Foamed or sprayed in place	2 Clab	1000	.016	B.F.		.43		.43	.71
0770	Loose fitting	1 Clab	3000	.003	C.F.		.07		.07	.12
0870	Rigid board		3450	.002	B.F.		.06		.06	.10
1120	Roll roofing, cold adhesive		12	.667	Sq.		17.75		17.75	29.50
1170	Roof accessories, adjustable metal chimney flashing		9	.889	Ea.		23.50		23.50	39.50
1325	Plumbing vent flashing		32	.250	"		6.65		6.65	11.15
1375	Ridge vent strip, aluminum		310	.026	L.F.		.69		.69	1.15
1620	Skylight to 10 S.F.		8	1	Ea.		26.50		26.50	44.50
2120	Roof edge, aluminum soffit and fascia		570	.014	L.F.		.37		.37	.62
2170	Concrete coping, up to 12" wide	2 Clab	160	.100			2.66		2.66	4.45
2220	Drip edge	1 Clab	1000	.008			.21		.21	.36
2270	Gravel stop		950	.008			.22		.22	.37
2370	Sheet metal coping, up to 12" wide		240	.033			.89		.89	1.48
2470	Roof insulation board, over 2" thick	B-2	7800	.005	B.F.		.14		.14	.23
2520	Up to 2" thick	"	3900	.010	S.F.		.28		.28	.46
2620	Roof ventilation, louvered gable vent	1 Clab	16	.500	Ea.		13.30		13.30	22.50
2670	Remove, roof hatch	G-3	15	2.133			69		69	116
2675	Rafter vents	1 Clab	960	.008			.22		.22	.37
2720	Soffit vent and/or fascia vent		575	.014	L.F.		.37		.37	.62
2775	Soffit vent strip, aluminum, 3" to 4" wide		160	.050			1.33		1.33	2.23
2820	Roofing accessories, shingle moulding, to 1" x 4"		1600	.005			.13		.13	.22
2870	Cant strip	B-2	2000	.020			.54		.54	.90
2920	Concrete block walkway	1 Clab	230	.035			.93		.93	1.55
3070	Roofing, felt paper, #15		70	.114	Sq.		3.04		3.04	5.10
3125	#30 felt		30	.267	"		7.10		7.10	11.85
3170	Asphalt shingles, 1 layer	B-2	3500	.011	S.F.		.31		.31	.52
3180	2 layers		1750	.023	"		.62		.62	1.03
3370	Modified bitumen		26	1.538	Sq.		41.50		41.50	69.50
3420	Built-up, no gravel, 3 ply		25	1.600			43		43	72.50
3470	4 ply		21	1.905			51.50		51.50	86
3620	5 ply		1600	.025	S.F.		.68		.68	1.13
3720	5 ply, with gravel		890	.045			1.21		1.21	2.03
3725	Loose gravel removal		5000	.008			.22		.22	.36
3730	Embedded gravel removal		2000	.020			.54		.54	.90
3870	Fiberglass sheet		1200	.033			.90		.90	1.51

416

07 05 Common Work Results for Thermal and Moisture Protection

07 05 05 – Selective Demolition for Thermal and Moisture Protection

07 05 05.10 Selective Demo., Thermal and Moist. Protection	Crew	Daily Output	Labor-Hours	Unit	Material	2017 Bare Costs Labor	Equipment	Total	Total Incl O&P
4120	Slate shingles	B-2	1900	.021	S.F.		.57		.57	.95
4170	Ridge shingles, clay or slate		2000	.020	L.F.		.54		.54	.90
4320	Single ply membrane, attached at seams		52	.769	Sq.		21		21	34.50
4370	Ballasted		75	.533			14.40		14.40	24
4420	Fully adhered		39	1.026			27.50		27.50	46.50
4550	Roof hatch, 2'-6" x 3'-0"	1 Clab	10	.800	Ea.		21.50		21.50	35.50
4670	Wood shingles	B-2	2200	.018	S.F.		.49		.49	.82
4820	Sheet metal roofing	"	2150	.019			.50		.50	.84
4970	Siding, horizontal wood clapboards	1 Clab	380	.021			.56		.56	.94
5025	Exterior insulation finish system	"	120	.067			1.77		1.77	2.97
5070	Tempered hardboard, remove and reset	1 Carp	380	.021			.74		.74	1.23
5120	Tempered hardboard sheet siding	"	375	.021			.75		.75	1.25
5170	Metal, corner strips	1 Clab	850	.009	L.F.		.25		.25	.42
5225	Horizontal strips		444	.018	S.F.		.48		.48	.80
5320	Vertical strips		400	.020			.53		.53	.89
5520	Wood shingles		350	.023			.61		.61	1.02
5620	Stucco siding		360	.022			.59		.59	.99
5670	Textured plywood		725	.011			.29		.29	.49
5720	Vinyl siding		510	.016			.42		.42	.70
5770	Corner strips		900	.009	L.F.		.24		.24	.40
5870	Wood, boards, vertical		400	.020	S.F.		.53		.53	.89
5880	Steel siding, corrugated/ribbed		402.50	.020	"		.53		.53	.88
5920	Waterproofing, protection/drain board	2 Clab	3900	.004	B.F.		.11		.11	.18
5970	Over 1/2" thick		1750	.009	S.F.		.24		.24	.41
6020	To 1/2" thick		2000	.008	"		.21		.21	.36

07 11 Dampproofing

07 11 13 – Bituminous Dampproofing

07 11 13.10 Bituminous Asphalt Coating

		Crew	Daily Output	Labor-Hours	Unit	Material	2017 Bare Costs Labor	Equipment	Total	Total Incl O&P
0010	**BITUMINOUS ASPHALT COATING**									
0030	Brushed on, below grade, 1 coat	1 Rofc	665	.012	S.F.	.22	.36		.58	.91
0100	2 coat		500	.016		.45	.48		.93	1.37
0300	Sprayed on, below grade, 1 coat		830	.010		.22	.29		.51	.78
0400	2 coat		500	.016		.44	.48		.92	1.36
0500	Asphalt coating, with fibers				Gal.	8.65			8.65	9.50
0600	Troweled on, asphalt with fibers, 1/16" thick	1 Rofc	500	.016	S.F.	.38	.48		.86	1.29
0700	1/8" thick		400	.020		.66	.60		1.26	1.83
1000	1/2" thick		350	.023		2.16	.68		2.84	3.63

07 11 16 – Cementitious Dampproofing

07 11 16.20 Cementitious Parging

		Crew	Daily Output	Labor-Hours	Unit	Material	2017 Bare Costs Labor	Equipment	Total	Total Incl O&P
0010	**CEMENTITIOUS PARGING**									
0020	Portland cement, 2 coats, 1/2" thick	D-1	250	.064	S.F.	.37	2.03		2.40	3.82
0100	Waterproofed Portland cement, 1/2" thick, 2 coats	"	250	.064	"	4.04	2.03		6.07	7.85

07 19 Water Repellents

07 19 19 - Silicone Water Repellents

07 19 19.10 Silicone Based Water Repellents		Crew	Daily Output	Labor-Hours	Unit	Material	2017 Bare Costs Labor	Equipment	Total	Total Incl O&P
0010	**SILICONE BASED WATER REPELLENTS**									
0020	Water base liquid, roller applied	2 Rofc	7000	.002	S.F.	.49	.07		.56	.67
0200	Silicone or stearate, sprayed on CMU, 1 coat	1 Rofc	4000	.002		.37	.06		.43	.52
0300	2 coats	"	3000	.003	↓	.74	.08		.82	.97

07 21 Thermal Insulation

07 21 13 - Board Insulation

07 21 13.10 Rigid Insulation

			Crew	Daily Output	Labor-Hours	Unit	Material	2017 Bare Costs Labor	Equipment	Total	Total Incl O&P
0010	**RIGID INSULATION**, for walls										
0040	Fiberglass, 1.5#/C.F., unfaced, 1" thick, R4.1	G	1 Carp	1000	.008	S.F.	.30	.28		.58	.80
0060	1-1/2" thick, R6.2	G		1000	.008		.39	.28		.67	.90
0080	2" thick, R8.3	G		1000	.008		.49	.28		.77	1.01
0120	3" thick, R12.4	G		800	.010		.57	.35		.92	1.21
0370	3#/C.F., unfaced, 1" thick, R4.3	G		1000	.008		.52	.28		.80	1.04
0390	1-1/2" thick, R6.5	G		1000	.008		.78	.28		1.06	1.33
0400	2" thick, R8.7	G		890	.009		1.05	.31		1.36	1.69
0420	2-1/2" thick, R10.9	G		800	.010		1.10	.35		1.45	1.79
0440	3" thick, R13	G		800	.010		1.59	.35		1.94	2.33
0520	Foil faced, 1" thick, R4.3	G		1000	.008		.90	.28		1.18	1.46
0540	1-1/2" thick, R6.5	G		1000	.008		1.35	.28		1.63	1.96
0560	2" thick, R8.7	G		890	.009		1.70	.31		2.01	2.40
0580	2-1/2" thick, R10.9	G		800	.010		2	.35		2.35	2.78
0600	3" thick, R13	G	↓	800	.010	↓	2.25	.35		2.60	3.06
1600	Isocyanurate, 4' x 8' sheet, foil faced, both sides										
1610	1/2" thick	G	1 Carp	800	.010	S.F.	.31	.35		.66	.92
1620	5/8" thick	G		800	.010		.33	.35		.68	.94
1630	3/4" thick	G		800	.010		.39	.35		.74	1.01
1640	1" thick	G		800	.010		.52	.35		.87	1.15
1650	1-1/2" thick	G		730	.011		.60	.38		.98	1.30
1660	2" thick	G		730	.011		.76	.38		1.14	1.48
1670	3" thick	G		730	.011		1.90	.38		2.28	2.73
1680	4" thick	G		730	.011		2.15	.38		2.53	3.01
1700	Perlite, 1" thick, R2.77	G		800	.010		.45	.35		.80	1.08
1750	2" thick, R5.55	G		730	.011		.78	.38		1.16	1.50
1900	Extruded polystyrene, 25 PSI compressive strength, 1" thick, R5	G		800	.010		.57	.35		.92	1.21
1940	2" thick, R10	G		730	.011		1.14	.38		1.52	1.89
1960	3" thick, R15	G		730	.011		1.59	.38		1.97	2.39
2100	Expanded polystyrene, 1" thick, R3.85	G		800	.010		.26	.35		.61	.87
2120	2" thick, R7.69	G		730	.011		.52	.38		.90	1.21
2140	3" thick, R11.49	G	↓	730	.011	↓	.78	.38		1.16	1.50

07 21 13.13 Foam Board Insulation

			Crew	Daily Output	Labor-Hours	Unit	Material	2017 Bare Costs Labor	Equipment	Total	Total Incl O&P
0010	**FOAM BOARD INSULATION**										
0600	Polystyrene, expanded, 1" thick, R4	G	1 Carp	680	.012	S.F.	.26	.41		.67	.98
0700	2" thick, R8	G	"	675	.012	"	.52	.41		.93	1.26

07 21 Thermal Insulation

07 21 16 – Blanket Insulation

07 21 16.10 Blanket Insulation for Floors/Ceilings

		Crew	Daily Output	Labor-Hours	Unit	Material	2017 Bare Costs Labor	Equipment	Total	Total Incl O&P
0010	**BLANKET INSULATION FOR FLOORS/CEILINGS**									
0020	Including spring type wire fasteners									
2000	Fiberglass, blankets or batts, paper or foil backing									
2100	3-1/2" thick, R13	G	1 Carp	700	.011	S.F.	.40	.40		.80	1.11
2150	6-1/4" thick, R19	G		600	.013		.52	.47		.99	1.35
2210	9-1/2" thick, R30	G		500	.016		.75	.56		1.31	1.77
2220	12" thick, R38	G		475	.017		1.08	.59		1.67	2.17
3000	Unfaced, 3-1/2" thick, R13	G		600	.013		.34	.47		.81	1.15
3010	6-1/4" thick, R19	G		500	.016		.40	.56		.96	1.38
3020	9-1/2" thick, R30	G		450	.018		.62	.62		1.24	1.72
3030	12" thick, R38	G	▼	425	.019	▼	.77	.66		1.43	1.95

07 21 16.20 Blanket Insulation for Walls

		Crew	Daily Output	Labor-Hours	Unit	Material	2017 Bare Costs Labor	Equipment	Total	Total Incl O&P
0010	**BLANKET INSULATION FOR WALLS**									
0020	Kraft faced fiberglass, 3-1/2" thick, R11, 15" wide	G	1 Carp	1350	.006	S.F.	.32	.21		.53	.70
0030	23" wide	G		1600	.005		.32	.17		.49	.64
0060	R13, 11" wide	G		1150	.007		.33	.24		.57	.77
0080	15" wide	G		1350	.006		.33	.21		.54	.71
0100	23" wide	G		1600	.005		.33	.17		.50	.65
0110	R15, 11" wide	G		1150	.007		.51	.24		.75	.97
0120	15" wide	G		1350	.006		.51	.21		.72	.91
0140	6" thick, R19, 11" wide	G		1150	.007		.45	.24		.69	.91
0160	15" wide	G		1350	.006		.45	.21		.66	.85
0180	23" wide	G		1600	.005		.45	.17		.62	.79
0201	9" thick, R30, 15" wide	G		1350	.006		.75	.21		.96	1.18
0241	12" thick, R38, 15" wide	G		1350	.006		1.08	.21		1.29	1.54
0410	Foil faced fiberglass, 3-1/2" thick, R13, 11" wide	G		1150	.007		.48	.24		.72	.94
0420	15" wide	G		1350	.006		.48	.21		.69	.88
0442	R15, 11" wide	G		1150	.007		.50	.24		.74	.96
0444	15" wide	G		1350	.006		.50	.21		.71	.90
0461	6" thick, R19, 15" wide	G		1600	.005		.64	.17		.81	.99
0482	R21, 11" wide	G		1150	.007		.66	.24		.90	1.14
0501	9" thick, R30, 15" wide	G		1350	.006		.97	.21		1.18	1.42
0620	Unfaced fiberglass, 3-1/2" thick, R13, 11" wide	G		1150	.007		.34	.24		.58	.78
0821	15" wide	G		1600	.005		.34	.17		.51	.66
0832	R15, 11" wide	G		1150	.007		.47	.24		.71	.93
0834	15" wide	G		1350	.006		.47	.21		.68	.87
0861	6" thick, R19, 15" wide	G		1350	.006		.40	.21		.61	.79
0901	9" thick, R30, 15" wide	G		1150	.007		.62	.24		.86	1.09
0941	12" thick, R38, 15" wide	G	▼	1150	.007	▼	.77	.24		1.01	1.26
1300	Wall or ceiling insulation, mineral wool batts									
1320	3-1/2" thick, R15	G	1 Carp	1600	.005	S.F.	.70	.17		.87	1.06
1340	5-1/2" thick, R23	G		1600	.005		1.10	.17		1.27	1.50
1380	7-1/4" thick, R30	G		1350	.006		1.45	.21		1.66	1.95
1700	Non-rigid insul, recycled blue cotton fiber, unfaced batts, R13, 16" wide	G		1600	.005		.99	.17		1.16	1.38
1710	R19, 16" wide	G		1600	.005	▼	1.35	.17		1.52	1.78
1850	Friction fit wire insulation supports, 16" O.C.		▼	960	.008	Ea.	.07	.29		.36	.57

07 21 19 – Foamed In Place Insulation

07 21 19.10 Masonry Foamed In Place Insulation

		Crew	Daily Output	Labor-Hours	Unit	Material	2017 Bare Costs Labor	Equipment	Total	Total Incl O&P
0010	**MASONRY FOAMED IN PLACE INSULATION**									
0100	Amino-plast foam, injected into block core, 6" block	G	G-2A	6000	.004	Ea.	.16	.11	.11	.38	.49
0110	8" block	G	▼	5000	.005	▼	.20	.13	.13	.46	.59

For customer support on your Residential Costs with RSMeans Data, call 800.448.8182.

419

07 21 Thermal Insulation

07 21 19 – Foamed In Place Insulation

07 21 19.10 Masonry Foamed In Place Insulation		Crew	Daily Output	Labor-Hours	Unit	Material	2017 Bare Costs Labor	Equipment	Total	Total Incl O&P
0120	10" block	G	G-2A	4000	.006	Ea.	.25	.16	.17	.58	.73
0130	12" block	G		3000	.008		.33	.21	.22	.76	.98
0140	Injected into cavity wall	G		13000	.002	B.F.	.06	.05	.05	.16	.21
0150	Preparation, drill holes into mortar joint every 4 VLF, 5/8" diameter		1 Clab	960	.008	Ea.		.22		.22	.37
0160	7/8" diameter			680	.012			.31		.31	.52
0170	Patch drilled holes, 5/8" diameter			1800	.004		.04	.12		.16	.24
0180	7/8" diameter			1200	.007		.05	.18		.23	.36

07 21 23 – Loose-Fill Insulation

07 21 23.10 Poured Loose-Fill Insulation

			Crew	Daily Output	Labor-Hours	Unit	Material	2017 Bare Costs Labor	Equipment	Total	Total Incl O&P
0010	**POURED LOOSE-FILL INSULATION**										
0020	Cellulose fiber, R3.8 per inch	G	1 Carp	200	.040	C.F.	.69	1.40		2.09	3.10
0021	4" thick	G		1000	.008	S.F.	.17	.28		.45	.65
0022	6" thick	G		800	.010	"	.28	.35		.63	.89
0080	Fiberglass wool, R4 per inch	G		200	.040	C.F.	.55	1.40		1.95	2.94
0081	4" thick	G		600	.013	S.F.	.19	.47		.66	.99
0082	6" thick	G		400	.020	"	.26	.70		.96	1.46
0100	Mineral wool, R3 per inch	G		200	.040	C.F.	.45	1.40		1.85	2.84
0101	4" thick	G		600	.013	S.F.	.15	.47		.62	.94
0102	6" thick	G		400	.020	"	.23	.70		.93	1.42
0300	Polystyrene, R4 per inch	G		200	.040	C.F.	1.60	1.40		3	4.10
0301	4" thick	G		600	.013	S.F.	.53	.47		1	1.36
0302	6" thick	G		400	.020	"	.80	.70		1.50	2.05
0400	Perlite, R2.78 per inch	G		200	.040	C.F.	5.30	1.40		6.70	8.15
0401	4" thick	G		1000	.008	S.F.	1.76	.28		2.04	2.41
0402	6" thick	G		800	.010	"	2.65	.35		3	3.49

07 21 23.20 Masonry Loose-Fill Insulation

			Crew	Daily Output	Labor-Hours	Unit	Material	2017 Bare Costs Labor	Equipment	Total	Total Incl O&P
0010	**MASONRY LOOSE-FILL INSULATION**, vermiculite or perlite										
0100	In cores of concrete block, 4" thick wall, .115 C.F./S.F.	G	D-1	4800	.003	S.F.	.61	.11		.72	.85
0700	Foamed in place, urethane in 2-5/8" cavity	G	G-2A	1035	.023		1.36	.61	.65	2.62	3.29
0800	For each 1" added thickness, add	G	"	2372	.010		.52	.27	.28	1.07	1.35

07 21 26 – Blown Insulation

07 21 26.10 Blown Insulation

			Crew	Daily Output	Labor-Hours	Unit	Material	2017 Bare Costs Labor	Equipment	Total	Total Incl O&P
0010	**BLOWN INSULATION** Ceilings, with open access										
0020	Cellulose, 3-1/2" thick, R13	G	G-4	5000	.005	S.F.	.24	.13	.07	.44	.56
0030	5-3/16" thick, R19	G		3800	.006		.35	.17	.10	.62	.78
0050	6-1/2" thick, R22	G		3000	.008		.45	.22	.12	.79	.99
0100	8-11/16" thick, R30	G		2600	.009		.61	.25	.14	1	1.24
0120	10-7/8" thick, R38	G		1800	.013		.78	.36	.20	1.34	1.68
1000	Fiberglass, 5.5" thick, R11	G		3800	.006		.19	.17	.10	.46	.59
1050	6" thick, R12	G		3000	.008		.26	.22	.12	.60	.78
1100	8.8" thick, R19	G		2200	.011		.33	.30	.16	.79	1.04
1200	10" thick, R22	G		1800	.013		.38	.36	.20	.94	1.25
1300	11.5" thick, R26	G		1500	.016		.46	.44	.24	1.14	1.49
1350	13" thick, R30	G		1400	.017		.53	.47	.26	1.26	1.64
1450	16" thick, R38	G		1145	.021		.68	.57	.32	1.57	2.05
1500	20" thick, R49	G		920	.026		.89	.71	.39	1.99	2.60

07 21 27 – Reflective Insulation

07 21 27.10 Reflective Insulation Options

			Crew	Daily Output	Labor-Hours	Unit	Material	2017 Bare Costs Labor	Equipment	Total	Total Incl O&P
0010	**REFLECTIVE INSULATION OPTIONS**										
0020	Aluminum foil on reinforced scrim	G	1 Carp	19	.421	C.S.F.	15	14.70		29.70	41
0100	Reinforced with woven polyolefin	G		19	.421		22	14.70		36.70	49

07 21 Thermal Insulation

07 21 27 – Reflective Insulation

07 21 27.10 Reflective Insulation Options		Crew	Daily Output	Labor-Hours	Unit	Material	2017 Bare Costs Labor	Equipment	Total	Total Incl O&P
0500	With single bubble air space, R8.8	G 1 Carp	15	.533	C.S.F.	26	18.65		44.65	60
0600	With double bubble air space, R9.8	G ▼	15	.533	▼	31.50	18.65		50.15	65.50

07 21 29 – Sprayed Insulation

07 21 29.10 Sprayed-On Insulation

		Crew	Daily Output	Labor-Hours	Unit	Material	Labor	Equipment	Total	Total Incl O&P
0010	**SPRAYED-ON INSULATION**									
0300	Closed cell, spray polyurethane foam, 2 pounds per cubic foot density									
0310	1" thick	G G-2A	6000	.004	S.F.	.52	.11	.11	.74	.88
0320	2" thick	G	3000	.008		1.04	.21	.22	1.47	1.76
0330	3" thick	G	2000	.012		1.55	.32	.34	2.21	2.64
0335	3-1/2" thick	G	1715	.014		1.81	.37	.39	2.57	3.08
0340	4" thick	G	1500	.016		2.07	.42	.45	2.94	3.52
0350	5" thick	G	1200	.020		2.59	.53	.56	3.68	4.41
0355	5-1/2" thick	G	1090	.022		2.85	.58	.62	4.05	4.84
0360	6" thick	G ▼	1000	.024	▼	3.11	.63	.67	4.41	5.30

07 22 Roof and Deck Insulation

07 22 16 – Roof Board Insulation

07 22 16.10 Roof Deck Insulation

		Crew	Daily Output	Labor-Hours	Unit	Material	Labor	Equipment	Total	Total Incl O&P
0010	**ROOF DECK INSULATION**, fastening excluded									
0016	Asphaltic cover board, fiberglass lined, 1/8" thick	1 Rofc	1400	.006	S.F.	.47	.17		.64	.83
0018	1/4" thick		1400	.006		.94	.17		1.11	1.34
0020	Fiberboard low density, 1/2" thick R1.39	G	1300	.006		.33	.18		.51	.70
0030	1" thick R2.78	G	1040	.008		.56	.23		.79	1.04
0080	1-1/2" thick R4.17	G	1040	.008		.85	.23		1.08	1.36
0100	2" thick R5.56	G	1040	.008		1.10	.23		1.33	1.63
0110	Fiberboard high density, 1/2" thick R1.3	G	1300	.006		.30	.18		.48	.67
0120	1" thick R2.5	G	1040	.008		.56	.23		.79	1.04
0130	1-1/2" thick R3.8	G	1040	.008		.86	.23		1.09	1.37
0200	Fiberglass, 3/4" thick R2.78	G	1300	.006		.61	.18		.79	1.01
0400	15/16" thick R3.70	G	1300	.006		.81	.18		.99	1.23
0460	1-1/16" thick R4.17	G	1300	.006		1.04	.18		1.22	1.48
0600	1-5/16" thick R5.26	G	1300	.006		1.40	.18		1.58	1.88
0650	2-1/16" thick R8.33	G	1040	.008		1.50	.23		1.73	2.07
0700	2-7/16" thick R10	G	1040	.008		1.70	.23		1.93	2.29
0800	Gypsum cover board, fiberglass mat facer, 1/4" thick		1400	.006		.47	.17		.64	.83
0810	1/2" thick		1300	.006		.57	.18		.75	.97
0820	5/8" thick		1200	.007		.61	.20		.81	1.04
0830	Primed fiberglass mat facer, 1/4" thick		1400	.006		.48	.17		.65	.84
0840	1/2" thick		1300	.006		.57	.18		.75	.97
0850	5/8" thick		1200	.007		.60	.20		.80	1.03
1650	Perlite, 1/2" thick R1.32	G	1365	.006		.26	.17		.43	.61
1655	3/4" thick R2.08	G	1040	.008		.37	.23		.60	.83
1660	1" thick R2.78	G	1040	.008		.53	.23		.76	1
1670	1-1/2" thick R4.17	G	1040	.008		.78	.23		1.01	1.28
1680	2" thick R5.56	G	910	.009		1.07	.26		1.33	1.66
1685	2-1/2" thick R6.67	G	910	.009	▼	1.45	.26		1.71	2.08
1690	Tapered for drainage	G	1040	.008	B.F.	1.05	.23		1.28	1.58
1700	Polyisocyanurate, 2#/C.F. density, 3/4" thick	G	1950	.004	S.F.	.42	.12		.54	.68
1705	1" thick	G	1820	.004		.43	.13		.56	.71
1715	1-1/2" thick	G	1625	.005	▼	.59	.15		.74	.92

07 22 Roof and Deck Insulation

07 22 16 – Roof Board Insulation

07 22 16.10 Roof Deck Insulation		Crew	Daily Output	Labor-Hours	Unit	Material	2017 Bare Costs Labor	Equipment	Total	Total Incl O&P
1725	2" thick	G 1 Rofc	1430	.006	S.F.	.75	.17		.92	1.14
1735	2-1/2" thick	G	1365	.006		1.01	.17		1.18	1.43
1745	3" thick	G	1300	.006		1.12	.18		1.30	1.57
1755	3-1/2" thick	G	1300	.006		1.74	.18		1.92	2.25
1765	Tapered for drainage	G	1820	.004	B.F.	.59	.13		.72	.89
1900	Extruded polystyrene									
1910	15 PSI compressive strength, 1" thick, R5	G 1 Rofc	1950	.004	S.F.	.61	.12		.73	.89
1920	2" thick, R10	G	1625	.005		.79	.15		.94	1.14
1930	3" thick, R15	G	1300	.006		1.59	.18		1.77	2.08
1932	4" thick, R20	G	1300	.006		2.14	.18		2.32	2.69
1934	Tapered for drainage	G	1950	.004	B.F.	.63	.12		.75	.91
1940	25 PSI compressive strength, 1" thick, R5	G	1950	.004	S.F.	.69	.12		.81	.98
1942	2" thick, R10	G	1625	.005		1.31	.15		1.46	1.71
1944	3" thick, R15	G	1300	.006		2	.18		2.18	2.54
1946	4" thick, R20	G	1300	.006		2.76	.18		2.94	3.38
1948	Tapered for drainage	G	1950	.004	B.F.	.62	.12		.74	.90
1950	40 PSI compressive strength, 1" thick, R5	G	1950	.004	S.F.	.54	.12		.66	.81
1952	2" thick, R10	G	1625	.005		1.03	.15		1.18	1.40
1954	3" thick, R15	G	1300	.006		1.49	.18		1.67	1.97
1956	4" thick, R20	G	1300	.006		1.94	.18		2.12	2.48
1958	Tapered for drainage	G	1820	.004	B.F.	.77	.13		.90	1.09
1960	60 PSI compressive strength, 1" thick, R5	G	1885	.004	S.F.	.75	.13		.88	1.06
1962	2" thick, R10	G	1560	.005		1.43	.15		1.58	1.85
1964	3" thick, R15	G	1270	.006		2.33	.19		2.52	2.90
1966	4" thick, R20	G	1235	.006		2.89	.19		3.08	3.53
1968	Tapered for drainage	G	1820	.004	B.F.	.97	.13		1.10	1.31
2010	Expanded polystyrene, 1#/C.F. density, 3/4" thick, R2.89	G	1950	.004	S.F.	.20	.12		.32	.43
2020	1" thick, R3.85	G	1950	.004		.26	.12		.38	.51
2100	2" thick, R7.69	G	1625	.005		.52	.15		.67	.84
2110	3" thick, R11.49	G	1625	.005		.78	.15		.93	1.13
2120	4" thick, R15.38	G	1625	.005		1.04	.15		1.19	1.41
2130	5" thick, R19.23	G	1495	.005		1.30	.16		1.46	1.72
2140	6" thick, R23.26	G	1495	.005		1.56	.16		1.72	2.01
2150	Tapered for drainage	G	1950	.004	B.F.	.54	.12		.66	.81
2400	Composites with 2" EPS									
2410	1" fiberboard	G 1 Rofc	1325	.006	S.F.	1.40	.18		1.58	1.87
2420	7/16" oriented strand board	G	1040	.008		1.13	.23		1.36	1.66
2430	1/2" plywood	G	1040	.008		1.40	.23		1.63	1.96
2440	1" perlite	G	1040	.008		1.14	.23		1.37	1.67
2450	Composites with 1-1/2" polyisocyanurate									
2460	1" fiberboard	G 1 Rofc	1040	.008	S.F.	1.09	.23		1.32	1.62
2470	1" perlite	G	1105	.007		.97	.22		1.19	1.47
2480	7/16" oriented strand board	G	1040	.008		.85	.23		1.08	1.36
3000	Fastening alternatives, coated screws, 2" long		3744	.002	Ea.	.06	.06		.12	.19
3010	4" long		3120	.003		.11	.08		.19	.26
3020	6" long		2675	.003		.19	.09		.28	.37
3030	8" long		2340	.003		.28	.10		.38	.50
3040	10" long		1872	.004		.47	.13		.60	.75
3050	Pre-drill and drive wedge spike, 2-1/2"		1248	.006		.40	.19		.59	.79
3060	3-1/2"		1101	.007		.57	.22		.79	1.03
3070	4-1/2"		936	.009		.64	.25		.89	1.17
3075	3" galvanized deck plates		7488	.001		.08	.03		.11	.15
3080	Spot mop asphalt	G-1	295	.190	Sq.	5.65	5.30	1.79	12.74	17.95

07 22 Roof and Deck Insulation

07 22 16 – Roof Board Insulation

07 22 16.10 Roof Deck Insulation		Crew	Daily Output	Labor-Hours	Unit	Material	2017 Bare Costs Labor	Equipment	Total	Total Incl O&P
3090	Full mop asphalt	G-1	192	.292	Sq.	11.35	8.15	2.75	22.25	30.50
3110	Low-rise polyurethane adhesive, from 5 gallon kit, 12" OC beads	1 Rofc	45	.178		33	5.30		38.30	46.50
3120	6" OC beads		32	.250		66	7.45		73.45	86
3130	4" OC beads		30	.267		99	7.95		106.95	124

07 24 Exterior Insulation and Finish Systems

07 24 13 – Polymer-Based Exterior Insulation and Finish System

07 24 13.10 Exterior Insulation and Finish Systems			Crew	Daily Output	Labor-Hours	Unit	Material	2017 Bare Costs Labor	Equipment	Total	Total Incl O&P
0010	**EXTERIOR INSULATION AND FINISH SYSTEMS**										
0095	Field applied, 1" EPS insulation	G	J-1	390	.103	S.F.	1.95	3.27	.35	5.57	7.90
0100	With 1/2" cement board sheathing	G		268	.149		2.73	4.77	.50	8	11.35
0105	2" EPS insulation	G		390	.103		2.21	3.27	.35	5.83	8.15
0110	With 1/2" cement board sheathing	G		268	.149		2.99	4.77	.50	8.26	11.65
0115	3" EPS insulation	G		390	.103		2.47	3.27	.35	6.09	8.45
0120	With 1/2" cement board sheathing	G		268	.149		3.25	4.77	.50	8.52	11.95
0125	4" EPS insulation	G		390	.103		2.73	3.27	.35	6.35	8.75
0130	With 1/2" cement board sheathing	G		268	.149		4.29	4.77	.50	9.56	13.05
0140	Premium finish add			1265	.032		.35	1.01	.11	1.47	2.17
0150	Heavy duty reinforcement add			914	.044		.85	1.40	.15	2.40	3.39
0160	2.5#/S.Y. metal lath substrate add		1 Lath	75	.107	S.Y.	3.02	3.68		6.70	9.25
0170	3.4#/S.Y. metal lath substrate add		"	75	.107	"	4.40	3.68		8.08	10.80
0180	Color or texture change		J-1	1265	.032	S.F.	.82	1.01	.11	1.94	2.68
0190	With substrate leveling base coat		1 Plas	530	.015		.83	.51		1.34	1.75
0210	With substrate sealing base coat		1 Pord	1224	.007		.12	.19		.31	.45
0370	V groove shape in panel face					L.F.	.66			.66	.73
0380	U groove shape in panel face					"	.85			.85	.94

07 25 Weather Barriers

07 25 10 – Weather Barriers or Wraps

07 25 10.10 Weather Barriers		Crew	Daily Output	Labor-Hours	Unit	Material	2017 Bare Costs Labor	Equipment	Total	Total Incl O&P
0010	**WEATHER BARRIERS**									
0400	Asphalt felt paper, 15#	1 Carp	37	.216	Sq.	5.30	7.55		12.85	18.50
0401	Per square foot	"	3700	.002	S.F.	.05	.08		.13	.19
0450	Housewrap, exterior, spun bonded polypropylene									
0470	Small roll	1 Carp	3800	.002	S.F.	.15	.07		.22	.29
0480	Large roll	"	4000	.002	"	.14	.07		.21	.27
2100	Asphalt felt roof deck vapor barrier, class 1 metal decks	1 Rofc	37	.216	Sq.	22	6.45		28.45	36
2200	For all other decks	"	37	.216		16.65	6.45		23.10	30
2800	Asphalt felt, 50% recycled content, 15 lb., 4 sq. per roll	1 Carp	36	.222		5.50	7.75		13.25	19.05
2810	30 lb., 2 sq. per roll	"	36	.222		11	7.75		18.75	25
3000	Building wrap, spun bonded polyethylene	2 Carp	8000	.002	S.F.	.16	.07		.23	.30

For customer support on your Residential Costs with RSMeans Data, call 800.448.8182.

423

07 26 Vapor Retarders

07 26 10 – Above-Grade Vapor Retarders

07 26 10.10 Building Paper		Crew	Daily Output	Labor-Hours	Unit	Material	2017 Bare Costs Labor	Equipment	Total	Total Incl O&P
0011	**BUILDING PAPER,** aluminum and kraft laminated, foil 1 side	1 Carp	3700	.002	S.F.	.12	.08		.20	.26
0101	Foil 2 sides G		3700	.002		.14	.08		.22	.28
0601	Polyethylene vapor barrier, standard, 2 mil G		3700	.002		.02	.08		.10	.15
0701	4 mil G		3700	.002		.03	.08		.11	.16
0901	6 mil G		3700	.002		.04	.08		.12	.17
1201	10 mil G		3700	.002		.08	.08		.16	.22
1801	Reinf. waterproof, 2 mil polyethylene backing, 1 side		3700	.002		.06	.08		.14	.20
1901	2 sides		3700	.002		.08	.08		.16	.22

07 27 Air Barriers

07 27 13 – Modified Bituminous Sheet Air Barriers

07 27 13.10 Modified Bituminous Sheet Air Barrier

		Crew	Daily Output	Labor-Hours	Unit	Material	2017 Bare Costs Labor	Equipment	Total	Total Incl O&P
0010	**MODIFIED BITUMINOUS SHEET AIR BARRIER**									
0100	SBS modified sheet laminated to polyethylene sheet, 40 mils, 4" wide	1 Carp	1200	.007	L.F.	.37	.23		.60	.80
0120	6" wide		1100	.007		.51	.25		.76	.98
0140	9" wide		1000	.008		.71	.28		.99	1.25
0160	12" wide		900	.009		.91	.31		1.22	1.52
0180	18" wide	2 Carp	1700	.009	S.F.	.85	.33		1.18	1.48
0200	36" wide	"	1800	.009		.83	.31		1.14	1.43
0220	Adhesive for above	1 Carp	1400	.006		.35	.20		.55	.71

07 27 26 – Fluid-Applied Membrane Air Barriers

07 27 26.10 Fluid Applied Membrane Air Barrier

		Crew	Daily Output	Labor-Hours	Unit	Material	2017 Bare Costs Labor	Equipment	Total	Total Incl O&P
0010	**FLUID APPLIED MEMBRANE AIR BARRIER**									
0100	Spray applied vapor barrier, 25 S.F./gallon	1 Pord	1375	.006	S.F.	.01	.17		.18	.30

07 31 Shingles and Shakes

07 31 13 – Asphalt Shingles

07 31 13.10 Asphalt Roof Shingles

		Crew	Daily Output	Labor-Hours	Unit	Material	2017 Bare Costs Labor	Equipment	Total	Total Incl O&P
0010	**ASPHALT ROOF SHINGLES**									
0100	Standard strip shingles									
0150	Inorganic, class A, 25 year	1 Rofc	5.50	1.455	Sq.	81.50	43.50		125	169
0155	Pneumatic nailed		7	1.143		81.50	34		115.50	152
0200	30 year		5	1.600		95	47.50		142.50	193
0205	Pneumatic nailed		6.25	1.280		95	38		133	175
0250	Standard laminated multi-layered shingles									
0300	Class A, 240-260 lb./square	1 Rofc	4.50	1.778	Sq.	109	53		162	218
0305	Pneumatic nailed		5.63	1.422		109	42.50		151.50	198
0350	Class A, 250-270 lb./square		4	2		109	59.50		168.50	230
0355	Pneumatic nailed		5	1.600		109	47.50		156.50	208
0400	Premium, laminated multi-layered shingles									
0450	Class A, 260-300 lb./square	1 Rofc	3.50	2.286	Sq.	158	68		226	299
0455	Pneumatic nailed		4.37	1.831		158	54.50		212.50	274
0500	Class A, 300-385 lb./square		3	2.667		242	79.50		321.50	410
0505	Pneumatic nailed		3.75	2.133		242	63.50		305.50	385
0800	#15 felt underlayment		64	.125		5.30	3.72		9.02	12.70
0825	#30 felt underlayment		58	.138		10.35	4.10		14.45	18.95
0850	Self adhering polyethylene and rubberized asphalt underlayment		22	.364		77	10.80		87.80	104
0900	Ridge shingles		330	.024	L.F.	2.25	.72		2.97	3.81
0905	Pneumatic nailed		412.50	.019	"	2.25	.58		2.83	3.54

07 31 Shingles and Shakes

07 31 13 – Asphalt Shingles

07 31 13.10 Asphalt Roof Shingles	Crew	Daily Output	Labor-Hours	Unit	Material	2017 Bare Costs Labor	Equipment	Total	Total Incl O&P
1000	For steep roofs (7 to 12 pitch or greater), add						50%			

07 31 26 – Slate Shingles

07 31 26.10 Slate Roof Shingles

		Crew	Daily Output	Labor-Hours	Unit	Material	Labor	Equipment	Total	Total Incl O&P
0010	**SLATE ROOF SHINGLES** R073126-20									
0100	Buckingham Virginia black, 3/16" - 1/4" thick [G]	1 Rots	1.75	4.571	Sq.	550	137		687	855
0200	1/4" thick [G]		1.75	4.571		550	137		687	855
0900	Pennsylvania black, Bangor, #1 clear [G]		1.75	4.571		495	137		632	795
1200	Vermont, unfading, green, mottled green [G]		1.75	4.571		495	137		632	795
1300	Semi-weathering green & gray [G]		1.75	4.571		360	137		497	645
1400	Purple [G]		1.75	4.571		435	137		572	730
1500	Black or gray [G]		1.75	4.571		475	137		612	775
2700	Ridge shingles, slate		200	.040	L.F.	10	1.20		11.20	13.20

07 31 29 – Wood Shingles and Shakes

07 31 29.13 Wood Shingles

		Crew	Daily Output	Labor-Hours	Unit	Material	Labor	Equipment	Total	Total Incl O&P
0010	**WOOD SHINGLES**									
0012	16" No. 1 red cedar shingles, 5" exposure, on roof	1 Carp	2.50	3.200	Sq.	282	112		394	495
0015	Pneumatic nailed		3.25	2.462		282	86		368	455
0200	7-1/2" exposure, on walls		2.05	3.902		188	136		324	435
0205	Pneumatic nailed		2.67	2.996		188	105		293	380
0300	18" No. 1 red cedar perfections, 5-1/2" exposure, on roof		2.75	2.909		250	102		352	445
0305	Pneumatic nailed		3.57	2.241		250	78.50		328.50	405
0500	7-1/2" exposure, on walls		2.25	3.556		184	124		308	410
0505	Pneumatic nailed		2.92	2.740		184	96		280	360
0600	Resquared and rebutted, 5-1/2" exposure, on roof		3	2.667		288	93		381	470
0605	Pneumatic nailed		3.90	2.051		288	71.50		359.50	435
0900	7-1/2" exposure, on walls		2.45	3.265		211	114		325	425
0905	Pneumatic nailed		3.18	2.516		211	88		299	380
1000	Add to above for fire retardant shingles					56			56	61.50
1060	Preformed ridge shingles	1 Carp	400	.020	L.F.	5	.70		5.70	6.65
2000	White cedar shingles, 16" long, extras, 5" exposure, on roof		2.40	3.333	Sq.	195	117		312	410
2005	Pneumatic nailed		3.12	2.564		195	89.50		284.50	365
2050	5" exposure on walls		2	4		195	140		335	450
2055	Pneumatic nailed		2.60	3.077		195	108		303	395
2100	7-1/2" exposure, on walls		2	4		139	140		279	385
2105	Pneumatic nailed		2.60	3.077		139	108		247	335
2150	"B" grade, 5" exposure on walls		2	4		165	140		305	415
2155	Pneumatic nailed		2.60	3.077		165	108		273	360
2300	For 15# organic felt underlayment on roof, 1 layer, add		64	.125		5.30	4.37		9.67	13.15
2400	2 layers, add		32	.250		10.60	8.75		19.35	26.50
2600	For steep roofs (7/12 pitch or greater), add to above						50%			
2700	Panelized systems, No.1 cedar shingles on 5/16" CDX plywood									
2800	On walls, 8' strips, 7" or 14" exposure	2 Carp	700	.023	S.F.	6	.80		6.80	7.95
3000	Ridge shakes or shingle, wood	1 Carp	280	.029	L.F.	4.50	1		5.50	6.60

07 31 29.16 Wood Shakes

		Crew	Daily Output	Labor-Hours	Unit	Material	Labor	Equipment	Total	Total Incl O&P
0010	**WOOD SHAKES**									
1100	Hand-split red cedar shakes, 1/2" thick x 24" long, 10" exp. on roof	1 Carp	2.50	3.200	Sq.	287	112		399	500
1105	Pneumatic nailed		3.25	2.462		287	86		373	460
1110	3/4" thick x 24" long, 10" exp. on roof		2.25	3.556		287	124		411	525
1115	Pneumatic nailed		2.92	2.740		287	96		383	475
1200	1/2" thick, 18" long, 8-1/2" exp. on roof		2	4		179	140		319	430
1205	Pneumatic nailed		2.60	3.077		179	108		287	375

07 31 Shingles and Shakes

07 31 29 – Wood Shingles and Shakes

07 31 29.16 Wood Shakes		Crew	Daily Output	Labor-Hours	Unit	Material	2017 Bare Costs Labor	Equipment	Total	Total Incl O&P
1210	3/4" thick x 18" long, 8-1/2" exp. on roof	1 Carp	1.80	4.444	Sq.	179	155		334	455
1215	Pneumatic nailed		2.34	3.419		179	119		298	395
1255	10" exposure on walls		2	4		173	140		313	425
1260	10" exposure on walls, pneumatic nailed		2.60	3.077		173	108		281	370
1700	Add to above for fire retardant shakes, 24" long					56			56	61.50
1800	18" long					56			56	61.50
1810	Ridge shakes	1 Carp	350	.023	L.F.	5.75	.80		6.55	7.70

07 32 Roof Tiles

07 32 13 – Clay Roof Tiles

07 32 13.10 Clay Tiles

		Crew	Daily Output	Labor-Hours	Unit	Material	2017 Bare Costs Labor	Equipment	Total	Total Incl O&P
0010	**CLAY TILES**, including accessories									
0300	Flat shingle, interlocking, 15", 166 pcs/sq, fireflashed blend	3 Rots	6	4	Sq.	470	120		590	735
0500	Terra cotta red		6	4		520	120		640	790
0600	Roman pan and top, 18", 102 pcs/sq, fireflashed blend		5.50	4.364		505	130		635	795
0640	Terra cotta red	1 Rots	2.40	3.333		570	99.50		669.50	810
1100	Barrel mission tile, 18", 166 pcs/sq, fireflashed blend	3 Rots	5.50	4.364		415	130		545	695
1140	Terra cotta red		5.50	4.364		420	130		550	700
1700	Scalloped edge flat shingle, 14", 145 pcs/sq, fireflashed blend		6	4		1,150	120		1,270	1,500
1800	Terra cotta red		6	4		1,050	120		1,170	1,375
3010	#15 felt underlayment	1 Rofc	64	.125		5.30	3.72		9.02	12.70
3020	#30 felt underlayment		58	.138		10.35	4.10		14.45	18.95
3040	Polyethylene and rubberized asph. underlayment		22	.364		77	10.80		87.80	104

07 32 16 – Concrete Roof Tiles

07 32 16.10 Concrete Tiles

		Crew	Daily Output	Labor-Hours	Unit	Material	2017 Bare Costs Labor	Equipment	Total	Total Incl O&P
0010	**CONCRETE TILES**									
0020	Corrugated, 13" x 16-1/2", 90 per sq., 950 lb. per sq.									
0050	Earthtone colors, nailed to wood deck	1 Rots	1.35	5.926	Sq.	105	177		282	440
0150	Blues		1.35	5.926		105	177		282	440
0200	Greens		1.35	5.926		106	177		283	440
0250	Premium colors		1.35	5.926		106	177		283	440
0500	Shakes, 13" x 16-1/2", 90 per sq., 950 lb. per sq.									
0600	All colors, nailed to wood deck	1 Rots	1.50	5.333	Sq.	126	159		285	430
1500	Accessory pieces, ridge & hip, 10" x 16-1/2", 8 lb. each	"	120	.067	Ea.	3.80	1.99		5.79	7.85
1700	Rake, 6-1/2" x 16-3/4", 9 lb. each					3.80			3.80	4.18
1800	Mansard hip, 10" x 16-1/2", 9.2 lb. each					3.80			3.80	4.18
1900	Hip starter, 10" x 16-1/2", 10.5 lb. each					10.50			10.50	11.55
2000	3 or 4 way apex, 10" each side, 11.5 lb. each					12			12	13.20

07 33 63 - Vegetated Roofing

07 33 63.10 Green Roof Systems

		Crew	Daily Output	Labor-Hours	Unit	Material	2017 Bare Costs Labor	Equipment	Total	Total Incl O&P
0010	**GREEN ROOF SYSTEMS**									
0020	Soil mixture for green roof 30% sand, 55% gravel, 15% soil									
0100	Hoist and spread soil mixture 4 inch depth up to five stories tall roof	G B-13B	4000	.014	S.F.	.24	.41	.27	.92	1.24
0150	6 inch depth	G	2667	.021		.35	.61	.40	1.36	1.85
0200	8 inch depth	G	2000	.028		.47	.82	.54	1.83	2.48
0250	10 inch depth	G	1600	.035		.59	1.02	.67	2.28	3.10
0300	12 inch depth	G	1335	.042		.71	1.23	.81	2.75	3.72
0310	Alt. man-made soil mix, hoist & spread, 4" deep up to 5 stories tall roof	G	4000	.014		1.92	.41	.27	2.60	3.09
0350	Mobilization 55 ton crane to site	G 1 Eqhv	3.60	2.222	Ea.		83		83	137
0355	Hoisting cost to five stories per day (Avg. 28 picks per day)	G B-13B	1	56	Day		1,650	1,075	2,725	3,900
0360	Mobilization or demobilization, 100 ton crane to site driver & escort	G A-3E	2.50	6.400	Ea.		223	56	279	430
0365	Hoisting cost six to ten stories per day (Avg. 21 picks per day)	G B-13C	1	56	Day		1,650	1,800	3,450	4,700
0370	Hoist and spread soil mixture 4 inch depth six to ten stories tall roof	G	4000	.014	S.F.	.24	.41	.45	1.10	1.44
0375	6 inch depth	G	2667	.021		.35	.61	.68	1.64	2.15
0380	8 inch depth	G	2000	.028		.47	.82	.90	2.19	2.88
0385	10 inch depth	G	1600	.035		.59	1.02	1.13	2.74	3.60
0390	12 inch depth	G	1335	.042		.71	1.23	1.35	3.29	4.32
0400	Green roof edging treated lumber 4" x 4", no hoisting included	G 2 Carp	400	.040	L.F.	1.37	1.40		2.77	3.85
0410	4" x 6"	G	400	.040		2.06	1.40		3.46	4.60
0420	4" x 8"	G	360	.044		3.84	1.55		5.39	6.85
0430	4" x 6" double stacked	G	300	.053		4.11	1.86		5.97	7.65
0500	Green roof edging redwood lumber 4" x 4", no hoisting included	G	400	.040		6.45	1.40		7.85	9.40
0510	4" x 6"	G	400	.040		12.60	1.40		14	16.20
0520	4" x 8"	G	360	.044		23.50	1.55		25.05	28.50
0530	4" x 6" double stacked	G	300	.053		25	1.86		26.86	30.50
0550	Components, not including membrane or insulation:									
0560	Fluid applied rubber membrane, reinforced, 215 mil thick	G G-5	350	.114	S.F.	.30	3.11	.52	3.93	6.65
0570	Root barrier	G 2 Rofc	775	.021		.70	.61		1.31	1.90
0580	Moisture retention barrier and reservoir	G "	900	.018		2.66	.53		3.19	3.90
0600	Planting sedum, light soil, potted, 2-1/4" diameter, two per S.F.	G 1 Clab	420	.019		5.70	.51		6.21	7.10
0610	one per S.F.	G "	840	.010		2.85	.25		3.10	3.56
0630	Planting sedum mat per S.F. including shipping (4000 S.F. min)	G 4 Clab	4000	.008		6.85	.21		7.06	7.85
0640	Installation sedum mat system (no soil required) per S.F. (4000 S.F. min)	G "	4000	.008		9.50	.21		9.71	10.80
0645	Note: pricing of sedum mats shipped in full truck loads (4000-5000 S.F.)									

07 41 Roof Panels

07 41 13 - Metal Roof Panels

07 41 13.10 Aluminum Roof Panels

		Crew	Daily Output	Labor-Hours	Unit	Material	Labor	Equipment	Total	Total Incl O&P
0010	**ALUMINUM ROOF PANELS**									
0020	Corrugated or ribbed, .0155" thick, natural	G-3	1200	.027	S.F.	1	.87		1.87	2.55
0300	Painted	"	1200	.027	"	1.45	.87		2.32	3.05

07 41 33 - Plastic Roof Panels

07 41 33.10 Fiberglass Panels

		Crew	Daily Output	Labor-Hours	Unit	Material	Labor	Equipment	Total	Total Incl O&P
0010	**FIBERGLASS PANELS**									
0012	Corrugated panels, roofing, 8 oz. per S.F.	G-3	1000	.032	S.F.	2.24	1.04		3.28	4.20
0100	12 oz. per S.F.		1000	.032		4.32	1.04		5.36	6.50
0300	Corrugated siding, 6 oz. per S.F.		880	.036		1.93	1.18		3.11	4.09
0400	8 oz. per S.F.		880	.036		2.24	1.18		3.42	4.43
0500	Fire retardant		880	.036		3.80	1.18		4.98	6.15
0600	12 oz. siding, textured		880	.036		3.80	1.18		4.98	6.15

07 41 Roof Panels

07 41 33 – Plastic Roof Panels

07 41 33.10 Fiberglass Panels	Crew	Daily Output	Labor-Hours	Unit	Material	2017 Bare Costs Labor	Equipment	Total	Total Incl O&P
0700	Fire retardant	G-3	880	.036	S.F.	4.45	1.18		5.63	6.85
0900	Flat panels, 6 oz. per S.F., clear or colors		880	.036		2.45	1.18		3.63	4.67
1100	Fire retardant, class A		880	.036		3.50	1.18		4.68	5.80
1300	8 oz. per S.F., clear or colors		880	.036		2.55	1.18		3.73	4.78

07 42 Wall Panels

07 42 13 – Metal Wall Panels

07 42 13.20 Aluminum Siding

		Crew	Daily Output	Labor-Hours	Unit	Material	Labor	Equipment	Total	Total Incl O&P
0011	**ALUMINUM SIDING**									
6040	.024 thick smooth white single 8" wide	2 Carp	515	.031	S.F.	2.75	1.09		3.84	4.85
6060	Double 4" pattern		515	.031		2.82	1.09		3.91	4.92
6080	Double 5" pattern		550	.029		2.75	1.02		3.77	4.73
6120	Embossed white, 8" wide		515	.031		2.76	1.09		3.85	4.86
6140	Double 4" pattern		515	.031		2.80	1.09		3.89	4.90
6160	Double 5" pattern		550	.029		2.82	1.02		3.84	4.80
6170	Vertical, embossed white, 12" wide		590	.027		2.83	.95		3.78	4.70
6320	.019 thick, insulated, smooth white, 8" wide		515	.031		2.47	1.09		3.56	4.54
6340	Double 4" pattern		515	.031		2.45	1.09		3.54	4.52
6360	Double 5" pattern		550	.029		2.46	1.02		3.48	4.41
6400	Embossed white, 8" wide		515	.031		2.85	1.09		3.94	4.96
6420	Double 4" pattern		515	.031		2.87	1.09		3.96	4.98
6440	Double 5" pattern		550	.029		2.87	1.02		3.89	4.86
6500	Shake finish 10" wide white		550	.029		3.10	1.02		4.12	5.10
6600	Vertical pattern, 12" wide, white		590	.027		2.35	.95		3.30	4.18
6640	For colors add					.15			.15	.17
6700	Accessories, white									
6720	Starter strip 2-1/8"	2 Carp	610	.026	L.F.	.48	.92		1.40	2.06
6740	Sill trim		450	.036		.65	1.24		1.89	2.80
6760	Inside corner		610	.026		1.72	.92		2.64	3.42
6780	Outside corner post		610	.026		3.63	.92		4.55	5.50
6800	Door & window trim		440	.036		.62	1.27		1.89	2.81
6820	For colors add					.14			.14	.15
6900	Soffit & fascia 1' overhang solid	2 Carp	110	.145		4.47	5.10		9.57	13.40
6920	Vented		110	.145		4.50	5.10		9.60	13.45
6940	2' overhang solid		100	.160		6.50	5.60		12.10	16.50
6960	Vented		100	.160		6.50	5.60		12.10	16.50

07 42 13.30 Steel Siding

		Crew	Daily Output	Labor-Hours	Unit	Material	Labor	Equipment	Total	Total Incl O&P
0010	**STEEL SIDING**									
0020	Beveled, vinyl coated, 8" wide	1 Carp	265	.030	S.F.	1.85	1.06		2.91	3.80
0050	10" wide	"	275	.029		1.95	1.02		2.97	3.85
0081	Galv., corrugated or ribbed, on steel frame, 30 ga.	G-3	775	.041		1.25	1.34		2.59	3.62
0101	28 ga.		775	.041		1.35	1.34		2.69	3.73
0301	26 ga.		775	.041		1.83	1.34		3.17	4.25
0401	24 ga.		775	.041		2	1.34		3.34	4.44
0601	22 ga.		775	.041		2.25	1.34		3.59	4.72
0701	Colored, corrugated/ribbed, on steel frame, 10 yr. finish, 28 ga.		775	.041		2.05	1.34		3.39	4.50
0901	26 ga.		775	.041		2.17	1.34		3.51	4.63
1001	24 ga.		775	.041		2.43	1.34		3.77	4.91

07 46 Siding

07 46 23 – Wood Siding

07 46 23.10 Wood Board Siding	Crew	Daily Output	Labor-Hours	Unit	Material	2017 Bare Costs Labor	Equipment	Total	Total Incl O&P
0010 **WOOD BOARD SIDING**									
2000 Board & batten, cedar, "B" grade, 1" x 10"	1 Carp	375	.021	S.F.	5.55	.75		6.30	7.40
2200 Redwood, clear, vertical grain, 1" x 10"		375	.021		5.50	.75		6.25	7.30
2400 White pine, #2 & better, 1" x 10"		375	.021		3.18	.75		3.93	4.75
2410 White pine #2 & better, 1" x 12"		420	.019		3.18	.67		3.85	4.61
3200 Wood, cedar bevel, A grade, 1/2" x 6"		295	.027		4.38	.95		5.33	6.40
3300 1/2" x 8"		330	.024		6.70	.85		7.55	8.75
3500 3/4" x 10", clear grade		375	.021		6.65	.75		7.40	8.55
3600 "B" grade		375	.021		3.79	.75		4.54	5.40
3800 Cedar, rough sawn, 1" x 4", A grade, natural		220	.036		6.55	1.27		7.82	9.40
3900 Stained		220	.036		6.70	1.27		7.97	9.50
4100 1" x 12", board & batten, #3 & Btr., natural		420	.019		4.48	.67		5.15	6.05
4200 Stained		420	.019		4.81	.67		5.48	6.40
4400 1" x 8" channel siding, #3 & Btr., natural		330	.024		4.57	.85		5.42	6.40
4500 Stained		330	.024		4.92	.85		5.77	6.80
4700 Redwood, clear, beveled, vertical grain, 1/2" x 4"		220	.036		4.20	1.27		5.47	6.75
4750 1/2" x 6"		295	.027		4.80	.95		5.75	6.90
4800 1/2" x 8"		330	.024		5.20	.85		6.05	7.10
5000 3/4" x 10"		375	.021		4.95	.75		5.70	6.70
5200 Channel siding, 1" x 10", B grade		375	.021		4.60	.75		5.35	6.30
5250 Redwood, T&G boards, B grade, 1" x 4"		220	.036		3.30	1.27		4.57	5.75
5270 1" x 8"		330	.024		5.25	.85		6.10	7.20
5400 White pine, rough sawn, 1" x 8", natural		330	.024		2.19	.85		3.04	3.83
5500 Stained		330	.024		2.19	.85		3.04	3.83
5600 Tongue and groove, 1" x 8"		330	.024		2.19	.85		3.04	3.83

07 46 29 – Plywood Siding

07 46 29.10 Plywood Siding Options	Crew	Daily Output	Labor-Hours	Unit	Material	Labor	Equipment	Total	Total Incl O&P
0010 **PLYWOOD SIDING OPTIONS**									
0900 Plywood, medium density overlaid, 3/8" thick	2 Carp	750	.021	S.F.	1.24	.75		1.99	2.61
1000 1/2" thick		700	.023		1.50	.80		2.30	2.99
1100 3/4" thick		650	.025		1.84	.86		2.70	3.46
1600 Texture 1-11, cedar, 5/8" thick, natural		675	.024		2.67	.83		3.50	4.33
1700 Factory stained		675	.024		2.80	.83		3.63	4.47
1900 Texture 1-11, fir, 5/8" thick, natural		675	.024		1.45	.83		2.28	2.99
2000 Factory stained		675	.024		1.80	.83		2.63	3.37
2050 Texture 1-11, S.Y.P., 5/8" thick, natural		675	.024		1.37	.83		2.20	2.90
2100 Factory stained		675	.024		1.44	.83		2.27	2.97
2200 Rough sawn cedar, 3/8" thick, natural		675	.024		1.25	.83		2.08	2.77
2300 Factory stained		675	.024		1.50	.83		2.33	3.04
2500 Rough sawn fir, 3/8" thick, natural		675	.024		.90	.83		1.73	2.38
2600 Factory stained		675	.024		1.04	.83		1.87	2.53
2800 Redwood, textured siding, 5/8" thick		675	.024		1.92	.83		2.75	3.50

07 46 33 – Plastic Siding

07 46 33.10 Vinyl Siding	Crew	Daily Output	Labor-Hours	Unit	Material	Labor	Equipment	Total	Total Incl O&P
0010 **VINYL SIDING**									
3995 Clapboard profile, woodgrain texture, .048 thick, double 4	2 Carp	495	.032	S.F.	1.06	1.13		2.19	3.06
4000 Double 5		550	.029		1.06	1.02		2.08	2.87
4005 Single 8		495	.032		1.37	1.13		2.50	3.40
4010 Single 10		550	.029		1.65	1.02		2.67	3.51
4015 .044 thick, double 4		495	.032		1.04	1.13		2.17	3.04
4020 Double 5		550	.029		1.06	1.02		2.08	2.87
4025 .042 thick, double 4		495	.032		1.06	1.13		2.19	3.06

For customer support on your Residential Costs with RSMeans Data, call 800.448.8182.

429

07 46 33.10 Vinyl Siding

		Crew	Daily Output	Labor-Hours	Unit	Material	2017 Bare Costs Labor	Equipment	Total	Total Incl O&P
4030	Double 5	2 Carp	550	.029	S.F.	1.06	1.02		2.08	2.87
4035	Cross sawn texture, .040 thick, double 4		495	.032		.72	1.13		1.85	2.69
4040	Double 5		550	.029		.66	1.02		1.68	2.43
4045	Smooth texture, .042 thick, double 4		495	.032		.79	1.13		1.92	2.76
4050	Double 5		550	.029		.79	1.02		1.81	2.57
4055	Single 8		495	.032		.79	1.13		1.92	2.76
4060	Cedar texture, .044 thick, double 4		495	.032		1.13	1.13		2.26	3.14
4065	Double 6		600	.027		1.13	.93		2.06	2.81
4070	Dutch lap profile, woodgrain texture, .048 thick, double 5		550	.029		1.08	1.02		2.10	2.89
4075	.044 thick, double 4.5		525	.030		1.08	1.07		2.15	2.97
4080	.042 thick, double 4.5		525	.030		.91	1.07		1.98	2.79
4085	.040 thick, double 4.5		525	.030		.72	1.07		1.79	2.58
4100	Shake profile, 10" wide		400	.040		3.66	1.40		5.06	6.35
4105	Vertical pattern, .046 thick, double 5		550	.029		1.57	1.02		2.59	3.43
4110	.044 thick, triple 3		550	.029		1.76	1.02		2.78	3.64
4115	.040 thick, triple 4		550	.029		1.66	1.02		2.68	3.53
4120	.040 thick, triple 2.66		550	.029		1.76	1.02		2.78	3.64
4125	Insulation, fan folded extruded polystyrene, 1/4"		2000	.008		.29	.28		.57	.79
4130	3/8"		2000	.008		.32	.28		.60	.82
4135	Accessories, J channel, 5/8" pocket		700	.023	L.F.	.50	.80		1.30	1.89
4140	3/4" pocket		695	.023		.55	.80		1.35	1.95
4145	1-1/4" pocket		680	.024		.85	.82		1.67	2.31
4150	Flexible, 3/4" pocket		600	.027		2.37	.93		3.30	4.16
4155	Under sill finish trim		500	.032		.55	1.12		1.67	2.47
4160	Vinyl starter strip		700	.023		.66	.80		1.46	2.06
4165	Aluminum starter strip		700	.023		.29	.80		1.09	1.66
4170	Window casing, 2-1/2" wide, 3/4" pocket		510	.031		1.69	1.10		2.79	3.69
4175	Outside corner, woodgrain finish, 4" face, 3/4" pocket		700	.023		2.11	.80		2.91	3.67
4180	5/8" pocket		700	.023		2.11	.80		2.91	3.67
4185	Smooth finish, 4" face, 3/4" pocket		700	.023		2.11	.80		2.91	3.67
4190	7/8" pocket		690	.023		2.01	.81		2.82	3.58
4195	1-1/4" pocket		700	.023		1.41	.80		2.21	2.90
4200	Soffit and fascia, 1' overhang, solid		120	.133		4.67	4.66		9.33	12.95
4205	Vented		120	.133		4.67	4.66		9.33	12.95
4207	18" overhang, solid		110	.145		5.45	5.10		10.55	14.50
4208	Vented		110	.145		5.45	5.10		10.55	14.50
4210	2' overhang, solid		100	.160		6.25	5.60		11.85	16.20
4215	Vented		100	.160		6.25	5.60		11.85	16.20
4217	3' overhang, solid		100	.160		7.80	5.60		13.40	17.95
4218	Vented		100	.160		7.80	5.60		13.40	17.95
4220	Colors for siding and soffits, add				S.F.	.15			.15	.17
4225	Colors for accessories and trim, add				L.F.	.31			.31	.34

07 46 33.20 Polypropylene Siding

		Crew	Daily Output	Labor-Hours	Unit	Material	2017 Bare Costs Labor	Equipment	Total	Total Incl O&P
0010	**POLYPROPYLENE SIDING**									
4090	Shingle profile, random grooves, double 7	2 Carp	400	.040	S.F.	3.21	1.40		4.61	5.90
4092	Cornerpost for above	1 Carp	365	.022	L.F.	13	.77		13.77	15.60
4095	Triple 5	2 Carp	400	.040	S.F.	3.21	1.40		4.61	5.90
4097	Cornerpost for above	1 Carp	365	.022	L.F.	12.20	.77		12.97	14.70
5000	Staggered butt, double 7"	2 Carp	400	.040	S.F.	3.66	1.40		5.06	6.35
5002	Cornerpost for above	1 Carp	365	.022	L.F.	13	.77		13.77	15.60
5010	Half round, double 6-1/4"	2 Carp	360	.044	S.F.	3.66	1.55		5.21	6.65
5020	Shake profile, staggered butt, double 9"	"	510	.031	"	3.66	1.10		4.76	5.85

07 46 Siding

07 46 33 – Plastic Siding

07 46 33.20 Polypropylene Siding	Crew	Daily Output	Labor-Hours	Unit	Material	2017 Bare Costs Labor	Equipment	Total	Total Incl O&P
5022	Cornerpost for above	1 Carp	365	.022	L.F.	9.70	.77		10.47	11.95
5030	Straight butt, double 7"	2 Carp	400	.040	S.F.	3.66	1.40		5.06	6.35
5032	Cornerpost for above	1 Carp	365	.022	L.F.	12.85	.77		13.62	15.45
6000	Accessories, J channel, 5/8" pocket	2 Carp	700	.023		.50	.80		1.30	1.89
6010	3/4" pocket		695	.023		.55	.80		1.35	1.95
6020	1-1/4" pocket		680	.024		.85	.82		1.67	2.31
6030	Aluminum starter strip	↓	700	.023	↓	.29	.80		1.09	1.66

07 46 46 – Fiber Cement Siding

07 46 46.10 Fiber Cement Siding

		Crew	Daily Output	Labor-Hours	Unit	Material	2017 Bare Costs Labor	Equipment	Total	Total Incl O&P
0010	**FIBER CEMENT SIDING**									
0020	Lap siding, 5/16" thick, 6" wide, 4-3/4" exposure, smooth texture	2 Carp	415	.039	S.F.	1.29	1.35		2.64	3.66
0025	Woodgrain texture		415	.039		1.29	1.35		2.64	3.66
0030	7-1/2" wide, 6-1/4" exposure, smooth texture		425	.038		1.61	1.32		2.93	3.97
0035	Woodgrain texture		425	.038		1.61	1.32		2.93	3.97
0040	8" wide, 6-3/4" exposure, smooth texture		425	.038		1.21	1.32		2.53	3.53
0045	Rough sawn texture		425	.038		1.21	1.32		2.53	3.53
0050	9-1/2" wide, 8-1/4" exposure, smooth texture		440	.036		1.28	1.27		2.55	3.54
0055	Woodgrain texture		440	.036		1.28	1.27		2.55	3.54
0060	12" wide, 10-3/8" exposure, smooth texture		455	.035		2.06	1.23		3.29	4.33
0065	Woodgrain texture		455	.035		2.06	1.23		3.29	4.33
0070	Panel siding, 5/16" thick, smooth texture		750	.021		1.31	.75		2.06	2.69
0075	Stucco texture		750	.021		1.31	.75		2.06	2.69
0080	Grooved woodgrain texture		750	.021		1.31	.75		2.06	2.69
0085	V - grooved woodgrain texture		750	.021		1.31	.75		2.06	2.69
0088	Shingle siding, 48" x 15-1/4" panels, 7" exposure		700	.023	↓	4.15	.80		4.95	5.90
0090	Wood starter strip		400	.040	L.F.	.44	1.40		1.84	2.82
0200	Fiber cement siding, accessories, fascia, 5/4" x 3-1/2"		275	.058		.82	2.03		2.85	4.30
0210	5/4" x 5-1/2"		250	.064		1.98	2.24		4.22	5.90
0220	5/4" x 7-1/2"		225	.071		2.75	2.49		5.24	7.20
0230	5/4" x 9-1/2"	↓	210	.076	↓	3.30	2.66		5.96	8.10

07 46 73 – Soffit

07 46 73.10 Soffit Options

		Crew	Daily Output	Labor-Hours	Unit	Material	2017 Bare Costs Labor	Equipment	Total	Total Incl O&P
0010	**SOFFIT OPTIONS**									
0012	Aluminum, residential, .020" thick	1 Carp	210	.038	S.F.	2.05	1.33		3.38	4.49
0100	Baked enamel on steel, 16 or 18 ga.		105	.076		6	2.66		8.66	11.05
0300	Polyvinyl chloride, white, solid		230	.035		2.15	1.22		3.37	4.40
0400	Perforated	↓	230	.035		2.15	1.22		3.37	4.40
0500	For colors, add				↓	.15			.15	.17

07 51 Built-Up Bituminous Roofing

07 51 13 – Built-Up Asphalt Roofing

07 51 13.10 Built-Up Roofing Components

		Crew	Daily Output	Labor-Hours	Unit	Material	2017 Bare Costs Labor	Equipment	Total	Total Incl O&P
0010	**BUILT-UP ROOFING COMPONENTS**									
0012	Asphalt saturated felt, #30, 2 square per roll	1 Rofc	58	.138	Sq.	10.35	4.10		14.45	18.95
0200	#15, 4 sq. per roll, plain or perforated, not mopped		58	.138		5.30	4.10		9.40	13.40
0250	Perforated		58	.138		5.30	4.10		9.40	13.40
0300	Roll roofing, smooth, #65		15	.533		10.15	15.85		26	40
0500	#90		12	.667		44.50	19.85		64.35	85.50
0520	Mineralized		12	.667		35.50	19.85		55.35	75.50
0540	D.C. (double coverage), 19" selvage edge	↓	10	.800	↓	54	24		78	103

07 51 Built-Up Bituminous Roofing

07 51 13 – Built-Up Asphalt Roofing

07 51 13.10 Built-Up Roofing Components

		Crew	Daily Output	Labor-Hours	Unit	Material	2017 Bare Costs Labor	2017 Bare Costs Equipment	Total	Total Incl O&P
0580	Adhesive (lap cement)				Gal.	8.45			8.45	9.30

07 51 13.20 Built-Up Roofing Systems

		Crew	Daily Output	Labor-Hours	Unit	Material	2017 Bare Costs Labor	2017 Bare Costs Equipment	Total	Total Incl O&P
0010	**BUILT-UP ROOFING SYSTEMS**									
0120	Asphalt flood coat with gravel/slag surfacing, not including									
0140	Insulation, flashing or wood nailers									
0200	Asphalt base sheet, 3 plies #15 asphalt felt, mopped	G-1	22	2.545	Sq.	101	71	24	196	269
0350	On nailable decks		21	2.667		104	74.50	25	203.50	280
0500	4 plies #15 asphalt felt, mopped		20	2.800		139	78.50	26.50	244	325
0550	On nailable decks	↓	19	2.947	↓	123	82.50	28	233.50	320
2000	Asphalt flood coat, smooth surface									
2200	Asphalt base sheet & 3 plies #15 asphalt felt, mopped	G-1	24	2.333	Sq.	108	65	22	195	262
2400	On nailable decks		23	2.435		99.50	68	23	190.50	261
2600	4 plies #15 asphalt felt, mopped		24	2.333		126	65	22	213	283
2700	On nailable decks	↓	23	2.435	↓	118	68	23	209	281
4500	Coal tar pitch with gravel/slag surfacing									
4600	4 plies #15 tarred felt, mopped	G-1	21	2.667	Sq.	201	74.50	25	300.50	385
4800	3 plies glass fiber felt (type IV), mopped	"	19	2.947	"	166	82.50	28	276.50	365

07 51 13.30 Cants

		Crew	Daily Output	Labor-Hours	Unit	Material	2017 Bare Costs Labor	2017 Bare Costs Equipment	Total	Total Incl O&P
0010	**CANTS**									
0012	Lumber, treated, 4" x 4" cut diagonally	1 Rofc	325	.025	L.F.	1.83	.73		2.56	3.36
0300	Mineral or fiber, trapezoidal, 1" x 4" x 48"		325	.025		.30	.73		1.03	1.68
0400	1-1/2" x 5-5/8" x 48"	↓	325	.025	↓	.48	.73		1.21	1.88

07 52 Modified Bituminous Membrane Roofing

07 52 13 – Atactic-Polypropylene-Modified Bituminous Membrane Roofing

07 52 13.10 APP Modified Bituminous Membrane

		Crew	Daily Output	Labor-Hours	Unit	Material	2017 Bare Costs Labor	2017 Bare Costs Equipment	Total	Total Incl O&P
0010	**APP MODIFIED BITUMINOUS MEMBRANE**	R075213-30								
0020	Base sheet, #15 glass fiber felt, nailed to deck	1 Rofc	58	.138	Sq.	12.15	4.10		16.25	21
0030	Spot mopped to deck	G-1	295	.190		16.50	5.30	1.79	23.59	30
0040	Fully mopped to deck	"	192	.292		22	8.15	2.75	32.90	42.50
0050	#15 organic felt, nailed to deck	1 Rofc	58	.138		6.60	4.10		10.70	14.80
0060	Spot mopped to deck	G-1	295	.190		10.95	5.30	1.79	18.04	24
0070	Fully mopped to deck	"	192	.292	↓	16.65	8.15	2.75	27.55	36.50
2100	APP mod., smooth surf. cap sheet, poly. reinf., torched, 160 mils	G-5	2100	.019	S.F.	.74	.52	.09	1.35	1.86
2150	170 mils		2100	.019		.75	.52	.09	1.36	1.88
2200	Granule surface cap sheet, poly. reinf., torched, 180 mils		2000	.020		.94	.54	.09	1.57	2.13
2250	Smooth surface flashing, torched, 160 mils		1260	.032		.74	.86	.15	1.75	2.56
2300	170 mils		1260	.032		.75	.86	.15	1.76	2.58
2350	Granule surface flashing, torched, 180 mils	↓	1260	.032		.94	.86	.15	1.95	2.78
2400	Fibrated aluminum coating	1 Rofc	3800	.002	↓	.09	.06		.15	.22
2450	Seam heat welding	"	205	.039	L.F.	.09	1.16		1.25	2.24

07 52 16 – Styrene-Butadiene-Styrene Modified Bituminous Membrane Roofing

07 52 16.10 SBS Modified Bituminous Membrane

		Crew	Daily Output	Labor-Hours	Unit	Material	2017 Bare Costs Labor	2017 Bare Costs Equipment	Total	Total Incl O&P
0010	**SBS MODIFIED BITUMINOUS MEMBRANE**									
0080	Mod bit rfng, SBS mod, gran surf cap sheet, poly reinf									
0650	120 to 149 mils thick	G-1	2000	.028	S.F.	1.27	.78	.26	2.31	3.13
0750	150 to 160 mils	"	2000	.028		1.72	.78	.26	2.76	3.62
1150	For reflective granules, add									
1600	Smooth surface cap sheet, mopped, 145 mils	G-1	2100	.027		.80	.75	.25	1.80	2.53
1620	Lightweight base sheet, fiberglass reinforced, 35 to 47 mil	↓	2100	.027	↓	.28	.75	.25	1.28	1.96

07 52 Modified Bituminous Membrane Roofing

07 52 16 – Styrene-Butadiene-Styrene Modified Bituminous Membrane Roofing

07 52 16.10 SBS Modified Bituminous Membrane		Crew	Daily Output	Labor-Hours	Unit	Material	2017 Bare Costs Labor	Equipment	Total	Total Incl O&P
1625	Heavyweight base/ply sheet, reinforced, 87 to 120 mil thick	G-1	2100	.027	S.F.	.89	.75	.25	1.89	2.63
1650	Granulated walkpad, 180 to 220 mils	1 Rofc	400	.020		1.79	.60		2.39	3.07
1700	Smooth surface flashing, 145 mils	G-1	1260	.044		.80	1.24	.42	2.46	3.63
1800	150 mils		1260	.044		.50	1.24	.42	2.16	3.30
1900	Granular surface flashing, 150 mils		1260	.044		.70	1.24	.42	2.36	3.52
2000	160 mils	▼	1260	.044		.73	1.24	.42	2.39	3.55
2010	Elastomeric asphalt primer	1 Rofc	2600	.003		.16	.09		.25	.35
2015	Roofing asphalt, 30 lb. per square	G-1	19000	.003		.14	.08	.03	.25	.34
2020	Cold process adhesive, 20 to 30 mils thick	1 Rofc	750	.011		.24	.32		.56	.84
2025	Self adhering vapor retarder, 30 to 45 mils thick	G-5	2150	.019	▼	1.02	.51	.09	1.62	2.14
2050	Seam heat welding	1 Rofc	205	.039	L.F.	.09	1.16		1.25	2.24

07 57 Coated Foamed Roofing

07 57 13 – Sprayed Polyurethane Foam Roofing

07 57 13.10 Sprayed Polyurethane Foam Roofing (S.P.F.)		Crew	Daily Output	Labor-Hours	Unit	Material	2017 Bare Costs Labor	Equipment	Total	Total Incl O&P
0010	**SPRAYED POLYURETHANE FOAM ROOFING (S.P.F.)**									
0100	Primer for metal substrate (when required)	G-2A	3000	.008	S.F.	.49	.21	.22	.92	1.16
0200	Primer for non-metal substrate (when required)		3000	.008		.19	.21	.22	.62	.83
0300	Closed cell spray, polyurethane foam, 3 lb. per C.F. density, 1", R6.7		15000	.002		.65	.04	.04	.73	.85
0400	2", R13.4		13125	.002		1.30	.05	.05	1.40	1.58
0500	3", R18.6		11485	.002		1.96	.05	.06	2.07	2.31
0550	4", R24.8		10080	.002		2.61	.06	.07	2.74	3.05
0700	Spray-on silicone coating	▼	2500	.010		1.24	.25	.27	1.76	2.11
0800	Warranty 5-20 year manufacturer's				▼				.15	.15
0900	Warranty 20 year, no dollar limit								.20	.20

07 58 Roll Roofing

07 58 10 – Asphalt Roll Roofing

07 58 10.10 Roll Roofing		Crew	Daily Output	Labor-Hours	Unit	Material	2017 Bare Costs Labor	Equipment	Total	Total Incl O&P
0010	**ROLL ROOFING**									
0100	Asphalt, mineral surface									
0200	1 ply #15 organic felt, 1 ply mineral surfaced									
0300	Selvage roofing, lap 19", nailed & mopped	G-1	27	2.074	Sq.	76.50	58	19.60	154.10	213
0400	3 plies glass fiber felt (type IV), 1 ply mineral surfaced									
0500	Selvage roofing, lapped 19", mopped	G-1	25	2.240	Sq.	132	62.50	21	215.50	284
0600	Coated glass fiber base sheet, 2 plies of glass fiber									
0700	Felt (type IV), 1 ply mineral surfaced selvage									
0800	Roofing, lapped 19", mopped	G-1	25	2.240	Sq.	139	62.50	21	222.50	291
0900	On nailable decks	"	24	2.333	"	127	65	22	214	284
1000	3 plies glass fiber felt (type III), 1 ply mineral surfaced									
1100	Selvage roofing, lapped 19", mopped	G-1	25	2.240	Sq.	132	62.50	21	215.50	284

For customer support on your Residential Costs with RSMeans Data, call 800.448.8182.

433

07 61 Sheet Metal Roofing

07 61 13 – Standing Seam Sheet Metal Roofing

07 61 13.10 Standing Seam Sheet Metal Roofing, Field Fab.

		Crew	Daily Output	Labor-Hours	Unit	Material	2017 Bare Costs Labor	Equipment	Total	Total Incl O&P
0010	**STANDING SEAM SHEET METAL ROOFING, FIELD FABRICATED**									
0400	Copper standing seam roofing, over 10 squares, 16 oz., 125 lb. per sq.	1 Shee	1.30	6.154	Sq.	990	236		1,226	1,500
0600	18 oz., 140 lb. per sq.	"	1.20	6.667		1,100	255		1,355	1,650
1200	For abnormal conditions or small areas, add					25%	100%			
1300	For lead-coated copper, add					25%				

07 61 16 – Batten Seam Sheet Metal Roofing

07 61 16.10 Batten Seam Sheet Metal Roofing, Field Fabricated

		Crew	Daily Output	Labor-Hours	Unit	Material	2017 Bare Costs Labor	Equipment	Total	Total Incl O&P
0010	**BATTEN SEAM SHEET METAL ROOFING, FIELD FABRICATED**									
0012	Copper batten seam roofing, over 10 sq., 16 oz., 130 lb. per sq.	1 Shee	1.10	7.273	Sq.	1,250	279		1,529	1,850
0100	Zinc/copper alloy batten seam roofing, .020" thick		1.20	6.667		1,325	255		1,580	1,875
0200	Copper roofing, batten seam, over 10 sq., 18 oz., 145 lb. per sq.		1	8		1,400	305		1,705	2,050
0800	Zinc, copper alloy roofing, batten seam, .027" thick		1.15	6.957		1,675	266		1,941	2,275
0900	.032" thick		1.10	7.273		1,900	279		2,179	2,575
1000	.040" thick		1.05	7.619		2,375	292		2,667	3,125

07 61 19 – Flat Seam Sheet Metal Roofing

07 61 19.10 Flat Seam Sheet Metal Roofing, Field Fabricated

		Crew	Daily Output	Labor-Hours	Unit	Material	2017 Bare Costs Labor	Equipment	Total	Total Incl O&P
0010	**FLAT SEAM SHEET METAL ROOFING, FIELD FABRICATED**									
0900	Copper flat seam roofing, over 10 squares, 16 oz., 115 lb./sq.	1 Shee	1.20	6.667	Sq.	920	255		1,175	1,425
0950	18 oz., 130 lb./sq.		1.15	6.957		1,025	266		1,291	1,575
1000	20 oz., 145 lb./sq.		1.10	7.273		1,225	279		1,504	1,825
1008	Zinc flat seam roofing, .020" thick		1.20	6.667		1,125	255		1,380	1,675
1010	.027" thick		1.15	6.957		1,425	266		1,691	2,025
1020	.032" thick		1.12	7.143		1,625	274		1,899	2,225
1030	.040" thick		1.05	7.619		2,025	292		2,317	2,725
1100	Lead flat seam roofing, 5 lb. per S.F.		1.30	6.154		1,200	236		1,436	1,700

07 62 Sheet Metal Flashing and Trim

07 62 10 – Sheet Metal Trim

07 62 10.10 Sheet Metal Cladding

		Crew	Daily Output	Labor-Hours	Unit	Material	2017 Bare Costs Labor	Equipment	Total	Total Incl O&P
0010	**SHEET METAL CLADDING**									
0100	Aluminum, up to 6 bends, .032" thick, window casing	1 Carp	180	.044	S.F.	1.70	1.55		3.25	4.47
0200	Window sill		72	.111	L.F.	1.70	3.88		5.58	8.35
0300	Door casing		180	.044	S.F.	1.70	1.55		3.25	4.47
0400	Fascia		250	.032		1.70	1.12		2.82	3.74
0500	Rake trim		225	.036		1.70	1.24		2.94	3.95
0700	.024" thick, window casing		180	.044		1.50	1.55		3.05	4.25
0800	Window sill		72	.111	L.F.	1.50	3.88		5.38	8.15
0900	Door casing		180	.044	S.F.	1.50	1.55		3.05	4.25
1000	Fascia		250	.032		1.50	1.12		2.62	3.52
1100	Rake trim		225	.036		1.50	1.24		2.74	3.73
1200	Vinyl coated aluminum, up to 6 bends, window casing		180	.044		1.59	1.55		3.14	4.35
1300	Window sill		72	.111	L.F.	1.59	3.88		5.47	8.25
1400	Door casing		180	.044	S.F.	1.59	1.55		3.14	4.35
1500	Fascia		250	.032		1.59	1.12		2.71	3.62
1600	Rake trim		225	.036		1.59	1.24		2.83	3.83

07 65 Flexible Flashing

07 65 10 – Sheet Metal Flashing

07 65 10.10 Sheet Metal Flashing and Counter Flashing

		Crew	Daily Output	Labor-Hours	Unit	Material	2017 Bare Costs Labor	Equipment	Total	Total Incl O&P
0010	**SHEET METAL FLASHING AND COUNTER FLASHING**									
0011	Including up to 4 bends									
0020	Aluminum, mill finish, .013" thick	1 Rofc	145	.055	S.F.	.83	1.64		2.47	3.93
0030	.016" thick		145	.055		.98	1.64		2.62	4.10
0060	.019" thick		145	.055		1.27	1.64		2.91	4.42
0100	.032" thick		145	.055		1.38	1.64		3.02	4.54
0200	.040" thick		145	.055		2.35	1.64		3.99	5.60
0300	.050" thick		145	.055		2.75	1.64		4.39	6.05
0325	Mill finish 5" x 7" step flashing, .016" thick		1920	.004	Ea.	.15	.12		.27	.40
0350	Mill finish 12" x 12" step flashing, .016" thick		1600	.005	"	.55	.15		.70	.88
0400	Painted finish, add				S.F.	.33			.33	.36
1600	Copper, 16 oz. sheets, under 1000 lb.	1 Rofc	115	.070		7.90	2.07		9.97	12.50
1900	20 oz. sheets, under 1000 lb.		110	.073		10.50	2.16		12.66	15.55
2200	24 oz. sheets, under 1000 lb.		105	.076		14.75	2.27		17.02	20.50
2500	32 oz. sheets, under 1000 lb.		100	.080		19	2.38		21.38	25.50
2700	W shape for valleys, 16 oz., 24" wide		100	.080	L.F.	16.25	2.38		18.63	22.50
5800	Lead, 2.5 lb. per S.F., up to 12" wide		135	.059	S.F.	5.50	1.76		7.26	9.30
5900	Over 12" wide		135	.059		4	1.76		5.76	7.65
8900	Stainless steel sheets, 32 ga.		155	.052		3.35	1.54		4.89	6.50
9000	28 ga.		155	.052		4.25	1.54		5.79	7.50
9100	26 ga.		155	.052		4.50	1.54		6.04	7.80
9200	24 ga.		155	.052		5	1.54		6.54	8.35
9290	For mechanically keyed flashing, add					40%				
9320	Steel sheets, galvanized, 20 ga.	1 Rofc	130	.062	S.F.	1.27	1.83		3.10	4.77
9322	22 ga.		135	.059		1.23	1.76		2.99	4.59
9324	24 ga.		140	.057		.93	1.70		2.63	4.15
9326	26 ga.		148	.054		.81	1.61		2.42	3.85
9328	28 ga.		155	.052		.70	1.54		2.24	3.60
9340	30 ga.		160	.050		.59	1.49		2.08	3.39
9400	Terne coated stainless steel, .015" thick, 28 ga		155	.052		8.10	1.54		9.64	11.75
9500	.018" thick, 26 ga		155	.052		9.05	1.54		10.59	12.80
9600	Zinc and copper alloy (brass), .020" thick		155	.052		10.25	1.54		11.79	14.15
9700	.027" thick		155	.052		12.25	1.54		13.79	16.35
9800	.032" thick		155	.052		15.50	1.54		17.04	19.90
9900	.040" thick		155	.052		20.50	1.54		22.04	25.50

07 65 13 – Laminated Sheet Flashing

07 65 13.10 Laminated Sheet Flashing

		Crew	Daily Output	Labor-Hours	Unit	Material	Labor	Equipment	Total	Total Incl O&P
0010	**LAMINATED SHEET FLASHING**, Including up to 4 bends									
8550	Shower pan, 3 ply copper and fabric, 3 oz.	1 Rofc	155	.052	S.F.	4	1.54		5.54	7.25
8600	7 oz.	"	155	.052	"	4.20	1.54		5.74	7.45

07 65 19 – Plastic Sheet Flashing

07 65 19.10 Plastic Sheet Flashing and Counter Flashing

		Crew	Daily Output	Labor-Hours	Unit	Material	Labor	Equipment	Total	Total Incl O&P
0010	**PLASTIC SHEET FLASHING AND COUNTER FLASHING**									
7300	Polyvinyl chloride, black, 10 mil	1 Rofc	285	.028	S.F.	.21	.84		1.05	1.77
7400	20 mil		285	.028		.26	.84		1.10	1.83
7600	30 mil		285	.028		.34	.84		1.18	1.91
7700	60 mil		285	.028		.82	.84		1.66	2.44
8060	PVC tape, 5" x 45 mils, for joint covers, 100 L.F./roll				Ea.	175			175	193

For customer support on your Residential Costs with RSMeans Data, call 800.448.8182.

435

07 65 Flexible Flashing

07 65 23 – Rubber Sheet Flashing

07 65 23.10 Rubber Sheet Flashing and Counter Flashing	Crew	Daily Output	Labor-Hours	Unit	Material	2017 Bare Costs Labor	Equipment	Total	Total Incl O&P
0010 **RUBBER SHEET FLASHING AND COUNTER FLASHING**									
4810 EPDM 90 mils, 1" diameter pipe flashing	1 Rofc	32	.250	Ea.	19.50	7.45		26.95	35
4820 2" diameter		30	.267		19.45	7.95		27.40	36
4830 3" diameter		28	.286		21	8.50		29.50	38.50
4840 4" diameter		24	.333		24	9.90		33.90	45
4850 6" diameter		22	.364	↓	24	10.80		34.80	46.50
8100 Rubber, butyl, 1/32" thick		285	.028	S.F.	2	.84		2.84	3.74
8200 1/16" thick		285	.028		2.75	.84		3.59	4.57
8300 Neoprene, cured, 1/16" thick		285	.028		2.60	.84		3.44	4.40
8400 1/8" thick	↓	285	.028	↓	6.10	.84		6.94	8.25

07 65 26 – Self-Adhering Sheet Flashing

07 65 26.10 Self-Adhering Sheet or Roll Flashing	Crew	Daily Output	Labor-Hours	Unit	Material	Labor	Equipment	Total	Total Incl O&P
0010 **SELF-ADHERING SHEET OR ROLL FLASHING**									
0020 Self-adhered flashing, 25 mil cross laminated HDPE, 4" wide	1 Rofc	960	.008	L.F.	.20	.25		.45	.68
0040 6" wide		896	.009		.30	.27		.57	.81
0060 9" wide		832	.010		.44	.29		.73	1.02
0080 12" wide	↓	768	.010	↓	.59	.31		.90	1.22

07 71 Roof Specialties

07 71 19 – Manufactured Gravel Stops and Fasciae

07 71 19.10 Gravel Stop

07 71 19.10 Gravel Stop	Crew	Daily Output	Labor-Hours	Unit	Material	Labor	Equipment	Total	Total Incl O&P
0010 **GRAVEL STOP**									
0020 Aluminum, .050" thick, 4" face height, mill finish	1 Shee	145	.055	L.F.	6.55	2.11		8.66	10.75
0080 Duranodic finish		145	.055		7.40	2.11		9.51	11.70
0100 Painted		145	.055		7.50	2.11		9.61	11.80
1200 Copper, 16 oz., 3" face height		145	.055		24.50	2.11		26.61	30
1300 6" face height		135	.059		33.50	2.27		35.77	41
1350 Galv steel, 24 ga., 4" leg, plain, with continuous cleat, 4" face		145	.055		6.35	2.11		8.46	10.55
1360 6" face height		145	.055		6.55	2.11		8.66	10.75
1500 Polyvinyl chloride, 6" face height		135	.059		5.75	2.27		8.02	10.15
1800 Stainless steel, 24 ga., 6" face height	↓	135	.059	↓	15.50	2.27		17.77	21

07 71 19.30 Fascia

07 71 19.30 Fascia	Crew	Daily Output	Labor-Hours	Unit	Material	Labor	Equipment	Total	Total Incl O&P
0010 **FASCIA**									
0100 Aluminum, reverse board and batten, .032" thick, colored, no furring incl	1 Shee	145	.055	S.F.	6.85	2.11		8.96	11.10
0200 Residential type, aluminum	1 Carp	200	.040	L.F.	2	1.40		3.40	4.54
0220 Vinyl	"	200	.040	"	2.15	1.40		3.55	4.71
0300 Steel, galv and enameled, stock, no furring, long panels	1 Shee	145	.055	S.F.	5.30	2.11		7.41	9.40
0600 Short panels	"	115	.070	"	5.95	2.66		8.61	11

07 71 23 – Manufactured Gutters and Downspouts

07 71 23.10 Downspouts

07 71 23.10 Downspouts	Crew	Daily Output	Labor-Hours	Unit	Material	Labor	Equipment	Total	Total Incl O&P
0010 **DOWNSPOUTS**									
0020 Aluminum, embossed, .020" thick, 2" x 3"	1 Shee	190	.042	L.F.	1.08	1.61		2.69	3.89
0100 Enameled		190	.042		1.42	1.61		3.03	4.26
0300 .024" thick, 2" x 3"		180	.044		2.10	1.70		3.80	5.15
0400 3" x 4"		140	.057		2.42	2.19		4.61	6.30
0600 Round, corrugated aluminum, 3" diameter, .020" thick		190	.042		2.03	1.61		3.64	4.93
0700 4" diameter, .025" thick		140	.057	↓	3	2.19		5.19	6.95
0900 Wire strainer, round, 2" diameter		155	.052	Ea.	1.90	1.98		3.88	5.40
1000 4" diameter	↓	155	.052	↓	2.50	1.98		4.48	6.05

07 71 Roof Specialties

07 71 23 – Manufactured Gutters and Downspouts

07 71 23.10 Downspouts	Crew	Daily Output	Labor-Hours	Unit	Material	2017 Bare Costs Labor	Equipment	Total	Total Incl O&P
1200	Rectangular, perforated, 2" x 3"	1 Shee	145	.055	Ea.	2.30	2.11		4.41	6.05
1300	3" x 4"		145	.055	▼	3.30	2.11		5.41	7.15
1500	Copper, round, 16 oz., stock, 2" diameter		190	.042	L.F.	7.70	1.61		9.31	11.15
1600	3" diameter		190	.042		8.15	1.61		9.76	11.65
1800	4" diameter		145	.055		9.85	2.11		11.96	14.40
1900	5" diameter		130	.062		15.85	2.36		18.21	21.50
2100	Rectangular, corrugated copper, stock, 2" x 3"		190	.042		8.80	1.61		10.41	12.40
2200	3" x 4"		145	.055		10.50	2.11		12.61	15.10
2400	Rectangular, plain copper, stock, 2" x 3"		190	.042		11.25	1.61		12.86	15.10
2500	3" x 4"		145	.055	▼	14	2.11		16.11	18.95
2700	Wire strainers, rectangular, 2" x 3"		145	.055	Ea.	17.20	2.11		19.31	22.50
2800	3" x 4"		145	.055		17.95	2.11		20.06	23.50
3000	Round, 2" diameter		145	.055		6.50	2.11		8.61	10.70
3100	3" diameter		145	.055		7.25	2.11		9.36	11.55
3300	4" diameter		145	.055		12.25	2.11		14.36	17.05
3400	5" diameter		115	.070	▼	22.50	2.66		25.16	29.50
3600	Lead-coated copper, round, stock, 2" diameter		190	.042	L.F.	22.50	1.61		24.11	27
3700	3" diameter		190	.042		23	1.61		24.61	27.50
3900	4" diameter		145	.055		23.50	2.11		25.61	29.50
4000	5" diameter, corrugated		130	.062		23	2.36		25.36	29.50
4200	6" diameter, corrugated		105	.076		30.50	2.92		33.42	38.50
4300	Rectangular, corrugated, stock, 2" x 3"		190	.042		15.75	1.61		17.36	20
4500	Plain, stock, 2" x 3"		190	.042		24	1.61		25.61	29
4600	3" x 4"		145	.055		33.50	2.11		35.61	40
4800	Steel, galvanized, round, corrugated, 2" or 3" diameter, 28 ga.		190	.042		2.15	1.61		3.76	5.05
4900	4" diameter, 28 ga.		145	.055		2.59	2.11		4.70	6.40
5700	Rectangular, corrugated 28 ga., 2" x 3"		190	.042		2	1.61		3.61	4.90
5800	3" x 4"		145	.055		1.85	2.11		3.96	5.55
6000	Rectangular, plain, 28 ga., galvanized, 2" x 3"		190	.042		3.75	1.61		5.36	6.85
6100	3" x 4"		145	.055		4.12	2.11		6.23	8.05
6300	Epoxy painted, 24 ga., corrugated, 2" x 3"		190	.042		2.37	1.61		3.98	5.30
6400	3" x 4"		145	.055	▼	2.88	2.11		4.99	6.70
6600	Wire strainers, rectangular, 2" x 3"		145	.055	Ea.	17.10	2.11		19.21	22.50
6700	3" x 4"		145	.055		17.85	2.11		19.96	23
6900	Round strainers, 2" or 3" diameter		145	.055		3.95	2.11		6.06	7.90
7000	4" diameter		145	.055	▼	5.95	2.11		8.06	10.10
8200	Vinyl, rectangular, 2" x 3"		210	.038	L.F.	2.15	1.46		3.61	4.81
8300	Round, 2-1/2"	▼	220	.036	"	1.35	1.39		2.74	3.82

07 71 23.20 Downspout Elbows

		Crew	Daily Output	Labor-Hours	Unit	Material	2017 Bare Costs Labor	Equipment	Total	Total Incl O&P
0010	**DOWNSPOUT ELBOWS**									
0020	Aluminum, embossed, 2" x 3", .020" thick	1 Shee	100	.080	Ea.	.96	3.06		4.02	6.15
0100	Enameled		100	.080		1.75	3.06		4.81	7.05
0200	Embossed, 3" x 4", .025" thick		100	.080		4.55	3.06		7.61	10.10
0300	Enameled		100	.080		3.85	3.06		6.91	9.35
0400	Embossed, corrugated, 3" diameter, .020" thick		100	.080		2.75	3.06		5.81	8.15
0500	4" diameter, .025" thick		100	.080		5.90	3.06		8.96	11.60
0600	Copper, 16 oz., 2" diameter		100	.080		9.50	3.06		12.56	15.55
0700	3" diameter		100	.080		9.15	3.06		12.21	15.15
0800	4" diameter		100	.080		14	3.06		17.06	20.50
1000	Rectangular, 2" x 3" corrugated		100	.080		9.65	3.06		12.71	15.70
1100	3" x 4" corrugated		100	.080		13.35	3.06		16.41	19.80
1300	Vinyl, 2-1/2" diameter, 45 or 75 degree bend	▼	100	.080	▼	3.99	3.06		7.05	9.50

For customer support on your Residential Costs with RSMeans Data, call 800.448.8182.

437

07 71 23 – Manufactured Gutters and Downspouts

07 71 23.20 Downspout Elbows	Crew	Daily Output	Labor-Hours	Unit	Material	2017 Bare Costs Labor	2017 Bare Costs Equipment	Total	Total Incl O&P
1400	Tee Y junction	1 Shee	75	.107	Ea.	13	4.09		17.09	21

07 71 23.30 Gutters

		Crew	Daily Output	Labor-Hours	Unit	Material	Labor	Equipment	Total	Total Incl O&P
0010	**GUTTERS**									
0012	Aluminum, stock units, 5" K type, .027" thick, plain	1 Shee	125	.064	L.F.	2.86	2.45		5.31	7.25
0100	Enameled		125	.064		2.86	2.45		5.31	7.25
0300	5" K type, .032" thick, plain		125	.064		3.53	2.45		5.98	8
0400	Enameled		125	.064		3.64	2.45		6.09	8.10
0700	Copper, half round, 16 oz., stock units, 4" wide		125	.064		9.60	2.45		12.05	14.65
0900	5" wide		125	.064		7.40	2.45		9.85	12.25
1000	6" wide		118	.068		12.10	2.60		14.70	17.65
1200	K type, 16 oz., stock, 5" wide		125	.064		8.10	2.45		10.55	13
1300	6" wide		125	.064		8.60	2.45		11.05	13.55
1500	Lead coated copper, 16 oz., half round, stock, 4" wide		125	.064		15	2.45		17.45	20.50
1600	6" wide		118	.068		22.50	2.60		25.10	29
1800	K type, stock, 5" wide		125	.064		18.50	2.45		20.95	24.50
1900	6" wide		125	.064		19.90	2.45		22.35	26
2100	Copper clad stainless steel, K type, 5" wide		125	.064		7.75	2.45		10.20	12.65
2200	6" wide		125	.064		9.80	2.45		12.25	14.90
2400	Steel, galv, half round or box, 28 ga., 5" wide, plain		125	.064		2.15	2.45		4.60	6.45
2500	Enameled		125	.064		2.23	2.45		4.68	6.55
2700	26 ga., stock, 5" wide		125	.064		2.45	2.45		4.90	6.80
2800	6" wide		125	.064		2.83	2.45		5.28	7.20
3000	Vinyl, O.G., 4" wide	1 Carp	115	.070		1.33	2.43		3.76	5.55
3100	5" wide		115	.070		1.62	2.43		4.05	5.85
3200	4" half round, stock units		115	.070		1.38	2.43		3.81	5.60
3250	Joint connectors				Ea.	3			3	3.30
3300	Wood, clear treated cedar, fir or hemlock, 3" x 4"	1 Carp	100	.080	L.F.	10	2.80		12.80	15.70
3400	4" x 5"	"	100	.080	"	16.75	2.80		19.55	23
5000	Accessories, end cap, K type, aluminum 5"	1 Shee	625	.013	Ea.	.71	.49		1.20	1.60
5010	6"		625	.013		1.54	.49		2.03	2.51
5020	Copper, 5"		625	.013		3.25	.49		3.74	4.40
5030	6"		625	.013		3.75	.49		4.24	4.95
5040	Lead coated copper, 5"		625	.013		12.50	.49		12.99	14.55
5050	6"		625	.013		13.50	.49		13.99	15.65
5060	Copper clad stainless steel, 5"		625	.013		3	.49		3.49	4.12
5070	6"		625	.013		3.60	.49		4.09	4.78
5080	Galvanized steel, 5"		625	.013		1.35	.49		1.84	2.31
5090	6"		625	.013		2.20	.49		2.69	3.24
5100	Vinyl, 4"	1 Carp	625	.013		13.25	.45		13.70	15.35
5110	5"	"	625	.013		13.25	.45		13.70	15.35
5120	Half round, copper, 4"	1 Shee	625	.013		4.55	.49		5.04	5.80
5130	5"		625	.013		4.55	.49		5.04	5.80
5140	6"		625	.013		7.75	.49		8.24	9.35
5150	Lead coated copper, 5"		625	.013		14.20	.49		14.69	16.40
5160	6"		625	.013		21.50	.49		21.99	24.50
5170	Copper clad stainless steel, 5"		625	.013		4.50	.49		4.99	5.75
5180	6"		625	.013		4.50	.49		4.99	5.75
5190	Galvanized steel, 5"		625	.013		2.30	.49		2.79	3.35
5200	6"		625	.013		2.85	.49		3.34	3.96
5210	Outlet, aluminum, 2" x 3"		420	.019		.65	.73		1.38	1.94
5220	3" x 4"		420	.019		1.05	.73		1.78	2.38
5230	2-3/8" round		420	.019		.55	.73		1.28	1.83

07 71 Roof Specialties

07 71 23 – Manufactured Gutters and Downspouts

07 71 23.30 Gutters

		Crew	Daily Output	Labor-Hours	Unit	Material	2017 Bare Costs Labor	Equipment	Total	Total Incl O&P
5240	Copper, 2" x 3"	1 Shee	420	.019	Ea.	6.55	.73		7.28	8.40
5250	3" x 4"		420	.019		7.90	.73		8.63	9.90
5260	2-3/8" round		420	.019		4.75	.73		5.48	6.45
5270	Lead coated copper, 2" x 3"		420	.019		25.50	.73		26.23	29
5280	3" x 4"		420	.019		29	.73		29.73	33
5290	2-3/8" round		420	.019		25.50	.73		26.23	29
5300	Copper clad stainless steel, 2" x 3"		420	.019		6.50	.73		7.23	8.35
5310	3" x 4"		420	.019		8	.73		8.73	10
5320	2-3/8" round		420	.019		4.75	.73		5.48	6.45
5330	Galvanized steel, 2" x 3"		420	.019		3.25	.73		3.98	4.80
5340	3" x 4"		420	.019		5	.73		5.73	6.70
5350	2-3/8" round		420	.019		4	.73		4.73	5.60
5360	K type mitres, aluminum		65	.123		3.10	4.71		7.81	11.30
5370	Copper		65	.123		17.50	4.71		22.21	27
5380	Lead coated copper		65	.123		54.50	4.71		59.21	68
5390	Copper clad stainless steel		65	.123		27.50	4.71		32.21	38.50
5400	Galvanized steel		65	.123		23	4.71		27.71	33
5420	Half round mitres, copper		65	.123		64	4.71		68.71	78.50
5430	Lead coated copper		65	.123		90	4.71		94.71	107
5440	Copper clad stainless steel		65	.123		56.50	4.71		61.21	70
5450	Galvanized steel		65	.123		25.50	4.71		30.21	36
5460	Vinyl mitres and outlets		65	.123		10	4.71		14.71	18.90
5470	Sealant		940	.009	L.F.	.01	.33		.34	.55
5480	Soldering		96	.083	"	.25	3.19		3.44	5.65

07 71 23.35 Gutter Guard

		Crew	Daily Output	Labor-Hours	Unit	Material	2017 Bare Costs Labor	Equipment	Total	Total Incl O&P
0010	**GUTTER GUARD**									
0020	6" wide strip, aluminum mesh	1 Carp	500	.016	L.F.	2.55	.56		3.11	3.75
0100	Vinyl mesh	"	500	.016	"	2.75	.56		3.31	3.97

07 71 43 – Drip Edge

07 71 43.10 Drip Edge, Rake Edge, Ice Belts

		Crew	Daily Output	Labor-Hours	Unit	Material	2017 Bare Costs Labor	Equipment	Total	Total Incl O&P
0010	**DRIP EDGE, RAKE EDGE, ICE BELTS**									
0020	Aluminum, .016" thick, 5" wide, mill finish	1 Carp	400	.020	L.F.	.57	.70		1.27	1.80
0100	White finish		400	.020		.63	.70		1.33	1.86
0200	8" wide, mill finish		400	.020		1.50	.70		2.20	2.82
0300	Ice belt, 28" wide, mill finish		100	.080		7.75	2.80		10.55	13.25
0310	Vented, mill finish		400	.020		1.99	.70		2.69	3.36
0320	Painted finish		400	.020		2.24	.70		2.94	3.63
0400	Galvanized, 5" wide		400	.020		.60	.70		1.30	1.83
0500	8" wide, mill finish		400	.020		.82	.70		1.52	2.07
0510	Rake edge, aluminum, 1-1/2" x 1-1/2"		400	.020		.33	.70		1.03	1.53
0520	3-1/2" x 1-1/2"		400	.020		.45	.70		1.15	1.67

For customer support on your Residential Costs with RSMeans Data, call 800.448.8182.

439

07 72 Roof Accessories

07 72 23 – Relief Vents

07 72 23.20 Vents

07 72 23.20 Vents		Crew	Daily Output	Labor-Hours	Unit	Material	2017 Bare Costs Labor	Equipment	Total	Total Incl O&P
0010	**VENTS**									
0100	Soffit or eave, aluminum, mill finish, strips, 2-1/2" wide	1 Carp	200	.040	L.F.	.46	1.40		1.86	2.85
0200	3" wide		200	.040		.48	1.40		1.88	2.87
0300	Enamel finish, 3" wide		200	.040		.51	1.40		1.91	2.90
0400	Mill finish, rectangular, 4" x 16"		72	.111	Ea.	1.52	3.88		5.40	8.15
0500	8" x 16"		72	.111		2.33	3.88		6.21	9.05
2420	Roof ventilator	Q-9	16	1		55	34.50		89.50	118
2500	Vent, roof vent	1 Rofc	24	.333		27.50	9.90		37.40	49

07 72 26 – Ridge Vents

07 72 26.10 Ridge Vents and Accessories

		Crew	Daily Output	Labor-Hours	Unit	Material	Labor	Equipment	Total	Total Incl O&P
0010	**RIDGE VENTS AND ACCESSORIES**									
0100	Aluminum strips, mill finish	1 Rofc	160	.050	L.F.	2.88	1.49		4.37	5.90
0150	Painted finish		160	.050	"	4.13	1.49		5.62	7.30
0200	Connectors		48	.167	Ea.	4.80	4.96		9.76	14.45
0300	End caps		48	.167	"	2.08	4.96		7.04	11.45
0400	Galvanized strips		160	.050	L.F.	3.63	1.49		5.12	6.75
0430	Molded polyethylene, shingles not included		160	.050	"	2.75	1.49		4.24	5.75
0440	End plugs		48	.167	Ea.	2.08	4.96		7.04	11.45
0450	Flexible roll, shingles not included		160	.050	L.F.	2.35	1.49		3.84	5.35
2300	Ridge vent strip, mill finish	1 Shee	155	.052	"	3.95	1.98		5.93	7.65

07 72 53 – Snow Guards

07 72 53.10 Snow Guard Options

		Crew	Daily Output	Labor-Hours	Unit	Material	Labor	Equipment	Total	Total Incl O&P
0010	**SNOW GUARD OPTIONS**									
0100	Slate & asphalt shingle roofs, fastened with nails	1 Rofc	160	.050	Ea.	12.55	1.49		14.04	16.55
0200	Standing seam metal roofs, fastened with set screws		48	.167		16.95	4.96		21.91	28
0300	Surface mount for metal roofs, fastened with solder		48	.167		8.45	4.96		13.41	18.45
0400	Double rail pipe type, including pipe		130	.062	L.F.	34	1.83		35.83	41

07 72 80 – Vents

07 72 80.30 Vent Options

		Crew	Daily Output	Labor-Hours	Unit	Material	Labor	Equipment	Total	Total Incl O&P
0010	**VENT OPTIONS**									
0800	Polystyrene baffles, 12" wide for 16" O.C. rafter spacing	1 Carp	90	.089	Ea.	.44	3.11		3.55	5.70
0900	For 24" O.C. rafter spacing	"	110	.073	"	.78	2.54		3.32	5.10

07 76 Roof Pavers

07 76 16 – Roof Decking Pavers

07 76 16.10 Roof Pavers and Supports

		Crew	Daily Output	Labor-Hours	Unit	Material	Labor	Equipment	Total	Total Incl O&P
0010	**ROOF PAVERS AND SUPPORTS**									
1000	Roof decking pavers, concrete blocks, 2" thick, natural	1 Clab	115	.070	S.F.	3.37	1.85		5.22	6.80
1100	Colors		115	.070	"	3.73	1.85		5.58	7.20
1200	Support pedestal, bottom cap		960	.008	Ea.	3	.22		3.22	3.67
1300	Top cap		960	.008		4.80	.22		5.02	5.65
1400	Leveling shims, 1/16"		1920	.004		1.20	.11		1.31	1.51
1500	1/8"		1920	.004		1.20	.11		1.31	1.51
1600	Buffer pad		960	.008		2.50	.22		2.72	3.12
1700	PVC legs (4" SDR 35)		2880	.003	Inch	.13	.07		.20	.26
2000	Alternate pricing method, system in place		101	.079	S.F.	7	2.11		9.11	11.20

07 91 Preformed Joint Seals

07 91 13 – Compression Seals

07 91 13.10 Compression Seals

		Crew	Daily Output	Labor-Hours	Unit	Material	2017 Bare Costs Labor	Equipment	Total	Total Incl O&P
0010	**COMPRESSION SEALS**									
4900	O-ring type cord, 1/4"	1 Bric	472	.017	L.F.	.43	.59		1.02	1.46
4910	1/2"		440	.018		1.21	.63		1.84	2.39
4920	3/4"		424	.019		2.43	.66		3.09	3.77
4930	1"		408	.020		4.10	.68		4.78	5.65
4940	1-1/4"		384	.021		7.50	.73		8.23	9.45
4950	1-1/2"		368	.022		9.25	.76		10.01	11.40
4960	1-3/4"		352	.023		18.75	.79		19.54	22
4970	2"		344	.023		22.50	.81		23.31	26.50

07 91 16 – Joint Gaskets

07 91 16.10 Joint Gaskets

		Crew	Daily Output	Labor-Hours	Unit	Material	Labor	Equipment	Total	Total Incl O&P
0010	**JOINT GASKETS**									
4400	Joint gaskets, neoprene, closed cell w/adh, 1/8" x 3/8"	1 Bric	240	.033	L.F.	.32	1.16		1.48	2.30
4500	1/4" x 3/4"		215	.037		.62	1.30		1.92	2.86
4700	1/2" x 1"		200	.040		1.45	1.39		2.84	3.94
4800	3/4" x 1-1/2"		165	.048		1.60	1.69		3.29	4.60

07 91 23 – Backer Rods

07 91 23.10 Backer Rods

		Crew	Daily Output	Labor-Hours	Unit	Material	Labor	Equipment	Total	Total Incl O&P
0010	**BACKER RODS**									
0030	Backer rod, polyethylene, 1/4" diameter	1 Bric	4.60	1.739	C.L.F.	2.37	60.50		62.87	105
0050	1/2" diameter		4.60	1.739		4.28	60.50		64.78	107
0070	3/4" diameter		4.60	1.739		6.75	60.50		67.25	109
0090	1" diameter		4.60	1.739		12.10	60.50		72.60	115

07 91 26 – Joint Fillers

07 91 26.10 Joint Fillers

		Crew	Daily Output	Labor-Hours	Unit	Material	Labor	Equipment	Total	Total Incl O&P
0010	**JOINT FILLERS**									
4360	Butyl rubber filler, 1/4" x 1/4"	1 Bric	290	.028	L.F.	.23	.96		1.19	1.86
4365	1/2" x 1/2"		250	.032		.90	1.12		2.02	2.86
4370	1/2" x 3/4"		210	.038		1.35	1.33		2.68	3.72
4375	3/4" x 3/4"		230	.035		2.03	1.21		3.24	4.26
4380	1" x 1"		180	.044		2.71	1.55		4.26	5.60
4390	For coloring, add					12%				
4980	Polyethylene joint backing, 1/4" x 2"	1 Bric	2.08	3.846	C.L.F.	13.20	134		147.20	240
4990	1/4" x 6"		1.28	6.250	"	29	218		247	395
5600	Silicone, room temp vulcanizing foam seal, 1/4" x 1/2"		1312	.006	L.F.	.46	.21		.67	.87
5610	1/2" x 1/2"		656	.012		.93	.43		1.36	1.73
5620	1/2" x 3/4"		442	.018		1.39	.63		2.02	2.59
5630	3/4" x 3/4"		328	.024		2.08	.85		2.93	3.72
5640	1/8" x 1"		1312	.006		.46	.21		.67	.87
5650	1/8" x 3"		442	.018		1.39	.63		2.02	2.59
5670	1/4" x 3"		295	.027		2.78	.95		3.73	4.65
5680	1/4" x 6"		148	.054		5.55	1.88		7.43	9.25
5690	1/2" x 6"		82	.098		11.10	3.40		14.50	17.90
5700	1/2" x 9"		52.50	.152		16.65	5.30		21.95	27.50
5710	1/2" x 12"		33	.242		22	8.45		30.45	38.50

For customer support on your Residential Costs with RSMeans Data, call 800.448.8182.

441

07 92 Joint Sealants

07 92 13 – Elastomeric Joint Sealants

07 92 13.20 Caulking and Sealant Options

		Crew	Daily Output	Labor-Hours	Unit	Material	2017 Bare Costs Labor	Equipment	Total	Total Incl O&P
0010	**CAULKING AND SEALANT OPTIONS**									
0050	Latex acrylic based, bulk				Gal.	27			27	29.50
0055	Bulk in place 1/4" x 1/4" bead	1 Bric	300	.027	L.F.	.08	.93		1.01	1.65
0060	1/4" x 3/8"		294	.027		.14	.95		1.09	1.74
0065	1/4" x 1/2"		288	.028		.19	.97		1.16	1.84
0075	3/8" x 3/8"		284	.028		.21	.98		1.19	1.88
0080	3/8" x 1/2"		280	.029		.28	1		1.28	1.98
0085	3/8" x 5/8"		276	.029		.35	1.01		1.36	2.09
0095	3/8" x 3/4"		272	.029		.42	1.02		1.44	2.18
0100	1/2" x 1/2"		275	.029		.38	1.01		1.39	2.11
0105	1/2" x 5/8"		269	.030		.47	1.04		1.51	2.26
0110	1/2" x 3/4"		263	.030		.56	1.06		1.62	2.40
0115	1/2" x 7/8"		256	.031		.66	1.09		1.75	2.55
0120	1/2" x 1"		250	.032		.75	1.12		1.87	2.70
0125	3/4" x 3/4"		244	.033		.85	1.14		1.99	2.85
0130	3/4" x 1"		225	.036		1.13	1.24		2.37	3.32
0135	1" x 1"	▼	200	.040	▼	1.50	1.39		2.89	3.99
0190	Cartridges				Gal.	33			33	36
0200	11 fl. oz. cartridge				Ea.	2.82			2.82	3.10
0500	1/4" x 1/2"	1 Bric	288	.028	L.F.	.23	.97		1.20	1.88
0600	1/2" x 1/2"		275	.029		.46	1.01		1.47	2.21
0800	3/4" x 3/4"		244	.033		1.04	1.14		2.18	3.06
0900	3/4" x 1"		225	.036		1.38	1.24		2.62	3.60
1000	1" x 1"	▼	200	.040	▼	1.73	1.39		3.12	4.24
1400	Butyl based, bulk				Gal.	37			37	40.50
1500	Cartridges				"	40.50			40.50	44.50
1700	1/4" x 1/2", 154 L.F./gal.	1 Bric	288	.028	L.F.	.24	.97		1.21	1.89
1800	1/2" x 1/2", 77 L.F./gal.	"	275	.029	"	.48	1.01		1.49	2.23
2300	Polysulfide compounds, 1 component, bulk				Gal.	84			84	92.50
2400	Cartridges				"	130			130	143
2600	1 or 2 component, in place, 1/4" x 1/4", 308 L.F./gal.	1 Bric	300	.027	L.F.	.27	.93		1.20	1.86
2700	1/2" x 1/4", 154 L.F./gal.		288	.028		.55	.97		1.52	2.23
2900	3/4" x 3/8", 68 L.F./gal.		272	.029		1.24	1.02		2.26	3.08
3000	1" x 1/2", 38 L.F./gal.		250	.032	▼	2.21	1.12		3.33	4.30
3200	Polyurethane, 1 or 2 component				Gal.	53.50			53.50	58.50
3300	Cartridges				"	67			67	73.50
3500	Bulk, in place, 1/4" x 1/4"	1 Bric	300	.027	L.F.	.17	.93		1.10	1.75
3655	1/2" x 1/4"		288	.028		.35	.97		1.32	2.01
3800	3/4" x 3/8"		272	.029		.78	1.02		1.80	2.58
3900	1" x 1/2"		250	.032	▼	1.38	1.12		2.50	3.39
4100	Silicone rubber, bulk				Gal.	54			54	59.50
4200	Cartridges				"	53			53	58.50

07 92 19 – Acoustical Joint Sealants

07 92 19.10 Acoustical Sealant

		Crew	Daily Output	Labor-Hours	Unit	Material	Labor	Equipment	Total	Total Incl O&P
0010	**ACOUSTICAL SEALANT**									
0020	Acoustical sealant, elastomeric, cartridges				Ea.	8.50			8.50	9.35
0025	In place, 1/4" x 1/4"	1 Bric	300	.027	L.F.	.35	.93		1.28	1.94
0030	1/4" x 1/2"		288	.028		.69	.97		1.66	2.39
0035	1/2" x 1/2"		275	.029		1.39	1.01		2.40	3.23
0040	1/2" x 3/4"		263	.030		2.08	1.06		3.14	4.07
0045	3/4" x 3/4"		244	.033		3.13	1.14		4.27	5.35
0050	1" x 1"	▼	200	.040	▼	5.55	1.39		6.94	8.45

442

Estimating Tips
08 10 00 Doors and Frames

All exterior doors should be addressed for their energy conservation (insulation and seals).

- Most metal doors and frames look alike, but there may be significant differences among them. When estimating these items, be sure to choose the line item that most closely compares to the specification or door schedule requirements regarding:
  - □ type of metal
  - □ metal gauge
  - □ door core material
  - □ fire rating
  - □ finish

- Wood and plastic doors vary considerably in price. The primary determinant is the veneer material. Lauan, birch, and oak are the most common veneers. Other variables include the following:
  - □ hollow or solid core
  - □ fire rating
  - □ flush or raised panel
  - □ finish

- Door pricing includes bore for cylindrical locksets and mortise for hinges.

08 30 00 Specialty Doors and Frames

- There are many varieties of special doors, and they are usually priced per each. Add frames, hardware, or operators required for a complete installation.

08 40 00 Entrances, Storefronts, and Curtain Walls

- Glazed curtain walls consist of the metal tube framing and the glazing material. The cost data in this subdivision is presented for the metal tube framing alone or the composite wall. If your estimate requires a detailed takeoff of the framing, be sure to add the glazing cost and any tints.

08 50 00 Windows

- Steel windows are unglazed and aluminum can be glazed or unglazed. Some metal windows are priced without glass. Refer to 08 80 00 Glazing for glass pricing. The grade C indicates commercial grade windows, usually ASTM C-35.

- All wood windows and vinyl are priced preglazed. The glazing is insulating glass. Add the cost of screens and grills if required and not already included.

08 70 00 Hardware

- Hardware costs add considerably to the cost of a door. The most efficient method to determine the hardware requirements for a project is to review the door and hardware schedule together. One type of door may have different hardware, depending on the door usage.

- Door hinges are priced by the pair, with most doors requiring 1-1/2 pairs per door. The hinge prices do not include installation labor, because it is included in door installation.

Hinges are classified according to the frequency of use, base material, and finish.

08 80 00 Glazing

- Different openings require different types of glass. The most common types are:
  - □ float
  - □ tempered
  - □ insulating
  - □ impact-resistant
  - □ ballistic-resistant

- Most exterior windows are glazed with insulating glass. Entrance doors and window walls, where the glass is less than 18" from the floor, are generally glazed with tempered glass. Interior windows and some residential windows are glazed with float glass.

- Coastal communities require the use of impact-resistant glass, dependent on wind speed.

- The insulation or 'u' value is a strong consideration, along with solar heat gain, to determine total energy efficiency.

Reference Numbers

Reference numbers are shown at the beginning of some major classifications. These numbers refer to related items in the Reference Section. The reference information may be an estimating procedure, an alternate pricing method, or technical information.

Note: Not all subdivisions listed here necessarily appear. ∎

08 01 53.81 Solid Vinyl Replacement Windows		Crew	Daily Output	Labor-Hours	Unit	Material	2017 Bare Costs Labor	Equipment	Total	Total Incl O&P
0010	**SOLID VINYL REPLACEMENT WINDOWS** R085313-20									
0020	Double hung, insulated glass, up to 83 united inches	G	2 Carp	8	2	Ea.	350	70		420	500
0040	84 to 93	G		8	2		400	70		470	555
0060	94 to 101	G		6	2.667		400	93		493	595
0080	102 to 111	G		6	2.667		420	93		513	615
0100	112 to 120	G		6	2.667		445	93		538	645
0120	For each united inch over 120, add	G		800	.020	Inch	5.60	.70		6.30	7.30
0140	Casement windows, one operating sash, 42 to 60 united inches	G		8	2	Ea.	224	70		294	365
0160	61 to 70	G		8	2		254	70		324	395
0180	71 to 80	G		8	2		277	70		347	420
0200	81 to 96	G		8	2		293	70		363	435
0220	Two operating sash, 58 to 78 united inches	G		8	2		445	70		515	605
0240	79 to 88	G		8	2		490	70		560	650
0260	89 to 98	G		8	2		515	70		585	685
0280	99 to 108	G		6	2.667		540	93		633	750
0300	109 to 121	G		6	2.667		585	93		678	795
0320	Two operating, one fixed sash, 73 to 108 united inches	G		8	2		705	70		775	890
0340	109 to 118	G		8	2		740	70		810	925
0360	119 to 128	G		6	2.667		760	93		853	990
0380	129 to 138	G		6	2.667		820	93		913	1,050
0400	139 to 156	G		6	2.667		860	93		953	1,100
0420	Four operating sash, 98 to 118 united inches	G		8	2		1,000	70		1,070	1,225
0440	119 to 128	G		8	2		1,075	70		1,145	1,300
0460	129 to 138	G		6	2.667		1,150	93		1,243	1,400
0480	139 to 148	G		6	2.667		1,200	93		1,293	1,475
0500	149 to 168	G		6	2.667		1,275	93		1,368	1,550
0520	169 to 178	G		6	2.667		1,400	93		1,493	1,675
0560	Fixed picture window, up to 63 united inches	G		8	2		170	70		240	305
0580	64 to 83	G		8	2		200	70		270	335
0600	84 to 101	G		8	2		240	70		310	380
0620	For each united inch over 101, add	G		900	.018	Inch	2.85	.62		3.47	4.18
0800	Cellulose fiber insulation, poured into sash balance cavity	G	1 Carp	36	.222	C.F.	.69	7.75		8.44	13.75
0820	Silicone caulking at perimeter	G	"	800	.010	L.F.	.17	.35		.52	.77
2000	Impact resistant replacement windows										
2005	Laminated glass, 120 mph rating, measure in united inches										
2010	Installation labor does not cover any rework of the window opening										
2020	Double hung, insulated glass, up to 101 united inches		2 Carp	8	2	Ea.	520	70		590	685
2025	For each united inch over 101, add			80	.200	Inch	3.30	7		10.30	15.35
2100	Casement windows, impact resistant, up to 60 united inches			8	2	Ea.	480	70		550	640
2120	61 to 70			8	2		505	70		575	670
2130	71 to 80			8	2		535	70		605	700
2140	81 to 100			8	2		550	70		620	715
2150	For each united inch over 100, add			80	.200	Inch	4.65	7		11.65	16.80
2200	Awning windows, impact resistant, up to 60 united inches			8	2	Ea.	490	70		560	655
2220	61 to 70			8	2		515	70		585	680
2230	71 to 80			8	2		525	70		595	690
2240	For each united inch over 80, add			80	.200	Inch	4.65	7		11.65	16.80
2300	Picture windows, impact resistant, up to 63 united inches			8	2	Ea.	355	70		425	505
2320	63 to 83			8	2		385	70		455	535
2330	84 to 101			8	2		420	70		490	575
2340	For each united inch over 101, add			80	.200	Inch	3.30	7		10.30	15.35

08 05 05 – Selective Demolition for Openings

08 05 05.10 Selective Demolition Doors		Crew	Daily Output	Labor-Hours	Unit	Material	2017 Bare Costs Labor	Equipment	Total	Total Incl O&P
0010	**SELECTIVE DEMOLITION DOORS** R024119-10									
0200	Doors, exterior, 1-3/4" thick, single, 3' x 7' high	1 Clab	16	.500	Ea.		13.30		13.30	22.50
0210	3' x 8' high		10	.800			21.50		21.50	35.50
0215	Double, 3' x 8' high		6	1.333			35.50		35.50	59.50
0220	Double, 6' x 7' high		12	.667			17.75		17.75	29.50
0500	Interior, 1-3/8" thick, single, 3' x 7' high		20	.400			10.65		10.65	17.80
0520	Double, 6' x 7' high		16	.500			13.30		13.30	22.50
0700	Bi-folding, 3' x 6'-8" high		20	.400			10.65		10.65	17.80
0720	6' x 6'-8" high		18	.444			11.80		11.80	19.80
0900	Bi-passing, 3' x 6'-8" high		16	.500			13.30		13.30	22.50
0940	6' x 6'-8" high		14	.571			15.20		15.20	25.50
0960	Interior metal door 1-3/4" thick, 3'-0" x 6'-8"		18	.444			11.80		11.80	19.80
0980	Interior metal door 1-3/4" thick, 3'-0" x 7'-0"		18	.444			11.80		11.80	19.80
1000	Interior wood door 1-3/4" thick, 3'-0" x 6'-8"		20	.400			10.65		10.65	17.80
1020	Interior wood door 1-3/4" thick, 3'-0" x 7'-0"		20	.400			10.65		10.65	17.80
1100	Door demo, floor door	2 Sswk	5	3.200			123		123	223
1500	Remove and reset, hollow core	1 Carp	8	1			35		35	58.50
1520	Solid		6	1.333			46.50		46.50	78
2000	Frames, including trim, metal		8	1			35		35	58.50
2200	Wood	2 Carp	32	.500			17.50		17.50	29
2201	Alternate pricing method	1 Carp	200	.040	L.F.		1.40		1.40	2.34
3000	Special doors, counter doors	2 Carp	6	2.667	Ea.		93		93	156
3300	Glass, sliding, including frames		12	1.333			46.50		46.50	78
3400	Overhead, commercial, 12' x 12' high		4	4			140		140	234
3500	Residential, 9' x 7' high		8	2			70		70	117
3540	16' x 7' high		7	2.286			80		80	134
3600	Remove and reset, small		4	4			140		140	234
3620	Large		2.50	6.400			224		224	375
3660	Remove and reset elec. garage door opener	1 Carp	8	1			35		35	58.50
4000	Residential lockset, exterior		28	.286			10		10	16.70
4010	Residential lockset, exterior w/deadbolt		26	.308			10.75		10.75	18
4020	Residential lockset, interior		30	.267			9.30		9.30	15.60
4200	Deadbolt lock		32	.250			8.75		8.75	14.60
4224	Pocket door, no frame		8	1			35		35	58.50
5590	Remove mail slot	1 Clab	45	.178			4.73		4.73	7.90
5600	Remove door sidelight	1 Carp	6	1.333			46.50		46.50	78

08 05 05.20 Selective Demolition of Windows

08 05 05.20 Selective Demolition of Windows		Crew	Daily Output	Labor-Hours	Unit	Material	Labor	Equipment	Total	Total Incl O&P
0010	**SELECTIVE DEMOLITION OF WINDOWS** R024119-10									
0200	Aluminum, including trim, to 12 S.F.	1 Clab	16	.500	Ea.		13.30		13.30	22.50
0240	To 25 S.F.		11	.727			19.35		19.35	32.50
0280	To 50 S.F.		5	1.600			42.50		42.50	71
0320	Storm windows/screens, to 12 S.F.		27	.296			7.90		7.90	13.20
0360	To 25 S.F.		21	.381			10.15		10.15	16.95
0400	To 50 S.F.		16	.500			13.30		13.30	22.50
0500	Screens, incl. aluminum frame, small		20	.400			10.65		10.65	17.80
0510	Large		16	.500			13.30		13.30	22.50
0600	Glass, up to 10 S.F. per window		200	.040	S.F.		1.06		1.06	1.78
0620	Over 10 S.F. per window		150	.053	"		1.42		1.42	2.37
2000	Wood, including trim, to 12 S.F.		22	.364	Ea.		9.65		9.65	16.20
2020	To 25 S.F.		18	.444			11.80		11.80	19.80
2060	To 50 S.F.		13	.615			16.35		16.35	27.50
2065	To 180 S.F.		8	1			26.50		26.50	44.50

08 05 Common Work Results for Openings

08 05 05 – Selective Demolition for Openings

08 05 05.20 Selective Demolition of Windows		Crew	Daily Output	Labor-Hours	Unit	Material	2017 Bare Costs Labor	Equipment	Total	Total Incl O&P
4300	Remove bay/bow window	2 Carp	6	2.667	Ea.		93		93	156
4410	Remove skylight, plstc domes, flush/curb mtd	"	395	.041	S.F.		1.42		1.42	2.37
4420	Remove skylight, plstc/glass up to 2' x 3'	1 Carp	15	.533	Ea.		18.65		18.65	31
4440	Remove skylight, plstc/glass up to 4' x 6'	2 Carp	10	1.600			56		56	93.50
4480	Remove roof window up to 3' x 4'	1 Carp	8	1			35		35	58.50
4500	Remove roof window up to 4' x 6'	2 Carp	6	2.667			93		93	156
5020	Remove and reset window, up to a 2' x 2' window	1 Carp	6	1.333			46.50		46.50	78
5040	Up to a 3' x 3' window		4	2			70		70	117
5080	Up to a 4' x 5' window	▼	2	4	▼		140		140	234
6000	Screening only	1 Clab	4000	.002	S.F.		.05		.05	.09
9100	Window awning, residential	"	80	.100	L.F.		2.66		2.66	4.45

08 11 Metal Doors and Frames

08 11 63 – Metal Screen and Storm Doors and Frames

08 11 63.23 Aluminum Screen and Storm Doors and Frames

08 11 63.23 Aluminum Screen and Storm Doors and Frames		Crew	Daily Output	Labor-Hours	Unit	Material	2017 Bare Costs Labor	Equipment	Total	Total Incl O&P
0010	**ALUMINUM SCREEN AND STORM DOORS AND FRAMES**									
0020	Combination storm and screen									
0420	Clear anodic coating, 2'-8" wide	2 Carp	14	1.143	Ea.	208	40		248	295
0440	3'-0" wide	"	14	1.143	"	180	40		220	265
0500	For 7'-0" door height, add					8%				
1020	Mill finish, 2'-8" wide	2 Carp	14	1.143	Ea.	245	40		285	335
1040	3'-0" wide	"	14	1.143		265	40		305	360
1100	For 7'-0" door, add					8%				
1520	White painted, 2'-8" wide	2 Carp	14	1.143		288	40		328	380
1540	3'-0" wide		14	1.143		300	40		340	395
1541	Storm door, painted, alum., insul., 6'-8" x 2'-6" wide		14	1.143		280	40		320	375
1545	2'-8" wide	▼	14	1.143		285	40		325	380
1600	For 7'-0" door, add					8%				
1800	Aluminum screen door, 6'-8" x 2'-8" wide	2 Carp	14	1.143		159	40		199	242
1810	3'-0" wide	"	14	1.143	▼	275	40		315	370
2000	Wood door & screen, see Section 08 14 33.20									

08 12 Metal Frames

08 12 13 – Hollow Metal Frames

08 12 13.13 Standard Hollow Metal Frames

08 12 13.13 Standard Hollow Metal Frames			Crew	Daily Output	Labor-Hours	Unit	Material	2017 Bare Costs Labor	Equipment	Total	Total Incl O&P
0010	**STANDARD HOLLOW METAL FRAMES**										
0020	16 ga., up to 5-3/4" jamb depth										
0025	3'-0" x 6'-8" single	G	2 Carp	16	1	Ea.	149	35		184	223
0028	3'-6" wide, single	G		16	1		163	35		198	238
0030	4'-0" wide, single	G		16	1		162	35		197	237
0040	6'-0" wide, double	G		14	1.143		207	40		247	294
0045	8'-0" wide, double	G		14	1.143		217	40		257	305
0100	3'-0" x 7'-0" single	G		16	1		157	35		192	232
0110	3'-6" wide, single	G		16	1		168	35		203	244
0112	4'-0" wide, single	G		16	1		168	35		203	244
0140	6'-0" wide, double	G		14	1.143		198	40		238	285
0145	8'-0" wide, double	G		14	1.143		234	40		274	325
1000	16 ga., up to 4-7/8" deep, 3'-0" x 7'-0" single	G		16	1		180	35		215	256
1140	6'-0" wide, double	G	▼	14	1.143	▼	203	40		243	290

446

08 12 Metal Frames

08 12 13 – Hollow Metal Frames

08 12 13.13 Standard Hollow Metal Frames		Crew	Daily Output	Labor-Hours	Unit	Material	2017 Bare Costs Labor	Equipment	Total	Total Incl O&P
1200	16 ga., 8-3/4" deep, 3'-0" x 7'-0" single	G 2 Carp	16	1	Ea.	202	35		237	281
1240	6'-0" wide, double	G	14	1.143		237	40		277	330
2800	14 ga., up to 3-7/8" deep, 3'-0" x 7'-0" single	G	16	1		185	35		220	263
2840	6'-0" wide, double	G	14	1.143		219	40		259	305
3000	14 ga., up to 5-3/4" deep, 3'-0" x 6'-8" single	G	16	1		155	35		190	230
3002	3'-6" wide, single	G	16	1		208	35		243	288
3005	4'-0" wide, single	G	16	1		214	35		249	295
3600	up to 5-3/4" jamb depth, 4'-0" x 7'-0" single	G	15	1.067		185	37.50		222.50	267
3620	6'-0" wide, double	G	12	1.333		237	46.50		283.50	340
3640	8'-0" wide, double	G	12	1.333		247	46.50		293.50	350
3700	8'-0" high, 4'-0" wide, single	G	15	1.067		237	37.50		274.50	325
3740	8'-0" wide, double	G	12	1.333		293	46.50		339.50	400
4000	6-3/4" deep, 4'-0" x 7'-0" single	G	15	1.067		225	37.50		262.50	310
4020	6'-0" wide, double	G	12	1.333		277	46.50		323.50	385
4040	8'-0" wide, double	G	12	1.333		292	46.50		338.50	400
4100	8'-0" high, 4'-0" wide, single	G	15	1.067		280	37.50		317.50	370
4140	8'-0" wide, double	G	12	1.333		325	46.50		371.50	440
4400	8-3/4" deep, 4'-0" x 7'-0", single	G	15	1.067		254	37.50		291.50	340
4440	8'-0" wide, double	G	12	1.333		315	46.50		361.50	425
4500	4'-0" x 8'-0", single	G	15	1.067		289	37.50		326.50	385
4540	8'-0" wide, double	G	12	1.333		360	46.50		406.50	475
4900	For welded frames, add					65			65	71.50
5400	14 ga., "B" label, up to 5-3/4" deep, 4'-0" x 7'-0" single	G 2 Carp	15	1.067		213	37.50		250.50	298
5440	8'-0" wide, double	G	12	1.333		279	46.50		325.50	385
5800	6-3/4" deep, 7'-0" high, 4'-0" wide, single	G	15	1.067		221	37.50		258.50	305
5840	8'-0" wide, double	G	12	1.333		390	46.50		436.50	510
6200	8-3/4" deep, 4'-0" x 7'-0" single	G	15	1.067		299	37.50		336.50	395
6240	8'-0" wide, double	G	12	1.333		380	46.50		426.50	500
6300	For "A" label use same price as "B" label									
6400	For baked enamel finish, add					30%	15%			
6500	For galvanizing, add					20%				
6600	For hospital stop, add				Ea.	300			300	330
6620	For hospital stop, stainless steel, add				"	395			395	435
7900	Transom lite frames, fixed, add		2 Carp	155	.103	S.F.	55	3.61		58.61	66.50
8000	Movable, add		"	130	.123	"	70	4.30		74.30	84

08 13 Metal Doors

08 13 13 – Hollow Metal Doors

08 13 13.15 Metal Fire Doors

		Crew	Daily Output	Labor-Hours	Unit	Material	2017 Bare Costs Labor	Equipment	Total	Total Incl O&P
0010	**METAL FIRE DOORS** R081313-20									
0015	Steel, flush, "B" label, 90 minute									
0020	Full panel, 20 ga., 2'-0" x 6'-8"	2 Carp	20	.800	Ea.	425	28		453	510
0040	2'-8" x 6'-8"		18	.889		440	31		471	535
0060	3'-0" x 6'-8"		17	.941		440	33		473	540
0080	3'-0" x 7'-0"		17	.941		455	33		488	555
0140	18 ga., 3'-0" x 6'-8"		16	1		505	35		540	615
0160	2'-8" x 7'-0"		17	.941		535	33		568	640
0180	3'-0" x 7'-0"		16	1		515	35		550	630
0200	4'-0" x 7'-0"		15	1.067		650	37.50		687.50	780
0220	For "A" label, 3 hour, 18 ga., use same price as "B" label									
0240	For vision lite, add				Ea.	163			163	179

447

08 13 Metal Doors

08 13 13 – Hollow Metal Doors

08 13 13.15 Metal Fire Doors

		Crew	Daily Output	Labor-Hours	Unit	Material	2017 Bare Costs Labor	Equipment	Total	Total Incl O&P
0520	Flush, "B" label, 90 min., egress core, 20 ga., 2'-0" x 6'-8"	2 Carp	18	.889	Ea.	665	31		696	785
0540	2'-8" x 6'-8"		17	.941		670	33		703	790
0560	3'-0" x 6'-8"		16	1		675	35		710	800
0580	3'-0" x 7'-0"		16	1		700	35		735	830
0640	Flush, "A" label, 3 hour, egress core, 18 ga., 3'-0" x 6'-8"		15	1.067		730	37.50		767.50	865
0660	2'-8" x 7'-0"		16	1		765	35		800	900
0680	3'-0" x 7'-0"		15	1.067		750	37.50		787.50	885
0700	4'-0" x 7'-0"		14	1.143		910	40		950	1,075

08 13 13.20 Residential Steel Doors

			Crew	Daily Output	Labor-Hours	Unit	Material	2017 Bare Costs Labor	Equipment	Total	Total Incl O&P
0010	**RESIDENTIAL STEEL DOORS**										
0020	Prehung, insulated, exterior										
0030	Embossed, full panel, 2'-8" x 6'-8"	G	2 Carp	17	.941	Ea.	320	33		353	410
0040	3'-0" x 6'-8"	G		15	1.067		280	37.50		317.50	375
0060	3'-0" x 7'-0"	G		15	1.067		350	37.50		387.50	450
0070	5'-4" x 6'-8", double	G		8	2		650	70		720	830
0220	Half glass, 2'-8" x 6'-8"	G		17	.941		335	33		368	420
0240	3'-0" x 6'-8"	G		16	1		335	35		370	425
0260	3'-0" x 7'-0"	G		16	1		395	35		430	495
0270	5'-4" x 6'-8", double	G		8	2		710	70		780	900
1320	Flush face, full panel, 2'-8" x 6'-8"	G		16	1		287	35		322	375
1340	3'-0" x 6'-8"	G		15	1.067		287	37.50		324.50	380
1360	3'-0" x 7'-0"	G		15	1.067		310	37.50		347.50	405
1380	5'-4" x 6'-8", double	G		8	2		575	70		645	745
1420	Half glass, 2'-8" x 6'-8"	G		17	.941		350	33		383	440
1440	3'-0" x 6'-8"	G		16	1		350	35		385	445
1460	3'-0" x 7'-0"	G		16	1		435	35		470	535
1480	5'-4" x 6'-8", double	G		8	2		660	70		730	840
1500	Sidelight, full lite, 1'-0" x 6'-8" with grille	G					270			270	297
1510	1'-0" x 6'-8", low e	G					290			290	320
1520	1'-0" x 6'-8", half lite	G					300			300	330
1530	1'-0" x 6'-8", half lite, low e	G					292			292	320
2300	Interior, residential, closet, bi-fold, 2'-0" x 6'-8"	G	2 Carp	16	1		175	35		210	252
2330	3'-0" wide	G		16	1		205	35		240	285
2360	4'-0" wide	G		15	1.067		280	37.50		317.50	375
2400	5'-0" wide	G		14	1.143		325	40		365	425
2420	6'-0" wide	G		13	1.231		300	43		343	400
2510	Bi-passing closet, incl. hardware, no frame or trim incl.										
2511	Mirrored, metal frame, 4'-0" x 6'-8"		2 Carp	10	1.600	Opng.	234	56		290	350
2512	5'-0" wide			10	1.600		264	56		320	385
2513	6'-0" wide			10	1.600		293	56		349	420
2514	7'-0" wide			9	1.778		285	62		347	420
2515	8'-0" wide			9	1.778		425	62		487	575
2611	Mirrored, metal, 4'-0" x 8'-0"			10	1.600		315	56		371	440
2612	5'-0" wide			10	1.600		325	56		381	450
2613	6'-0" wide			10	1.600		380	56		436	510
2614	7'-0" wide			9	1.778		400	62		462	540
2615	8'-0" wide			9	1.778		445	62		507	590

08 14 Wood Doors

08 14 13 – Carved Wood Doors

08 14 13.10 Types of Wood Doors, Carved	Crew	Daily Output	Labor-Hours	Unit	Material	2017 Bare Costs Labor	Equipment	Total	Total Incl O&P
0010 **TYPES OF WOOD DOORS, CARVED**									
3000 Solid wood, 1-3/4" thick stile and rail									
3020 Mahogany, 3'-0" x 7'-0", six panel	2 Carp	14	1.143	Ea.	1,300	40		1,340	1,500
3030 With two lites		10	1.600		1,975	56		2,031	2,275
3040 3'-6" x 8'-0", six panel		10	1.600		1,550	56		1,606	1,825
3050 With two lites		8	2		2,700	70		2,770	3,100
3100 Pine, 3'-0" x 7'-0", six panel		14	1.143		560	40		600	680
3110 With two lites		10	1.600		825	56		881	1,000
3120 3'-6" x 8'-0", six panel		10	1.600		1,000	56		1,056	1,200
3130 With two lites		8	2		1,900	70		1,970	2,225
3200 Red oak, 3'-0" x 7'-0", six panel		14	1.143		1,850	40		1,890	2,100
3210 With two lites		10	1.600		2,550	56		2,606	2,900
3220 3'-6" x 8'-0", six panel		10	1.600		2,575	56		2,631	2,925
3230 With two lites		8	2		3,525	70		3,595	4,025
4000 Hand carved door, mahogany									
4020 3'-0" x 7'-0", simple design	2 Carp	14	1.143	Ea.	1,750	40		1,790	2,000
4030 Intricate design		11	1.455		3,700	51		3,751	4,150
4040 3'-6" x 8'-0", simple design		10	1.600		3,000	56		3,056	3,400
4050 Intricate design		8	2		3,700	70		3,770	4,200
4400 For custom finish, add					475			475	525
4600 Side light, mahogany, 7'-0" x 1'-6" wide, 4 lites	2 Carp	18	.889		1,100	31		1,131	1,250
4610 6 lites		14	1.143		2,550	40		2,590	2,875
4620 8'-0" x 1'-6" wide, 4 lites		14	1.143		1,800	40		1,840	2,050
4630 6 lites		10	1.600		2,100	56		2,156	2,400
4640 Side light, oak, 7'-0" x 1'-6" wide, 4 lites		18	.889		1,200	31		1,231	1,375
4650 6 lites		14	1.143		2,100	40		2,140	2,375
4660 8'-0" x 1'-6" wide, 4 lites		14	1.143		1,100	40		1,140	1,275
4670 6 lites		10	1.600		2,100	56		2,156	2,400

08 14 16 – Flush Wood Doors

08 14 16.09 Smooth Wood Doors

	Crew	Daily Output	Labor-Hours	Unit	Material	2017 Bare Costs Labor	Equipment	Total	Total Incl O&P
0010 **SMOOTH WOOD DOORS**									
0015 Flush, interior, hollow core									
0025 Lauan face, 1-3/8", 3'-0" x 6'-8"	2 Carp	17	.941	Ea.	55	33		88	116
0030 4'-0" x 6'-8"		16	1		126	35		161	198
0140 Birch face, 1-3/8", 2'-6" x 6'-8"		17	.941		90	33		123	154
0180 3'-0" x 6'-8"		17	.941		97.50	33		130.50	162
0200 4'-0" x 6'-8"		16	1		158	35		193	233
0202 1-3/4", 2'-0" x 6'-8"		17	.941		60.50	33		93.50	122
0204 2'-4" x 7'-0"		16	1		123	35		158	195
0206 2'-6" x 7'-0"		16	1		127	35		162	198
0208 2'-8" x 7'-0"		16	1		133	35		168	206
0210 3'-0" x 7'-0"		16	1		139	35		174	212
0212 3'-4" x 7'-0"		15	1.067		212	37.50		249.50	296
0214 Pair of 3'-0" x 7'-0"		9	1.778	Pr.	266	62		328	395
0480 For prefinishing, clear, add				Ea.	47			47	51.50
0500 For prefinishing, stain, add				"	59			59	65
0620 For dutch door with shelf, add					140%				
1320 M.D. overlay on hardboard, 1-3/8", 2'-0" x 6'-8"	2 Carp	17	.941	Ea.	120	33		153	187
1340 2'-6" x 6'-8"		17	.941		121	33		154	188
1380 3'-0" x 6'-8"		17	.941		130	33		163	198
1400 4'-0" x 6'-8"		16	1		185	35		220	263
1720 H.P. plastic laminate, 1-3/8", 2'-0" x 6'-8"		16	1		275	35		310	365

08 14 Wood Doors

08 14 16 – Flush Wood Doors

08 14 16.09 Smooth Wood Doors	Crew	Daily Output	Labor-Hours	Unit	Material	2017 Bare Costs Labor	Equipment	Total	Total Incl O&P
1740	2'-6" x 6'-8"	2 Carp	16	1	Ea.	270	35		305	355
1780	3'-0" x 6'-8"	↓	15	1.067		299	37.50		336.50	395
1785	Door, plastic laminate, 3'-0" x 6'-8"					299			299	330
1800	4'-0" x 6'-8"	2 Carp	14	1.143		395	40		435	500
2020	Particle core, lauan face, 1-3/8", 2'-6" x 6'-8"		15	1.067		97	37.50		134.50	170
2040	3'-0" x 6'-8"		14	1.143		99	40		139	176
2120	Birch face, 1-3/8", 2'-6" x 6'-8"		15	1.067		108	37.50		145.50	182
2140	3'-0" x 6'-8"		14	1.143		119	40		159	198
3320	M.D. overlay on hardboard, 1-3/8", 2'-6" x 6'-8"		14	1.143		106	40		146	184
3340	3'-0" x 6'-8"		13	1.231		115	43		158	199
4000	Exterior, flush, solid core, birch, 1-3/4" x 2'-6" x 7'-0"		15	1.067		185	37.50		222.50	267
4020	2'-8" wide		15	1.067		163	37.50		200.50	242
4040	3'-0" wide	↓	14	1.143		214	40		254	300
4045	3'-0" x 8'-0"	1 Carp	8	1		430	35		465	535
4100	Oak faced 1-3/4" x 2'-6" x 7'-0"	2 Carp	15	1.067		225	37.50		262.50	310
4120	2'-8" wide		15	1.067		245	37.50		282.50	335
4140	3'-0" wide	↓	14	1.143		240	40		280	330
4160	Walnut faced, 1-3/4" x 3'-0" x 6'-8"	1 Carp	17	.471		305	16.45		321.45	365
4180	3'-6" wide	"	17	.471		365	16.45		381.45	435
4200	Walnut faced, 1-3/4" x 2'-6" x 7'-0"	2 Carp	15	1.067		330	37.50		367.50	430
4220	2'-8" wide		15	1.067		335	37.50		372.50	435
4240	3'-0" wide	↓	14	1.143		325	40		365	425
4250	3'-6" wide	1 Carp	14	.571		420	19.95		439.95	500
4260	3'-0" x 8'-0"		8	1		385	35		420	485
4270	3'-6" wide		8	1		465	35		500	570
4285	Cherry faced, flush, sc, 1-3/4" x 3'-0" x 8'-0" wide	↓	8	1	↓	465	35		500	570

08 14 16.10 Wood Doors Decorator

		Crew	Daily Output	Labor-Hours	Unit	Material	Labor	Equipment	Total	Total Incl O&P
0010	**WOOD DOORS DECORATOR**									
1800	Exterior, flush, solid wood core, birch 1-3/4" x 2'-6" x 7'-0"	2 Carp	15	1.067	Ea.	320	37.50		357.50	415
1820	2'-8" wide		15	1.067		330	37.50		367.50	430
1840	3'-0" wide		14	1.143		335	40		375	435
1900	Oak faced, 1-3/4" x 2'-6" x 7'-0"		15	1.067		340	37.50		377.50	440
1920	2'-8" wide		15	1.067		340	37.50		377.50	440
1940	3'-0" wide		14	1.143		350	40		390	450
2100	Walnut faced, 1-3/4" x 2'-6" x 7'-0"		15	1.067		385	37.50		422.50	490
2120	2'-8" wide		15	1.067		400	37.50		437.50	505
2140	3'-0" wide	↓	14	1.143	↓	430	40		470	540

08 14 33 – Stile and Rail Wood Doors

08 14 33.10 Wood Doors Paneled

		Crew	Daily Output	Labor-Hours	Unit	Material	Labor	Equipment	Total	Total Incl O&P
0010	**WOOD DOORS PANELED**									
0020	Interior, six panel, hollow core, 1-3/8" thick									
0040	Molded hardboard, 2'-0" x 6'-8"	2 Carp	17	.941	Ea.	62	33		95	123
0060	2'-6" x 6'-8"		17	.941		64	33		97	126
0070	2'-8" x 6'-8"		17	.941		67	33		100	129
0080	3'-0" x 6'-8"		17	.941		72	33		105	134
0140	Embossed print, molded hardboard, 2'-0" x 6'-8"		17	.941		64	33		97	126
0160	2'-6" x 6'-8"		17	.941		64	33		97	126
0180	3'-0" x 6'-8"		17	.941		72	33		105	134
0540	Six panel, solid, 1-3/8" thick, pine, 2'-0" x 6'-8"		15	1.067		155	37.50		192.50	234
0560	2'-6" x 6'-8"		14	1.143		170	40		210	254
0580	3'-0" x 6'-8"		13	1.231		145	43		188	232
1020	Two panel, bored rail, solid, 1-3/8" thick, pine, 1'-6" x 6'-8"	↓	16	1	↓	270	35		305	355

08 14 Wood Doors

08 14 33 – Stile and Rail Wood Doors

08 14 33.10 Wood Doors Paneled

		Crew	Daily Output	Labor-Hours	Unit	Material	2017 Bare Costs Labor	Equipment	Total	Total Incl O&P
1040	2'-0" x 6'-8"	2 Carp	15	1.067	Ea.	355	37.50		392.50	455
1060	2'-6" x 6'-8"		14	1.143		400	40		440	505
1340	Two panel, solid, 1-3/8" thick, fir, 2'-0" x 6'-8"		15	1.067		160	37.50		197.50	239
1360	2'-6" x 6'-8"		14	1.143		210	40		250	298
1380	3'-0" x 6'-8"		13	1.231		415	43		458	525
1740	Five panel, solid, 1-3/8" thick, fir, 2'-0" x 6'-8"		15	1.067		280	37.50		317.50	375
1760	2'-6" x 6'-8"		14	1.143		420	40		460	525
1780	3'-0" x 6'-8"		13	1.231		420	43		463	530
4190	Exterior, Knotty pine, paneled, 1-3/4", 3'-0" x 6'-8"		16	1		780	35		815	920
4195	Double 1-3/4", 3'-0" x 6'-8"		16	1		1,550	35		1,585	1,775
4200	Ash, paneled, 1-3/4", 3'-0" x 6'-8"		16	1		890	35		925	1,050
4205	Double 1-3/4", 3'-0" x 6'-8"		16	1		1,775	35		1,810	2,000
4210	Cherry, paneled, 1-3/4", 3'-0" x 6'-8"		16	1		1,000	35		1,035	1,150
4215	Double 1-3/4", 3'-0" x 6'-8"		16	1		2,000	35		2,035	2,250
4230	Ash, paneled, 1-3/4", 3'-0" x 8'-0"		16	1		1,050	35		1,085	1,200
4235	Double 1-3/4", 3'-0" x 8'-0"		16	1		2,100	35		2,135	2,350
4240	Hard maple, paneled, 1-3/4", 3'-0" x 8'-0"		16	1		1,050	35		1,085	1,200
4245	Double 1-3/4", 3'-0" x 8'-0"		16	1		2,100	35		2,135	2,350
4250	Cherry, paneled, 1-3/4", 3'-0" x 8'-0"		16	1		1,175	35		1,210	1,350
4255	Double 1-3/4", 3'-0" x 8'-0"		16	1		2,375	35		2,410	2,650

08 14 33.20 Wood Doors Residential

		Crew	Daily Output	Labor-Hours	Unit	Material	2017 Bare Costs Labor	Equipment	Total	Total Incl O&P
0010	**WOOD DOORS RESIDENTIAL**									
0200	Exterior, combination storm & screen, pine									
0260	2'-8" wide	2 Carp	10	1.600	Ea.	315	56		371	440
0280	3'-0" wide		9	1.778		320	62		382	455
0300	7'-1" x 3'-0" wide		9	1.778		365	62		427	510
0400	Full lite, 6'-9" x 2'-6" wide		11	1.455		325	51		376	440
0420	2'-8" wide		10	1.600		325	56		381	455
0440	3'-0" wide		9	1.778		335	62		397	470
0500	7'-1" x 3'-0" wide		9	1.778		365	62		427	505
0604	Door, screen, plain full		12	1.333		385	46.50		431.50	505
0614	Divided		12	1.333		410	46.50		456.50	530
0634	Decor full		12	1.333		460	46.50		506.50	585
0700	Dutch door, pine, 1-3/4" x 2'-8" x 6'-8", 6 panel		12	1.333		745	46.50		791.50	900
0720	Half glass		10	1.600		930	56		986	1,125
0800	3'-0" wide, 6 panel		12	1.333		745	46.50		791.50	900
0820	Half glass		10	1.600		880	56		936	1,050
1000	Entrance door, colonial, 1-3/4" x 6'-8" x 2'-8" wide		16	1		560	35		595	675
1020	6 panel pine, 3'-0" wide		15	1.067		435	37.50		472.50	545
1100	8 panel pine, 2'-8" wide		16	1		610	35		645	730
1120	3'-0" wide		15	1.067		600	37.50		637.50	725
1200	For tempered safety glass lites (min of 2), add					80			80	88
1300	Flush, birch, solid core, 1-3/4" x 6'-8" x 2'-8" wide	2 Carp	16	1		111	35		146	181
1320	3'-0" wide		15	1.067		119	37.50		156.50	193
1350	7'-0" x 2'-8" wide		16	1		133	35		168	206
1360	3'-0" wide		15	1.067		155	37.50		192.50	233
1420	6'-8" x 3'-0" wide, fir		16	1		475	35		510	585
1720	Carved mahogany 3'-0" x 6'-8"		15	1.067		1,375	37.50		1,412.50	1,600
1760	Mahogany, 3'-0" x 6'-8"		15	1.067		710	37.50		747.50	845
1930	For dutch door with shelf, add					140%				
2700	Interior, closet, bi-fold, w/hardware, no frame or trim incl.									
2720	Flush, birch, 2'-6" x 6'-8"	2 Carp	13	1.231	Ea.	71	43		114	150

For customer support on your Residential Costs with RSMeans Data, call 800.448.8182.

451

08 14 Wood Doors

08 14 33 – Stile and Rail Wood Doors

08 14 33.20 Wood Doors Residential		Crew	Daily Output	Labor-Hours	Unit	Material	2017 Bare Costs Labor	Equipment	Total	Total Incl O&P
2740	3'-0" wide	2 Carp	13	1.231	Ea.	73	43		116	152
2760	4'-0" wide		12	1.333		113	46.50		159.50	202
2780	5'-0" wide		11	1.455		113	51		164	209
2800	6'-0" wide		10	1.600		132	56		188	239
2804	Flush lauan 2'-0" x 6'-8"		14	1.143		49	40		89	121
2810	8'-0" wide		9	1.778		199	62		261	325
2817	6'-0" wide		9	1.778		128	62		190	244
2820	Flush, hardboard, primed, 6'-8" x 2'-6" wide		13	1.231		71.50	43		114.50	151
2840	3'-0" wide		13	1.231		82	43		125	162
2860	4'-0" wide		12	1.333		141	46.50		187.50	233
2880	5'-0" wide		11	1.455		168	51		219	270
2900	6'-0" wide		10	1.600		175	56		231	287
2920	Hardboard, primed 7'-0" x 4'-0", wide		12	1.333		184	46.50		230.50	280
2930	6'-0" wide		10	1.600		178	56		234	290
3000	Raised panel pine, 6'-6" or 6'-8" x 2'-6" wide		13	1.231		214	43		257	305
3020	3'-0" wide		13	1.231		281	43		324	380
3040	4'-0" wide		12	1.333		310	46.50		356.50	420
3060	5'-0" wide		11	1.455		395	51		446	520
3080	6'-0" wide		10	1.600		435	56		491	570
3180	Louvered, pine, 6'-6" or 6'-8" x 1'-6" wide		13	1.231		190	43		233	281
3190	2'-0" wide		14	1.143		169	40		209	253
3200	Louvered, pine, 6'-6" or 6'-8" x 2'-6" wide		13	1.231		152	43		195	239
3220	3'-0" wide	↓	13	1.231		228	43		271	325
3225	Door, interior louvered bi-fold, pine, 3'-0" x 6'-8"					228			228	251
3240	4'-0" wide	2 Carp	12	1.333		244	46.50		290.50	345
3260	5'-0" wide		11	1.455		272	51		323	385
3280	6'-0" wide		10	1.600		300	56		356	425
3290	8'-0" wide		10	1.600		460	56		516	600
3300	7'-0" x 3'-0" wide		12	1.333		276	46.50		322.50	385
3320	6'-0" wide	↓	10	1.600	↓	340	56		396	465
4400	Bi-passing closet, incl. hardware and frame, no trim incl.									
4420	Flush, lauan, 6'-8" x 4'-0" wide	2 Carp	12	1.333	Opng.	180	46.50		226.50	276
4440	5'-0" wide		11	1.455		193	51		244	298
4460	6'-0" wide		10	1.600		217	56		273	330
4600	Flush, birch, 6'-8" x 4'-0" wide		12	1.333		248	46.50		294.50	350
4620	5'-0" wide		11	1.455		216	51		267	320
4640	6'-0" wide		10	1.600		293	56		349	415
4800	Louvered, pine, 6'-8" x 4'-0" wide		12	1.333		490	46.50		536.50	615
4820	5'-0" wide		11	1.455		535	51		586	675
4840	6'-0" wide		10	1.600	↓	630	56		686	790
4900	Mirrored, 6'-8" x 4'-0" wide		12	1.333	Ea.	320	46.50		366.50	430
5000	Paneled, pine, 6'-8" x 4'-0" wide		12	1.333	Opng.	475	46.50		521.50	600
5020	5'-0" wide		11	1.455		550	51		601	690
5040	6'-0" wide		10	1.600		735	56		791	905
5042	8'-0" wide		12	1.333		950	46.50		996.50	1,125
5061	Hardboard, 6'-8" x 4'-0" wide		10	1.600		206	56		262	320
5062	5'-0" wide		10	1.600		207	56		263	320
5063	6'-0" wide	↓	10	1.600	↓	230	56		286	345
6100	Folding accordion, closet, including track and frame									
6200	Rigid PVC	2 Carp	10	1.600	Ea.	59.50	56		115.50	159
7310	Passage doors, flush, no frame included									
7320	Hardboard, hollow core, 1-3/8" x 6'-8" x 1'-6" wide	2 Carp	18	.889	Ea.	42	31		73	98
7330	2'-0" wide	↓	18	.889	↓	44.50	31		75.50	101

08 14 Wood Doors

08 14 33 – Stile and Rail Wood Doors

08 14 33.20 Wood Doors Residential	Crew	Daily Output	Labor-Hours	Unit	Material	2017 Bare Costs Labor	Equipment	Total	Total Incl O&P
7340	2'-6" wide	2 Carp	18	.889	Ea.	51	31		82	108
7350	2'-8" wide		18	.889		52	31		83	109
7360	3'-0" wide		17	.941		54	33		87	115
7420	Lauan, hollow core, 1-3/8" x 6'-8" x 1'-6" wide		18	.889		37	31		68	92.50
7440	2'-0" wide		18	.889		36	31		67	91.50
7450	2'-4" wide		18	.889		39.50	31		70.50	95.50
7460	2'-6" wide		18	.889		40	31		71	95.50
7480	2'-8" wide		18	.889		41.50	31		72.50	97.50
7500	3'-0" wide		17	.941		43.50	33		76.50	103
7540	2'-6" wide		16	1		64.50	35		99.50	130
7560	2'-8" wide		16	1		69	35		104	135
7580	3'-0" wide		16	1		71.50	35		106.50	137
7595	Pair of 3'-0" wide		9	1.778	Pr.	141	62		203	259
7700	Birch, hollow core, 1-3/8" x 6'-8" x 1'-6" wide		18	.889	Ea.	43.50	31		74.50	100
7720	2'-0" wide		18	.889		38.50	31		69.50	94.50
7740	2'-6" wide		18	.889		51.50	31		82.50	109
7760	2'-8" wide		18	.889		51.50	31		82.50	109
7780	3'-0" wide		17	.941		52.50	33		85.50	113
7790	2'-6" ash/oak door with hinges		18	.889		95	31		126	157
7910	2'-8" wide		16	1		86.50	35		121.50	154
7920	3'-0" wide		16	1		91.50	35		126.50	160
7940	Pair of 3'-0" wide		9	1.778	Pr.	187	62		249	310
8000	Pine louvered, 1-3/8" x 6'-8" x 1'-6" wide		19	.842	Ea.	112	29.50		141.50	172
8020	2'-0" wide		18	.889		131	31		162	196
8040	2'-6" wide		18	.889		149	31		180	215
8060	2'-8" wide		18	.889		156	31		187	224
8080	3'-0" wide		17	.941		168	33		201	240
8300	Pine paneled, 1-3/8" x 6'-8" x 1'-6" wide		19	.842		121	29.50		150.50	182
8320	2'-0" wide		18	.889		163	31		194	231
8330	2'-4" wide		18	.889		178	31		209	248
8340	2'-6" wide		18	.889		184	31		215	254
8360	2'-8" wide		18	.889		184	31		215	254
8380	3'-0" wide		17	.941		196	33		229	270
8450	French door, pine, 15 lites, 1-3/8" x 6'-8" x 2'-6" wide		18	.889		207	31		238	279
8470	2'-8" wide		18	.889		259	31		290	335
8490	3'-0" wide		17	.941		286	33		319	370
8804	Pocket door, 6 panel pine, 2'-6" x 6'-8" with frame		10.50	1.524		360	53.50		413.50	485
8814	2'-8" x 6'-8"		10.50	1.524		355	53.50		408.50	480
8824	3'-0" x 6'-8"		10.50	1.524		370	53.50		423.50	495
9000	Passage doors, flush, no frame, birch, solid core, 1-3/8" x 2'-4" x 7'-0"		16	1		122	35		157	193
9020	2'-8" wide		16	1		129	35		164	201
9040	3'-0" wide		16	1		141	35		176	214
9060	3'-4" wide		15	1.067		161	37.50		198.50	240
9080	Pair of 3'-0" wide		9	1.778	Pr.	281	62		343	415
9100	Lauan, solid core, 1-3/8" x 7'-0" x 2'-4" wide		16	1	Ea.	142	35		177	215
9120	2'-8" wide		16	1		151	35		186	225
9140	3'-0" wide		16	1		160	35		195	235
9160	3'-4" wide		15	1.067		164	37.50		201.50	244
9180	Pair of 3'-0" wide		9	1.778	Pr.	287	62		349	420
9200	Hardboard, solid core, 1-3/8" x 7'-0" x 2'-4" wide		16	1	Ea.	171	35		206	247
9220	2'-8" wide		16	1		178	35		213	255
9240	3'-0" wide		16	1		184	35		219	261
9260	3'-4" wide		15	1.067		202	37.50		239.50	285

For customer support on your Residential Costs with RSMeans Data, call 800.448.8182.

453

08 14 Wood Doors

08 14 35 – Torrified Doors

08 14 35.10 Torrified Exterior Doors		Crew	Daily Output	Labor-Hours	Unit	Material	2017 Bare Costs Labor	Equipment	Total	Total Incl O&P
0010	**TORRIFIED EXTERIOR DOORS**									
0020	Wood doors made from torrified wood, exterior									
0030	All doors require a finish be applied, all glass is insulated									
0040	All doors require pilot holes for all fasteners									
0100	6 panel, paint grade poplar, 1-3/4" x 3'-0" x 6'-8"	2 Carp	12	1.333	Ea.	1,075	46.50		1,121.50	1,250
0120	Half glass 3'-0" x 6'-8"	"	12	1.333		1,175	46.50		1,221.50	1,375
0200	Side lite, full glass, 1-3/4" x 1'-2" x 6'-8"					905			905	995
0220	Side lite, half glass, 1-3/4" x 1'-2" x 6'-8"					905			905	995
0300	Raised face, 2 panel, paint grade poplar, 1-3/4" x 3'-0" x 7'-0"	2 Carp	12	1.333		1,275	46.50		1,321.50	1,475
0320	Side lite, raised face, half glass, 1-3/4" x 1'-2" x 7'-0"					1,050			1,050	1,175
0500	6 panel, Fir, 1-3/4" x 3'-0" x 6'-8"	2 Carp	12	1.333		1,550	46.50		1,596.50	1,775
0520	Half glass 3'-0" x 6'-8"	"	12	1.333		1,650	46.50		1,696.50	1,900
0600	Side lite, full glass, 1-3/4" x 1'-2" x 6'-8"					1,150			1,150	1,275
0620	Side lite, half glass, 1-3/4" x 1'-2" x 6'-8"					1,450			1,450	1,600
0700	6 panel, Mahogany, 1-3/4" x 3'-0" x 6'-8"	2 Carp	12	1.333		1,625	46.50		1,671.50	1,850
0800	Side lite, full glass, 1-3/4" x 1'-2" x 6'-8"					1,225			1,225	1,350
0820	Side lite, half glass, 1-3/4" x 1'-2" x 6'-8"					1,200			1,200	1,325

08 14 40 – Interior Cafe Doors

08 14 40.10 Cafe Style Doors		Crew	Daily Output	Labor-Hours	Unit	Material	2017 Bare Costs Labor	Equipment	Total	Total Incl O&P
0010	**CAFE STYLE DOORS**									
6520	Interior cafe doors, 2'-6" opening, stock, panel pine	2 Carp	16	1	Ea.	203	35		238	282
6540	3'-0" opening	"	16	1	"	251	35		286	335
6550	Louvered pine									
6560	2'-6" opening	2 Carp	16	1	Ea.	169	35		204	245
8000	3'-0" opening		16	1		195	35		230	274
8010	2'-6" opening, hardwood		16	1		272	35		307	360
8020	3'-0" opening		16	1		298	35		333	385

08 16 Composite Doors

08 16 13 – Fiberglass Doors

08 16 13.10 Entrance Doors, Fibrous Glass			Crew	Daily Output	Labor-Hours	Unit	Material	2017 Bare Costs Labor	Equipment	Total	Total Incl O&P
0010	**ENTRANCE DOORS, FIBROUS GLASS**										
0020	Exterior, fiberglass, door, 2'-8" wide x 6'-8" high	G	2 Carp	15	1.067	Ea.	281	37.50		318.50	375
0040	3'-0" wide x 6'-8" high	G		15	1.067		274	37.50		311.50	365
0060	3'-0" wide x 7'-0" high	G		15	1.067		490	37.50		527.50	600
0080	3'-0" wide x 6'-8" high, with two lites	G		15	1.067		340	37.50		377.50	440
0100	3'-0" wide x 8'-0" high, with two lites	G		15	1.067		525	37.50		562.50	645
0110	Half glass, 3'-0" wide x 6'-8" high	G		15	1.067		450	37.50		487.50	560
0120	3'-0" wide x 6'-8" high, low e	G		15	1.067		490	37.50		527.50	600
0130	3'-0" wide x 8'-0" high	G		15	1.067		585	37.50		622.50	710
0140	3'-0" wide x 8'-0" high, low e	G		15	1.067		675	37.50		712.50	810
0150	Side lights, 1'-0" wide x 6'-8" high	G					281			281	310
0160	1'-0" wide x 6'-8" high, low e	G					289			289	320
0180	1'-0" wide x 6'-8" high, full glass	G					340			340	370
0190	1'-0" wide x 6'-8" high, low e	G					360			360	395

08 16 Composite Doors

08 16 14 – French Doors

08 16 14.10 Exterior Doors With Glass Lites	Crew	Daily Output	Labor-Hours	Unit	Material	2017 Bare Costs Labor	Equipment	Total	Total Incl O&P
0010	**EXTERIOR DOORS WITH GLASS LITES**								
0020	French, Fir, 1-3/4", 3'-0" wide x 6'-8" high	2 Carp	12	1.333	Ea.	620	46.50		666.50	760
0025	Double		12	1.333		1,250	46.50		1,296.50	1,425
0030	Maple, 1-3/4", 3'-0" wide x 6'-8" high		12	1.333		695	46.50		741.50	845
0035	Double		12	1.333		1,400	46.50		1,446.50	1,600
0040	Cherry, 1-3/4", 3'-0" wide x 6'-8" high		12	1.333		810	46.50		856.50	970
0045	Double		12	1.333		1,625	46.50		1,671.50	1,850
0100	Mahogany, 1-3/4", 3'-0" wide x 8'-0" high		10	1.600		825	56		881	1,000
0105	Double		10	1.600		1,650	56		1,706	1,925
0110	Fir, 1-3/4", 3'-0" wide x 8'-0" high		10	1.600		1,225	56		1,281	1,450
0115	Double		10	1.600		2,475	56		2,531	2,825
0120	Oak, 1-3/4", 3'-0" wide x 8'-0" high		10	1.600		1,875	56		1,931	2,175
0125	Double		10	1.600		3,750	56		3,806	4,225

08 17 Integrated Door Opening Assemblies

08 17 23 – Integrated Wood Door Opening Assemblies

08 17 23.10 Pre-Hung Doors	Crew	Daily Output	Labor-Hours	Unit	Material	2017 Bare Costs Labor	Equipment	Total	Total Incl O&P
0010	**PRE-HUNG DOORS**								
0300	Exterior, wood, comb. storm & screen, 6'-9" x 2'-6" wide	2 Carp	15	1.067	Ea.	299	37.50		336.50	395
0320	2'-8" wide		15	1.067		300	37.50		337.50	395
0340	3'-0" wide		15	1.067		310	37.50		347.50	405
0360	For 7'-0" high door, add					32			32	35
1600	Entrance door, flush, birch, solid core									
1620	4-5/8" solid jamb, 1-3/4" x 6'-8" x 2'-8" wide	2 Carp	16	1	Ea.	305	35		340	395
1640	3'-0" wide		16	1		395	35		430	495
1642	5-5/8" jamb		16	1		335	35		370	425
1680	For 7'-0" high door, add					25			25	27.50
2000	Entrance door, colonial, 6 panel pine									
2020	4-5/8" solid jamb, 1-3/4" x 6'-8" x 2'-8" wide	2 Carp	16	1	Ea.	645	35		680	770
2040	3'-0" wide	"	16	1		675	35		710	805
2060	For 7'-0" high door, add					55			55	60
2200	For 5-5/8" solid jamb, add					45			45	49.50
2230	French style, exterior, 1 lite, 1-3/4" x 3'-0" x 6'-8"	1 Carp	14	.571		615	19.95		634.95	710
2235	9 lites	"	14	.571		660	19.95		679.95	760
2245	15 lites	2 Carp	14	1.143		695	40		735	830
2250	Double, 15 lites, 2'-0" x 6'-8", 4'-0" opening		7	2.286	Pr.	1,225	80		1,305	1,450
2260	2'-6" x 6'-8", 5'-0" opening		7	2.286		1,350	80		1,430	1,600
2280	3'-0" x 6'-8", 6'-0" opening		7	2.286		1,450	80		1,530	1,725
2430	3'-0" x 7'-0", 15 lites		14	1.143	Ea.	975	40		1,015	1,150
2432	Two 3'-0" x 7'-0"		7	2.286	Pr.	2,025	80		2,105	2,350
2435	3'-0" x 8'-0"		14	1.143	Ea.	1,025	40		1,065	1,200
2437	Two, 3'-0" x 8'-0"		7	2.286	Pr.	2,125	80		2,205	2,450
2500	Exterior, metal face, insulated, incl. jamb, brickmold and									
2520	Threshold, flush, 2'-8" x 6'-8"	2 Carp	16	1	Ea.	290	35		325	380
2550	3'-0" x 6'-8"		16	1		290	35		325	380
3500	Embossed, 6 panel, 2'-8" x 6'-8"		16	1		330	35		365	420
3550	3'-0" x 6'-8"		16	1		330	35		365	425
3600	2 narrow lites, 2'-8" x 6'-8"		16	1		305	35		340	395
3650	3'-0" x 6'-8"		16	1		310	35		345	400
3700	Half glass, 2'-8" x 6'-8"		16	1		325	35		360	420

08 17 Integrated Door Opening Assemblies

08 17 23 – Integrated Wood Door Opening Assemblies

08 17 23.10 Pre-Hung Doors	Crew	Daily Output	Labor-Hours	Unit	Material	2017 Bare Costs Labor	Equipment	Total	Total Incl O&P
3750	3'-0" x 6'-8"	2 Carp	16	1	Ea.	345	35		380	440
3800	2 top lites, 2'-8" x 6'-8"		16	1		320	35		355	410
3850	3'-0" x 6'-8"		16	1		355	35		390	450
4000	Interior, passage door, 4-5/8" solid jamb									
4370	Pine, louvered, 2'-8" x 6'-8"	2 Carp	17	.941	Ea.	203	33		236	278
4380	3'-0"		17	.941		210	33		243	286
4400	Lauan, flush, solid core, 1-3/8" x 6'-8" x 2'-6" wide		17	.941		188	33		221	261
4420	2'-8" wide		17	.941		188	33		221	261
4440	3'-0" wide		16	1		204	35		239	283
4600	Hollow core, 1-3/8" x 6'-8" x 2'-6" wide		17	.941		129	33		162	197
4620	2'-8" wide		17	.941		131	33		164	199
4640	3'-0" wide		16	1		143	35		178	216
4700	For 7'-0" high door, add					38			38	42
5000	Birch, flush, solid core, 1-3/8" x 6'-8" x 2'-6" wide	2 Carp	17	.941		279	33		312	360
5020	2'-8" wide		17	.941		203	33		236	278
5040	3'-0" wide		16	1		305	35		340	395
5200	Hollow core, 1-3/8" x 6'-8" x 2'-6" wide		17	.941		230	33		263	310
5220	2'-8" wide		17	.941		249	33		282	330
5240	3'-0" wide		16	1		248	35		283	330
5280	For 7'-0" high door, add					32			32	35
5500	Hardboard paneled, 1-3/8" x 6'-8" x 2'-6" wide	2 Carp	17	.941		151	33		184	221
5520	2'-8" wide		17	.941		158	33		191	228
5540	3'-0" wide		16	1		156	35		191	231
6000	Pine paneled, 1-3/8" x 6'-8" x 2'-6" wide		17	.941		267	33		300	350
6020	2'-8" wide		17	.941		284	33		317	365
6040	3'-0" wide		16	1		292	35		327	380
7200	Prehung, bifold, mirrored, 6'-8" x 5'-0"	1 Carp	9	.889		390	31		421	480
7220	6'-8" x 6'-0"		9	.889		390	31		421	480
7240	6'-8" x 8'-0"		6	1.333		645	46.50		691.50	790
7600	Oak, 6 panel, 1-3/4" x 6'-8" x 3'-0"		17	.471		905	16.45		921.45	1,025
8500	Pocket door frame with lauan, flush, hollow core, 1-3/8" x 3'-0" x 6'-8"		17	.471		236	16.45		252.45	288

08 31 Access Doors and Panels

08 31 13 – Access Doors and Frames

08 31 13.20 Bulkhead/Cellar Doors

0010	BULKHEAD/CELLAR DOORS									
0020	Steel, not incl. sides, 44" x 62"	1 Carp	5.50	1.455	Ea.	610	51		661	755
0100	52" x 73"		5.10	1.569		885	55		940	1,050
0500	With sides and foundation plates, 57" x 45" x 24"		4.70	1.702		920	59.50		979.50	1,100
0600	42" x 49" x 51"		4.30	1.860		935	65		1,000	1,125

08 31 13.40 Kennel Doors

0010	KENNEL DOORS									
0020	2 way, swinging type, 13" x 19" opening	2 Carp	11	1.455	Opng.	90	51		141	184
0100	17" x 29" opening		11	1.455		99	51		150	194
0200	9" x 9" opening, electronic with accessories		11	1.455		120	51		171	217

08 32 Sliding Glass Doors

08 32 13 – Sliding Aluminum-Framed Glass Doors

08 32 13.10 Sliding Aluminum Doors

		Crew	Daily Output	Labor-Hours	Unit	Material	2017 Bare Costs Labor	Equipment	Total	Total Incl O&P
0010	**SLIDING ALUMINUM DOORS**									
0350	Aluminum, 5/8" tempered insulated glass, 6' wide									
0400	Premium	2 Carp	4	4	Ea.	1,550	140		1,690	1,925
0450	Economy		4	4		820	140		960	1,150
0500	8' wide, premium		3	5.333		1,675	186		1,861	2,125
0550	Economy		3	5.333		1,450	186		1,636	1,875
0600	12' wide, premium		2.50	6.400		3,000	224		3,224	3,675
0650	Economy		2.50	6.400		1,575	224		1,799	2,100
4000	Aluminum, baked on enamel, temp glass, 6'-8" x 10'-0" wide		4	4		1,100	140		1,240	1,425
4020	Insulating glass, 6'-8" x 6'-0" wide		4	4		955	140		1,095	1,275
4040	8'-0" wide		3	5.333		1,125	186		1,311	1,525
4060	10'-0" wide		2	8		1,375	280		1,655	1,975
4080	Anodized, temp glass, 6'-8" x 6'-0" wide		4	4		455	140		595	735
4100	8'-0" wide		3	5.333		575	186		761	945
4120	10'-0" wide		2	8		645	280		925	1,175

08 32 19 – Sliding Wood-Framed Glass Doors

08 32 19.10 Sliding Wood Doors

		Crew	Daily Output	Labor-Hours	Unit	Material	2017 Bare Costs Labor	Equipment	Total	Total Incl O&P
0010	**SLIDING WOOD DOORS**									
0020	Wood, tempered insul. glass, 6' wide, premium	2 Carp	4	4	Ea.	1,450	140		1,590	1,825
0100	Economy		4	4		1,200	140		1,340	1,550
0150	8' wide, wood, premium		3	5.333		1,850	186		2,036	2,325
0200	Economy		3	5.333		1,525	186		1,711	1,975
0235	10' wide, wood, premium		2.50	6.400		2,675	224		2,899	3,300
0240	Economy		2.50	6.400		2,275	224		2,499	2,875
0250	12' wide, wood, premium		2.50	6.400		3,100	224		3,324	3,775
0300	Economy		2.50	6.400		2,475	224		2,699	3,100

08 32 19.15 Sliding Glass Vinyl-Clad Wood Doors

			Crew	Daily Output	Labor-Hours	Unit	Material	2017 Bare Costs Labor	Equipment	Total	Total Incl O&P
0010	**SLIDING GLASS VINYL-CLAD WOOD DOORS**										
0020	Glass, sliding vinyl clad, insul. glass, 6'-0" x 6'-8"	G	2 Carp	4	4	Opng.	1,525	140		1,665	1,900
0025	6'-0" x 6'-10" high	G		4	4		1,700	140		1,840	2,075
0030	6'-0" x 8'-0" high	G		4	4		2,050	140		2,190	2,475
0050	5'-0" x 6'-8" high	G		4	4		1,575	140		1,715	1,975
0100	8'-0" x 6'-10" high	G		4	4		2,025	140		2,165	2,450
0104	8'-0" x 6'-8" high	G		4	4		2,025	140		2,165	2,450
0150	8'-0" x 8'-0" high	G		4	4		2,350	140		2,490	2,825
0500	4 leaf, 9'-0" x 6'-10" high	G		3	5.333		3,350	186		3,536	4,000
0550	9'-0" x 8'-0" high	G		3	5.333		3,925	186		4,111	4,600
0600	12'-0" x 6'-10" high	G		3	5.333		4,025	186		4,211	4,725

08 36 Panel Doors

08 36 13 – Sectional Doors

08 36 13.20 Residential Garage Doors

		Crew	Daily Output	Labor-Hours	Unit	Material	2017 Bare Costs Labor	Equipment	Total	Total Incl O&P
0010	**RESIDENTIAL GARAGE DOORS**									
0050	Hinged, wood, custom, double door, 9' x 7'	2 Carp	4	4	Ea.	820	140		960	1,150
0070	16' x 7'		3	5.333		1,250	186		1,436	1,675
0200	Overhead, sectional, incl. hardware, fiberglass, 9' x 7', standard		5	3.200		975	112		1,087	1,250
0220	Deluxe		5	3.200		1,150	112		1,262	1,450
0300	16' x 7', standard		6	2.667		1,575	93		1,668	1,875
0320	Deluxe		6	2.667		2,150	93		2,243	2,500
0500	Hardboard, 9' x 7', standard		8	2		685	70		755	870

For customer support on your Residential Costs with RSMeans Data, call 800.448.8182.

457

08 36 Panel Doors

08 36 13 – Sectional Doors

08 36 13.20 Residential Garage Doors		Crew	Daily Output	Labor-Hours	Unit	Material	2017 Bare Costs Labor	Equipment	Total	Total Incl O&P
0520	Deluxe	2 Carp	8	2	Ea.	815	70		885	1,025
0600	16' x 7', standard		6	2.667		1,225	93		1,318	1,500
0620	Deluxe		6	2.667		1,425	93		1,518	1,725
0700	Metal, 9' x 7', standard		8	2		835	70		905	1,025
0720	Deluxe		6	2.667		960	93		1,053	1,200
0800	16' x 7', standard		6	2.667		1,025	93		1,118	1,275
0820	Deluxe		5	3.200		1,400	112		1,512	1,725
0900	Wood, 9' x 7', standard		8	2		970	70		1,040	1,200
0920	Deluxe		8	2		2,150	70		2,220	2,475
1000	16' x 7', standard		6	2.667		1,625	93		1,718	1,950
1020	Deluxe		6	2.667		3,025	93		3,118	3,475
1800	Door hardware, sectional	1 Carp	4	2		350	70		420	500
1810	Door tracks only		4	2		164	70		234	297
1820	One side only		7	1.143		120	40		160	199
4000	For electric operator, economy, add		8	1		425	35		460	530
4100	Deluxe, including remote control		8	1		610	35		645	735
4500	For transmitter/receiver control, add to operator				Total	110			110	121
4600	Transmitters, additional				"	60			60	66
6000	Replace section, on sectional door, fiberglass, 9' x 7'	1 Carp	4	2	Ea.	650	70		720	830
6020	16' x 7'		3.50	2.286		790	80		870	1,000
6200	Hardboard, 9' x 7'		4	2		157	70		227	290
6220	16' x 7'		3.50	2.286		230	80		310	385
6300	Metal, 9' x 7'		4	2		200	70		270	335
6320	16' x 7'		3.50	2.286		320	80		400	485
6500	Wood, 9' x 7'		4	2		120	70		190	249
6520	16' x 7'		3.50	2.286		240	80		320	400
7010	Garage doors, row of lites					120			120	132

08 51 Metal Windows

08 51 13 – Aluminum Windows

08 51 13.20 Aluminum Windows

08 51 13.20 Aluminum Windows		Crew	Daily Output	Labor-Hours	Unit	Material	2017 Bare Costs Labor	Equipment	Total	Total Incl O&P
0010	**ALUMINUM WINDOWS**, incl. frame and glazing, commercial grade									
1000	Stock units, casement, 3'-1" x 3'-2" opening	2 Sswk	10	1.600	Ea.	380	61.50		441.50	530
1040	Insulating glass	"	10	1.600		515	61.50		576.50	675
1050	Add for storms					122			122	134
1600	Projected, with screen, 3'-1" x 3'-2" opening	2 Sswk	10	1.600		360	61.50		421.50	505
1650	Insulating glass	"	10	1.600		390	61.50		451.50	535
1700	Add for storms					119			119	131
2000	4'-5" x 5'-3" opening	2 Sswk	8	2		410	77		487	590
2050	Insulating glass	"	8	2		475	77		552	665
2100	Add for storms					128			128	141
2500	Enamel finish windows, 3'-1" x 3'-2"	2 Sswk	10	1.600		365	61.50		426.50	515
2550	Insulating glass		10	1.600		315	61.50		376.50	455
2600	4'-5" x 5'-3"		8	2		415	77		492	595
2700	Insulating glass		8	2		415	77		492	595
3000	Single hung, 2' x 3' opening, enameled, standard glazed		10	1.600		212	61.50		273.50	345
3100	Insulating glass		10	1.600		257	61.50		318.50	395
3300	2'-8" x 6'-8" opening, standard glazed		8	2		370	77		447	545
3400	Insulating glass		8	2		480	77		557	670
3700	3'-4" x 5'-0" opening, standard glazed		9	1.778		305	68.50		373.50	460
3800	Insulating glass		9	1.778		340	68.50		408.50	500

458

08 51 Metal Windows

08 51 13 – Aluminum Windows

08 51 13.20 Aluminum Windows

		Crew	Daily Output	Labor-Hours	Unit	Material	2017 Bare Costs Labor	Equipment	Total	Total Incl O&P
4000	Sliding aluminum, 3' x 2' opening, standard glazed	2 Sswk	10	1.600	Ea.	220	61.50		281.50	355
4100	Insulating glass		10	1.600		236	61.50		297.50	370
4300	5' x 3' opening, standard glazed		9	1.778		335	68.50		403.50	495
4400	Insulating glass		9	1.778		390	68.50		458.50	555
4600	8' x 4' opening, standard glazed		6	2.667		355	103		458	580
4700	Insulating glass		6	2.667		575	103		678	820
5000	9' x 5' opening, standard glazed		4	4		540	154		694	875
5100	Insulating glass		4	4		850	154		1,004	1,225
5500	Sliding, with thermal barrier and screen, 6' x 4', 2 track		8	2		725	77		802	935
5700	4 track		8	2		910	77		987	1,150
6000	For above units with bronze finish, add					15%				
6200	For installation in concrete openings, add					8%				

08 51 13.30 Impact Resistant Aluminum Windows

		Crew	Daily Output	Labor-Hours	Unit	Material	2017 Bare Costs Labor	Equipment	Total	Total Incl O&P
0010	**IMPACT RESISTANT ALUMINUM WINDOWS**, incl. frame and glazing									
0100	Single hung, impact resistant, 2'-8" x 5'-0"	2 Carp	9	1.778	Ea.	1,250	62		1,312	1,475
0120	3'-0" x 5'-0"		9	1.778		1,300	62		1,362	1,550
0130	4'-0" x 5'-0"		9	1.778		1,300	62		1,362	1,550
0250	Horizontal slider, impact resistant, 5'-5" x 5'-2"		9	1.778		1,550	62		1,612	1,825

08 51 23 – Steel Windows

08 51 23.40 Basement Utility Windows

		Crew	Daily Output	Labor-Hours	Unit	Material	2017 Bare Costs Labor	Equipment	Total	Total Incl O&P
0010	**BASEMENT UTILITY WINDOWS**									
0015	1'-3" x 2'-8"	1 Carp	16	.500	Ea.	139	17.50		156.50	182
1100	1'-7" x 2'-8"		16	.500		143	17.50		160.50	186
1200	1'-11" x 2'-8"		14	.571		146	19.95		165.95	195

08 51 66 – Metal Window Screens

08 51 66.10 Screens

		Crew	Daily Output	Labor-Hours	Unit	Material	2017 Bare Costs Labor	Equipment	Total	Total Incl O&P
0010	**SCREENS**									
0020	For metal sash, aluminum or bronze mesh, flat screen	2 Sswk	1200	.013	S.F.	4.40	.51		4.91	5.75
0500	Wicket screen, inside window	"	1000	.016	"	6.70	.62		7.32	8.45
0600	Residential, aluminum mesh and frame, 2' x 3'	2 Carp	32	.500	Ea.	17	17.50		34.50	47.50
0610	Rescreen		50	.320		13.50	11.20		24.70	33.50
0620	3' x 5'		32	.500		56.50	17.50		74	91
0630	Rescreen		45	.356		35	12.45		47.45	59.50
0640	4' x 8'		25	.640		87	22.50		109.50	133
0650	Rescreen		40	.400		51	14		65	79.50
0660	Patio door		25	.640		200	22.50		222.50	258
0680	Rescreening		1600	.010	S.F.	2.50	.35		2.85	3.33
1000	Screens for solar louvers	2 Sswk	160	.100	"	24.50	3.86		28.36	34

08 52 Wood Windows

08 52 10 – Plain Wood Windows

08 52 10.10 Wood Windows

		Crew	Daily Output	Labor-Hours	Unit	Material	2017 Bare Costs Labor	Equipment	Total	Total Incl O&P
0010	**WOOD WINDOWS**, including frame, screens and grilles									
0020	Residential, stock units									
0050	Awning type, double insulated glass, 2'-10" x 1'-9" opening	2 Carp	12	1.333	Opng.	230	46.50		276.50	330
0100	2'-10" x 6'-0" opening	1 Carp	8	1		555	35		590	670
0200	4'-0" x 3'-6" single pane		10	.800		375	28		403	460
0300	6' x 5' single pane		8	1	Ea.	510	35		545	620
1000	Casement, 2'-0" x 3'-4" high	2 Carp	20	.800		258	28		286	330
1020	2'-0" x 4'-0"		18	.889		273	31		304	350

08 52 Wood Windows

08 52 10 – Plain Wood Windows

08 52 10.10 Wood Windows		Crew	Daily Output	Labor-Hours	Unit	Material	2017 Bare Costs Labor	Equipment	Total	Total Incl O&P
1040	2'-0" x 5'-0"	2 Carp	17	.941	Ea.	315	33		348	405
1060	2'-0" x 6'-0"		16	1		315	35		350	405
1080	4'-0" x 3'-4"		15	1.067		590	37.50		627.50	715
1100	4'-0" x 4'-0"		15	1.067		665	37.50		702.50	795
1120	4'-0" x 5'-0"		14	1.143		750	40		790	890
1140	4'-0" x 6'-0"		12	1.333	↓	845	46.50		891.50	1,000
1600	Casement units, 8' x 5', with screens, double insulated glass		2.50	6.400	Opng.	1,500	224		1,724	2,025
1700	Low E glass		2.50	6.400		1,625	224		1,849	2,175
2300	Casements, including screens, 2'-0" x 3'-4", dbl. insulated glass		11	1.455		275	51		326	390
2400	Low E glass		11	1.455		275	51		326	390
2600	2 lite, 4'-0" x 4'-0", double insulated glass		9	1.778		500	62		562	655
2700	Low E glass		9	1.778		515	62		577	670
2900	3 lite, 5'-2" x 5'-0", double insulated glass		7	2.286		760	80		840	970
3000	Low E glass		7	2.286		805	80		885	1,025
3200	4 lite, 7'-0" x 5'-0", double insulated glass		6	2.667		1,075	93		1,168	1,350
3300	Low E glass		6	2.667		1,150	93		1,243	1,425
3500	5 lite, 8'-6" x 5'-0", double insulated glass		5	3.200		1,450	112		1,562	1,750
3600	Low E glass	↓	5	3.200	↓	1,450	112		1,562	1,750
3800	For removable wood grilles, diamond pattern, add				Leaf	39			39	43
3900	Rectangular pattern, add				"	39			39	43
4000	Bow, fixed lites, 8' x 5', double insulated glass	2 Carp	3	5.333	Opng.	1,450	186		1,636	1,875
4100	Low E glass	"	3	5.333	"	1,975	186		2,161	2,475
4150	6'-0" x 5'-0"	1 Carp	8	1	Ea.	1,275	35		1,310	1,450
4300	Fixed lites, 9'-9" x 5'-0", double insulated glass	2 Carp	2	8	Opng.	995	280		1,275	1,575
4400	Low E glass	"	2	8	"	1,075	280		1,355	1,675
5000	Bow, casement, 8'-1" x 4'-8" high	3 Carp	8	3	Ea.	1,600	105		1,705	1,925
5020	9'-6" x 4'-8"		8	3		1,725	105		1,830	2,075
5040	8'-1" x 5'-1"		8	3		1,925	105		2,030	2,300
5060	9'-6" x 5'-1"		6	4		1,950	140		2,090	2,375
5080	8'-1" x 6'-0"		6	4		1,925	140		2,065	2,350
5100	9'-6" x 6'-0"	↓	6	4	↓	2,050	140		2,190	2,475
5800	Skylights, hatches, vents, and sky roofs, see Section 08 62 13.00									

08 52 10.20 Awning Window

		Crew	Daily Output	Labor-Hours	Unit	Material	2017 Bare Costs Labor	Equipment	Total	Total Incl O&P
0010	**AWNING WINDOW**, Including frame, screens and grilles									
0100	34" x 22", insulated glass	1 Carp	10	.800	Ea.	276	28		304	350
0200	Low E glass		10	.800		298	28		326	375
0300	40" x 28", insulated glass		9	.889		315	31		346	395
0400	Low E glass		9	.889		345	31		376	430
0500	48" x 36", insulated glass		8	1		470	35		505	575
0600	Low E glass	↓	8	1	↓	495	35		530	605

08 52 10.30 Wood Windows

		Crew	Daily Output	Labor-Hours	Unit	Material	2017 Bare Costs Labor	Equipment	Total	Total Incl O&P
0010	**WOOD WINDOWS**, double hung									
0020	Including frame, double insulated glass, screens and grilles									
0040	Double hung, 2'-2" x 3'-4" high	2 Carp	15	1.067	Ea.	215	37.50		252.50	300
0060	2'-2" x 4'-4"		14	1.143		234	40		274	325
0080	2'-6" x 3'-4"		13	1.231		225	43		268	320
0100	2'-6" x 4'-0"		12	1.333		233	46.50		279.50	335
0120	2'-6" x 4'-8"		12	1.333		253	46.50		299.50	355
0140	2'-10" x 3'-4"		10	1.600		227	56		283	345
0160	2'-10" x 4'-0"		10	1.600		252	56		308	370
0180	3'-7" x 3'-4"		9	1.778		259	62		321	390
0200	3'-7" x 5'-4"	↓	9	1.778		294	62		356	430

460

08 52 Wood Windows

08 52 10 – Plain Wood Windows

08 52 10.30 Wood Windows

		Crew	Daily Output	Labor-Hours	Unit	Material	2017 Bare Costs Labor	Equipment	Total	Total Incl O&P
0220	3'-10" x 5'-4"	2 Carp	8	2	Ea.	520	70		590	685
3800	Triple glazing for above, add				▼	25%				

08 52 10.40 Casement Window

			Crew	Daily Output	Labor-Hours	Unit	Material	2017 Bare Costs Labor	Equipment	Total	Total Incl O&P
0010	**CASEMENT WINDOW**, including frame, screen and grilles	R085216-10									
0100	2'-0" x 3'-0" H, dbl. insulated glass	G	1 Carp	10	.800	Ea.	274	28		302	345
0150	Low E glass	G		10	.800		266	28		294	340
0200	2'-0" x 4'-6" high, double insulated glass	G		9	.889		375	31		406	465
0250	Low E glass	G		9	.889		375	31		406	465
0260	Casement 4'-2" x 4'-2" double insulated glass	G		11	.727		890	25.50		915.50	1,025
0270	4'-0" x 4'-0" Low E glass	G		11	.727		550	25.50		575.50	645
0290	6'-4" x 5'-7" Low E glass	G		9	.889		1,125	31		1,156	1,300
0300	2'-4" x 6'-0" high, double insulated glass	G		8	1		445	35		480	550
0350	Low E glass	G		8	1		440	35		475	545
0522	Vinyl clad, premium, double insulated glass, 2'-0" x 3'-0"	G		10	.800		276	28		304	350
0524	2'-0" x 4'-0"	G		9	.889		320	31		351	400
0525	2'-0" x 5'-0"	G		8	1		380	35		415	480
0528	2'-0" x 6'-0"	G		8	1		390	35		425	490
0600	3'-0" x 5'-0"	G		8	1		675	35		710	805
0700	4'-0" x 3'-0"	G		8	1		740	35		775	875
0710	4'-0" x 4'-0"	G		8	1		635	35		670	760
0720	4'-8" x 4'-0"	G		8	1		700	35		735	830
0730	4'-8" x 5'-0"	G		6	1.333		800	46.50		846.50	960
0740	4'-8" x 6'-0"	G		6	1.333		900	46.50		946.50	1,075
0750	6'-0" x 4'-0"	G		6	1.333		820	46.50		866.50	980
0800	6'-0" x 5'-0"	G		6	1.333		900	46.50		946.50	1,075
0900	5'-6" x 5'-6"	G	2 Carp	15	1.067	▼	1,450	37.50		1,487.50	1,650
2000	Bay, casement units, 8' x 5', w/screens, dbl. insul. glass			2.50	6.400	Opng.	1,625	224		1,849	2,175
2100	Low E glass		▼	2.50	6.400	"	1,725	224		1,949	2,250
3020	Vinyl clad, premium, double insulated glass, multiple leaf units										
3080	Single unit, 1'-6" x 5'-0"	G	2 Carp	20	.800	Ea.	320	28		348	395
3100	2'-0" x 2'-0"	G		20	.800		225	28		253	295
3140	2'-0" x 2'-6"	G		20	.800		276	28		304	350
3220	2'-0" x 3'-6"	G		20	.800		281	28		309	355
3260	2'-0" x 4'-0"	G		19	.842		320	29.50		349.50	400
3300	2'-0" x 4'-6"	G		19	.842		325	29.50		354.50	410
3340	2'-0" x 5'-0"	G		18	.889		380	31		411	470
3460	2'-4" x 3'-0"	G		20	.800		281	28		309	355
3500	2'-4" x 4'-0"	G		19	.842		350	29.50		379.50	435
3540	2'-4" x 5'-0"	G		18	.889		415	31		446	505
3700	Double unit, 2'-8" x 5'-0"	G		18	.889		580	31		611	690
3740	2'-8" x 6'-0"	G		17	.941		675	33		708	800
3840	3'-0" x 4'-6"	G		18	.889		525	31		556	630
3860	3'-0" x 5'-0"	G		17	.941		675	33		708	800
3880	3'-0" x 6'-0"	G		17	.941		730	33		763	860
3980	3'-4" x 2'-6"	G		19	.842		445	29.50		474.50	540
4000	3'-4" x 3'-0"	G		12	1.333		450	46.50		496.50	575
4030	3'-4" x 4'-0"	G		18	.889		545	31		576	650
4050	3'-4" x 5'-0"	G		12	1.333		680	46.50		726.50	830
4100	3'-4" x 6'-0"	G		11	1.455		730	51		781	890
4200	3'-6" x 3'-0"	G		18	.889		525	31		556	630
4340	4'-0" x 3'-0"	G		18	.889		505	31		536	605
4380	4'-0" x 3'-6"	G	▼	17	.941	▼	545	33		578	655

For customer support on your Residential Costs with RSMeans Data, call 800.448.8182.

461

08 52 Wood Windows

08 52 10 – Plain Wood Windows

08 52 10.40 Casement Window		Crew	Daily Output	Labor-Hours	Unit	Material	2017 Bare Costs Labor	Equipment	Total	Total Incl O&P
4420	4'-0" x 4'-0" [G]	2 Carp	16	1	Ea.	635	35		670	760
4460	4'-0" x 4'-4" [G]		16	1		640	35		675	760
4540	4'-0" x 5'-0" [G]		16	1		695	35		730	825
4580	4'-0" x 6'-0" [G]		15	1.067		790	37.50		827.50	930
4740	4'-8" x 3'-0" [G]		18	.889		565	31		596	670
4780	4'-8" x 3'-6" [G]		17	.941		600	33		633	715
4820	4'-8" x 4'-0" [G]		16	1		700	35		735	830
4860	4'-8" x 5'-0" [G]		15	1.067		800	37.50		837.50	945
4900	4'-8" x 6'-0" [G]		15	1.067		900	37.50		937.50	1,050
5060	5'-0" x 5'-0" [G]		15	1.067		1,050	37.50		1,087.50	1,225
5100	Triple unit, 5'-6" x 3'-0" [G]		17	.941		715	33		748	840
5140	5'-6" x 3'-6" [G]		16	1		825	35		860	970
5180	5'-6" x 4'-6" [G]		15	1.067		865	37.50		902.50	1,025
5220	5'-6" x 5'-6" [G]		15	1.067		1,125	37.50		1,162.50	1,325
5300	6'-0" x 4'-6" [G]		15	1.067		900	37.50		937.50	1,050
5850	5'-0" x 3'-0" [G]		12	1.333		600	46.50		646.50	740
5900	5'-0" x 4'-0" [G]		11	1.455		960	51		1,011	1,125
6100	5'-0" x 5'-6" [G]		10	1.600		1,075	56		1,131	1,275
6150	5'-0" x 6'-0" [G]		10	1.600		1,200	56		1,256	1,425
6200	6'-0" x 3'-0" [G]		12	1.333		1,175	46.50		1,221.50	1,350
6250	6'-0" x 3'-4" [G]		12	1.333		675	46.50		721.50	825
6300	6'-0" x 4'-0" [G]		11	1.455		835	51		886	1,000
6350	6'-0" x 5'-0" [G]		10	1.600		920	56		976	1,100
6400	6'-0" x 6'-0" [G]		10	1.600		1,175	56		1,231	1,375
6500	Quadruple unit, 7'-0" x 4'-0" [G]		9	1.778		1,150	62		1,212	1,350
6700	8'-0" x 4'-6" [G]		9	1.778		1,425	62		1,487	1,675
6950	6'-8" x 4'-0" [G]		10	1.600		1,100	56		1,156	1,300
7000	6'-8" x 6'-0" [G]		10	1.600		1,475	56		1,531	1,700
8190	For installation, add per leaf						15%			
8200	For multiple leaf units, deduct for stationary sash									
8220	2' high				Ea.	23.50			23.50	25.50
8240	4'-6" high					26.50			26.50	29
8260	6' high					35			35	38.50

08 52 10.50 Double Hung

		Crew	Daily Output	Labor-Hours	Unit	Material	Labor	Equipment	Total	Total Incl O&P
0010	**DOUBLE HUNG,** Including frame, screens and grilles									
0100	2'-0" x 3'-0" high, low E insul. glass [G]	1 Carp	10	.800	Ea.	193	28		221	259
0200	3'-0" x 4'-0" high, double insulated glass [G]		9	.889		283	31		314	360
0300	4'-0" x 4'-6" high, low E insulated glass [G]		8	1		330	35		365	425

08 52 10.55 Picture Window

		Crew	Daily Output	Labor-Hours	Unit	Material	Labor	Equipment	Total	Total Incl O&P
0010	**PICTURE WINDOW,** Including frame and grilles									
0100	3'-6" x 4'-0" high, dbl. insulated glass	2 Carp	12	1.333	Ea.	435	46.50		481.50	560
0150	Low E glass		12	1.333		445	46.50		491.50	570
0200	4'-0" x 4'-6" high, double insulated glass		11	1.455		550	51		601	690
0250	Low E glass		11	1.455		530	51		581	670
0300	5'-0" x 4'-0" high, double insulated glass		11	1.455		580	51		631	725
0350	Low E glass		11	1.455		605	51		656	750
0400	6'-0" x 4'-6" high, double insulated glass		10	1.600		640	56		696	795
0450	Low E glass		10	1.600		640	56		696	800

08 52 10.65 Wood Sash

		Crew	Daily Output	Labor-Hours	Unit	Material	Labor	Equipment	Total	Total Incl O&P
0010	**WOOD SASH,** Including glazing but not trim									
0050	Custom, 5'-0" x 4'-0", 1" dbl. glazed, 3/16" thick lites	2 Carp	3.20	5	Ea.	233	175		408	550
0100	1/4" thick lites		5	3.200		263	112		375	475

08 52 Wood Windows

08 52 10 – Plain Wood Windows

08 52 10.65 Wood Sash

		Crew	Daily Output	Labor-Hours	Unit	Material	2017 Bare Costs Labor	Equipment	Total	Total Incl O&P
0200	1" thick, triple glazed	2 Carp	5	3.200	Ea.	430	112		542	660
0300	7'-0" x 4'-6" high, 1" double glazed, 3/16" thick lites		4.30	3.721		430	130		560	685
0400	1/4" thick lites		4.30	3.721		490	130		620	750
0500	1" thick, triple glazed		4.30	3.721		560	130		690	830
0600	8'-6" x 5'-0" high, 1" double glazed, 3/16" thick lites		3.50	4.571		580	160		740	905
0700	1/4" thick lites		3.50	4.571		640	160		800	965
0800	1" thick, triple glazed		3.50	4.571		675	160		835	1,000
0900	Window frames only, based on perimeter length				L.F.	4.13			4.13	4.54

08 52 10.70 Sliding Windows

				Crew	Daily Output	Labor-Hours	Unit	Material	2017 Bare Costs Labor	Equipment	Total	Total Incl O&P
0010	**SLIDING WINDOWS**											
0100	3'-0" x 3'-0" high, double insulated	G		1 Carp	10	.800	Ea.	293	28		321	365
0120	Low E glass	G			10	.800		320	28		348	395
0200	4'-0" x 3'-6" high, double insulated	G			9	.889		380	31		411	470
0220	Low E glass	G			9	.889		385	31		416	470
0300	6'-0" x 5'-0" high, double insulated	G			8	1		505	35		540	615
0320	Low E glass	G			8	1		550	35		585	665
6000	Sliding, insulating glass, including screens,											
6100	3'-0" x 3'-0"				2 Carp	6.50	2.462	Ea.	330	86		416	510
6200	4'-0" x 3'-6"					6.30	2.540		335	89		424	520
6300	5'-0" x 4'-0"					6	2.667		415	93		508	615

08 52 13 – Metal-Clad Wood Windows

08 52 13.10 Awning Windows, Metal-Clad

		Crew	Daily Output	Labor-Hours	Unit	Material	2017 Bare Costs Labor	Equipment	Total	Total Incl O&P
0010	**AWNING WINDOWS, METAL-CLAD**									
2000	Metal-clad, awning deluxe, double insulated glass, 34" x 22"	1 Carp	9	.889	Ea.	255	31		286	335
2050	36" x 25"		9	.889		276	31		307	355
2100	40" x 22"		9	.889		295	31		326	375
2150	40" x 30"		9	.889		340	31		371	425
2200	48" x 28"		8	1		350	35		385	445
2250	60" x 36"		8	1		375	35		410	470

08 52 13.20 Casement Windows, Metal-Clad

			Crew	Daily Output	Labor-Hours	Unit	Material	2017 Bare Costs Labor	Equipment	Total	Total Incl O&P
0010	**CASEMENT WINDOWS, METAL-CLAD**										
0100	Metal-clad, deluxe, dbl. insul. glass, 2'-0" x 3'-0" high	G	1 Carp	10	.800	Ea.	285	28		313	360
0120	2'-0" x 4'-0" high	G		9	.889		320	31		351	400
0130	2'-0" x 5'-0" high	G		8	1		330	35		365	425
0140	2'-0" x 6'-0" high	G		8	1		370	35		405	465
0150	Casement window, metal clad, double insul. glass, 3'-6" x 3'-6"	G		8.90	.899		490	31.50		521.50	595
0300	Metal-clad, casement, bldrs mdl, 6'-0" x 4'-0", dbl. insltd gls, 3 panels		2 Carp	10	1.600		1,200	56		1,256	1,425
0310	9'-0" x 4'-0", 4 panels			8	2		1,550	70		1,620	1,825
0320	10'-0" x 5'-0", 5 panels			7	2.286		2,100	80		2,180	2,450
0330	12'-0" x 6'-0", 6 panels			6	2.667		2,700	93		2,793	3,100

08 52 13.30 Double-Hung Windows, Metal-Clad

			Crew	Daily Output	Labor-Hours	Unit	Material	2017 Bare Costs Labor	Equipment	Total	Total Incl O&P
0010	**DOUBLE-HUNG WINDOWS, METAL-CLAD**										
0100	Metal-clad, deluxe, dbl. insul. glass, 2'-6" x 3'-0" high	G	1 Carp	10	.800	Ea.	280	28		308	355
0120	3'-0" x 3'-6" high	G		10	.800		320	28		348	395
0140	3'-0" x 4'-0" high	G		9	.889		335	31		366	420
0160	3'-0" x 4'-6" high	G		9	.889		350	31		381	435
0180	3'-0" x 5'-0" high	G		8	1		380	35		415	475
0200	3'-6" x 6'-0" high	G		8	1		455	35		490	565

For customer support on your Residential Costs with RSMeans Data, call 800.448.8182.

463

08 52 13 – Metal-Clad Wood Windows

08 52 13.35 Picture and Sliding Windows Metal-Clad		Crew	Daily Output	Labor-Hours	Unit	Material	2017 Bare Costs		Total	Total Incl O&P
							Labor	Equipment		
0010	**PICTURE AND SLIDING WINDOWS METAL-CLAD**									
2000	Metal-clad, dlx picture, dbl. insul. glass, 4'-0" x 4'-0" high	2 Carp	12	1.333	Ea.	380	46.50		426.50	500
2100	4'-0" x 6'-0" high		11	1.455		560	51		611	700
2200	5'-0" x 6'-0" high		10	1.600		620	56		676	775
2300	6'-0" x 6'-0" high		10	1.600		710	56		766	875
2400	Metal-clad, dlx sliding, double insulated glass, 3'-0" x 3'-0" high G	1 Carp	10	.800		330	28		358	405
2420	4'-0" x 3'-6" high G		9	.889		400	31		431	490
2440	5'-0" x 4'-0" high G		9	.889		480	31		511	575
2460	6'-0" x 5'-0" high G		8	1		745	35		780	880

08 52 13.40 Bow and Bay Windows, Metal-Clad

		Crew	Daily Output	Labor-Hours	Unit	Material	Labor	Equipment	Total	Total Incl O&P
0010	**BOW AND BAY WINDOWS, METAL-CLAD**									
0100	Metal-clad, deluxe, dbl. insul. glass, 8'-0" x 5'-0" high, 4 panels	2 Carp	10	1.600	Ea.	1,700	56		1,756	1,975
0120	10'-0" x 5'-0" high, 5 panels		8	2		1,825	70		1,895	2,125
0140	10'-0" x 6'-0" high, 5 panels		7	2.286		2,150	80		2,230	2,500
0160	12'-0" x 6'-0" high, 6 panels		6	2.667		2,925	93		3,018	3,375
0400	Double hung, bldrs. model, bay, 8' x 4' high, dbl. insulated glass		10	1.600		1,350	56		1,406	1,575
0440	Low E glass		10	1.600		1,450	56		1,506	1,700
0460	9'-0" x 5'-0" high, double insulated glass		6	2.667		1,450	93		1,543	1,750
0480	Low E glass		6	2.667		1,525	93		1,618	1,825
0500	Metal-clad, deluxe, dbl. insul. glass, 7'-0" x 4'-0" high		10	1.600		1,300	56		1,356	1,525
0520	8'-0" x 4'-0" high		8	2		1,350	70		1,420	1,600
0540	8'-0" x 5'-0" high		7	2.286		1,375	80		1,455	1,650
0560	9'-0" x 5'-0" high		6	2.667		1,475	93		1,568	1,775

08 52 16 – Plastic-Clad Wood Windows

08 52 16.10 Bow Window

		Crew	Daily Output	Labor-Hours	Unit	Material	Labor	Equipment	Total	Total Incl O&P
0010	**BOW WINDOW** Including frames, screens, and grilles									
0020	End panels operable									
1000	Bow type, casement, wood, bldrs. mdl., 8' x 5' dbl. insltd glass, 4 panel	2 Carp	10	1.600	Ea.	1,575	56		1,631	1,825
1050	Low E glass		10	1.600		1,325	56		1,381	1,550
1100	10'-0" x 5'-0", double insulated glass, 6 panels		6	2.667		1,350	93		1,443	1,650
1200	Low E glass, 6 panels		6	2.667		1,450	93		1,543	1,750
1300	Vinyl clad, bldrs. model, double insulated glass, 6'-0" x 4'-0", 3 panel		10	1.600		1,050	56		1,106	1,250
1340	9'-0" x 4'-0", 4 panel		8	2		1,425	70		1,495	1,700
1380	10'-0" x 6'-0", 5 panels		7	2.286		2,350	80		2,430	2,700
1420	12'-0" x 6'-0", 6 panels		6	2.667		3,075	93		3,168	3,525
2000	Bay window, 8' x 5', dbl. insul glass		10	1.600		1,925	56		1,981	2,200
2050	Low E glass		10	1.600		2,325	56		2,381	2,650
2100	12'-0" x 6'-0", double insulated glass, 6 panels		6	2.667		2,400	93		2,493	2,775
2200	Low E glass		6	2.667		3,250	93		3,343	3,725
2280	6'-0" x 4'-0"		11	1.455		1,250	51		1,301	1,450
2300	Vinyl clad, premium, double insulated glass, 8'-0" x 5'-0"		10	1.600		1,800	56		1,856	2,075
2340	10'-0" x 5'-0"		8	2		2,400	70		2,470	2,775
2380	10'-0" x 6'-0"		7	2.286		2,800	80		2,880	3,200
2420	12'-0" x 6'-0		6	2.667		3,350	93		3,443	3,850
2430	14'-0" x 3'-0"		7	2.286		3,050	80		3,130	3,475
2440	14'-0" x 6'-0"		5	3.200		5,100	112		5,212	5,775
3300	Vinyl clad, premium, double insulated glass, 7'-0" x 4'-6"		10	1.600		1,400	56		1,456	1,625
3340	8'-0" x 4'-6"		8	2		1,425	70		1,495	1,675
3380	8'-0" x 5'-0"		7	2.286		1,500	80		1,580	1,775
3420	9'-0" x 5'-0"		6	2.667		1,525	93		1,618	1,825

08 52 Wood Windows

08 52 16 – Plastic-Clad Wood Windows

08 52 16.15 Awning Window Vinyl-Clad

		Crew	Daily Output	Labor-Hours	Unit	Material	2017 Bare Costs Labor	2017 Bare Costs Equipment	Total	Total Incl O&P
0010	**AWNING WINDOW VINYL-CLAD** Including frames, screens, and grilles									
0200	Vinyl-clad, premium, double insulated glass, 24" x 17"	1 Carp	12	.667	Ea.	213	23.50		236.50	274
0210	24" x 28"		11	.727		261	25.50		286.50	330
0250	36" x 17"		9	.889		268	31		299	345
0280	36" x 28"		9	.889		305	31		336	390
0300	36" x 36"		9	.889		350	31		381	435
0320	36" x 40"		9	.889		400	31		431	490
0340	40" x 22"		10	.800		295	28		323	370
0360	48" x 28"		8	1		370	35		405	470
0380	60" x 36"		8	1		520	35		555	630

08 52 16.20 Half Round, Vinyl Clad

		Crew	Daily Output	Labor-Hours	Unit	Material	2017 Bare Costs Labor	2017 Bare Costs Equipment	Total	Total Incl O&P
0010	**HALF ROUND, VINYL CLAD**, double insulated glass, incl. grille									
0800	14" height x 24" base	2 Carp	9	1.778	Ea.	420	62		482	565
1040	15" height x 25" base		8	2		405	70		475	560
1060	16" height x 28" base		7	2.286		430	80		510	605
1080	17" height x 29" base		7	2.286		445	80		525	620
2000	19" height x 33" base	1 Carp	6	1.333		490	46.50		536.50	615
2100	20" height x 35" base		6	1.333		485	46.50		531.50	610
2200	21" height x 37" base		6	1.333		495	46.50		541.50	625
2250	23" height x 41" base	2 Carp	6	2.667		535	93		628	740
2300	26" height x 48" base		6	2.667		555	93		648	765
2350	30" height x 56" base		6	2.667		645	93		738	865
3000	36" height x 67" base	1 Carp	4	2		1,150	70		1,220	1,375
3040	38" height x 71" base	2 Carp	5	3.200		1,000	112		1,112	1,275
3050	40" height x 75" base	"	5	3.200		1,325	112		1,437	1,625
5000	Elliptical, 71" x 16"	1 Carp	11	.727		995	25.50		1,020.50	1,150
5100	95" x 21"	"	10	.800		1,425	28		1,453	1,625

08 52 16.30 Palladian Windows

		Crew	Daily Output	Labor-Hours	Unit	Material	2017 Bare Costs Labor	2017 Bare Costs Equipment	Total	Total Incl O&P
0010	**PALLADIAN WINDOWS**									
0020	Vinyl-clad, double insulated glass, including frame and grilles									
0040	3'-2" x 2'-6" high	2 Carp	11	1.455	Ea.	1,275	51		1,326	1,475
0060	3'-2" x 4'-10"		11	1.455		1,750	51		1,801	2,000
0080	3'-2" x 6'-4"		10	1.600		1,750	56		1,806	2,025
0100	4'-0" x 4'-0"		10	1.600		1,575	56		1,631	1,825
0120	4'-0" x 5'-4"	3 Carp	10	2.400		1,875	84		1,959	2,225
0140	4'-0" x 6'-0"		9	2.667		1,875	93		1,968	2,225
0160	4'-0" x 7'-4"		9	2.667		2,125	93		2,218	2,500
0180	5'-5" x 4'-10"		9	2.667		2,300	93		2,393	2,675
0200	5'-5" x 6'-10"		9	2.667		2,650	93		2,743	3,050
0220	5'-5" x 7'-9"		9	2.667		2,800	93		2,893	3,250
0240	6'-0" x 7'-11"		8	3		3,575	105		3,680	4,125
0260	8'-0" x 6'-0"		8	3		3,200	105		3,305	3,675

08 52 16.35 Double-Hung Window

			Crew	Daily Output	Labor-Hours	Unit	Material	2017 Bare Costs Labor	2017 Bare Costs Equipment	Total	Total Incl O&P
0010	**DOUBLE-HUNG WINDOW** Including frames, screens, and grilles										
0300	Vinyl clad, premium, double insulated glass, 2'-6" x 3'-0"	G	1 Carp	10	.800	Ea.	340	28		368	415
0305	2'-6" x 4'-0"	G		10	.800		375	28		403	460
0400	3'-0" x 3'-6"	G		10	.800		340	28		368	415
0500	3'-0" x 4'-0"	G		9	.889		395	31		426	485
0600	3'-0" x 4'-6"	G		9	.889		420	31		451	510
0700	3'-0" x 5'-0"	G		8	1		450	35		485	555
0790	3'-4" x 5'-0"	G		8	1		450	35		485	555

For customer support on your Residential Costs with RSMeans Data, call 800.448.8182.

465

08 52 Wood Windows

08 52 16 – Plastic-Clad Wood Windows

08 52 16.35 Double-Hung Window

		Crew	Daily Output	Labor-Hours	Unit	Material	2017 Bare Costs Labor	Equipment	Total	Total Incl O&P
0800	3'-6" x 6'-0" G	1 Carp	8	1	Ea.	505	35		540	615
0820	4'-0" x 5'-0" G		7	1.143		565	40		605	685
0830	4'-0" x 6'-0" G		7	1.143		715	40		755	850

08 52 16.40 Transom Windows

		Crew	Daily Output	Labor-Hours	Unit	Material	2017 Bare Costs Labor	Equipment	Total	Total Incl O&P
0010	**TRANSOM WINDOWS**									
0050	Vinyl clad, premium, double insulated glass, 32" x 8"	1 Carp	16	.500	Ea.	191	17.50		208.50	239
0100	36" x 8"		16	.500		206	17.50		223.50	256
0110	36" x 12"		16	.500		221	17.50		238.50	272
1000	Vinyl clad, premium, dbl. insul. glass, 4'-0" x 4'-0"	2 Carp	12	1.333		530	46.50		576.50	665
1100	4'-0" x 6'-0"		11	1.455		975	51		1,026	1,150
1200	5'-0" x 6'-0"		10	1.600		1,075	56		1,131	1,300
1300	6'-0" x 6'-0"		10	1.600		1,150	56		1,206	1,350

08 52 16.45 Trapezoid Windows

		Crew	Daily Output	Labor-Hours	Unit	Material	2017 Bare Costs Labor	Equipment	Total	Total Incl O&P
0010	**TRAPEZOID WINDOWS**									
0100	Vinyl clad, including frame and exterior trim									
0900	20" base x 44" leg x 53" leg	2 Carp	13	1.231	Ea.	400	43		443	510
1000	24" base x 90" leg x 102" leg		8	2		700	70		770	885
3000	36" base x 40" leg x 22" leg		12	1.333		440	46.50		486.50	565
3010	36" base x 44" leg x 25" leg		13	1.231		465	43		508	580
3050	36" base x 26" leg x 48" leg		9	1.778		470	62		532	620
3100	36" base x 42" legs, 50" peak		9	1.778		555	62		617	715
3200	36" base x 60" leg x 81" leg		11	1.455		730	51		781	885
4320	44" base x 23" leg x 56" leg		11	1.455		570	51		621	710
4350	44" base x 59" leg x 92" leg		10	1.600		880	56		936	1,075
4500	46" base x 15" leg x 46" leg		8	2		440	70		510	600
4550	46" base x 16" leg x 48" leg		8	2		465	70		535	625
4600	46" base x 50" leg x 80" leg		7	2.286		700	80		780	905
6600	66" base x 12" leg x 42" leg		8	2		600	70		670	775
6650	66" base x 12" legs, 28" peak		9	1.778		480	62		542	635
6700	68" base x 23" legs, 31" peak		8	2		600	70		670	775

08 52 16.70 Vinyl Clad, Premium, Dbl. Insulated Glass

		Crew	Daily Output	Labor-Hours	Unit	Material	2017 Bare Costs Labor	Equipment	Total	Total Incl O&P
0010	**VINYL CLAD, PREMIUM, DBL. INSULATED GLASS**									
1000	Sliding, 3'-0" x 3'-0" G	1 Carp	10	.800	Ea.	625	28		653	730
1020	4'-0" x 1'-11" G		11	.727		600	25.50		625.50	705
1040	4'-0" x 3'-0" G		10	.800		750	28		778	870
1050	4'-0" x 3'-6" G		9	.889		690	31		721	810
1090	4'-0" x 5'-0" G		9	.889		940	31		971	1,075
1100	5'-0" x 4'-0" G		9	.889		920	31		951	1,050
1120	5'-0" x 5'-0" G		8	1		1,075	35		1,110	1,250
1140	6'-0" x 4'-0" G		8	1		1,125	35		1,160	1,275
1150	6'-0" x 5'-0" G		8	1		1,175	35		1,210	1,325

08 52 50 – Window Accessories

08 52 50.10 Window Grille or Muntin

		Crew	Daily Output	Labor-Hours	Unit	Material	2017 Bare Costs Labor	Equipment	Total	Total Incl O&P
0010	**WINDOW GRILLE OR MUNTIN**, snap in type									
0020	Standard pattern interior grilles									
2000	Wood, awning window, glass size, 28" x 16" high	1 Carp	30	.267	Ea.	30.50	9.30		39.80	49
2060	44" x 24" high		32	.250		44	8.75		52.75	63
2100	Casement, glass size, 20" x 36" high		30	.267		33.50	9.30		42.80	52.50
2180	20" x 56" high		32	.250		46.50	8.75		55.25	65.50
2200	Double hung, glass size, 16" x 24" high		24	.333	Set	56	11.65		67.65	81
2280	32" x 32" high		34	.235	"	140	8.20		148.20	168

08 52 Wood Windows

08 52 50 – Window Accessories

		Crew	Daily Output	Labor-Hours	Unit	Material	2017 Bare Costs Labor	Equipment	Total	Total Incl O&P
08 52 50.10 Window Grille or Muntin										
2500	Picture, glass size, 48" x 48" high	1 Carp	30	.267	Ea.	128	9.30		137.30	157
2580	60" x 68" high		28	.286	"	196	10		206	233
2600	Sliding, glass size, 14" x 36" high		24	.333	Set	37.50	11.65		49.15	61
2680	36" x 36" high	▼	22	.364	"	45	12.70		57.70	71

08 52 66 – Wood Window Screens

		Crew	Daily Output	Labor-Hours	Unit	Material	2017 Bare Costs Labor	Equipment	Total	Total Incl O&P
08 52 66.10 Wood Screens										
0010	**WOOD SCREENS**									
0020	Over 3 S.F., 3/4" frames	2 Carp	375	.043	S.F.	4.75	1.49		6.24	7.75
0100	1-1/8" frames	"	375	.043	"	8.45	1.49		9.94	11.80

08 52 69 – Wood Storm Windows

			Crew	Daily Output	Labor-Hours	Unit	Material	2017 Bare Costs Labor	Equipment	Total	Total Incl O&P
08 52 69.10 Storm Windows											
0010	**STORM WINDOWS**, aluminum residential										
0300	Basement, mill finish, incl. fiberglass screen										
0320	1'-10" x 1'-0" high	G	2 Carp	30	.533	Ea.	36	18.65		54.65	70.50
0340	2'-9" x 1'-6" high	G		30	.533		39	18.65		57.65	74
0360	3'-4" x 2'-0" high	G	▼	30	.533	▼	46	18.65		64.65	81.50
1600	Double-hung, combination, storm & screen										
1700	Custom, clear anodic coating, 2'-0" x 3'-5" high		2 Carp	30	.533	Ea.	99	18.65		117.65	140
1720	2'-6" x 5'-0" high			28	.571		120	19.95		139.95	166
1740	4'-0" x 6'-0" high			25	.640		235	22.50		257.50	297
1800	White painted, 2'-0" x 3'-5" high			30	.533		115	18.65		133.65	158
1820	2'-6" x 5'-0" high			28	.571		175	19.95		194.95	227
1840	4'-0" x 6'-0" high			25	.640		290	22.50		312.50	360
2000	Clear anodic coating, 2'-0" x 3'-5" high	G		30	.533		97	18.65		115.65	138
2020	2'-6" x 5'-0" high	G		28	.571		124	19.95		143.95	170
2040	4'-0" x 6'-0" high	G		25	.640		135	22.50		157.50	187
2400	White painted, 2'-0" x 3'-5" high	G		30	.533		95	18.65		113.65	136
2420	2'-6" x 5'-0" high	G		28	.571		100	19.95		119.95	144
2440	4'-0" x 6'-0" high	G		25	.640		115	22.50		137.50	165
2600	Mill finish, 2'-0" x 3'-5" high	G		30	.533		90	18.65		108.65	130
2620	2'-6" x 5'-0" high	G		28	.571		95	19.95		114.95	139
2640	4'-0" x 6'-8" high	G	▼	25	.640	▼	115	22.50		137.50	165
4000	Picture window, storm, 1 lite, white or bronze finish										
4020	4'-6" x 4'-6" high		2 Carp	25	.640	Ea.	140	22.50		162.50	192
4040	5'-8" x 4'-6" high			20	.800		155	28		183	218
4400	Mill finish, 4'-6" x 4'-6" high			25	.640		140	22.50		162.50	192
4420	5'-8" x 4'-6" high		▼	20	.800	▼	160	28		188	223
4600	3 lite, white or bronze finish										
4620	4'-6" x 4'-6" high		2 Carp	25	.640	Ea.	165	22.50		187.50	220
4640	5'-8" x 4'-6" high			20	.800		175	28		203	240
4800	Mill finish, 4'-6" x 4'-6" high			25	.640		160	22.50		182.50	214
4820	5'-8" x 4'-6" high		▼	20	.800	▼	165	28		193	229
6000	Sliding window, storm, 2 lite, white or bronze finish										
6020	3'-4" x 2'-7" high		2 Carp	28	.571	Ea.	143	19.95		162.95	191
6040	4'-4" x 3'-3" high			25	.640		160	22.50		182.50	214
6060	5'-4" x 6'-0" high		▼	20	.800	▼	216	28		244	285
9000	Interior storm window										
9100	Storm window interior glass		1 Glaz	107	.075	S.F.	6.20	2.54		8.74	11.05

08 53 Plastic Windows

08 53 13 – Vinyl Windows

08 53 13.10 Solid Vinyl Windows		Crew	Daily Output	Labor-Hours	Unit	Material	2017 Bare Costs Labor	2017 Bare Costs Equipment	Total	Total Incl O&P
0010	**SOLID VINYL WINDOWS**									
0020	Double hung, including frame and screen, 2'-0" x 2'-6"	2 Carp	15	1.067	Ea.	205	37.50		242.50	289
0040	2'-0" x 3'-6"		14	1.143		215	40		255	305
0060	2'-6" x 4'-6"		13	1.231		256	43		299	355
0080	3'-0" x 4'-0"		10	1.600		227	56		283	345
0100	3'-0" x 4'-6"		9	1.778		292	62		354	425
0120	3'-6" x 4'-6"		8	2		310	70		380	455
0140	3'-6" x 6'-0"		7	2.286		385	80		465	560

08 53 13.20 Vinyl Single Hung Windows

			Crew	Daily Output	Labor-Hours	Unit	Material	Labor	Equipment	Total	Total Incl O&P
0010	**VINYL SINGLE HUNG WINDOWS**, insulated glass										
0020	Grids, low e, J fin, extension jambs										
0130	25" x 41"	G	2 Carp	20	.800	Ea.	210	28		238	278
0140	25" x 49"	G		18	.889		220	31		251	294
0150	25" x 57"	G		17	.941		230	33		263	310
0160	25" x 65"	G		16	1		250	35		285	335
0170	29" x 41"	G		18	.889		210	31		241	283
0180	29" x 53"	G		18	.889		230	31		261	305
0190	29" x 57"	G		17	.941		240	33		273	320
0200	29" x 65"	G		16	1		250	35		285	335
0210	33" x 41"	G		20	.800		225	28		253	295
0220	33" x 53"	G		18	.889		245	31		276	320
0230	33" x 57"	G		17	.941		250	33		283	330
0240	33" x 65"	G		16	1		260	35		295	345
0250	37" x 41"	G		20	.800		250	28		278	320
0260	37" x 53"	G		18	.889		275	31		306	355
0270	37" x 57"	G		17	.941		285	33		318	370
0280	37" x 65"	G		16	1		300	35		335	390
0500	Vinyl clad, premium, double insulated glass, circle, 24" diameter		1 Carp	6	1.333		490	46.50		536.50	615
1000	2'-4" diameter			6	1.333		565	46.50		611.50	700
1500	2'-11" diameter			6	1.333		655	46.50		701.50	800

08 53 13.30 Vinyl Double Hung Windows

			Crew	Daily Output	Labor-Hours	Unit	Material	Labor	Equipment	Total	Total Incl O&P
0010	**VINYL DOUBLE HUNG WINDOWS**, insulated glass										
0100	Grids, low E, J fin, ext. jambs, 21" x 53"	G	2 Carp	18	.889	Ea.	220	31		251	294
0102	21" x 37"	G		18	.889		230	31		261	305
0104	21" x 41"	G		18	.889		240	31		271	315
0106	21" x 49"	G		18	.889		250	31		281	325
0110	21" x 57"	G		17	.941		270	33		303	350
0120	21" x 65"	G		16	1		285	35		320	375
0128	25" x 37"	G		20	.800		240	28		268	310
0130	25" x 41"	G		20	.800		250	28		278	320
0140	25" x 49"	G		18	.889		260	31		291	340
0145	25" x 53"	G		18	.889		275	31		306	355
0150	25" x 57"	G		17	.941		280	33		313	365
0160	25" x 65"	G		16	1		295	35		330	385
0162	25" x 69"	G		16	1		300	35		335	390
0164	25" x 77"	G		16	1		325	35		360	420
0168	29" x 37"	G		18	.889		250	31		281	325
0170	29" x 41"	G		18	.889		260	31		291	340
0172	29" x 49"	G		18	.889		270	31		301	350
0180	29" x 53"	G		18	.889		280	31		311	360
0190	29" x 57"	G		17	.941		290	33		323	375
0200	29" x 65"	G		16	1		310	35		345	400

For customer support on your Residential Costs with RSMeans Data, call 800.448.8182.

08 53 Plastic Windows

08 53 13 – Vinyl Windows

08 53 13.30 Vinyl Double Hung Windows		Crew	Daily Output	Labor-Hours	Unit	Material	2017 Bare Costs Labor	Equipment	Total	Total Incl O&P
0202	29" x 69" [G]	2 Carp	16	1	Ea.	315	35		350	405
0205	29" x 77" [G]		16	1		340	35		375	435
0208	33" x 37" [G]		20	.800		265	28		293	340
0210	33" x 41" [G]		20	.800		270	28		298	345
0215	33" x 49" [G]		20	.800		285	28		313	360
0220	33" x 53" [G]		18	.889		290	31		321	370
0230	33" x 57" [G]		17	.941		300	33		333	385
0240	33" x 65" [G]		16	1		320	35		355	410
0242	33" x 69" [G]		16	1		330	35		365	425
0246	33" x 77" [G]		16	1		350	35		385	445
0250	37" x 41" [G]		20	.800		295	28		323	370
0255	37" x 49" [G]		20	.800		297	28		325	370
0260	37" x 53" [G]		18	.889		320	31		351	400
0270	37" x 57" [G]		17	.941		340	33		373	430
0280	37" x 65" [G]		16	1		360	35		395	455
0282	37" x 69" [G]		16	1		365	35		400	460
0286	37" x 77" [G]		16	1		380	35		415	480
0300	Solid vinyl, average quality, double insulated glass, 2'-0" x 3'-0" [G]	1 Carp	10	.800		291	28		319	365
0310	3'-0" x 4'-0" [G]		9	.889		214	31		245	287
0330	Premium, double insulated glass, 2'-6" x 3'-0" [G]		10	.800		276	28		304	350
0340	3'-0" x 3'-6" [G]		9	.889		310	31		341	390
0350	3'-0" x 4"-0" [G]		9	.889		330	31		361	415
0360	3'-0" x 4'-6" [G]		9	.889		335	31		366	420
0370	3'-0" x 5'-0" [G]		8	1		360	35		395	455
0380	3'-6" x 6'-0" [G]		8	1		395	35		430	495

08 53 13.40 Vinyl Casement Windows

		Crew	Daily Output	Labor-Hours	Unit	Material	2017 Bare Costs Labor	Equipment	Total	Total Incl O&P
0010	**VINYL CASEMENT WINDOWS**, insulated glass									
0015	Grids, low E, J fin, extension jambs, screens									
0100	One lite, 21" x 41" [G]	2 Carp	20	.800	Ea.	300	28		328	375
0110	21" x 47" [G]		20	.800		330	28		358	410
0120	21" x 53" [G]		20	.800		350	28		378	430
0128	24" x 35" [G]		19	.842		285	29.50		314.50	365
0130	24" x 41" [G]		19	.842		320	29.50		349.50	400
0140	24" x 47" [G]		19	.842		340	29.50		369.50	425
0150	24" x 53" [G]		19	.842		365	29.50		394.50	450
0158	28" x 35" [G]		19	.842		310	29.50		339.50	390
0160	28" x 41" [G]		19	.842		340	29.50		369.50	425
0170	28" x 47" [G]		19	.842		360	29.50		389.50	445
0180	28" x 53" [G]		19	.842		390	29.50		419.50	480
0184	28" x 59" [G]		19	.842		400	29.50		429.50	490
0188	Two lites, 33" x 35" [G]		18	.889		475	31		506	575
0190	33" x 41" [G]		18	.889		510	31		541	610
0200	33" x 47" [G]		18	.889		540	31		571	645
0210	33" x 53" [G]		18	.889		580	31		611	690
0212	33" x 59" [G]		18	.889		610	31		641	720
0215	33" x 72" [G]		18	.889		640	31		671	755
0220	41" x 41" [G]		18	.889		550	31		581	655
0230	41" x 47" [G]		18	.889		585	31		616	695
0240	41" x 53" [G]		17	.941		625	33		658	745
0242	41" x 59" [G]		17	.941		660	33		693	780
0246	41" x 72" [G]		17	.941		690	33		723	815
0250	47" x 41" [G]		17	.941		560	33		593	670

08 53 Plastic Windows

08 53 13 – Vinyl Windows

08 53 13.40 Vinyl Casement Windows

			Crew	Daily Output	Labor-Hours	Unit	Material	2017 Bare Costs Labor	Equipment	Total	Total Incl O&P
0260	47" x 47"	G	2 Carp	17	.941	Ea.	600	33		633	715
0270	47" x 53"	G		17	.941		640	33		673	760
0272	47" x 59"	G		17	.941		695	33		728	820
0280	56" x 41"	G		15	1.067		600	37.50		637.50	725
0290	56" x 47"	G		15	1.067		640	37.50		677.50	770
0300	56" x 53"	G		15	1.067		695	37.50		732.50	830
0302	56" x 59"	G		15	1.067		720	37.50		757.50	855
0310	56" x 72"	G		15	1.067		775	37.50		812.50	920
0340	Solid vinyl, premium, double insulated glass, 2'-0" x 3'-0" high	G	1 Carp	10	.800		270	28		298	345
0360	2'-0" x 4'-0" high	G		9	.889		299	31		330	380
0380	2'-0" x 5'-0" high	G		8	1		335	35		370	430

08 53 13.50 Vinyl Picture Windows

		Crew	Daily Output	Labor-Hours	Unit	Material	2017 Bare Costs Labor	Equipment	Total	Total Incl O&P
0010	**VINYL PICTURE WINDOWS**, insulated glass									
0120	Grids, low e, J fin, ext. jambs, 47" x 35"	2 Carp	12	1.333	Ea.	305	46.50		351.50	415
0130	47" x 41"		12	1.333		400	46.50		446.50	520
0140	47" x 47"		12	1.333		350	46.50		396.50	465
0150	47" x 53"		11	1.455		375	51		426	500
0160	71" x 35"		11	1.455		400	51		451	525
0170	71" x 41"		11	1.455		420	51		471	545
0180	71" x 47"		11	1.455		450	51		501	580

08 53 13.60 Vinyl Half Round Windows

		Crew	Daily Output	Labor-Hours	Unit	Material	2017 Bare Costs Labor	Equipment	Total	Total Incl O&P
0010	**VINYL HALF ROUND WINDOWS**, Including grille, j fin, low E, ext. jambs									
0100	10" height x 20" base	2 Carp	8	2	Ea.	475	70		545	640
0110	15" height x 30" base		8	2		480	70		550	645
0120	17" height x 34" base		7	2.286		395	80		475	570
0130	19" height x 38" base		7	2.286		440	80		520	620
0140	19" height x 33" base		7	2.286		575	80		655	770
0150	24" height x 48" base	1 Carp	6	1.333		500	46.50		546.50	630
0160	25" height x 50" base	"	6	1.333		775	46.50		821.50	935
0170	30" height x 60" base	2 Carp	6	2.667		795	93		888	1,025

08 54 Composite Windows

08 54 13 – Fiberglass Windows

08 54 13.10 Fiberglass Single Hung Windows

			Crew	Daily Output	Labor-Hours	Unit	Material	2017 Bare Costs Labor	Equipment	Total	Total Incl O&P
0010	**FIBERGLASS SINGLE HUNG WINDOWS**										
0100	Grids, low E, 18" x 24"	G	2 Carp	18	.889	Ea.	335	31		366	420
0110	18" x 40"	G		17	.941		340	33		373	430
0130	24" x 40"	G		20	.800		360	28		388	440
0230	36" x 36"	G		17	.941		370	33		403	460
0250	36" x 48"	G		20	.800		405	28		433	490
0260	36" x 60"	G		18	.889		445	31		476	540
0280	36" x 72"	G		16	1		470	35		505	575
0290	48" x 40"	G		16	1		470	35		505	575

08 54 13.30 Fiberglass Slider Windows

			Crew	Daily Output	Labor-Hours	Unit	Material	2017 Bare Costs Labor	Equipment	Total	Total Incl O&P
0010	**FIBERGLASS SLIDER WINDOWS**										
0100	Grids, low E, 36" x 24"	G	2 Carp	20	.800	Ea.	340	28		368	420
0110	36" x 36"	G	"	20	.800	"	390	28		418	475

08 54 13.50 Fiberglass Bay Windows

			Crew	Daily Output	Labor-Hours	Unit	Material	2017 Bare Costs Labor	Equipment	Total	Total Incl O&P
0010	**FIBERGLASS BAY WINDOWS**										
0150	48" x 36"	G	2 Carp	11	1.455	Ea.	1,100	51		1,151	1,275

470

08 61 Roof Windows

08 61 13 – Metal Roof Windows

08 61 13.10 Roof Windows

		Crew	Daily Output	Labor-Hours	Unit	Material	2017 Bare Costs Labor	Equipment	Total	Total Incl O&P
0010	**ROOF WINDOWS**, fixed high perf tmpd glazing, metallic framed									
0020	46" x 21-1/2", Flashed for shingled roof	1 Carp	8	1	Ea.	281	35		316	370
0100	46" x 28"		8	1		305	35		340	395
0125	57" x 44"		6	1.333		375	46.50		421.50	495
0130	72" x 28"		7	1.143		375	40		415	480
0150	Fixed, laminated tempered glazing, 46" x 21-1/2"		8	1		465	35		500	570
0175	46" x 28"		8	1		515	35		550	625
0200	57" x 44"		6	1.333		485	46.50		531.50	610
0500	Vented flashing set for shingled roof, 46" x 21-1/2"		7	1.143		465	40		505	575
0525	46" x 28"		6	1.333		515	46.50		561.50	645
0550	57" x 44"		5	1.600		645	56		701	805
0560	72" x 28"		5	1.600		645	56		701	805
0575	Flashing set for low pitched roof, 46" x 21-1/2"		7	1.143		535	40		575	655
0600	46" x 28"		7	1.143		585	40		625	710
0625	57" x 44"		5	1.600		730	56		786	895
0650	Flashing set for curb 46" x 21-1/2"		7	1.143		620	40		660	745
0675	46" x 28"		7	1.143		670	40		710	805
0700	57" x 44"		5	1.600		825	56		881	1,000

08 61 16 – Wood Roof Windows

08 61 16.16 Roof Windows, Wood Framed

		Crew	Daily Output	Labor-Hours	Unit	Material	2017 Bare Costs Labor	Equipment	Total	Total Incl O&P
0010	**ROOF WINDOWS, WOOD FRAMED**									
5600	Roof window incl. frame, flashing, double insulated glass & screens,									
5610	complete unit, 22" x 38"	2 Carp	3	5.333	Ea.	755	186		941	1,150
5650	2'-5" x 3'-8"		3.20	5		945	175		1,120	1,350
5700	3'-5" x 4'-9"		3.40	4.706		1,050	164		1,214	1,425

08 62 Unit Skylights

08 62 13 – Domed Unit Skylights

08 62 13.10 Domed Skylights

			Crew	Daily Output	Labor-Hours	Unit	Material	2017 Bare Costs Labor	Equipment	Total	Total Incl O&P
0010	**DOMED SKYLIGHTS**										
0020	Skylight, fixed dome type, 22" x 22"	G	G-3	12	2.667	Ea.	216	86.50		302.50	385
0030	22" x 46"	G		10	3.200		269	104		373	470
0040	30" x 30"	G		12	2.667		286	86.50		372.50	460
0050	30" x 46"	G		10	3.200		380	104		484	595
0110	Fixed, double glazed, 22" x 27"	G		12	2.667		275	86.50		361.50	450
0120	22" x 46"	G		10	3.200		293	104		397	495
0130	44" x 46"	G		10	3.200		430	104		534	650
0210	Operable, double glazed, 22" x 27"	G		12	2.667		405	86.50		491.50	590
0220	22" x 46"	G		10	3.200		465	104		569	690
0230	44" x 46"	G		10	3.200		925	104		1,029	1,200

08 62 13.20 Skylights

			Crew	Daily Output	Labor-Hours	Unit	Material	2017 Bare Costs Labor	Equipment	Total	Total Incl O&P
0010	**SKYLIGHTS**, flush or curb mounted										
2120	Ventilating insulated plexiglass dome with										
2130	curb mounting, 36" x 36"	G	G-3	12	2.667	Ea.	480	86.50		566.50	675
2150	52" x 52"	G		12	2.667		670	86.50		756.50	880
2160	28" x 52"	G		10	3.200		490	104		594	715
2170	36" x 52"	G		10	3.200		545	104		649	770
2180	For electric opening system, add	G					315			315	345
2210	Operating skylight, with thermopane glass, 24" x 48"	G	G-3	10	3.200		585	104		689	820
2220	32" x 48"	G	"	9	3.556		615	115		730	870

08 62 Unit Skylights

08 62 13 – Domed Unit Skylights

08 62 13.20 Skylights		Crew	Daily Output	Labor-Hours	Unit	Material	2017 Bare Costs Labor	Equipment	Total	Total Incl O&P
2310	Non venting insulated plexiglass dome skylight with									
2320	Flush mount 22" x 46"	G	G-3	15.23	2.101	Ea.	330	68		398	480
2330	30" x 30"	G		16	2		305	65		370	445
2340	46" x 46"	G		13.91	2.301		565	74.50		639.50	745
2350	Curb mount 22" x 46"	G		15.23	2.101		365	68		433	515
2360	30" x 30"	G		16	2		405	65		470	560
2370	46" x 46"	G		13.91	2.301		625	74.50		699.50	815
2381	Non-insulated flush mount 22" x 46"			15.23	2.101		225	68		293	360
2382	30" x 30"			16	2		202	65		267	330
2383	46" x 46"			13.91	2.301		380	74.50		454.50	545
2384	Curb mount 22" x 46"			15.23	2.101		189	68		257	320
2385	30" x 30"		↓	16	2		188	65		253	315
4000	Skylight, solar tube kit, incl dome, flashing, diffuser, 1 pipe, 10" dia.	G	1 Carp	2	4		300	140		440	565
4010	14" diam.	G		2	4		400	140		540	675
4020	21" diam.	G		2	4		490	140		630	775
4030	Accessories for, 1' long x 9" dia pipe	G		24	.333		50	11.65		61.65	74.50
4040	2' long x 9" dia pipe	G		24	.333		43	11.65		54.65	67
4050	4' long x 9" dia pipe	G		20	.400		75	14		89	106
4060	1' long x 13" dia pipe	G		24	.333		70	11.65		81.65	96.50
4070	2' long x 13" dia pipe	G		24	.333		55	11.65		66.65	80
4080	4' long x 13" dia pipe	G		20	.400		102	14		116	136
4090	6.5" turret ext for 21" dia pipe	G		16	.500		110	17.50		127.50	150
4100	12' long x 21" dia flexible pipe	G		12	.667		90	23.50		113.50	138
4110	45 degree elbow, 10"	G		16	.500		155	17.50		172.50	200
4120	14"	G		16	.500		85	17.50		102.50	123
4130	Interior decorative ring, 9"	G		20	.400		45	14		59	73
4140	13"	G	↓	20	.400	↓	60	14		74	89.50

08 71 Door Hardware

08 71 20 – Hardware

08 71 20.15 Hardware

		Crew	Daily Output	Labor-Hours	Unit	Material	2017 Bare Costs Labor	Equipment	Total	Total Incl O&P
0010	**HARDWARE**									
0020	Average percentage for hardware, total job cost									
0500	Total hardware for building, average distribution					Job	85%	15%			
1000	Door hardware, apartment, interior		1 Carp	4	2	Door	465	70		535	630
1300	Average, door hardware, motel/hotel interior, with access card			4	2	"	615	70		685	795
2100	Pocket door			6	1.333	Ea.	110	46.50		156.50	199
4000	Door knocker, bright brass			32	.250		75	8.75		83.75	97
4100	Mail slot, bright brass, 2" x 11"		↓	25	.320		60	11.20		71.20	84.50
4200	Peep hole, add to price of door					↓	12			12	13.20

08 71 20.40 Lockset

		Crew	Daily Output	Labor-Hours	Unit	Material	2017 Bare Costs Labor	Equipment	Total	Total Incl O&P
0010	**LOCKSET**, Standard duty									
0020	Non-keyed, passage, w/sect. trim		1 Carp	12	.667	Ea.	72.50	23.50		96	119
0100	Privacy			12	.667		80	23.50		103.50	127
0400	Keyed, single cylinder function			10	.800		113	28		141	171
0500	Lever handled, keyed, single cylinder function		↓	10	.800	↓	126	28		154	185

08 71 20.41 Dead Locks

		Crew	Daily Output	Labor-Hours	Unit	Material	2017 Bare Costs Labor	Equipment	Total	Total Incl O&P
0010	**DEAD LOCKS**									
1203	Deadlock night latch		1 Carp	7.70	1.039	Ea.	50	36.50		86.50	116
1420	Deadbolt lock, single cylinder		↓	10	.800		50	28		78	102

08 71 Door Hardware

08 71 20 – Hardware

08 71 20.41 Dead Locks	Crew	Daily Output	Labor-Hours	Unit	Material	2017 Bare Costs Labor	Equipment	Total	Total Incl O&P
1440 Double cylinder	1 Carp	10	.800	Ea.	64.50	28		92.50	118

08 71 20.42 Mortise Locksets

	Crew	Daily Output	Labor-Hours	Unit	Material	Labor	Equipment	Total	Total Incl O&P
0010 **MORTISE LOCKSETS**, Comm., wrought knobs & full escutcheon trim									
0015 Assumes mortise is cut									
0020 Non-keyed, passage, Grade 3	1 Carp	9	.889	Ea.	155	31		186	223
0030 Grade 1		8	1		405	35		440	505
0040 Privacy set, Grade 3		9	.889		169	31		200	238
0050 Grade 1		8	1		455	35		490	560
0100 Keyed, office/entrance/apartment, Grade 2		8	1		197	35		232	276
0110 Grade 1		7	1.143		515	40		555	635
0120 Single cylinder, typical, Grade 3		8	1		189	35		224	267
0130 Grade 1		7	1.143		500	40		540	615
0200 Hotel, room, Grade 3		7	1.143		190	40		230	276
0210 Grade 1 (see also Section 08 71 20.15)		6	1.333		510	46.50		556.50	640
0300 Double cylinder, Grade 3		8	1		225	35		260	305
0310 Grade 1		7	1.143		515	40		555	635
1000 Wrought knobs and sectional trim, non-keyed, passage, Grade 3		10	.800		130	28		158	190
1010 Grade 1		9	.889		405	31		436	495
1040 Privacy, Grade 3		10	.800		150	28		178	212
1050 Grade 1		9	.889		455	31		486	550
1100 Keyed, entrance, office/apartment, Grade 3		9	.889		220	31		251	294
1103 Install lockset		6.92	1.156		220	40.50		260.50	310
1110 Grade 1		8	1		520	35		555	630
1120 Single cylinder, Grade 3		9	.889		225	31		256	300
1130 Grade 1		8	1		500	35		535	610
2000 Cast knobs and full escutcheon trim									
2010 Non-keyed, passage, Grade 3	1 Carp	9	.889	Ea.	275	31		306	355
2020 Grade 1		8	1		380	35		415	480
2040 Privacy, Grade 3		9	.889		320	31		351	400
2050 Grade 1		8	1		440	35		475	545
2120 Keyed, single cylinder, Grade 3		8	1		330	35		365	425
2123 Mortise lock		6.15	1.301		330	45.50		375.50	440
2130 Grade 1		7	1.143		525	40		565	645

08 71 20.50 Door Stops

	Crew	Daily Output	Labor-Hours	Unit	Material	Labor	Equipment	Total	Total Incl O&P
0010 **DOOR STOPS**									
0020 Holder & bumper, floor or wall	1 Carp	32	.250	Ea.	35.50	8.75		44.25	53.50
1300 Wall bumper, 4" diameter, with rubber pad, aluminum		32	.250		12.30	8.75		21.05	28
1600 Door bumper, floor type, aluminum		32	.250		8.70	8.75		17.45	24
1620 Brass		32	.250		10.25	8.75		19	26
1630 Bronze		32	.250		18.40	8.75		27.15	35
1900 Plunger type, door mounted		32	.250		30	8.75		38.75	47.50
2520 Wall type, aluminum		32	.250		35.50	8.75		44.25	54
2540 Plunger type, aluminum		32	.250		30	8.75		38.75	47.50
2560 Brass		32	.250		45.50	8.75		54.25	64.50
3020 Floor mounted, US3		3	2.667		325	93		418	510

08 71 20.60 Entrance Locks

	Crew	Daily Output	Labor-Hours	Unit	Material	Labor	Equipment	Total	Total Incl O&P
0010 **ENTRANCE LOCKS**									
0015 Cylinder, grip handle deadlocking latch	1 Carp	9	.889	Ea.	175	31		206	245
0020 Deadbolt		8	1		190	35		225	268
0100 Push and pull plate, dead bolt		8	1		225	35		260	305
0900 For handicapped lever, add					150			150	165

For customer support on your Residential Costs with RSMeans Data, call 800.448.8182.

473

08 71 Door Hardware

08 71 20 – Hardware

08 71 20.65 Thresholds		Crew	Daily Output	Labor-Hours	Unit	Material	2017 Bare Costs Labor	Equipment	Total	Total Incl O&P
0010	**THRESHOLDS**									
0011	Threshold 3' long saddles aluminum	1 Carp	48	.167	L.F.	9.70	5.85		15.55	20.50
0100	Aluminum, 8" wide, 1/2" thick		12	.667	Ea.	49	23.50		72.50	92.50
0500	Bronze		60	.133	L.F.	44	4.66		48.66	56.50
0600	Bronze, panic threshold, 5" wide, 1/2" thick		12	.667	Ea.	158	23.50		181.50	212
0700	Rubber, 1/2" thick, 5-1/2" wide		20	.400		40	14		54	67.50
0800	2-3/4" wide		20	.400		45.50	14		59.50	73.50
1950	ADA Compliant Thresholds									
2000	Threshold, wood oak 3-1/2" wide x 24" long	1 Carp	12	.667	Ea.	11.40	23.50		34.90	51.50
2010	3-1/2" wide x 36" long		12	.667		15.60	23.50		39.10	56
2020	3-1/2" wide x 48" long		12	.667		21	23.50		44.50	62
2030	4-1/2" wide x 24" long		12	.667		13.50	23.50		37	54
2040	4-1/2" wide x 36" long		12	.667		19.70	23.50		43.20	60.50
2050	4-1/2" wide x 48" long		12	.667		26	23.50		49.50	67.50
2060	6-1/2" wide x 24" long		12	.667		18.70	23.50		42.20	59.50
2070	6-1/2" wide x 36" long		12	.667		28	23.50		51.50	70
2080	6-1/2" wide x 48" long		12	.667		37.50	23.50		61	80
2090	Threshold, wood cherry 3-1/2" wide x 24" long		12	.667		15.60	23.50		39.10	56
2100	3-1/2" wide x 36" long		12	.667		23	23.50		46.50	64
2110	3-1/2" wide x 48" long		12	.667		30	23.50		53.50	72
2120	4-1/2" wide x 24" long		12	.667		19.75	23.50		43.25	60.50
2130	4-1/2" wide x 36" long		12	.667		29	23.50		52.50	71
2140	4-1/2" wide x 48" long		12	.667		38.50	23.50		62	81.50
2150	6-1/2" wide x 24" long		12	.667		28	23.50		51.50	70
2160	6-1/2" wide x 36" long		12	.667		41.50	23.50		65	85
2170	6-1/2" wide x 48" long		12	.667		55	23.50		78.50	99.50
2180	Threshold, wood walnut 3-1/2" wide x 24" long		12	.667		18.70	23.50		42.20	59.50
2190	3-1/2" wide x 36" long		12	.667		28	23.50		51.50	70
2200	3-1/2" wide x 48" long		12	.667		37.50	23.50		61	80
2210	4-1/2" wide x 24" long		12	.667		27	23.50		50.50	69
2220	4-1/2" wide x 36" long		12	.667		39.50	23.50		63	82.50
2230	4-1/2" wide x 48" long		12	.667		52	23.50		75.50	96
2240	6-1/2" wide x 24" long		12	.667		44.50	23.50		68	88
2250	6-1/2" wide x 36" long		12	.667		65	23.50		88.50	111
2260	6-1/2" wide x 48" long		12	.667		87	23.50		110.50	135
2300	Threshold, aluminum 4" wide x 36" long		12	.667		34.50	23.50		58	76.50
2310	4" wide x 48" long		12	.667		42.50	23.50		66	86
2320	4" wide x 72" long		12	.667		68.50	23.50		92	115
2330	5" wide x 36" long		12	.667		47	23.50		70.50	90.50
2340	5" wide x 48" long		12	.667		58	23.50		81.50	103
2350	5" wide x 72" long		12	.667		92.50	23.50		116	141
2360	6" wide x 36" long		12	.667		55	23.50		78.50	99.50
2370	6" wide x 48" long		12	.667		70.50	23.50		94	117
2380	6" wide x 72" long		12	.667		108	23.50		131.50	158
2390	7" wide x 36" long		12	.667		71	23.50		94.50	117
2400	7" wide x 48" long		12	.667		93	23.50		116.50	141
2410	7" wide x 72" long		12	.667		140	23.50		163.50	193
2500	Threshold, ramp, aluminum or rubber 24" x 24"		12	.667		195	23.50		218.50	254

08 71 20.75 Door Hardware Accessories

		Crew	Daily Output	Labor-Hours	Unit	Material	2017 Bare Costs Labor	Equipment	Total	Total Incl O&P
0010	**DOOR HARDWARE ACCESSORIES**									
1000	Knockers, brass, standard	1 Carp	16	.500	Ea.	50	17.50		67.50	84
1100	Deluxe		10	.800		112	28		140	170

08 71 Door Hardware

08 71 20 – Hardware

08 71 20.75 Door Hardware Accessories

		Crew	Daily Output	Labor-Hours	Unit	Material	2017 Bare Costs Labor	Equipment	Total	Total Incl O&P
4500	Rubber door silencers	1 Carp	540	.015	Ea.	.50	.52		1.02	1.42

08 71 20.90 Hinges

		Crew	Daily Output	Labor-Hours	Unit	Material	Labor	Equipment	Total	Total Incl O&P
0010	**HINGES**									
0012	Full mortise, avg. freq., steel base, USP, 4-1/2" x 4-1/2"				Pr.	39.50			39.50	43.50
0100	5" x 5", USP					59			59	65
0200	6" x 6", USP					124			124	137
0400	Brass base, 4-1/2" x 4-1/2", US10					62.50			62.50	69
0500	5" x 5", US10					89			89	98
0600	6" x 6", US10					164			164	180
0800	Stainless steel base, 4-1/2" x 4-1/2", US32					77.50			77.50	85
0900	For non removable pin, add (security item)				Ea.	5.55			5.55	6.10
0910	For floating pin, driven tips, add					3.40			3.40	3.74
0930	For hospital type tip on pin, add					14.20			14.20	15.60
0940	For steeple type tip on pin, add					19.30			19.30	21
0950	Full mortise, high frequency, steel base, 3-1/2" x 3-1/2", US26D				Pr.	30.50			30.50	33.50
1000	4-1/2" x 4-1/2", USP					66.50			66.50	73
1100	5" x 5", USP					52.50			52.50	57.50
1200	6" x 6", USP					139			139	153
1400	Brass base, 3-1/2" x 3-1/2", US4					53.50			53.50	59
1430	4-1/2" x 4-1/2", US10					76			76	83.50
1500	5" x 5", US10					127			127	139
1600	6" x 6", US10					171			171	188
1800	Stainless steel base, 4-1/2" x 4-1/2", US32					104			104	115
1810	5" x 4-1/2", US32					140			140	154
1930	For hospital type tip on pin, add				Ea.	14.60			14.60	16.05
1950	Full mortise, low frequency, steel base, 3-1/2" x 3-1/2", US26D				Pr.	27.50			27.50	30
2000	4-1/2" x 4-1/2", USP					23.50			23.50	25.50
2100	5" x 5", USP					49			49	54
2200	6" x 6", USP					94			94	103
2300	4-1/2" x 4-1/2", US3					17.50			17.50	19.25
2310	5" x 5", US3					42.50			42.50	46.50
2400	Brass bass, 4-1/2" x 4-1/2", US10					55			55	60.50
2500	5" x 5", US10					79			79	86.50
2800	Stainless steel base, 4-1/2" x 4-1/2", US32					76.50			76.50	84.50
8000	Install hinge	1 Carp	34	.235			8.20		8.20	13.75

08 71 20.91 Special Hinges

		Crew	Daily Output	Labor-Hours	Unit	Material	Labor	Equipment	Total	Total Incl O&P
0010	**SPECIAL HINGES**									
8000	Continuous hinges									
8010	Steel, piano, 2" x 72"	1 Carp	20	.400	Ea.	23	14		37	49
8020	Brass, piano, 1-1/16" x 30"		30	.267		9	9.30		18.30	25.50
8030	Acrylic, piano, 1-3/4" x 12"		40	.200		16	7		23	29.50

08 71 20.92 Mortised Hinges

		Crew	Daily Output	Labor-Hours	Unit	Material	Labor	Equipment	Total	Total Incl O&P
0010	**MORTISED HINGES**									
0200	Average frequency, steel plated, ball bearing, 3-1/2" x 3-1/2"				Pr.	30.50			30.50	33.50
0300	Bronze, ball bearing					35			35	38.50
0900	High frequency, steel plated, ball bearing					78.50			78.50	86.50
1100	Bronze, ball bearing					78.50			78.50	86.50
1300	Average frequency, steel plated, ball bearing, 4-1/2" x 4-1/2"					38			38	41.50
1500	Bronze, ball bearing, to 36" wide					39.50			39.50	43.50
1700	Low frequency, steel, plated, plain bearing					22			22	24
1900	Bronze, plain bearing					29			29	32

08 71 Door Hardware

08 71 20 – Hardware

08 71 20.95 Kick Plates

		Crew	Daily Output	Labor-Hours	Unit	Material	2017 Bare Costs Labor	Equipment	Total	Total Incl O&P
0010	**KICK PLATES**									
0020	Stainless steel, .050", 16 ga., 8" x 28", US32	1 Carp	15	.533	Ea.	40	18.65		58.65	75
0080	Mop/Kick, 4" x 28"		15	.533		35.50	18.65		54.15	70.50
0090	4" x 30"		15	.533		38	18.65		56.65	72.50
0100	4" x 34"		15	.533		43	18.65		61.65	78.50
0110	6" x 28"		15	.533		45	18.65		63.65	80.50
0120	6" x 30"		15	.533		49.50	18.65		68.15	85.50
0130	6" x 34"		15	.533		55.50	18.65		74.15	92

08 71 21 – Astragals

08 71 21.10 Exterior Mouldings, Astragals

		Crew	Daily Output	Labor-Hours	Unit	Material	2017 Bare Costs Labor	Equipment	Total	Total Incl O&P
0010	**EXTERIOR MOULDINGS, ASTRAGALS**									
4170	Astragal for double doors, aluminum	1 Carp	4	2	Opng.	35.50	70		105.50	156
4174	Bronze	"	4	2	"	49	70		119	171

08 71 25 – Weatherstripping

08 71 25.10 Mechanical Seals, Weatherstripping

		Crew	Daily Output	Labor-Hours	Unit	Material	2017 Bare Costs Labor	Equipment	Total	Total Incl O&P
0010	**MECHANICAL SEALS, WEATHERSTRIPPING**									
1000	Doors, wood frame, interlocking, for 3' x 7' door, zinc	1 Carp	3	2.667	Opng.	44	93		137	205
1100	Bronze		3	2.667		56	93		149	218
1300	6' x 7' opening, zinc		2	4		54	140		194	294
1400	Bronze		2	4		65	140		205	305
1500	Vinyl V strip		6.40	1.250	Ea.	12.15	43.50		55.65	86.50
1700	Wood frame, spring type, bronze									
1800	3' x 7' door	1 Carp	7.60	1.053	Opng.	23.50	37		60.50	87.50
1900	6' x 7' door		7	1.143		31	40		71	101
1920	Felt, 3' x 7' door		14	.571		4	19.95		23.95	38
1930	6' x 7' door		13	.615		4.63	21.50		26.13	41
1950	Rubber, 3' x 7' door		7.60	1.053		9.25	37		46.25	71.50
1960	6' x 7' door		7	1.143		11.40	40		51.40	79.50
2200	Metal frame, spring type, bronze									
2300	3' x 7' door	1 Carp	3	2.667	Opng.	47.50	93		140.50	208
2400	6' x 7' door	"	2.50	3.200	"	52	112		164	244
2500	For stainless steel, spring type, add					133%				
2700	Metal frame, extruded sections, 3' x 7' door, aluminum	1 Carp	3	2.667	Opng.	28	93		121	187
2800	Bronze		3	2.667		82	93		175	246
3100	6' x 7' door, aluminum		1.50	5.333		35	186		221	350
3200	Bronze		1.50	5.333		137	186		323	460
3500	Threshold weatherstripping									
3650	Door sweep, flush mounted, aluminum	1 Carp	25	.320	Ea.	19	11.20		30.20	39.50
3700	Vinyl		25	.320		18	11.20		29.20	38.50
5000	Garage door bottom weatherstrip, 12' aluminum, clear		14	.571		25	19.95		44.95	61
5010	Bronze		14	.571		90	19.95		109.95	133
5050	Bottom protection, rubber		14	.571		38	19.95		57.95	75
5100	Threshold		14	.571		74.50	19.95		94.45	116

08 75 Window Hardware

08 75 10 - Window Handles and Latches

08 75 10.10 Handles and Latches

08 75 10.10 Handles and Latches	Crew	Daily Output	Labor-Hours	Unit	Material	2017 Bare Costs Labor	Equipment	Total	Total Incl O&P
0010 **HANDLES AND LATCHES**									
1000 Handles, surface mounted, aluminum	1 Carp	24	.333	Ea.	4.85	11.65		16.50	25
1020 Brass		24	.333		6.45	11.65		18.10	26.50
1040 Chrome		24	.333		7.40	11.65		19.05	27.50
1500 Recessed, aluminum		12	.667		3.05	23.50		26.55	42.50
1520 Brass		12	.667		4.45	23.50		27.95	44
1540 Chrome		12	.667		3.69	23.50		27.19	43
2000 Latches, aluminum		20	.400		3.60	14		17.60	27.50
2020 Brass		20	.400		5.15	14		19.15	29
2040 Chrome		20	.400		3.68	14		17.68	27.50

08 75 30 - Weatherstripping

08 75 30.10 Mechanical Weather Seals

08 75 30.10 Mechanical Weather Seals	Crew	Daily Output	Labor-Hours	Unit	Material	2017 Bare Costs Labor	Equipment	Total	Total Incl O&P
0010 **MECHANICAL WEATHER SEALS**, Window, double hung, 3' x 5'									
0020 Zinc	1 Carp	7.20	1.111	Opng.	21	39		60	88
0100 Bronze		7.20	1.111		40	39		79	109
0200 Vinyl V strip		7	1.143		9.75	40		49.75	78
0500 As above but heavy duty, zinc		4.60	1.739		20	61		81	124
0600 Bronze		4.60	1.739		70	61		131	179

08 79 Hardware Accessories

08 79 20 - Door Accessories

08 79 20.10 Door Hardware Accessories

08 79 20.10 Door Hardware Accessories	Crew	Daily Output	Labor-Hours	Unit	Material	2017 Bare Costs Labor	Equipment	Total	Total Incl O&P
0010 **DOOR HARDWARE ACCESSORIES**									
0140 Door bolt, surface, 4"	1 Carp	32	.250	Ea.	15	8.75		23.75	31
0160 Door latch	"	12	.667	"	8.55	23.50		32.05	48.50
0200 Sliding closet door									
0220 Track and hanger, single	1 Carp	10	.800	Ea.	65	28		93	119
0240 Double		8	1		80	35		115	147
0260 Door guide, single		48	.167		30	5.85		35.85	43
0280 Double		48	.167		40	5.85		45.85	54
0600 Deadbolt and lock cover plate, brass or stainless steel		30	.267		28	9.30		37.30	46.50
0620 Hole cover plate, brass or chrome		35	.229		8	8		16	22
2240 Mortise lockset, passage, lever handle		9	.889		160	31		191	228
4000 Security chain, standard		18	.444		11.50	15.55		27.05	38.50
4100 Deluxe		18	.444		45	15.55		60.55	75.50

08 81 Glass Glazing

08 81 10 - Float Glass

08 81 10.10 Various Types and Thickness of Float Glass

08 81 10.10 Various Types and Thickness of Float Glass	Crew	Daily Output	Labor-Hours	Unit	Material	2017 Bare Costs Labor	Equipment	Total	Total Incl O&P
0010 **VARIOUS TYPES AND THICKNESS OF FLOAT GLASS**									
0020 3/16" plain	2 Glaz	130	.123	S.F.	6.90	4.18		11.08	14.55
0200 Tempered, clear		130	.123		7.10	4.18		11.28	14.75
0300 Tinted		130	.123		6.90	4.18		11.08	14.55
0600 1/4" thick, clear, plain		120	.133		10.05	4.53		14.58	18.55
0700 Tinted		120	.133		9.15	4.53		13.68	17.55
0800 Tempered, clear		120	.133		6.90	4.53		11.43	15.10
0900 Tinted		120	.133		11.70	4.53		16.23	20.50
1600 3/8" thick, clear, plain		75	.213		10.80	7.25		18.05	24
1700 Tinted		75	.213		16	7.25		23.25	29.50

08 81 Glass Glazing

08 81 10 – Float Glass

08 81 10.10 Various Types and Thickness of Float Glass

		Crew	Daily Output	Labor-Hours	Unit	Material	2017 Bare Costs Labor	Equipment	Total	Total Incl O&P
1800	Tempered, clear	2 Glaz	75	.213	S.F.	17.10	7.25		24.35	31
1900	Tinted		75	.213		19.40	7.25		26.65	33.50
2200	1/2" thick, clear, plain		55	.291		18.45	9.90		28.35	37
2300	Tinted		55	.291		28	9.90		37.90	47.50
2400	Tempered, clear		55	.291		25.50	9.90		35.40	44.50
2500	Tinted		55	.291		27	9.90		36.90	46
2800	5/8" thick, clear, plain		45	.356		28	12.05		40.05	51
2900	Tempered, clear		45	.356		32	12.05		44.05	55

08 81 25 – Glazing Variables

08 81 25.10 Applications of Glazing

		Crew	Daily Output	Labor-Hours	Unit	Material	2017 Bare Costs Labor	Equipment	Total	Total Incl O&P
0010	**APPLICATIONS OF GLAZING**									
0600	For glass replacement, add				S.F.		100%			
0700	For gasket settings, add				L.F.	5.85			5.85	6.45
0900	For sloped glazing, add				S.F.		26%			
2000	Fabrication, polished edges, 1/4" thick				Inch	.56			.56	.62
2100	1/2" thick					1.32			1.32	1.45
2500	Mitered edges, 1/4" thick					1.32			1.32	1.45
2600	1/2" thick					2.19			2.19	2.41

08 81 30 – Insulating Glass

08 81 30.10 Reduce Heat Transfer Glass

			Crew	Daily Output	Labor-Hours	Unit	Material	2017 Bare Costs Labor	Equipment	Total	Total Incl O&P
0010	**REDUCE HEAT TRANSFER GLASS**										
0015	2 lites 1/8" float, 1/2" thk under 15 S.F.										
0100	Tinted	G	2 Glaz	95	.168	S.F.	14.65	5.70		20.35	25.50
0280	Double glazed, 5/8" thk unit, 3/16" float, 15 to 30 S.F., clear			90	.178		13.95	6.05		20	25.50
0400	1" thk, dbl. glazed, 1/4" float, 30 to 70 S.F., clear	G		75	.213		17.60	7.25		24.85	31.50
0500	Tinted	G		75	.213		24	7.25		31.25	38.50
2000	Both lites, light & heat reflective	G		85	.188		32	6.40		38.40	45.50
2500	Heat reflective, film inside, 1" thick unit, clear	G		85	.188		28	6.40		34.40	41.50
2600	Tinted	G		85	.188		29	6.40		35.40	42.50
3000	Film on weatherside, clear, 1/2" thick unit	G		95	.168		20	5.70		25.70	31.50
3100	5/8" thick unit	G		90	.178		20	6.05		26.05	32
3200	1" thick unit	G		85	.188		27.50	6.40		33.90	41
5000	Spectrally selective film, on ext, blocks solar gain/allows 70% of light	G		95	.168		14.25	5.70		19.95	25

08 81 40 – Plate Glass

08 81 40.10 Plate Glass

		Crew	Daily Output	Labor-Hours	Unit	Material	2017 Bare Costs Labor	Equipment	Total	Total Incl O&P
0010	**PLATE GLASS** Twin ground, polished,									
0015	3/16" thick, material				S.F.	5.50			5.50	6.05
0020	3/16" thick	2 Glaz	100	.160		5.50	5.45		10.95	15.05
0100	1/4" thick		94	.170		7.55	5.80		13.35	17.90
0200	3/8" thick		60	.267		12.85	9.05		21.90	29
0300	1/2" thick		40	.400		25	13.60		38.60	50

08 81 55 – Window Glass

08 81 55.10 Sheet Glass

		Crew	Daily Output	Labor-Hours	Unit	Material	2017 Bare Costs Labor	Equipment	Total	Total Incl O&P
0010	**SHEET GLASS** (window), clear float, stops, putty bed									
0015	1/8" thick, clear float	2 Glaz	480	.033	S.F.	3.78	1.13		4.91	6.05
0500	3/16" thick, clear		480	.033		6.10	1.13		7.23	8.60
0600	Tinted		480	.033		7.60	1.13		8.73	10.25
0700	Tempered		480	.033		9.40	1.13		10.53	12.25

08 83 Mirrors

08 83 13 - Mirrored Glass Glazing

08 83 13.10 Mirrors	Crew	Daily Output	Labor-Hours	Unit	Material	2017 Bare Costs Labor	Equipment	Total	Total Incl O&P
0010 **MIRRORS**, No frames, wall type, 1/4" plate glass, polished edge									
0100 Up to 5 S.F.	2 Glaz	125	.128	S.F.	9.70	4.35		14.05	17.85
0200 Over 5 S.F.		160	.100		9.45	3.40		12.85	16.05
0500 Door type, 1/4" plate glass, up to 12 S.F.		160	.100		9	3.40		12.40	15.55
1000 Float glass, up to 10 S.F., 1/8" thick		160	.100		6.05	3.40		9.45	12.30
1100 3/16" thick		150	.107		7.45	3.62		11.07	14.20
1500 12" x 12" wall tiles, square edge, clear		195	.082		2.51	2.79		5.30	7.40
1600 Veined		195	.082		6.35	2.79		9.14	11.60
2010 Bathroom, unframed, laminated		160	.100		14.25	3.40		17.65	21.50

08 87 Glazing Surface Films

08 87 26 - Bird Control Film

08 87 26.10 Bird Control Film	Crew	Daily Output	Labor-Hours	Unit	Material	2017 Bare Costs Labor	Equipment	Total	Total Incl O&P
0010 **BIRD CONTROL FILM**									
0050 Patterned, adhered to glass	2 Glaz	180	.089	S.F.	20	3.02		23.02	27
0200 Decals small, adhered to glass	1 Glaz	50	.160	Ea.	2.50	5.45		7.95	11.75
0250 Decals large, adhered to glass		50	.160	"	9	5.45		14.45	18.90
0300 Decals set of 4, adhered to glass		25	.320	Set	8	10.85		18.85	27
0350 Decals set of 6, adhered to glass		20	.400	"	20	13.60		33.60	44.50
0400 Bird control film tape		10	.800	Roll	22	27		49	69

08 87 33 - Electrically Tinted Window Film

08 87 33.20 Window Film	Crew	Daily Output	Labor-Hours	Unit	Material	2017 Bare Costs Labor	Equipment	Total	Total Incl O&P
0010 **WINDOW FILM** adhered on glass (glass not included)									
0015 Film is pre-wired and can be trimmed									
0100 Window film 4 S.F. adhered on glass	1 Glaz	200	.040	S.F.	242	1.36		243.36	268
0120 6 S.F.		180	.044		360	1.51		361.51	405
0160 9 S.F.		170	.047		540	1.60		541.60	600
0180 10 S.F.		150	.053		605	1.81		606.81	670
0200 12 S.F.		144	.056		720	1.89		721.89	795
0220 14 S.F.		140	.057		840	1.94		841.94	930
0240 16 S.F.		128	.063		960	2.12		962.12	1,050
0260 18 S.F.		126	.063		1,075	2.16		1,077.16	1,200
0280 20 S.F.		120	.067		1,200	2.26		1,202.26	1,325

08 87 53 - Security Films On Glass

08 87 53.10 Security Film Adhered On Glass	Crew	Daily Output	Labor-Hours	Unit	Material	2017 Bare Costs Labor	Equipment	Total	Total Incl O&P
0010 **SECURITY FILM ADHERED ON GLASS** (glass not included)									
0020 Security film, clear, 7 mil	1 Glaz	200	.040	S.F.	1.18	1.36		2.54	3.56
0030 8 mil		200	.040		1.95	1.36		3.31	4.41
0040 9 mil		200	.040		2.10	1.36		3.46	4.57
0050 10 mil		200	.040		2.25	1.36		3.61	4.74
0060 12 mil		200	.040		2.10	1.36		3.46	4.57
0075 15 mil		200	.040		2.45	1.36		3.81	4.96
0100 Security film, sealed with structural adhesive, 7 mil		180	.044		5.65	1.51		7.16	8.70
0110 8 mil		180	.044		6.55	1.51		8.06	9.70
0140 14 mil		180	.044		7.15	1.51		8.66	10.35

For customer support on your Residential Costs with RSMeans Data, call 800.448.8182.

479

08 91 Louvers

08 91 19 – Fixed Louvers

08 91 19.10 Aluminum Louvers		Crew	Daily Output	Labor-Hours	Unit	Material	2017 Bare Costs Labor	2017 Bare Costs Equipment	Total	Total Incl O&P
0010	**ALUMINUM LOUVERS**									
0020	Aluminum with screen, residential, 8" x 8"	1 Carp	38	.211	Ea.	20	7.35		27.35	34.50
0100	12" x 12"		38	.211		16	7.35		23.35	30
0200	12" x 18"		35	.229		20	8		28	35.50
0250	14" x 24"		30	.267		29	9.30		38.30	47.50
0300	18" x 24"		27	.296		32	10.35		42.35	52.50
0500	24" x 30"		24	.333		61.50	11.65		73.15	87
0700	Triangle, adjustable, small		20	.400		58.50	14		72.50	88
0800	Large		15	.533		80.50	18.65		99.15	120
2100	Midget, aluminum, 3/4" deep, 1" diameter		85	.094		.77	3.29		4.06	6.35
2150	3" diameter		60	.133		2.73	4.66		7.39	10.80
2200	4" diameter		50	.160		5.10	5.60		10.70	14.95
2250	6" diameter	↓	30	.267	↓	4.10	9.30		13.40	20

08 95 Vents

08 95 13 – Soffit Vents

08 95 13.10 Wall Louvers

		Crew	Daily Output	Labor-Hours	Unit	Material	Labor	Equipment	Total	Total Incl O&P
0010	**WALL LOUVERS**									
2400	Under eaves vent, aluminum, mill finish, 16" x 4"	1 Carp	48	.167	Ea.	1.86	5.85		7.71	11.80
2500	16" x 8"	"	48	.167	"	2.23	5.85		8.08	12.20

08 95 16 – Wall Vents

08 95 16.10 Louvers

		Crew	Daily Output	Labor-Hours	Unit	Material	Labor	Equipment	Total	Total Incl O&P
0010	**LOUVERS**									
0020	Redwood, 2'-0" diameter, full circle	1 Carp	16	.500	Ea.	200	17.50		217.50	249
0100	Half circle		16	.500		183	17.50		200.50	230
0200	Octagonal		16	.500		150	17.50		167.50	194
0300	Triangular, 5/12 pitch, 5'-0" at base		16	.500		210	17.50		227.50	260
1000	Rectangular, 1'-4" x 1'-3"		16	.500		21	17.50		38.50	52
1100	Rectangular, 1'-4" x 1'-8"		16	.500		30	17.50		47.50	62
1200	1'-4" x 2'-2"		15	.533		32	18.65		50.65	66
1300	1'-9" x 2'-2"		15	.533		39.50	18.65		58.15	74.50
1400	2'-3" x 2'-2"		14	.571		49	19.95		68.95	87
1700	2'-4" x 2'-11"		13	.615		49	21.50		70.50	89.50
2000	Aluminum, 12" x 16"		25	.320		20.50	11.20		31.70	41
2010	16" x 20"		25	.320		28.50	11.20		39.70	50
2020	24" x 30"		25	.320		60	11.20		71.20	84.50
2100	6' triangle		12	.667		180	23.50		203.50	237
3100	Round, 2'-2" diameter		16	.500		133	17.50		150.50	176
7000	Vinyl gable vent, 8" x 8"		38	.211		15	7.35		22.35	29
7020	12" x 12"		38	.211		28	7.35		35.35	43.50
7080	12" x 18"		35	.229		37	8		45	54
7200	18" x 24"	↓	30	.267	↓	45	9.30		54.30	65

Estimating Tips
General
- Room Finish Schedule: A complete set of plans should contain a room finish schedule. If one is not available, it would be well worth the time and effort to obtain one.

09 20 00 Plaster and Gypsum Board
- Lath is estimated by the square yard plus a 5% allowance for waste. Furring, channels, and accessories are measured by the linear foot. An extra foot should be allowed for each accessory miter or stop.
- Plaster is also estimated by the square yard. Deductions for openings vary by preference, from zero deduction to 50% of all openings over 2 feet in width. The estimator should allow one extra square foot for each linear foot of horizontal interior or exterior angle located below the ceiling level. Also, double the areas of small radius work.
- Drywall accessories, studs, track, and acoustical caulking are all measured by the linear foot. Drywall taping is figured by the square foot. Gypsum wallboard is estimated by the square foot. No material deductions should be made for door or window openings under 32 S.F.

09 60 00 Flooring
- Tile and terrazzo areas are taken off on a square foot basis. Trim and base materials are measured by the linear foot. Accent tiles are listed per each. Two basic methods of installation are

used. Mud set is approximately 30% more expensive than thin set. The cost of grout is included with tile unit price lines unless otherwise noted. In terrazzo work, be sure to include the linear footage of embedded decorative strips, grounds, machine rubbing, and power cleanup.
- Wood flooring is available in strip, parquet, or block configuration. The latter two types are set in adhesives with quantities estimated by the square foot. The laying pattern will influence labor costs and material waste. In addition to the material and labor for laying wood floors, the estimator must make allowances for sanding and finishing these areas, unless the flooring is prefinished.
- Sheet flooring is measured by the square yard. Roll widths vary, so consideration should be given to use the most economical width, as waste must be figured into the total quantity. Consider also the installation methods available—direct glue down or stretched. Direct glue-down installation is assumed with sheet carpet unit price lines unless otherwise noted.

09 70 00 Wall Finishes
- Wall coverings are estimated by the square foot. The area to be covered is measured—length by height of the wall above the baseboards—to calculate the square footage of each wall. This figure is divided by the number of square feet in the single roll which is being used. Deduct, in full,

the areas of openings such as doors and windows. Where a pattern match is required allow 25%–30% waste.

09 80 00 Acoustic Treatment
- Acoustical systems fall into several categories. The takeoff of these materials should be by the square foot of area with a 5% allowance for waste. Do not forget about scaffolding, if applicable, when estimating these systems.

09 90 00 Painting and Coating
- A major portion of the work in painting involves surface preparation. Be sure to include cleaning, sanding, filling, and masking costs in the estimate.
- Protection of adjacent surfaces is not included in painting costs. When considering the method of paint application, an important factor is the amount of protection and masking required. These must be estimated separately and may be the determining factor in choosing the method of application.

Reference Numbers
Reference numbers are shown at the beginning of some major classifications. These numbers refer to related items in the Reference Section. The reference information may be an estimating procedure, an alternate pricing method, or technical information.

Note: Not all subdivisions listed here necessarily appear. ■

Did you know?
Our online estimating solution gives you the same access to RSMeans' data with 24/7 access:
- Quickly locate costs in the searchable database.
- Build cost lists, estimates, and reports in minutes.
- Adjust costs to any location in the U.S. and Canada with the click of a button.

Start your free trial today at
www.RSMeansOnline.com

09 01 Maintenance of Finishes

09 01 70 – Maintenance of Wall Finishes

09 01 70.10 Gypsum Wallboard Repairs	Crew	Daily Output	Labor-Hours	Unit	Material	2017 Bare Costs Labor	Equipment	Total	Total Incl O&P
0010 **GYPSUM WALLBOARD REPAIRS**									
0100 Fill and sand, pin/nail holes	1 Carp	960	.008	Ea.		.29		.29	.49
0110 Screw head pops		480	.017			.58		.58	.97
0120 Dents, up to 2" square		48	.167		.01	5.85		5.86	9.75
0130 2" to 4" square		24	.333		.03	11.65		11.68	19.55
0140 Cut square, patch, sand and finish, holes, up to 2" square		12	.667		.04	23.50		23.54	39
0150 2" to 4" square		11	.727		.09	25.50		25.59	42.50
0160 4" to 8" square		10	.800		.25	28		28.25	47.50
0170 8" to 12" square		8	1		.49	35		35.49	59
0180 12" to 32" square		6	1.333		1.61	46.50		48.11	80
0210 16" by 48"		5	1.600		2.77	56		58.77	96.50
0220 32" by 48"		4	2		4.54	70		74.54	122
0230 48" square		3.50	2.286		6.40	80		86.40	141
0240 60" square		3.20	2.500		10	87.50		97.50	157
0500 Skim coat surface with joint compound		1600	.005	S.F.	.03	.17		.20	.32
0510 Prepare, retape and refinish joints		60	.133	L.F.	.63	4.66		5.29	8.50

09 05 Common Work Results for Finishes

09 05 05 – Selective Demolition for Finishes

09 05 05.10 Selective Demolition, Ceilings

	Crew	Daily Output	Labor-Hours	Unit	Material	2017 Bare Costs Labor	Equipment	Total	Total Incl O&P
0010 **SELECTIVE DEMOLITION, CEILINGS** R024119-10									
0200 Ceiling, gypsum wall board, furred and nailed or screwed	2 Clab	800	.020	S.F.		.53		.53	.89
1000 Plaster, lime and horse hair, on wood lath, incl. lath		700	.023			.61		.61	1.02
1200 Suspended ceiling, mineral fiber, 2' x 2' or 2' x 4'		1500	.011			.28		.28	.47
1250 On suspension system, incl. system		1200	.013			.35		.35	.59
1500 Tile, wood fiber, 12" x 12", glued		900	.018			.47		.47	.79
1540 Stapled		1500	.011			.28		.28	.47
2000 Wood, tongue and groove, 1" x 4"		1000	.016			.43		.43	.71
2040 1" x 8"		1100	.015			.39		.39	.65
2400 Plywood or wood fiberboard, 4' x 8' sheets		1200	.013			.35		.35	.59

09 05 05.20 Selective Demolition, Flooring

	Crew	Daily Output	Labor-Hours	Unit	Material	2017 Bare Costs Labor	Equipment	Total	Total Incl O&P
0010 **SELECTIVE DEMOLITION, FLOORING** R024119-10									
0200 Brick with mortar	2 Clab	475	.034	S.F.		.90		.90	1.50
0400 Carpet, bonded, including surface scraping		2000	.008			.21		.21	.36
0480 Tackless		9000	.002			.05		.05	.08
0550 Carpet tile, releasable adhesive		5000	.003			.09		.09	.14
0560 Permanent adhesive		1850	.009			.23		.23	.38
0800 Resilient, sheet goods		1400	.011			.30		.30	.51
0850 Vinyl or rubber cove base	1 Clab	1000	.008	L.F.		.21		.21	.36
0860 Vinyl or rubber cove base, molded corner	"	1000	.008	Ea.		.21		.21	.36
0870 For glued and caulked installation, add to labor						50%			
0900 Vinyl composition tile, 12" x 12"	2 Clab	1000	.016	S.F.		.43		.43	.71
2000 Tile, ceramic, thin set		675	.024			.63		.63	1.05
2020 Mud set		625	.026			.68		.68	1.14
3000 Wood, block, on end	1 Carp	400	.020			.70		.70	1.17
3200 Parquet		450	.018			.62		.62	1.04
3400 Strip flooring, interior, 2-1/4" x 25/32" thick		325	.025			.86		.86	1.44
3500 Exterior, porch flooring, 1" x 4"		220	.036			1.27		1.27	2.13
3800 Subfloor, tongue and groove, 1" x 6"		325	.025			.86		.86	1.44
3820 1" x 8"		430	.019			.65		.65	1.09
3840 1" x 10"		520	.015			.54		.54	.90

09 05 Common Work Results for Finishes

09 05 05 – Selective Demolition for Finishes

09 05 05.20 Selective Demolition, Flooring

09 05 05.20 Selective Demolition, Flooring		Crew	Daily Output	Labor-Hours	Unit	Material	2017 Bare Costs Labor	Equipment	Total	Total Incl O&P
4000	Plywood, nailed	1 Carp	600	.013	S.F.		.47		.47	.78
4100	Glued and nailed		400	.020			.70		.70	1.17
4200	Hardboard, 1/4" thick		760	.011			.37		.37	.62

09 05 05.30 Selective Demolition, Walls and Partitions

09 05 05.30		Crew	Daily Output	Labor-Hours	Unit	Material	2017 Bare Costs Labor	Equipment	Total	Total Incl O&P
0010	**SELECTIVE DEMOLITION, WALLS AND PARTITIONS** R024119-10									
0020	Walls, concrete, reinforced	B-39	120	.400	C.F.		10.75	1.78	12.53	19.95
0025	Plain	"	160	.300	"		8.10	1.33	9.43	14.95
1000	Gypsum wallboard, nailed or screwed	1 Clab	1000	.008	S.F.		.21		.21	.36
1010	2 layers		400	.020			.53		.53	.89
1500	Fiberboard, nailed		900	.009			.24		.24	.40
1568	Plenum barrier, sheet lead		300	.027			.71		.71	1.19
2200	Metal or wood studs, finish 2 sides, fiberboard	B-1	520	.046			1.26		1.26	2.10
2250	Lath and plaster		260	.092			2.52		2.52	4.21
2300	Gypsum wallboard		520	.046			1.26		1.26	2.10
2350	Plywood		450	.053			1.45		1.45	2.43
2800	Paneling, 4' x 8' sheets	1 Clab	475	.017			.45		.45	.75
3000	Plaster, lime and horsehair, on wood lath		400	.020			.53		.53	.89
3020	On metal lath		335	.024			.64		.64	1.06
3450	Plaster, interior gypsum, acoustic, or cement		60	.133	S.Y.		3.55		3.55	5.95
3500	Stucco, on masonry		145	.055			1.47		1.47	2.46
3510	Commercial 3-coat		80	.100			2.66		2.66	4.45
3520	Interior stucco		25	.320			8.50		8.50	14.25
3760	Tile, ceramic, on walls, thin set		300	.027	S.F.		.71		.71	1.19
3765	Mud set		250	.032	"		.85		.85	1.42

09 22 Supports for Plaster and Gypsum Board

09 22 03 – Fastening Methods for Finishes

09 22 03.20 Drilling Plaster/Drywall

09 22 03.20 Drilling Plaster/Drywall		Crew	Daily Output	Labor-Hours	Unit	Material	2017 Bare Costs Labor	Equipment	Total	Total Incl O&P
0010	**DRILLING PLASTER/DRYWALL**									
1100	Drilling & layout for drywall/plaster walls, up to 1" deep, no anchor									
1200	Holes, 1/4" diameter	1 Carp	150	.053	Ea.	.01	1.86		1.87	3.13
1300	3/8" diameter		140	.057		.01	2		2.01	3.35
1400	1/2" diameter		130	.062		.01	2.15		2.16	3.61
1500	3/4" diameter		120	.067		.02	2.33		2.35	3.92
1600	1" diameter		110	.073		.02	2.54		2.56	4.27
1700	1-1/4" diameter		100	.080		.04	2.80		2.84	4.72
1800	1-1/2" diameter		90	.089		.05	3.11		3.16	5.25
1900	For ceiling installations, add						40%			

09 22 13 – Metal Furring

09 22 13.13 Metal Channel Furring

09 22 13.13 Metal Channel Furring		Crew	Daily Output	Labor-Hours	Unit	Material	2017 Bare Costs Labor	Equipment	Total	Total Incl O&P
0010	**METAL CHANNEL FURRING**									
0030	Beams and columns, 7/8" channels, galvanized, 12" O.C.	1 Lath	155	.052	S.F.	.43	1.78		2.21	3.37
0050	16" O.C.		170	.047		.35	1.62		1.97	3.02
0070	24" O.C.		185	.043		.24	1.49		1.73	2.68
0100	Ceilings, on steel, 7/8" channels, galvanized, 12" O.C.		210	.038		.39	1.31		1.70	2.56
0300	16" O.C.		290	.028		.35	.95		1.30	1.93
0400	24" O.C.		420	.019		.24	.66		.90	1.32
0600	1-5/8" channels, galvanized, 12" O.C.		190	.042		.53	1.45		1.98	2.93
0700	16" O.C.		260	.031		.47	1.06		1.53	2.24
0900	24" O.C.		390	.021		.32	.71		1.03	1.50

09 22 Supports for Plaster and Gypsum Board

09 22 13 – Metal Furring

09 22 13.13 Metal Channel Furring		Crew	Daily Output	Labor-Hours	Unit	Material	2017 Bare Costs Labor	Equipment	Total	Total Incl O&P
0930	7/8" channels with sound isolation clips, 12" O.C.	1 Lath	120	.067	S.F.	1.89	2.30		4.19	5.80
0940	16" O.C.		100	.080		1.42	2.76		4.18	6.05
0950	24" O.C.		165	.048		.95	1.67		2.62	3.75
0960	1-5/8" channels, galvanized, 12" O.C.		110	.073		2.02	2.51		4.53	6.30
0970	16" O.C.		100	.080		1.52	2.76		4.28	6.15
0980	24" O.C.		155	.052		1.01	1.78		2.79	4
1000	Walls, 7/8" channels, galvanized, 12" O.C.		235	.034		.39	1.17		1.56	2.33
1200	16" O.C.		265	.030		.35	1.04		1.39	2.08
1300	24" O.C.		350	.023		.24	.79		1.03	1.54
1500	1-5/8" channels, galvanized, 12" O.C.		210	.038		.53	1.31		1.84	2.71
1600	16" O.C.		240	.033		.47	1.15		1.62	2.38
1800	24" O.C.		305	.026		.32	.90		1.22	1.82
1920	7/8" channels with sound isolation clips, 12" O.C.		125	.064		1.89	2.21		4.10	5.65
1940	16" O.C.		100	.080		1.42	2.76		4.18	6.05
1950	24" O.C.		150	.053		.95	1.84		2.79	4.02
1960	1-5/8" channels, galvanized, 12" O.C.		115	.070		2.02	2.40		4.42	6.10
1970	16" O.C.		95	.084		1.52	2.91		4.43	6.40
1980	24" O.C.		140	.057		1.01	1.97		2.98	4.30

09 22 16 – Non-Structural Metal Framing

09 22 16.13 Non-Structural Metal Stud Framing

		Crew	Daily Output	Labor-Hours	Unit	Material	2017 Bare Costs Labor	Equipment	Total	Total Incl O&P
0010	**NON-STRUCTURAL METAL STUD FRAMING**									
1600	Non-load bearing, galv., 8' high, 25 ga. 1-5/8" wide, 16" O.C.	1 Carp	619	.013	S.F.	.27	.45		.72	1.06
1610	24" O.C.		950	.008		.20	.29		.49	.71
1620	2-1/2" wide, 16" O.C.		613	.013		.36	.46		.82	1.15
1630	24" O.C.		938	.009		.27	.30		.57	.79
1640	3-5/8" wide, 16" O.C.		600	.013		.40	.47		.87	1.22
1650	24" O.C.		925	.009		.30	.30		.60	.84
1660	4" wide, 16" O.C.		594	.013		.45	.47		.92	1.28
1670	24" O.C.		925	.009		.33	.30		.63	.88
1680	6" wide, 16" O.C.		588	.014		.53	.48		1.01	1.38
1690	24" O.C.		906	.009		.40	.31		.71	.96
1700	20 ga. studs, 1-5/8" wide, 16" O.C.		494	.016		.34	.57		.91	1.33
1710	24" O.C.		763	.010		.26	.37		.63	.89
1720	2-1/2" wide, 16" O.C.		488	.016		.44	.57		1.01	1.44
1730	24" O.C.		750	.011		.33	.37		.70	.98
1740	3-5/8" wide, 16" O.C.		481	.017		.50	.58		1.08	1.52
1750	24" O.C.		738	.011		.37	.38		.75	1.04
1760	4" wide, 16" O.C.		475	.017		.60	.59		1.19	1.64
1770	24" O.C.		738	.011		.45	.38		.83	1.13
1780	6" wide, 16" O.C.		469	.017		.71	.60		1.31	1.79
1790	24" O.C.		725	.011		.54	.39		.93	1.23
2000	Non-load bearing, galv., 10' high, 25 ga. 1-5/8" wide, 16" O.C.		495	.016		.25	.56		.81	1.22
2100	24" O.C.		760	.011		.19	.37		.56	.83
2200	2-1/2" wide, 16" O.C.		490	.016		.34	.57		.91	1.32
2250	24" O.C.		750	.011		.25	.37		.62	.89
2300	3-5/8" wide, 16" O.C.		480	.017		.38	.58		.96	1.39
2350	24" O.C.		740	.011		.28	.38		.66	.94
2400	4" wide, 16" O.C.		475	.017		.42	.59		1.01	1.45
2450	24" O.C.		740	.011		.31	.38		.69	.97
2500	6" wide, 16" O.C.		470	.017		.50	.59		1.09	1.54
2550	24" O.C.		725	.011		.37	.39		.76	1.05
2600	20 ga. studs, 1-5/8" wide, 16" O.C.		395	.020		.32	.71		1.03	1.54

09 22 16 – Non-Structural Metal Framing

09 22 16.13 Non-Structural Metal Stud Framing	Crew	Daily Output	Labor-Hours	Unit	Material	2017 Bare Costs Labor	Equipment	Total	Total Incl O&P
2650	24" O.C.	1 Carp	610	.013	S.F.	.24	.46		.70	1.03
2700	2-1/2" wide, 16" O.C.		390	.021		.41	.72		1.13	1.65
2750	24" O.C.		600	.013		.30	.47		.77	1.11
2800	3-5/8" wide, 16" O.C.		385	.021		.47	.73		1.20	1.73
2850	24" O.C.		590	.014		.35	.47		.82	1.17
2900	4" wide, 16" O.C.		380	.021		.57	.74		1.31	1.86
2950	24" O.C.		590	.014		.42	.47		.89	1.25
3000	6" wide, 16" O.C.		375	.021		.68	.75		1.43	1.99
3050	24" O.C.		580	.014		.50	.48		.98	1.36
3060	Non-load bearing, galv., 12' high, 25 ga. 1-5/8" wide, 16" O.C.		413	.019		.24	.68		.92	1.40
3070	24" O.C.		633	.013		.18	.44		.62	.94
3080	2-1/2" wide, 16" O.C.		408	.020		.32	.69		1.01	1.51
3090	24" O.C.		625	.013		.24	.45		.69	1.01
3100	3-5/8" wide, 16" O.C.		400	.020		.36	.70		1.06	1.57
3110	24" O.C.		617	.013		.26	.45		.71	1.05
3120	4" wide, 16" O.C.		396	.020		.40	.71		1.11	1.62
3130	24" O.C.		617	.013		.30	.45		.75	1.08
3140	6" wide, 16" O.C.		392	.020		.48	.71		1.19	1.72
3150	24" O.C.		604	.013		.35	.46		.81	1.16
3160	20 ga. studs, 1-5/8" wide, 16" O.C.		329	.024		.31	.85		1.16	1.76
3170	24" O.C.		508	.016		.23	.55		.78	1.17
3180	2-1/2" wide, 16" O.C.		325	.025		.40	.86		1.26	1.87
3190	24" O.C.		500	.016		.29	.56		.85	1.26
3200	3-5/8" wide, 16" O.C.		321	.025		.45	.87		1.32	1.96
3210	24" O.C.		492	.016		.33	.57		.90	1.31
3220	4" wide, 16" O.C.		317	.025		.55	.88		1.43	2.08
3230	24" O.C.		492	.016		.40	.57		.97	1.39
3240	6" wide, 16" O.C.		313	.026		.65	.89		1.54	2.20
3250	24" O.C.	▼	483	.017	▼	.47	.58		1.05	1.49
5000	For load bearing studs, see Section 05 41 13.30									

09 22 26 – Suspension Systems

09 22 26.13 Ceiling Suspension Systems

		Crew	Daily Output	Labor-Hours	Unit	Material	Labor	Equipment	Total	Total Incl O&P
0010	**CEILING SUSPENSION SYSTEMS** for gypsum board or plaster									
8000	Suspended ceilings, including carriers									
8200	1-1/2" carriers, 24" O.C. with:									
8300	7/8" channels, 16" O.C.	1 Lath	275	.029	S.F.	.57	1		1.57	2.26
8320	24" O.C.		310	.026		.46	.89		1.35	1.94
8400	1-5/8" channels, 16" O.C.		205	.039		.69	1.35		2.04	2.94
8420	24" O.C.	▼	250	.032	▼	.53	1.10		1.63	2.38
8600	2" carriers, 24" O.C. with:									
8700	7/8" channels, 16" O.C.	1 Lath	250	.032	S.F.	.62	1.10		1.72	2.48
8720	24" O.C.		285	.028		.51	.97		1.48	2.13
8800	1-5/8" channels, 16" O.C.		190	.042		.74	1.45		2.19	3.17
8820	24" O.C.	▼	225	.036	▼	.59	1.23		1.82	2.63

09 22 36 – Lath

09 22 36.13 Gypsum Lath

		Crew	Daily Output	Labor-Hours	Unit	Material	Labor	Equipment	Total	Total Incl O&P
0011	**GYPSUM LATH** Plain or perforated, nailed, 3/8" thick	1 Lath	765	.010	S.F.	.35	.36		.71	.97
0101	1/2" thick, nailed		720	.011		.28	.38		.66	.93
0301	Clipped to steel studs, 3/8" thick		675	.012		.35	.41		.76	1.05
0401	1/2" thick		630	.013		.28	.44		.72	1.02
0601	Firestop gypsum base, to steel studs, 3/8" thick		630	.013		.28	.44		.72	1.02
0701	1/2" thick	▼	585	.014	▼	.33	.47		.80	1.12

09 22 Supports for Plaster and Gypsum Board

09 22 36 – Lath

09 22 36.13 Gypsum Lath

		Crew	Daily Output	Labor-Hours	Unit	Material	2017 Bare Costs Labor	Equipment	Total	Total Incl O&P
0901	Foil back, to steel studs, 3/8" thick	1 Lath	675	.012	S.F.	.34	.41		.75	1.03
1001	1/2" thick		630	.013		.38	.44		.82	1.13
1501	For ceiling installations, add		1950	.004			.14		.14	.23
1601	For columns and beams, add		1550	.005			.18		.18	.29

09 22 36.23 Metal Lath

		Crew	Daily Output	Labor-Hours	Unit	Material	2017 Bare Costs Labor	Equipment	Total	Total Incl O&P
0010	**METAL LATH** R092000-50									
3601	2.5 lb. diamond painted, on wood framing, on walls	1 Lath	765	.010	S.F.	.41	.36		.77	1.03
3701	On ceilings		675	.012		.41	.41		.82	1.11
4201	3.4 lb. diamond painted, wired to steel framing, on walls		675	.012		.45	.41		.86	1.16
4301	On ceilings		540	.015		.45	.51		.96	1.33
5101	Rib lath, painted, wired to steel, on walls, 2.75 lb.		675	.012		.36	.41		.77	1.06
5201	3.4 lb.		630	.013		.45	.44		.89	1.21
5701	Suspended ceiling system, incl. 3.4 lb. diamond lath, painted		135	.059		.51	2.04		2.55	3.87
5801	Galvanized		135	.059		.54	2.04		2.58	3.90

09 22 36.83 Accessories, Plaster

		Crew	Daily Output	Labor-Hours	Unit	Material	2017 Bare Costs Labor	Equipment	Total	Total Incl O&P
0010	**ACCESSORIES, PLASTER**									
0020	Casing bead, expanded flange, galvanized	1 Lath	2.70	2.963	C.L.F.	53.50	102		155.50	225
0200	Foundation weep screed, galvanized	"	2.70	2.963		52	102		154	223
0900	Channels, cold rolled, 16 ga., 3/4" deep, galvanized					39.50			39.50	43.50
1620	Corner bead, expanded bullnose, 3/4" radius, #10, galvanized	1 Lath	2.60	3.077		26.50	106		132.50	201
1650	#1, galvanized		2.55	3.137		48.50	108		156.50	228
1670	Expanded wing, 2-3/4" wide, #1, galvanized		2.65	3.019		40	104		144	213
1700	Inside corner (corner rite), 3" x 3", painted		2.60	3.077		20.50	106		126.50	195
1750	Strip-ex, 4" wide, painted		2.55	3.137		23	108		131	200
1800	Expansion joint, 3/4" grounds, limited expansion, galv., 1 piece		2.70	2.963		73	102		175	246
2100	Extreme expansion, galvanized, 2 piece		2.60	3.077		151	106		257	340

09 23 Gypsum Plastering

09 23 13 – Acoustical Gypsum Plastering

09 23 13.10 Perlite or Vermiculite Plaster

		Crew	Daily Output	Labor-Hours	Unit	Material	2017 Bare Costs Labor	Equipment	Total	Total Incl O&P
0010	**PERLITE OR VERMICULITE PLASTER** R092000-50									
0020	In 100 lb. bags, under 200 bags				Bag	17.65			17.65	19.40
0301	2 coats, no lath included, on walls	J-1	830	.048	S.F.	.65	1.54	.16	2.35	3.42
0401	On ceilings		710	.056		.65	1.80	.19	2.64	3.88
0901	3 coats, no lath included, on walls		665	.060		.71	1.92	.20	2.83	4.15
1001	On ceilings		565	.071		.71	2.26	.24	3.21	4.75
1700	For irregular or curved surfaces, add to above				S.Y.		30%			
1800	For columns and beams, add to above						50%			
1900	For soffits, add to ceiling prices						40%			

09 23 20 – Gypsum Plaster

09 23 20.10 Gypsum Plaster On Walls and Ceilings

		Crew	Daily Output	Labor-Hours	Unit	Material	2017 Bare Costs Labor	Equipment	Total	Total Incl O&P
0010	**GYPSUM PLASTER ON WALLS AND CEILINGS** R092000-50									
0020	80# bag, less than 1 ton				Bag	15.80			15.80	17.40
0302	2 coats, no lath included, on walls	J-1	750	.053	S.F.	.41	1.70	.18	2.29	3.44
0402	On ceilings		660	.061		.41	1.94	.20	2.55	3.84
0903	3 coats, no lath included, on walls		620	.065		.59	2.06	.22	2.87	4.27
1002	On ceilings		560	.071		1.05	2.28	.24	3.57	5.15
1600	For irregular or curved surfaces, add						30%			
1800	For columns & beams, add						50%			

09 24 Cement Plastering

09 24 23 – Cement Stucco

09 24 23.40 Stucco

		Crew	Daily Output	Labor-Hours	Unit	Material	2017 Bare Costs Labor	Equipment	Total	Total Incl O&P
0010	**STUCCO** R092000-50									
0011	3 coats 1" thick, float finish, with mesh, on wood frame	J-2	470	.102	S.F.	1.05	3.30	.29	4.64	6.85
0101	On masonry construction	J-1	495	.081		.37	2.58	.27	3.22	4.93
0151	2 coats, 5/8" thick, float finish, no lath incl.	"	980	.041		.35	1.30	.14	1.79	2.68
0301	For trowel finish, add	1 Plas	1530	.005			.18		.18	.29
0600	For coloring, add	J-1	685	.058	S.Y.	.41	1.86	.20	2.47	3.73
0700	For special texture, add		200	.200	"	1.44	6.40	.67	8.51	12.80
1001	Stucco, with bonding agent, 3 coats, on walls		1800	.022	S.F.	.47	.71	.07	1.25	1.75
1201	Ceilings		1620	.025		.37	.79	.08	1.24	1.79
1301	Beams		720	.056		.37	1.77	.19	2.33	3.53
1501	Columns		900	.044		.37	1.42	.15	1.94	2.90
1601	Mesh, galvanized, nailed to wood, 1.8 lb.	1 Lath	540	.015		.80	.51		1.31	1.71
1801	3.6 lb.		495	.016		.46	.56		1.02	1.41
1901	Wired to steel, galvanized, 1.8 lb.		477	.017		.80	.58		1.38	1.82
2101	3.6 lb.		450	.018		.46	.61		1.07	1.50

09 25 Other Plastering

09 25 23 – Lime Based Plastering

09 25 23.10 Venetian Plaster

		Crew	Daily Output	Labor-Hours	Unit	Material	2017 Bare Costs Labor	Equipment	Total	Total Incl O&P
0010	**VENETIAN PLASTER**									
0100	Walls, 1 coat primer, roller applied	1 Plas	950	.008	S.F.	.16	.29		.45	.65
0210	For pigment, light colors add per S.F. plaster					.02			.02	.02
0220	For pigment, dark colors add per S.F. plaster					.05			.05	.06
0300	For sealer/wax coat incl. burnishing, add	1 Plas	300	.027		.41	.91		1.32	1.94

09 26 Veneer Plastering

09 26 13 – Gypsum Veneer Plastering

09 26 13.20 Blueboard

		Crew	Daily Output	Labor-Hours	Unit	Material	2017 Bare Costs Labor	Equipment	Total	Total Incl O&P
0010	**BLUEBOARD** For use with thin coat									
0100	plaster application see Section 09 26 13.80									
1000	3/8" thick, on walls or ceilings, standard, no finish included	2 Carp	1900	.008	S.F.	.34	.29		.63	.86
1100	With thin coat plaster finish		875	.018		.45	.64		1.09	1.57
1400	On beams, columns, or soffits, standard, no finish included		675	.024		.39	.83		1.22	1.82
1450	With thin coat plaster finish		475	.034		.50	1.18		1.68	2.52
3000	1/2" thick, on walls or ceilings, standard, no finish included		1900	.008		.35	.29		.64	.88
3100	With thin coat plaster finish		875	.018		.46	.64		1.10	1.58
3300	Fire resistant, no finish included		1900	.008		.35	.29		.64	.88
3400	With thin coat plaster finish		875	.018		.46	.64		1.10	1.58
3450	On beams, columns, or soffits, standard, no finish included		675	.024		.40	.83		1.23	1.83
3500	With thin coat plaster finish		475	.034		.51	1.18		1.69	2.54
3700	Fire resistant, no finish included		675	.024		.40	.83		1.23	1.83
3800	With thin coat plaster finish		475	.034		.51	1.18		1.69	2.54
5000	5/8" thick, on walls or ceilings, fire resistant, no finish included		1900	.008		.33	.29		.62	.85
5100	With thin coat plaster finish		875	.018		.44	.64		1.08	1.56
5500	On beams, columns, or soffits, no finish included		675	.024		.38	.83		1.21	1.81
5600	With thin coat plaster finish		475	.034		.49	1.18		1.67	2.51
6000	For high ceilings, over 8' high, add		3060	.005			.18		.18	.31
6500	For over 3 stories high, add per story		6100	.003			.09		.09	.15

For customer support on your Residential Costs with RSMeans Data, call 800.448.8182.

487

09 26 Veneer Plastering

09 26 13 – Gypsum Veneer Plastering

09 26 13.80 Thin Coat Plaster		Crew	Daily Output	Labor-Hours	Unit	Material	2017 Bare Costs Labor	2017 Bare Costs Equipment	Total	Total Incl O&P
0010	**THIN COAT PLASTER**	R092000-50								
0012	1 coat veneer, not incl. lath		J-1	3600	.011	S.F.	.11	.35	.04	.50	.74
1000	In 50 lb. bags					Bag	15.05			15.05	16.55

09 28 Backing Boards and Underlayments

09 28 13 – Cementitious Backing Boards

09 28 13.10 Cementitious Backerboard

		Crew	Daily Output	Labor-Hours	Unit	Material	Labor	Equipment	Total	Total Incl O&P
0010	**CEMENTITIOUS BACKERBOARD**									
0070	Cementitious backerboard, on floor, 3' x 4' x 1/2" sheets	2 Carp	525	.030	S.F.	.86	1.07		1.93	2.73
0080	3' x 5' x 1/2" sheets		525	.030		.81	1.07		1.88	2.67
0090	3' x 6' x 1/2" sheets		525	.030		.78	1.07		1.85	2.64
0100	3' x 4' x 5/8" sheets		525	.030		.99	1.07		2.06	2.87
0110	3' x 5' x 5/8" sheets		525	.030		.98	1.07		2.05	2.86
0120	3' x 6' x 5/8" sheets		525	.030		.96	1.07		2.03	2.83
0150	On wall, 3' x 4' x 1/2" sheets		350	.046		.86	1.60		2.46	3.62
0160	3' x 5' x 1/2" sheets		350	.046		.81	1.60		2.41	3.56
0170	3' x 6' x 1/2" sheets		350	.046		.78	1.60		2.38	3.53
0180	3' x 4' x 5/8" sheets		350	.046		.99	1.60		2.59	3.76
0190	3' x 5' x 5/8" sheets		350	.046		.98	1.60		2.58	3.75
0200	3' x 6' x 5/8" sheets		350	.046		.96	1.60		2.56	3.72
0250	On counter, 3' x 4' x 1/2" sheets		180	.089		.86	3.11		3.97	6.15
0260	3' x 5' x 1/2" sheets		180	.089		.81	3.11		3.92	6.10
0270	3' x 6' x 1/2" sheets		180	.089		.78	3.11		3.89	6.05
0300	3' x 4' x 5/8" sheets		180	.089		.99	3.11		4.10	6.30
0310	3' x 5' x 5/8" sheets		180	.089		.98	3.11		4.09	6.30
0320	3' x 6' x 5/8" sheets		180	.089		.96	3.11		4.07	6.25

09 29 Gypsum Board

09 29 10 – Gypsum Board Panels

09 29 10.20 Taping and Finishing

		Crew	Daily Output	Labor-Hours	Unit	Material	Labor	Equipment	Total	Total Incl O&P
0010	**TAPING AND FINISHING**									
3600	For taping and finishing joints, add	2 Carp	2000	.008	S.F.	.05	.28		.33	.52
4500	For thin coat plaster instead of taping, add	J-1	3600	.011	"	.11	.35	.04	.50	.74

09 29 10.30 Gypsum Board

		Crew	Daily Output	Labor-Hours	Unit	Material	Labor	Equipment	Total	Total Incl O&P
0010	**GYPSUM BOARD** on walls & ceilings	R092910-10								
0100	Nailed or screwed to studs unless otherwise noted									
0110	1/4" thick, on walls or ceilings, standard, no finish included	2 Carp	1330	.012	S.F.	.37	.42		.79	1.11
0115	1/4" thick, on walls or ceilings, flexible, no finish included		1050	.015		.53	.53		1.06	1.47
0117	1/4" thick, on columns or soffits, flexible, no finish included		1050	.015		.53	.53		1.06	1.47
0130	1/4" thick, standard, no finish included, less than 800 S.F.		510	.031		.37	1.10		1.47	2.24
0150	3/8" thick, on walls, standard, no finish included		2000	.008		.36	.28		.64	.87
0200	On ceilings, standard, no finish included		1800	.009		.36	.31		.67	.92
0250	On beams, columns, or soffits, no finish included		675	.024		.36	.83		1.19	1.79
0300	1/2" thick, on walls, standard, no finish included		2000	.008		.34	.28		.62	.84
0350	Taped and finished (level 4 finish)		965	.017		.39	.58		.97	1.40
0390	With compound skim coat (level 5 finish)		775	.021		.44	.72		1.16	1.69
0400	Fire resistant, no finish included		2000	.008		.37	.28		.65	.88
0450	Taped and finished (level 4 finish)		965	.017		.42	.58		1	1.43

09 29 10.30 Gypsum Board		Crew	Daily Output	Labor-Hours	Unit	Material	2017 Bare Costs Labor	Equipment	Total	Total Incl O&P
0490	With compound skim coat (level 5 finish)	2 Carp	775	.021	S.F.	.47	.72		1.19	1.73
0500	Water resistant, no finish included		2000	.008		.42	.28		.70	.93
0550	Taped and finished (level 4 finish)		965	.017		.47	.58		1.05	1.48
0590	With compound skim coat (level 5 finish)		775	.021		.52	.72		1.24	1.78
0600	Prefinished, vinyl, clipped to studs		900	.018		.51	.62		1.13	1.60
0700	Mold resistant, no finish included		2000	.008		.44	.28		.72	.95
0710	Taped and finished (level 4 finish)		965	.017		.49	.58		1.07	1.51
0720	With compound skim coat (level 5 finish)		775	.021		.54	.72		1.26	1.80
1000	On ceilings, standard, no finish included		1800	.009		.34	.31		.65	.89
1050	Taped and finished (level 4 finish)		765	.021		.39	.73		1.12	1.65
1090	With compound skim coat (level 5 finish)		610	.026		.44	.92		1.36	2.01
1100	Fire resistant, no finish included		1800	.009		.37	.31		.68	.93
1150	Taped and finished (level 4 finish)		765	.021		.42	.73		1.15	1.68
1195	With compound skim coat (level 5 finish)		610	.026		.47	.92		1.39	2.05
1200	Water resistant, no finish included		1800	.009		.42	.31		.73	.98
1250	Taped and finished (level 4 finish)		765	.021		.47	.73		1.20	1.73
1290	With compound skim coat (level 5 finish)		610	.026		.52	.92		1.44	2.10
1310	Mold resistant, no finish included		1800	.009		.44	.31		.75	1
1320	Taped and finished (level 4 finish)		765	.021		.49	.73		1.22	1.76
1330	With compound skim coat (level 5 finish)		610	.026		.54	.92		1.46	2.12
1350	Sag resistant, no finish included		1600	.010		.36	.35		.71	.98
1360	Taped and finished (level 4 finish)		765	.021		.41	.73		1.14	1.67
1370	With compound skim coat (level 5 finish)		610	.026		.46	.92		1.38	2.03
1500	On beams, columns, or soffits, standard, no finish included		675	.024		.39	.83		1.22	1.82
1550	Taped and finished (level 4 finish)		540	.030		.39	1.04		1.43	2.16
1590	With compound skim coat (level 5 finish)		475	.034		.44	1.18		1.62	2.45
1600	Fire resistant, no finish included		675	.024		.37	.83		1.20	1.80
1650	Taped and finished (level 4 finish)		540	.030		.42	1.04		1.46	2.19
1690	With compound skim coat (level 5 finish)		475	.034		.47	1.18		1.65	2.49
1700	Water resistant, no finish included		675	.024		.48	.83		1.31	1.92
1750	Taped and finished (level 4 finish)		540	.030		.47	1.04		1.51	2.24
1790	With compound skim coat (level 5 finish)		475	.034		.52	1.18		1.70	2.54
1800	Mold resistant, no finish included		675	.024		.51	.83		1.34	1.95
1810	Taped and finished (level 4 finish)		540	.030		.49	1.04		1.53	2.27
1820	With compound skim coat (level 5 finish)		475	.034		.54	1.18		1.72	2.56
1850	Sag resistant, no finish included		675	.024		.41	.83		1.24	1.85
1860	Taped and finished (level 4 finish)		540	.030		.41	1.04		1.45	2.18
1870	With compound skim coat (level 5 finish)		475	.034		.46	1.18		1.64	2.47
2000	5/8" thick, on walls, standard, no finish included		2000	.008		.35	.28		.63	.86
2050	Taped and finished (level 4 finish)		965	.017		.40	.58		.98	1.41
2090	With compound skim coat (level 5 finish)		775	.021		.45	.72		1.17	1.70
2100	Fire resistant, no finish included		2000	.008		.36	.28		.64	.87
2150	Taped and finished (level 4 finish)		965	.017		.41	.58		.99	1.42
2195	With compound skim coat (level 5 finish)		775	.021		.46	.72		1.18	1.71
2200	Water resistant, no finish included		2000	.008		.44	.28		.72	.95
2250	Taped and finished (level 4 finish)		965	.017		.49	.58		1.07	1.51
2290	With compound skim coat (level 5 finish)		775	.021		.54	.72		1.26	1.80
2300	Prefinished, vinyl, clipped to studs		900	.018		.79	.62		1.41	1.91
2510	Mold resistant, no finish included		2000	.008		.49	.28		.77	1.01
2520	Taped and finished (level 4 finish)		965	.017		.54	.58		1.12	1.56
2530	With compound skim coat (level 5 finish)		775	.021		.59	.72		1.31	1.86
3000	On ceilings, standard, no finish included		1800	.009		.35	.31		.66	.91
3050	Taped and finished (level 4 finish)		765	.021		.40	.73		1.13	1.66

09 29 10.30 Gypsum Board	Crew	Daily Output	Labor-Hours	Unit	Material	2017 Bare Costs Labor	2017 Bare Costs Equipment	Total	Total Incl O&P
3090 With compound skim coat (level 5 finish)	2 Carp	615	.026	S.F.	.45	.91		1.36	2.01
3100 Fire resistant, no finish included		1800	.009		.36	.31		.67	.92
3150 Taped and finished (level 4 finish)		765	.021		.41	.73		1.14	1.67
3190 With compound skim coat (level 5 finish)		615	.026		.46	.91		1.37	2.02
3200 Water resistant, no finish included		1800	.009		.44	.31		.75	1
3250 Taped and finished (level 4 finish)		765	.021		.49	.73		1.22	1.76
3290 With compound skim coat (level 5 finish)		615	.026		.54	.91		1.45	2.11
3300 Mold resistant, no finish included		1800	.009		.49	.31		.80	1.06
3310 Taped and finished (level 4 finish)		765	.021		.54	.73		1.27	1.81
3320 With compound skim coat (level 5 finish)		615	.026		.59	.91		1.50	2.17
3500 On beams, columns, or soffits, no finish included		675	.024		.40	.83		1.23	1.83
3550 Taped and finished (level 4 finish)		475	.034		.46	1.18		1.64	2.47
3590 With compound skim coat (level 5 finish)		380	.042		.52	1.47		1.99	3.03
3600 Fire resistant, no finish included		675	.024		.41	.83		1.24	1.85
3650 Taped and finished (level 4 finish)		475	.034		.47	1.18		1.65	2.48
3690 With compound skim coat (level 5 finish)		380	.042		.46	1.47		1.93	2.96
3700 Water resistant, no finish included		675	.024		.51	.83		1.34	1.95
3750 Taped and finished (level 4 finish)		475	.034		.54	1.18		1.72	2.56
3790 With compound skim coat (level 5 finish)		380	.042		.56	1.47		2.03	3.08
3800 Mold resistant, no finish included		675	.024		.56	.83		1.39	2.01
3810 Taped and finished (level 4 finish)		475	.034		.59	1.18		1.77	2.62
3820 With compound skim coat (level 5 finish)		380	.042		.62	1.47		2.09	3.14
4000 Fireproofing, beams or columns, 2 layers, 1/2" thick, incl finish		330	.048		.83	1.69		2.52	3.75
4010 Mold resistant		330	.048		.97	1.69		2.66	3.90
4050 5/8" thick		300	.053		.81	1.86		2.67	4.01
4060 Mold resistant		300	.053		1.07	1.86		2.93	4.30
4100 3 layers, 1/2" thick		225	.071		1.25	2.49		3.74	5.55
4110 Mold resistant		225	.071		1.46	2.49		3.95	5.75
4150 5/8" thick		210	.076		1.22	2.66		3.88	5.80
4160 Mold resistant		210	.076		1.61	2.66		4.27	6.20
5200 For work over 8' high, add		3060	.005			.18		.18	.31
5270 For textured spray, add	2 Lath	1600	.010		.04	.35		.39	.60
5350 For finishing inner corners, add	2 Carp	950	.017	L.F.	.10	.59		.69	1.09
5355 For finishing outer corners, add	"	1250	.013		.24	.45		.69	1.01
5500 For acoustical sealant, add per bead	1 Carp	500	.016		.04	.56		.60	.99
5550 Sealant, 1 quart tube				Ea.	7.05			7.05	7.80
6000 Gypsum sound dampening panels									
6010 1/2" thick on walls, multi-layer, light weight, no finish included	2 Carp	1500	.011	S.F.	2.08	.37		2.45	2.91
6015 Taped and finished (level 4 finish)		725	.022		2.13	.77		2.90	3.63
6020 With compound skim coat (level 5 finish)		580	.028		2.18	.96		3.14	4.01
6025 5/8" thick on walls, for wood studs, no finish included		1500	.011		2.21	.37		2.58	3.05
6030 Taped and finished (level 4 finish)		725	.022		2.26	.77		3.03	3.77
6035 With compound skim coat (level 5 finish)		580	.028		2.31	.96		3.27	4.15
6040 For metal stud, no finish included		1500	.011		2.20	.37		2.57	3.04
6045 Taped and finished (level 4 finish)		725	.022		2.25	.77		3.02	3.76
6050 With compound skim coat (level 5 finish)		580	.028		2.30	.96		3.26	4.14
6055 Abuse resist, no finish included		1500	.011		3.95	.37		4.32	4.97
6060 Taped and finished (level 4 finish)		725	.022		4	.77		4.77	5.70
6065 With compound skim coat (level 5 finish)		580	.028		4.05	.96		5.01	6.05
6070 Shear rated, no finish included		1500	.011		4.95	.37		5.32	6.05
6075 Taped and finished (level 4 finish)		725	.022		5	.77		5.77	6.80
6080 With compound skim coat (level 5 finish)		580	.028		5.05	.96		6.01	7.15
6085 For SCIF applications, no finish included		1500	.011		4.96	.37		5.33	6.05

09 29 Gypsum Board

09 29 10 – Gypsum Board Panels

09 29 10.30 Gypsum Board		Crew	Daily Output	Labor-Hours	Unit	Material	2017 Bare Costs Labor	Equipment	Total	Total Incl O&P
6090	Taped and finished (level 4 finish)	2 Carp	725	.022	S.F.	5	.77		5.77	6.80
6095	With compound skim coat (level 5 finish)		580	.028		5.05	.96		6.01	7.15
6100	1-3/8" thick on walls, THX Certified, no finish included		1500	.011		8.75	.37		9.12	10.20
6105	Taped and finished (level 4 finish)		725	.022		8.80	.77		9.57	10.95
6110	With compound skim coat (level 5 finish)		580	.028		8.85	.96		9.81	11.30
6115	5/8" thick on walls, score & snap installation, no finish included		2000	.008		1.96	.28		2.24	2.63
6120	Taped and finished (level 4 finish)		965	.017		2.01	.58		2.59	3.18
6125	With compound skim coat (level 5 finish)		775	.021		2.06	.72		2.78	3.47
7020	5/8" thick on ceilings, for wood joists, no finish included		1200	.013		2.21	.47		2.68	3.21
7025	Taped and finished (level 4 finish)		510	.031		2.26	1.10		3.36	4.31
7030	With compound skim coat (level 5 finish)		410	.039		2.31	1.36		3.67	4.82
7035	For metal joists, no finish included		1200	.013		2.20	.47		2.67	3.20
7040	Taped and finished (level 4 finish)		510	.031		2.25	1.10		3.35	4.30
7045	With compound skim coat (level 5 finish)		410	.039		2.30	1.36		3.66	4.81
7050	Abuse resist, no finish included		1200	.013		3.95	.47		4.42	5.15
7055	Taped and finished (level 4 finish)		510	.031		4	1.10		5.10	6.25
7060	With compound skim coat (level 5 finish)		410	.039		4.05	1.36		5.41	6.75
7065	Shear rated, no finish included		1200	.013		4.95	.47		5.42	6.25
7070	Taped and finished (level 4 finish)		510	.031		5	1.10		6.10	7.35
7075	With compound skim coat (level 5 finish)		410	.039		5.05	1.36		6.41	7.85
7080	For SCIF applications, no finish included		1200	.013		4.96	.47		5.43	6.25
7085	Taped and finished (level 4 finish)		510	.031		5	1.10		6.10	7.35
7090	With compound skim coat (level 5 finish)		410	.039		5.05	1.36		6.41	7.85
8010	5/8" thick on ceilings, score & snap installation, no finish included		1600	.010		1.96	.35		2.31	2.74
8015	Taped and finished (level 4 finish)		680	.024		2.01	.82		2.83	3.59
8020	With compound skim coat (level 5 finish)		545	.029		2.06	1.03		3.09	3.98

09 29 15 – Gypsum Board Accessories

09 29 15.10 Accessories, Drywall

		Crew	Daily Output	Labor-Hours	Unit	Material	2017 Bare Costs Labor	Equipment	Total	Total Incl O&P
0011	**ACCESSORIES, DRYWALL** Casing bead, galvanized steel	1 Carp	290	.028	L.F.	.24	.96		1.20	1.87
0101	Vinyl		290	.028		.23	.96		1.19	1.86
0401	Corner bead, galvanized steel, 1-1/4" x 1-1/4"		350	.023		.17	.80		.97	1.53
0411	1-1/4" x 1-1/4", 10' long		35	.229	Ea.	1.70	8		9.70	15.20
0601	Vinyl corner bead		400	.020	L.F.	.20	.70		.90	1.39
0901	Furring channel, galv. steel, 7/8" deep, standard		260	.031		.34	1.08		1.42	2.17
1001	Resilient		260	.031		.25	1.08		1.33	2.08
1101	J trim, galvanized steel, 1/2" wide		300	.027			.93		.93	1.56
1121	5/8" wide		300	.027		.32	.93		1.25	1.91
1160	Screws #6 x 1" A				M	10.25			10.25	11.30
1170	#6 x 1-5/8" A				"	15.10			15.10	16.60
1501	Z stud, galvanized steel, 1-1/2" wide	1 Carp	260	.031	L.F.	.41	1.08		1.49	2.25

For customer support on your Residential Costs with RSMeans Data, call 800.448.8182.

491

09 30 Tiling

09 30 13 – Ceramic Tiling

09 30 13.45 Ceramic Tile Accessories	Crew	Daily Output	Labor-Hours	Unit	Material	2017 Bare Costs Labor	Equipment	Total	Total Incl O&P
0010 **CERAMIC TILE ACCESSORIES**									
0100 Spacers, 1/8"				C	1.98			1.98	2.18
1310 Sealer for natural stone tile, installed	1 Tilf	650	.012	S.F.	.05	.41		.46	.73

09 30 29 – Metal Tiling

09 30 29.10 Metal Tile	Crew	Daily Output	Labor-Hours	Unit	Material	2017 Bare Costs Labor	Equipment	Total	Total Incl O&P
0010 **METAL TILE** 4' x 4' sheet, 24 ga., tile pattern, nailed									
0200 Stainless steel	2 Carp	512	.031	S.F.	28.50	1.09		29.59	33.50
0400 Aluminized steel	"	512	.031	"	15.40	1.09		16.49	18.75

09 30 95 – Tile & Stone Setting Materials and Specialties

09 30 95.10 Moisture Resistant, Anti-Fracture Membrane	Crew	Daily Output	Labor-Hours	Unit	Material	2017 Bare Costs Labor	Equipment	Total	Total Incl O&P
0010 **MOISTURE RESISTANT, ANTI-FRACTURE MEMBRANE**									
0200 Elastomeric membrane, 1/16" thick	D-7	275	.058	S.F.	1.05	1.73		2.78	3.97

09 31 Thin-Set Tiling

09 31 13 – Thin-Set Ceramic Tiling

09 31 13.10 Thin-Set Ceramic Tile	Crew	Daily Output	Labor-Hours	Unit	Material	2017 Bare Costs Labor	Equipment	Total	Total Incl O&P
0010 **THIN-SET CERAMIC TILE**									
0020 Backsplash, average grade tiles	1 Tilf	50	.160	S.F.	2.80	5.35		8.15	11.80
0022 Custom grade tiles		50	.160		5.60	5.35		10.95	14.85
0024 Luxury grade tiles		50	.160		11.20	5.35		16.55	21
0026 Economy grade tiles		50	.160		2.56	5.35		7.91	11.50
0100 Base, using 1' x 4" high piece with 1" x 1" tiles	D-7	128	.125	L.F.	5	3.73		8.73	11.55
0300 For 6" high base, 1" x 1" tile face, add					1.23			1.23	1.35
0400 For 2" x 2" tile face, add to above					.72			.72	.79
0700 Cove base, 4-1/4" x 4-1/4"	D-7	128	.125		4.08	3.73		7.81	10.55
1000 6" x 4-1/4" high		137	.117		4.30	3.48		7.78	10.40
1300 Sanitary cove base, 6" x 4-1/4" high		124	.129		4.63	3.85		8.48	11.35
1600 6" x 6" high		117	.137		5.35	4.08		9.43	12.50
1800 Bathroom accessories, average (soap dish, tooth brush holder)		82	.195	Ea.	9.75	5.80		15.55	20
1900 Bathtub, 5', rec. 4-1/4" x 4-1/4" tile wainscot, adhesive set 6' high		2.90	5.517		175	164		339	460
2100 7' high wainscot		2.50	6.400		204	191		395	535
2200 8' high wainscot		2.20	7.273		233	217		450	605
2500 Bullnose trim, 4-1/4" x 4-1/4"		128	.125	L.F.	4.11	3.73		7.84	10.55
2800 2" x 6"		124	.129	"	4.27	3.85		8.12	10.95
3300 Ceramic tile, porcelain type, 1 color, color group 2, 1" x 1"		183	.087	S.F.	6.40	2.61		9.01	11.30
3310 2" x 2" or 2" x 1"		190	.084		6.65	2.51		9.16	11.35
3350 For random blend, 2 colors, add					1			1	1.10
3360 4 colors, add					1.50			1.50	1.65
4300 Specialty tile, 4-1/4" x 4-1/4" x 1/2", decorator finish	D-7	183	.087		12.65	2.61		15.26	18.20
4500 Add for epoxy grout, 1/16" joint, 1" x 1" tile		800	.020		.68	.60		1.28	1.72
4600 2" x 2" tile		820	.020		.62	.58		1.20	1.62
4610 Add for epoxy grout, 1/8" joint, 8" x 8" x 3/8" tile, add		900	.018		1.41	.53		1.94	2.41
4800 Pregrouted sheets, walls, 4-1/4" x 4-1/4", 6" x 4-1/4"									
4810 and 8-1/2" x 4-1/4", 4 S.F. sheets, silicone grout	D-7	240	.067	S.F.	5.60	1.99		7.59	9.45
5100 Floors, unglazed, 2 S.F. sheets,									
5110 urethane adhesive	D-7	180	.089	S.F.	2.03	2.65		4.68	6.55
5400 Walls, interior, 4-1/4" x 4-1/4" tile		190	.084		2.61	2.51		5.12	6.95
5500 6" x 4-1/4" tile		190	.084		3.15	2.51		5.66	7.55
5700 8-1/2" x 4-1/4" tile		190	.084		5.55	2.51		8.06	10.15
5800 6" x 6" tile		175	.091		3.59	2.72		6.31	8.35

For customer support on your Residential Costs with RSMeans Data, call 800.448.8182.

09 31 Thin-Set Tiling

09 31 13 – Thin-Set Ceramic Tiling

09 31 13.10 Thin-Set Ceramic Tile

		Crew	Daily Output	Labor-Hours	Unit	Material	2017 Bare Costs Labor	2017 Bare Costs Equipment	Total	Total Incl O&P
5810	8" x 8" tile	D-7	170	.094	S.F.	4.83	2.80		7.63	9.85
5820	12" x 12" tile		160	.100		4.63	2.98		7.61	9.95
5830	16" x 16" tile		150	.107		5.15	3.18		8.33	10.80
6000	Decorated wall tile, 4-1/4" x 4-1/4", color group 1		270	.059		3.67	1.77		5.44	6.90
6100	Color group 4		180	.089		52.50	2.65		55.15	62
9300	Ceramic tiles, recycled glass, standard colors, 2" x 2" thru 6" x 6" [G]		190	.084		22	2.51		24.51	28.50
9310	6" x 6" [G]		175	.091		22	2.72		24.72	29
9320	8" x 8" [G]		170	.094		23.50	2.80		26.30	30.50
9330	12" x 12" [G]		160	.100		23.50	2.98		26.48	31
9340	Earthtones, 2" x 2" to 4" x 8" [G]		190	.084		26	2.51		28.51	32.50
9350	6" x 6" [G]		175	.091		26	2.72		28.72	33
9360	8" x 8" [G]		170	.094		27	2.80		29.80	34
9370	12" x 12" [G]		160	.100		27	2.98		29.98	34.50
9380	Deep colors, 2" x 2" to 4" x 8" [G]		190	.084		30.50	2.51		33.01	38
9390	6" x 6" [G]		175	.091		30.50	2.72		33.22	38
9400	8" x 8" [G]		170	.094		32	2.80		34.80	40
9410	12" x 12" [G]		160	.100		32	2.98		34.98	40.50

09 31 33 – Thin-Set Stone Tiling

09 31 33.10 Tiling, Thin-Set Stone

		Crew	Daily Output	Labor-Hours	Unit	Material	2017 Bare Costs Labor	2017 Bare Costs Equipment	Total	Total Incl O&P
0010	**TILING, THIN-SET STONE**									
3000	Floors, natural clay, random or uniform, color group 1	D-7	183	.087	S.F.	4.30	2.61		6.91	8.95
3100	Color group 2		183	.087		5.90	2.61		8.51	10.75
3255	Floors, glazed, 6" x 6", color group 1		300	.053		5.25	1.59		6.84	8.40
3260	8" x 8" tile		300	.053		5.25	1.59		6.84	8.35
3270	12" x 12" tile		290	.055		5.85	1.64		7.49	9.05
3280	16" x 16" tile		280	.057		7.50	1.70		9.20	11
3281	18" x 18" tile		270	.059		6.85	1.77		8.62	10.40
3282	20" x 20" tile		260	.062		9.95	1.83		11.78	13.95
3283	24" x 24" tile		250	.064		11.30	1.91		13.21	15.55
3285	Border, 6" x 12" tile		200	.080		11.55	2.38		13.93	16.55
3290	3" x 12" tile		200	.080		10.60	2.38		12.98	15.50

09 32 Mortar-Bed Tiling

09 32 13 – Mortar-Bed Ceramic Tiling

09 32 13.10 Ceramic Tile

		Crew	Daily Output	Labor-Hours	Unit	Material	2017 Bare Costs Labor	2017 Bare Costs Equipment	Total	Total Incl O&P
0010	**CERAMIC TILE**									
0050	Base, using 1' x 4" high pc. with 1" x 1" tiles	D-7	82	.195	L.F.	5.25	5.80		11.05	15.25
0600	Cove base, 4-1/4" x 4-1/4" high		91	.176		4.21	5.25		9.46	13.15
0900	6" x 4-1/4" high		100	.160		4.43	4.77		9.20	12.65
1200	Sanitary cove base, 6" x 4-1/4" high		93	.172		4.76	5.15		9.91	13.55
1500	6" x 6" high		84	.190		5.50	5.70		11.20	15.25
2400	Bullnose trim, 4-1/4" x 4-1/4"		82	.195		4.20	5.80		10	14.05
2700	2" x 6" bullnose trim		84	.190		4.34	5.70		10.04	13.95
6210	Wall tile, 4-1/4" x 4-1/4", better grade	1 Tilf	50	.160	S.F.	9.50	5.35		14.85	19.15
6240	2" x 2"		50	.160		6.50	5.35		11.85	15.85
6250	6" x 6"		55	.145		10.15	4.87		15.02	19.05
6260	8" x 8"		60	.133		9.40	4.46		13.86	17.55
6600	Crystalline glazed, 4-1/4" x 4-1/4", plain	D-7	100	.160		4.66	4.77		9.43	12.90
6700	4-1/4" x 4-1/4", scored tile		100	.160		6.50	4.77		11.27	14.90
6900	6" x 6" plain		93	.172		7	5.15		12.15	16

09 32 Mortar-Bed Tiling

09 32 13 – Mortar-Bed Ceramic Tiling

09 32 13.10 Ceramic Tile

		Crew	Daily Output	Labor-Hours	Unit	Material	2017 Bare Costs Labor	Equipment	Total	Total Incl O&P
7000	For epoxy grout, 1/16" joints, 4-1/4" tile, add	D-7	800	.020	S.F.	.41	.60		1.01	1.42
7200	For tile set in dry mortar, add		1735	.009			.27		.27	.45
7300	For tile set in Portland cement mortar, add		290	.055		.18	1.64		1.82	2.86

09 32 16 – Mortar-Bed Quarry Tiling

09 32 16.10 Quarry Tile

		Crew	Daily Output	Labor-Hours	Unit	Material	2017 Bare Costs Labor	Equipment	Total	Total Incl O&P
0010	**QUARRY TILE**									
0100	Base, cove or sanitary, to 5" high, 1/2" thick	D-7	110	.145	L.F.	6.45	4.33		10.78	14.15
0300	Bullnose trim, red, 6" x 6" x 1/2" thick		120	.133		5.40	3.97		9.37	12.40
0400	4" x 4" x 1/2" thick		110	.145		5	4.33		9.33	12.55
0600	4" x 8" x 1/2" thick, using 8" as edge		130	.123		5.40	3.67		9.07	11.85
0700	Floors, 1,000 S.F. lots, red, 4" x 4" x 1/2" thick		120	.133	S.F.	8.70	3.97		12.67	16
0900	6" x 6" x 1/2" thick		140	.114		8.45	3.41		11.86	14.85
1000	4" x 8" x 1/2" thick		130	.123		9.95	3.67		13.62	16.90
1300	For waxed coating, add					.76			.76	.84
1500	For non-standard colors, add					.46			.46	.51
1600	For abrasive surface, add					.52			.52	.57
1800	Brown tile, imported, 6" x 6" x 3/4"	D-7	120	.133		7.75	3.97		11.72	14.95
1900	8" x 8" x 1"		110	.145		9.50	4.33		13.83	17.50
2100	For thin set mortar application, deduct		700	.023			.68		.68	1.11
2700	Stair tread, 6" x 6" x 3/4", plain		50	.320		8.40	9.55		17.95	25
2800	Abrasive		47	.340		7.85	10.15		18	25
3000	Wainscot, 6" x 6" x 1/2", thin set, red		105	.152		5.95	4.54		10.49	13.90
3100	Non-standard colors		105	.152		5.90	4.54		10.44	13.85
3300	Window sill, 6" wide, 3/4" thick		90	.178	L.F.	8.30	5.30		13.60	17.75
3400	Corners		80	.200	Ea.	6.55	5.95		12.50	16.90

09 32 23 – Mortar-Bed Glass Mosaic Tiling

09 32 23.10 Glass Mosaics

		Crew	Daily Output	Labor-Hours	Unit	Material	2017 Bare Costs Labor	Equipment	Total	Total Incl O&P
0010	**GLASS MOSAICS** 3/4" tile on 12" sheets, standard grout									
1020	1" tile on 12" sheets, opalescent finish	D-7	73	.219	S.F.	18.10	6.55		24.65	30.50
1040	1" x 2" tile on 12" sheet, blend		73	.219		20.50	6.55		27.05	33
1060	2" tile on 12" sheet, blend		73	.219		17.30	6.55		23.85	29.50
1080	5/8" x random tile, linear, on 12" sheet, blend		73	.219		25.50	6.55		32.05	38.50
1600	Dots on 12" sheet		73	.219		25.50	6.55		32.05	39
1700	For glass mosaic tiles set in dry mortar, add		290	.055		.45	1.64		2.09	3.17
1720	For glass mosaic tiles set in Portland cement mortar, add		290	.055		.01	1.64		1.65	2.68
1730	For polyblend sanded tile grout		96.15	.166	Lb.	2.19	4.96		7.15	10.45

09 34 Waterproofing-Membrane Tiling

09 34 13 – Waterproofing-Membrane Ceramic Tiling

09 34 13.10 Ceramic Tile Waterproofing Membrane

		Crew	Daily Output	Labor-Hours	Unit	Material	2017 Bare Costs Labor	Equipment	Total	Total Incl O&P
0010	**CERAMIC TILE WATERPROOFING MEMBRANE**									
0020	On floors, including thinset									
0030	Fleece laminated polyethylene grid, 1/8" thick	D-7	250	.064	S.F.	2.28	1.91		4.19	5.60
0040	5/16" thick	"	250	.064	"	2.60	1.91		4.51	5.95
0050	On walls, including thinset									
0060	Fleece laminated polyethylene sheet, 8 mil thick	D-7	480	.033	S.F.	2.28	.99		3.27	4.11
0070	Accessories, including thinset									
0080	Joint and corner sheet, 4 mils thick, 5" wide	1 Tilf	240	.033	L.F.	1.35	1.11		2.46	3.29
0090	7-1/4" wide		180	.044		1.71	1.49		3.20	4.29
0100	10" wide		120	.067		2.08	2.23		4.31	5.90

For customer support on your Residential Costs with RSMeans Data, call 800.448.8182.

09 34 Waterproofing-Membrane Tiling

09 34 13 – Waterproofing-Membrane Ceramic Tiling

09 34 13.10 Ceramic Tile Waterproofing Membrane	Crew	Daily Output	Labor-Hours	Unit	Material	2017 Bare Costs Labor	Equipment	Total	Total Incl O&P
0110	Pre-formed corners, inside	1 Tilf	32	.250	Ea.	7.50	8.35		15.85	22
0120	Outside		32	.250		7.65	8.35		16	22
0130	2" flanged floor drain with 6" stainless steel grate		16	.500	↓	370	16.75		386.75	435
0140	EPS, sloped shower floor		480	.017	S.F.	4.97	.56		5.53	6.35
0150	Curb	↓	32	.250	L.F.	14.05	8.35		22.40	29

09 51 Acoustical Ceilings

09 51 13 – Acoustical Panel Ceilings

09 51 13.10 Ceiling, Acoustical Panel

		Crew	Daily Output	Labor-Hours	Unit	Material	2017 Bare Costs Labor	Equipment	Total	Total Incl O&P
0010	**CEILING, ACOUSTICAL PANEL**									
0100	Fiberglass boards, film faced, 2' x 2' or 2' x 4', 5/8" thick	1 Carp	625	.013	S.F.	1.29	.45		1.74	2.17
0120	3/4" thick		600	.013		2.66	.47		3.13	3.71
0130	3" thick, thermal, R11		450	.018		3.50	.62		4.12	4.89

09 51 14 – Acoustical Fabric-Faced Panel Ceilings

09 51 14.10 Ceiling, Acoustical Fabric-Faced Panel

		Crew	Daily Output	Labor-Hours	Unit	Material	2017 Bare Costs Labor	Equipment	Total	Total Incl O&P
0010	**CEILING, ACOUSTICAL FABRIC-FACED PANEL**									
0100	Glass cloth faced fiberglass, 3/4" thick	1 Carp	500	.016	S.F.	2.81	.56		3.37	4.03
0120	1" thick		485	.016		3.41	.58		3.99	4.71
0130	1-1/2" thick, nubby face		475	.017		2.67	.59		3.26	3.92

09 51 23 – Acoustical Tile Ceilings

09 51 23.10 Suspended Acoustic Ceiling Tiles

		Crew	Daily Output	Labor-Hours	Unit	Material	2017 Bare Costs Labor	Equipment	Total	Total Incl O&P
0010	**SUSPENDED ACOUSTIC CEILING TILES**, not including									
0100	suspension system									
1110	Mineral fiber tile, lay-in, 2' x 2' or 2' x 4', 5/8" thick, fine texture	1 Carp	625	.013	S.F.	.96	.45		1.41	1.81
1115	Rough textured		625	.013		.89	.45		1.34	1.73
1125	3/4" thick, fine textured		600	.013		2.07	.47		2.54	3.06
1130	Rough textured		600	.013		1.65	.47		2.12	2.60
1135	Fissured		600	.013		2.04	.47		2.51	3.02
1150	Tegular, 5/8" thick, fine textured		470	.017		1.08	.59		1.67	2.18
1155	Rough textured		470	.017		1.32	.59		1.91	2.44
1165	3/4" thick, fine textured		450	.018		2.25	.62		2.87	3.52
1170	Rough textured		450	.018		1.45	.62		2.07	2.64
1175	Fissured		450	.018		2.21	.62		2.83	3.47
1185	For plastic film face, add					.83			.83	.91
1190	For fire rating, add					.48			.48	.53
3750	Wood fiber in cementitious binder, 2' x 2' or 4', painted, 1" thick	1 Carp	600	.013		2.12	.47		2.59	3.11
3760	2" thick		550	.015		3.71	.51		4.22	4.93
3770	2-1/2" thick		500	.016		4.63	.56		5.19	6.05
3780	3" thick		450	.018		5.55	.62		6.17	7.20

09 51 23.30 Suspended Ceilings, Complete

		Crew	Daily Output	Labor-Hours	Unit	Material	2017 Bare Costs Labor	Equipment	Total	Total Incl O&P
0010	**SUSPENDED CEILINGS, COMPLETE**, including standard									
0100	suspension system but not incl. 1-1/2" carrier channels									
0600	Fiberglass ceiling board, 2' x 4' x 5/8", plain faced	1 Carp	500	.016	S.F.	2.08	.56		2.64	3.23
0700	Offices, 2' x 4' x 3/4"		380	.021		3.45	.74		4.19	5
1800	Tile, Z bar suspension, 5/8" mineral fiber tile		150	.053		2.35	1.86		4.21	5.70
1900	3/4" mineral fiber tile		150	.053		2.41	1.86		4.27	5.75

09 51 Acoustical Ceilings

09 51 53 – Direct-Applied Acoustical Ceilings

09 51 53.10 Ceiling Tile	Crew	Daily Output	Labor-Hours	Unit	Material	2017 Bare Costs Labor	Equipment	Total	Total Incl O&P
0010 **CEILING TILE**, stapled or cemented									
0100　12" x 12" or 12" x 24", not including furring									
0600　Mineral fiber, vinyl coated, 5/8" thick	1 Carp	300	.027	S.F.	2.34	.93		3.27	4.13
0700　　3/4" thick		300	.027		3.03	.93		3.96	4.89
0900　　Fire rated, 3/4" thick, plain faced		300	.027		1.36	.93		2.29	3.06
1000　　　Plastic coated face		300	.027		2.07	.93		3	3.84
1200　　　Aluminum faced, 5/8" thick, plain	▼	300	.027		1.83	.93		2.76	3.57
3300　For flameproofing, add					.09			.09	.10
3400　For sculptured 3 dimensional, add					.32			.32	.35
3900　For ceiling primer, add					.13			.13	.14
4000　For ceiling cement, add				▼	.40			.40	.44

09 53 Acoustical Ceiling Suspension Assemblies

09 53 23 – Metal Acoustical Ceiling Suspension Assemblies

09 53 23.30 Ceiling Suspension Systems

09 53 23.30 Ceiling Suspension Systems	Crew	Daily Output	Labor-Hours	Unit	Material	2017 Bare Costs Labor	Equipment	Total	Total Incl O&P
0010 **CEILING SUSPENSION SYSTEMS** for boards and tile									
0050　Class A suspension system, 15/16" T bar, 2' x 4' grid	1 Carp	800	.010	S.F.	.79	.35		1.14	1.45
0300　　2' x 2' grid	"	650	.012		1.02	.43		1.45	1.84
0350　For 9/16" grid, add					.16			.16	.18
0360　For fire rated grid, add					.09			.09	.10
0370　For colored grid, add					.21			.21	.23
0400　Concealed Z bar suspension system, 12" module	1 Carp	520	.015		.89	.54		1.43	1.88
0600　1-1/2" carrier channels, 4' O.C., add		470	.017		.12	.59		.71	1.12
0650　　1-1/2" x 3-1/2" channels	▼	470	.017	▼	.32	.59		.91	1.34
0700　Carrier channels for ceilings with									
0900　　recessed lighting fixtures, add	1 Carp	460	.017	S.F.	.22	.61		.83	1.26
5000　Wire hangers, #12 wire	"	300	.027	Ea.	.06	.93		.99	1.63

09 54 Specialty Ceilings

09 54 16 – Luminous Ceilings

09 54 16.10 Ceiling, Luminous

09 54 16.10 Ceiling, Luminous	Crew	Daily Output	Labor-Hours	Unit	Material	2017 Bare Costs Labor	Equipment	Total	Total Incl O&P
0010 **CEILING, LUMINOUS**									
0020　Translucent lay-in panels, 2' x 2'	1 Carp	500	.016	S.F.	23	.56		23.56	26
0030　　2' x 6'	"	500	.016	"	17.80	.56		18.36	20.50

09 54 23 – Linear Metal Ceilings

09 54 23.10 Metal Ceilings

09 54 23.10 Metal Ceilings	Crew	Daily Output	Labor-Hours	Unit	Material	2017 Bare Costs Labor	Equipment	Total	Total Incl O&P
0010 **METAL CEILINGS**									
0015　Solid alum. planks, 3-1/4" x 12', open reveal	1 Carp	500	.016	S.F.	2.35	.56		2.91	3.53
0020　　Closed reveal		500	.016		3	.56		3.56	4.24
0030　　7-1/4" x 12', open reveal		500	.016		4	.56		4.56	5.35
0040　　Closed reveal		500	.016		5.10	.56		5.66	6.55
0050　Metal, open cell, 2' x 2', 6" cell		500	.016		8.70	.56		9.26	10.50
0060　　8" cell		500	.016		9.60	.56		10.16	11.50
0070　　2' x 4', 6" cell		500	.016		5.70	.56		6.26	7.20
0080　　8" cell	▼	500	.016	▼	5.70	.56		6.26	7.20

09 61 Flooring Treatment

09 61 19 - Concrete Floor Staining

09 61 19.40 Floors, Interior

		Crew	Daily Output	Labor-Hours	Unit	Material	2017 Bare Costs Labor	2017 Bare Costs Equipment	Total	Total Incl O&P
0010	**FLOORS, INTERIOR**									
0300	Acid stain and sealer									
0310	Stain, one coat	1 Pord	650	.012	S.F.	.12	.36		.48	.73
0320	Two coats		570	.014		.25	.41		.66	.95
0330	Acrylic sealer, one coat		2600	.003		.22	.09		.31	.39
0340	Two coats	↓	1400	.006	↓	.44	.17		.61	.77

09 62 Specialty Flooring

09 62 19 - Laminate Flooring

09 62 19.10 Floating Floor

		Crew	Daily Output	Labor-Hours	Unit	Material	2017 Bare Costs Labor	2017 Bare Costs Equipment	Total	Total Incl O&P
0010	**FLOATING FLOOR**									
8300	Floating floor, laminate, wood pattern strip, complete	1 Clab	133	.060	S.F.	4.30	1.60		5.90	7.40
8310	Components, T & G wood composite strips					3.81			3.81	4.19
8320	Film					.17			.17	.18
8330	Foam					.26			.26	.29
8340	Adhesive					.48			.48	.53
8350	Installation kit				↓	.19			.19	.21
8360	Trim, 2" wide x 3' long				L.F.	4.30			4.30	4.73
8370	Reducer moulding				"	5.70			5.70	6.25

09 62 23 - Bamboo Flooring

09 62 23.10 Flooring, Bamboo

			Crew	Daily Output	Labor-Hours	Unit	Material	2017 Bare Costs Labor	2017 Bare Costs Equipment	Total	Total Incl O&P
0010	**FLOORING, BAMBOO**										
8600	Flooring, wood, bamboo strips, unfinished, 5/8" x 4" x 3'	G	1 Carp	255	.031	S.F.	4.69	1.10		5.79	7
8610	5/8" x 4" x 4'	G		275	.029		4.87	1.02		5.89	7.05
8620	5/8" x 4" x 6'	G		295	.027		5.35	.95		6.30	7.45
8630	Finished, 5/8" x 4" x 3'	G		255	.031		5.15	1.10		6.25	7.55
8640	5/8" x 4" x 4'	G		275	.029		5.40	1.02		6.42	7.65
8650	5/8" x 4" x 6'	G		295	.027	↓	4.94	.95		5.89	7.05
8660	Stair treads, unfinished, 1-1/16" x 11-1/2" x 4'	G		18	.444	Ea.	45	15.55		60.55	75.50
8670	Finished, 1-1/16" x 11-1/2" x 4'	G		18	.444		82	15.55		97.55	117
8680	Stair risers, unfinished, 5/8" x 7-1/2" x 4'	G		18	.444		16.60	15.55		32.15	44.50
8690	Finished, 5/8" x 7-1/2" x 4'	G		18	.444		31.50	15.55		47.05	60.50
8700	Stair nosing, unfinished, 6' long	G		16	.500		37	17.50		54.50	69.50
8710	Finished, 6' long	G	↓	16	.500	↓	42	17.50		59.50	75

09 62 29 - Cork Flooring

09 62 29.10 Cork Tile Flooring

			Crew	Daily Output	Labor-Hours	Unit	Material	2017 Bare Costs Labor	2017 Bare Costs Equipment	Total	Total Incl O&P
0010	**CORK TILE FLOORING**										
2200	Cork tile, standard finish, 1/8" thick	G	1 Tilf	315	.025	S.F.	6.80	.85		7.65	8.85
2250	3/16" thick	G		315	.025		5.80	.85		6.65	7.75
2300	5/16" thick	G		315	.025		8.35	.85		9.20	10.60
2350	1/2" thick	G		315	.025		10.95	.85		11.80	13.40
2500	Urethane finish, 1/8" thick	G		315	.025		8.10	.85		8.95	10.30
2550	3/16" thick	G		315	.025		8.25	.85		9.10	10.45
2600	5/16" thick	G		315	.025		8.85	.85		9.70	11.15
2650	1/2" thick	G	↓	315	.025	↓	12.15	.85		13	14.75

09 63 Masonry Flooring

09 63 13 – Brick Flooring

09 63 13.10 Miscellaneous Brick Flooring		Crew	Daily Output	Labor-Hours	Unit	Material	2017 Bare Costs Labor	Equipment	Total	Total Incl O&P
0010	**MISCELLANEOUS BRICK FLOORING**									
0020	Acid-proof shales, red, 8" x 3-3/4" x 1-1/4" thick	D-7	.43	37.209	M	710	1,100		1,810	2,575
0050	2-1/4" thick	D-1	.40	40	"	985	1,275		2,260	3,200
0260	Cast ceramic, pressed, 4" x 8" x 1/2", unglazed	D-7	100	.160	S.F.	6.45	4.77		11.22	14.85
0270	Glazed		100	.160		8.60	4.77		13.37	17.25
0280	Hand molded flooring, 4" x 8" x 3/4", unglazed		95	.168		8.55	5		13.55	17.55
0290	Glazed		95	.168		10.75	5		15.75	19.95
0300	8" hexagonal, 3/4" thick, unglazed		85	.188		9.35	5.60		14.95	19.40
0310	Glazed	▼	85	.188		16.90	5.60		22.50	27.50
0450	Acid-proof joints, 1/4" wide	D-1	65	.246		1.49	7.80		9.29	14.80
0500	Pavers, 8" x 4", 1" to 1-1/4" thick, red	D-7	95	.168		3.76	5		8.76	12.30
0510	Ironspot	"	95	.168		5.30	5		10.30	14
0540	1-3/8" to 1-3/4" thick, red	D-1	95	.168		3.63	5.35		8.98	13
0560	Ironspot		95	.168		5.25	5.35		10.60	14.80
0580	2-1/4" thick, red		90	.178		3.69	5.65		9.34	13.55
0590	Ironspot		90	.178		5.75	5.65		11.40	15.80
0700	Paver, adobe brick, 6" x 12", 1/2" joint [G]	▼	42	.381		1.37	12.10		13.47	22
0710	Mexican red, 12" x 12" [G]	1 Tilf	48	.167		1.72	5.60		7.32	10.95
0720	Saltillo, 12" x 12" [G]	"	48	.167	▼	1.49	5.60		7.09	10.70
0800	For sidewalks and patios with pavers, see Section 32 14 16.10									
0870	For epoxy joints, add	D-1	600	.027	S.F.	2.87	.85		3.72	4.58
0880	For Furan underlayment, add	"	600	.027		2.38	.85		3.23	4.04
0890	For waxed surface, steam cleaned, add	A-1H	1000	.008	▼	.20	.21	.08	.49	.66

09 63 40 – Stone Flooring

09 63 40.10 Marble

		Crew	Daily Output	Labor-Hours	Unit	Material	2017 Bare Costs Labor	Equipment	Total	Total Incl O&P
0010	**MARBLE**									
0020	Thin gauge tile, 12" x 6", 3/8", white Carara	D-7	60	.267	S.F.	15.70	7.95		23.65	30
0100	Travertine		60	.267		10.45	7.95		18.40	24.50
0200	12" x 12" x 3/8", thin set, floors		60	.267		10.45	7.95		18.40	24.50
0300	On walls		52	.308	▼	9.85	9.15		19	26
1000	Marble threshold, 4" wide x 36" long x 5/8" thick, white	▼	60	.267	Ea.	10.45	7.95		18.40	24.50

09 63 40.20 Slate Tile

		Crew	Daily Output	Labor-Hours	Unit	Material	2017 Bare Costs Labor	Equipment	Total	Total Incl O&P
0010	**SLATE TILE**									
0020	Vermont, 6" x 6" x 1/4" thick, thin set	D-7	180	.089	S.F.	7.60	2.65		10.25	12.70

09 64 Wood Flooring

09 64 23 – Wood Parquet Flooring

09 64 23.10 Wood Parquet

		Crew	Daily Output	Labor-Hours	Unit	Material	2017 Bare Costs Labor	Equipment	Total	Total Incl O&P
0010	**WOOD PARQUET** flooring									
5200	Parquetry, 5/16" thk, no finish, oak, plain pattern	1 Carp	160	.050	S.F.	5.45	1.75		7.20	8.85
5300	Intricate pattern		100	.080		9.80	2.80		12.60	15.45
5500	Teak, plain pattern		160	.050		6.30	1.75		8.05	9.85
5600	Intricate pattern		100	.080		10.70	2.80		13.50	16.45
5650	13/16" thick, select grade oak, plain pattern		160	.050		9.75	1.75		11.50	13.65
5700	Intricate pattern		100	.080		17.25	2.80		20.05	23.50
5800	Custom parquetry, including finish, plain pattern		100	.080		17.05	2.80		19.85	23.50
5900	Intricate pattern		50	.160		25	5.60		30.60	37
6700	Parquetry, prefinished white oak, 5/16" thick, plain pattern		160	.050		7.95	1.75		9.70	11.60
6800	Intricate pattern		100	.080		8.55	2.80		11.35	14.10
7000	Walnut or teak, parquetry, plain pattern		160	.050		8.40	1.75		10.15	12.15

09 64 Wood Flooring

09 64 23 – Wood Parquet Flooring

09 64 23.10 Wood Parquet	Crew	Daily Output	Labor-Hours	Unit	Material	2017 Bare Costs Labor	Equipment	Total	Total Incl O&P
7100	Intricate pattern	1 Carp	100	.080	S.F.	13.50	2.80		16.30	19.55
7200	Acrylic wood parquet blocks, 12" x 12" x 5/16",									
7210	Irradiated, set in epoxy	1 Carp	160	.050	S.F.	10.40	1.75		12.15	14.35

09 64 29 – Wood Strip and Plank Flooring

09 64 29.10 Wood

		Crew	Daily Output	Labor-Hours	Unit	Material	Labor	Equipment	Total	Total Incl O&P
0010	**WOOD**									
0020	Fir, vertical grain, 1" x 4", not incl. finish, grade B & better	1 Carp	255	.031	S.F.	2.85	1.10		3.95	4.97
0100	Grade C & better		255	.031		2.68	1.10		3.78	4.78
0300	Flat grain, 1" x 4", not incl. finish, B & better		255	.031		3.25	1.10		4.35	5.40
0400	C & better		255	.031		3.13	1.10		4.23	5.25
4000	Maple, strip, 25/32" x 2-1/4", not incl. finish, select		170	.047		4.90	1.64		6.54	8.15
4100	#2 & better		170	.047		4.79	1.64		6.43	8
4300	33/32" x 3-1/4", not incl. finish, #1 grade		170	.047		4.65	1.64		6.29	7.85
4400	#2 & better		170	.047		4.14	1.64		5.78	7.30
4600	Oak, white or red, 25/32" x 2-1/4", not incl. finish									
4700	#1 common	1 Carp	170	.047	S.F.	3.39	1.64		5.03	6.50
4900	Select quartered, 2-1/4" wide		170	.047		4.29	1.64		5.93	7.45
5000	Clear		170	.047		4.19	1.64		5.83	7.35
6100	Prefinished, white oak, prime grade, 2-1/4" wide		170	.047		5.20	1.64		6.84	8.45
6200	3-1/4" wide		185	.043		5.65	1.51		7.16	8.75
6400	Ranch plank		145	.055		7.20	1.93		9.13	11.15
6500	Hardwood blocks, 9" x 9", 25/32" thick		160	.050		6.15	1.75		7.90	9.65
7400	Yellow pine, 3/4" x 3-1/8", T & G, C & better, not incl. finish		200	.040		1.65	1.40		3.05	4.16
7500	Refinish wood floor, sand, 2 coats poly, wax, soft wood	1 Clab	400	.020		.92	.53		1.45	1.90
7600	Hardwood		130	.062		1.37	1.64		3.01	4.25
7800	Sanding and finishing, 2 coats polyurethane		295	.027		.92	.72		1.64	2.22
7900	Subfloor and underlayment, see Section 06 16									
8015	Transition molding, 2-1/4" wide, 5' long	1 Carp	19.20	.417	Ea.	10.85	14.55		25.40	36.50

09 65 Resilient Flooring

09 65 10 – Resilient Tile Underlayment

09 65 10.10 Latex Underlayment

		Crew	Daily Output	Labor-Hours	Unit	Material	Labor	Equipment	Total	Total Incl O&P
0010	**LATEX UNDERLAYMENT**									
3600	Latex underlayment, 1/8" thk., cementitious for resilient flooring	1 Tilf	160	.050	S.F.	1.25	1.67		2.92	4.10
4000	Liquid, fortified				Gal.	31			31	34

09 65 13 – Resilient Base and Accessories

09 65 13.13 Resilient Base

		Crew	Daily Output	Labor-Hours	Unit	Material	Labor	Equipment	Total	Total Incl O&P
0010	**RESILIENT BASE**									
0690	1/8" vinyl base, 2-1/2" H, straight or cove, standard colors	1 Tilf	315	.025	L.F.	.63	.85		1.48	2.07
0700	4" high		315	.025		1.17	.85		2.02	2.67
0710	6" high		315	.025		1.30	.85		2.15	2.81
0720	Corners, 2-1/2" high		315	.025	Ea.	2.05	.85		2.90	3.64
0730	4" high		315	.025		2.23	.85		3.08	3.83
0740	6" high		315	.025		2.53	.85		3.38	4.16
0800	1/8" rubber base, 2-1/2" H, straight or cove, standard colors		315	.025	L.F.	1.01	.85		1.86	2.49
1100	4" high		315	.025		1.14	.85		1.99	2.63
1110	6" high		315	.025		1.87	.85		2.72	3.44
1150	Corners, 2-1/2" high		315	.025	Ea.	2.19	.85		3.04	3.79
1153	4" high		315	.025		2.27	.85		3.12	3.88
1155	6" high		315	.025		2.77	.85		3.62	4.43

09 65 Resilient Flooring

09 65 13 – Resilient Base and Accessories

09 65 13.13 Resilient Base	Crew	Daily Output	Labor-Hours	Unit	Material	2017 Bare Costs Labor	Equipment	Total	Total Incl O&P
1450	For premium color/finish add					50%				
1500	Millwork profile	1 Tilf	315	.025	L.F.	5.90	.85		6.75	7.85

09 65 16 – Resilient Sheet Flooring

09 65 16.10 Rubber and Vinyl Sheet Flooring

		Crew	Daily Output	Labor-Hours	Unit	Material	Labor	Equipment	Total	Total Incl O&P
0010	**RUBBER AND VINYL SHEET FLOORING**									
5500	Linoleum, sheet goods G	1 Tilf	360	.022	S.F.	3.59	.74		4.33	5.15
5900	Rubber, sheet goods, 36" wide, 1/8" thick		120	.067		7.10	2.23		9.33	11.40
5950	3/16" thick		100	.080		10.45	2.68		13.13	15.85
6000	1/4" thick		90	.089		12.30	2.97		15.27	18.40
8000	Vinyl sheet goods, backed, .065" thick, plain pattern/colors		250	.032		3.69	1.07		4.76	5.80
8050	Intricate pattern/colors		200	.040		4.34	1.34		5.68	6.95
8100	.080" thick, plain pattern/colors		230	.035		4.12	1.16		5.28	6.40
8150	Intricate pattern/colors		200	.040		6.45	1.34		7.79	9.25
8200	.125" thick, plain pattern/colors		230	.035		3.87	1.16		5.03	6.15
8250	Intricate pattern/colors		200	.040		7.50	1.34		8.84	10.40
8700	Adhesive cement, 1 gallon per 200 to 300 S.F.				Gal.	30.50			30.50	33.50
8800	Asphalt primer, 1 gallon per 300 S.F.					14.60			14.60	16.05
8900	Emulsion, 1 gallon per 140 S.F.					19.60			19.60	21.50

09 65 19 – Resilient Tile Flooring

09 65 19.19 Vinyl Composition Tile Flooring

		Crew	Daily Output	Labor-Hours	Unit	Material	Labor	Equipment	Total	Total Incl O&P
0010	**VINYL COMPOSITION TILE FLOORING**									
7000	Vinyl composition tile, 12" x 12", 1/16" thick	1 Tilf	500	.016	S.F.	1.22	.54		1.76	2.21
7050	Embossed		500	.016		2.25	.54		2.79	3.35
7100	Marbleized		500	.016		2.25	.54		2.79	3.35
7150	Solid		500	.016		2.91	.54		3.45	4.07
7200	3/32" thick, embossed		500	.016		1.47	.54		2.01	2.49
7250	Marbleized		500	.016		2.59	.54		3.13	3.72
7300	Solid		500	.016		2.41	.54		2.95	3.52
7350	1/8" thick, marbleized		500	.016		2.44	.54		2.98	3.55
7400	Solid		500	.016		1.55	.54		2.09	2.58
7450	Conductive		500	.016		6.05	.54		6.59	7.50

09 65 19.23 Vinyl Tile Flooring

		Crew	Daily Output	Labor-Hours	Unit	Material	Labor	Equipment	Total	Total Incl O&P
0010	**VINYL TILE FLOORING**									
7500	Vinyl tile, 12" x 12", 3/32" thick, standard colors/patterns	1 Tilf	500	.016	S.F.	3.71	.54		4.25	4.95
7550	1/8" thick, standard colors/patterns		500	.016		5.20	.54		5.74	6.55
7600	1/8" thick, premium colors/patterns		500	.016		7	.54		7.54	8.55
7650	Solid colors		500	.016		3.27	.54		3.81	4.47
7700	Marbleized or Travertine pattern		500	.016		6.05	.54		6.59	7.50
7750	Florentine pattern		500	.016		6.45	.54		6.99	7.95
7800	Premium colors/patterns		500	.016		6.25	.54		6.79	7.70

09 65 19.33 Rubber Tile Flooring

		Crew	Daily Output	Labor-Hours	Unit	Material	Labor	Equipment	Total	Total Incl O&P
0010	**RUBBER TILE FLOORING**									
6050	Rubber tile, marbleized colors, 12" x 12", 1/8" thick	1 Tilf	400	.020	S.F.	5.70	.67		6.37	7.35
6100	3/16" thick		400	.020		9.05	.67		9.72	11.05
6300	Special tile, plain colors, 1/8" thick		400	.020		7.95	.67		8.62	9.85
6350	3/16" thick		400	.020		9.05	.67		9.72	11.05

09 65 Resilient Flooring

09 65 33 – Conductive Resilient Flooring

09 65 33.10 Conductive Rubber and Vinyl Flooring	Crew	Daily Output	Labor-Hours	Unit	Material	2017 Bare Costs Labor	Equipment	Total	Total Incl O&P
0010 **CONDUCTIVE RUBBER AND VINYL FLOORING**									
1700 Conductive flooring, rubber tile, 1/8" thick	1 Tilf	315	.025	S.F.	6.95	.85		7.80	9.05
1800 Homogeneous vinyl tile, 1/8" thick	"	315	.025	"	6.70	.85		7.55	8.80

09 66 Terrazzo Flooring

09 66 13 – Portland Cement Terrazzo Flooring

09 66 13.10 Portland Cement Terrazzo

	Crew	Daily Output	Labor-Hours	Unit	Material	Labor	Equipment	Total	Total Incl O&P
0010 **PORTLAND CEMENT TERRAZZO**, cast-in-place									
4300 Stone chips, onyx gemstone, per 50 lb. bag				Bag	16.80			16.80	18.50

09 66 16 – Terrazzo Floor Tile

09 66 16.13 Portland Cement Terrazzo Floor Tile

	Crew	Daily Output	Labor-Hours	Unit	Material	Labor	Equipment	Total	Total Incl O&P
0010 **PORTLAND CEMENT TERRAZZO FLOOR TILE**									
1200 Floor tiles, non-slip, 1" thick, 12" x 12"	D-1	60	.267	S.F.	20.50	8.45		28.95	36.50
1300 1-1/4" thick, 12" x 12"		60	.267		21	8.45		29.45	37
1500 16" x 16"		50	.320		23	10.15		33.15	42
1600 1-1/2" thick, 16" x 16"	↓	45	.356	↓	21	11.30		32.30	42

09 66 16.30 Terrazzo, Precast

	Crew	Daily Output	Labor-Hours	Unit	Material	Labor	Equipment	Total	Total Incl O&P
0010 **TERRAZZO, PRECAST**									
0020 Base, 6" high, straight	1 Mstz	70	.114	L.F.	12.35	3.83		16.18	19.80
0100 Cove		60	.133		13.70	4.47		18.17	22.50
0300 8" high, straight		60	.133		12.25	4.47		16.72	21
0400 Cove	↓	50	.160		18.05	5.35		23.40	28.50
0600 For white cement, add					.46			.46	.51
0700 For 16 ga. zinc toe strip, add					1.81			1.81	1.99
0900 Curbs, 4" x 4" high	1 Mstz	40	.200		33.50	6.70		40.20	47.50
1000 8" x 8" high		30	.267	↓	38.50	8.95		47.45	57
4800 Wainscot, 12" x 12" x 1" tiles		12	.667	S.F.	7.30	22.50		29.80	44.50
4900 16" x 16" x 1-1/2" tiles	↓	8	1	"	14.50	33.50		48	70.50

09 68 Carpeting

09 68 05 – Carpet Accessories

09 68 05.11 Flooring Transition Strip

	Crew	Daily Output	Labor-Hours	Unit	Material	Labor	Equipment	Total	Total Incl O&P
0010 **FLOORING TRANSITION STRIP**									
0107 Clamp down brass divider, 12' strip, vinyl to carpet	1 Tilf	31.25	.256	Ea.	14.65	8.55		23.20	30
0117 Vinyl to hard surface	"	31.25	.256	"	14.65	8.55		23.20	30

09 68 10 – Carpet Pad

09 68 10.10 Commercial Grade Carpet Pad

	Crew	Daily Output	Labor-Hours	Unit	Material	Labor	Equipment	Total	Total Incl O&P
0010 **COMMERCIAL GRADE CARPET PAD**									
9001 Sponge rubber pad, 20 oz./sq. yd.	1 Tilf	1350	.006	S.F.	.52	.20		.72	.89
9101 40 to 62 oz./sq. yd.		1350	.006		.97	.20		1.17	1.39
9201 Felt pad, 20 to 32 oz./sq. yd.		1350	.006		.65	.20		.85	1.04
9301 Maximum		1350	.006		1.18	.20		1.38	1.62
9401 Bonded urethane pad, 2.7 density		1350	.006		.66	.20		.86	1.05
9501 13.0 density		1350	.006		.89	.20		1.09	1.30
9601 Prime urethane pad, 2.7 density		1350	.006		.39	.20		.59	.75
9701 13.0 density	↓	1350	.006	↓	.73	.20		.93	1.13

For customer support on your Residential Costs with RSMeans Data, call 800.448.8182.

501

09 68 Carpeting

09 68 13 – Tile Carpeting

09 68 13.10 Carpet Tile

		Crew	Daily Output	Labor-Hours	Unit	Material	2017 Bare Costs Labor	Equipment	Total	Total Incl O&P
0010	**CARPET TILE**									
0100	Tufted nylon, 18" x 18", hard back, 20 oz.	1 Tilf	80	.100	S.Y.	23.50	3.35		26.85	31
0110	26 oz.		80	.100		26	3.35		29.35	34
0200	Cushion back, 20 oz.		80	.100		23.50	3.35		26.85	31.50
0210	26 oz.		80	.100		36.50	3.35		39.85	45.50

09 68 16 – Sheet Carpeting

09 68 16.10 Sheet Carpet

		Crew	Daily Output	Labor-Hours	Unit	Material	2017 Bare Costs Labor	Equipment	Total	Total Incl O&P
0010	**SHEET CARPET**									
0701	Nylon, level loop, 26 oz., light to medium traffic	1 Tilf	675	.012	S.F.	2.41	.40		2.81	3.29
0901	32 oz., medium traffic		675	.012		4.39	.40		4.79	5.45
1101	40 oz., medium to heavy traffic		675	.012		5	.40		5.40	6.15
2101	Nylon, plush, 20 oz., light traffic		675	.012		2.03	.40		2.43	2.88
2801	24 oz., light to medium traffic		675	.012		2.12	.40		2.52	2.97
2901	30 oz., medium traffic		675	.012		3.44	.40		3.84	4.42
3001	36 oz., medium traffic		675	.012		3.88	.40		4.28	4.91
3101	42 oz., medium to heavy traffic		630	.013		5	.42		5.42	6.20
3201	46 oz., medium to heavy traffic		630	.013		5.85	.42		6.27	7.15
3301	54 oz., heavy traffic		630	.013		6.45	.42		6.87	7.80
3501	Olefin, 15 oz., light traffic		675	.012		1.67	.40		2.07	2.48
3651	22 oz., light traffic		675	.012		1.65	.40		2.05	2.45
4501	50 oz., medium to heavy traffic, level loop		630	.013		11.15	.42		11.57	13
4701	32 oz., medium to heavy traffic, patterned		630	.013		10.10	.42		10.52	11.85
4901	48 oz., heavy traffic, patterned		630	.013		11.15	.42		11.57	13
5000	For less than full roll (approx. 1500 S.F.), add					25%				
5100	For small rooms, less than 12' wide, add						25%			
5200	For large open areas (no cuts), deduct						25%			
5600	For bound carpet baseboard, add	1 Tilf	300	.027	L.F.	3	.89		3.89	4.75
5610	For stairs, not incl. price of carpet, add	"	30	.267	Riser		8.90		8.90	14.50
8950	For tackless, stretched installation, add padding from 09 68 10.10 to above									
9850	For brand-named specific fiber, add				S.Y.	25%				

09 68 20 – Athletic Carpet

09 68 20.10 Indoor Athletic Carpet

		Crew	Daily Output	Labor-Hours	Unit	Material	2017 Bare Costs Labor	Equipment	Total	Total Incl O&P
0010	**INDOOR ATHLETIC CARPET**									
3700	Polyethylene, in rolls, no base incl., landscape surfaces	1 Tilf	275	.029	S.F.	4.23	.97		5.20	6.25
3800	Nylon action surface, 1/8" thick		275	.029		3.84	.97		4.81	5.80
3900	1/4" thick		275	.029		5.55	.97		6.52	7.70
4000	3/8" thick		275	.029		6.95	.97		7.92	9.25

09 72 Wall Coverings

09 72 13 – Cork Wall Coverings

09 72 13.10 Covering, Cork Wall

		Crew	Daily Output	Labor-Hours	Unit	Material	2017 Bare Costs Labor	Equipment	Total	Total Incl O&P
0010	**COVERING, CORK WALL**									
0600	Cork tiles, light or dark, 12" x 12" x 3/16"	1 Pape	240	.033	S.F.	4.33	.98		5.31	6.35
0700	5/16" thick		235	.034		3.16	1		4.16	5.15
0900	1/4" basketweave		240	.033		3.50	.98		4.48	5.45
1000	1/2" natural, non-directional pattern		240	.033		6.75	.98		7.73	9.05
1100	3/4" natural, non-directional pattern		240	.033		11.95	.98		12.93	14.75
1200	Granular surface, 12" x 36", 1/2" thick		385	.021		1.34	.61		1.95	2.47
1300	1" thick		370	.022		1.71	.63		2.34	2.93

09 72 Wall Coverings

09 72 13 – Cork Wall Coverings

09 72 13.10 Covering, Cork Wall

		Crew	Daily Output	Labor-Hours	Unit	Material	2017 Bare Costs Labor	Equipment	Total	Total Incl O&P
1500	Polyurethane coated, 12" x 12" x 3/16" thick	1 Pape	240	.033	S.F.	4.16	.98		5.14	6.20
1600	5/16" thick		235	.034		6.60	1		7.60	8.90
1800	Cork wallpaper, paperbacked, natural		480	.017		1.90	.49		2.39	2.90
1900	Colors		480	.017		2.93	.49		3.42	4.03

09 72 16 – Vinyl-Coated Fabric Wall Coverings

09 72 16.13 Flexible Vinyl Wall Coverings

		Crew	Daily Output	Labor-Hours	Unit	Material	2017 Bare Costs Labor	Equipment	Total	Total Incl O&P
0010	**FLEXIBLE VINYL WALL COVERINGS**									
3000	Vinyl wall covering, fabric-backed, lightweight, type 1 (12-15 oz./S.Y.)	1 Pape	640	.013	S.F.	1	.37		1.37	1.70
3300	Medium weight, type 2 (20-24 oz./S.Y.)		480	.017		.91	.49		1.40	1.81
3400	Heavy weight, type 3 (28 oz./S.Y.)		435	.018		1.40	.54		1.94	2.43
3600	Adhesive, 5 gal. lots (18 S.Y./gal.)				Gal.	12.10			12.10	13.30

09 72 16.16 Rigid-Sheet Vinyl Wall Coverings

		Crew	Daily Output	Labor-Hours	Unit	Material	2017 Bare Costs Labor	Equipment	Total	Total Incl O&P
0010	**RIGID-SHEET VINYL WALL COVERINGS**									
0100	Acrylic, modified, semi-rigid PVC, .028" thick	2 Carp	330	.048	S.F.	1.28	1.69		2.97	4.24
0110	.040" thick	"	320	.050	"	1.91	1.75		3.66	5

09 72 19 – Textile Wall Coverings

09 72 19.10 Textile Wall Covering

		Crew	Daily Output	Labor-Hours	Unit	Material	2017 Bare Costs Labor	Equipment	Total	Total Incl O&P
0010	**TEXTILE WALL COVERING**, including sizing; add 10-30% waste @ takeoff									
0020	Silk	1 Pape	640	.013	S.F.	4.23	.37		4.60	5.25
0030	Cotton		640	.013		6.75	.37		7.12	8.05
0040	Linen		640	.013		1.89	.37		2.26	2.68
0050	Blend		640	.013		3.03	.37		3.40	3.93
0060	Linen wall covering, paper backed									
0070	Flame treatment				S.F.	1.09			1.09	1.20
0080	Stain resistance treatment					1.82			1.82	2
0100	Grass cloths with lining paper [G]	1 Pape	400	.020		.90	.59		1.49	1.96
0110	Premium texture/color [G]	"	350	.023		3.15	.67		3.82	4.58

09 72 20 – Natural Fiber Wall Covering

09 72 20.10 Natural Fiber Wall Covering

		Crew	Daily Output	Labor-Hours	Unit	Material	2017 Bare Costs Labor	Equipment	Total	Total Incl O&P
0010	**NATURAL FIBER WALL COVERING**, including sizing; add 10-30% waste @ takeoff									
0015	Bamboo	1 Pape	640	.013	S.F.	2.31	.37		2.68	3.14
0030	Burlap		640	.013		2.07	.37		2.44	2.88
0045	Jute		640	.013		1.32	.37		1.69	2.05
0060	Sisal		640	.013		1.49	.37		1.86	2.24

09 72 23 – Wallpapering

09 72 23.10 Wallpaper

		Crew	Daily Output	Labor-Hours	Unit	Material	2017 Bare Costs Labor	Equipment	Total	Total Incl O&P
0010	**WALLPAPER** including sizing; add 10-30% waste @ takeoff R097223-10									
0050	Aluminum foil	1 Pape	275	.029	S.F.	1.06	.85		1.91	2.58
0100	Copper sheets, .025" thick, vinyl backing		240	.033		5.65	.98		6.63	7.85
0300	Phenolic backing		240	.033		7.35	.98		8.33	9.70
2400	Gypsum-based, fabric-backed, fire resistant									
2500	for masonry walls, 21 oz./S.Y.	1 Pape	800	.010	S.F.	.77	.29		1.06	1.33
2600	Average		720	.011		1.30	.33		1.63	1.97
2700	Small quantities		640	.013		.70	.37		1.07	1.37
3700	Wallpaper, average workmanship, solid pattern, low cost paper		640	.013		.59	.37		.96	1.25
3900	Basic patterns (matching required), avg. cost paper		535	.015		1.17	.44		1.61	2.01
4000	Paper at $85 per double roll, quality workmanship		435	.018		1.82	.54		2.36	2.89

09 74 Flexible Wood Sheets

09 74 16 – Flexible Wood Veneers

09 74 16.10 Veneer, Flexible Wood	Crew	Daily Output	Labor-Hours	Unit	Material	2017 Bare Costs Labor	Equipment	Total	Total Incl O&P
0010 **VENEER, FLEXIBLE WOOD**									
0100 Flexible wood veneer, 1/32" thick, plain woods	1 Pape	100	.080	S.F.	2.49	2.34		4.83	6.60
0110 Exotic woods	"	95	.084	"	3.76	2.47		6.23	8.20

09 91 Painting

09 91 03 – Paint Restoration

09 91 03.20 Sanding

	Crew	Daily Output	Labor-Hours	Unit	Material	2017 Bare Costs Labor	Equipment	Total	Total Incl O&P
0010 **SANDING** and puttying interior trim, compared to									
0100 Painting 1 coat, on quality work				L.F.		100%			
0300 Medium work						50%			
0400 Industrial grade				▼		25%			
0500 Surface protection, placement and removal									
0510 Surface protection, placement and removal, basic drop cloths	1 Pord	6400	.001	S.F.		.04		.04	.06
0520 Masking with paper		800	.010		.07	.29		.36	.56
0530 Volume cover up (using plastic sheathing or building paper)	▼	16000	.001	▼		.01		.01	.02

09 91 03.30 Exterior Surface Preparation

	Crew	Daily Output	Labor-Hours	Unit	Material	2017 Bare Costs Labor	Equipment	Total	Total Incl O&P
0010 **EXTERIOR SURFACE PREPARATION**									
0015 Doors, per side, not incl. frames or trim									
0020 Scrape & sand									
0030 Wood, flush	1 Pord	616	.013	S.F.		.38		.38	.63
0040 Wood, detail		496	.016			.47		.47	.78
0050 Wood, louvered		280	.029			.83		.83	1.38
0060 Wood, overhead	▼	616	.013	▼		.38		.38	.63
0070 Wire brush									
0080 Metal, flush	1 Pord	640	.013	S.F.		.37		.37	.60
0090 Metal, detail		520	.015			.45		.45	.74
0100 Metal, louvered		360	.022			.65		.65	1.07
0110 Metal or fibr., overhead		640	.013			.37		.37	.60
0120 Metal, roll up		560	.014			.42		.42	.69
0130 Metal, bulkhead	▼	640	.013	▼		.37		.37	.60
0140 Power wash, based on 2500 lb. operating pressure									
0150 Metal, flush	A-1H	2240	.004	S.F.		.10	.03	.13	.20
0160 Metal, detail		2120	.004			.10	.04	.14	.21
0170 Metal, louvered		2000	.004			.11	.04	.15	.22
0180 Metal or fibr., overhead		2400	.003			.09	.03	.12	.18
0190 Metal, roll up		2400	.003			.09	.03	.12	.18
0200 Metal, bulkhead	▼	2200	.004	▼		.10	.03	.13	.20
0400 Windows, per side, not incl. trim									
0410 Scrape & sand									
0420 Wood, 1-2 lite	1 Pord	320	.025	S.F.		.73		.73	1.21
0430 Wood, 3-6 lite		280	.029			.83		.83	1.38
0440 Wood, 7-10 lite		240	.033			.97		.97	1.61
0450 Wood, 12 lite		200	.040			1.17		1.17	1.93
0460 Wood, Bay/Bow	▼	320	.025	▼		.73		.73	1.21
0470 Wire brush									
0480 Metal, 1-2 lite	1 Pord	480	.017	S.F.		.49		.49	.80
0490 Metal, 3-6 lite		400	.020			.58		.58	.96
0500 Metal, Bay/Bow	▼	480	.017	▼		.49		.49	.80
0510 Power wash, based on 2500 lb. operating pressure									
0520 1-2 lite	A-1H	4400	.002	S.F.		.05	.02	.07	.10
0530 3-6 lite	▼	4320	.002	▼		.05	.02	.07	.10

09 91 Painting

09 91 03 – Paint Restoration

09 91 03.30 Exterior Surface Preparation	Crew	Daily Output	Labor-Hours	Unit	Material	2017 Bare Costs Labor	Equipment	Total	Total Incl O&P
0540	7-10 lite	A-1H	4240	.002	S.F.		.05	.02	.07	.10
0550	12 lite		4160	.002			.05	.02	.07	.11
0560	Bay/Bow	▼	4400	.002	▼		.05	.02	.07	.10
0600	Siding, scrape and sand, light=10-30%, med.=30-70%									
0610	Heavy=70-100% of surface to sand									
0650	Texture 1-11, light	1 Pord	480	.017	S.F.		.49		.49	.80
0660	Med.		440	.018			.53		.53	.88
0670	Heavy		360	.022			.65		.65	1.07
0680	Wood shingles, shakes, light		440	.018			.53		.53	.88
0690	Med.		360	.022			.65		.65	1.07
0700	Heavy		280	.029			.83		.83	1.38
0710	Clapboard, light		520	.015			.45		.45	.74
0720	Med.		480	.017			.49		.49	.80
0730	Heavy	▼	400	.020	▼		.58		.58	.96
0740	Wire brush									
0750	Aluminum, light	1 Pord	600	.013	S.F.		.39		.39	.64
0760	Med.		520	.015			.45		.45	.74
0770	Heavy	▼	440	.018	▼		.53		.53	.88
0780	Pressure wash, based on 2500 lb. operating pressure									
0790	Stucco	A-1H	3080	.003	S.F.		.07	.02	.09	.15
0800	Aluminum or vinyl		3200	.003			.07	.02	.09	.14
0810	Siding, masonry, brick & block	▼	2400	.003	▼		.09	.03	.12	.18
1300	Miscellaneous, wire brush									
1310	Metal, pedestrian gate	1 Pord	100	.080	S.F.		2.34		2.34	3.86

09 91 03.40 Interior Surface Preparation

		Crew	Daily Output	Labor-Hours	Unit	Material	2017 Bare Costs Labor	Equipment	Total	Total Incl O&P
0010	**INTERIOR SURFACE PREPARATION**									
0020	Doors, per side, not incl. frames or trim									
0030	Scrape & sand									
0040	Wood, flush	1 Pord	616	.013	S.F.		.38		.38	.63
0050	Wood, detail		496	.016			.47		.47	.78
0060	Wood, louvered	▼	280	.029	▼		.83		.83	1.38
0070	Wire brush									
0080	Metal, flush	1 Pord	640	.013	S.F.		.37		.37	.60
0090	Metal, detail		520	.015			.45		.45	.74
0100	Metal, louvered	▼	360	.022	▼		.65		.65	1.07
0110	Hand wash									
0120	Wood, flush	1 Pord	2160	.004	S.F.		.11		.11	.18
0130	Wood, detail		2000	.004			.12		.12	.19
0140	Wood, louvered		1360	.006			.17		.17	.28
0150	Metal, flush		2160	.004			.11		.11	.18
0160	Metal, detail		2000	.004			.12		.12	.19
0170	Metal, louvered	▼	1360	.006	▼		.17		.17	.28
0400	Windows, per side, not incl. trim									
0410	Scrape & sand									
0420	Wood, 1-2 lite	1 Pord	360	.022	S.F.		.65		.65	1.07
0430	Wood, 3-6 lite		320	.025			.73		.73	1.21
0440	Wood, 7-10 lite		280	.029			.83		.83	1.38
0450	Wood, 12 lite		240	.033			.97		.97	1.61
0460	Wood, Bay/Bow	▼	360	.022	▼		.65		.65	1.07
0470	Wire brush									
0480	Metal, 1-2 lite	1 Pord	520	.015	S.F.		.45		.45	.74
0490	Metal, 3-6 lite		440	.018			.53		.53	.88

For customer support on your Residential Costs with RSMeans Data, call 800.448.8182.

505

09 91 Painting

09 91 03 – Paint Restoration

09 91 03.40 Interior Surface Preparation

		Crew	Daily Output	Labor-Hours	Unit	Material	2017 Bare Costs Labor	Equipment	Total	Total Incl O&P
0500	Metal, Bay/Bow	1 Pord	520	.015	S.F.		.45		.45	.74
0600	Walls, sanding, light=10-30%, medium=30-70%,									
0610	heavy=70-100% of surface to sand									
0650	Walls, sand									
0660	Gypsum board or plaster, light	1 Pord	3077	.003	S.F.		.08		.08	.13
0670	Gypsum board or plaster, medium		2160	.004			.11		.11	.18
0680	Gypsum board or plaster, heavy		923	.009			.25		.25	.42
0690	Wood, T&G, light		2400	.003			.10		.10	.16
0700	Wood, T&G, med.		1600	.005			.15		.15	.24
0710	Wood, T&G, heavy	↓	800	.010	↓		.29		.29	.48
0720	Walls, wash									
0730	Gypsum board or plaster	1 Pord	3200	.003	S.F.		.07		.07	.12
0740	Wood, T&G		3200	.003			.07		.07	.12
0750	Masonry, brick & block, smooth		2800	.003			.08		.08	.14
0760	Masonry, brick & block, coarse	↓	2000	.004	↓		.12		.12	.19
8000	For chemical washing, see Section 04 01 30									

09 91 03.41 Scrape After Fire Damage

		Crew	Daily Output	Labor-Hours	Unit	Material	2017 Bare Costs Labor	Equipment	Total	Total Incl O&P
0010	**SCRAPE AFTER FIRE DAMAGE**									
0050	Boards, 1" x 4"	1 Pord	336	.024	L.F.		.70		.70	1.15
0060	1" x 6"		260	.031			.90		.90	1.48
0070	1" x 8"		207	.039			1.13		1.13	1.86
0080	1" x 10"		174	.046			1.34		1.34	2.22
0500	Framing, 2" x 4"		265	.030			.88		.88	1.46
0510	2" x 6"		221	.036			1.06		1.06	1.74
0520	2" x 8"		190	.042			1.23		1.23	2.03
0530	2" x 10"		165	.048			1.42		1.42	2.34
0540	2" x 12"		144	.056			1.62		1.62	2.68
1000	Heavy framing, 3" x 4"		226	.035			1.03		1.03	1.71
1010	4" x 4"		210	.038			1.11		1.11	1.84
1020	4" x 6"		191	.042			1.22		1.22	2.02
1030	4" x 8"		165	.048			1.42		1.42	2.34
1040	4" x 10"		144	.056			1.62		1.62	2.68
1060	4" x 12"		131	.061	↓		1.78		1.78	2.94
2900	For sealing, light damage		825	.010	S.F.	.14	.28		.42	.62
2920	Heavy damage	↓	460	.017	"	.32	.51		.83	1.19

09 91 13 – Exterior Painting

09 91 13.30 Fences

		Crew	Daily Output	Labor-Hours	Unit	Material	2017 Bare Costs Labor	Equipment	Total	Total Incl O&P
0010	**FENCES** R099100-20									
0100	Chain link or wire metal, one side, water base									
0110	Roll & brush, first coat	1 Pord	960	.008	S.F.	.07	.24		.31	.48
0120	Second coat		1280	.006		.07	.18		.25	.37
0130	Spray, first coat		2275	.004		.07	.10		.17	.25
0140	Second coat	↓	2600	.003	↓	.07	.09		.16	.23
0150	Picket, water base									
0160	Roll & brush, first coat	1 Pord	865	.009	S.F.	.07	.27		.34	.53
0170	Second coat		1050	.008		.07	.22		.29	.45
0180	Spray, first coat		2275	.004		.07	.10		.17	.25
0190	Second coat		2600	.003		.07	.09		.16	.23
0200	Stockade, water base									
0210	Roll & brush, first coat	1 Pord	1040	.008	S.F.	.07	.22		.29	.45
0220	Second coat		1200	.007		.07	.19		.26	.40
0230	Spray, first coat		2275	.004		.07	.10		.17	.25

09 91 Painting

09 91 13 – Exterior Painting

09 91 13.30 Fences	Crew	Daily Output	Labor-Hours	Unit	Material	2017 Bare Costs Labor	Equipment	Total	Total Incl O&P
0240 Second coat	1 Pord	2600	.003	S.F.	.07	.09		.16	.23

09 91 13.42 Miscellaneous, Exterior

	Crew	Daily Output	Labor-Hours	Unit	Material	Labor	Equipment	Total	Total Incl O&P
0010 **MISCELLANEOUS, EXTERIOR** R099100-20									
0100 Railing, ext., decorative wood, incl. cap & baluster									
0110 Newels & spindles @ 12" O.C.									
0120 Brushwork, stain, sand, seal & varnish									
0130 First coat	1 Pord	90	.089	L.F.	.90	2.60		3.50	5.25
0140 Second coat	"	120	.067	"	.90	1.95		2.85	4.20
0150 Rough sawn wood, 42" high, 2" x 2" verticals, 6" O.C.									
0160 Brushwork, stain, each coat	1 Pord	90	.089	L.F.	.29	2.60		2.89	4.59
0170 Wrought iron, 1" rail, 1/2" sq. verticals									
0180 Brushwork, zinc chromate, 60" high, bars 6" O.C.									
0190 Primer	1 Pord	130	.062	L.F.	.88	1.80		2.68	3.94
0200 Finish coat		130	.062		1.13	1.80		2.93	4.21
0210 Additional coat	↓	190	.042	↓	1.32	1.23		2.55	3.48
0220 Shutters or blinds, single panel, 2' x 4', paint all sides									
0230 Brushwork, primer	1 Pord	20	.400	Ea.	.68	11.70		12.38	20
0240 Finish coat, exterior latex		20	.400		.56	11.70		12.26	19.90
0250 Primer & 1 coat, exterior latex		13	.615		1.09	17.95		19.04	30.50
0260 Spray, primer		35	.229		.99	6.65		7.64	12.10
0270 Finish coat, exterior latex		35	.229		1.20	6.65		7.85	12.30
0280 Primer & 1 coat, exterior latex	↓	20	.400	↓	1.06	11.70		12.76	20.50
0290 For louvered shutters, add				S.F.	10%				
0300 Stair stringers, exterior, metal									
0310 Roll & brush, zinc chromate, to 14", each coat	1 Pord	320	.025	L.F.	.38	.73		1.11	1.62
0320 Rough sawn wood, 4" x 12"									
0330 Roll & brush, exterior latex, each coat	1 Pord	215	.037	L.F.	.08	1.09		1.17	1.88
0340 Trellis/lattice, 2" x 2" @ 3" O.C. with 2" x 8" supports									
0350 Spray, latex, per side, each coat	1 Pord	475	.017	S.F.	.08	.49		.57	.90
0450 Decking, ext., sealer, alkyd, brushwork, sealer coat		1140	.007		.10	.21		.31	.45
0460 1st coat		1140	.007		.11	.21		.32	.46
0470 2nd coat		1300	.006		.08	.18		.26	.39
0500 Paint, alkyd, brushwork, primer coat		1140	.007		.11	.21		.32	.46
0510 1st coat		1140	.007		.14	.21		.35	.49
0520 2nd coat		1300	.006		.10	.18		.28	.41
0600 Sand paint, alkyd, brushwork, 1 coat	↓	150	.053	↓	.14	1.56		1.70	2.72

09 91 13.60 Siding Exterior

	Crew	Daily Output	Labor-Hours	Unit	Material	Labor	Equipment	Total	Total Incl O&P
0010 **SIDING EXTERIOR**, Alkyd (oil base)									
0450 Steel siding, oil base, paint 1 coat, brushwork	2 Pord	2015	.008	S.F.	.11	.23		.34	.50
0500 Spray		4550	.004		.16	.10		.26	.35
0800 Paint 2 coats, brushwork		1300	.012		.22	.36		.58	.83
1000 Spray		2750	.006		.18	.17		.35	.48
1200 Stucco, rough, oil base, paint 2 coats, brushwork		1300	.012		.22	.36		.58	.83
1400 Roller		1625	.010		.23	.29		.52	.72
1600 Spray		2925	.005		.24	.16		.40	.53
1800 Texture 1-11 or clapboard, oil base, primer coat, brushwork		1300	.012		.15	.36		.51	.75
2000 Spray		4550	.004		.15	.10		.25	.33
2100 Paint 1 coat, brushwork		1300	.012		.16	.36		.52	.77
2200 Spray		4550	.004		.16	.10		.26	.35
2400 Paint 2 coats, brushwork		810	.020		.32	.58		.90	1.30
2600 Spray		2600	.006		.35	.18		.53	.69
3000 Stain 1 coat, brushwork		1520	.011		.10	.31		.41	.61

09 91 13.60 Siding Exterior

		Crew	Daily Output	Labor-Hours	Unit	Material	2017 Bare Costs Labor	Equipment	Total	Total Incl O&P
3200	Spray	2 Pord	5320	.003	S.F.	.11	.09		.20	.27
3400	Stain 2 coats, brushwork		950	.017		.19	.49		.68	1.02
4000	Spray		3050	.005		.21	.15		.36	.48
4200	Wood shingles, oil base primer coat, brushwork		1300	.012		.14	.36		.50	.74
4400	Spray		3900	.004		.13	.12		.25	.34
4600	Paint 1 coat, brushwork		1300	.012		.13	.36		.49	.74
4800	Spray		3900	.004		.16	.12		.28	.38
5000	Paint 2 coats, brushwork		810	.020		.27	.58		.85	1.24
5200	Spray		2275	.007		.25	.21		.46	.62
5800	Stain 1 coat, brushwork		1500	.011		.10	.31		.41	.61
6000	Spray		3900	.004		.10	.12		.22	.30
6500	Stain 2 coats, brushwork		950	.017		.19	.49		.68	1.02
7000	Spray		2660	.006		.26	.18		.44	.58
8000	For latex paint, deduct					10%				
8100	For work over 12' H, from pipe scaffolding, add						15%			
8200	For work over 12' H, from extension ladder, add						25%			
8300	For work over 12' H, from swing staging, add						35%			

09 91 13.62 Siding, Misc.

		Crew	Daily Output	Labor-Hours	Unit	Material	2017 Bare Costs Labor	Equipment	Total	Total Incl O&P
0010	**SIDING, MISC.,** latex paint R099100-10									
0100	Aluminum siding									
0110	Brushwork, primer	2 Pord	2275	.007	S.F.	.06	.21		.27	.41
0120	Finish coat, exterior latex		2275	.007		.06	.21		.27	.40
0130	Primer & 1 coat exterior latex		1300	.012		.13	.36		.49	.73
0140	Primer & 2 coats exterior latex		975	.016		.19	.48		.67	1
0150	Mineral fiber shingles									
0160	Brushwork, primer	2 Pord	1495	.011	S.F.	.15	.31		.46	.68
0170	Finish coat, industrial enamel		1495	.011		.18	.31		.49	.72
0180	Primer & 1 coat enamel		810	.020		.33	.58		.91	1.31
0190	Primer & 2 coats enamel		540	.030		.50	.87		1.37	1.98
0200	Roll, primer		1625	.010		.16	.29		.45	.65
0210	Finish coat, industrial enamel		1625	.010		.19	.29		.48	.68
0220	Primer & 1 coat enamel		975	.016		.36	.48		.84	1.18
0230	Primer & 2 coats enamel		650	.025		.55	.72		1.27	1.79
0240	Spray, primer		3900	.004		.13	.12		.25	.34
0250	Finish coat, industrial enamel		3900	.004		.16	.12		.28	.38
0260	Primer & 1 coat enamel		2275	.007		.29	.21		.50	.66
0270	Primer & 2 coats enamel		1625	.010		.45	.29		.74	.96
0280	Waterproof sealer, first coat		4485	.004		.10	.10		.20	.28
0290	Second coat		5235	.003		.09	.09		.18	.25
0300	Rough wood incl. shingles, shakes or rough sawn siding									
0310	Brushwork, primer	2 Pord	1280	.013	S.F.	.14	.37		.51	.75
0320	Finish coat, exterior latex		1280	.013		.10	.37		.47	.71
0330	Primer & 1 coat exterior latex		960	.017		.24	.49		.73	1.06
0340	Primer & 2 coats exterior latex		700	.023		.34	.67		1.01	1.48
0350	Roll, primer		2925	.005		.18	.16		.34	.46
0360	Finish coat, exterior latex		2925	.005		.12	.16		.28	.40
0370	Primer & 1 coat exterior latex		1790	.009		.31	.26		.57	.77
0380	Primer & 2 coats exterior latex		1300	.012		.43	.36		.79	1.06
0390	Spray, primer		3900	.004		.15	.12		.27	.37
0400	Finish coat, exterior latex		3900	.004		.10	.12		.22	.31
0410	Primer & 1 coat exterior latex		2600	.006		.25	.18		.43	.58
0420	Primer & 2 coats exterior latex		2080	.008		.35	.22		.57	.75

09 91 Painting

09 91 13 – Exterior Painting

09 91 13.62 Siding, Misc.

		Crew	Daily Output	Labor-Hours	Unit	Material	2017 Bare Costs Labor	Equipment	Total	Total Incl O&P
0430	Waterproof sealer, first coat	2 Pord	4485	.004	S.F.	.18	.10		.28	.36
0440	Second coat	↓	4485	.004	↓	.10	.10		.20	.28
0450	Smooth wood incl. butt, T&G, beveled, drop or B&B siding									
0460	Brushwork, primer	2 Pord	2325	.007	S.F.	.10	.20		.30	.44
0470	Finish coat, exterior latex		1280	.013		.10	.37		.47	.71
0480	Primer & 1 coat exterior latex		800	.020		.20	.58		.78	1.18
0490	Primer & 2 coats exterior latex		630	.025		.30	.74		1.04	1.56
0500	Roll, primer		2275	.007		.11	.21		.32	.46
0510	Finish coat, exterior latex		2275	.007		.11	.21		.32	.46
0520	Primer & 1 coat exterior latex		1300	.012		.22	.36		.58	.83
0530	Primer & 2 coats exterior latex		975	.016		.33	.48		.81	1.16
0540	Spray, primer		4550	.004		.09	.10		.19	.26
0550	Finish coat, exterior latex		4550	.004		.10	.10		.20	.28
0560	Primer & 1 coat exterior latex		2600	.006		.18	.18		.36	.50
0570	Primer & 2 coats exterior latex		1950	.008		.28	.24		.52	.70
0580	Waterproof sealer, first coat		5230	.003		.10	.09		.19	.26
0590	Second coat	↓	5980	.003		.10	.08		.18	.24
0600	For oil base paint, add				↓	10%				

09 91 13.70 Doors and Windows, Exterior

		Crew	Daily Output	Labor-Hours	Unit	Material	2017 Bare Costs Labor	Equipment	Total	Total Incl O&P
0010	**DOORS AND WINDOWS, EXTERIOR** R099100-10									
0100	Door frames & trim, only									
0110	Brushwork, primer R099100-20	1 Pord	512	.016	L.F.	.06	.46		.52	.82
0120	Finish coat, exterior latex		512	.016		.07	.46		.53	.83
0130	Primer & 1 coat, exterior latex		300	.027		.13	.78		.91	1.44
0140	Primer & 2 coats, exterior latex	↓	265	.030	↓	.20	.88		1.08	1.68
0150	Doors, flush, both sides, incl. frame & trim									
0160	Roll & brush, primer	1 Pord	10	.800	Ea.	4.70	23.50		28.20	43.50
0170	Finish coat, exterior latex		10	.800		5.35	23.50		28.85	44.50
0180	Primer & 1 coat, exterior latex		7	1.143		10.05	33.50		43.55	66
0190	Primer & 2 coats, exterior latex		5	1.600		15.40	46.50		61.90	94
0200	Brushwork, stain, sealer & 2 coats polyurethane	↓	4	2	↓	32	58.50		90.50	132
0210	Doors, French, both sides, 10-15 lite, incl. frame & trim									
0220	Brushwork, primer	1 Pord	6	1.333	Ea.	2.35	39		41.35	67
0230	Finish coat, exterior latex		6	1.333		2.68	39		41.68	67.50
0240	Primer & 1 coat, exterior latex		3	2.667		5.05	78		83.05	135
0250	Primer & 2 coats, exterior latex		2	4		7.55	117		124.55	201
0260	Brushwork, stain, sealer & 2 coats polyurethane	↓	2.50	3.200	↓	11.40	93.50		104.90	167
0270	Doors, louvered, both sides, incl. frame & trim									
0280	Brushwork, primer	1 Pord	7	1.143	Ea.	4.70	33.50		38.20	60
0290	Finish coat, exterior latex		7	1.143		5.35	33.50		38.85	61
0300	Primer & 1 coat, exterior latex		4	2		10.05	58.50		68.55	108
0310	Primer & 2 coats, exterior latex		3	2.667		15.10	78		93.10	146
0320	Brushwork, stain, sealer & 2 coats polyurethane	↓	4.50	1.778	↓	32	52		84	121
0330	Doors, panel, both sides, incl. frame & trim									
0340	Roll & brush, primer	1 Pord	6	1.333	Ea.	4.70	39		43.70	69.50
0350	Finish coat, exterior latex		6	1.333		5.35	39		44.35	70.50
0360	Primer & 1 coat, exterior latex		3	2.667		10.05	78		88.05	140
0370	Primer & 2 coats, exterior latex		2.50	3.200		15.10	93.50		108.60	171
0380	Brushwork, stain, sealer & 2 coats polyurethane	↓	3	2.667	↓	32	78		110	165
0400	Windows, per ext. side, based on 15 S.F.									
0410	1 to 6 lite									
0420	Brushwork, primer	1 Pord	13	.615	Ea.	.93	17.95		18.88	30.50

For customer support on your Residential Costs with RSMeans Data, call 800.448.8182.

509

09 91 13.70 Doors and Windows, Exterior

		Crew	Daily Output	Labor-Hours	Unit	Material	2017 Bare Costs Labor	Equipment	Total	Total Incl O&P
0430	Finish coat, exterior latex	1 Pord	13	.615	Ea.	1.06	17.95		19.01	30.50
0440	Primer & 1 coat, exterior latex		8	1		1.98	29		30.98	50
0450	Primer & 2 coats, exterior latex		6	1.333		2.98	39		41.98	68
0460	Stain, sealer & 1 coat varnish	▼	7	1.143	▼	4.50	33.50		38	60
0470	7 to 10 lite									
0480	Brushwork, primer	1 Pord	11	.727	Ea.	.93	21		21.93	36
0490	Finish coat, exterior latex		11	.727		1.06	21		22.06	36
0500	Primer & 1 coat, exterior latex		7	1.143		1.98	33.50		35.48	57
0510	Primer & 2 coats, exterior latex		5	1.600		2.98	46.50		49.48	80.50
0520	Stain, sealer & 1 coat varnish	▼	6	1.333	▼	4.50	39		43.50	69.50
0530	12 lite									
0540	Brushwork, primer	1 Pord	10	.800	Ea.	.93	23.50		24.43	39.50
0550	Finish coat, exterior latex		10	.800		1.06	23.50		24.56	39.50
0560	Primer & 1 coat, exterior latex		6	1.333		1.98	39		40.98	66.50
0570	Primer & 2 coats, exterior latex		5	1.600		2.98	46.50		49.48	80.50
0580	Stain, sealer & 1 coat varnish	▼	6	1.333		4.41	39		43.41	69.50
0590	For oil base paint, add				▼	10%				

09 91 13.80 Trim, Exterior

		Crew	Daily Output	Labor-Hours	Unit	Material	2017 Bare Costs Labor	Equipment	Total	Total Incl O&P
0010	**TRIM, EXTERIOR** R099100-10									
0100	Door frames & trim (see Doors, interior or exterior)									
0110	Fascia, latex paint, one coat coverage									
0120	1" x 4", brushwork	1 Pord	640	.013	L.F.	.02	.37		.39	.62
0130	Roll		1280	.006		.02	.18		.20	.33
0140	Spray		2080	.004		.02	.11		.13	.21
0150	1" x 6" to 1" x 10", brushwork		640	.013		.07	.37		.44	.68
0160	Roll		1230	.007		.08	.19		.27	.40
0170	Spray		2100	.004		.06	.11		.17	.25
0180	1" x 12", brushwork		640	.013		.07	.37		.44	.68
0190	Roll		1050	.008		.08	.22		.30	.46
0200	Spray	▼	2200	.004	▼	.06	.11		.17	.25
0210	Gutters & downspouts, metal, zinc chromate paint									
0220	Brushwork, gutters, 5", first coat	1 Pord	640	.013	L.F.	.40	.37		.77	1.04
0230	Second coat		960	.008		.38	.24		.62	.81
0240	Third coat		1280	.006		.30	.18		.48	.64
0250	Downspouts, 4", first coat		640	.013		.40	.37		.77	1.04
0260	Second coat		960	.008		.38	.24		.62	.81
0270	Third coat	▼	1280	.006	▼	.30	.18		.48	.64
0280	Gutters & downspouts, wood									
0290	Brushwork, gutters, 5", primer	1 Pord	640	.013	L.F.	.06	.37		.43	.67
0300	Finish coat, exterior latex		640	.013		.06	.37		.43	.67
0310	Primer & 1 coat exterior latex		400	.020		.13	.58		.71	1.11
0320	Primer & 2 coats exterior latex		325	.025		.20	.72		.92	1.41
0330	Downspouts, 4", primer		640	.013		.06	.37		.43	.67
0340	Finish coat, exterior latex		640	.013		.06	.37		.43	.67
0350	Primer & 1 coat exterior latex		400	.020		.13	.58		.71	1.11
0360	Primer & 2 coats exterior latex		325	.025		.10	.72		.82	1.30
0370	Molding, exterior, up to 14" wide									
0380	Brushwork, primer	1 Pord	640	.013	L.F.	.07	.37		.44	.68
0390	Finish coat, exterior latex		640	.013		.08	.37		.45	.68
0400	Primer & 1 coat exterior latex		400	.020		.16	.58		.74	1.13
0410	Primer & 2 coats exterior latex		315	.025		.16	.74		.90	1.39
0420	Stain & fill	▼	1050	.008		.11	.22		.33	.50

For customer support on your Residential Costs with RSMeans Data, call 800.448.8182.

09 91 13 – Exterior Painting

09 91 13.80 Trim, Exterior

	Crew	Daily Output	Labor-Hours	Unit	Material	2017 Bare Costs Labor	Equipment	Total	Total Incl O&P
0430 Shellac	1 Pord	1850	.004	L.F.	.14	.13		.27	.37
0440 Varnish		1275	.006		.10	.18		.28	.41

09 91 13.90 Walls, Masonry (CMU), Exterior

	Crew	Daily Output	Labor-Hours	Unit	Material	2017 Bare Costs Labor	Equipment	Total	Total Incl O&P
0010 **WALLS, MASONRY (CMU), EXTERIOR**									
0360 Concrete masonry units (CMU), smooth surface									
0370 Brushwork, latex, first coat	1 Pord	640	.013	S.F.	.07	.37		.44	.68
0380 Second coat		960	.008		.06	.24		.30	.46
0390 Waterproof sealer, first coat		736	.011		.27	.32		.59	.81
0400 Second coat		1104	.007		.27	.21		.48	.64
0410 Roll, latex, paint, first coat		1465	.005		.09	.16		.25	.35
0420 Second coat		1790	.004		.06	.13		.19	.29
0430 Waterproof sealer, first coat		1680	.005		.27	.14		.41	.52
0440 Second coat		2060	.004		.27	.11		.38	.48
0450 Spray, latex, paint, first coat		1950	.004		.07	.12		.19	.27
0460 Second coat		2600	.003		.05	.09		.14	.21
0470 Waterproof sealer, first coat		2245	.004		.27	.10		.37	.46
0480 Second coat		2990	.003		.27	.08		.35	.42
0490 Concrete masonry unit (CMU), porous									
0500 Brushwork, latex, first coat	1 Pord	640	.013	S.F.	.14	.37		.51	.76
0510 Second coat		960	.008		.07	.24		.31	.48
0520 Waterproof sealer, first coat		736	.011		.27	.32		.59	.81
0530 Second coat		1104	.007		.27	.21		.48	.64
0540 Roll latex, first coat		1465	.005		.11	.16		.27	.38
0550 Second coat		1790	.004		.07	.13		.20	.30
0560 Waterproof sealer, first coat		1680	.005		.27	.14		.41	.52
0570 Second coat		2060	.004		.27	.11		.38	.48
0580 Spray latex, first coat		1950	.004		.08	.12		.20	.29
0590 Second coat		2600	.003		.05	.09		.14	.21
0600 Waterproof sealer, first coat		2245	.004		.27	.10		.37	.46
0610 Second coat		2990	.003		.27	.08		.35	.42

09 91 23 – Interior Painting

09 91 23.20 Cabinets and Casework

	Crew	Daily Output	Labor-Hours	Unit	Material	2017 Bare Costs Labor	Equipment	Total	Total Incl O&P
0010 **CABINETS AND CASEWORK**									
1000 Primer coat, oil base, brushwork	1 Pord	650	.012	S.F.	.06	.36		.42	.66
2000 Paint, oil base, brushwork, 1 coat		650	.012		.11	.36		.47	.71
2500 2 coats		400	.020		.22	.58		.80	1.20
3000 Stain, brushwork, wipe off		650	.012		.10	.36		.46	.69
4000 Shellac, 1 coat, brushwork		650	.012		.12	.36		.48	.72
4500 Varnish, 3 coats, brushwork, sand after 1st coat		325	.025		.25	.72		.97	1.46
5000 For latex paint, deduct					10%				

09 91 23.33 Doors and Windows, Interior Alkyd (Oil Base)

	Crew	Daily Output	Labor-Hours	Unit	Material	2017 Bare Costs Labor	Equipment	Total	Total Incl O&P
0010 **DOORS AND WINDOWS, INTERIOR ALKYD (OIL BASE)**									
0500 Flush door & frame, 3' x 7', oil, primer, brushwork	1 Pord	10	.800	Ea.	3.74	23.50		27.24	42.50
1000 Paint, 1 coat		10	.800		3.91	23.50		27.41	43
1200 2 coats		6	1.333		4.61	39		43.61	69.50
1400 Stain, brushwork, wipe off		18	.444		2	13		15	23.50
1600 Shellac, 1 coat, brushwork		25	.320		2.52	9.35		11.87	18.15
1800 Varnish, 3 coats, brushwork, sand after 1st coat		9	.889		5.15	26		31.15	48.50
2000 Panel door & frame, 3' x 7', oil, primer, brushwork		6	1.333		2.45	39		41.45	67
2200 Paint, 1 coat		6	1.333		3.91	39		42.91	69
2400 2 coats		3	2.667		10.30	78		88.30	140
2600 Stain, brushwork, panel door, 3' x 7', not incl. frame		16	.500		2	14.60		16.60	26

511

09 91 Painting

09 91 23 – Interior Painting

09 91 23.33 Doors and Windows, Interior Alkyd (Oil Base)		Crew	Daily Output	Labor-Hours	Unit	Material	2017 Bare Costs Labor	Equipment	Total	Total Incl O&P
2800	Shellac, 1 coat, brushwork	1 Pord	22	.364	Ea.	2.52	10.60		13.12	20.50
3000	Varnish, 3 coats, brushwork, sand after 1st coat	↓	7.50	1.067	↓	5.15	31		36.15	57
3020	French door, incl. 3' x 7', 6 lites, frame & trim									
3022	Paint, 1 coat, over existing paint	1 Pord	5	1.600	Ea.	7.85	46.50		54.35	85.50
3024	2 coats, over existing paint		5	1.600		15.20	46.50		61.70	94
3026	Primer & 1 coat		3.50	2.286		12.70	66.50		79.20	124
3028	Primer & 2 coats		3	2.667		20.50	78		98.50	152
3032	Varnish or polyurethane, 1 coat		5	1.600		9.25	46.50		55.75	87
3034	2 coats, sanding between	↓	3	2.667	↓	18.50	78		96.50	150
4400	Windows, including frame and trim, per side									
4600	Colonial type, 6/6 lites, 2' x 3', oil, primer, brushwork	1 Pord	14	.571	Ea.	.39	16.70		17.09	28
5800	Paint, 1 coat		14	.571		.62	16.70		17.32	28
6000	2 coats		9	.889		1.20	26		27.20	44.50
6200	3' x 5' opening, 6/6 lites, primer coat, brushwork		12	.667		.97	19.45		20.42	33
6400	Paint, 1 coat		12	.667		1.55	19.45		21	33.50
6600	2 coats		7	1.143		3	33.50		36.50	58.50
6800	4' x 8' opening, 6/6 lites, primer coat, brushwork		8	1		2.06	29		31.06	50.50
7000	Paint, 1 coat		8	1		3.30	29		32.30	51.50
7200	2 coats		5	1.600		6.40	46.50		52.90	84
8000	Single lite type, 2' x 3', oil base, primer coat, brushwork		33	.242		.39	7.10		7.49	12.15
8200	Paint, 1 coat		33	.242		.62	7.10		7.72	12.40
8400	2 coats		20	.400		1.20	11.70		12.90	20.50
8600	3' x 5' opening, primer coat, brushwork		20	.400		.97	11.70		12.67	20.50
8800	Paint, 1 coat		20	.400		1.55	11.70		13.25	21
8900	2 coats		13	.615		3	17.95		20.95	33
9200	4' x 8' opening, primer coat, brushwork		14	.571		2.06	16.70		18.76	30
9400	Paint, 1 coat		14	.571		3.30	16.70		20	31
9600	2 coats	↓	8	1	↓	6.40	29		35.40	55

09 91 23.35 Doors and Windows, Interior Latex

		Crew	Daily Output	Labor-Hours	Unit	Material	Labor	Equipment	Total	Total Incl O&P
0010	**DOORS & WINDOWS, INTERIOR LATEX**　R099100-10									
0100	Doors, flush, both sides, incl. frame & trim									
0110	Roll & brush, primer	1 Pord	10	.800	Ea.	4.25	23.50		27.75	43
0120	Finish coat, latex		10	.800		5.45	23.50		28.95	44.50
0130	Primer & 1 coat latex		7	1.143		9.70	33.50		43.20	65.50
0140	Primer & 2 coats latex		5	1.600		14.80	46.50		61.30	93.50
0160	Spray, both sides, primer		20	.400		4.47	11.70		16.17	24
0170	Finish coat, latex		20	.400		5.70	11.70		17.40	25.50
0180	Primer & 1 coat latex		11	.727		10.25	21		31.25	46.50
0190	Primer & 2 coats latex	↓	8	1	↓	15.70	29		44.70	65.50
0200	Doors, French, both sides, 10-15 lite, incl. frame & trim									
0210	Roll & brush, primer	1 Pord	6	1.333	Ea.	2.12	39		41.12	67
0220	Finish coat, latex		6	1.333		2.72	39		41.72	67.50
0230	Primer & 1 coat latex		3	2.667		4.84	78		82.84	134
0240	Primer & 2 coats latex	↓	2	4	↓	7.40	117		124.40	201
0260	Doors, louvered, both sides, incl. frame & trim									
0270	Roll & brush, primer	1 Pord	7	1.143	Ea.	4.25	33.50		37.75	59.50
0280	Finish coat, latex		7	1.143		5.45	33.50		38.95	61
0290	Primer & 1 coat, latex		4	2		9.45	58.50		67.95	107
0300	Primer & 2 coats, latex		3	2.667		15.15	78		93.15	146
0320	Spray, both sides, primer		20	.400		4.47	11.70		16.17	24
0330	Finish coat, latex		20	.400		5.70	11.70		17.40	25.50
0340	Primer & 1 coat, latex		11	.727		10.25	21		31.25	46.50

09 91 Painting

09 91 23 – Interior Painting

09 91 23.35 Doors and Windows, Interior Latex		Crew	Daily Output	Labor-Hours	Unit	Material	2017 Bare Costs Labor	Equipment	Total	Total Incl O&P
0350	Primer & 2 coats, latex	1 Pord	8	1	Ea.	16.05	29		45.05	65.50
0360	Doors, panel, both sides, incl. frame & trim									
0370	Roll & brush, primer	1 Pord	6	1.333	Ea.	4.47	39		43.47	69.50
0380	Finish coat, latex		6	1.333		5.45	39		44.45	70.50
0390	Primer & 1 coat, latex		3	2.667		9.70	78		87.70	140
0400	Primer & 2 coats, latex		2.50	3.200		15.15	93.50		108.65	171
0420	Spray, both sides, primer		10	.800		4.47	23.50		27.97	43.50
0430	Finish coat, latex		10	.800		5.70	23.50		29.20	45
0440	Primer & 1 coat, latex		5	1.600		10.25	46.50		56.75	88.50
0450	Primer & 2 coats, latex	↓	4	2	↓	16.05	58.50		74.55	114
0460	Windows, per interior side, based on 15 S.F.									
0470	1 to 6 lite									
0480	Brushwork, primer	1 Pord	13	.615	Ea.	.84	17.95		18.79	30.50
0490	Finish coat, enamel		13	.615		1.07	17.95		19.02	30.50
0500	Primer & 1 coat enamel		8	1		1.91	29		30.91	50
0510	Primer & 2 coats enamel	↓	6	1.333	↓	2.99	39		41.99	68
0530	7 to 10 lite									
0540	Brushwork, primer	1 Pord	11	.727	Ea.	.84	21		21.84	36
0550	Finish coat, enamel		11	.727		1.07	21		22.07	36
0560	Primer & 1 coat enamel		7	1.143		1.91	33.50		35.41	57
0570	Primer & 2 coats enamel	↓	5	1.600		2.99	46.50		49.49	80.50
0590	12 lite									
0600	Brushwork, primer	1 Pord	10	.800	Ea.	.84	23.50		24.34	39.50
0610	Finish coat, enamel		10	.800		1.07	23.50		24.57	39.50
0620	Primer & 1 coat enamel		6	1.333		1.91	39		40.91	66.50
0630	Primer & 2 coats enamel	↓	5	1.600		2.99	46.50		49.49	80.50
0650	For oil base paint, add				↓	10%				

09 91 23.39 Doors and Windows, Interior Latex, Zero Voc

			Crew	Daily Output	Labor-Hours	Unit	Material	Labor	Equipment	Total	Total Incl O&P
0010	**DOORS & WINDOWS, INTERIOR LATEX, ZERO VOC**										
0100	Doors flush, both sides, incl. frame & trim										
0110	Roll & brush, primer	G	1 Pord	10	.800	Ea.	5.05	23.50		28.55	44
0120	Finish coat, latex	G		10	.800		5.75	23.50		29.25	45
0130	Primer & 1 coat latex	G		7	1.143		10.80	33.50		44.30	67
0140	Primer & 2 coats latex	G		5	1.600		16.20	46.50		62.70	95
0160	Spray, both sides, primer	G		20	.400		5.30	11.70		17	25
0170	Finish coat, latex	G		20	.400		6.05	11.70		17.75	26
0180	Primer & 1 coat latex	G		11	.727		11.40	21		32.40	47.50
0190	Primer & 2 coats latex	G	↓	8	1	↓	17.15	29		46.15	67
0200	Doors, French, both sides, 10-15 lite, incl. frame & trim										
0210	Roll & brush, primer	G	1 Pord	6	1.333	Ea.	2.52	39		41.52	67.50
0220	Finish coat, latex	G		6	1.333		2.88	39		41.88	67.50
0230	Primer & 1 coat latex	G		3	2.667		5.40	78		83.40	135
0240	Primer & 2 coats latex	G	↓	2	4	↓	8.10	117		125.10	202
0360	Doors, panel, both sides, incl. frame & trim										
0370	Roll & brush, primer	G	1 Pord	6	1.333	Ea.	5.30	39		44.30	70.50
0380	Finish coat, latex	G		6	1.333		5.75	39		44.75	71
0390	Primer & 1 coat, latex	G		3	2.667		10.80	78		88.80	141
0400	Primer & 2 coats, latex	G		2.50	3.200		16.55	93.50		110.05	172
0420	Spray, both sides, primer	G		10	.800		5.30	23.50		28.80	44.50
0430	Finish coat, latex	G		10	.800		6.05	23.50		29.55	45
0440	Primer & 1 coat, latex	G		5	1.600		11.40	46.50		57.90	89.50
0450	Primer & 2 coats, latex	G	↓	4	2		17.55	58.50		76.05	116

For customer support on your Residential Costs with RSMeans Data, call 800.448.8182.

513

09 91 Painting

09 91 23 – Interior Painting

09 91 23.39 Doors and Windows, Interior Latex, Zero Voc

		Crew	Daily Output	Labor-Hours	Unit	Material	2017 Bare Costs Labor	Equipment	Total	Total Incl O&P
0460	Windows, per interior side, based on 15 S.F.									
0470	1 to 6 lite									
0480	Brushwork, primer G	1 Pord	13	.615	Ea.	.99	17.95		18.94	30.50
0490	Finish coat, enamel G		13	.615		1.14	17.95		19.09	31
0500	Primer & 1 coat enamel G		8	1		2.13	29		31.13	50.50
0510	Primer & 2 coats enamel G		6	1.333		3.27	39		42.27	68

09 91 23.40 Floors, Interior

		Crew	Daily Output	Labor-Hours	Unit	Material	2017 Bare Costs Labor	Equipment	Total	Total Incl O&P
0010	**FLOORS, INTERIOR**									
0100	Concrete paint, latex									
0110	Brushwork									
0120	1st coat	1 Pord	975	.008	S.F.	.14	.24		.38	.55
0130	2nd coat		1150	.007		.09	.20		.29	.44
0140	3rd coat		1300	.006		.07	.18		.25	.38
0150	Roll									
0160	1st coat	1 Pord	2600	.003	S.F.	.19	.09		.28	.36
0170	2nd coat		3250	.002		.11	.07		.18	.24
0180	3rd coat		3900	.002		.08	.06		.14	.19
0190	Spray									
0200	1st coat	1 Pord	2600	.003	S.F.	.16	.09		.25	.33
0210	2nd coat		3250	.002		.09	.07		.16	.22
0220	3rd coat		3900	.002		.07	.06		.13	.18

09 91 23.52 Miscellaneous, Interior

		Crew	Daily Output	Labor-Hours	Unit	Material	2017 Bare Costs Labor	Equipment	Total	Total Incl O&P
0010	**MISCELLANEOUS, INTERIOR**									
2400	Floors, conc./wood, oil base, primer/sealer coat, brushwork	2 Pord	1950	.008	S.F.	.09	.24		.33	.50
2450	Roller		5200	.003		.10	.09		.19	.26
2600	Spray		6000	.003		.10	.08		.18	.23
2650	Paint 1 coat, brushwork		1950	.008		.10	.24		.34	.51
2800	Roller		5200	.003		.11	.09		.20	.27
2850	Spray		6000	.003		.11	.08		.19	.25
3000	Stain, wood floor, brushwork, 1 coat		4550	.004		.10	.10		.20	.27
3200	Roller		5200	.003		.10	.09		.19	.26
3250	Spray		6000	.003		.10	.08		.18	.24
3400	Varnish, wood floor, brushwork		4550	.004		.08	.10		.18	.26
3450	Roller		5200	.003		.09	.09		.18	.25
3600	Spray		6000	.003		.09	.08		.17	.23
3800	Grilles, per side, oil base, primer coat, brushwork	1 Pord	520	.015		.13	.45		.58	.88
3850	Spray		1140	.007		.13	.21		.34	.49
3880	Paint 1 coat, brushwork		520	.015		.21	.45		.66	.97
3900	Spray		1140	.007		.23	.21		.44	.59
3920	Paint 2 coats, brushwork		325	.025		.40	.72		1.12	1.63
3940	Spray		650	.012		.46	.36		.82	1.09
4500	Louvers, 1 side, primer, brushwork		524	.015		.09	.45		.54	.84
4520	Paint 1 coat, brushwork		520	.015		.10	.45		.55	.85
4530	Spray		1140	.007		.11	.21		.32	.46
4540	Paint 2 coats, brushwork		325	.025		.19	.72		.91	1.40
4550	Spray		650	.012		.21	.36		.57	.82
4560	Paint 3 coats, brushwork		270	.030		.28	.87		1.15	1.74
4570	Spray		500	.016		.31	.47		.78	1.11
5000	Pipe, 1" - 4" diameter, primer or sealer coat, oil base, brushwork	2 Pord	1250	.013	L.F.	.10	.37		.47	.73
5100	Spray		2165	.007		.09	.22		.31	.46
5200	Paint 1 coat, brushwork		1250	.013		.11	.37		.48	.74
5300	Spray		2165	.007		.10	.22		.32	.47

514

09 91 23.52 Miscellaneous, Interior

		Crew	Daily Output	Labor-Hours	Unit	Material	2017 Bare Costs Labor	Equipment	Total	Total Incl O&P
5350	Paint 2 coats, brushwork	2 Pord	775	.021	L.F.	.20	.60		.80	1.22
5400	Spray		1240	.013		.22	.38		.60	.86
5450	5" - 8" diameter, primer or sealer coat, brushwork		620	.026		.19	.75		.94	1.45
5500	Spray		1085	.015		.31	.43		.74	1.06
5550	Paint 1 coat, brushwork		620	.026		.30	.75		1.05	1.57
5600	Spray		1085	.015		.33	.43		.76	1.08
5650	Paint 2 coats, brushwork		385	.042		.39	1.21		1.60	2.43
5700	Spray		620	.026		.44	.75		1.19	1.72
6600	Radiators, per side, primer, brushwork	1 Pord	520	.015	S.F.	.09	.45		.54	.84
6620	Paint, 1 coat		520	.015		.09	.45		.54	.83
6640	2 coats		340	.024		.19	.69		.88	1.34
6660	3 coats		283	.028		.28	.83		1.11	1.67
7000	Trim, wood, incl. puttying, under 6" wide									
7200	Primer coat, oil base, brushwork	1 Pord	650	.012	L.F.	.03	.36		.39	.63
7250	Paint, 1 coat, brushwork		650	.012		.05	.36		.41	.65
7400	2 coats		400	.020		.10	.58		.68	1.07
7450	3 coats		325	.025		.15	.72		.87	1.35
7500	Over 6" wide, primer coat, brushwork		650	.012		.06	.36		.42	.66
7550	Paint, 1 coat, brushwork		650	.012		.10	.36		.46	.70
7600	2 coats		400	.020		.20	.58		.78	1.18
7650	3 coats		325	.025		.30	.72		1.02	1.52
8000	Cornice, simple design, primer coat, oil base, brushwork		650	.012	S.F.	.06	.36		.42	.66
8250	Paint, 1 coat		650	.012		.10	.36		.46	.70
8300	2 coats		400	.020		.20	.58		.78	1.18
8350	Ornate design, primer coat		350	.023		.06	.67		.73	1.17
8400	Paint, 1 coat		350	.023		.10	.67		.77	1.21
8450	2 coats		400	.020		.20	.58		.78	1.18
8600	Balustrades, primer coat, oil base, brushwork		520	.015		.06	.45		.51	.81
8650	Paint, 1 coat		520	.015		.10	.45		.55	.85
8700	2 coats		325	.025		.20	.72		.92	1.41
8900	Trusses and wood frames, primer coat, oil base, brushwork		800	.010		.06	.29		.35	.55
8950	Spray		1200	.007		.07	.19		.26	.39
9000	Paint 1 coat, brushwork		750	.011		.10	.31		.41	.62
9200	Spray		1200	.007		.11	.19		.30	.45
9220	Paint 2 coats, brushwork		500	.016		.20	.47		.67	.99
9240	Spray		600	.013		.22	.39		.61	.88
9260	Stain, brushwork, wipe off		600	.013		.10	.39		.49	.74
9280	Varnish, 3 coats, brushwork		275	.029		.25	.85		1.10	1.67
9350	For latex paint, deduct					10%				

09 91 23.72 Walls and Ceilings, Interior

		Crew	Daily Output	Labor-Hours	Unit	Material	2017 Bare Costs Labor	Equipment	Total	Total Incl O&P
0010	**WALLS AND CEILINGS, INTERIOR**									
0100	Concrete, drywall or plaster, latex, primer or sealer coat									
0200	Smooth finish, brushwork	1 Pord	1150	.007	S.F.	.06	.20		.26	.41
0240	Roller		1350	.006		.06	.17		.23	.36
0280	Spray		2750	.003		.06	.09		.15	.20
0300	Sand finish, brushwork		975	.008		.06	.24		.30	.47
0340	Roller		1150	.007		.06	.20		.26	.41
0380	Spray		2275	.004		.06	.10		.16	.23
0400	Paint 1 coat, smooth finish, brushwork		1200	.007		.07	.19		.26	.40
0440	Roller		1300	.006		.07	.18		.25	.38
0480	Spray		2275	.004		.06	.10		.16	.23
0500	Sand finish, brushwork		1050	.008		.06	.22		.28	.44

09 91 23.72 Walls and Ceilings, Interior	Crew	Daily Output	Labor-Hours	Unit	Material	2017 Bare Costs Labor	Equipment	Total	Total Incl O&P
0540	Roller	1 Pord	1600	.005	S.F.	.07	.15		.22	.32
0580	Spray		2100	.004		.02	.11		.13	.21
0800	Paint 2 coats, smooth finish, brushwork		680	.012		.14	.34		.48	.72
0840	Roller		800	.010		.14	.29		.43	.63
0880	Spray		1625	.005		.13	.14		.27	.38
0900	Sand finish, brushwork		605	.013		.14	.39		.53	.79
0940	Roller		1020	.008		.14	.23		.37	.53
0980	Spray		1700	.005		.13	.14		.27	.37
1200	Paint 3 coats, smooth finish, brushwork		510	.016		.21	.46		.67	.99
1240	Roller		650	.012		.21	.36		.57	.82
1280	Spray		850	.009		.19	.27		.46	.66
1300	Sand finish, brushwork		454	.018		.32	.51		.83	1.20
1340	Roller		680	.012		.34	.34		.68	.95
1380	Spray		1133	.007		.29	.21		.50	.66
1600	Glaze coating, 2 coats, spray, clear		1200	.007		.49	.19		.68	.86
1640	Multicolor		1200	.007		1.05	.19		1.24	1.47
1660	Painting walls, complete, including surface prep, primer &									
1670	2 coats finish, on drywall or plaster, with roller	1 Pord	325	.025	S.F.	.21	.72		.93	1.42
1700	For oil base paint, add					10%				
1800	For ceiling installations, add						25%			
2000	Masonry or concrete block, primer/sealer, latex paint									
2100	Primer, smooth finish, brushwork	1 Pord	1000	.008	S.F.	.15	.23		.38	.55
2110	Roller		1150	.007		.11	.20		.31	.46
2180	Spray		2400	.003		.10	.10		.20	.27
2200	Sand finish, brushwork		850	.009		.11	.27		.38	.57
2210	Roller		975	.008		.11	.24		.35	.52
2280	Spray		2050	.004		.10	.11		.21	.30
2400	Finish coat, smooth finish, brush		1100	.007		.08	.21		.29	.44
2410	Roller		1300	.006		.08	.18		.26	.39
2480	Spray		2400	.003		.07	.10		.17	.24
2500	Sand finish, brushwork		950	.008		.08	.25		.33	.50
2510	Roller		1090	.007		.08	.21		.29	.44
2580	Spray		2040	.004		.07	.11		.18	.27
2800	Primer plus one finish coat, smooth brush		525	.015		.30	.45		.75	1.06
2810	Roller		615	.013		.19	.38		.57	.84
2880	Spray		1200	.007		.17	.19		.36	.51
2900	Sand finish, brushwork		450	.018		.19	.52		.71	1.07
2910	Roller		515	.016		.19	.45		.64	.96
2980	Spray		1025	.008		.17	.23		.40	.57
3200	Primer plus 2 finish coats, smooth, brush		355	.023		.27	.66		.93	1.39
3210	Roller		415	.019		.27	.56		.83	1.23
3280	Spray		800	.010		.24	.29		.53	.74
3300	Sand finish, brushwork		305	.026		.27	.77		1.04	1.56
3310	Roller		350	.023		.27	.67		.94	1.40
3380	Spray		675	.012		.24	.35		.59	.83
3600	Glaze coating, 3 coats, spray, clear		900	.009		.70	.26		.96	1.20
3620	Multicolor		900	.009		1.23	.26		1.49	1.78
4000	Block filler, 1 coat, brushwork		425	.019		.12	.55		.67	1.05
4100	Silicone, water repellent, 2 coats, spray		2000	.004		.37	.12		.49	.60
4120	For oil base paint, add					10%				
8200	For work 8' - 15' H, add						10%			
8300	For work over 15' H, add						20%			
8400	For light textured surfaces, add						10%			

516

For customer support on your Residential Costs with RSMeans Data, call 800.448.8182.

09 91 Painting

09 91 23 – Interior Painting

09 91 23.72 Walls and Ceilings, Interior

	Crew	Daily Output	Labor-Hours	Unit	Material	2017 Bare Costs Labor	Equipment	Total	Total Incl O&P
8410 Heavy textured, add				S.F.		25%			

09 91 23.74 Walls and Ceilings, Interior, Zero VOC Latex

		Crew	Daily Output	Labor-Hours	Unit	Material	2017 Bare Costs Labor	Equipment	Total	Total Incl O&P
0010	**WALLS AND CEILINGS, INTERIOR, ZERO VOC LATEX**									
0100	Concrete, dry wall or plaster, latex, primer or sealer coat									
0200	Smooth finish, brushwork	G 1 Pord	1150	.007	S.F.	.07	.20		.27	.41
0240	Roller	G	1350	.006		.06	.17		.23	.36
0280	Spray	G	2750	.003		.05	.09		.14	.19
0300	Sand finish, brushwork	G	975	.008		.06	.24		.30	.47
0340	Roller	G	1150	.007		.07	.20		.27	.42
0380	Spray	G	2275	.004		.05	.10		.15	.23
0400	Paint 1 coat, smooth finish, brushwork	G	1200	.007		.08	.19		.27	.40
0440	Roller	G	1300	.006		.08	.18		.26	.38
0480	Spray	G	2275	.004		.07	.10		.17	.24
0500	Sand finish, brushwork	G	1050	.008		.07	.22		.29	.45
0540	Roller	G	1600	.005		.08	.15		.23	.32
0580	Spray	G	2100	.004		.07	.11		.18	.25
0800	Paint 2 coats, smooth finish, brushwork	G	680	.012		.15	.34		.49	.73
0840	Roller	G	800	.010		.15	.29		.44	.65
0880	Spray	G	1625	.005		.13	.14		.27	.38
0900	Sand finish, brushwork	G	605	.013		.14	.39		.53	.80
0940	Roller	G	1020	.008		.15	.23		.38	.55
0980	Spray	G	1700	.005		.13	.14		.27	.37
1200	Paint 3 coats, smooth finish, brushwork	G	510	.016		.21	.46		.67	1
1240	Roller	G	650	.012		.23	.36		.59	.84
1280	Spray	G	850	.009		.20	.27		.47	.66
1800	For ceiling installations, add	G					25%			
8200	For work 8' - 15' H, add						10%			
8300	For work over 15' H, add						20%			

09 91 23.75 Dry Fall Painting

		Crew	Daily Output	Labor-Hours	Unit	Material	2017 Bare Costs Labor	Equipment	Total	Total Incl O&P
0010	**DRY FALL PAINTING**									
0100	Sprayed on walls, gypsum board or plaster									
0220	One coat	1 Pord	2600	.003	S.F.	.08	.09		.17	.24
0250	Two coats		1560	.005		.16	.15		.31	.42
0280	Concrete or textured plaster, one coat		1560	.005		.08	.15		.23	.34
0310	Two coats		1300	.006		.16	.18		.34	.47
0340	Concrete block, one coat		1560	.005		.08	.15		.23	.34
0370	Two coats		1300	.006		.16	.18		.34	.47
0400	Wood, one coat		877	.009		.08	.27		.35	.53
0430	Two coats		650	.012		.16	.36		.52	.76
0440	On ceilings, gypsum board or plaster									
0470	One coat	1 Pord	1560	.005	S.F.	.08	.15		.23	.34
0500	Two coats		1300	.006		.16	.18		.34	.47
0530	Concrete or textured plaster, one coat		1560	.005		.08	.15		.23	.34
0560	Two coats		1300	.006		.16	.18		.34	.47
0570	Structural steel, bar joists or metal deck, one coat		1560	.005		.08	.15		.23	.34
0580	Two coats		1040	.008		.16	.22		.38	.54

For customer support on your Residential Costs with RSMeans Data, call 800.448.8182.

517

09 93 Staining and Transparent Finishing

09 93 23 – Interior Staining and Finishing

09 93 23.10 Varnish	Crew	Daily Output	Labor-Hours	Unit	Material	2017 Bare Costs Labor	Equipment	Total	Total Incl O&P
0010 **VARNISH**									
0012 1 coat + sealer, on wood trim, brush, no sanding included	1 Pord	400	.020	S.F.	.07	.58		.65	1.04
0020 1 coat + sealer, on wood trim, brush, no sanding included, no VOC		400	.020		.22	.58		.80	1.20
0100 Hardwood floors, 2 coats, no sanding included, roller		1890	.004		.15	.12		.27	.37

09 96 High-Performance Coatings

09 96 56 – Epoxy Coatings

09 96 56.20 Wall Coatings	Crew	Daily Output	Labor-Hours	Unit	Material	2017 Bare Costs Labor	Equipment	Total	Total Incl O&P
0010 **WALL COATINGS**									
0100 Acrylic glazed coatings, matte	1 Pord	525	.015	S.F.	.32	.45		.77	1.08
0200 Gloss		305	.026		.66	.77		1.43	1.99
0300 Epoxy coatings, solvent based		525	.015		.41	.45		.86	1.18
0400 Water based		170	.047		.29	1.37		1.66	2.59
0600 Exposed aggregate, troweled on, 1/16" to 1/4", solvent based		235	.034		.63	.99		1.62	2.33
0700 Water based (epoxy or polyacrylate)		130	.062		1.36	1.80		3.16	4.47
0900 1/2" to 5/8" aggregate, solvent based		130	.062		1.22	1.80		3.02	4.31
1000 Water based		80	.100		2.12	2.92		5.04	7.15
1200 1" aggregate size, solvent based		90	.089		2.16	2.60		4.76	6.65
1300 Water based		55	.145		3.29	4.25		7.54	10.60
1500 Exposed aggregate, sprayed on, 1/8" aggregate, solvent based		295	.027		.58	.79		1.37	1.95
1600 Water based		145	.055		1.07	1.61		2.68	3.84

Estimating Tips
General
- The items in this division are usually priced per square foot or each.
- Many items in Division 10 require some type of support system or special anchors that are not usually furnished with the item. The required anchors must be added to the estimate in the appropriate division.
- Some items in Division 10, such as lockers, may require assembly before installation. Verify the amount of assembly required. Assembly can often exceed installation time.

10 20 00 Interior Specialties
- Support angles and blocking are not included in the installation of toilet compartments, shower/dressing compartments, or cubicles. Appropriate line items from Division 5 or 6 may need to be added to support the installations.
- Toilet partitions are priced by the stall. A stall consists of a side wall, pilaster, and door with hardware. Toilet tissue holders and grab bars are extra.
- The required acoustical rating of a folding partition can have a significant impact on costs. Verify the sound transmission coefficient rating of the panel priced against the specification requirements.

- Grab bar installation does not include supplemental blocking or backing to support the required load. When grab bars are installed at an existing facility, provisions must be made to attach the grab bars to a solid structure.

Reference Numbers
Reference numbers are shown at the beginning of some major classifications. These numbers refer to related items in the Reference Section. The reference information may be an estimating procedure, an alternate pricing method, or technical information.

Note: Not all subdivisions listed here necessarily appear. ■

10 28 Toilet, Bath, and Laundry Accessories

10 28 13 – Toilet Accessories

10 28 13.13 Commercial Toilet Accessories

10 28 13.13 Commercial Toilet Accessories	Crew	Daily Output	Labor-Hours	Unit	Material	2017 Bare Costs Labor	Equipment	Total	Total Incl O&P
0010 **COMMERCIAL TOILET ACCESSORIES**									
0200 Curtain rod, stainless steel, 5' long, 1" diameter	1 Carp	13	.615	Ea.	28	21.50		49.50	66.50
0300 1-1/4" diameter		13	.615		32.50	21.50		54	71.50
0800 Grab bar, straight, 1-1/4" diameter, stainless steel, 18" long		24	.333		30	11.65		41.65	52.50
1100 36" long		20	.400		35	14		49	62
1105 42" long		20	.400		36.50	14		50.50	63.50
1120 Corner, 36" long		20	.400		93.50	14		107.50	127
3000 Mirror, with stainless steel 3/4" square frame, 18" x 24"		20	.400		47	14		61	75.50
3100 36" x 24"		15	.533		111	18.65		129.65	153
3300 72" x 24"		6	1.333		283	46.50		329.50	390
4300 Robe hook, single, regular		96	.083		21	2.91		23.91	28.50
4400 Heavy duty, concealed mounting		56	.143		23.50	4.99		28.49	34.50
6400 Towel bar, stainless steel, 18" long		23	.348		44.50	12.15		56.65	69.50
6500 30" long		21	.381		61	13.30		74.30	90
7400 Tumbler holder, for tumbler only		30	.267		19.10	9.30		28.40	36.50
7410 Tumbler holder, recessed		20	.400		8	14		22	32.50
7500 Soap, tumbler & toothbrush		30	.267		19.60	9.30		28.90	37
7510 Tumbler & toothbrush holder		20	.400		13.65	14		27.65	38.50

10 28 16 – Bath Accessories

10 28 16.20 Medicine Cabinets

	Crew	Daily Output	Labor-Hours	Unit	Material	2017 Bare Costs Labor	Equipment	Total	Total Incl O&P
0010 **MEDICINE CABINETS**									
0020 With mirror, sst frame, 16" x 22", unlighted	1 Carp	14	.571	Ea.	107	19.95		126.95	152
0100 Wood frame		14	.571		140	19.95		159.95	188
0300 Sliding mirror doors, 20" x 16" x 4-3/4", unlighted		7	1.143		128	40		168	207
0400 24" x 19" x 8-1/2", lighted		5	1.600		189	56		245	300
0600 Triple door, 30" x 32", unlighted, plywood body		7	1.143		350	40		390	450
0700 Steel body		7	1.143		375	40		415	475
0900 Oak door, wood body, beveled mirror, single door		7	1.143		196	40		236	282
1000 Double door		6	1.333		415	46.50		461.50	535

10 28 19 – Tub and Shower Enclosures

10 28 19.10 Partitions, Shower

	Crew	Daily Output	Labor-Hours	Unit	Material	2017 Bare Costs Labor	Equipment	Total	Total Incl O&P
0010 **PARTITIONS, SHOWER** floor mounted, no plumbing									
0400 Cabinet, one piece, fiberglass, 32" x 32"	2 Carp	5	3.200	Ea.	540	112		652	780
0420 36" x 36"		5	3.200		655	112		767	905
0440 36" x 48"		5	3.200		1,375	112		1,487	1,700
0460 Acrylic, 32" x 32"		5	3.200		350	112		462	570
0480 36" x 36"		5	3.200		1,050	112		1,162	1,325
0500 36" x 48"		5	3.200		1,475	112		1,587	1,800
0520 Shower door for above, clear plastic, 24" wide	1 Carp	8	1		192	35		227	271
0540 28" wide		8	1		213	35		248	293
0560 Tempered glass, 24" wide		8	1		205	35		240	285
0580 28" wide		8	1		235	35		270	320
2400 Glass stalls, with doors, no receptors, chrome on brass	2 Shee	3	5.333		1,700	204		1,904	2,225
2700 Anodized aluminum	"	4	4		1,175	153		1,328	1,550
3200 Receptors, precast terrazzo, 32" x 32"	2 Marb	14	1.143		350	39.50		389.50	450
3300 48" x 34"		9.50	1.684		465	58.50		523.50	610
3500 Plastic, simulated terrazzo receptor, 32" x 32"		14	1.143		160	39.50		199.50	243
3600 32" x 48"		12	1.333		230	46		276	330
3800 Precast concrete, colors, 32" x 32"		14	1.143		218	39.50		257.50	305
3900 48" x 48"		8	2		279	69.50		348.50	420
4100 Shower doors, economy plastic, 24" wide	1 Shee	9	.889		144	34		178	215
4200 Tempered glass door, economy		8	1		267	38.50		305.50	360

520

10 28 Toilet, Bath, and Laundry Accessories

10 28 19 – Tub and Shower Enclosures

10 28 19.10 Partitions, Shower	Crew	Daily Output	Labor-Hours	Unit	Material	Labor	Equipment	Total	Total Incl O&P
4400 Folding, tempered glass, aluminum frame	1 Shee	6	1.333	Ea.	420	51		471	545
4700 Deluxe, tempered glass, chrome on brass frame, 42" to 44"		8	1		415	38.50		453.50	520
4800 39" to 48" wide		1	8		700	305		1,005	1,275
4850 On anodized aluminum frame, obscure glass		2	4		575	153		728	885
4900 Clear glass		1	8		700	305		1,005	1,275
5100 Shower enclosure, tempered glass, anodized alum. frame									
5120 2 panel & door, corner unit, 32" x 32"	1 Shee	2	4	Ea.	1,100	153		1,253	1,475
5140 Neo-angle corner unit, 16" x 24" x 16"	"	2	4		1,125	153		1,278	1,475
5200 Shower surround, 3 wall, polypropylene, 32" x 32"	1 Carp	4	2		520	70		590	685
5220 PVC, 32" x 32"		4	2		405	70		475	560
5240 Fiberglass		4	2		420	70		490	575
5250 2 wall, polypropylene, 32" x 32"		4	2		325	70		395	475
5270 PVC		4	2		395	70		465	550
5290 Fiberglass		4	2		400	70		470	555
5300 Tub doors, tempered glass & frame, obscure glass	1 Shee	8	1		234	38.50		272.50	320
5400 Clear glass		6	1.333		545	51		596	685
5600 Chrome plated, brass frame, obscure glass		8	1		310	38.50		348.50	405
5700 Clear glass		6	1.333		755	51		806	920
5900 Tub/shower enclosure, temp. glass, alum. frame, obscure glass		2	4		420	153		573	715
6200 Clear glass		1.50	5.333		875	204		1,079	1,300
6500 On chrome-plated brass frame, obscure glass		2	4		580	153		733	890
6600 Clear glass		1.50	5.333		1,225	204		1,429	1,700
6800 Tub surround, 3 wall, polypropylene	1 Carp	4	2		264	70		334	405
6900 PVC		4	2		390	70		460	545
7000 Fiberglass, obscure glass		4	2		410	70		480	565
7100 Clear glass		3	2.667		695	93		788	920

10 28 23 – Laundry Accessories

10 28 23.13 Built-In Ironing Boards

	Crew	Daily Output	Labor-Hours	Unit	Material	Labor	Equipment	Total	Total Incl O&P
0010 **BUILT-IN IRONING BOARDS**									
0020 Including cabinet, board & light, 42"	1 Carp	2	4	Ea.	455	140		595	735

10 31 Manufactured Fireplaces

10 31 13 – Manufactured Fireplace Chimneys

10 31 13.10 Fireplace Chimneys

	Crew	Daily Output	Labor-Hours	Unit	Material	Labor	Equipment	Total	Total Incl O&P
0010 **FIREPLACE CHIMNEYS**									
0500 Chimney dbl. wall, all stainless, over 8'-6", 7" diam., add to fireplace	1 Carp	33	.242	V.L.F.	87.50	8.45		95.95	110
0600 10" diameter, add to fireplace		32	.250		112	8.75		120.75	139
0700 12" diameter, add to fireplace		31	.258		172	9		181	205
0800 14" diameter, add to fireplace		30	.267		227	9.30		236.30	266
1000 Simulated brick chimney top, 4' high, 16" x 16"		10	.800	Ea.	440	28		468	530
1100 24" x 24"		7	1.143	"	560	40		600	680

10 31 13.20 Chimney Accessories

	Crew	Daily Output	Labor-Hours	Unit	Material	Labor	Equipment	Total	Total Incl O&P
0010 **CHIMNEY ACCESSORIES**									
0020 Chimney screens, galv., 13" x 13" flue	1 Bric	8	1	Ea.	58.50	35		93.50	123
0050 24" x 24" flue		5	1.600		124	56		180	231
0200 Stainless steel, 13" x 13" flue		8	1		97.50	35		132.50	166
0250 20" x 20" flue		5	1.600		152	56		208	261
2400 Squirrel and bird screens, galvanized, 8" x 8" flue		16	.500		60	17.45		77.45	95.50
2450 13" x 13" flue		12	.667		62.50	23		85.50	108

10 31 Manufactured Fireplaces

10 31 16 – Manufactured Fireplace Forms

10 31 16.10 Fireplace Forms	Crew	Daily Output	Labor-Hours	Unit	Material	2017 Bare Costs Labor	Equipment	Total	Total Incl O&P
0010 **FIREPLACE FORMS**									
1800 Fireplace forms, no accessories, 32" opening	1 Bric	3	2.667	Ea.	720	93		813	945
1900 36" opening		2.50	3.200		915	112		1,027	1,175
2000 40" opening		2	4		1,225	139		1,364	1,550
2100 78" opening	↓	1.50	5.333	↓	1,775	186		1,961	2,250

10 31 23 – Prefabricated Fireplaces

10 31 23.10 Fireplace, Prefabricated

	Crew	Daily Output	Labor-Hours	Unit	Material	2017 Bare Costs Labor	Equipment	Total	Total Incl O&P
0010 **FIREPLACE, PREFABRICATED**, free standing or wall hung									
0100 With hood & screen, painted	1 Carp	1.30	6.154	Ea.	1,525	215		1,740	2,025
0150 Average		1	8		1,750	280		2,030	2,400
0200 Stainless steel		.90	8.889		3,200	310		3,510	4,025
1500 Simulated logs, gas fired, 40,000 BTU, 2' long, manual safety pilot		7	1.143	Set	475	40		515	585
1600 Adjustable flame remote pilot		6	1.333		1,250	46.50		1,296.50	1,450
1700 Electric, 1,500 BTU, 1'-6" long, incandescent flame		7	1.143		218	40		258	305
1800 1,500 BTU, LED flame		6	1.333	↓	335	46.50		381.50	445
2000 Fireplace, built-in, 36" hearth, radiant		1.30	6.154	Ea.	700	215		915	1,125
2100 Recirculating, small fan		1	8		905	280		1,185	1,475
2150 Large fan		.90	8.889		2,000	310		2,310	2,725
2200 42" hearth, radiant		1.20	6.667		950	233		1,183	1,450
2300 Recirculating, small fan		.90	8.889		1,225	310		1,535	1,875
2350 Large fan		.80	10		1,400	350		1,750	2,125
2400 48" hearth, radiant		1.10	7.273		2,275	254		2,529	2,925
2500 Recirculating, small fan		.80	10		2,600	350		2,950	3,450
2550 Large fan		.70	11.429		2,700	400		3,100	3,650
3000 See through, including doors		.80	10		2,275	350		2,625	3,075
3200 Corner (2 wall)	↓	1	8	↓	3,700	280		3,980	4,550

10 32 Fireplace Specialties

10 32 13 – Fireplace Dampers

10 32 13.10 Dampers

	Crew	Daily Output	Labor-Hours	Unit	Material	2017 Bare Costs Labor	Equipment	Total	Total Incl O&P
0010 **DAMPERS**									
0800 Damper, rotary control, steel, 30" opening	1 Bric	6	1.333	Ea.	119	46.50		165.50	209
0850 Cast iron, 30" opening		6	1.333		125	46.50		171.50	215
1200 Steel plate, poker control, 60" opening		8	1		320	35		355	415
1250 84" opening, special order		5	1.600		585	56		641	740
1400 "Universal" type, chain operated, 32" x 20" opening		8	1		250	35		285	335
1450 48" x 24" opening	↓	5	1.600	↓	375	56		431	505

10 32 23 – Fireplace Doors

10 32 23.10 Doors

	Crew	Daily Output	Labor-Hours	Unit	Material	2017 Bare Costs Labor	Equipment	Total	Total Incl O&P
0010 **DOORS**									
0400 Cleanout doors and frames, cast iron, 8" x 8"	1 Bric	12	.667	Ea.	47.50	23		70.50	91
0450 12" x 12"		10	.800		89	28		117	145
0500 18" x 24"		8	1		150	35		185	224
0550 Cast iron frame, steel door, 24" x 30"		5	1.600		315	56		371	440
1600 Dutch Oven door and frame, cast iron, 12" x 15" opening		13	.615		131	21.50		152.50	181
1650 Copper plated, 12" x 15" opening	↓	13	.615	↓	257	21.50		278.50	320

10 35 Stoves

10 35 13 – Heating Stoves

10 35 13.10 Woodburning Stoves	Crew	Daily Output	Labor-Hours	Unit	Material	2017 Bare Costs Labor	Equipment	Total	Total Incl O&P
0010 **WOODBURNING STOVES**									
0015 Cast iron, less than 1500 S.F.	2 Carp	1.30	12.308	Ea.	1,300	430		1,730	2,175
0020 1500 to 2000 S.F.		1	16		2,050	560		2,610	3,175
0030 greater than 2,000 S.F.	↓	.80	20		2,800	700		3,500	4,250
0050 For gas log lighter, add				↓	46			46	50.50

10 44 Fire Protection Specialties

10 44 16 – Fire Extinguishers

10 44 16.13 Portable Fire Extinguishers

	Crew	Daily Output	Labor-Hours	Unit	Material	2017 Bare Costs Labor	Equipment	Total	Total Incl O&P
0010 **PORTABLE FIRE EXTINGUISHERS**									
0140 CO_2, with hose and "H" horn, 10 lb.				Ea.	296			296	325
1000 Dry chemical, pressurized									
1040 Standard type, portable, painted, 2-1/2 lb.				Ea.	40.50			40.50	44.50
1080 10 lb.					83.50			83.50	92
1100 20 lb.					136			136	149
1120 30 lb.					405			405	445
2000 ABC all purpose type, portable, 2-1/2 lb.					22.50			22.50	24.50
2080 9-1/2 lb.				↓	49			49	54

10 55 Postal Specialties

10 55 23 – Mail Boxes

10 55 23.10 Mail Boxes

	Crew	Daily Output	Labor-Hours	Unit	Material	2017 Bare Costs Labor	Equipment	Total	Total Incl O&P
0011 **MAIL BOXES**									
1900 Letter slot, residential	1 Carp	20	.400	Ea.	80	14		94	112
2400 Residential, galv. steel, small 20" x 7" x 9"	1 Clab	16	.500		200	13.30		213.30	243
2410 With galv. steel post, 54" long		6	1.333		250	35.50		285.50	335
2420 Large, 24" x 12" x 15"		16	.500		200	13.30		213.30	243
2430 With galv. steel post, 54" long		6	1.333		240	35.50		275.50	325
2440 Decorative, polyethylene, 22" x 10" x 10"		16	.500		60	13.30		73.30	88.50
2450 With alum. post, decorative, 54" long	↓	6	1.333	↓	200	35.50		235.50	280

10 56 Storage Assemblies

10 56 13 – Metal Storage Shelving

10 56 13.10 Shelving

	Crew	Daily Output	Labor-Hours	Unit	Material	2017 Bare Costs Labor	Equipment	Total	Total Incl O&P
0010 **SHELVING**									
0020 Metal, industrial, cross-braced, 3' wide, 12" deep	1 Sswk	175	.046	SF Shlf	7.20	1.76		8.96	11.10
0100 24" deep		330	.024		5.20	.93		6.13	7.40
2200 Wide span, 1600 lb. capacity per shelf, 6' wide, 24" deep		380	.021		6.95	.81		7.76	9.05
2400 36" deep	↓	440	.018	↓	6.10	.70		6.80	7.95
3000 Residential, vinyl covered wire, wardrobe, 12" deep	1 Carp	195	.041	L.F.	15.25	1.43		16.68	19.15
3100 16" deep		195	.041		11	1.43		12.43	14.50
3200 Standard, 6" deep		195	.041		4.49	1.43		5.92	7.35
3300 9" deep		195	.041		6	1.43		7.43	9
3400 12" deep		195	.041		7.90	1.43		9.33	11.10
3500 16" deep		195	.041		18	1.43		19.43	22
3600 20" deep		195	.041		21.50	1.43		22.93	26
3700 Support bracket	↓	80	.100	Ea.	6.40	3.50		9.90	12.90

10 57 Wardrobe and Closet Specialties

10 57 23 – Closet and Utility Shelving

10 57 23.19 Wood Closet and Utility Shelving	Crew	Daily Output	Labor-Hours	Unit	Material	2017 Bare Costs Labor	Equipment	Total	Total Incl O&P
0010 **WOOD CLOSET AND UTILITY SHELVING**									
0020 Pine, clear grade, no edge band, 1" x 8"	1 Carp	115	.070	L.F.	3.21	2.43		5.64	7.60
0100 1" x 10"		110	.073		3.99	2.54		6.53	8.65
0200 1" x 12"		105	.076		4.81	2.66		7.47	9.75
0450 1" x 18"		95	.084		7.20	2.94		10.14	12.85
0460 1" x 24"		85	.094		9.60	3.29		12.89	16.10
0600 Plywood, 3/4" thick with lumber edge, 12" wide		75	.107		1.89	3.73		5.62	8.35
0700 24" wide		70	.114	↓	3.38	3.99		7.37	10.40
0900 Bookcase, clear grade pine, shelves 12" O.C., 8" deep, per S.F. shelf		70	.114	S.F.	10.40	3.99		14.39	18.15
1000 12" deep shelves		65	.123	"	15.65	4.30		19.95	24.50
1200 Adjustable closet rod and shelf, 12" wide, 3' long		20	.400	Ea.	11.60	14		25.60	36.50
1300 8' long		15	.533	"	19.95	18.65		38.60	53
1500 Prefinished shelves with supports, stock, 8" wide		75	.107	L.F.	4.98	3.73		8.71	11.75
1600 10" wide		70	.114	"	5.70	3.99		9.69	12.95

10 73 Protective Covers

10 73 16 – Canopies

10 73 16.10 Canopies, Residential

	Crew	Daily Output	Labor-Hours	Unit	Material	2017 Bare Costs Labor	Equipment	Total	Total Incl O&P
0010 **CANOPIES, RESIDENTIAL** Prefabricated									
0500 Carport, free standing, baked enamel, alum., .032", 40 psf									
0520 16' x 8', 4 posts	2 Carp	3	5.333	Ea.	4,825	186		5,011	5,625
0600 20' x 10', 6 posts		2	8		4,950	280		5,230	5,925
0605 30' x 10', 8 posts		2	8		7,425	280		7,705	8,650
1000 Door canopies, extruded alum., .032", 42" projection, 4' wide	1 Carp	8	1		210	35		245	290
1020 6' wide	"	6	1.333		295	46.50		341.50	405
1040 8' wide	2 Carp	9	1.778		405	62		467	550
1060 10' wide		7	2.286		415	80		495	590
1080 12' wide		5	3.200		655	112		767	905
1200 54" projection, 4' wide	1 Carp	8	1		258	35		293	345
1220 6' wide	"	6	1.333		310	46.50		356.50	425
1240 8' wide	2 Carp	9	1.778		375	62		437	520
1260 10' wide		7	2.286		545	80		625	735
1280 12' wide		5	3.200		590	112		702	835
1300 Painted, add					20%				
1310 Bronze anodized, add					50%				
3000 Window awnings, aluminum, window 3' high, 4' wide	1 Carp	10	.800		133	28		161	193
3020 6' wide	"	8	1		191	35		226	269
3040 9' wide	2 Carp	9	1.778		320	62		382	460
3060 12' wide	"	5	3.200		320	112		432	540
3100 Window, 4' high, 4' wide	1 Carp	10	.800		168	28		196	232
3120 6' wide	"	8	1		242	35		277	325
3140 9' wide	2 Carp	9	1.778		395	62		457	540
3160 12' wide	"	5	3.200		395	112		507	620
3200 Window, 6' high, 4' wide	1 Carp	10	.800		320	28		348	400
3220 6' wide	"	8	1		370	35		405	470
3240 9' wide	2 Carp	9	1.778		970	62		1,032	1,175
3260 12' wide	"	5	3.200		1,275	112		1,387	1,575
3400 Roll-up aluminum, 2'-6" wide	1 Carp	14	.571		181	19.95		200.95	233
3420 3' wide		12	.667		185	23.50		208.50	243
3440 4' wide		10	.800		232	28		260	300
3460 6' wide		8	1		275	35		310	365

10 73 Protective Covers

10 73 16 – Canopies

10 73 16.10 Canopies, Residential	Crew	Daily Output	Labor-Hours	Unit	Material	2017 Bare Costs Labor	Equipment	Total	Total Incl O&P
3480	9' wide	2 Carp	9	1.778	Ea.	380	62		442	525
3500	12' wide	"	5	3.200	↓	505	112		617	745
3600	Window awnings, canvas, 24" drop, 3' wide	1 Carp	30	.267	L.F.	53	9.30		62.30	73.50
3620	4' wide		40	.200		44.50	7		51.50	60.50
3700	30" drop, 3' wide		30	.267		56.50	9.30		65.80	77.50
3720	4' wide		40	.200		47.50	7		54.50	63.50
3740	5' wide		45	.178		43.50	6.20		49.70	58.50
3760	6' wide		48	.167		40.50	5.85		46.35	54.50
3780	8' wide		48	.167		37.50	5.85		43.35	51
3800	10' wide	↓	50	.160	↓	41.50	5.60		47.10	55

10 74 Manufactured Exterior Specialties

10 74 23 – Cupolas

10 74 23.10 Wood Cupolas

		Crew	Daily Output	Labor-Hours	Unit	Material	2017 Bare Costs Labor	Equipment	Total	Total Incl O&P
0010	**WOOD CUPOLAS**									
0020	Stock units, pine, painted, 18" sq., 28" high, alum. roof	1 Carp	4.10	1.951	Ea.	207	68		275	340
0100	Copper roof		3.80	2.105		289	73.50		362.50	445
0300	23" square, 33" high, aluminum roof		3.70	2.162		440	75.50		515.50	610
0400	Copper roof		3.30	2.424		530	84.50		614.50	720
0600	30" square, 37" high, aluminum roof		3.70	2.162		600	75.50		675.50	785
0700	Copper roof		3.30	2.424		715	84.50		799.50	930
0900	Hexagonal, 31" wide, 46" high, copper roof		4	2		930	70		1,000	1,150
1000	36" wide, 50" high, copper roof	↓	3.50	2.286		1,550	80		1,630	1,850
1200	For deluxe stock units, add to above					25%				
1400	For custom built units, add to above			↓		50%	50%			

10 74 33 – Weathervanes

10 74 33.10 Residential Weathervanes

		Crew	Daily Output	Labor-Hours	Unit	Material	2017 Bare Costs Labor	Equipment	Total	Total Incl O&P
0010	**RESIDENTIAL WEATHERVANES**									
0020	Residential types, 18" to 24"	1 Carp	8	1	Ea.	99	35		134	168
0100	24" to 48"	"	2	4	"	1,775	140		1,915	2,175

10 74 46 – Window Wells

10 74 46.10 Area Window Wells

		Crew	Daily Output	Labor-Hours	Unit	Material	2017 Bare Costs Labor	Equipment	Total	Total Incl O&P
0010	**AREA WINDOW WELLS**, Galvanized steel									
0020	20 ga., 3'-2" wide, 1' deep	1 Sswk	29	.276	Ea.	16.95	10.65		27.60	38
0100	2' deep		23	.348		31	13.40		44.40	58.50
0300	16 ga., 3'-2" wide, 1' deep		29	.276		23	10.65		33.65	44.50
0400	3' deep		23	.348		47	13.40		60.40	75.50
0600	Welded grating for above, 15 lb., painted		45	.178		91.50	6.85		98.35	113
0700	Galvanized		45	.178		124	6.85		130.85	149
0900	Translucent plastic cap for above	↓	60	.133	↓	20.50	5.15		25.65	32

For customer support on your Residential Costs with RSMeans Data, call 800.448.8182.

525

10 75 16.10 Flagpoles	Crew	Daily Output	Labor-Hours	Unit	Material	2017 Bare Costs Labor	Equipment	Total	Total Incl O&P
0010 **FLAGPOLES**, ground set									
0050 Not including base or foundation									
0100 Aluminum, tapered, ground set 20' high	K-1	2	8	Ea.	1,075	267	135	1,477	1,775
0200 25' high		1.70	9.412		1,175	315	159	1,649	1,975
0300 30' high		1.50	10.667		1,400	355	180	1,935	2,350
0500 40' high		1.20	13.333		2,975	445	225	3,645	4,275

Estimating Tips
General

- The items in this division are usually priced per square foot or each. Many of these items are purchased by the owner for installation by the contractor. Check the specifications for responsibilities and include time for receiving, storage, installation, and mechanical and electrical hookups in the appropriate divisions.

- Many items in Division 11 require some type of support system that is not usually furnished with the item. Examples of these systems include blocking for the attachment of casework and support angles for ceiling-hung projection screens. The required blocking or supports must be added to the estimate in the appropriate division.

- Some items in Division 11 may require assembly or electrical hookups. Verify the amount of assembly required or the need for a hard electrical connection and add the appropriate costs.

Reference Numbers

Reference numbers are shown at the beginning of some major classifications. These numbers refer to related items in the Reference Section. The reference information may be an estimating procedure, an alternate pricing method, or technical information.

Note: Not all subdivisions listed here necessarily appear. ■

Did you know?

Our online estimating solution gives you the same access to RSMeans' data with 24/7 access:

- Quickly locate costs in the searchable database.
- Build cost lists, estimates, and reports in minutes.
- Adjust costs to any location in the U.S. and Canada with the click of a button.

Start your free trial today at
www.RSMeansOnline.com

11 30 Residential Equipment

11 30 13 – Residential Appliances

11 30 13.15 Cooking Equipment

		Crew	Daily Output	Labor-Hours	Unit	Material	2017 Bare Costs Labor	2017 Bare Costs Equipment	Total	Total Incl O&P
0010	**COOKING EQUIPMENT**									
0020	Cooking range, 30" free standing, 1 oven, minimum	2 Clab	10	1.600	Ea.	485	42.50		527.50	600
0050	Maximum		4	4		1,975	106		2,081	2,350
0150	2 oven, minimum		10	1.600		1,350	42.50		1,392.50	1,550
0200	Maximum	▼	10	1.600		2,675	42.50		2,717.50	3,025
0350	Built-in, 30" wide, 1 oven, minimum	1 Elec	6	1.333		900	53.50		953.50	1,075
0400	Maximum	2 Carp	2	8		1,650	280		1,930	2,300
0500	2 oven, conventional, minimum		4	4		1,350	140		1,490	1,700
0550	1 conventional, 1 microwave, maximum	▼	2	8		2,650	280		2,930	3,375
0700	Free standing, 1 oven, 21" wide range, minimum	2 Clab	10	1.600		515	42.50		557.50	640
0750	21" wide, maximum	"	4	4		610	106		716	850
0900	Countertop cooktops, 4 burner, standard, minimum	1 Elec	6	1.333		340	53.50		393.50	465
0950	Maximum		3	2.667		1,775	107		1,882	2,125
1050	As above, but with grill and griddle attachment, minimum		6	1.333		1,550	53.50		1,603.50	1,800
1100	Maximum		3	2.667		3,825	107		3,932	4,375
1250	Microwave oven, minimum		4	2		119	80.50		199.50	263
1300	Maximum		2	4		475	161		636	790
5380	Oven, built-in, standard		4	2		900	80.50		980.50	1,125
5390	Deluxe	▼	2	4	▼	2,700	161		2,861	3,250

11 30 13.16 Refrigeration Equipment

		Crew	Daily Output	Labor-Hours	Unit	Material	2017 Bare Costs Labor	2017 Bare Costs Equipment	Total	Total Incl O&P
0010	**REFRIGERATION EQUIPMENT**									
2000	Deep freeze, 15 to 23 C.F., minimum	2 Clab	10	1.600	Ea.	595	42.50		637.50	725
2050	Maximum		5	3.200		785	85		870	1,000
2200	30 C.F., minimum		8	2		690	53		743	850
2250	Maximum	▼	3	5.333		850	142		992	1,175
5200	Icemaker, automatic, 20 lb. per day	1 Plum	7	1.143		1,100	45		1,145	1,275
5350	51 lb. per day	"	2	4		1,500	158		1,658	1,900
5450	Refrigerator, no frost, 6 C.F.	2 Clab	15	1.067		240	28.50		268.50	315
5500	Refrigerator, no frost, 10 C.F. to 12 C.F., minimum		10	1.600		515	42.50		557.50	635
5600	Maximum		6	2.667		535	71		606	710
5750	14 C.F. to 16 C.F., minimum		9	1.778		590	47.50		637.50	730
5800	Maximum		5	3.200		715	85		800	925
5950	18 C.F. to 20 C.F., minimum		8	2		750	53		803	910
6000	Maximum		4	4		1,750	106		1,856	2,100
6150	21 C.F. to 29 C.F., minimum		7	2.286		1,175	61		1,236	1,375
6200	Maximum	▼	3	5.333		3,500	142		3,642	4,075
6790	Energy-star qualified, 18 C.F., minimum [G]	2 Carp	4	4		675	140		815	975
6795	Maximum [G]		2	8		1,600	280		1,880	2,225
6797	21.7 C.F., minimum [G]		4	4		1,250	140		1,390	1,600
6799	Maximum [G]	▼	4	4	▼	2,200	140		2,340	2,650

11 30 13.17 Kitchen Cleaning Equipment

		Crew	Daily Output	Labor-Hours	Unit	Material	2017 Bare Costs Labor	2017 Bare Costs Equipment	Total	Total Incl O&P
0010	**KITCHEN CLEANING EQUIPMENT**									
2750	Dishwasher, built-in, 2 cycles, minimum	L-1	4	2.500	Ea.	315	99		414	510
2800	Maximum		2	5		550	198		748	930
2950	4 or more cycles, minimum		4	2.500		415	99		514	625
2960	Average		4	2.500		555	99		654	775
3000	Maximum		2	5		1,250	198		1,448	1,700
3100	Energy-star qualified, minimum [G]		4	2.500		480	99		579	695
3110	Maximum [G]	▼	2	5	▼	1,650	198		1,848	2,150

11 30 Residential Equipment

11 30 13 – Residential Appliances

11 30 13.18 Waste Disposal Equipment

		Crew	Daily Output	Labor-Hours	Unit	Material	2017 Bare Costs Labor	2017 Bare Costs Equipment	Total	Total Incl O&P
0010	**WASTE DISPOSAL EQUIPMENT**									
1750	Compactor, residential size, 4 to 1 compaction, minimum	1 Carp	5	1.600	Ea.	690	56		746	855
1800	Maximum	"	3	2.667		1,150	93		1,243	1,425
3300	Garbage disposal, sink type, minimum	L-1	10	1		97.50	39.50		137	173
3350	Maximum	"	10	1		246	39.50		285.50	335

11 30 13.19 Kitchen Ventilation Equipment

		Crew	Daily Output	Labor-Hours	Unit	Material	2017 Bare Costs Labor	2017 Bare Costs Equipment	Total	Total Incl O&P
0010	**KITCHEN VENTILATION EQUIPMENT**									
4150	Hood for range, 2 speed, vented, 30" wide, minimum	L-3	5	2	Ea.	85.50	72		157.50	214
4200	Maximum		3	3.333		925	120		1,045	1,225
4300	42" wide, minimum		5	2		153	72		225	289
4330	Custom		5	2		1,600	72		1,672	1,900
4350	Maximum		3	3.333		1,950	120		2,070	2,350
4500	For ventless hood, 2 speed, add					22			22	24
4650	For vented 1 speed, deduct from maximum					66			66	72.50

11 30 13.24 Washers

		Crew	Daily Output	Labor-Hours	Unit	Material	2017 Bare Costs Labor	2017 Bare Costs Equipment	Total	Total Incl O&P
0010	**WASHERS**									
6650	Washing machine, automatic, minimum	1 Plum	3	2.667	Ea.	565	105		670	795
6700	Maximum		1	8		1,525	315		1,840	2,200
6750	Energy star qualified, front loading, minimum [G]		3	2.667		670	105		775	915
6760	Maximum [G]		1	8		1,700	315		2,015	2,400
6764	Top loading, minimum [G]		3	2.667		575	105		680	810
6766	Maximum [G]		3	2.667		1,450	105		1,555	1,750

11 30 13.25 Dryers

		Crew	Daily Output	Labor-Hours	Unit	Material	2017 Bare Costs Labor	2017 Bare Costs Equipment	Total	Total Incl O&P
0010	**DRYERS**									
6770	Electric, front loading, energy-star qualified, minimum [G]	L-2	3	5.333	Ea.	645	164		809	985
6780	Maximum [G]	"	2	8		1,525	246		1,771	2,100
7450	Vent kits for dryers	1 Carp	10	.800		40	28		68	91

11 30 15 – Miscellaneous Residential Appliances

11 30 15.13 Sump Pumps

		Crew	Daily Output	Labor-Hours	Unit	Material	2017 Bare Costs Labor	2017 Bare Costs Equipment	Total	Total Incl O&P
0010	**SUMP PUMPS**									
6400	Cellar drainer, pedestal, 1/3 H.P., molded PVC base	1 Plum	3	2.667	Ea.	141	105		246	330
6450	Solid brass	"	2	4	"	300	158		458	590
6460	Sump pump, see also Section 22 14 29.16									

11 30 15.23 Water Heaters

		Crew	Daily Output	Labor-Hours	Unit	Material	2017 Bare Costs Labor	2017 Bare Costs Equipment	Total	Total Incl O&P
0010	**WATER HEATERS**									
6900	Electric, glass lined, 30 gallon, minimum	L-1	5	2	Ea.	970	79.50		1,049.50	1,200
6950	Maximum		3	3.333		1,350	132		1,482	1,700
7100	80 gallon, minimum		2	5		1,800	198		1,998	2,300
7150	Maximum		1	10		2,500	395		2,895	3,400
7180	Gas, glass lined, 30 gallon, minimum	2 Plum	5	3.200		1,725	127		1,852	2,100
7220	Maximum		3	5.333		2,400	211		2,611	3,000
7260	50 gallon, minimum		2.50	6.400		1,875	253		2,128	2,475
7300	Maximum		1.50	10.667		2,600	420		3,020	3,575
7310	Water heater, see also Section 22 33 30.13									

11 30 15.43 Air Quality

		Crew	Daily Output	Labor-Hours	Unit	Material	2017 Bare Costs Labor	2017 Bare Costs Equipment	Total	Total Incl O&P
0010	**AIR QUALITY**									
2450	Dehumidifier, portable, automatic, 15 pint	1 Elec	4	2	Ea.	191	80.50		271.50	340
2550	40 pint		3.75	2.133		218	86		304	380
3550	Heater, electric, built-in, 1250 watt, ceiling type, minimum		4	2		123	80.50		203.50	267
3600	Maximum		3	2.667		194	107		301	390

For customer support on your Residential Costs with RSMeans Data, call 800.448.8182.

529

11 30 Residential Equipment

11 30 15 – Miscellaneous Residential Appliances

11 30 15.43 Air Quality

		Crew	Daily Output	Labor-Hours	Unit	Material	2017 Bare Costs Labor	Equipment	Total	Total Incl O&P
3700	Wall type, minimum	1 Elec	4	2	Ea.	181	80.50		261.50	330
3750	Maximum		3	2.667		186	107		293	380
3900	1500 watt wall type, with blower		4	2		181	80.50		261.50	330
3950	3000 watt		3	2.667		445	107		552	665
4850	Humidifier, portable, 8 gallons per day					157			157	173
5000	15 gallons per day					224			224	246

11 30 33 – Retractable Stairs

11 30 33.10 Disappearing Stairway

		Crew	Daily Output	Labor-Hours	Unit	Material	2017 Bare Costs Labor	Equipment	Total	Total Incl O&P
0010	**DISAPPEARING STAIRWAY** No trim included									
0020	One piece, yellow pine, 8'-0" ceiling	2 Carp	4	4	Ea.	230	140		370	485
0030	9'-0" ceiling		4	4		272	140		412	535
0040	10'-0" ceiling		3	5.333		254	186		440	590
0050	11'-0" ceiling		3	5.333		325	186		511	670
0060	12'-0" ceiling		3	5.333		340	186		526	685
0100	Custom grade, pine, 8'-6" ceiling, minimum	1 Carp	4	2		222	70		292	360
0150	Average		3.50	2.286		245	80		325	405
0200	Maximum		3	2.667		294	93		387	480
0500	Heavy duty, pivoted, from 7'-7" to 12'-10" floor to floor		3	2.667		1,025	93		1,118	1,275
0600	16'-0" ceiling		2	4		1,600	140		1,740	1,975
0800	Economy folding, pine, 8'-6" ceiling		4	2		179	70		249	315
0900	9'-6" ceiling		4	2		207	70		277	345
1100	Automatic electric, aluminum, floor to floor height, 8' to 9'	2 Carp	1	16		9,450	560		10,010	11,300

11 32 Unit Kitchens

11 32 13 – Metal Unit Kitchens

11 32 13.10 Commercial Unit Kitchens

		Crew	Daily Output	Labor-Hours	Unit	Material	2017 Bare Costs Labor	Equipment	Total	Total Incl O&P
0010	**COMMERCIAL UNIT KITCHENS**									
1500	Combination range, refrigerator and sink, 30" wide, minimum	L-1	2	5	Ea.	1,100	198		1,298	1,550
1550	Maximum		1	10		1,350	395		1,745	2,125
1570	60" wide, average		1.40	7.143		1,475	283		1,758	2,100
1590	72" wide, average		1.20	8.333		1,850	330		2,180	2,575

11 41 Foodservice Storage Equipment

11 41 13 – Refrigerated Food Storage Cases

11 41 13.30 Wine Cellar

		Crew	Daily Output	Labor-Hours	Unit	Material	2017 Bare Costs Labor	Equipment	Total	Total Incl O&P
0010	**WINE CELLAR**, refrigerated, Redwood interior, carpeted, walk-in type									
0020	6'-8" high, including racks									
0200	80" W x 48" D for 900 bottles	2 Carp	1.50	10.667	Ea.	4,250	375		4,625	5,300
0250	80" W x 72" D for 1300 bottles		1.33	12.030		5,175	420		5,595	6,400
0300	80" W x 94" D for 1900 bottles		1.17	13.675		6,275	480		6,755	7,700

11 81 Facility Maintenance Equipment

11 81 19 – Vacuum Cleaning Systems

11 81 19.10 Vacuum Cleaning	Crew	Daily Output	Labor-Hours	Unit	Material	2017 Bare Costs Labor	Equipment	Total	Total Incl O&P
0010 **VACUUM CLEANING**									
0020 Central, 3 inlet, residential	1 Skwk	.90	8.889	Total	1,175	320		1,495	1,800
0400 5 inlet system, residential		.50	16		1,675	570		2,245	2,800
0600 7 inlet system, commercial		.40	20		1,900	715		2,615	3,300
0800 9 inlet system, residential	↓	.30	26.667		4,050	955		5,005	6,075
4010 Rule of thumb: First 1200 S.F., installed								1,425	1,575
4020 For each additional S.F., add				S.F.				.26	.26

Division Notes

	CREW	DAILY OUTPUT	LABOR-HOURS	UNIT	BARE COSTS				TOTAL INCL O&P
					MAT.	LABOR	EQUIP.	TOTAL	

Estimating Tips
General

- The items in this division are usually priced per square foot or each. Most of these items are purchased by the owner and installed by the contractor. Do not assume the items in Division 12 will be purchased and installed by the contractor. Check the specifications for responsibilities and include receiving, storage, installation, and mechanical and electrical hookups in the appropriate divisions.

- Some items in this division require some type of support system that is not usually furnished with the item. Examples of these systems include blocking for the attachment of casework and heavy drapery rods. The required blocking must be added to the estimate in the appropriate division.

Reference Numbers

Reference numbers are shown at the beginning of some major classifications. These numbers refer to related items in the Reference Section. The reference information may be an estimating procedure, an alternate pricing method, or technical information.

Note: Not all subdivisions listed here necessarily appear. ■

12 21 Window Blinds

12 21 13 – Horizontal Louver Blinds

12 21 13.13 Metal Horizontal Louver Blinds	Crew	Daily Output	Labor-Hours	Unit	Material	2017 Bare Costs Labor	Equipment	Total	Total Incl O&P
0010 **METAL HORIZONTAL LOUVER BLINDS**									
0020 Horizontal, 1" aluminum slats, solid color, stock	1 Carp	590	.014	S.F.	4.61	.47		5.08	5.85

12 21 13.33 Vinyl Horizontal Louver Blinds	Crew	Daily Output	Labor-Hours	Unit	Material	Labor	Equipment	Total	Total Incl O&P
0010 **VINYL HORIZONTAL LOUVER BLINDS**									
0015 1" composite, 48" wide, 48" high	1 Carp	30	.267	Ea.	37	9.30		46.30	56.50
0020 72" high		30	.267		45.50	9.30		54.80	65.50
0030 60" wide, 60" high		30	.267		54.50	9.30		63.80	75
0040 72" high		30	.267		54.50	9.30		63.80	75
0050 72" wide x 72" high		30	.267		65	9.30		74.30	87

12 22 Curtains and Drapes

12 22 16 – Drapery Track and Accessories

12 22 16.10 Drapery Hardware

	Crew	Daily Output	Labor-Hours	Unit	Material	Labor	Equipment	Total	Total Incl O&P
0010 **DRAPERY HARDWARE**									
0030 Standard traverse, per foot, minimum	1 Carp	59	.136	L.F.	6.35	4.74		11.09	14.95
0100 Maximum		51	.157	"	12.35	5.50		17.85	22.50
0200 Decorative traverse, 28"-48", minimum		22	.364	Ea.	25.50	12.70		38.20	49.50
0220 Maximum		21	.381		56.50	13.30		69.80	84.50
0300 48"-84", minimum		20	.400		27.50	14		41.50	54
0320 Maximum		19	.421		72	14.70		86.70	104
0400 66"-120", minimum		18	.444		38	15.55		53.55	67.50
0420 Maximum		17	.471		110	16.45		126.45	149
0500 84"-156", minimum		16	.500		48.50	17.50		66	82.50
0520 Maximum		15	.533		150	18.65		168.65	196
0600 130"-240", minimum		14	.571		70.50	19.95		90.45	111
0620 Maximum		13	.615		208	21.50		229.50	265
0700 Slide rings, each, minimum					1.28			1.28	1.41
0720 Maximum					2.15			2.15	2.37
4000 Traverse rods, adjustable, 28" to 48"	1 Carp	22	.364		32	12.70		44.70	56.50
4020 48" to 84"		20	.400		40.50	14		54.50	68
4040 66" to 120"		18	.444		49.50	15.55		65.05	80
4060 84" to 156"		16	.500		56	17.50		73.50	90.50
4080 100" to 180"		14	.571		65.50	19.95		85.45	106
4100 228" to 312"		13	.615		90.50	21.50		112	136
4500 Curtain rod, 28" to 48", single		22	.364		7	12.70		19.70	29
4510 Double		22	.364		11.90	12.70		24.60	34.50
4520 48" to 86", single		20	.400		11.95	14		25.95	36.50
4530 Double		20	.400		19.95	14		33.95	45.50
4540 66" to 120", single		18	.444		20	15.55		35.55	48
4550 Double		18	.444		31	15.55		46.55	60.50
4600 Valance, pinch pleated fabric, 12" deep, up to 54" long, minimum					41.50			41.50	45.50
4610 Maximum					103			103	113
4620 Up to 77" long, minimum					73			73	80.50
4630 Maximum					166			166	183
5000 Stationary rods, first 2'					8.45			8.45	9.30

12 23 Interior Shutters

12 23 10 – Wood Interior Shutters

12 23 10.10 Wood Interior Shutters

	Crew	Daily Output	Labor-Hours	Unit	Material	2017 Bare Costs Labor	Equipment	Total	Total Incl O&P
0010 **WOOD INTERIOR SHUTTERS**, louvered									
0200 Two panel, 27" wide, 36" high	1 Carp	5	1.600	Set	161	56		217	272
0300 33" wide, 36" high		5	1.600		208	56		264	325
0500 47" wide, 36" high		5	1.600		279	56		335	400
1000 Four panel, 27" wide, 36" high		5	1.600		160	56		216	270
1100 33" wide, 36" high		5	1.600		205	56		261	320
1300 47" wide, 36" high		5	1.600		274	56		330	395
1400 Plantation shutters, 16" x 48"		5	1.600	Ea.	183	56		239	295
1450 16" x 96"		4	2		300	70		370	445
1460 36" x 96"		3	2.667		660	93		753	880

12 23 10.13 Wood Panels

	Crew	Daily Output	Labor-Hours	Unit	Material	2017 Bare Costs Labor	Equipment	Total	Total Incl O&P
0010 **WOOD PANELS**									
3000 Wood folding panels with movable louvers, 7" x 20" each	1 Carp	17	.471	Pr.	87	16.45		103.45	123
3300 8" x 28" each		17	.471		87	16.45		103.45	123
3450 9" x 36" each		17	.471		100	16.45		116.45	138
3600 10" x 40" each		17	.471		109	16.45		125.45	148
4000 Fixed louver type, stock units, 8" x 20" each		17	.471		94	16.45		110.45	131
4150 10" x 28" each		17	.471		79.50	16.45		95.95	115
4300 12" x 36" each		17	.471		94	16.45		110.45	131
4450 18" x 40" each		17	.471		134	16.45		150.45	176
5000 Insert panel type, stock, 7" x 20" each		17	.471		22	16.45		38.45	51.50
5150 8" x 28" each		17	.471		40	16.45		56.45	71.50
5300 9" x 36" each		17	.471		51	16.45		67.45	83.50
5450 10" x 40" each		17	.471		54.50	16.45		70.95	87.50
5600 Raised panel type, stock, 10" x 24" each		17	.471		110	16.45		126.45	149
5650 12" x 26" each		17	.471		110	16.45		126.45	149
5700 14" x 30" each		17	.471		122	16.45		138.45	162
5750 16" x 36" each		17	.471		134	16.45		150.45	176
6000 For custom built pine, add					22%				
6500 For custom built hardwood blinds, add					42%				

12 24 Window Shades

12 24 13 – Roller Window Shades

12 24 13.10 Shades

	Crew	Daily Output	Labor-Hours	Unit	Material	2017 Bare Costs Labor	Equipment	Total	Total Incl O&P
0010 **SHADES**									
0020 Basswood, roll-up, stain finish, 3/8" slats	1 Carp	300	.027	S.F.	17.85	.93		18.78	21
5011 Insulative shades [G]		125	.064		12.50	2.24		14.74	17.50
6011 Solar screening, fiberglass [G]		85	.094		6.70	3.29		9.99	12.90
8011 Interior insulative shutter									
8111 Stock unit, 15" x 60" [G]	1 Carp	17	.471	Pr.	12.60	16.45		29.05	41.50

For customer support on your Residential Costs with RSMeans Data, call 800.448.8182.

535

12 32 Manufactured Wood Casework

12 32 23 – Hardwood Casework

12 32 23.10 Manufactured Wood Casework, Stock Units	Crew	Daily Output	Labor-Hours	Unit	Material	2017 Bare Costs Labor	Equipment	Total	Total Incl O&P
0010 **MANUFACTURED WOOD CASEWORK, STOCK UNITS**									
0700 Kitchen base cabinets, hardwood, not incl. counter tops,									
0710 24" deep, 35" high, prefinished									
0800 One top drawer, one door below, 12" wide	2 Carp	24.80	.645	Ea.	292	22.50		314.50	360
0820 15" wide		24	.667		305	23.50		328.50	375
0840 18" wide		23.30	.687		330	24		354	405
0860 21" wide		22.70	.705		340	24.50		364.50	415
0880 24" wide		22.30	.717		400	25		425	480
1000 Four drawers, 12" wide		24.80	.645		305	22.50		327.50	380
1020 15" wide		24	.667		310	23.50		333.50	385
1040 18" wide		23.30	.687		345	24		369	415
1060 24" wide		22.30	.717		380	25		405	455
1200 Two top drawers, two doors below, 27" wide		22	.727		435	25.50		460.50	520
1220 30" wide		21.40	.748		475	26		501	565
1240 33" wide		20.90	.766		490	27		517	585
1260 36" wide		20.30	.788		510	27.50		537.50	605
1280 42" wide		19.80	.808		535	28		563	635
1300 48" wide		18.90	.847		575	29.50		604.50	685
1500 Range or sink base, two doors below, 30" wide		21.40	.748		390	26		416	475
1520 33" wide		20.90	.766		420	27		447	505
1540 36" wide		20.30	.788		440	27.50		467.50	530
1560 42" wide		19.80	.808		465	28		493	555
1580 48" wide		18.90	.847		485	29.50		514.50	585
1800 For sink front units, deduct					174			174	191
2000 Corner base cabinets, 36" wide, standard	2 Carp	18	.889		725	31		756	850
2100 Lazy Susan with revolving door	"	16.50	.970		925	34		959	1,075
4000 Kitchen wall cabinets, hardwood, 12" deep with two doors									
4050 12" high, 30" wide	2 Carp	24.80	.645	Ea.	264	22.50		286.50	330
4100 36" wide		24	.667		315	23.50		338.50	385
4400 15" high, 30" wide		24	.667		269	23.50		292.50	335
4420 33" wide		23.30	.687		330	24		354	405
4440 36" wide		22.70	.705		325	24.50		349.50	395
4450 42" wide		22.70	.705		365	24.50		389.50	440
4700 24" high, 30" wide		23.30	.687		360	24		384	435
4720 36" wide		22.70	.705		395	24.50		419.50	475
4740 42" wide		22.30	.717		450	25		475	535
5000 30" high, one door, 12" wide		22	.727		253	25.50		278.50	320
5020 15" wide		21.40	.748		266	26		292	335
5040 18" wide		20.90	.766		292	27		319	365
5060 24" wide		20.30	.788		340	27.50		367.50	420
5300 Two doors, 27" wide		19.80	.808		375	28		403	460
5320 30" wide		19.30	.829		395	29		424	485
5340 36" wide		18.80	.851		455	29.50		484.50	550
5360 42" wide		18.50	.865		490	30		520	590
5380 48" wide		18.40	.870		555	30.50		585.50	660
6000 Corner wall, 30" high, 24" wide		18	.889		390	31		421	480
6050 30" wide		17.20	.930		410	32.50		442.50	510
6100 36" wide		16.50	.970		470	34		504	570
6500 Revolving Lazy Susan		15.20	1.053		530	37		567	640
7000 Broom cabinet, 84" high, 24" deep, 18" wide		10	1.600		725	56		781	895
7500 Oven cabinets, 84" high, 24" deep, 27" wide		8	2		1,100	70		1,170	1,325
7750 Valance board trim		396	.040	L.F.	17.55	1.41		18.96	21.50
7780 Toe kick trim	1 Carp	256	.031	"	3.35	1.09		4.44	5.50

536

For customer support on your Residential Costs with RSMeans Data, call 800.448.8182.

12 32 Manufactured Wood Casework

12 32 23 – Hardwood Casework

12 32 23.10 Manufactured Wood Casework, Stock Units	Crew	Daily Output	Labor-Hours	Unit	Material	2017 Bare Costs Labor	2017 Bare Costs Equipment	Total	Total Incl O&P
7790	Base cabinet corner filler	1 Carp	16	.500	Ea.	47	17.50		64.50	80.50
7800	Cabinet filler, 3" x 24"		20	.400		18.50	14		32.50	44
7810	3" x 30"		20	.400		23	14		37	49
7820	3" x 42"		18	.444		32.50	15.55		48.05	61.50
7830	3" x 80"		16	.500		61.50	17.50		79	97
7850	Cabinet panel		50	.160	S.F.	10.05	5.60		15.65	20.50
9000	For deluxe models of all cabinets, add					40%				
9500	For custom built in place, add					25%	10%			
9558	Rule of thumb, kitchen cabinets not including									
9560	appliances & counter top, minimum	2 Carp	30	.533	L.F.	196	18.65		214.65	247
9600	Maximum	"	25	.640	"	425	22.50		447.50	510

12 32 23.30 Manufactured Wood Casework Vanities

		Crew	Daily Output	Labor-Hours	Unit	Material	2017 Bare Costs Labor	2017 Bare Costs Equipment	Total	Total Incl O&P
0010	**MANUFACTURED WOOD CASEWORK VANITIES**									
8000	Vanity bases, 2 doors, 30" high, 21" deep, 24" wide	2 Carp	20	.800	Ea.	340	28		368	420
8050	30" wide		16	1		405	35		440	505
8100	36" wide		13.33	1.200		395	42		437	505
8150	48" wide		11.43	1.400		515	49		564	650
9000	For deluxe models of all vanities, add to above					40%				
9500	For custom built in place, add to above					25%	10%			

12 32 23.35 Manufactured Wood Casework Hardware

		Crew	Daily Output	Labor-Hours	Unit	Material	2017 Bare Costs Labor	2017 Bare Costs Equipment	Total	Total Incl O&P
0010	**MANUFACTURED WOOD CASEWORK HARDWARE**									
1000	Catches, minimum	1 Carp	235	.034	Ea.	1.30	1.19		2.49	3.42
1020	Average		119.40	.067		4	2.34		6.34	8.30
1040	Maximum		80	.100		7.75	3.50		11.25	14.40
2000	Door/drawer pulls, handles									
2200	Handles and pulls, projecting, metal, minimum	1 Carp	48	.167	Ea.	5.20	5.85		11.05	15.45
2220	Average		42	.190		7.90	6.65		14.55	19.85
2240	Maximum		36	.222		10.65	7.75		18.40	24.50
2300	Wood, minimum		48	.167		5.30	5.85		11.15	15.60
2320	Average		42	.190		7.10	6.65		13.75	18.95
2340	Maximum		36	.222		9.80	7.75		17.55	24
2600	Flush, metal, minimum		48	.167		5.30	5.85		11.15	15.60
2620	Average		42	.190		7.25	6.65		13.90	19.15
2640	Maximum		36	.222		9.90	7.75		17.65	24
3000	Drawer tracks/glides, minimum		48	.167	Pr.	8.95	5.85		14.80	19.60
3020	Average		32	.250		16	8.75		24.75	32
3040	Maximum		24	.333		26	11.65		37.65	48
4000	Cabinet hinges, minimum		160	.050		3.10	1.75		4.85	6.35
4020	Average		95.24	.084		7.60	2.94		10.54	13.25
4040	Maximum		68	.118		11.80	4.11		15.91	19.85

12 34 Manufactured Plastic Casework

12 34 16 – Manufactured Solid-Plastic Casework

12 34 16.10 Outdoor Casework		Crew	Daily Output	Labor-Hours	Unit	Material	2017 Bare Costs Labor	Equipment	Total	Total Incl O&P
0010	**OUTDOOR CASEWORK**									
0020	Cabinet, base, sink/range, 36"	2 Carp	20.30	.788	Ea.	1,725	27.50		1,752.50	1,950
0100	Base, 36"		20.30	.788		1,575	27.50		1,602.50	1,800
0200	Filler strip, 1" x 30"		158	.101		43	3.54		46.54	53

12 36 Countertops

12 36 16 – Metal Countertops

12 36 16.10 Stainless Steel Countertops

		Crew	Daily Output	Labor-Hours	Unit	Material	2017 Bare Costs Labor	Equipment	Total	Total Incl O&P
0010	**STAINLESS STEEL COUNTERTOPS**									
3200	Stainless steel, custom	1 Carp	24	.333	S.F.	159	11.65		170.65	195

12 36 19 – Wood Countertops

12 36 19.10 Maple Countertops

		Crew	Daily Output	Labor-Hours	Unit	Material	2017 Bare Costs Labor	Equipment	Total	Total Incl O&P
0010	**MAPLE COUNTERTOPS**									
2900	Solid, laminated, 1-1/2" thick, no splash	1 Carp	28	.286	L.F.	78.50	10		88.50	103
3000	With square splash		28	.286	"	93.50	10		103.50	120
3400	Recessed cutting block with trim, 16" x 20" x 1"		8	1	Ea.	95.50	35		130.50	164
3411	Replace cutting block only		16	.500	"	71.50	17.50		89	108

12 36 23 – Plastic Countertops

12 36 23.13 Plastic-Laminate-Clad Countertops

		Crew	Daily Output	Labor-Hours	Unit	Material	2017 Bare Costs Labor	Equipment	Total	Total Incl O&P
0010	**PLASTIC-LAMINATE-CLAD COUNTERTOPS**									
0020	Stock, 24" wide w/backsplash, minimum	1 Carp	30	.267	L.F.	16.35	9.30		25.65	33.50
0100	Maximum		25	.320		37.50	11.20		48.70	59.50
0300	Custom plastic, 7/8" thick, aluminum molding, no splash		30	.267		33	9.30		42.30	52
0400	Cove splash		30	.267		31	9.30		40.30	49.50
0600	1-1/4" thick, no splash		28	.286		39	10		49	59
0700	Square splash		28	.286		43	10		53	64
0900	Square edge, plastic face, 7/8" thick, no splash		30	.267		33.50	9.30		42.80	52.50
1000	With splash		30	.267		40	9.30		49.30	59.50
1200	For stainless channel edge, 7/8" thick, add					3.25			3.25	3.58
1300	1-1/4" thick, add					3.87			3.87	4.26
1500	For solid color suede finish, add					4.14			4.14	4.55
1700	For end splash, add				Ea.	18.65			18.65	20.50
1901	For cut outs, standard, add, minimum	1 Carp	32	.250			8.75		8.75	14.60
2000	Maximum		8	1		6.20	35		41.20	65.50
2010	Cut out in backsplash for elec. wall outlet		38	.211			7.35		7.35	12.30
2020	Cut out for sink		20	.400			14		14	23.50
2030	Cut out for stove top		18	.444			15.55		15.55	26
2100	Postformed, including backsplash and front edge		30	.267	L.F.	10.35	9.30		19.65	27
2110	Mitred, add		12	.667	Ea.		23.50		23.50	39
2200	Built-in place, 25" wide, plastic laminate		25	.320	L.F.	43	11.20		54.20	66

12 36 33 – Tile Countertops

12 36 33.10 Ceramic Tile Countertops

		Crew	Daily Output	Labor-Hours	Unit	Material	2017 Bare Costs Labor	Equipment	Total	Total Incl O&P
0010	**CERAMIC TILE COUNTERTOPS**									
2300	Ceramic tile mosaic	1 Carp	25	.320	L.F.	35	11.20		46.20	57

12 36 40 – Stone Countertops

12 36 40.10 Natural Stone Countertops

		Crew	Daily Output	Labor-Hours	Unit	Material	2017 Bare Costs Labor	Equipment	Total	Total Incl O&P
0010	**NATURAL STONE COUNTERTOPS**									
2500	Marble, stock, with splash, 1/2" thick, minimum	1 Bric	17	.471	L.F.	43.50	16.40		59.90	75.50
2700	3/4" thick, maximum		13	.615		109	21.50		130.50	156

12 36 Countertops

12 36 40 – Stone Countertops

12 36 40.10 Natural Stone Countertops	Crew	Daily Output	Labor-Hours	Unit	Material	2017 Bare Costs Labor	Equipment	Total	Total Incl O&P
2800	Granite, average, 1-1/4" thick, 24" wide, no splash	1 Bric	13.01	.615	L.F.	147	21.50		168.50	197

12 36 61 – Simulated Stone Countertops

12 36 61.16 Solid Surface Countertops

		Crew	Daily Output	Labor-Hours	Unit	Material	Labor	Equipment	Total	Total Incl O&P
0010	**SOLID SURFACE COUNTERTOPS**, Acrylic polymer									
2000	Pricing for order of 1 – 50 L.F.									
2100	25" wide, solid colors	2 Carp	20	.800	L.F.	79.50	28		107.50	135
2200	Patterned colors		20	.800		101	28		129	158
2300	Premium patterned colors		20	.800		128	28		156	188
2400	With silicone attached 4" backsplash, solid colors		19	.842		88.50	29.50		118	147
2500	Patterned colors		19	.842		112	29.50		141.50	172
2600	Premium patterned colors		19	.842		140	29.50		169.50	203
2700	With hard seam attached 4" backsplash, solid colors		15	1.067		88.50	37.50		126	160
2800	Patterned colors		15	1.067		112	37.50		149.50	186
2900	Premium patterned colors		15	1.067		140	37.50		177.50	217
3800	Sinks, pricing for order of 1 – 50 units									
3900	Single bowl, hard seamed, solid colors, 13" x 17"	1 Carp	2	4	Ea.	545	140		685	835
4000	10" x 15"		4.55	1.758		252	61.50		313.50	380
4100	Cutouts for sinks		5.25	1.524			53.50		53.50	89

12 36 61.17 Solid Surface Vanity Tops

		Crew	Daily Output	Labor-Hours	Unit	Material	Labor	Equipment	Total	Total Incl O&P
0010	**SOLID SURFACE VANITY TOPS**									
0015	Solid surface, center bowl, 17" x 19"	1 Carp	12	.667	Ea.	201	23.50		224.50	261
0020	19" x 25"		12	.667		206	23.50		229.50	265
0030	19" x 31"		12	.667		241	23.50		264.50	305
0040	19" x 37"		12	.667		281	23.50		304.50	350
0050	22" x 25"		10	.800		370	28		398	450
0060	22" x 31"		10	.800		430	28		458	515
0070	22" x 37"		10	.800		500	28		528	595
0080	22" x 43"		10	.800		575	28		603	680
0090	22" x 49"		10	.800		625	28		653	730
0110	22" x 55"		8	1		705	35		740	835
0120	22" x 61"		8	1		800	35		835	940
0220	Double bowl, 22" x 61"		8	1		900	35		935	1,050
0230	Double bowl, 22" x 73"		8	1		980	35		1,015	1,125
0240	For aggregate colors, add					35%				
0250	For faucets and fittings, see Section 22 41 39.10									

12 36 61.19 Quartz Agglomerate Countertops

		Crew	Daily Output	Labor-Hours	Unit	Material	Labor	Equipment	Total	Total Incl O&P
0010	**QUARTZ AGGLOMERATE COUNTERTOPS**									
0100	25" wide, 4" backsplash, color group A, minimum	2 Carp	15	1.067	L.F.	65	37.50		102.50	134
0110	Maximum		15	1.067		91	37.50		128.50	163
0120	Color group B, minimum		15	1.067		67	37.50		104.50	136
0130	Maximum		15	1.067		95	37.50		132.50	168
0140	Color group C, minimum		15	1.067		78	37.50		115.50	149
0150	Maximum		15	1.067		107	37.50		144.50	181
0160	Color group D, minimum		15	1.067		85	37.50		122.50	156
0170	Maximum		15	1.067		115	37.50		152.50	190

For customer support on your Residential Costs with RSMeans Data, call 800.448.8182.

539

Division Notes

		CREW	DAILY OUTPUT	LABOR-HOURS	UNIT	BARE COSTS				TOTAL INCL O&P
						MAT.	LABOR	EQUIP.	TOTAL	

Estimating Tips
General

- The items and systems in this division are usually estimated, purchased, supplied, and installed as a unit by one or more subcontractors. The estimator must ensure that all parties are operating from the same set of specifications and assumptions, and that all necessary items are estimated and will be provided. Many times the complex items and systems are covered, but the more common ones, such as excavation or a crane, are overlooked for the very reason that everyone assumes nobody could miss them. The estimator should be the central focus and be able to ensure that all systems are complete.

- Another area where problems can develop in this division is at the interface between systems. The estimator must ensure, for instance, that anchor bolts, nuts, and washers are estimated and included for the air-supported structures and pre-engineered buildings to be bolted to their foundations. Utility supply is a common area where essential items or pieces of equipment can be missed or overlooked, because each subcontractor may feel it is another's responsibility. The estimator should also be aware of certain items which may be supplied as part of a package but installed by others, and ensure that the installing contractor's estimate includes the cost of installation. Conversely, the estimator must also ensure that items are not costed by two different subcontractors, resulting in an inflated overall estimate.

13 30 00 Special Structures

- The foundations and floor slab, as well as rough mechanical and electrical, should be estimated, as this work is required for the assembly and erection of the structure. Generally, as noted in the data set, the pre-engineered building comes as a shell. Pricing is based on the size and structural design parameters stated in the reference section. Additional features, such as windows and doors with their related structural framing, must also be included by the estimator. Here again, the estimator must have a clear understanding of the scope of each portion of the work and all the necessary interfaces.

Reference Numbers

Reference numbers are shown at the beginning of some major classifications. These numbers refer to related items in the Reference Section. The reference information may be an estimating procedure, an alternate pricing method, or technical information.

Note: Not all subdivisions listed here necessarily appear. ■

13 11 Swimming Pools

13 11 13 – Below-Grade Swimming Pools

13 11 13.50 Swimming Pools

	13 11 13.50 Swimming Pools	Crew	Daily Output	Labor-Hours	Unit	Material	2017 Bare Costs Labor	Equipment	Total	Total Incl O&P
0010	**SWIMMING POOLS** Residential in-ground, vinyl lined									
0020	Concrete sides, w/equip, sand bottom	B-52	300	.187	SF Surf	26	5.55	2.14	33.69	40.50
0100	Metal or polystyrene sides R131113-20	B-14	410	.117		22	3.32	.89	26.21	30.50
0200	Add for vermiculite bottom				↓	1.67			1.67	1.84
0500	Gunite bottom and sides, white plaster finish									
0600	12' x 30' pool	B-52	145	.386	SF Surf	49	11.45	4.42	64.87	77.50
0720	16' x 32' pool		155	.361		44	10.70	4.13	58.83	71
0750	20' x 40' pool	↓	250	.224	↓	39.50	6.65	2.56	48.71	57
0810	Concrete bottom and sides, tile finish									
0820	12' x 30' pool	B-52	80	.700	SF Surf	49.50	20.50	8	78	97.50
0830	16' x 32' pool		95	.589		40.50	17.45	6.75	64.70	81.50
0840	20' x 40' pool	↓	130	.431	↓	32.50	12.75	4.93	50.18	62.50
1600	For water heating system, see Section 23 52 28.10									
1700	Filtration and deck equipment only, as % of total				Total				20%	20%
1800	Deck equipment, rule of thumb, 20' x 40' pool				SF Pool				1.18	1.30
3000	Painting pools, preparation + 3 coats, 20' x 40' pool, epoxy	2 Pord	.33	48.485	Total	1,825	1,425		3,250	4,325
3100	Rubber base paint, 18 gallons	"	.33	48.485	"	1,325	1,425		2,750	3,775

13 11 23 – On-Grade Swimming Pools

13 11 23.50 Swimming Pools

	13 11 23.50 Swimming Pools	Crew	Daily Output	Labor-Hours	Unit	Material	2017 Bare Costs Labor	Equipment	Total	Total Incl O&P
0010	**SWIMMING POOLS** Residential above ground, steel construction									
0100	Round, 15' dia.	B-80A	3	8	Ea.	840	213	90	1,143	1,375
0120	18' dia.		2.50	9.600		910	255	108	1,273	1,550
0140	21' dia.		2	12		1,050	320	135	1,505	1,825
0160	24' dia.		1.80	13.333		1,150	355	150	1,655	2,000
0180	27' dia.		1.50	16		1,350	425	180	1,955	2,375
0200	30' dia.		1	24		1,500	640	270	2,410	3,025
0220	Oval, 12' x 24'		2.30	10.435		1,575	278	118	1,971	2,325
0240	15' x 30'		1.80	13.333		1,750	355	150	2,255	2,675
0260	18' x 33'	↓	1	24	↓	1,975	640	270	2,885	3,525

13 11 46 – Swimming Pool Accessories

13 11 46.50 Swimming Pool Equipment

	13 11 46.50 Swimming Pool Equipment	Crew	Daily Output	Labor-Hours	Unit	Material	2017 Bare Costs Labor	Equipment	Total	Total Incl O&P
0010	**SWIMMING POOL EQUIPMENT**									
0020	Diving stand, stainless steel, 3 meter	2 Carp	.40	40	Ea.	16,100	1,400		17,500	20,100
0300	1 meter		2.70	5.926		9,775	207		9,982	11,100
0600	Diving boards, 16' long, aluminum		2.70	5.926		4,350	207		4,557	5,150
0700	Fiberglass		2.70	5.926		3,325	207		3,532	4,025
0800	14' long, aluminum		2.70	5.926		3,850	207		4,057	4,600
0850	Fiberglass	↓	2.70	5.926		3,325	207		3,532	4,000
1100	Bulkhead, movable, PVC, 8'-2" wide	2 Clab	8	2		2,475	53		2,528	2,825
1120	7'-9" wide		8	2		2,300	53		2,353	2,625
1140	7'-3" wide		8	2		2,050	53		2,103	2,375
1160	6'-9" wide	↓	8	2		2,050	53		2,103	2,375
1200	Ladders, heavy duty, stainless steel, 2 tread	2 Carp	7	2.286		870	80		950	1,100
1500	4 tread	"	6	2.667		1,150	93		1,243	1,425
2100	Lights, underwater, 12 volt, with transformer, 300 watt	1 Elec	1	8		350	320		670	910
2200	110 volt, 500 watt, standard	"	1	8	↓	293	320		613	845
3000	Pool covers, reinforced vinyl	3 Clab	1800	.013	S.F.	1.20	.35		1.55	1.91
3100	Vinyl, for winter, 400 S.F. max pool surface		3200	.008		.26	.20		.46	.62
3200	With water tubes, 400 S.F. max pool surface	↓	3000	.008		.33	.21		.54	.72
3250	Sealed air bubble polyethylene solar blanket, 16 mils				↓	.33			.33	.36
3300	Slides, tubular, fiberglass, aluminum handrails & ladder, 5'-0", straight	2 Carp	1.60	10	Ea.	3,650	350		4,000	4,600
3320	8'-0", curved	"	3	5.333	"	7,225	186		7,411	8,250

13 12 Fountains

13 12 13 – Exterior Fountains

13 12 13.10 Outdoor Fountains	Crew	Daily Output	Labor-Hours	Unit	Material	2017 Bare Costs Labor	Equipment	Total	Total Incl O&P
0010 **OUTDOOR FOUNTAINS**									
0100 Outdoor fountain, 48" high with bowl and figures	2 Clab	2	8	Ea.	570	213		783	980
0200 Commercial, concrete or cast stone, 40-60" H, simple		2	8		775	213		988	1,200
0220 Average		2	8		1,350	213		1,563	1,825
0240 Ornate		2	8		2,625	213		2,838	3,225
0260 Metal, 72" high		2	8		1,225	213		1,438	1,700
0280 90" high		2	8		1,875	213		2,088	2,400
0300 120" high		2	8		4,950	213		5,163	5,800
0320 Resin or fiberglass, 40-60" H, wall type		2	8		480	213		693	885
0340 Waterfall type		2	8		1,200	213		1,413	1,675

13 12 23 – Interior Fountains

13 12 23.10 Indoor Fountains	Crew	Daily Output	Labor-Hours	Unit	Material	2017 Bare Costs Labor	Equipment	Total	Total Incl O&P
0010 **INDOOR FOUNTAINS**									
0100 Commercial, floor type, resin or fiberglass, lighted, cascade type	2 Clab	2	8	Ea.	296	213		509	680
0120 Tiered type		2	8		284	213		497	665
0140 Waterfall type		2	8		300	213		513	685

13 17 Tubs and Pools

13 17 13 – Hot Tubs

13 17 13.10 Redwood Hot Tub System	Crew	Daily Output	Labor-Hours	Unit	Material	2017 Bare Costs Labor	Equipment	Total	Total Incl O&P
0010 **REDWOOD HOT TUB SYSTEM**									
7050 4' diameter x 4' deep	Q-1	1	16	Ea.	3,225	570		3,795	4,500
7150 6' diameter x 4' deep		.80	20		4,950	710		5,660	6,600
7200 8' diameter x 4' deep		.80	20		7,250	710		7,960	9,150

13 17 33 – Whirlpool Tubs

13 17 33.10 Whirlpool Bath	Crew	Daily Output	Labor-Hours	Unit	Material	2017 Bare Costs Labor	Equipment	Total	Total Incl O&P
0010 **WHIRLPOOL BATH**									
6000 Whirlpool, bath with vented overflow, molded fiberglass									
6100 66" x 36" x 24"	Q-1	1	16	Ea.	3,525	570		4,095	4,825
6400 72" x 36" x 21"		1	16		1,825	570		2,395	2,950
6500 60" x 34" x 21"		1	16		1,800	570		2,370	2,925
6600 72" x 42" x 23"		1	16		2,200	570		2,770	3,375

13 24 Special Activity Rooms

13 24 16 – Saunas

13 24 16.50 Saunas and Heaters	Crew	Daily Output	Labor-Hours	Unit	Material	2017 Bare Costs Labor	Equipment	Total	Total Incl O&P
0010 **SAUNAS AND HEATERS**									
0020 Prefabricated, incl. heater & controls, 7' high, 6' x 4', C/C	L-7	2.20	11.818	Ea.	5,350	355		5,705	6,500
0050 6' x 4', C/P		2	13		4,825	390		5,215	5,950
0400 6' x 5', C/C		2	13		6,025	390		6,415	7,275
0450 6' x 5', C/P		2	13		5,350	390		5,740	6,525
0600 6' x 6', C/C		1.80	14.444		6,325	435		6,760	7,675
0650 6' x 6', C/P		1.80	14.444		5,600	435		6,035	6,900
0800 6' x 9', C/C		1.60	16.250		8,200	490		8,690	9,850
0850 6' x 9', C/P		1.60	16.250		7,150	490		7,640	8,700
1000 8' x 12', C/C		1.10	23.636		10,900	715		11,615	13,200
1050 8' x 12', C/P		1.10	23.636		9,675	715		10,390	11,900
1200 8' x 8', C/C		1.40	18.571		8,600	560		9,160	10,400

For customer support on your Residential Costs with RSMeans Data, call 800.448.8182.

543

13 24 Special Activity Rooms

13 24 16 – Saunas

13 24 16.50 Saunas and Heaters

	13 24 16.50 Saunas and Heaters	Crew	Daily Output	Labor-Hours	Unit	Material	2017 Bare Costs Labor	Equipment	Total	Total Incl O&P
1250	8' x 8', C/P	L-7	1.40	18.571	Ea.	7,650	560		8,210	9,375
1400	8' x 10', C/C		1.20	21.667		9,400	655		10,055	11,400
1450	8' x 10', C/P		1.20	21.667		8,300	655		8,955	10,200
1600	10' x 12', C/C		1	26		12,600	785		13,385	15,200
1650	10' x 12', C/P		1	26		11,400	785		12,185	13,800
1700	Door only, cedar, 2'x6', with 1' x 4' tempered insulated glass window	2 Carp	3.40	4.706		645	164		809	980
1800	Prehung, incl. jambs, pulls & hardware	"	12	1.333		705	46.50		751.50	855
2500	Heaters only (incl. above), wall mounted, to 200 C.F.					800			800	880
2750	To 300 C.F.					1,075			1,075	1,175
3000	Floor standing, to 720 C.F., 10,000 watts, w/controls	1 Elec	3	2.667		2,625	107		2,732	3,075
3250	To 1,000 C.F., 16,000 watts	"	3	2.667		3,900	107		4,007	4,450

13 24 26 – Steam Baths

13 24 26.50 Steam Baths and Components

	13 24 26.50 Steam Baths and Components	Crew	Daily Output	Labor-Hours	Unit	Material	2017 Bare Costs Labor	Equipment	Total	Total Incl O&P
0010	**STEAM BATHS AND COMPONENTS**									
0020	Heater, timer & head, single, to 140 C.F.	1 Plum	1.20	6.667	Ea.	2,325	264		2,589	2,975
0500	To 300 C.F.	"	1.10	7.273		2,600	288		2,888	3,325
2700	Conversion unit for residential tub, including door					3,750			3,750	4,100

13 34 Fabricated Engineered Structures

13 34 13 – Glazed Structures

13 34 13.13 Greenhouses

	13 34 13.13 Greenhouses	Crew	Daily Output	Labor-Hours	Unit	Material	2017 Bare Costs Labor	Equipment	Total	Total Incl O&P
0010	**GREENHOUSES**, Shell only, stock units, not incl. 2' stub walls,									
0020	foundation, floors, heat or compartments									
0300	Residential type, free standing, 8'-6" long x 7'-6" wide	2 Carp	59	.271	SF Flr.	25	9.50		34.50	43.50
0400	10'-6" wide		85	.188		39.50	6.60		46.10	54.50
0600	13'-6" wide		108	.148		46	5.20		51.20	59
0700	17'-0" wide		160	.100		46	3.50		49.50	56.50
0900	Lean-to type, 3'-10" wide		34	.471		44	16.45		60.45	75.50
1000	6'-10" wide		58	.276		29	9.65		38.65	48
1100	Wall mounted to existing window, 3' x 3'	1 Carp	4	2	Ea.	1,850	70		1,920	2,150
1120	4' x 5'	"	3	2.667	"	2,025	93		2,118	2,375
1200	Deluxe quality, free standing, 7'-6" wide	2 Carp	55	.291	SF Flr.	86	10.15		96.15	112
1220	10'-6" wide		81	.198		64.50	6.90		71.40	82.50
1240	13'-6" wide		104	.154		53.50	5.40		58.90	68
1260	17'-0" wide		150	.107		49	3.73		52.73	60
1400	Lean-to type, 3'-10" wide		31	.516		105	18.05		123.05	146
1420	6'-10" wide		55	.291		70.50	10.15		80.65	94.50
1440	8'-0" wide		97	.165		60	5.75		65.75	75.50

13 34 13.19 Swimming Pool Enclosures

	13 34 13.19 Swimming Pool Enclosures	Crew	Daily Output	Labor-Hours	Unit	Material	2017 Bare Costs Labor	Equipment	Total	Total Incl O&P
0010	**SWIMMING POOL ENCLOSURES** Translucent, free standing									
0020	not including foundations, heat or light									
0200	Economy	2 Carp	200	.080	SF Hor.	33.50	2.80		36.30	41.50
0600	Deluxe	"	70	.229	"	93	8		101	115

13 34 63 – Natural Fiber Construction

13 34 63.50 Straw Bale Construction

	13 34 63.50 Straw Bale Construction	Crew	Daily Output	Labor-Hours	Unit	Material	2017 Bare Costs Labor	Equipment	Total	Total Incl O&P
0010	**STRAW BALE CONSTRUCTION**									
2020	Straw bales in walls w/modified post and beam frame [G]	2 Carp	320	.050	S.F.	6	1.75		7.75	9.50

For customer support on your Residential Costs with RSMeans Data, call 800.448.8182.

Estimating Tips
General
- Many products in Division 14 will require some type of support or blocking for installation not included with the item itself. Examples are supports for conveyors or tube systems, attachment points for lifts, and footings for hoists or cranes. Add these supports in the appropriate division.

14 10 00 Dumbwaiters
14 20 00 Elevators
- Dumbwaiters and elevators are estimated and purchased in a method similar to buying a car. The manufacturer has a base unit with standard features. Added to this base unit price will be whatever options the owner or specifications require. Increased load capacity, additional vertical travel, additional stops, higher speed, and cab finish options are items to be considered. When developing an estimate for dumbwaiters and elevators, remember that some items needed by the installers may have to be included as part of the general contract.

Examples are:
- ☐ shaftway
- ☐ rail support brackets
- ☐ machine room
- ☐ electrical supply
- ☐ sill angles
- ☐ electrical connections
- ☐ pits
- ☐ roof penthouses
- ☐ pit ladders

Check the job specifications and drawings before pricing.
- Installation of elevators and handicapped lifts in historic structures can require significant additional costs. The associated structural requirements may involve cutting into and repairing finishes, moldings, flooring, etc. The estimator must account for these special conditions.

14 30 00 Escalators and Moving Walks
- Escalators and moving walks are specialty items installed by specialty contractors. There are numerous options associated with these items. For specific options, contact a manufacturer or contractor. In a method similar to estimating dumbwaiters and elevators, you should verify the extent of general contract work and add items as necessary.

14 40 00 Lifts
14 90 00 Other Conveying Equipment
- Products such as correspondence lifts, chutes, and pneumatic tube systems, as well as other items specified in this subdivision, may require trained installers. The general contractor might not have any choice as to who will perform the installation or when it will be performed. Long lead times are often required for these products, making early decisions in scheduling necessary.

Reference Numbers
Reference numbers are shown at the beginning of some major classifications. These numbers refer to related items in the Reference Section. The reference information may be an estimating procedure, an alternate pricing method, or technical information.

Note: Not all subdivisions listed here necessarily appear. ■

Did you know?

Our online estimating solution gives you the same access to RSMeans' data with 24/7 access:

- Quickly locate costs in the searchable database.
- Build cost lists, estimates, and reports in minutes.
- Adjust costs to any location in the U.S. and Canada with the click of a button.

Start your free trial today at
www.RSMeansOnline.com

14 21 Electric Traction Elevators

14 21 33 - Electric Traction Residential Elevators

14 21 33.20 Residential Elevators	Crew	Daily Output	Labor-Hours	Unit	Material	2017 Bare Costs Labor	Equipment	Total	Total Incl O&P
0010 **RESIDENTIAL ELEVATORS**									
7000 Residential, cab type, 1 floor, 2 stop, economy model	2 Elev	.20	80	Ea.	11,600	4,325		15,925	19,900
7100 Custom model		.10	160		19,600	8,650		28,250	35,600
7200 2 floor, 3 stop, economy model		.12	133		17,200	7,200		24,400	30,700
7300 Custom model	↓	.06	266	↓	28,100	14,400		42,500	54,500

14 42 Wheelchair Lifts

14 42 13 - Inclined Wheelchair Lifts

14 42 13.10 Inclined Wheelchair Lifts and Stairclimbers

	Crew	Daily Output	Labor-Hours	Unit	Material	2017 Bare Costs Labor	Equipment	Total	Total Incl O&P
0010 **INCLINED WHEELCHAIR LIFTS AND STAIRCLIMBERS**									
7700 Stair climber (chair lift), single seat, minimum	2 Elev	1	16	Ea.	5,425	865		6,290	7,350
7800 Maximum	"	.20	80	"	7,425	4,325		11,750	15,200

Estimating Tips

Pipe for fire protection and all uses is located in Subdivisions 21 11 13 and 22 11 13.

The labor adjustment factors listed in Subdivision 22 01 02.20 also apply to Division 21.

Many, but not all, areas in the U.S. require backflow protection in the fire system. Insurance underwriters may have specific requirements for the type of materials to be installed or design requirements based on the hazard to be protected. Local jurisdictions may have requirements not covered by code. It is advisable to be aware of any special conditions.

For your reference, the following is a list of the most applicable Fire Codes and Standards which may be purchased from the NFPA, 1 Batterymarch Park, Quincy, MA 02169-7471.

- NFPA 1: Uniform Fire Code
- NFPA 10: Portable Fire Extinguishers
- NFPA 11: Low-, Medium-, and High-Expansion Foam
- NFPA 12: Carbon Dioxide Extinguishing Systems (Also companion 12A)
- NFPA 13: Installation of Sprinkler Systems (Also companion 13D, 13E, and 13R)
- NFPA 14: Installation of Standpipe and Hose Systems
- NFPA 15: Water Spray Fixed Systems for Fire Protection
- NFPA 16: Installation of Foam-Water Sprinkler and Foam-Water Spray Systems
- NFPA 17: Dry Chemical Extinguishing Systems (Also companion 17A)
- NFPA 18: Wetting Agents
- NFPA 20: Installation of Stationary Pumps for Fire Protection
- NFPA 22: Water Tanks for Private Fire Protection
- NFPA 24: Installation of Private Fire Service Mains and their Appurtenances
- NFPA 25: Inspection, Testing and Maintenance of Water-Based Fire Protection

Reference Numbers

Reference numbers are shown at the beginning of some major classifications. These numbers refer to related items in the Reference Section. The reference information may be an estimating procedure, an alternate pricing method, or technical information.

Note: Not all subdivisions listed here necessarily appear. ∎

Did you know?

Our online estimating solution gives you the same access to RSMeans' data with 24/7 access:

- Quickly locate costs in the searchable database.
- Build cost lists, estimates, and reports in minutes.
- Adjust costs to any location in the U.S. and Canada with the click of a button.

Start your free trial today at
www.RSMeansOnline.com

21 05 Common Work Results for Fire Suppression

21 05 23 – General-Duty Valves for Water-Based Fire-Suppression Piping

21 05 23.50 General-Duty Valves	Crew	Daily Output	Labor-Hours	Unit	Material	2017 Bare Costs Labor	Equipment	Total	Total Incl O&P
0010 **GENERAL-DUTY VALVES**, for water-based fire suppression									
6200 Valves and components									
6210 Wet alarm, includes									
6220 retard chamber, trim, gauges, alarm line strainer									
6260 3" size	Q-12	3	5.333	Ea.	1,775	187		1,962	2,250
6280 4" size	"	2	8		1,925	280		2,205	2,575
6300 6" size	Q-13	4	8	↓	1,825	280		2,105	2,500
6400 Dry alarm, includes									
6405 retard chamber, trim, gauges, alarm line strainer									
6410 1-1/2" size	Q-12	3	5.333	Ea.	4,075	187		4,262	4,775
6420 2" size		3	5.333		4,075	187		4,262	4,775
6430 3" size		3	5.333		3,925	187		4,112	4,600
6440 4" size	↓	2	8		4,425	280		4,705	5,325
6450 6" size	Q-13	3	10.667		5,100	375		5,475	6,225
6460 8" size	"	3	10.667	↓	7,475	375		7,850	8,850
6500 Check, swing, C.I. body, brass fittings, auto. ball drip									
6520 4" size	Q-12	3	5.333	Ea.	380	187		567	725
6800 Check, wafer, butterfly type, C.I. body, bronze fittings									
6820 4" size	Q-12	4	4	Ea.	1,200	140		1,340	1,525
8700 Floor control valve, includes trim and gauges, 2" size		6	2.667		715	93.50		808.50	940
8710 2-1/2" size		6	2.667		695	93.50		788.50	920
8720 3" size		6	2.667		715	93.50		808.50	940
8730 4" size		6	2.667		715	93.50		808.50	940
8740 6" size		5	3.200		715	112		827	970
8800 Flow control valve, includes trim and gauges, 2" size		2	8		4,725	280		5,005	5,675
8820 3" size	↓	1.50	10.667		5,675	375		6,050	6,875
8840 4" size	Q-13	2.80	11.429		5,675	400		6,075	6,900
8860 6" size	"	2	16		7,725	560		8,285	9,425
9200 Pressure operated relief valve, brass body	1 Spri	18	.444	↓	625	17.30		642.30	720
9600 Waterflow indicator, vane type, with recycling retard and									
9610 two single pole retard switches, 2" thru 6" pipe size	1 Spri	8	1	Ea.	163	39		202	245

21 05 53 – Identification For Fire-Suppression Piping and Equipment

21 05 53.50 Identification	Crew	Daily Output	Labor-Hours	Unit	Material	2017 Bare Costs Labor	Equipment	Total	Total Incl O&P
0010 **IDENTIFICATION**, for fire suppression piping and equipment									
3010 Plates and escutcheons for identification of fire dept. service/connections									
3100 Wall mount, round, aluminum									
3110 4"	1 Plum	96	.083	Ea.	22.50	3.30		25.80	30.50
3120 6"	"	96	.083	"	60	3.30		63.30	71.50
3200 Wall mount, round, cast brass									
3210 2-1/2"	1 Plum	70	.114	Ea.	54	4.52		58.52	67
3220 3"		70	.114		63	4.52		67.52	77
3230 4"		70	.114		108	4.52		112.52	126
3240 6"	↓	70	.114	↓	126	4.52		130.52	146
3250 For polished brass, add									
3260 For rough chrome, add									
3270 For polished chrome, add									
3300 Wall mount, square, cast brass									
3310 2-1/2"	1 Plum	70	.114	Ea.	144	4.52		148.52	165
3320 3"	"	70	.114	"	153	4.52		157.52	175
3330 For polished brass, add									
3340 For rough chrome, add									
3350 For polished chrome, add									

21 05 Common Work Results for Fire Suppression

21 05 53 – Identification For Fire-Suppression Piping and Equipment

21 05 53.50 Identification

	Crew	Daily Output	Labor-Hours	Unit	Material	2017 Bare Costs Labor	Equipment	Total	Total Incl O&P
3400 Wall mount, cast brass, multiple outlets									
3410 rect. 2 way	Q-1	5	3.200	Ea.	198	114		312	405
3420 rect. 3 way		4	4		470	142		612	750
3430 rect. 4 way		4	4		585	142		727	880
3440 square 4 way		4	4		585	142		727	880
3450 rect. 6 way		3	5.333		800	190		990	1,200
3460 For polished brass, add									
3470 For rough chrome, add									
3480 For polished chrome, add									
3500 Base mount, free standing fdc, cast brass									
3510 4"	1 Plum	60	.133	Ea.	108	5.25		113.25	128
3520 6"	"	60	.133	"	144	5.25		149.25	167
3530 For polished brass, add									
3540 For rough chrome, add									
3550 For polished chrome, add									

21 11 Facility Fire-Suppression Water-Service Piping

21 11 13 – Facility Water Distribution Piping

21 11 13.16 Pipe, Plastic

	Crew	Daily Output	Labor-Hours	Unit	Material	2017 Bare Costs Labor	Equipment	Total	Total Incl O&P
0010 **PIPE, PLASTIC**									
0020 CPVC, fire suppression (C-UL-S, FM, NFPA 13, 13D & 13R)									
0030 Socket joint, no couplings or hangers									
0100 SDR 13.5 (ASTM F442)									
0120 3/4" diameter	Q-12	420	.038	L.F.	1.67	1.34		3.01	4.05
0130 1" diameter		340	.047		2.58	1.65		4.23	5.55
0140 1-1/4" diameter		260	.062		4.10	2.16		6.26	8.10
0150 1-1/2" diameter		190	.084		5.65	2.95		8.60	11.15
0160 2" diameter		140	.114		9	4.01		13.01	16.50
0170 2-1/2" diameter		130	.123		16.65	4.31		20.96	25.50
0180 3" diameter		120	.133		25.50	4.67		30.17	36

21 11 13.18 Pipe Fittings, Plastic

	Crew	Daily Output	Labor-Hours	Unit	Material	2017 Bare Costs Labor	Equipment	Total	Total Incl O&P
0010 **PIPE FITTINGS, PLASTIC**									
0020 CPVC, fire suppression (C-UL-S, FM, NFPA 13, 13D & 13R)									
0030 Socket joint									
0100 90° Elbow									
0120 3/4"	1 Plum	26	.308	Ea.	1.78	12.15		13.93	22
0130 1"		22.70	.352		3.91	13.95		17.86	27.50
0140 1-1/4"		20.20	.396		4.94	15.65		20.59	31.50
0150 1-1/2"		18.20	.440		7	17.40		24.40	36
0160 2"	Q-1	33.10	.483		8.70	17.20		25.90	38
0170 2-1/2"		24.20	.661		16.75	23.50		40.25	57.50
0180 3"		20.80	.769		23	27.50		50.50	70
0200 45° Elbow									
0210 3/4"	1 Plum	26	.308	Ea.	2.45	12.15		14.60	22.50
0220 1"		22.70	.352		2.87	13.95		16.82	26
0230 1-1/4"		20.20	.396		4.15	15.65		19.80	30.50
0240 1-1/2"		18.20	.440		5.80	17.40		23.20	35
0250 2"	Q-1	33.10	.483		7.20	17.20		24.40	36.50
0260 2-1/2"		24.20	.661		12.95	23.50		36.45	53
0270 3"		20.80	.769		18.55	27.50		46.05	65.50
0300 Tee									

For customer support on your Residential Costs with RSMeans Data, call 800.448.8182.

549

21 11 13.18 Pipe Fittings, Plastic		Crew	Daily Output	Labor-Hours	Unit	Material	2017 Bare Costs Labor	Equipment	Total	Total Incl O&P
0310	3/4"	1 Plum	17.30	.462	Ea.	2.45	18.30		20.75	32.50
0320	1"		15.20	.526		4.82	21		25.82	40
0330	1-1/4"		13.50	.593		7.25	23.50		30.75	46.50
0340	1-1/2"		12.10	.661		10.70	26		36.70	55
0350	2"	Q-1	20	.800		15.80	28.50		44.30	64.50
0360	2-1/2"		16.20	.988		25.50	35		60.50	86
0370	3"		13.90	1.151		40	41		81	112
0400	Tee, reducing x any size									
0420	1"	1 Plum	15.20	.526	Ea.	4.09	21		25.09	39
0430	1-1/4"		13.50	.593		7.50	23.50		31	47
0440	1-1/2"		12.10	.661		9.10	26		35.10	53
0450	2"	Q-1	20	.800		15.50	28.50		44	64
0460	2-1/2"		16.20	.988		19.95	35		54.95	80
0470	3"		13.90	1.151		23	41		64	93
0500	Coupling									
0510	3/4"	1 Plum	26	.308	Ea.	1.71	12.15		13.86	22
0520	1"		22.70	.352		2.26	13.95		16.21	25.50
0530	1-1/4"		20.20	.396		3.29	15.65		18.94	29.50
0540	1-1/2"		18.20	.440		4.70	17.40		22.10	33.50
0550	2"	Q-1	33.10	.483		6.35	17.20		23.55	35.50
0560	2-1/2"		24.20	.661		9.70	23.50		33.20	49.50
0570	3"		20.80	.769		12.60	27.50		40.10	59
0600	Coupling, reducing									
0610	1" x 3/4"	1 Plum	22.70	.352	Ea.	2.26	13.95		16.21	25.50
0620	1-1/4" x 1"		20.20	.396		3.42	15.65		19.07	30
0630	1-1/2" x 3/4"		18.20	.440		5.15	17.40		22.55	34
0640	1-1/2" x 1"		18.20	.440		4.94	17.40		22.34	34
0650	1-1/2" x 1-1/4"		18.20	.440		4.70	17.40		22.10	33.50
0660	2" x 1"	Q-1	33.10	.483		6.60	17.20		23.80	36
0670	2" x 1-1/2"	"	33.10	.483		6.35	17.20		23.55	35.50
0700	Cross									
0720	3/4"	1 Plum	13	.615	Ea.	3.84	24.50		28.34	44
0730	1"		11.30	.708		4.82	28		32.82	51.50
0740	1-1/4"		10.10	.792		6.65	31.50		38.15	59
0750	1-1/2"		9.10	.879		9.20	35		44.20	67.50
0760	2"	Q-1	16.60	.964		15	34.50		49.50	73
0770	2-1/2"	"	12.10	1.322		33	47		80	114
0800	Cap									
0820	3/4"	1 Plum	52	.154	Ea.	1.04	6.10		7.14	11.20
0830	1"		45	.178		1.47	7.05		8.52	13.20
0840	1-1/4"		40	.200		2.38	7.90		10.28	15.65
0850	1-1/2"		36.40	.220		3.29	8.70		11.99	17.95
0860	2"	Q-1	66	.242		4.94	8.65		13.59	19.70
0870	2-1/2"		48.40	.331		7.15	11.75		18.90	27.50
0880	3"		41.60	.385		11.50	13.70		25.20	35
0900	Adapter, sprinkler head, female w/metal thd. insert (s x FNPT)									
0920	3/4" x 1/2"	1 Plum	52	.154	Ea.	4.61	6.10		10.71	15.10
0930	1" x 1/2"		45	.178		4.86	7.05		11.91	16.95
0940	1" x 3/4"		45	.178		7.65	7.05		14.70	20

21 11 Facility Fire-Suppression Water-Service Piping

21 11 16 – Facility Fire Hydrants

21 11 16.50 Fire Hydrants for Buildings	Crew	Daily Output	Labor-Hours	Unit	Material	2017 Bare Costs Labor	Equipment	Total	Total Incl O&P
0010 **FIRE HYDRANTS FOR BUILDINGS**									
3750 Hydrants, wall, w/caps, single, flush, polished brass									
3800 2-1/2" x 2-1/2"	Q-12	5	3.200	Ea.	248	112		360	460
3840 2-1/2" x 3"		5	3.200		500	112		612	735
3860 3" x 3"	↓	4.80	3.333	↓	405	117		522	640
3900 For polished chrome, add				↓	20%				
3950 Double, flush, polished brass									
4000 2-1/2" x 2-1/2" x 4"	Q-12	5	3.200	Ea.	765	112		877	1,025
4040 2-1/2" x 2-1/2" x 6"		4.60	3.478		875	122		997	1,150
4080 3" x 3" x 4"		4.90	3.265		1,125	114		1,239	1,450
4120 3" x 3" x 6"	↓	4.50	3.556		1,600	125		1,725	1,950
4200 For polished chrome, add				↓	10%				
4350 Double, projecting, polished brass									
4400 2-1/2" x 2-1/2" x 4"	Q-12	5	3.200	Ea.	296	112		408	510
4450 2-1/2" x 2-1/2" x 6"	"	4.60	3.478	"	605	122		727	865
4460 Valve control, dbl. flush/projecting hydrant, cap &									
4470 chain, extension rod & cplg., escutcheon, polished brass	Q-12	8	2	Ea.	272	70		342	415
4480 Four-way square, flush, polished brass									
4540 2-1/2" (4) x 6"	Q-12	3.60	4.444	Ea.	3,575	156		3,731	4,200

21 11 19 – Fire-Department Connections

21 11 19.50 Connections for the Fire-Department	Crew	Daily Output	Labor-Hours	Unit	Material	2017 Bare Costs Labor	Equipment	Total	Total Incl O&P
0010 **CONNECTIONS FOR THE FIRE-DEPARTMENT**									
4000 Storz type, with cap and chain									
6000 Roof manifold, horiz., brass, without valves & caps									
6040 2-1/2" x 2-1/2" x 4"	Q-12	4.80	3.333	Ea.	188	117		305	400
6060 2-1/2" x 2-1/2" x 6"		4.60	3.478		205	122		327	425
6080 2-1/2" x 2-1/2" x 2-1/2" x 4"		4.60	3.478		300	122		422	530
6090 2-1/2" x 2-1/2" x 2-1/2" x 6"	↓	4.60	3.478		310	122		432	540
7000 Sprinkler line tester, cast brass				↓	33.50			33.50	36.50
7140 Standpipe connections, wall, w/plugs & chains									
7160 Single, flush, brass, 2-1/2" x 2-1/2"	Q-12	5	3.200	Ea.	188	112		300	390
7180 2-1/2" x 3"	"	5	3.200	"	196	112		308	400
7240 For polished chrome, add					15%				
7280 Double, flush, polished brass									
7300 2-1/2" x 2-1/2" x 4"	Q-12	5	3.200	Ea.	655	112		767	905
7330 2-1/2" x 2-1/2" x 6"		4.60	3.478		890	122		1,012	1,175
7340 3" x 3" x 4"		4.90	3.265		1,025	114		1,139	1,325
7370 3" x 3" x 6"	↓	4.50	3.556	↓	1,250	125		1,375	1,575
7400 For polished chrome, add					15%				
7440 For sill cock combination, add				Ea.	96			96	105
7580 Double projecting, polished brass									
7600 2-1/2" x 2-1/2" x 4"	Q-12	5	3.200	Ea.	535	112		647	770
7630 2-1/2" x 2-1/2" x 6"	"	4.60	3.478	"	890	122		1,012	1,175
7680 For polished chrome, add					15%				
7900 Three way, flush, polished brass									
7920 2-1/2" (3) x 4"	Q-12	4.80	3.333	Ea.	1,950	117		2,067	2,350
7930 2-1/2" (3) x 6"	"	4.60	3.478	"	2,000	122		2,122	2,400
8000 For polished chrome, add				↓	9%				
8020 Three way, projecting, polished brass									
8040 2-1/2" (3) x 4"	Q-12	4.80	3.333	Ea.	850	117		967	1,125
8070 2-1/2" (3) x 6"	"	4.60	3.478	↓	1,750	122		1,872	2,125
8100 For polished chrome, add					12%				

21 11 Facility Fire-Suppression Water-Service Piping

21 11 19 – Fire-Department Connections

21 11 19.50 Connections for the Fire-Department

		Crew	Daily Output	Labor-Hours	Unit	Material	2017 Bare Costs Labor	Equipment	Total	Total Incl O&P
8200	Four way, square, flush, polished brass,									
8240	2-1/2" (4) x 6"	Q-12	3.60	4.444	Ea.	1,500	156		1,656	1,900
8300	For polished chrome, add				"	10%				
8550	Wall, vertical, flush, cast brass									
8600	Two way, 2-1/2" x 2-1/2" x 4"	Q-12	5	3.200	Ea.	395	112		507	620
8660	Four way, 2-1/2" (4) x 6"		3.80	4.211		1,325	148		1,473	1,700
8680	Six way, 2-1/2" (6) x 6"		3.40	4.706		1,550	165		1,715	2,000
8700	For polished chrome, add					10%				
8800	Free standing siamese unit, polished brass, two way									
8820	2-1/2" x 2-1/2" x 4"	Q-12	2.50	6.400	Ea.	735	224		959	1,175
8850	2-1/2" x 2-1/2" x 6"		2	8		915	280		1,195	1,475
8860	3" x 3" x 4"		2.50	6.400		500	224		724	920
8890	3" x 3" x 6"		2	8		1,325	280		1,605	1,925
8940	For polished chrome, add					12%				
9100	Free standing siamese unit, polished brass, three way									
9120	2-1/2" x 2-1/2" x 2-1/2" x 6"	Q-12	2	8	Ea.	950	280		1,230	1,525
9160	For polished chrome, add				"	15%				

21 12 Fire-Suppression Standpipes

21 12 19 – Fire-Suppression Hose Racks

21 12 19.50 Fire Hose Racks

		Crew	Daily Output	Labor-Hours	Unit	Material	2017 Bare Costs Labor	Equipment	Total	Total Incl O&P
0010	**FIRE HOSE RACKS**									
2600	Hose rack, swinging, for 1-1/2" diameter hose,									
2620	Enameled steel, 50' & 75' lengths of hose	Q-12	20	.800	Ea.	69	28		97	123
2640	100' and 125' lengths of hose		20	.800		86	28		114	141
2680	Chrome plated, 50' and 75' lengths of hose		20	.800		79.50	28		107.50	134
2700	100' and 125' lengths of hose		20	.800		139	28		167	200
2780	For hose rack nipple, 1-1/2" polished brass, add					30			30	33
2820	2-1/2" polished brass, add					58			58	63.50
2840	1-1/2" polished chrome, add					34			34	37.50
2860	2-1/2" polished chrome, add					58			58	64

21 12 23 – Fire-Suppression Hose Valves

21 12 23.70 Fire Hose Valves

		Crew	Daily Output	Labor-Hours	Unit	Material	2017 Bare Costs Labor	Equipment	Total	Total Incl O&P
0010	**FIRE HOSE VALVES**									
0020	Angle, combination pressure adjust/restricting, rough brass									
0030	1-1/2"	1 Spri	12	.667	Ea.	96	26		122	149
0040	2-1/2"	"	7	1.143	"	208	44.50		252.50	305
0042	Nonpressure adjustable/restricting, rough brass									
0044	1-1/2"	1 Spri	12	.667	Ea.	67	26		93	117
0046	2-1/2"	"	7	1.143	"	95.50	44.50		140	179
0050	For polished brass, add					30%				
0060	For polished chrome, add					40%				
1000	Ball drip, automatic, rough brass, 1/2"	1 Spri	20	.400	Ea.	23.50	15.60		39.10	51.50
1010	3/4"	"	20	.400	"	18.70	15.60		34.30	46.50
1100	Ball, 175 lb., sprinkler system, FM/UL, threaded, bronze									
1120	Slow close									
1150	1" size	1 Spri	19	.421	Ea.	246	16.40		262.40	298
1160	1-1/4" size		15	.533		266	21		287	330
1170	1-1/2" size		13	.615		380	24		404	455
1180	2" size		11	.727		425	28.50		453.50	515

21 12 Fire-Suppression Standpipes

21 12 23 – Fire-Suppression Hose Valves

21 12 23.70 Fire Hose Valves

		Crew	Daily Output	Labor-Hours	Unit	Material	2017 Bare Costs Labor	Equipment	Total	Total Incl O&P
1190	2-1/2" size	Q-12	15	1.067	Ea.	575	37.50		612.50	690
1230	For supervisory switch kit, all sizes									
1240	One circuit, add	1 Spri	48	.167	Ea.	169	6.50		175.50	197
1280	Quarter turn for trim									
1300	1/2" size	1 Spri	22	.364	Ea.	33.50	14.15		47.65	60
1310	3/4" size		20	.400		35.50	15.60		51.10	65.50
1320	1" size		19	.421		39.50	16.40		55.90	70.50
1330	1-1/4" size		15	.533		65	21		86	106
1340	1-1/2" size		13	.615		81.50	24		105.50	129
1350	2" size		11	.727		97	28.50		125.50	154
1400	Caps, polished brass with chain, 3/4"					44.50			44.50	49
1420	1"					57			57	62.50
1440	1-1/2"					20.50			20.50	22.50
1460	2-1/2"					31			31	34
1480	3"					38.50			38.50	42
1900	Escutcheon plate, for angle valves, polished brass, 1-1/2"					15.20			15.20	16.70
1920	2-1/2"					24.50			24.50	27
1940	3"					31			31	34
1980	For polished chrome, add					15%				
3000	Gate, hose, wheel handle, N.R.S., rough brass, 1-1/2"	1 Spri	12	.667		154	26		180	212
3040	2-1/2", 300 lb.	"	7	1.143		222	44.50		266.50	320
3080	For polished brass, add					40%				
3090	For polished chrome, add					50%				
5000	Pressure reducing rough brass, 1-1/2"	1 Spri	12	.667		340	26		366	420
5020	2-1/2"	"	7	1.143		480	44.50		524.50	605
5080	For polished brass, add					105%				
5090	For polished chrome, add					140%				

21 13 Fire-Suppression Sprinkler Systems

21 13 13 – Wet-Pipe Sprinkler Systems

21 13 13.50 Wet-Pipe Sprinkler System Components

		Crew	Daily Output	Labor-Hours	Unit	Material	2017 Bare Costs Labor	Equipment	Total	Total Incl O&P
0010	**WET-PIPE SPRINKLER SYSTEM COMPONENTS**									
1100	Alarm, electric pressure switch (circuit closer)	1 Spri	26	.308	Ea.	105	12		117	136
1140	For explosion proof, max 20 PSI, contacts close or open		26	.308		660	12		672	745
1220	Water motor, complete with gong		4	2		445	78		523	620
1900	Flexible sprinkler head connectors									
1910	Braided stainless steel hose with mounting bracket									
1920	1/2" and 3/4" outlet size									
1940	40" length	1 Spri	30	.267	Ea.	76	10.40		86.40	101
1960	60" length	"	22	.364	"	87.50	14.15		101.65	120
1982	May replace hard-pipe armovers									
1984	for wet and pre-action systems.									
2000	Release, emergency, manual, for hydraulic or pneumatic system	1 Spri	12	.667	Ea.	235	26		261	300
2060	Release, thermostatic, for hydraulic or pneumatic release line		20	.400		730	15.60		745.60	825
2200	Sprinkler cabinets, 6 head capacity		16	.500		85.50	19.50		105	126
2260	12 head capacity		16	.500		90.50	19.50		110	132
2340	Sprinkler head escutcheons, standard, brass tone, 1" size		40	.200		3.09	7.80		10.89	16.30
2360	Chrome, 1" size		40	.200		3.29	7.80		11.09	16.50
2400	Recessed type, bright brass		40	.200		10.90	7.80		18.70	25
2440	Chrome or white enamel		40	.200		3.63	7.80		11.43	16.90
2600	Sprinkler heads, not including supply piping									

21 13 13.50 Wet-Pipe Sprinkler System Components		Crew	Daily Output	Labor-Hours	Unit	Material	2017 Bare Costs Labor	Equipment	Total	Total Incl O&P
3700	Standard spray, pendent or upright, brass, 135°F to 286°F									
3720	1/2" NPT, 3/8" orifice	1 Spri	16	.500	Ea.	16.20	19.50		35.70	50
3730	1/2" NPT, 7/16" orifice		16	.500		16	19.50		35.50	49.50
3732	1/2" NPT, 7/16" orifice, chrome		16	.500		16.80	19.50		36.30	50.50
3740	1/2" NPT, 1/2" orifice		16	.500		10.40	19.50		29.90	43.50
3760	1/2" NPT, 17/32" orifice		16	.500		13.50	19.50		33	47
3780	3/4" NPT, 17/32" orifice		16	.500		12.45	19.50		31.95	45.50
3840	For chrome, add					3.70			3.70	4.07
4200	Sidewall, vertical brass, 135°F to 286°F									
4240	1/2" NPT, 1/2" orifice	1 Spri	16	.500	Ea.	26.50	19.50		46	61.50
4280	3/4" NPT, 17/32" orifice	"	16	.500		74	19.50		93.50	113
4360	For satin chrome, add					3.70			3.70	4.07
4500	Sidewall, horizontal, brass, 135°F to 286°F									
4520	1/2" NPT, 1/2" orifice	1 Spri	16	.500	Ea.	26.50	19.50		46	61.50
5600	Concealed, complete with cover plate									
5620	1/2" NPT, 1/2" orifice, 135°F to 212°F	1 Spri	9	.889	Ea.	25.50	34.50		60	85
6025	Residential sprinkler components (one and two family)									
6026	Water motor alarm with strainer	1 Spri	4	2	Ea.	445	78		523	620
6027	Fast response, glass bulb, 135°F to 155°F									
6028	1/2" NPT, pendent, brass	1 Spri	16	.500	Ea.	28.50	19.50		48	63.50
6029	1/2" NPT, sidewall, brass		16	.500		28.50	19.50		48	63.50
6030	1/2" NPT, pendent, brass, extended coverage		16	.500		25	19.50		44.50	59.50
6031	1/2" NPT, sidewall, brass, extended coverage		16	.500		25	19.50		44.50	59.50
6032	3/4" NPT sidewall, brass, extended coverage		16	.500		25.50	19.50		45	60
6033	For chrome, add					15%				
6034	For polyester/teflon coating add					20%				
6100	Sprinkler head wrenches, standard head				Ea.	26			26	28.50
6120	Recessed head					39.50			39.50	43.50
6160	Tamper switch (valve supervisory switch)	1 Spri	16	.500		238	19.50		257.50	294
6165	Flow switch (valve supervisory switch)	"	16	.500		238	19.50		257.50	294

21 13 16 – Dry-Pipe Sprinkler Systems

21 13 16.50 Dry-Pipe Sprinkler System Components		Crew	Daily Output	Labor-Hours	Unit	Material	2017 Bare Costs Labor	Equipment	Total	Total Incl O&P
0010	**DRY-PIPE SPRINKLER SYSTEM COMPONENTS**									
0600	Accelerator	1 Spri	8	1	Ea.	820	39		859	965
0800	Air compressor for dry pipe system, automatic, complete									
0820	30 gal. system capacity, 3/4 HP	1 Spri	1.30	6.154	Ea.	860	240		1,100	1,350
0860	30 gal. system capacity, 1 HP		1.30	6.154		860	240		1,100	1,350
0960	Air pressure maintenance control		24	.333		375	13		388	430
1600	Dehydrator package, incl. valves and nipples		12	.667		770	26		796	890
2600	Sprinkler heads, not including supply piping									
2640	Dry, pendent, 1/2" orifice, 3/4" or 1" NPT									
2660	1/2" to 6" length	1 Spri	14	.571	Ea.	132	22.50		154.50	182
2670	6-1/4" to 8" length		14	.571		137	22.50		159.50	187
2680	8-1/4" to 12" length		14	.571		143	22.50		165.50	194
2800	For each inch or fraction, add					3.70			3.70	4.07
6330	Valves and components									
6340	Alarm test/shut off valve, 1/2"	1 Spri	20	.400	Ea.	23.50	15.60		39.10	51.50
8000	Dry pipe air check valve, 3" size	Q-12	2	8		1,925	280		2,205	2,575
8200	Dry pipe valve, incl. trim and gauges, 3" size		2	8		2,800	280		3,080	3,550
8220	4" size		1	16		3,075	560		3,635	4,325
8240	6" size	Q-13	2	16		3,625	560		4,185	4,900
8280	For accelerator trim with gauges, add	1 Spri	8	1		258	39		297	350

For customer support on your Residential Costs with RSMeans Data, call 800.448.8182.

Estimating Tips
22 10 00 Plumbing
Piping and Pumps

This subdivision is primarily basic pipe and related materials. The pipe may be used by any of the mechanical disciplines, i.e., plumbing, fire protection, heating, and air conditioning.

Note: CPVC plastic piping approved for fire protection is located in 21 11 13.

- The labor adjustment factors listed in Subdivision 22 01 02.20 apply throughout Divisions 21, 22, and 23. CAUTION: the correct percentage may vary for the same items. For example, the percentage add for the basic pipe installation should be based on the maximum height that the installer must install for that particular section. If the pipe is to be located 14' above the floor but it is suspended on threaded rod from beams, the bottom flange of which is 18' high (4' rods), then the height is actually 18' and the add is 20%. The pipe cover, however, does not have to go above the 14', and so the add should be 10%.

- Most pipe is priced first as straight pipe with a joint (coupling, weld, etc.) every 10' and a hanger usually every 10'. There are exceptions with hanger spacing such as for cast iron pipe (5')

and plastic pipe (3 per 10'). Following each type of pipe there are several lines listing sizes and the amount to be subtracted to delete couplings and hangers. This is for pipe that is to be buried or supported together on trapeze hangers. The reason that the couplings are deleted is that these runs are usually long, and frequently longer lengths of pipe are used. By deleting the couplings, the estimator is expected to look up and add back the correct reduced number of couplings.

- When preparing an estimate, it may be necessary to approximate the fittings. Fittings usually run between 25% and 50% of the cost of the pipe. The lower percentage is for simpler runs, and the higher number is for complex areas, such as mechanical rooms.

- For historic restoration projects, the systems must be as invisible as possible, and pathways must be sought for pipes, conduit, and ductwork. While installations in accessible spaces (such as basements and attics) are relatively straightforward to estimate, labor costs may be more difficult to determine when delivery systems must be concealed.

22 40 00 Plumbing Fixtures

- Plumbing fixture costs usually require two lines: the fixture itself and its "rough-in, supply, and waste."

- In the Assemblies Section (Plumbing D2010) for the desired fixture, the System Components Group at the center of the page shows the fixture on the first line. The rest of the list (fittings, pipe, tubing, etc.) will total up to what we refer to in the Unit Price section as "Rough-in, supply, waste, and vent." Note that for most fixtures we allow a nominal 5' of tubing to reach from the fixture to a main or riser.

- Remember that gas- and oil-fired units need venting.

Reference Numbers

Reference numbers are shown at the beginning of some major classifications. These numbers refer to related items in the Reference Section. The reference information may be an estimating procedure, an alternate pricing method, or technical information.

Note: Not all subdivisions listed here necessarily appear. ■

22 05 Common Work Results for Plumbing

22 05 05 – Selective Demolition for Plumbing

22 05 05.10 Plumbing Demolition

		Crew	Daily Output	Labor-Hours	Unit	Material	2017 Bare Costs Labor	Equipment	Total	Total Incl O&P
0010	**PLUMBING DEMOLITION**									
1020	Fixtures, including 10' piping									
1101	Bathtubs, cast iron	1 Clab	4	2	Ea.		53		53	89
1121	Fiberglass		6	1.333			35.50		35.50	59.50
1141	Steel		5	1.600			42.50		42.50	71
1200	Lavatory, wall hung	1 Plum	10	.800			31.50		31.50	52
1221	Counter top	1 Clab	16	.500			13.30		13.30	22.50
1301	Sink, single compartment		16	.500			13.30		13.30	22.50
1321	Double		10	.800			21.50		21.50	35.50
1400	Water closet, floor mounted	1 Plum	8	1			39.50		39.50	65
1421	Wall mounted	1 Clab	7	1.143			30.50		30.50	51
2001	Piping, metal, to 1-1/2" diameter		200	.040	L.F.		1.06		1.06	1.78
2051	2" thru 3-1/2" diameter		150	.053			1.42		1.42	2.37
2101	4" thru 6" diameter		100	.080			2.13		2.13	3.56
2160	Plastic pipe with fittings, up thru 1-1/2" diameter	1 Plum	250	.032			1.27		1.27	2.09
2162	2" thru 3" diameter	"	200	.040			1.58		1.58	2.61
2164	4" thru 6" diameter	Q-1	200	.080			2.85		2.85	4.70
2166	8" thru 14" diameter		150	.107			3.80		3.80	6.25
2168	16" diameter		100	.160			5.70		5.70	9.40
3000	Submersible sump pump	1 Plum	24	.333	Ea.		13.20		13.20	21.50
6000	Remove and reset fixtures, easy access		6	1.333			52.50		52.50	87
6100	Difficult access		4	2			79		79	130

22 05 23 – General-Duty Valves for Plumbing Piping

22 05 23.20 Valves, Bronze

		Crew	Daily Output	Labor-Hours	Unit	Material	2017 Bare Costs Labor	Equipment	Total	Total Incl O&P
0010	**VALVES, BRONZE**									
1750	Check, swing, class 150, regrinding disc, threaded									
1860	3/4"	1 Plum	20	.400	Ea.	96	15.80		111.80	131
1870	1"	"	19	.421	"	138	16.65		154.65	180
2850	Gate, N.R.S., soldered, 125 psi									
2940	3/4"	1 Plum	20	.400	Ea.	63	15.80		78.80	95
2950	1"	"	19	.421	"	81.50	16.65		98.15	118
5600	Relief, pressure & temperature, self-closing, ASME, threaded									
5640	3/4"	1 Plum	28	.286	Ea.	206	11.30		217.30	245
5650	1"		24	.333		330	13.20		343.20	380
5660	1-1/4"		20	.400		675	15.80		690.80	770
6400	Pressure, water, ASME, threaded									
6440	3/4"	1 Plum	28	.286	Ea.	153	11.30		164.30	187
6450	1"	"	24	.333	"	287	13.20		300.20	335
6900	Reducing, water pressure									
6920	300 psi to 25-75 psi, threaded or sweat									
6940	1/2"	1 Plum	24	.333	Ea.	435	13.20		448.20	495
6950	3/4"		20	.400		445	15.80		460.80	515
6960	1"		19	.421		690	16.65		706.65	785
8350	Tempering, water, sweat connections									
8400	1/2"	1 Plum	24	.333	Ea.	118	13.20		131.20	152
8440	3/4"	"	20	.400	"	137	15.80		152.80	176
8650	Threaded connections									
8700	1/2"	1 Plum	24	.333	Ea.	141	13.20		154.20	177
8740	3/4"	"	20	.400	"	845	15.80		860.80	955
8800	Water heater water & gas safety shut off									
8810	Protection against a leaking water heater									
8814	Shut off valve	1 Plum	16	.500	Ea.	186	19.80		205.80	238

22 05 Common Work Results for Plumbing

22 05 23 – General-Duty Valves for Plumbing Piping

22 05 23.20 Valves, Bronze		Crew	Daily Output	Labor-Hours	Unit	Material	2017 Bare Costs Labor	Equipment	Total	Total Incl O&P
8818	Water heater dam	1 Plum	32	.250	Ea.	31.50	9.90		41.40	51
8822	Gas control wiring harness	↓	32	.250	↓	24	9.90		33.90	43
8830	Whole house flood safety shut off									
8834	Connections									
8838	3/4" NPT	1 Plum	12	.667	Ea.	935	26.50		961.50	1,075
8842	1" NPT		11	.727		960	29		989	1,100
8846	1-1/4" NPT	↓	10	.800	↓	995	31.50		1,026.50	1,150

22 05 29 – Hangers and Supports for Plumbing Piping and Equipment

22 05 29.10 Hangers & Supp. for Plumb'g/HVAC Pipe/Equip.

		Crew	Daily Output	Labor-Hours	Unit	Material	2017 Bare Costs Labor	Equipment	Total	Total Incl O&P
0010	**HANGERS AND SUPPORTS FOR PLUMB'G/HVAC PIPE/EQUIP.**									
8000	Pipe clamp, plastic, 1/2" CTS	1 Plum	80	.100	Ea.	.23	3.96		4.19	6.75
8010	3/4" CTS		73	.110		.24	4.33		4.57	7.40
8020	1" CTS		68	.118		.53	4.65		5.18	8.25
8080	Economy clamp, 1/4" CTS		175	.046		.04	1.81		1.85	3.02
8090	3/8" CTS		168	.048		.04	1.88		1.92	3.14
8100	1/2" CTS		160	.050		.04	1.98		2.02	3.30
8110	3/4" CTS		145	.055		.05	2.18		2.23	3.66
8200	Half clamp, 1/2" CTS		80	.100		.07	3.96		4.03	6.60
8210	3/4" CTS		73	.110		.10	4.33		4.43	7.25
8300	Suspension clamp, 1/2" CTS		80	.100		.20	3.96		4.16	6.70
8310	3/4" CTS		73	.110		.21	4.33		4.54	7.40
8320	1" CTS		68	.118		.46	4.65		5.11	8.15
8400	Insulator, 1/2" CTS		80	.100		.33	3.96		4.29	6.85
8410	3/4" CTS		73	.110		.34	4.33		4.67	7.50
8420	1" CTS		68	.118		.35	4.65		5	8.05
8500	J hook clamp with nail, 1/2" CTS		240	.033		.11	1.32		1.43	2.29
8501	3/4" CTS	↓	240	.033	↓	.11	1.32		1.43	2.29

22 05 48 – Vibration and Seismic Controls for Plumbing Piping and Equipment

22 05 48.10 Seismic Bracing Supports

		Crew	Daily Output	Labor-Hours	Unit	Material	2017 Bare Costs Labor	Equipment	Total	Total Incl O&P
0010	**SEISMIC BRACING SUPPORTS**									
0020	Clamps									
0030	C-clamp, for mounting on steel beam									
0040	3/8" threaded rod	1 Skwk	160	.050	Ea.	2.41	1.79		4.20	5.65
0050	1/2" threaded rod		160	.050		2.45	1.79		4.24	5.70
0060	5/8" threaded rod		160	.050		3.72	1.79		5.51	7.10
0070	3/4" threaded rod	↓	160	.050	↓	4.58	1.79		6.37	8.05
0100	Brackets									
0110	Beam side or wall malleable iron									
0120	3/8" threaded rod	1 Skwk	48	.167	Ea.	3.74	5.95		9.69	14.10
0130	1/2" threaded rod		48	.167		3.41	5.95		9.36	13.75
0140	5/8" threaded rod		48	.167		10.35	5.95		16.30	21.50
0150	3/4" threaded rod		48	.167		12.10	5.95		18.05	23.50
0160	7/8" threaded rod	↓	48	.167	↓	12.50	5.95		18.45	24
0170	For concrete installation, add						30%			
0180	Wall, welded steel									
0190	0 size 12" wide 18" deep	1 Skwk	34	.235	Ea.	171	8.40		179.40	202
0200	1 size 18" wide 24" deep		34	.235		228	8.40		236.40	265
0210	2 size 24" wide 30" deep	↓	34	.235		299	8.40		307.40	345
0300	Rod, carbon steel									
0310	Continuous thread									
0320	1/4" thread	1 Skwk	144	.056	L.F.	2.18	1.99		4.17	5.75
0330	3/8" thread	↓	144	.056	↓	2.33	1.99		4.32	5.90

For customer support on your Residential Costs with RSMeans Data, call 800.448.8182.

557

22 05 48 – Vibration and Seismic Controls for Plumbing Piping and Equipment

22 05 48.10 Seismic Bracing Supports		Crew	Daily Output	Labor-Hours	Unit	Material	2017 Bare Costs Labor	Equipment	Total	Total Incl O&P
0340	1/2" thread	1 Skwk	144	.056	L.F.	3.67	1.99		5.66	7.35
0350	5/8" thread		144	.056		5.20	1.99		7.19	9.05
0360	3/4" thread		144	.056		9.15	1.99		11.14	13.45
0370	7/8" thread		144	.056		11.50	1.99		13.49	16
0380	For galvanized, add					30%				
0400	Channel, steel									
0410	3/4" x 1-1/2"	1 Skwk	80	.100	L.F.	2.47	3.58		6.05	8.70
0420	1-1/2" x 1-1/2"		70	.114		3.16	4.09		7.25	10.35
0430	1-7/8" x 1-1/2"		60	.133		23	4.77		27.77	33.50
0440	3" x 1-1/2"		50	.160		39.50	5.70		45.20	53
0450	Spring nuts									
0460	3/8"	1 Skwk	100	.080	Ea.	1.49	2.86		4.35	6.45
0470	1/2"	"	80	.100	"	1.69	3.58		5.27	7.85
0500	Welding, field									
0510	Cleaning and welding plates, bars, or rods									
0520	To existing beams, columns, or trusses									
0530	1" weld	1 Skwk	144	.056	Ea.	.23	1.99		2.22	3.58
0540	2" weld		72	.111		.46	3.97		4.43	7.15
0550	3" weld		54	.148		.69	5.30		5.99	9.65
0560	4" weld		36	.222		.92	7.95		8.87	14.35
0570	5" weld		30	.267		1.15	9.55		10.70	17.25
0580	6" weld		24	.333		1.38	11.90		13.28	21.50
0600	Vibration absorbers									
0610	Hangers, neoprene flex									
0620	10-120 lb. capacity	1 Skwk	8	1	Ea.	25.50	36		61.50	88
0630	75-550 lb. capacity		8	1		40.50	36		76.50	105
0640	250-1100 lb. capacity		6	1.333		82.50	47.50		130	171
0650	1000-4000 lb. capacity		6	1.333		147	47.50		194.50	242

22 05 76 – Facility Drainage Piping Cleanouts

22 05 76.10 Cleanouts

		Crew	Daily Output	Labor-Hours	Unit	Material	Labor	Equipment	Total	Total Incl O&P
0010	**CLEANOUTS**									
0060	Floor type									
0080	Round or square, scoriated nickel bronze top									
0100	2" pipe size	1 Plum	10	.800	Ea.	172	31.50		203.50	241
0120	3" pipe size		8	1		280	39.50		319.50	375
0140	4" pipe size		6	1.333		280	52.50		332.50	395

22 05 76.20 Cleanout Tees

		Crew	Daily Output	Labor-Hours	Unit	Material	Labor	Equipment	Total	Total Incl O&P
0010	**CLEANOUT TEES**									
0100	Cast iron, B&S, with countersunk plug									
0220	3" pipe size	1 Plum	3.60	2.222	Ea.	238	88		326	405
0240	4" pipe size	"	3.30	2.424	"	296	96		392	485
0500	For round smooth access cover, same price									
4000	Plastic, tees and adapters. Add plugs									
4010	ABS, DWV									
4020	Cleanout tee, 1-1/2" pipe size	1 Plum	15	.533	Ea.	10.95	21		31.95	47

22 07 Plumbing Insulation

22 07 16 – Plumbing Equipment Insulation

22 07 16.10 Insulation for Plumbing Equipment		Crew	Daily Output	Labor-Hours	Unit	Material	2017 Bare Costs Labor	Equipment	Total	Total Incl O&P
0010	**INSULATION FOR PLUMBING EQUIPMENT**									
2900	Domestic water heater wrap kit									
2920	1-1/2" with vinyl jacket, 20 to 60 gal.	G	1 Plum	8	1	Ea.	16.50	39.50		56	83

22 07 19 – Plumbing Piping Insulation

22 07 19.10 Piping Insulation

		Crew	Daily Output	Labor-Hours	Unit	Material	2017 Bare Costs Labor	Equipment	Total	Total Incl O&P
0010	**PIPING INSULATION**									
0230	Insulated protectors (ADA)									
0235	For exposed piping under sinks or lavatories									
0240	Vinyl coated foam, velcro tabs									
0245	P Trap, 1-1/4" or 1-1/2"	1 Plum	32	.250	Ea.	17	9.90		26.90	35
0260	Valve and supply cover									
0265	1/2", 3/8", and 7/16" pipe size	1 Plum	32	.250	Ea.	16.60	9.90		26.50	34.50
0285	1-1/4" pipe size	"	32	.250	"	13.80	9.90		23.70	31.50
0600	Pipe covering (price copper tube one size less than IPS)									
6600	Fiberglass, with all service jacket									
6840	1" wall, 1/2" iron pipe size	G	Q-14	240	.067	L.F.	.85	2.15		3	4.58
6860	3/4" iron pipe size	G		230	.070		.92	2.24		3.16	4.81
6870	1" iron pipe size	G		220	.073		.99	2.34		3.33	5.05
6900	2" iron pipe size	G		200	.080		1.53	2.58		4.11	6.05
7879	Rubber tubing, flexible closed cell foam									
8100	1/2" wall, 1/4" iron pipe size	G	1 Asbe	90	.089	L.F.	.72	3.18		3.90	6.20
8130	1/2" iron pipe size	G		89	.090		.84	3.22		4.06	6.35
8140	3/4" iron pipe size	G		89	.090		.85	3.22		4.07	6.40
8150	1" iron pipe size	G		88	.091		.82	3.25		4.07	6.40
8170	1-1/2" iron pipe size	G		87	.092		1.49	3.29		4.78	7.25
8180	2" iron pipe size	G		86	.093		1.91	3.33		5.24	7.75
8300	3/4" wall, 1/4" iron pipe size	G		90	.089		.89	3.18		4.07	6.40
8330	1/2" iron pipe size	G		89	.090		1.09	3.22		4.31	6.65
8340	3/4" iron pipe size	G		89	.090		1.54	3.22		4.76	7.15
8350	1" iron pipe size	G		88	.091		1.77	3.25		5.02	7.45
8380	2" iron pipe size	G		86	.093		3.04	3.33		6.37	9
8444	1" wall, 1/2" iron pipe size	G		86	.093		2.32	3.33		5.65	8.20
8445	3/4" iron pipe size	G		84	.095		2.81	3.41		6.22	8.90
8446	1" iron pipe size	G		84	.095		3.39	3.41		6.80	9.55
8447	1-1/4" iron pipe size	G		82	.098		3.75	3.49		7.24	10.05
8448	1-1/2" iron pipe size	G		82	.098		4.88	3.49		8.37	11.25
8449	2" iron pipe size	G		80	.100		6.10	3.58		9.68	12.75
8450	2-1/2" iron pipe size	G		80	.100		7.45	3.58		11.03	14.25
8456	Rubber insulation tape, 1/8" x 2" x 30'	G				Ea.	21			21	23

22 11 Facility Water Distribution

22 11 13 – Facility Water Distribution Piping

22 11 13.23 Pipe/Tube, Copper

		Crew	Daily Output	Labor-Hours	Unit	Material	2017 Bare Costs Labor	Equipment	Total	Total Incl O&P
0010	**PIPE/TUBE, COPPER**, Solder joints									
1000	Type K tubing, couplings & clevis hanger assemblies 10' O.C.									
1180	3/4" diameter	1 Plum	74	.108	L.F.	7.50	4.28		11.78	15.30
1200	1" diameter	"	66	.121	"	12.60	4.79		17.39	22
2000	Type L tubing, couplings & clevis hanger assemblies 10' O.C.									
2140	1/2" diameter	1 Plum	81	.099	L.F.	3.54	3.91		7.45	10.35
2160	5/8" diameter		79	.101		4.99	4.01		9	12.10

For customer support on your Residential Costs with RSMeans Data, call 800.448.8182.

559

22 11 Facility Water Distribution

22 11 13 – Facility Water Distribution Piping

22 11 13.23 Pipe/Tube, Copper

		Crew	Daily Output	Labor-Hours	Unit	Material	2017 Bare Costs Labor	Equipment	Total	Total Incl O&P
2180	3/4" diameter	1 Plum	76	.105	L.F.	4.90	4.16		9.06	12.25
2200	1" diameter		68	.118		9.80	4.65		14.45	18.40
2220	1-1/4" diameter		58	.138		12.25	5.45		17.70	22.50
3000	Type M tubing, couplings & clevis hanger assemblies 10' O.C.									
3140	1/2" diameter	1 Plum	84	.095	L.F.	3.13	3.77		6.90	9.65
3180	3/4" diameter		78	.103		4.18	4.06		8.24	11.30
3200	1" diameter		70	.114		9.05	4.52		13.57	17.45
3220	1-1/4" diameter		60	.133		11.40	5.25		16.65	21.50
3240	1-1/2" diameter		54	.148		14	5.85		19.85	25
3260	2" diameter		44	.182		19.50	7.20		26.70	33.50
4000	Type DWV tubing, couplings & clevis hanger assemblies 10' O.C.									
4100	1-1/4" diameter	1 Plum	60	.133	L.F.	11.40	5.25		16.65	21.50
4120	1-1/2" diameter		54	.148		13.30	5.85		19.15	24.50
4140	2" diameter		44	.182		16.50	7.20		23.70	30
4160	3" diameter	Q-1	58	.276		24.50	9.80		34.30	43
4180	4" diameter	"	40	.400		44.50	14.25		58.75	72.50

22 11 13.25 Pipe/Tube Fittings, Copper

		Crew	Daily Output	Labor-Hours	Unit	Material	2017 Bare Costs Labor	Equipment	Total	Total Incl O&P
0010	**PIPE/TUBE FITTINGS, COPPER**, Wrought unless otherwise noted									
0040	Solder joints, copper x copper									
0070	90° elbow, 1/4"	1 Plum	22	.364	Ea.	3.57	14.40		17.97	27.50
0100	1/2"		20	.400		1.23	15.80		17.03	27.50
0120	3/4"		19	.421		2.75	16.65		19.40	30.50
0250	45° elbow, 1/4"		22	.364		6.35	14.40		20.75	30.50
0280	1/2"		20	.400		2.24	15.80		18.04	28.50
0290	5/8"		19	.421		9.55	16.65		26.20	38
0300	3/4"		19	.421		3.82	16.65		20.47	31.50
0310	1"		16	.500		9.60	19.80		29.40	43
0320	1-1/4"		15	.533		12.85	21		33.85	49
0450	Tee, 1/4"		14	.571		7.15	22.50		29.65	45.50
0480	1/2"		13	.615		2.09	24.50		26.59	42.50
0490	5/8"		12	.667		13.10	26.50		39.60	58
0500	3/4"		12	.667		5.05	26.50		31.55	49
0510	1"		10	.800		15.15	31.50		46.65	68.50
0520	1-1/4"		9	.889		21	35		56	81
0612	Tee, reducing on the outlet, 1/4"		15	.533		11.70	21		32.70	48
0613	3/8"		15	.533		11.30	21		32.30	47.50
0614	1/2"		14	.571		10.45	22.50		32.95	49
0615	5/8"		13	.615		21	24.50		45.50	63
0616	3/4"		12	.667		6.75	26.50		33.25	51
0617	1"		11	.727		18.80	29		47.80	68
0618	1-1/4"		10	.800		22.50	31.50		54	77
0619	1-1/2"		9	.889		24	35		59	84.50
0620	2"		8	1		50.50	39.50		90	121
0621	2-1/2"	Q-1	9	1.778		108	63.50		171.50	223
0622	3"		8	2		112	71		183	240
0623	4"		6	2.667		225	95		320	405
0624	5"		5	3.200		1,225	114		1,339	1,550
0625	6"	Q-2	7	3.429		1,600	118		1,718	1,950
0626	8"	"	6	4		6,475	137		6,612	7,350
0630	Tee, reducing on the run, 1/4"	1 Plum	15	.533		15.10	21		36.10	51.50
0631	3/8"		15	.533		21.50	21		42.50	58.50
0632	1/2"		14	.571		13.60	22.50		36.10	52.50

22 11 13 – Facility Water Distribution Piping

22 11 13.25 Pipe/Tube Fittings, Copper		Crew	Daily Output	Labor-Hours	Unit	Material	2017 Bare Costs Labor	Equipment	Total	Total Incl O&P
0633	5/8"	1 Plum	13	.615	Ea.	21.50	24.50		46	63.50
0634	3/4"		12	.667		17.85	26.50		44.35	63
0635	1"		11	.727		18.45	29		47.45	68
0636	1-1/4"		10	.800		29	31.50		60.50	84
0637	1-1/2"		9	.889		51	35		86	114
0638	2"		8	1		65.50	39.50		105	137
0639	2-1/2"	Q-1	9	1.778		139	63.50		202.50	257
0640	3"		8	2		204	71		275	340
0641	4"		6	2.667		415	95		510	610
0642	5"		5	3.200		1,175	114		1,289	1,475
0643	6"	Q-2	7	3.429		1,775	118		1,893	2,150
0644	8"	"	6	4		7,050	137		7,187	7,975
0650	Coupling, 1/4"	1 Plum	24	.333		.84	13.20		14.04	22.50
0680	1/2"		22	.364		.93	14.40		15.33	24.50
0690	5/8"		21	.381		2.72	15.05		17.77	28
0700	3/4"		21	.381		1.87	15.05		16.92	27
0710	1"		18	.444		3.69	17.60		21.29	33
0715	1-1/4"		17	.471		6.35	18.60		24.95	37.50
2000	DWV, solder joints, copper x copper									
2030	90° Elbow, 1-1/4"	1 Plum	13	.615	Ea.	13.10	24.50		37.60	54.50
2050	1-1/2"		12	.667		17.40	26.50		43.90	62.50
2070	2"		10	.800		28	31.50		59.50	82.50
2090	3"	Q-1	10	1.600		67.50	57		124.50	168
2100	4"	"	9	1.778		325	63.50		388.50	465
2250	Tee, Sanitary, 1-1/4"	1 Plum	9	.889		23	35		58	83.50
2270	1-1/2"		8	1		28.50	39.50		68	96.50
2290	2"		7	1.143		39	45		84	118
2310	3"	Q-1	7	2.286		150	81.50		231.50	299
2330	4"	"	6	2.667		360	95		455	555
2400	Coupling, 1-1/4"	1 Plum	14	.571		5.45	22.50		27.95	43.50
2420	1-1/2"		13	.615		6.75	24.50		31.25	47.50
2440	2"		11	.727		9.40	29		38.40	58
2460	3"	Q-1	11	1.455		22	52		74	110
2480	4"	"	10	1.600		48	57		105	147

22 11 13.44 Pipe, Steel

		Crew	Daily Output	Labor-Hours	Unit	Material	2017 Bare Costs Labor	Equipment	Total	Total Incl O&P
0010	**PIPE, STEEL**									
0050	Schedule 40, threaded, with couplings, and clevis hanger									
0060	assemblies sized for covering, 10' O.C.									
0540	Black, 1/4" diameter	1 Plum	66	.121	L.F.	7.80	4.79		12.59	16.50
0560	1/2" diameter		63	.127		5.95	5		10.95	14.85
0570	3/4" diameter		61	.131		6.25	5.20		11.45	15.40
0580	1" diameter		53	.151		4.58	5.95		10.53	14.90
0590	1-1/4" diameter	Q-1	89	.180		5.40	6.40		11.80	16.50
0600	1-1/2" diameter		80	.200		5.95	7.10		13.05	18.30
0610	2" diameter		64	.250		12.55	8.90		21.45	28.50

22 11 13.45 Pipe Fittings, Steel, Threaded

		Crew	Daily Output	Labor-Hours	Unit	Material	2017 Bare Costs Labor	Equipment	Total	Total Incl O&P
0010	**PIPE FITTINGS, STEEL, THREADED**									
5000	Malleable iron, 150 lb.									
5020	Black									
5040	90° elbow, straight									
5090	3/4"	1 Plum	14	.571	Ea.	4.17	22.50		26.67	42
5100	1"	"	13	.615		7.25	24.50		31.75	48

22 11 13.45 Pipe Fittings, Steel, Threaded		Crew	Daily Output	Labor-Hours	Unit	Material	2017 Bare Costs Labor	Equipment	Total	Total Incl O&P
5120	1-1/2"	Q-1	20	.800	Ea.	15.70	28.50		44.20	64.50
5130	2"	"	18	.889	↓	27	31.50		58.50	82
5450	Tee, straight									
5500	3/4"	1 Plum	9	.889	Ea.	6.65	35		41.65	65.50
5510	1"	"	8	1		11.35	39.50		50.85	77.50
5520	1-1/4"	Q-1	14	1.143		18.40	40.50		58.90	87
5530	1-1/2"	↓	13	1.231		23	44		67	97.50
5540	2"	↓	11	1.455	↓	39	52		91	129
5650	Coupling									
5700	3/4"	1 Plum	18	.444	Ea.	5.60	17.60		23.20	35
5710	1"	"	15	.533		8.40	21		29.40	44
5720	1-1/4"	Q-1	26	.615		10.85	22		32.85	48
5730	1-1/2"	↓	24	.667		14.65	23.50		38.15	55
5740	2"	↓	21	.762	↓	21.50	27		48.50	68.50

22 11 13.74 Pipe, Plastic		Crew	Daily Output	Labor-Hours	Unit	Material	2017 Bare Costs Labor	Equipment	Total	Total Incl O&P
0010	**PIPE, PLASTIC**									
1800	PVC, couplings 10' O.C., clevis hanger assemblies, 3 per 10'									
1820	Schedule 40									
1860	1/2" diameter	1 Plum	54	.148	L.F.	5	5.85		10.85	15.15
1870	3/4" diameter		51	.157		5.30	6.20		11.50	16.10
1880	1" diameter		46	.174		14.40	6.90		21.30	27
1890	1-1/4" diameter		42	.190		15.10	7.55		22.65	29
1900	1-1/2" diameter	↓	36	.222		15.30	8.80		24.10	31.50
1910	2" diameter	Q-1	59	.271		16.55	9.65		26.20	34
1920	2-1/2" diameter		56	.286		10	10.15		20.15	28
1930	3" diameter		53	.302		12.20	10.75		22.95	31
1940	4" diameter	↓	48	.333	↓	30	11.85		41.85	52.50
4100	DWV type, schedule 40, couplings 10' O.C., clevis hanger assy's, 3 per 10'									
4210	ABS, schedule 40, foam core type									
4212	Plain end black									
4214	1-1/2" diameter	1 Plum	39	.205	L.F.	13.90	8.10		22	28.50
4216	2" diameter	Q-1	62	.258		14.20	9.20		23.40	31
4218	3" diameter		56	.286		8.05	10.15		18.20	25.50
4220	4" diameter		51	.314		25	11.15		36.15	46
4222	6" diameter	↓	42	.381	↓	18.55	13.55		32.10	43
4240	To delete coupling & hangers, subtract									
4244	1-1/2" diam. to 6" diam.					43%	48%			
4400	PVC									
4410	1-1/4" diameter	1 Plum	42	.190	L.F.	14.15	7.55		21.70	28
4420	1-1/2" diameter	"	36	.222		13.85	8.80		22.65	30
4460	2" diameter	Q-1	59	.271		14.25	9.65		23.90	31.50
4470	3" diameter		53	.302		8.05	10.75		18.80	26.50
4480	4" diameter	↓	48	.333		10.05	11.85		21.90	30.50
5300	CPVC, socket joint, couplings 10' O.C., clevis hanger assemblies, 3 per 10'									
5302	Schedule 40									
5304	1/2" diameter	1 Plum	54	.148	L.F.	6.20	5.85		12.05	16.45
5305	3/4" diameter		51	.157		7	6.20		13.20	17.95
5306	1" diameter		46	.174		17.05	6.90		23.95	30
5307	1-1/4" diameter		42	.190		18.65	7.55		26.20	33
5308	1-1/2" diameter	↓	36	.222		18.55	8.80		27.35	35
5309	2" diameter	Q-1	59	.271	↓	20	9.65		29.65	38
5360	CPVC, threaded, couplings 10' O.C., clevis hanger assemblies, 3 per 10'									

22 11 13.74 Pipe, Plastic	Crew	Daily Output	Labor-Hours	Unit	Material	2017 Bare Costs Labor	2017 Bare Costs Equipment	Total	Total Incl O&P
5380	Schedule 40									
5460	1/2" diameter	1 Plum	54	.148	L.F.	7	5.85		12.85	17.35
5470	3/4" diameter		51	.157		8.40	6.20		14.60	19.45
5480	1" diameter		46	.174		18.50	6.90		25.40	32
5490	1-1/4" diameter		42	.190		19.75	7.55		27.30	34
5500	1-1/2" diameter		36	.222		19.50	8.80		28.30	36
5510	2" diameter	Q-1	59	.271		21.50	9.65		31.15	39.50
6500	Residential installation, plastic pipe									
6510	Couplings 10' O.C., strap hangers 3 per 10'									
6520	PVC, Schedule 40									
6530	1/2" diameter	1 Plum	138	.058	L.F.	.95	2.29		3.24	4.83
6540	3/4" diameter		128	.063		1.02	2.47		3.49	5.20
6550	1" diameter		119	.067		1.52	2.66		4.18	6.05
6560	1-1/4" diameter		111	.072		1.89	2.85		4.74	6.80
6570	1-1/2" diameter		104	.077		2.02	3.04		5.06	7.20
6580	2" diameter	Q-1	197	.081		2.58	2.89		5.47	7.60
6590	2-1/2" diameter		162	.099		4.25	3.52		7.77	10.50
6600	4" diameter		123	.130		7.10	4.63		11.73	15.50
6700	PVC, DWV, Schedule 40									
6720	1-1/4" diameter	1 Plum	100	.080	L.F.	1.77	3.16		4.93	7.15
6730	1-1/2" diameter	"	94	.085		1.52	3.37		4.89	7.20
6740	2" diameter	Q-1	178	.090		1.81	3.20		5.01	7.30
6760	4" diameter	"	110	.145		5	5.20		10.20	14.05
7280	PEX, flexible, no couplings or hangers									
7282	Note: For labor costs add 25% to the couplings and fittings labor total.									
7285	For fittings see section 23 83 16.10 7000									
7300	Non-barrier type, hot/cold tubing rolls									
7310	1/4" diameter x 100'				L.F.	.49			.49	.54
7350	3/8" diameter x 100'					.55			.55	.61
7360	1/2" diameter x 100'					.61			.61	.67
7370	1/2" diameter x 500'					.61			.61	.67
7380	1/2" diameter x 1000'					.61			.61	.67
7400	3/4" diameter x 100'					.92			.92	1.01
7410	3/4" diameter x 500'					1.11			1.11	1.22
7420	3/4" diameter x 1000'					1.11			1.11	1.22
7460	1" diameter x 100'					1.90			1.90	2.09
7470	1" diameter x 300'					1.90			1.90	2.09
7480	1" diameter x 500'					1.90			1.90	2.09
7500	1-1/4" diameter x 100'					3.23			3.23	3.55
7510	1-1/4" diameter x 300'					3.23			3.23	3.55
7540	1-1/2" diameter x 100'					4.40			4.40	4.84
7550	1-1/2" diameter x 300'					4.40			4.40	4.84
7596	Most sizes available in red or blue									
7700	Non-barrier type, hot/cold tubing straight lengths									
7710	1/2" diameter x 20'				L.F.	.61			.61	.67
7750	3/4" diameter x 20'					1.11			1.11	1.22
7760	1" diameter x 20'					1.90			1.90	2.09
7770	1-1/4" diameter x 20'					3.23			3.23	3.55
7780	1-1/2" diameter x 20'					4.40			4.40	4.84
7790	2" diameter					8.60			8.60	9.45
7796	Most sizes available in red or blue									

22 11 13.76 Pipe Fittings, Plastic		Crew	Daily Output	Labor-Hours	Unit	Material	2017 Bare Costs Labor	Equipment	Total	Total Incl O&P
0010	**PIPE FITTINGS, PLASTIC**									
2700	PVC (white), schedule 40, socket joints									
2760	90° elbow, 1/2"	1 Plum	33.30	.240	Ea.	.48	9.50		9.98	16.20
2770	3/4"		28.60	.280		.54	11.05		11.59	18.85
2780	1"		25	.320		.97	12.65		13.62	22
2790	1-1/4"		22.20	.360		1.71	14.25		15.96	25.50
2800	1-1/2"		20	.400		1.85	15.80		*17.65	28
2810	2"	Q-1	36.40	.440		2.89	15.65		18.54	29
2820	2-1/2"		26.70	.599		8.80	21.50		30.30	44.50
2830	3"		22.90	.699		10.50	25		35.50	52.50
2840	4"		18.20	.879		18.80	31.50		50.30	72
3180	Tee, 1/2"	1 Plum	22.20	.360		.60	14.25		14.85	24
3190	3/4"		19	.421		.69	16.65		17.34	28.50
3200	1"		16.70	.479		1.29	18.95		20.24	32.50
3210	1-1/4"		14.80	.541		2.01	21.50		23.51	37
3220	1-1/2"		13.30	.602		2.45	24		26.45	41.50
3230	2"	Q-1	24.20	.661		3.56	23.50		27.06	43
3240	2-1/2"		17.80	.899		11.75	32		43.75	66
3250	3"		15.20	1.053		15.45	37.50		52.95	79
3260	4"		12.10	1.322		28	47		75	108
3380	Coupling, 1/2"	1 Plum	33.30	.240		.32	9.50		9.82	16
3390	3/4"		28.60	.280		.44	11.05		11.49	18.75
3400	1"		25	.320		.77	12.65		13.42	22
3410	1-1/4"		22.20	.360		1.06	14.25		15.31	24.50
3420	1-1/2"		20	.400		1.13	15.80		16.93	27
3430	2"	Q-1	36.40	.440		1.72	15.65		17.37	28
3440	2-1/2"		26.70	.599		3.81	21.50		25.31	39
3450	3"		22.90	.699		5.95	25		30.95	47.50
3460	4"		18.20	.879		8.65	31.50		40.15	61
4500	DWV, ABS, non pressure, socket joints									
4540	1/4 Bend, 1-1/4"	1 Plum	20.20	.396	Ea.	3.60	15.65		19.25	30
4560	1-1/2"	"	18.20	.440		2.69	17.40		20.09	31.50
4570	2"	Q-1	33.10	.483		4.28	17.20		21.48	33
4650	1/8 Bend, same as 1/4 Bend									
4800	Tee, sanitary									
4820	1-1/4"	1 Plum	13.50	.593	Ea.	4.79	23.50		28.29	44
4830	1-1/2"	"	12.10	.661		4.11	26		30.11	47.50
4840	2"	Q-1	20	.800		6.35	28.50		34.85	54
5000	DWV, PVC, schedule 40, socket joints									
5040	1/4 bend, 1-1/4"	1 Plum	20.20	.396	Ea.	7.25	15.65		22.90	34
5060	1-1/2"	"	18.20	.440		2.08	17.40		19.48	31
5070	2"	Q-1	33.10	.483		3.27	17.20		20.47	32
5080	3"		20.80	.769		9.60	27.50		37.10	55.50
5090	4"		16.50	.970		18.95	34.50		53.45	78
5110	1/4 bend, long sweep, 1-1/2"	1 Plum	18.20	.440		4.81	17.40		22.21	34
5112	2"	Q-1	33.10	.483		5.35	17.20		22.55	34.50
5114	3"		20.80	.769		12.35	27.50		39.85	58.50
5116	4"		16.50	.970		23.50	34.50		58	83
5250	Tee, sanitary 1-1/4"	1 Plum	13.50	.593		7.80	23.50		31.30	47
5254	1-1/2"	"	12.10	.661		3.62	26		29.62	47
5255	2"	Q-1	20	.800		5.35	28.50		33.85	53
5256	3"		13.90	1.151		14.05	41		55.05	83

22 11 13.76 Pipe Fittings, Plastic		Crew	Daily Output	Labor-Hours	Unit	Material	2017 Bare Costs Labor	Equipment	Total	Total Incl O&P
5257	4"	Q-1	11	1.455	Ea.	26	52		78	114
5259	6"	↓	6.70	2.388		103	85		188	254
5261	8"	Q-2	6.20	3.871		229	133		362	470
5264	2" x 1-1/2"	Q-1	22	.727		4.70	26		30.70	47.50
5266	3" x 1-1/2"		15.50	1.032		10.25	37		47.25	72
5268	4" x 3"		12.10	1.322		30	47		77	111
5271	6" x 4"		6.90	2.319		100	82.50		182.50	246
5314	Combination Y & 1/8 bend, 1-1/2"	1 Plum	12.10	.661		8.85	26		34.85	52.50
5315	2"	Q-1	20	.800		9.40	28.50		37.90	57.50
5317	3"		13.90	1.151		24	41		65	94
5318	4"	↓	11	1.455	↓	48	52		100	138
5324	Combination Y & 1/8 bend, reducing									
5325	2" x 2" x 1-1/2"	Q-1	22	.727	Ea.	12.40	26		38.40	56
5327	3" x 3" x 1-1/2"		15.50	1.032		22	37		59	85
5328	3" x 3" x 2"		15.30	1.046		16.50	37		53.50	79.50
5329	4" x 4" x 2"	↓	12.20	1.311		25	46.50		71.50	105
5331	Wye, 1-1/4"	1 Plum	13.50	.593		9.95	23.50		33.45	49.50
5332	1-1/2"	"	12.10	.661		6.65	26		32.65	50.50
5333	2"	Q-1	20	.800		6.50	28.50		35	54
5334	3"		13.90	1.151		17.50	41		58.50	87
5335	4"		11	1.455		32	52		84	121
5336	6"	↓	6.70	2.388		92.50	85		177.50	242
5337	8"	Q-2	6.20	3.871		163	133		296	400
5341	2" x 1-1/2"	Q-1	22	.727		8	26		34	51.50
5342	3" x 1-1/2"		15.50	1.032		11.80	37		48.80	73.50
5343	4" x 3"		12.10	1.322		26	47		73	106
5344	6" x 4"	↓	6.90	2.319		70.50	82.50		153	214
5345	8" x 6"	Q-2	6.40	3.750		154	129		283	380
5347	Double wye, 1-1/2"	1 Plum	9.10	.879		14.90	35		49.90	74
5348	2"	Q-1	16.60	.964		16.65	34.50		51.15	75
5349	3"		10.40	1.538		34.50	55		89.50	129
5350	4"	↓	8.25	1.939	↓	70.50	69		139.50	192
5353	Double wye, reducing									
5354	2" x 2" x 1-1/2" x 1-1/2"	Q-1	16.80	.952	Ea.	15.20	34		49.20	73
5355	3" x 3" x 2" x 2"		10.60	1.509		26	53.50		79.50	117
5356	4" x 4" x 3" x 3"		8.45	1.893		55.50	67.50		123	172
5357	6" x 6" x 4" x 4"		7.25	2.207		195	78.50		273.50	345
5374	Coupling, 1-1/4"	1 Plum	20.20	.396		4.70	15.65		20.35	31
5376	1-1/2"	"	18.20	.440		.97	17.40		18.37	29.50
5378	2"	Q-1	33.10	.483		1.34	17.20		18.54	30
5380	3"		20.80	.769		4.66	27.50		32.16	50
5390	4"		16.50	.970		7.90	34.50		42.40	65.50
5410	Reducer bushing, 2" x 1-1/4"		36.50	.438		3.35	15.60		18.95	29
5412	3" x 1-1/2"		27.30	.586		8.20	21		29.20	43.50
5414	4" x 2"		18.20	.879		14.25	31.50		45.75	67
5416	6" x 4"	↓	11.10	1.441		36.50	51.50		88	125
5418	8" x 6"	Q-2	10.20	2.353	↓	71.50	80.50		152	212
5500	CPVC, Schedule 80, threaded joints									
5540	90° Elbow, 1/4"	1 Plum	32	.250	Ea.	12.15	9.90		22.05	29.50
5560	1/2"		30.30	.264		7.05	10.45		17.50	25
5570	3/4"		26	.308		10.55	12.15		22.70	31.50
5580	1"		22.70	.352		14.80	13.95		28.75	39.50
5590	1-1/4"	↓	20.20	.396	↓	28.50	15.65		44.15	57.50

22 11 13 – Facility Water Distribution Piping

22 11 13.76 Pipe Fittings, Plastic		Crew	Daily Output	Labor-Hours	Unit	Material	2017 Bare Costs Labor	Equipment	Total	Total Incl O&P
5600	1-1/2"	1 Plum	18.20	.440	Ea.	30.50	17.40		47.90	62
5610	2"	Q-1	33.10	.483		41	17.20		58.20	73.50
5730	Coupling, 1/4"	1 Plum	32	.250		15.45	9.90		25.35	33.50
5732	1/2"		30.30	.264		12.75	10.45		23.20	31
5734	3/4"		26	.308		20.50	12.15		32.65	42.50
5736	1"		22.70	.352		23.50	13.95		37.45	48.50
5738	1-1/4"		20.20	.396		25	15.65		40.65	53
5740	1-1/2"	▼	18.20	.440		26.50	17.40		43.90	58
5742	2"	Q-1	33.10	.483	▼	31.50	17.20		48.70	63
5900	CPVC, Schedule 80, socket joints									
5904	90° Elbow, 1/4"	1 Plum	32	.250	Ea.	11.55	9.90		21.45	29
5906	1/2"		30.30	.264		4.53	10.45		14.98	22
5908	3/4"		26	.308		5.80	12.15		17.95	26.50
5910	1"		22.70	.352		9.20	13.95		23.15	33
5912	1-1/4"		20.20	.396		19.85	15.65		35.50	48
5914	1-1/2"	▼	18.20	.440		22	17.40		39.40	53
5916	2"	Q-1	33.10	.483		26.50	17.20		43.70	58
5930	45° Elbow, 1/4"	1 Plum	32	.250		17.20	9.90		27.10	35
5932	1/2"		30.30	.264		5.55	10.45		16	23.50
5934	3/4"		26	.308		8	12.15		20.15	29
5936	1"		22.70	.352		12.75	13.95		26.70	37
5938	1-1/4"		20.20	.396		25	15.65		40.65	53.50
5940	1-1/2"	▼	18.20	.440		25.50	17.40		42.90	56.50
5942	2"	Q-1	33.10	.483		29	17.20		46.20	60
5990	Coupling, 1/4"	1 Plum	32	.250		12.30	9.90		22.20	30
5992	1/2"		30.30	.264		4.79	10.45		15.24	22.50
5994	3/4"		26	.308		6.70	12.15		18.85	27.50
5996	1"		22.70	.352		9	13.95		22.95	33
5998	1-1/4"		20.20	.396		13.50	15.65		29.15	41
6000	1-1/2"	▼	18.20	.440		17	17.40		34.40	47
6002	2"	Q-1	33.10	.483	▼	19.75	17.20		36.95	50

22 11 19 – Domestic Water Piping Specialties

22 11 19.38 Water Supply Meters

		Crew	Daily Output	Labor-Hours	Unit	Material	2017 Bare Costs Labor	Equipment	Total	Total Incl O&P
0010	**WATER SUPPLY METERS**									
2000	Domestic/commercial, bronze									
2020	Threaded									
2060	5/8" diameter, to 20 GPM	1 Plum	16	.500	Ea.	50.50	19.80		70.30	88
2080	3/4" diameter, to 30 GPM		14	.571		92	22.50		114.50	139
2100	1" diameter, to 50 GPM	▼	12	.667	▼	140	26.50		166.50	198

22 11 19.42 Backflow Preventers

		Crew	Daily Output	Labor-Hours	Unit	Material	2017 Bare Costs Labor	Equipment	Total	Total Incl O&P
0010	**BACKFLOW PREVENTERS**, Includes valves									
0020	and four test cocks, corrosion resistant, automatic operation									
4000	Reduced pressure principle									
4100	Threaded, bronze, valves are ball									
4120	3/4" pipe size	1 Plum	16	.500	Ea.	300	19.80		319.80	365

22 11 19.50 Vacuum Breakers

		Crew	Daily Output	Labor-Hours	Unit	Material	2017 Bare Costs Labor	Equipment	Total	Total Incl O&P
0010	**VACUUM BREAKERS**									
0013	See also backflow preventers Section 22 11 19.42									
1000	Anti-siphon continuous pressure type									
1010	Max. 150 PSI - 210°F									
1020	Bronze body									
1030	1/2" size	1 Stpi	24	.333	Ea.	166	13.70		179.70	205

22 11 Facility Water Distribution

22 11 19 – Domestic Water Piping Specialties

22 11 19.50 Vacuum Breakers

		Crew	Daily Output	Labor-Hours	Unit	Material	2017 Bare Costs Labor	Equipment	Total	Total Incl O&P
1040	3/4" size	1 Stpi	20	.400	Ea.	166	16.45		182.45	209
1050	1" size		19	.421		170	17.30		187.30	216
1060	1-1/4" size		15	.533		335	22		357	405
1070	1-1/2" size		13	.615		415	25.50		440.50	495
1080	2" size	↓	11	.727	↓	425	30		455	520
1200	Max. 125 PSI with atmospheric vent									
1210	Brass, in-line construction									
1220	1/4" size	1 Stpi	24	.333	Ea.	129	13.70		142.70	165
1230	3/8" size	"	24	.333		129	13.70		142.70	165
1260	For polished chrome finish, add				↓	13%				
2000	Anti-siphon, non-continuous pressure type									
2010	Hot or cold water 125 PSI - 210°F									
2020	Bronze body									
2030	1/4" size	1 Stpi	24	.333	Ea.	71	13.70		84.70	101
2040	3/8" size		24	.333		71	13.70		84.70	101
2050	1/2" size		24	.333		80	13.70		93.70	111
2060	3/4" size		20	.400		95	16.45		111.45	132
2070	1" size		19	.421		148	17.30		165.30	191
2080	1-1/4" size		15	.533		258	22		280	320
2090	1-1/2" size		13	.615		305	25.50		330.50	375
2100	2" size		11	.727		470	30		500	570
2110	2-1/2" size		8	1		1,350	41		1,391	1,575
2120	3" size	↓	6	1.333	↓	1,800	55		1,855	2,075
2150	For polished chrome finish, add					50%				

22 11 19.54 Water Hammer Arresters/Shock Absorbers

		Crew	Daily Output	Labor-Hours	Unit	Material	2017 Bare Costs Labor	Equipment	Total	Total Incl O&P
0010	**WATER HAMMER ARRESTERS/SHOCK ABSORBERS**									
0490	Copper									
0500	3/4" male I.P.S. For 1 to 11 fixtures	1 Plum	12	.667	Ea.	28.50	26.50		55	74.50

22 13 Facility Sanitary Sewerage

22 13 16 – Sanitary Waste and Vent Piping

22 13 16.20 Pipe, Cast Iron

		Crew	Daily Output	Labor-Hours	Unit	Material	2017 Bare Costs Labor	Equipment	Total	Total Incl O&P
0010	**PIPE, CAST IRON**, Soil, on clevis hanger assemblies, 5' O.C. R221113-50									
0020	Single hub, service wt., lead & oakum joints 10' O.C.									
2120	2" diameter	Q-1	63	.254	L.F.	21	9.05		30.05	38
2140	3" diameter		60	.267		20	9.50		29.50	37.50
2160	4" diameter	↓	55	.291	↓	35	10.35		45.35	55.50
4000	No hub, couplings 10' O.C.									
4100	1-1/2" diameter	Q-1	71	.225	L.F.	19.95	8		27.95	35.50
4120	2" diameter		67	.239		21	8.50		29.50	37
4140	3" diameter		64	.250		19.80	8.90		28.70	36.50
4160	4" diameter	↓	58	.276		35	9.80		44.80	54.50

22 13 16.30 Pipe Fittings, Cast Iron

		Crew	Daily Output	Labor-Hours	Unit	Material	2017 Bare Costs Labor	Equipment	Total	Total Incl O&P
0010	**PIPE FITTINGS, CAST IRON**, Soil									
0040	Hub and spigot, service weight, lead & oakum joints									
0080	1/4 bend, 2"	Q-1	16	1	Ea.	20.50	35.50		56	81
0120	3"		14	1.143		27.50	40.50		68	97
0140	4"		13	1.231		43	44		87	120
0340	1/8 bend, 2"		16	1		14.65	35.50		50.15	74.50
0350	3"	↓	14	1.143	↓	23	40.50		63.50	92

22 13 16.30 Pipe Fittings, Cast Iron		Crew	Daily Output	Labor-Hours	Unit	Material	2017 Bare Costs Labor	Equipment	Total	Total Incl O&P
0360	4"	Q-1	13	1.231	Ea.	33.50	44		77.50	110
0500	Sanitary tee, 2"		10	1.600		28.50	57		85.50	126
0540	3"		9	1.778		46.50	63.50		110	155
0620	4"		8	2		57	71		128	180
5990	No hub									
6000	Cplg. & labor required at joints not incl. in fitting									
6010	price. Add 1 coupling per joint for installed price									
6020	1/4 Bend, 1-1/2"				Ea.	10.55			10.55	11.65
6060	2"					11.55			11.55	12.70
6080	3"					16.10			16.10	17.70
6120	4"					24			24	26
6184	1/4 Bend, long sweep, 1-1/2"					27			27	29.50
6186	2"					25			25	27.50
6188	3"					30.50			30.50	33.50
6189	4"					48.50			48.50	53.50
6190	5"					94			94	103
6191	6"					107			107	118
6192	8"					291			291	320
6193	10"					585			585	645
6200	1/8 Bend, 1-1/2"					8.90			8.90	9.80
6210	2"					9.95			9.95	10.95
6212	3"					13.30			13.30	14.65
6214	4"					17.45			17.45	19.15
6380	Sanitary tee, tapped, 1-1/2"					21			21	23
6382	2" x 1-1/2"					18.60			18.60	20.50
6384	2"					19.95			19.95	22
6386	3" x 2"					29.50			29.50	32.50
6388	3"					51			51	56.50
6390	4" x 1-1/2"					26.50			26.50	29
6392	4" x 2"					30			30	33
6393	4"					30			30	33
6394	6" x 1-1/2"					68.50			68.50	75.50
6396	6" x 2"					70			70	77
6459	Sanitary tee, 1-1/2"					14.85			14.85	16.30
6460	2"					15.90			15.90	17.50
6470	3"					19.60			19.60	21.50
6472	4"					37			37	41
8000	Coupling, standard (by CISPI Mfrs.)									
8020	1-1/2"	Q-1	48	.333	Ea.	15.10	11.85		26.95	36
8040	2"		44	.364		15.10	12.95		28.05	38
8080	3"		38	.421		18	15		33	44.50
8120	4"		33	.485		21	17.25		38.25	52

22 13 16.50 Shower Drains

		Crew	Daily Output	Labor-Hours	Unit	Material	2017 Bare Costs Labor	Equipment	Total	Total Incl O&P
0010	**SHOWER DRAINS**									
2780	Shower, with strainer, uniform diam. trap, bronze top									
2800	2" and 3" pipe size	Q-1	8	2	Ea.	345	71		416	495
2820	4" pipe size	"	7	2.286		380	81.50		461.50	555
2840	For galvanized body, add					135			135	149

22 13 16.60 Traps		Crew	Daily Output	Labor-Hours	Unit	Material	2017 Bare Costs Labor	Equipment	Total	Total Incl O&P
0010	**TRAPS**									
0030	Cast iron, service weight									
0050	Running P trap, without vent									
1100	2"	Q-1	16	1	Ea.	148	35.50		183.50	222
1150	4"	"	13	1.231		148	44		192	236
1160	6"	Q-2	17	1.412		655	48.50		703.50	800
3000	P trap, B&S, 2" pipe size	Q-1	16	1		35	35.50		70.50	97
3040	3" pipe size	"	14	1.143		52.50	40.50		93	125
4700	Copper, drainage, drum trap									
4840	3" x 6" swivel, 1-1/2" pipe size	1 Plum	16	.500	Ea.	144	19.80		163.80	191
5100	P trap, standard pattern									
5200	1-1/4" pipe size	1 Plum	18	.444	Ea.	58.50	17.60		76.10	93.50
5240	1-1/2" pipe size		17	.471		78	18.60		96.60	117
5260	2" pipe size		15	.533		121	21		142	168
5280	3" pipe size		11	.727		350	29		379	435
6710	ABS DWV P trap, solvent weld joint									
6720	1-1/2" pipe size	1 Plum	18	.444	Ea.	8.80	17.60		26.40	38.50
6722	2" pipe size		17	.471		11.60	18.60		30.20	43.50
6724	3" pipe size		15	.533		46	21		67	85.50
6726	4" pipe size		14	.571		92	22.50		114.50	139
6732	PVC DWV P trap, solvent weld joint									
6733	1-1/2" pipe size	1 Plum	18	.444	Ea.	6.95	17.60		24.55	36.50
6734	2" pipe size		17	.471		9.40	18.60		28	41
6735	3" pipe size		15	.533		32	21		53	70
6736	4" pipe size		14	.571		72	22.50		94.50	117
6860	PVC DWV hub x hub, basin trap, 1-1/4" pipe size		18	.444		51.50	17.60		69.10	85.50
6870	Sink P trap, 1-1/2" pipe size		18	.444		12.70	17.60		30.30	43
6880	Tubular S trap, 1-1/2" pipe size		17	.471		26.50	18.60		45.10	59.50
6890	PVC sch. 40 DWV, drum trap									
6900	1-1/2" pipe size	1 Plum	16	.500	Ea.	34.50	19.80		54.30	70
6910	P trap, 1-1/2" pipe size		18	.444		7.75	17.60		25.35	37.50
6920	2" pipe size		17	.471		10.40	18.60		29	42
6930	3" pipe size		15	.533		35.50	21		56.50	74
6940	4" pipe size		14	.571		80	22.50		102.50	126
6950	P trap w/clean out, 1-1/2" pipe size		18	.444		12.70	17.60		30.30	43
6960	2" pipe size		17	.471		21.50	18.60		40.10	54

22 13 16.80 Vent Flashing and Caps

		Crew	Daily Output	Labor-Hours	Unit	Material	2017 Bare Costs Labor	Equipment	Total	Total Incl O&P
0010	**VENT FLASHING AND CAPS**									
0120	Vent caps									
0140	Cast iron									
0160	1-1/4" - 1-1/2" pipe	1 Plum	23	.348	Ea.	30.50	13.75		44.25	56
0170	2" - 2-1/8" pipe		22	.364		35.50	14.40		49.90	62.50
0180	2-1/2" - 3-5/8" pipe		21	.381		35.50	15.05		50.55	64
0190	4" - 4-1/8" pipe		19	.421		56.50	16.65		73.15	90
0200	5" - 6" pipe		17	.471		99.50	18.60		118.10	141
0300	PVC									
0320	1-1/4" - 1-1/2" pipe	1 Plum	24	.333	Ea.	9.30	13.20		22.50	31.50
0330	2" - 2-1/8" pipe	"	23	.348	"	9.40	13.75		23.15	33
0900	Vent flashing									
1350	Copper with neoprene ring									
1400	1-1/4" pipe	1 Plum	20	.400	Ea.	68	15.80		83.80	101
1430	1-1/2" pipe		20	.400		68	15.80		83.80	101

22 13 Facility Sanitary Sewerage

22 13 16 – Sanitary Waste and Vent Piping

22 13 16.80 Vent Flashing and Caps	Crew	Daily Output	Labor-Hours	Unit	Material	2017 Bare Costs Labor	Equipment	Total	Total Incl O&P
1440	2" pipe	1 Plum	18	.444	Ea.	68	17.60		85.60	104
1450	3" pipe		17	.471		82	18.60		100.60	121
1460	4" pipe	↓	16	.500	↓	82	19.80		101.80	123
2980	Neoprene, one piece									
3000	1-1/4" pipe	1 Plum	24	.333	Ea.	2.96	13.20		16.16	25
3030	1-1/2" pipe		24	.333		2.98	13.20		16.18	25
3040	2" pipe		23	.348		2.98	13.75		16.73	26
3050	3" pipe		21	.381		3.42	15.05		18.47	29
3060	4" pipe	↓	20	.400	↓	5.05	15.80		20.85	31.50

22 13 19 – Sanitary Waste Piping Specialties

22 13 19.13 Sanitary Drains

	22 13 19.13 Sanitary Drains	Crew	Daily Output	Labor-Hours	Unit	Material	Labor	Equipment	Total	Total Incl O&P
0010	**SANITARY DRAINS**									
2000	Floor, medium duty, C.I., deep flange, 7" diam. top									
2040	2" and 3" pipe size	Q-1	12	1.333	Ea.	164	47.50		211.50	259
2080	For galvanized body, add					69			69	76
2120	With polished bronze top				↓	255			255	281

22 14 Facility Storm Drainage

22 14 26 – Facility Storm Drains

22 14 26.13 Roof Drains

	22 14 26.13 Roof Drains	Crew	Daily Output	Labor-Hours	Unit	Material	Labor	Equipment	Total	Total Incl O&P
0010	**ROOF DRAINS**									
3860	Roof, flat metal deck, C.I. body, 12" C.I. dome									
3890	3" pipe size	Q-1	14	1.143	Ea.	298	40.50		338.50	395

22 14 29 – Sump Pumps

22 14 29.16 Submersible Sump Pumps

	22 14 29.16 Submersible Sump Pumps	Crew	Daily Output	Labor-Hours	Unit	Material	Labor	Equipment	Total	Total Incl O&P
0010	**SUBMERSIBLE SUMP PUMPS**									
7000	Sump pump, automatic									
7100	Plastic, 1-1/4" discharge, 1/4 HP	1 Plum	6.40	1.250	Ea.	150	49.50		199.50	247
7500	Cast iron, 1-1/4" discharge, 1/4 HP	"	6	1.333	"	211	52.50		263.50	320

22 31 Domestic Water Softeners

22 31 13 – Residential Domestic Water Softeners

22 31 13.10 Residential Water Softeners

	22 31 13.10 Residential Water Softeners	Crew	Daily Output	Labor-Hours	Unit	Material	Labor	Equipment	Total	Total Incl O&P
0010	**RESIDENTIAL WATER SOFTENERS**									
7350	Water softener, automatic, to 30 grains per gallon	2 Plum	5	3.200	Ea.	380	127		507	630
7400	To 100 grains per gallon	"	4	4	"	815	158		973	1,150

22 33 Electric Domestic Water Heaters

22 33 30 – Residential, Electric Domestic Water Heaters

22 33 30.13 Residential, Small-Capacity Elec. Water Heaters		Crew	Daily Output	Labor-Hours	Unit	Material	2017 Bare Costs Labor	Equipment	Total	Total Incl O&P
0010	**RESIDENTIAL, SMALL-CAPACITY ELECTRIC DOMESTIC WATER HEATERS**									
1000	Residential, electric, glass lined tank, 5 yr., 10 gal., single element	1 Plum	2.30	3.478	Ea.	465	138		603	735
1060	30 gallon, double element		2.20	3.636		1,075	144		1,219	1,425
1080	40 gallon, double element		2	4		1,150	158		1,308	1,525
1100	52 gallon, double element		2	4		1,300	158		1,458	1,700
1120	66 gallon, double element		1.80	4.444		1,775	176		1,951	2,250
1140	80 gallon, double element		1.60	5		2,000	198		2,198	2,525

22 34 Fuel-Fired Domestic Water Heaters

22 34 13 – Instantaneous, Tankless, Gas Domestic Water Heaters

22 34 13.10 Instantaneous, Tankless, Gas Water Heaters

			Crew	Daily Output	Labor-Hours	Unit	Material	Labor	Equipment	Total	Total Incl O&P
0010	**INSTANTANEOUS, TANKLESS, GAS WATER HEATERS**										
9410	Natural gas/propane, 3.2 GPM	G	1 Plum	2	4	Ea.	540	158		698	855
9420	6.4 GPM	G		1.90	4.211		770	167		937	1,125
9430	8.4 GPM	G		1.80	4.444		925	176		1,101	1,325
9440	9.5 GPM	G		1.60	5		1,075	198		1,273	1,525

22 34 30 – Residential Gas Domestic Water Heaters

22 34 30.13 Residential, Atmos, Gas Domestic Wtr Heaters

		Crew	Daily Output	Labor-Hours	Unit	Material	Labor	Equipment	Total	Total Incl O&P
0010	**RESIDENTIAL, ATMOSPHERIC, GAS DOMESTIC WATER HEATERS**									
2000	Gas fired, foam lined tank, 10 yr., vent not incl.									
2040	30 gallon	1 Plum	2	4	Ea.	1,925	158		2,083	2,375
2100	75 gallon	"	1.50	5.333	"	2,925	211		3,136	3,575
3000	Tank leak safety, water & gas shut off see 22 05 23.20 8800									

22 34 46 – Oil-Fired Domestic Water Heaters

22 34 46.10 Residential Oil-Fired Water Heaters

		Crew	Daily Output	Labor-Hours	Unit	Material	Labor	Equipment	Total	Total Incl O&P
0010	**RESIDENTIAL OIL-FIRED WATER HEATERS**									
3000	Oil fired, glass lined tank, 5 yr., vent not included, 30 gallon	1 Plum	2	4	Ea.	1,400	158		1,558	1,775
3040	50 gallon	"	1.80	4.444	"	1,700	176		1,876	2,175

22 41 Residential Plumbing Fixtures

22 41 13 – Residential Water Closets, Urinals, and Bidets

22 41 13.13 Water Closets

		Crew	Daily Output	Labor-Hours	Unit	Material	Labor	Equipment	Total	Total Incl O&P
0010	**WATER CLOSETS**									
0150	Tank type, vitreous china, incl. seat, supply pipe w/stop, 1.6 gpf or noted									
0200	Wall hung									
0400	Two piece, close coupled	Q-1	5.30	3.019	Ea.	435	107		542	655
0960	For rough-in, supply, waste, vent and carrier	"	2.73	5.861	"	1,150	209		1,359	1,625
0999	Floor mounted									
1020	One piece, low profile	Q-1	5.30	3.019	Ea.	610	107		717	845
1100	Two piece, close coupled		5.30	3.019		194	107		301	390
1102	Economy		5.30	3.019		108	107		215	295
1110	Two piece, close coupled, dual flush		5.30	3.019		267	107		374	470
1140	Two piece, close coupled, 1.28 gpf, ADA G		5.30	3.019		259	107		366	460
1960	For color, add					30%				
1980	For rough-in, supply, waste and vent	Q-1	3.05	5.246	Ea.	380	187		567	730

For customer support on your Residential Costs with RSMeans Data, call 800.448.8182.

571

22 41 16.13 Lavatories

		Crew	Daily Output	Labor-Hours	Unit	Material	2017 Bare Costs Labor	2017 Bare Costs Equipment	Total	Total Incl O&P
0010	**LAVATORIES**, With trim, white unless noted otherwise									
0500	Vanity top, porcelain enamel on cast iron									
0600	20" x 18"	Q-1	6.40	2.500	Ea.	320	89		409	495
0640	33" x 19" oval		6.40	2.500		480	89		569	670
0720	19" round	↓	6.40	2.500	↓	420	89		509	610
0860	For color, add					25%				
1000	Cultured marble, 19" x 17", single bowl	Q-1	6.40	2.500	Ea.	152	89		241	315
1120	25" x 22", single bowl		6.40	2.500		191	89		280	355
1160	37" x 22", single bowl		6.40	2.500	↓	222	89		311	390
1580	For color, same price									
1900	Stainless steel, self-rimming, 25" x 22", single bowl, ledge	Q-1	6.40	2.500	Ea.	345	89		434	520
1960	17" x 22", single bowl		6.40	2.500		335	89		424	510
2600	Steel, enameled, 20" x 17", single bowl		5.80	2.759		151	98		249	330
2900	Vitreous china, 20" x 16", single bowl		5.40	2.963		238	105		343	435
3200	22" x 13", single bowl		5.40	2.963		245	105		350	445
3580	Rough-in, supply, waste and vent for all above lavatories	↓	2.30	6.957	↓	209	248		457	640
4000	Wall hung									
4040	Porcelain enamel on cast iron, 16" x 14", single bowl	Q-1	8	2	Ea.	505	71		576	670
4180	20" x 18", single bowl	"	8	2	"	267	71		338	410
4580	For color, add					30%				
6000	Vitreous china, 18" x 15", single bowl with backsplash	Q-1	7	2.286	Ea.	188	81.50		269.50	340
6060	19" x 17", single bowl		7	2.286		149	81.50		230.50	298
6960	Rough-in, supply, waste and vent for above lavatories	↓	1.66	9.639	↓	390	345		735	995
7000	Pedestal type									
7600	Vitreous china, 27" x 21", white	Q-1	6.60	2.424	Ea.	685	86.50		771.50	895
7610	27" x 21", colored		6.60	2.424		870	86.50		956.50	1,100
7620	27" x 21", premium color		6.60	2.424		985	86.50		1,071.50	1,225
7660	26" x 20", white		6.60	2.424		675	86.50		761.50	885
7670	26" x 20", colored		6.60	2.424		855	86.50		941.50	1,075
7680	26" x 20", premium color		6.60	2.424		970	86.50		1,056.50	1,225
7700	24" x 20", white		6.60	2.424		400	86.50		486.50	580
7710	24" x 20", colored		6.60	2.424		495	86.50		581.50	685
7720	24" x 20", premium color		6.60	2.424		560	86.50		646.50	755
7760	21" x 18", white		6.60	2.424		280	86.50		366.50	450
7770	21" x 18", colored		6.60	2.424		340	86.50		426.50	515
7990	Rough-in, supply, waste and vent for pedestal lavatories	↓	1.66	9.639	↓	390	345		735	995

22 41 16.16 Sinks

		Crew	Daily Output	Labor-Hours	Unit	Material	2017 Bare Costs Labor	2017 Bare Costs Equipment	Total	Total Incl O&P
0010	**SINKS**, With faucets and drain									
2000	Kitchen, counter top style, P.E. on C.I., 24" x 21" single bowl	Q-1	5.60	2.857	Ea.	300	102		402	500
2100	31" x 22" single bowl		5.60	2.857		555	102		657	780
2200	32" x 21" double bowl		4.80	3.333		375	119		494	605
3000	Stainless steel, self rimming, 19" x 18" single bowl		5.60	2.857		610	102		712	840
3100	25" x 22" single bowl		5.60	2.857		675	102		777	915
3200	33" x 22" double bowl		4.80	3.333		975	119		1,094	1,275
3300	43" x 22" double bowl		4.80	3.333		1,125	119		1,244	1,450
4000	Steel, enameled, with ledge, 24" x 21" single bowl		5.60	2.857		530	102		632	755
4100	32" x 21" double bowl	↓	4.80	3.333	↓	525	119		644	770
4960	For color sinks except stainless steel, add					10%				
4980	For rough-in, supply, waste and vent, counter top sinks	Q-1	2.14	7.477		268	266		534	735
5000	Kitchen, raised deck, P.E. on C.I.									
5100	32" x 21", dual level, double bowl	Q-1	2.60	6.154	Ea.	445	219		664	850
5790	For rough-in, supply, waste & vent, sinks	"	1.85	8.649	"	268	310		578	805

22 41 Residential Plumbing Fixtures

22 41 19 – Residential Bathtubs

22 41 19.10 Baths

		Crew	Daily Output	Labor-Hours	Unit	Material	2017 Bare Costs Labor	Equipment	Total	Total Incl O&P
0010	**BATHS**									
0100	Tubs, recessed porcelain enamel on cast iron, with trim									
0180	48" x 42"	Q-1	4	4	Ea.	2,700	142		2,842	3,175
0220	72" x 36"	"	3	5.333	"	2,775	190		2,965	3,375
0300	Mat bottom									
0380	5' long	Q-1	4.40	3.636	Ea.	1,150	129		1,279	1,475
0480	Above floor drain, 5' long		4	4		840	142		982	1,150
0560	Corner 48" x 44"		4.40	3.636		2,700	129		2,829	3,175
2000	Enameled formed steel, 4'-6" long		5.80	2.759		490	98		588	695
4600	Module tub & showerwall surround, molded fiberglass									
4610	5' long x 34" wide x 76" high	Q-1	4	4	Ea.	830	142		972	1,150
9600	Rough-in, supply, waste and vent, for all above tubs, add	"	2.07	7.729	"	415	275		690	910

22 41 23 – Residential Showers

22 41 23.20 Showers

		Crew	Daily Output	Labor-Hours	Unit	Material	2017 Bare Costs Labor	Equipment	Total	Total Incl O&P
0010	**SHOWERS**									
1500	Stall, with drain only. Add for valve and door/curtain									
1520	32" square	Q-1	5	3.200	Ea.	1,175	114		1,289	1,500
1530	36" square		4.80	3.333		2,950	119		3,069	3,450
1540	Terrazzo receptor, 32" square		5	3.200		1,350	114		1,464	1,700
1560	36" square		4.80	3.333		1,475	119		1,594	1,825
1580	36" corner angle		4.80	3.333		1,750	119		1,869	2,125
3000	Fiberglass, one piece, with 3 walls, 32" x 32" square		5.50	2.909		340	104		444	545
3100	36" x 36" square		5.50	2.909		390	104		494	595
4200	Rough-in, supply, waste and vent for above showers		2.05	7.805		365	278		643	860

22 41 36 – Residential Laundry Trays

22 41 36.10 Laundry Sinks

		Crew	Daily Output	Labor-Hours	Unit	Material	2017 Bare Costs Labor	Equipment	Total	Total Incl O&P
0010	**LAUNDRY SINKS**, With trim									
0020	Porcelain enamel on cast iron, black iron frame									
0050	24" x 21", single compartment	Q-1	6	2.667	Ea.	595	95		690	810
0100	26" x 21", single compartment	"	6	2.667	"	620	95		715	840
3000	Plastic, on wall hanger or legs									
3020	18" x 23", single compartment	Q-1	6.50	2.462	Ea.	146	87.50		233.50	305
3100	20" x 24", single compartment		6.50	2.462		177	87.50		264.50	340
3200	36" x 23", double compartment		5.50	2.909		228	104		332	420
3300	40" x 24", double compartment		5.50	2.909		310	104		414	515
5000	Stainless steel, counter top, 22" x 17" single compartment		6	2.667		77	95		172	242
5200	33" x 22", double compartment		5	3.200		92	114		206	289
9600	Rough-in, supply, waste and vent, for all laundry sinks		2.14	7.477		268	266		534	735

22 41 39 – Residential Faucets, Supplies and Trim

22 41 39.10 Faucets and Fittings

		Crew	Daily Output	Labor-Hours	Unit	Material	2017 Bare Costs Labor	Equipment	Total	Total Incl O&P
0010	**FAUCETS AND FITTINGS**									
0150	Bath, faucets, diverter spout combination, sweat	1 Plum	8	1	Ea.	87	39.50		126.50	161
0200	For integral stops, IPS unions, add					111			111	122
0420	Bath, press-bal mix valve w/diverter, spout, shower head, arm/flange	1 Plum	8	1		173	39.50		212.50	255
0500	Drain, central lift, 1-1/2" IPS male		20	.400		49.50	15.80		65.30	80.50
0600	Trip lever, 1-1/2" IPS male		20	.400		55.50	15.80		71.30	87
1000	Kitchen sink faucets, top mount, cast spout		10	.800		78	31.50		109.50	138
1100	For spray, add		24	.333		17.10	13.20		30.30	40.50
1300	Single control lever handle									
1310	With pull out spray									

For customer support on your Residential Costs with RSMeans Data, call 800.448.8182.

573

22 41 39.10 Faucets and Fittings

		Crew	Daily Output	Labor-Hours	Unit	Material	2017 Bare Costs Labor	2017 Bare Costs Equipment	Total	Total Incl O&P
1320	Polished chrome	1 Plum	10	.800	Ea.	200	31.50		231.50	271
2000	Laundry faucets, shelf type, IPS or copper unions		12	.667		62	26.50		88.50	112
2100	Lavatory faucet, centerset, without drain		10	.800		64	31.50		95.50	123
2120	With pop-up drain	↓	6.66	1.201	↓	83.50	47.50		131	171
2210	Porcelain cross handles and pop-up drain									
2220	Polished chrome	1 Plum	6.66	1.201	Ea.	222	47.50		269.50	325
2230	Polished brass	"	6.66	1.201	"	335	47.50		382.50	450
2260	Single lever handle and pop-up drain									
2280	Satin nickel	1 Plum	6.66	1.201	Ea.	277	47.50		324.50	385
2290	Polished chrome		6.66	1.201		198	47.50		245.50	297
2800	Self-closing, center set		10	.800		150	31.50		181.50	217
4000	Shower by-pass valve with union		18	.444		57.50	17.60		75.10	92.50
4200	Shower thermostatic mixing valve, concealed, with shower head trim kit		8	1		340	39.50		379.50	440
4220	Shower pressure balancing mixing valve									
4230	With shower head, arm, flange and diverter tub spout									
4240	Chrome	1 Plum	6.14	1.303	Ea.	375	51.50		426.50	500
4250	Satin nickel		6.14	1.303		495	51.50		546.50	625
4260	Polished graphite		6.14	1.303		505	51.50		556.50	640
5000	Sillcock, compact, brass, IPS or copper to hose	↓	24	.333	↓	10.20	13.20		23.40	33

22 41 39.70 Washer/Dryer Accessories

		Crew	Daily Output	Labor-Hours	Unit	Material	2017 Bare Costs Labor	2017 Bare Costs Equipment	Total	Total Incl O&P
0010	**WASHER/DRYER ACCESSORIES**									
1020	Valves ball type single lever									
1030	1/2" diam., IPS	1 Plum	21	.381	Ea.	60.50	15.05		75.55	91.50
1040	1/2" diam., solder	"	21	.381	"	60.50	15.05		75.55	91.50
1050	Recessed box, 16 ga., two hose valves and drain									
1060	1/2" size, 1-1/2" drain	1 Plum	18	.444	Ea.	133	17.60		150.60	175
1070	1/2" size, 2" drain	"	17	.471	"	119	18.60		137.60	162
1080	With grounding electric receptacle									
1090	1/2" size, 1-1/2" drain	1 Plum	18	.444	Ea.	145	17.60		162.60	189
1100	1/2" size, 2" drain	"	17	.471	"	157	18.60		175.60	204
1110	With grounding and dryer receptacle									
1120	1/2" size, 1-1/2" drain	1 Plum	18	.444	Ea.	180	17.60		197.60	227
1130	1/2" size, 2" drain	"	17	.471	"	182	18.60		200.60	231
1140	Recessed box, 16 ga., ball valves with single lever and drain									
1150	1/2" size, 1-1/2" drain	1 Plum	19	.421	Ea.	251	16.65		267.65	305
1160	1/2" size, 2" drain	"	18	.444	"	218	17.60		235.60	268
1170	With grounding electric receptacle									
1180	1/2" size, 1-1/2" drain	1 Plum	19	.421	Ea.	249	16.65		265.65	300
1190	1/2" size, 2" drain	"	18	.444	"	241	17.60		258.60	295
1200	With grounding and dryer receptacles									
1210	1/2" size, 1-1/2" drain	1 Plum	19	.421	Ea.	238	16.65		254.65	289
1220	1/2" size, 2" drain	"	18	.444	"	264	17.60		281.60	320
1300	Recessed box, 20 ga., two hose valves and drain (economy type)									
1310	1/2" size, 1-1/2" drain	1 Plum	19	.421	Ea.	104	16.65		120.65	142
1320	1/2" size, 2" drain		18	.444		97	17.60		114.60	136
1330	Box with drain only		24	.333		60	13.20		73.20	87.50
1340	1/2" size, 1-1/2" ABS/PVC drain		19	.421		115	16.65		131.65	154
1350	1/2" size, 2" ABS/PVC drain		18	.444		112	17.60		129.60	152
1352	Box with drain and 15 A receptacle		24	.333		111	13.20		124.20	144
1360	1/2" size, 2" drain ABS/PVC, 15 A receptacle	↓	24	.333	↓	133	13.20		146.20	168
1400	Wall mounted									
1410	1/2" size, 1-1/2" plastic drain	1 Plum	19	.421	Ea.	30.50	16.65		47.15	61

22 41 Residential Plumbing Fixtures

22 41 39 – Residential Faucets, Supplies and Trim

22 41 39.70 Washer/Dryer Accessories	Crew	Daily Output	Labor-Hours	Unit	Material	2017 Bare Costs Labor	Equipment	Total	Total Incl O&P
1420	1/2" size, 2" plastic drain	1 Plum	18	.444	Ea.	17.50	17.60		35.10	48.50
1500	Dryer vent kit									
1510	8' flex duct, clamps and outside hood	1 Plum	20	.400	Ea.	13.10	15.80		28.90	40.50
1980	Rough-in, supply, waste, and vent for washer boxes		3.46	2.310		253	91.50		344.50	430
9605	Washing machine valve assembly, hot & cold water supply, recessed		8	1		76	39.50		115.50	149
9610	Washing machine valve assembly, hot & cold water supply, mounted		8	1		60.50	39.50		100	132

22 42 Commercial Plumbing Fixtures

22 42 13 – Commercial Water Closets, Urinals, and Bidets

22 42 13.13 Water Closets

		Crew	Daily Output	Labor-Hours	Unit	Material	2017 Bare Costs Labor	Equipment	Total	Total Incl O&P
0010	WATER CLOSETS									
3000	Bowl only, with flush valve, seat, 1.6 gpf unless noted									
3100	Wall hung	Q-1	5.80	2.759	Ea.	835	98		933	1,075
3200	For rough-in, supply, waste and vent, single WC		2.56	6.250		1,200	223		1,423	1,700
3300	Floor mounted		5.80	2.759		296	98		394	485
3370	For rough-in, supply, waste and vent, single WC		2.84	5.634		435	201		636	805
3390	Floor mounted children's size, 10-3/4" high									
3392	With automatic flush sensor, 1.6 gpf	Q-1	6.20	2.581	Ea.	590	92		682	800
3396	With automatic flush sensor, 1.28 gpf		6.20	2.581		590	92		682	800
3400	For rough-in, supply, waste and vent, single WC		2.84	5.634		435	201		636	805

22 42 16 – Commercial Lavatories and Sinks

22 42 16.13 Lavatories

0010	LAVATORIES, With trim, white unless noted otherwise
0020	Commercial lavatories same as residential. See Section 22 41 16

22 42 16.40 Service Sinks

		Crew	Daily Output	Labor-Hours	Unit	Material	2017 Bare Costs Labor	Equipment	Total	Total Incl O&P
0010	SERVICE SINKS									
6650	Service, floor, corner, P.E. on C.I., 28" x 28"	Q-1	4.40	3.636	Ea.	1,025	129		1,154	1,375
6750	Vinyl coated rim guard, add					62.50			62.50	68.50
6755	Mop sink, molded stone, 22" x 18"	1 Plum	3.33	2.402		273	95		368	455
6760	Mop sink, molded stone, 24" x 36"		3.33	2.402		257	95		352	440
6770	Mop sink, molded stone, 24" x 36", w/rim 3 sides		3.33	2.402		281	95		376	465
6790	For rough-in, supply, waste & vent, floor service sinks	Q-1	1.64	9.756		790	345		1,135	1,450

22 42 39 – Commercial Faucets, Supplies, and Trim

22 42 39.10 Faucets and Fittings

		Crew	Daily Output	Labor-Hours	Unit	Material	2017 Bare Costs Labor	Equipment	Total	Total Incl O&P
0010	FAUCETS AND FITTINGS									
2790	Faucets for lavatories									
2800	Self-closing, center set	1 Plum	10	.800	Ea.	150	31.50		181.50	217
2810	Automatic sensor and operator, with faucet head		6.15	1.301		460	51.50		511.50	590
3000	Service sink faucet, cast spout, pail hook, hose end		14	.571		76.50	22.50		99	122

22 42 39.30 Carriers and Supports

		Crew	Daily Output	Labor-Hours	Unit	Material	2017 Bare Costs Labor	Equipment	Total	Total Incl O&P
0010	CARRIERS AND SUPPORTS, For plumbing fixtures									
0600	Plate type with studs, top back plate	1 Plum	7	1.143	Ea.	96	45		141	181
3000	Lavatory, concealed arm									
3050	Floor mounted, single									
3100	High back fixture	1 Plum	6	1.333	Ea.	570	52.50		622.50	710
3200	Flat slab fixture	"	6	1.333	"	490	52.50		542.50	625
8200	Water closet, residential									
8220	Vertical centerline, floor mount									
8240	Single, 3" caulk, 2" or 3" vent	1 Plum	6	1.333	Ea.	655	52.50		707.50	810

22 42 Commercial Plumbing Fixtures

22 42 39 – Commercial Faucets, Supplies, and Trim

22 42 39.30 Carriers and Supports	Crew	Daily Output	Labor-Hours	Unit	Material	2017 Bare Costs Labor	Equipment	Total	Total Incl O&P
8260	4" caulk, 2" or 4" vent	1 Plum	6	1.333	Ea.	845	52.50		897.50	1,025

22 51 Swimming Pool Plumbing Systems

22 51 19 – Swimming Pool Water Treatment Equipment

22 51 19.50 Swimming Pool Filtration Equipment

		Crew	Daily Output	Labor-Hours	Unit	Material	2017 Bare Costs Labor	Equipment	Total	Total Incl O&P
0010	**SWIMMING POOL FILTRATION EQUIPMENT**									
0900	Filter system, sand or diatomite type, incl. pump, 6,000 gal./hr.	2 Plum	1.80	8.889	Total	2,325	350		2,675	3,125
1020	Add for chlorination system, 800 S.F. pool	"	3	5.333	Ea.	179	211		390	545

Estimating Tips

The labor adjustment factors listed in Subdivision 22 01 02.20 also apply to Division 23.

23 10 00 Facility Fuel Systems

- The prices in this subdivision for above- and below-ground storage tanks do not include foundations or hold-down slabs, unless noted. The estimator should refer to Divisions 3 and 31 for foundation system pricing. In addition to the foundations, required tank accessories, such as tank gauges, leak detection devices, and additional manholes and piping, must be added to the tank prices.

23 50 00 Central Heating Equipment

- When estimating the cost of an HVAC system, check to see who is responsible for providing and installing the temperature control system. It is possible to overlook controls, assuming that they would be included in the electrical estimate.
- When looking up a boiler, be careful on specified capacity. Some

manufacturers rate their products on output while others use input.

- Include HVAC insulation for pipe, boiler, and duct (wrap and liner).
- Be careful when looking up mechanical items to get the correct pressure rating and connection type (thread, weld, flange).

23 70 00 Central HVAC Equipment

- Combination heating and cooling units are sized by the air conditioning requirements. (See Reference No. R236000-20 for the preliminary sizing guide.)
- A ton of air conditioning is nominally 400 CFM.
- Rectangular duct is taken off by the linear foot for each size, but its cost is usually estimated by the pound. Remember that SMACNA standards now base duct on internal pressure.
- Prefabricated duct is estimated and purchased like pipe: straight sections and fittings.
- Note that cranes or other lifting equipment are not included on any

lines in Division 23. For example, if a crane is required to lift a heavy piece of pipe into place high above a gym floor, or to put a rooftop unit on the roof of a four-story building, etc., it must be added. Due to the potential for extreme variation—from nothing additional required to a major crane or helicopter—we feel that including a nominal amount for "lifting contingency" would be useless and detract from the accuracy of the estimate. When using equipment rental cost data from RSMeans, do not forget to include the cost of the operator(s).

Reference Numbers

Reference numbers are shown at the beginning of some major classifications. These numbers refer to related items in the Reference Section. The reference information may be an estimating procedure, an alternate pricing method, or technical information.

Note: Not all subdivisions listed here necessarily appear. ■

23 05 Common Work Results for HVAC

23 05 05 – Selective Demolition for HVAC

23 05 05.10 HVAC Demolition	Crew	Daily Output	Labor-Hours	Unit	Material	2017 Bare Costs Labor	Equipment	Total	Total Incl O&P
0010	**HVAC DEMOLITION**								
0100	Air conditioner, split unit, 3 ton	Q-5	2	8	Ea.		296		296	490
0150	Package unit, 3 ton	Q-6	3	8	"		285		285	470
0260	Baseboard, hydronic fin tube, 1/2"	Q-5	117	.137	L.F.		5.05		5.05	8.35
0298	Boilers									
0300	Electric, up thru 148 kW	Q-19	2	12	Ea.		455		455	750
0310	150 thru 518 kW	"	1	24			915		915	1,500
0320	550 thru 2000 kW	Q-21	.40	80			3,100		3,100	5,100
0330	2070 kW and up	"	.30	106			4,150		4,150	6,825
0340	Gas and/or oil, up thru 150 MBH	Q-7	2.20	14.545			540		540	885
0350	160 thru 2000 MBH		.80	40			1,475		1,475	2,450
0360	2100 thru 4500 MBH		.50	64			2,375		2,375	3,900
0370	4600 thru 7000 MBH		.30	106			3,950		3,950	6,500
0390	12,200 thru 25,000 MBH		.12	266			9,875		9,875	16,300
1000	Ductwork, 4" high, 8" wide	1 Clab	200	.040	L.F.		1.06		1.06	1.78
1100	6" high, 8" wide		165	.048			1.29		1.29	2.16
1200	10" high, 12" wide		125	.064			1.70		1.70	2.85
1300	12"-14" high, 16"-18" wide		85	.094			2.50		2.50	4.19
1500	30" high, 36" wide		56	.143			3.80		3.80	6.35
2200	Furnace, electric	Q-20	2	10	Ea.		355		355	595
2300	Gas or oil, under 120 MBH	Q-9	4	4			138		138	230
2340	Over 120 MBH	"	3	5.333			184		184	305
2800	Heat pump, package unit, 3 ton	Q-5	2.40	6.667			247		247	405
2840	Split unit, 3 ton		2	8			296		296	490
2950	Tank, steel, oil, 275 gal., above ground		10	1.600			59		59	97.50
2960	Remove and reset		3	5.333			197		197	325
5090	Remove refrigerant from system	1 Stpi	40	.200	Lb.		8.20		8.20	13.55

23 07 HVAC Insulation

23 07 13 – Duct Insulation

23 07 13.10 Duct Thermal Insulation

23 07 13.10 Duct Thermal Insulation	Crew	Daily Output	Labor-Hours	Unit	Material	2017 Bare Costs Labor	Equipment	Total	Total Incl O&P
0010	**DUCT THERMAL INSULATION**									
3000	Ductwork									
3020	Blanket type, fiberglass, flexible									
3030	Fire rated for grease and hazardous exhaust ducts									
3060	1-1/2" thick	Q-14	84	.190	S.F.	4.54	6.15		10.69	15.40
3090	Fire rated for plenums									
3100	1/2" x 24" x 25'	Q-14	1.94	8.247	Roll	167	266		433	635
3110	1/2" x 24" x 25'		98	.163	S.F.	3.35	5.25		8.60	12.60
3120	1/2" x 48" x 25'		1.04	15.385	Roll	335	495		830	1,200
3126	1/2" x 48" x 25'		104	.154	S.F.	3.35	4.96		8.31	12.10
3140	FSK vapor barrier wrap, .75 lb. density									
3160	1" thick	G	Q-14	350	.046	S.F.	.22	1.47		1.69	2.74
3170	1-1/2" thick	G	"	320	.050	"	.27	1.61		1.88	3.03
3210	Vinyl jacket, same as FSK									

23 09 Instrumentation and Control for HVAC

23 09 53 – Pneumatic and Electric Control System for HVAC

23 09 53.10 Control Components

23 09 53.10 Control Components	Crew	Daily Output	Labor-Hours	Unit	Material	2017 Bare Costs Labor	2017 Bare Costs Equipment	Total	Total Incl O&P
0010 **CONTROL COMPONENTS**									
5000 Thermostats									
5030 Manual	1 Stpi	8	1	Ea.	50.50	41		91.50	124
5040 1 set back, electric, timed G		8	1		76.50	41		117.50	153
5050 2 set back, electric, timed G		8	1		243	41		284	335

23 13 Facility Fuel-Storage Tanks

23 13 13 – Facility Underground Fuel-Oil, Storage Tanks

23 13 13.09 Single-Wall Steel Fuel-Oil Tanks

	Crew	Daily Output	Labor-Hours	Unit	Material	2017 Bare Costs Labor	2017 Bare Costs Equipment	Total	Total Incl O&P
0010 **SINGLE-WALL STEEL FUEL-OIL TANKS**									
5000 Tanks, steel ugnd., sti-p3, not incl. hold-down bars									
5500 Excavation, pad, pumps and piping not included									
5510 Single wall, 500 gallon capacity, 7 ga. shell	Q-5	2.70	5.926	Ea.	1,800	219		2,019	2,350
5520 1,000 gallon capacity, 7 ga. shell	"	2.50	6.400		2,525	237		2,762	3,175
5530 2,000 gallon capacity, 1/4" thick shell	Q-7	4.60	6.957		3,275	257		3,532	4,025
5535 2,500 gallon capacity, 7 ga. shell	Q-5	3	5.333		4,900	197		5,097	5,700
5610 25,000 gallon capacity, 3/8" thick shell	Q-7	1.30	24.615		26,500	910		27,410	30,700
5630 40,000 gallon capacity, 3/8" thick shell		.90	35.556		42,400	1,325		43,725	48,900
5640 50,000 gallon capacity, 3/8" thick shell		.80	40		47,100	1,475		48,575	54,500

23 13 13.23 Glass-Fiber-Reinfcd-Plastic, Fuel-Oil, Storage

	Crew	Daily Output	Labor-Hours	Unit	Material	2017 Bare Costs Labor	2017 Bare Costs Equipment	Total	Total Incl O&P
0010 **GLASS-FIBER-REINFCD-PLASTIC, UNDERGRND. FUEL-OIL, STORAGE**									
0210 Fiberglass, underground, single wall, U.L. listed, not including									
0220 manway or hold-down strap									
0230 1,000 gallon capacity	Q-5	2.46	6.504	Ea.	4,525	241		4,766	5,400
0240 2,000 gallon capacity	Q-7	4.57	7.002		6,550	259		6,809	7,650
0245 3,000 gallon capacity		3.90	8.205		7,850	305		8,155	9,150
0255 5,000 gallon capacity		3.20	10		10,100	370		10,470	11,800
0500 For manway, fittings and hold-downs, add					20%	15%			
2210 Fiberglass, underground, single wall, U.L. listed, including									
2220 hold-down straps, no manways									
2230 1,000 gallon capacity	Q-5	1.88	8.511	Ea.	5,000	315		5,315	6,050
2240 2,000 gallon capacity	Q-7	3.55	9.014	"	7,025	335		7,360	8,300

23 13 23 – Facility Aboveground Fuel-Oil, Storage Tanks

23 13 23.16 Steel

	Crew	Daily Output	Labor-Hours	Unit	Material	2017 Bare Costs Labor	2017 Bare Costs Equipment	Total	Total Incl O&P
3001 **STEEL**, storage, above ground, including supports, coating									
3020 fittings, not including foundation, pumps or piping									
3040 Single wall, 275 gallon	Q-5	5	3.200	Ea.	515	118		633	760
3060 550 gallon	"	2.70	5.926		4,125	219		4,344	4,900
3080 1,000 gallon	Q-7	5	6.400		6,775	237		7,012	7,850
3320 Double wall, 500 gallon capacity	Q-5	2.40	6.667		1,750	247		1,997	2,325
3330 2000 gallon capacity	Q-7	4.15	7.711		5,700	285		5,985	6,750
3340 4000 gallon capacity		3.60	8.889		12,500	330		12,830	14,300
3350 6000 gallon capacity		2.40	13.333		14,200	495		14,695	16,400
3360 8000 gallon capacity		2	16		16,800	590		17,390	19,500
3370 10000 gallon capacity		1.80	17.778		30,000	660		30,660	34,100
3380 15000 gallon capacity		1.50	21.333		40,000	790		40,790	45,300
3390 20000 gallon capacity		1.30	24.615		43,000	910		43,910	48,800
3400 25000 gallon capacity		1.15	27.826		53,500	1,025		54,525	60,500
3410 30000 gallon capacity		1	32		64,500	1,175		65,675	73,000

For customer support on your Residential Costs with RSMeans Data, call 800.448.8182.

579

23 13 Facility Fuel-Storage Tanks

23 13 23 – Facility Aboveground Fuel-Oil, Storage Tanks

23 13 23.26 Horizontal, Conc., Abvgrd Fuel-Oil, Stor. Tanks	Crew	Daily Output	Labor-Hours	Unit	Material	2017 Bare Costs Labor	Equipment	Total	Total Incl O&P
0010 **HORIZONTAL, CONCRETE, ABOVEGROUND FUEL-OIL, STORAGE TANKS**									
0050 Concrete, storage, aboveground, including pad & pump									
0100 500 gallon	F-3	2	20	Ea.	10,100	640	286	11,026	12,500
0200 1,000 gallon	"	2	20	"	14,100	640	286	15,026	17,000

23 21 Hydronic Piping and Pumps

23 21 20 – Hydronic HVAC Piping Specialties

23 21 20.46 Expansion Tanks

	Crew	Daily Output	Labor-Hours	Unit	Material	2017 Bare Costs Labor	Equipment	Total	Total Incl O&P
0010 **EXPANSION TANKS**									
1507 Underground fuel-oil storage tanks, see Section 23 13 13									
2000 Steel, liquid expansion, ASME, painted, 15 gallon capacity	Q-5	17	.941	Ea.	710	35		745	840
2040 30 gallon capacity		12	1.333		820	49.50		869.50	980
3000 Steel ASME expansion, rubber diaphragm, 19 gal. cap. accept.		12	1.333		2,700	49.50		2,749.50	3,050
3020 31 gallon capacity		8	2		3,000	74		3,074	3,425

23 21 23 – Hydronic Pumps

23 21 23.13 In-Line Centrifugal Hydronic Pumps

	Crew	Daily Output	Labor-Hours	Unit	Material	2017 Bare Costs Labor	Equipment	Total	Total Incl O&P
0010 **IN-LINE CENTRIFUGAL HYDRONIC PUMPS**									
0600 Bronze, sweat connections, 1/40 HP, in line									
0640 3/4" size	Q-1	16	1	Ea.	244	35.50		279.50	330
1000 Flange connection, 3/4" to 1-1/2" size									
1040 1/12 HP	Q-1	6	2.667	Ea.	635	95		730	855
1060 1/8 HP		6	2.667		1,100	95		1,195	1,350
2101 Pumps, circulating, 3/4" to 1-1/2" size, 1/3 HP		6	2.667		915	95		1,010	1,150

23 23 Refrigerant Piping

23 23 16 – Refrigerant Piping Specialties

23 23 16.16 Refrigerant Line Sets

	Crew	Daily Output	Labor-Hours	Unit	Material	2017 Bare Costs Labor	Equipment	Total	Total Incl O&P
0010 **REFRIGERANT LINE SETS**									
0100 Copper tube									
0110 1/2" insulation, both tubes									
0120 Combination 1/4" and 1/2" tubes									
0130 10' set	Q-5	42	.381	Ea.	70.50	14.10		84.60	101
0140 20' set		40	.400		110	14.80		124.80	146
0150 30' set		37	.432		148	16		164	189
0160 40' set		35	.457		193	16.90		209.90	241
0170 50' set		32	.500		229	18.50		247.50	283
0180 100' set		22	.727		520	27		547	620
0300 Combination 1/4" and 3/4" tubes									
0310 10' set	Q-5	40	.400	Ea.	78.50	14.80		93.30	111
0320 20' set		38	.421		139	15.60		154.60	179
0330 30' set		35	.457		208	16.90		224.90	257
0340 40' set		33	.485		272	17.95		289.95	330
0350 50' set		30	.533		345	19.75		364.75	410
0380 100' set		20	.800		780	29.50		809.50	910
0500 Combination 3/8" & 3/4" tubes									
0510 10' set	Q-5	28	.571	Ea.	90.50	21		111.50	135
0520 20' set		36	.444		141	16.45		157.45	182
0530 30' set		34	.471		191	17.40		208.40	240

23 23 Refrigerant Piping

23 23 16 – Refrigerant Piping Specialties

23 23 16.16 Refrigerant Line Sets		Crew	Daily Output	Labor-Hours	Unit	Material	2017 Bare Costs Labor	Equipment	Total	Total Incl O&P
0540	40' set	Q-5	31	.516	Ea.	252	19.10		271.10	310
0550	50' set		28	.571		296	21		317	360
0580	100' set		18	.889		875	33		908	1,025
0700	Combination 3/8" & 1-1/8" tubes									
0710	10' set	Q-5	36	.444	Ea.	158	16.45		174.45	201
0720	20' set		33	.485		265	17.95		282.95	320
0730	30' set		31	.516		355	19.10		374.10	420
0740	40' set		28	.571		535	21		556	620
0750	50' set		26	.615		615	23		638	720
0900	Combination 1/2" & 3/4" tubes									
0910	10' set	Q-5	37	.432	Ea.	95.50	16		111.50	132
0920	20' set		35	.457		169	16.90		185.90	214
0930	30' set		33	.485		255	17.95		272.95	310
0940	40' set		30	.533		335	19.75		354.75	405
0950	50' set		27	.593		420	22		442	500
0980	100' set		17	.941		950	35		985	1,100
2100	Combination 1/2" & 1-1/8" tubes									
2110	10' set	Q-5	35	.457	Ea.	163	16.90		179.90	207
2120	20' set		31	.516		279	19.10		298.10	335
2130	30' set		29	.552		420	20.50		440.50	495
2140	40' set		25	.640		565	23.50		588.50	660
2150	50' set		14	1.143		625	42.50		667.50	755
2300	For 1" thick insulation add					30%	15%			

23 31 HVAC Ducts and Casings

23 31 13 – Metal Ducts

23 31 13.13 Rectangular Metal Ducts

		Crew	Daily Output	Labor-Hours	Unit	Material	2017 Bare Costs Labor	Equipment	Total	Total Incl O&P
0010	**RECTANGULAR METAL DUCTS**									
0020	Fabricated rectangular, includes fittings, joints, supports,									
0021	allowance for flexible connections and field sketches.									
0030	Does not include "as-built dwgs." or insulation.									
0031	NOTE: Fabrication and installation are combined									
0040	as LABOR cost. Approx. 25% fittings assumed.									
0042	Fabrication/Inst. is to commercial quality standards									
0043	(SMACNA or equiv.) for structure, sealing, leak testing, etc.									
0100	Aluminum, alloy 3003-H14, under 100 lb.	Q-10	75	.320	Lb.	3.19	11.45		14.64	22.50
0110	100 to 500 lb.		80	.300		1.88	10.75		12.63	19.95
0120	500 to 1,000 lb.		95	.253		1.81	9.05		10.86	17.10
0140	1,000 to 2,000 lb.		120	.200		1.77	7.15		8.92	13.90
0500	Galvanized steel, under 200 lb.		235	.102		.57	3.65		4.22	6.75
0520	200 to 500 lb.		245	.098		.56	3.50		4.06	6.45
0540	500 to 1,000 lb.		255	.094		.55	3.36		3.91	6.20

For customer support on your Residential Costs with RSMeans Data, call 800.448.8182.

581

23 33 13 – Dampers

23 33 13.13 Volume-Control Dampers

		Crew	Daily Output	Labor-Hours	Unit	Material	2017 Bare Costs Labor	Equipment	Total	Total Incl O&P
0010	**VOLUME-CONTROL DAMPERS**									
6000	12" x 12"	1 Shee	21	.381	Ea.	30	14.60		44.60	57.50
8000	Multi-blade dampers, parallel blade									
8100	8" x 8"	1 Shee	24	.333	Ea.	83	12.75		95.75	113

23 33 13.16 Fire Dampers

		Crew	Daily Output	Labor-Hours	Unit	Material	2017 Bare Costs Labor	Equipment	Total	Total Incl O&P
0010	**FIRE DAMPERS**									
3000	Fire damper, curtain type, 1-1/2 hr. rated, vertical, 6" x 6"	1 Shee	24	.333	Ea.	24.50	12.75		37.25	48.50
3020	8" x 6"	"	22	.364	"	24.50	13.95		38.45	50.50

23 33 46 – Flexible Ducts

23 33 46.10 Flexible Air Ducts

		Crew	Daily Output	Labor-Hours	Unit	Material	2017 Bare Costs Labor	Equipment	Total	Total Incl O&P
0010	**FLEXIBLE AIR DUCTS**									
1300	Flexible, coated fiberglass fabric on corr. resist. metal helix									
1400	pressure to 12" (WG) UL-181									
1500	Noninsulated, 3" diameter	Q-9	400	.040	L.F.	1.20	1.38		2.58	3.62
1540	5" diameter		320	.050		1.38	1.72		3.10	4.40
1560	6" diameter		280	.057		1.60	1.97		3.57	5.05
1580	7" diameter		240	.067		1.78	2.30		4.08	5.80
1900	Insulated, 1" thick, PE jacket, 3" diameter [G]		380	.042		2.62	1.45		4.07	5.30
1910	4" diameter [G]		340	.047		2.80	1.62		4.42	5.80
1920	5" diameter [G]		300	.053		2.93	1.84		4.77	6.30
1940	6" diameter [G]		260	.062		3.11	2.12		5.23	6.95
1960	7" diameter [G]		220	.073		3.60	2.51		6.11	8.15
1980	8" diameter [G]		180	.089		3.80	3.06		6.86	9.30
2040	12" diameter [G]		100	.160		5.25	5.50		10.75	15

23 33 53 – Duct Liners

23 33 53.10 Duct Liner Board

		Crew	Daily Output	Labor-Hours	Unit	Material	2017 Bare Costs Labor	Equipment	Total	Total Incl O&P
0010	**DUCT LINER BOARD**									
3490	Board type, fiberglass liner, 3 lb. density									
3940	Board type, non-fibrous foam									
3950	Temperature, bacteria and fungi resistant									
3960	1" thick [G]	Q-14	150	.107	S.F.	2.57	3.44		6.01	8.65
3970	1-1/2" thick [G]		130	.123		4.19	3.97		8.16	11.30
3980	2" thick [G]		120	.133		4.02	4.30		8.32	11.70

23 34 HVAC Fans

23 34 23 – HVAC Power Ventilators

23 34 23.10 HVAC Power Circulators and Ventilators

		Crew	Daily Output	Labor-Hours	Unit	Material	2017 Bare Costs Labor	Equipment	Total	Total Incl O&P
0010	**HVAC POWER CIRCULATORS AND VENTILATORS**									
6650	Residential, bath exhaust, grille, back draft damper									
6660	50 CFM	Q-20	24	.833	Ea.	56.50	29.50		86	112
6670	110 CFM		22	.909		95	32.50		127.50	159
6900	Kitchen exhaust, grille, complete, 160 CFM		22	.909		116	32.50		148.50	181
6910	180 CFM		20	1		97	35.50		132.50	167
6920	270 CFM		18	1.111		184	39.50		223.50	268
6930	350 CFM		16	1.250		138	44.50		182.50	226
6940	Residential roof jacks and wall caps									
6944	Wall cap with back draft damper									
6946	3" & 4" diam. round duct	1 Shee	11	.727	Ea.	27	28		55	76
6948	6" diam. round duct	"	11	.727	"	64	28		92	117
6958	Roof jack with bird screen and back draft damper									

23 34 23.10 HVAC Power Circulators and Ventilators	Crew	Daily Output	Labor-Hours	Unit	Material	2017 Bare Costs Labor	Equipment	Total	Total Incl O&P
6960 3" & 4" diam. round duct	1 Shee	11	.727	Ea.	23.50	28		51.50	72.50
6962 3-1/4" x 10" rectangular duct	"	10	.800	"	47	30.50		77.50	103
8020 Attic, roof type									
8030 Aluminum dome, damper & curb									
8080 12" diameter, 1000 CFM (gravity)	1 Elec	10	.800	Ea.	600	32		632	715
8090 16" diameter, 1500 CFM (gravity)		9	.889		725	35.50		760.50	860
8100 20" diameter, 2500 CFM (gravity)		8	1		890	40		930	1,050
8160 Plastic, ABS dome									
8180 1050 CFM	1 Elec	14	.571	Ea.	177	23		200	233
8200 1600 CFM	"	12	.667	"	265	27		292	335
8240 Attic, wall type, with shutter, one speed									
8250 12" diameter, 1000 CFM	1 Elec	14	.571	Ea.	415	23		438	495
8260 14" diameter, 1500 CFM		12	.667		450	27		477	540
8270 16" diameter, 2000 CFM		9	.889		510	35.50		545.50	620
8290 Whole house, wall type, with shutter, one speed									
8300 30" diameter, 4800 CFM	1 Elec	7	1.143	Ea.	1,100	46		1,146	1,275
8310 36" diameter, 7000 CFM		6	1.333		1,175	53.50		1,228.50	1,400
8320 42" diameter, 10,000 CFM		5	1.600		1,325	64.50		1,389.50	1,550
8330 48" diameter, 16,000 CFM		4	2		1,650	80.50		1,730.50	1,950
8340 For two speed, add					99			99	109
8350 Whole house, lay-down type, with shutter, one speed									
8360 30" diameter, 4500 CFM	1 Elec	8	1	Ea.	1,150	40		1,190	1,350
8370 36" diameter, 6500 CFM		7	1.143		1,250	46		1,296	1,450
8380 42" diameter, 9000 CFM		6	1.333		1,375	53.50		1,428.50	1,600
8390 48" diameter, 12,000 CFM		5	1.600		1,550	64.50		1,614.50	1,800
8440 For two speed, add					74.50			74.50	82
8450 For 12 hour timer switch, add	1 Elec	32	.250		74.50	10.05		84.55	98.50

23 37 Air Outlets and Inlets

23 37 13 - Diffusers, Registers, and Grilles

23 37 13.10 Diffusers

	Crew	Daily Output	Labor-Hours	Unit	Material	2017 Bare Costs Labor	Equipment	Total	Total Incl O&P
0010 **DIFFUSERS**, Aluminum, opposed blade damper unless noted									
0100 Ceiling, linear, also for sidewall									
0120 2" wide	1 Shee	32	.250	L.F.	17.45	9.60		27.05	35
0160 4" wide		26	.308	"	23.50	11.80		35.30	45
0500 Perforated, 24" x 24" lay-in panel size, 6" x 6"		16	.500	Ea.	158	19.15		177.15	206
0520 8" x 8"		15	.533		166	20.50		186.50	217
0530 9" x 9"		14	.571		169	22		191	223
0590 16" x 16"		11	.727		197	28		225	264
1000 Rectangular, 1 to 4 way blow, 6" x 6"		16	.500		42	19.15		61.15	78
1010 8" x 8"		15	.533		58.50	20.50		79	98
1014 9" x 9"		15	.533		52.50	20.50		73	91.50
1016 10" x 10"		15	.533		80.50	20.50		101	123
1020 12" x 6"		15	.533		72	20.50		92.50	114
1040 12" x 9"		14	.571		76.50	22		98.50	121
1060 12" x 12"		12	.667		70.50	25.50		96	120
1070 14" x 6"		13	.615		78.50	23.50		102	126
1074 14" x 14"		12	.667		129	25.50		154.50	185
1150 18" x 18"		9	.889		114	34		148	182
1170 24" x 12"		10	.800		165	30.50		195.50	232
1180 24" x 24"		7	1.143		272	44		316	370

23 37 Air Outlets and Inlets

23 37 13 – Diffusers, Registers, and Grilles

23 37 13.10 Diffusers

		Crew	Daily Output	Labor-Hours	Unit	Material	2017 Bare Costs Labor	2017 Bare Costs Equipment	Total	Total Incl O&P
1500	Round, butterfly damper, steel, diffuser size, 6" diameter	1 Shee	18	.444	Ea.	11	17		28	40.50
1520	8" diameter		16	.500		11.70	19.15		30.85	45
2000	T bar mounting, 24" x 24" lay-in frame, 6" x 6"		16	.500		72.50	19.15		91.65	112
2020	8" x 8"		14	.571		72.50	22		94.50	117
2040	12" x 12"		12	.667		89	25.50		114.50	141
2060	16" x 16"		11	.727		120	28		148	179
2080	18" x 18"		10	.800		134	30.50		164.50	198
6000	For steel diffusers instead of aluminum, deduct					10%				

23 37 13.30 Grilles

		Crew	Daily Output	Labor-Hours	Unit	Material	2017 Bare Costs Labor	2017 Bare Costs Equipment	Total	Total Incl O&P
0010	**GRILLES**									
0020	Aluminum, unless noted otherwise									
1000	Air return, steel, 6" x 6"	1 Shee	26	.308	Ea.	19.80	11.80		31.60	41.50
1020	10" x 6"		24	.333		19.80	12.75		32.55	43.50
1080	16" x 8"		22	.364		28	13.95		41.95	54.50
1100	12" x 12"		22	.364		28	13.95		41.95	54.50
1120	24" x 12"		18	.444		37	17		54	69
1180	16" x 16"		22	.364		36	13.95		49.95	63

23 37 13.60 Registers

		Crew	Daily Output	Labor-Hours	Unit	Material	2017 Bare Costs Labor	2017 Bare Costs Equipment	Total	Total Incl O&P
0010	**REGISTERS**									
0980	Air supply									
3000	Baseboard, hand adj. damper, enameled steel									
3012	8" x 6"	1 Shee	26	.308	Ea.	6.85	11.80		18.65	27.50
3020	10" x 6"		24	.333		7.45	12.75		20.20	29.50
3040	12" x 5"		23	.348		6.05	13.30		19.35	29
3060	12" x 6"		23	.348		8.10	13.30		21.40	31.50
4000	Floor, toe operated damper, enameled steel									
4020	4" x 8"	1 Shee	32	.250	Ea.	12.70	9.60		22.30	30
4040	4" x 12"	"	26	.308	"	14.90	11.80		26.70	36
4300	Spiral pipe supply register									
4310	Steel, with air scoop									
4320	4" x 12", for 8" thru 13" diameter duct	1 Shee	25	.320	Ea.	78	12.25		90.25	107
4330	4" x 18", for 8" thru 13" diameter duct		18	.444		91.50	17		108.50	129
4340	6" x 12", for 14" thru 21" diameter duct		19	.421		83	16.15		99.15	119
4350	6" x 16", for 14" thru 21" diameter duct		18	.444		95	17		112	134
4360	6" x 20", for 14" thru 21" diameter duct		17	.471		104	18		122	144
4370	6" x 24", for 14" thru 21" diameter duct		16	.500		123	19.15		142.15	167
4380	8" x 16", for 22" thru 31" diameter duct		19	.421		99.50	16.15		115.65	137
4390	8" x 18", for 22" thru 31" diameter duct		18	.444		104	17		121	143
4400	8" x 24", for 22" thru 31" diameter duct		15	.533		128	20.50		148.50	175

23 41 Particulate Air Filtration

23 41 13 – Panel Air Filters

23 41 13.10 Panel Type Air Filters

		Crew	Daily Output	Labor-Hours	Unit	Material	2017 Bare Costs Labor	2017 Bare Costs Equipment	Total	Total Incl O&P
0010	**PANEL TYPE AIR FILTERS**									
2950	Mechanical media filtration units									
3000	High efficiency type, with frame, non-supported	G				MCFM	35			35	38.50
3100	Supported type	G				"	55			55	60.50
5500	Throwaway glass or paper media type, 12" x 36" x 1"					Ea.	2.39			2.39	2.63

23 41 Particulate Air Filtration

23 41 16 – Renewable-Media Air Filters

23 41 16.10 Disposable Media Air Filters	Crew	Daily Output	Labor-Hours	Unit	Material	2017 Bare Costs Labor	Equipment	Total	Total Incl O&P
0010 **DISPOSABLE MEDIA AIR FILTERS**									
5000 Renewable disposable roll				C.S.F.	5.25			5.25	5.75

23 41 19 – Washable Air Filters

23 41 19.10 Permanent Air Filters

	Crew	Daily Output	Labor-Hours	Unit	Material	Labor	Equipment	Total	Total Incl O&P
0010 **PERMANENT AIR FILTERS**									
4500 Permanent washable	G			MCFM	25			25	27.50

23 41 23 – Extended Surface Filters

23 41 23.10 Expanded Surface Filters

	Crew	Daily Output	Labor-Hours	Unit	Material	Labor	Equipment	Total	Total Incl O&P
0010 **EXPANDED SURFACE FILTERS**									
4000 Medium efficiency, extended surface	G			MCFM	6			6	6.60

23 42 Gas-Phase Air Filtration

23 42 13 – Activated-Carbon Air Filtration

23 42 13.10 Charcoal Type Air Filtration

	Crew	Daily Output	Labor-Hours	Unit	Material	Labor	Equipment	Total	Total Incl O&P
0010 **CHARCOAL TYPE AIR FILTRATION**									
0050 Activated charcoal type, full flow				MCFM	650			650	715
0060 Full flow, impregnated media 12" deep					225			225	248
0070 HEPA filter & frame for field erection					450			450	495
0080 HEPA filter-diffuser, ceiling install.				↓	350			350	385

23 43 Electronic Air Cleaners

23 43 13 – Washable Electronic Air Cleaners

23 43 13.10 Electronic Air Cleaners

	Crew	Daily Output	Labor-Hours	Unit	Material	Labor	Equipment	Total	Total Incl O&P
0010 **ELECTRONIC AIR CLEANERS**									
2000 Electronic air cleaner, duct mounted									
2150 1000 CFM	1 Shee	4	2	Ea.	430	76.50		506.50	605
2200 1200 CFM		3.80	2.105		505	80.50		585.50	690
2250 1400 CFM	↓	3.60	2.222	↓	530	85		615	725

23 51 Breechings, Chimneys, and Stacks

23 51 23 – Gas Vents

23 51 23.10 Gas Chimney Vents

	Crew	Daily Output	Labor-Hours	Unit	Material	Labor	Equipment	Total	Total Incl O&P
0010 **GAS CHIMNEY VENTS**, Prefab metal, U.L. listed									
0020 Gas, double wall, galvanized steel									
0080 3" diameter	Q-9	72	.222	V.L.F.	6.60	7.65		14.25	20
0100 4" diameter	"	68	.235	"	8.15	8.10		16.25	22.50

For customer support on your Residential Costs with RSMeans Data, call 800.448.8182.

585

23 52 Heating Boilers

23 52 13 – Electric Boilers

23 52 13.10 Electric Boilers, ASME

23 52 13.10 Electric Boilers, ASME	Crew	Daily Output	Labor-Hours	Unit	Material	2017 Bare Costs Labor	Equipment	Total	Total Incl O&P
0010 **ELECTRIC BOILERS, ASME**, Standard controls and trim									
1000 Steam, 6 KW, 20.5 MBH	Q-19	1.20	20	Ea.	4,100	760		4,860	5,750
1160 60 KW, 205 MBH		1	24		6,925	915		7,840	9,100
2000 Hot water, 7.5 KW, 25.6 MBH		1.30	18.462		4,950	705		5,655	6,600
2040 30 KW, 102 MBH		1.20	20		5,325	760		6,085	7,100
2060 45 KW, 164 MBH	↓	1.20	20	↓	5,425	760		6,185	7,200

23 52 23 – Cast-Iron Boilers

23 52 23.20 Gas-Fired Boilers

	Crew	Daily Output	Labor-Hours	Unit	Material	Labor	Equipment	Total	Total Incl O&P
0010 **GAS-FIRED BOILERS**, Natural or propane, standard controls, packaged									
1000 Cast iron, with insulated jacket									
3000 Hot water, gross output, 80 MBH	Q-7	1.46	21.918	Ea.	1,925	810		2,735	3,450
3020 100 MBH	"	1.35	23.704		2,450	875		3,325	4,150
7000 For tankless water heater, add					10%				
7050 For additional zone valves up to 312 MBH, add				↓	196			196	216

23 52 23.30 Gas/Oil Fired Boilers

	Crew	Daily Output	Labor-Hours	Unit	Material	Labor	Equipment	Total	Total Incl O&P
0010 **GAS/OIL FIRED BOILERS**, Combination with burners and controls, packaged									
1000 Cast iron with insulated jacket									
2000 Steam, gross output, 720 MBH	Q-7	.43	74.074	Ea.	14,200	2,750		16,950	20,100
2900 Hot water, gross output									
2910 200 MBH	Q-6	.62	39.024	Ea.	10,200	1,400		11,600	13,600
2920 300 MBH		.49	49.080		10,200	1,750		11,950	14,200
2930 400 MBH		.41	57.971		12,000	2,075		14,075	16,600
2940 500 MBH	↓	.36	67.039		12,900	2,400		15,300	18,200
3000 584 MBH	Q-7	.44	72.072	↓	14,300	2,675		16,975	20,100

23 52 23.40 Oil-Fired Boilers

	Crew	Daily Output	Labor-Hours	Unit	Material	Labor	Equipment	Total	Total Incl O&P
0010 **OIL-FIRED BOILERS**, Standard controls, flame retention burner, packaged									
1000 Cast iron, with insulated flush jacket									
2000 Steam, gross output, 109 MBH	Q-7	1.20	26.667	Ea.	2,225	985		3,210	4,075
2060 207 MBH	"	.90	35.556	"	3,025	1,325		4,350	5,500
3000 Hot water, same price as steam									

23 52 26 – Steel Boilers

23 52 26.40 Oil-Fired Boilers

	Crew	Daily Output	Labor-Hours	Unit	Material	Labor	Equipment	Total	Total Incl O&P
0010 **OIL-FIRED BOILERS**, Standard controls, flame retention burner									
5000 Steel, with insulated flush jacket									
7000 Hot water, gross output, 103 MBH	Q-6	1.60	15	Ea.	1,875	535		2,410	2,950
7020 122 MBH		1.45	16.506		2,000	590		2,590	3,175
7060 168 MBH		1.30	18.405		2,450	655		3,105	3,775
7080 225 MBH	↓	1.22	19.704	↓	3,250	700		3,950	4,725

23 52 28 – Swimming Pool Boilers

23 52 28.10 Swimming Pool Heaters

	Crew	Daily Output	Labor-Hours	Unit	Material	Labor	Equipment	Total	Total Incl O&P
0010 **SWIMMING POOL HEATERS**, Not including wiring, external									
0020 piping, base or pad									
0160 Gas fired, input, 155 MBH	Q-6	1.50	16	Ea.	1,975	570		2,545	3,125
0200 199 MBH		1	24		2,100	855		2,955	3,700
0280 500 MBH	↓	.40	60		8,725	2,150		10,875	13,100
2000 Electric, 12 KW, 4,800 gallon pool	Q-19	3	8		2,100	305		2,405	2,825
2020 15 KW, 7,200 gallon pool		2.80	8.571		2,150	325		2,475	2,875
2040 24 KW, 9,600 gallon pool		2.40	10		2,475	380		2,855	3,350
2100 57 KW, 24,000 gallon pool	↓	1.20	20		3,650	760		4,410	5,250

23 52 Heating Boilers

23 52 88 – Burners

23 52 88.10 Replacement Type Burners		Crew	Daily Output	Labor-Hours	Unit	Material	2017 Bare Costs Labor	Equipment	Total	Total Incl O&P
0010	**REPLACEMENT TYPE BURNERS**									
0990	Residential, conversion, gas fired, LP or natural									
1000	Gun type, atmospheric input 50 to 225 MBH	Q-1	2.50	6.400	Ea.	875	228		1,103	1,325
1020	100 to 400 MBH	"	2	8		1,450	285		1,735	2,075
1025	Burner, gas, 100 to 400 MBH ⬚G					1,450			1,450	1,600
1040	300 to 1000 MBH	Q-1	1.70	9.412		4,400	335		4,735	5,400

23 54 Furnaces

23 54 13 – Electric-Resistance Furnaces

23 54 13.10 Electric Furnaces

		Crew	Daily Output	Labor-Hours	Unit	Material	Labor	Equipment	Total	Total Incl O&P
0010	**ELECTRIC FURNACES**, Hot air, blowers, std. controls									
0011	not including gas, oil or flue piping									
1000	Electric, UL listed									
1100	34.1 MBH	Q-20	4.40	4.545	Ea.	530	162		692	855

23 54 16 – Fuel-Fired Furnaces

23 54 16.13 Gas-Fired Furnaces

		Crew	Daily Output	Labor-Hours	Unit	Material	Labor	Equipment	Total	Total Incl O&P
0010	**GAS-FIRED FURNACES**									
3000	Gas, AGA certified, upflow, direct drive models									
3020	45 MBH input	Q-9	4	4	Ea.	580	138		718	865
3040	60 MBH input		3.80	4.211		595	145		740	900
3060	75 MBH input		3.60	4.444		660	153		813	980
3100	100 MBH input		3.20	5		690	172		862	1,050
3120	125 MBH input		3	5.333		725	184		909	1,100
3130	150 MBH input		2.80	5.714		1,375	197		1,572	1,825
3140	200 MBH input		2.60	6.154		3,050	212		3,262	3,725
4000	For starter plenum, add		16	1		92	34.50		126.50	159

23 54 16.16 Oil-Fired Furnaces

		Crew	Daily Output	Labor-Hours	Unit	Material	Labor	Equipment	Total	Total Incl O&P
0010	**OIL-FIRED FURNACES**									
6000	Oil, UL listed, atomizing gun type burner									
6020	56 MBH output	Q-9	3.60	4.444	Ea.	2,475	153		2,628	2,975
6030	84 MBH output		3.50	4.571		2,525	158		2,683	3,075
6040	95 MBH output		3.40	4.706		2,550	162		2,712	3,075
6060	134 MBH output		3.20	5		2,575	172		2,747	3,125
6080	151 MBH output		3	5.333		2,750	184		2,934	3,325
6100	200 MBH input		2.60	6.154		3,425	212		3,637	4,100

23 54 16.21 Solid Fuel-Fired Furnaces

		Crew	Daily Output	Labor-Hours	Unit	Material	Labor	Equipment	Total	Total Incl O&P
0010	**SOLID FUEL-FIRED FURNACES**									
6020	Wood fired furnaces									
6030	Includes hot water coil, thermostat, and auto draft control									
6040	24" long firebox ⬚G	Q-9	4	4	Ea.	4,375	138		4,513	5,050
6050	30" long firebox ⬚G		3.60	4.444		5,100	153		5,253	5,875
6060	With fireplace glass doors ⬚G		3.20	5		6,450	172		6,622	7,400
6200	Wood/oil fired furnaces, includes two thermostats									
6210	Includes hot water coil and auto draft control									
6240	24" long firebox ⬚G	Q-9	3.40	4.706	Ea.	5,375	162		5,537	6,175
6250	30" long firebox ⬚G		3	5.333		5,975	184		6,159	6,875
6260	With fireplace glass doors ⬚G		2.80	5.714		7,275	197		7,472	8,350
6400	Wood/gas fired furnaces, includes two thermostats									
6410	Includes hot water coil and auto draft control									

23 54 Furnaces

23 54 16 – Fuel-Fired Furnaces

23 54 16.21 Solid Fuel-Fired Furnaces		Crew	Daily Output	Labor-Hours	Unit	Material	2017 Bare Costs Labor	Equipment	Total	Total Incl O&P
6440	24" long firebox	G	Q-9	2.80	5.714	Ea.	6,000	197		6,197	6,925
6450	30" long firebox	G		2.40	6.667		6,700	230		6,930	7,750
6460	With fireplace glass doors	G		2	8		7,975	276		8,251	9,225
6600	Wood/oil/gas fired furnaces, optional accessories										
6610	Hot air plenum		Q-9	16	1	Ea.	108	34.50		142.50	177
6620	Safety heat dump			24	.667		94	23		117	142
6630	Auto air intake			18	.889		148	30.50		178.50	214
6640	Cold air return package			14	1.143		159	39.50		198.50	241
6650	Wood fork						51			51	56
6700	Wood fired outdoor furnace										
6740	24" long firebox	G	Q-9	3.80	4.211	Ea.	4,275	145		4,420	4,950
6760	Wood fired outdoor furnace, optional accessories										
6770	Chimney section, stainless steel, 6" ID x 3' lg.	G	Q-9	36	.444	Ea.	176	15.30		191.30	220
6780	Chimney cap, stainless steel	G	"	40	.400	"	104	13.80		117.80	137
6800	Wood fired hot water furnace										
6820	Includes 200 gal. hot water storage, thermostat, and auto draft control										
6840	30" long firebox	G	Q-9	2.10	7.619	Ea.	8,350	263		8,613	9,650
6850	Water to air heat exchanger										
6870	Includes mounting kit and blower relay										
6880	140 MBH, 18.75" W x 18.75" L		Q-9	7.50	2.133	Ea.	375	73.50		448.50	535
6890	200 MBH, 24" W x 24" L		"	7	2.286	"	530	79		609	715
6900	Water to water heat exchanger										
6940	100 MBH		Q-9	6.50	2.462	Ea.	375	85		460	555
6960	290 MBH		"	6	2.667	"	540	92		632	750
7000	Optional accessories										
7010	Large volume circulation pump (2 included)		Q-9	14	1.143	Ea.	244	39.50		283.50	335
7020	Air bleed fittings (package)			24	.667		51	23		74	94.50
7030	Domestic water preheater			6	2.667		221	92		313	395
7040	Smoke pipe kit			4	4		88	138		226	325

23 54 24 – Furnace Components for Cooling

23 54 24.10 Furnace Components and Combinations

23 54 24.10 Furnace Components and Combinations		Crew	Daily Output	Labor-Hours	Unit	Material	2017 Bare Costs Labor	Equipment	Total	Total Incl O&P
0010	**FURNACE COMPONENTS AND COMBINATIONS**										
0080	Coils, A.C. evaporator, for gas or oil furnaces										
0090	Add-on, with holding charge										
0100	Upflow										
0120	1-1/2 ton cooling		Q-5	4	4	Ea.	208	148		356	475
0130	2 ton cooling			3.70	4.324		263	160		423	555
0140	3 ton cooling			3.30	4.848		425	179		604	760
0150	4 ton cooling			3	5.333		475	197		672	850
0160	5 ton cooling			2.70	5.926		510	219		729	925
0300	Downflow										
0330	2-1/2 ton cooling		Q-5	3	5.333	Ea.	300	197		497	655
0340	3-1/2 ton cooling			2.60	6.154		475	228		703	900
0350	5 ton cooling			2.20	7.273		510	269		779	1,000
0600	Horizontal										
0630	2 ton cooling		Q-5	3.90	4.103	Ea.	350	152		502	635
0640	3 ton cooling			3.50	4.571		390	169		559	710
0650	4 ton cooling			3.20	5		470	185		655	820
0660	5 ton cooling			2.90	5.517		470	204		674	850
2000	Cased evaporator coils for air handlers										
2100	1-1/2 ton cooling		Q-5	4.40	3.636	Ea.	277	135		412	525
2110	2 ton cooling			4.10	3.902		310	144		454	580

23 54 Furnaces

23 54 24 – Furnace Components for Cooling

23 54 24.10 Furnace Components and Combinations	Crew	Daily Output	Labor-Hours	Unit	Material	2017 Bare Costs Labor	Equipment	Total	Total Incl O&P
2120	2-1/2 ton cooling	Q-5	3.90	4.103	Ea.	325	152		477	610
2130	3 ton cooling		3.70	4.324		365	160		525	665
2140	3-1/2 ton cooling		3.50	4.571		525	169		694	855
2150	4 ton cooling		3.20	5		530	185		715	885
2160	5 ton cooling	↓	2.90	5.517	↓	540	204		744	930
3010	Air handler, modular									
3100	With cased evaporator cooling coil									
3120	1-1/2 ton cooling	Q-5	3.80	4.211	Ea.	875	156		1,031	1,225
3130	2 ton cooling		3.50	4.571		965	169		1,134	1,350
3140	2-1/2 ton cooling		3.30	4.848		1,025	179		1,204	1,425
3150	3 ton cooling		3.10	5.161		1,175	191		1,366	1,625
3160	3-1/2 ton cooling		2.90	5.517		1,350	204		1,554	1,800
3170	4 ton cooling		2.50	6.400		1,450	237		1,687	2,000
3180	5 ton cooling	↓	2.10	7.619	↓	1,750	282		2,032	2,400
3500	With no cooling coil									
3520	1-1/2 ton coil size	Q-5	12	1.333	Ea.	850	49.50		899.50	1,025
3530	2 ton coil size		10	1.600		885	59		944	1,075
3540	2-1/2 ton coil size		10	1.600		910	59		969	1,100
3554	3 ton coil size		9	1.778		970	66		1,036	1,175
3560	3-1/2 ton coil size		9	1.778		1,000	66		1,066	1,200
3570	4 ton coil size		8.50	1.882		1,050	69.50		1,119.50	1,275
3580	5 ton coil size	↓	8	2	↓	1,100	74		1,174	1,325
4000	With heater									
4120	5 kW, 17.1 MBH	Q-5	16	1	Ea.	455	37		492	560
4130	7.5 kW, 25.6 MBH		15.60	1.026		1,100	38		1,138	1,275
4140	10 kW, 34.2 MBH		15.20	1.053		1,175	39		1,214	1,375
4150	12.5 kW, 42.7 MBH		14.80	1.081		1,550	40		1,590	1,775
4160	15 kW, 51.2 MBH		14.40	1.111		1,700	41		1,741	1,950
4170	25 kW, 85.4 MBH		14	1.143		2,250	42.50		2,292.50	2,550
4180	30 kW, 102 MBH	↓	13	1.231	↓	2,600	45.50		2,645.50	2,950

23 62 Packaged Compressor and Condenser Units

23 62 13 – Packaged Air-Cooled Refrigerant Compressor and Condenser Units

23 62 13.10 Packaged Air-Cooled Refrig. Condensing Units

		Crew	Daily Output	Labor-Hours	Unit	Material	Labor	Equipment	Total	Total Incl O&P
0010	**PACKAGED AIR-COOLED REFRIGERANT CONDENSING UNITS**									
0020	Condensing unit									
0030	Air cooled, compressor, standard controls									
0050	1.5 ton	Q-5	2.50	6.400	Ea.	1,025	237		1,262	1,525
0100	2 ton		2.10	7.619		1,050	282		1,332	1,625
0200	2.5 ton		1.70	9.412		1,300	350		1,650	2,025
0300	3 ton		1.30	12.308		1,300	455		1,755	2,200
0350	3.5 ton		1.10	14.545		1,525	540		2,065	2,550
0400	4 ton		.90	17.778		1,725	660		2,385	2,975
0500	5 ton	↓	.60	26.667	↓	2,075	985		3,060	3,925

For customer support on your Residential Costs with RSMeans Data, call 800.448.8182.

589

23 74 Packaged Outdoor HVAC Equipment

23 74 33 – Dedicated Outdoor-Air Units

23 74 33.10 Rooftop Air Conditioners	Crew	Daily Output	Labor-Hours	Unit	Material	2017 Bare Costs Labor	Equipment	Total	Total Incl O&P
0010 **ROOFTOP AIR CONDITIONERS**, Standard controls, curb, economizer									
1000 Single zone, electric cool, gas heat									
1140 5 ton cooling, 112 MBH heating	Q-5	.56	28.521	Ea.	4,375	1,050		5,425	6,550
1150 7.5 ton cooling, 170 MBH heating		.50	32.258		5,825	1,200		7,025	8,375
1156 8.5 ton cooling, 170 MBH heating	↓	.46	34.783		7,075	1,275		8,350	9,900
1160 10 ton cooling, 200 MBH heating	Q-6	.67	35.982	↓	9,150	1,275		10,425	12,200

23 81 Decentralized Unitary HVAC Equipment

23 81 13 – Packaged Terminal Air-Conditioners

23 81 13.10 Packaged Cabinet Type Air-Conditioners

	Crew	Daily Output	Labor-Hours	Unit	Material	2017 Bare Costs Labor	Equipment	Total	Total Incl O&P
0010 **PACKAGED CABINET TYPE AIR-CONDITIONERS**, Cabinet, wall sleeve,									
0100 louver, electric heat, thermostat, manual changeover, 208 V									
0200 6,000 BTUH cooling, 8800 BTU heat	Q-5	6	2.667	Ea.	865	98.50		963.50	1,125
0220 9,000 BTUH cooling, 13,900 BTU heat		5	3.200		1,275	118		1,393	1,600
0240 12,000 BTUH cooling, 13,900 BTU heat		4	4		1,375	148		1,523	1,750
0260 15,000 BTUH cooling, 13,900 BTU heat	↓	3	5.333	↓	1,575	197		1,772	2,075

23 81 19 – Self-Contained Air-Conditioners

23 81 19.10 Window Unit Air Conditioners

	Crew	Daily Output	Labor-Hours	Unit	Material	2017 Bare Costs Labor	Equipment	Total	Total Incl O&P
0010 **WINDOW UNIT AIR CONDITIONERS**									
4000 Portable/window, 15 amp, 125 V grounded receptacle required									
4060 5000 BTUH	1 Carp	8	1	Ea.	345	35		380	440
4340 6000 BTUH		8	1		390	35		425	490
4480 8000 BTUH		6	1.333		495	46.50		541.50	625
4500 10,000 BTUH	↓	6	1.333		595	46.50		641.50	735
4520 12,000 BTUH	L-2	8	2	↓	1,925	61.50		1,986.50	2,200
4600 Window/thru-the-wall, 15 amp, 230 V grounded receptacle required									
4780 18,000 BTUH	L-2	6	2.667	Ea.	1,050	82		1,132	1,300
4940 25,000 BTUH		4	4		1,325	123		1,448	1,650
4960 29,000 BTUH	↓	4	4	↓	1,400	123		1,523	1,750

23 81 19.20 Self-Contained Single Package

	Crew	Daily Output	Labor-Hours	Unit	Material	2017 Bare Costs Labor	Equipment	Total	Total Incl O&P
0010 **SELF-CONTAINED SINGLE PACKAGE**									
0100 Air cooled, for free blow or duct, not incl. remote condenser									
0110 Constant volume									
0200 3 ton cooling	Q-5	1	16	Ea.	3,725	590		4,315	5,075
0210 4 ton cooling	"	.80	20	"	4,075	740		4,815	5,700
1000 Water cooled for free blow or duct, not including tower									
1010 Constant volume									
1100 3 ton cooling	Q-6	1	24	Ea.	3,625	855		4,480	5,375
1300 For hot water or steam heat coils, add				"	12%	10%			

23 81 26 – Split-System Air-Conditioners

23 81 26.10 Split Ductless Systems

	Crew	Daily Output	Labor-Hours	Unit	Material	2017 Bare Costs Labor	Equipment	Total	Total Incl O&P
0010 **SPLIT DUCTLESS SYSTEMS**									
0100 Cooling only, single zone									
0110 Wall mount									
0120 3/4 ton cooling	Q-5	2	8	Ea.	1,100	296		1,396	1,725
0130 1 ton cooling		1.80	8.889		1,225	330		1,555	1,900
0140 1-1/2 ton cooling		1.60	10		1,975	370		2,345	2,775
0150 2 ton cooling	↓	1.40	11.429	↓	2,250	425		2,675	3,175
1000 Ceiling mount									
1020 2 ton cooling	Q-5	1.40	11.429	Ea.	2,000	425		2,425	2,900

23 81 Decentralized Unitary HVAC Equipment

23 81 26 – Split-System Air-Conditioners

23 81 26.10 Split Ductless Systems

		Crew	Daily Output	Labor-Hours	Unit	Material	2017 Bare Costs Labor	Equipment	Total	Total Incl O&P
1030	3 ton cooling	Q-5	1.20	13.333	Ea.	2,550	495		3,045	3,625
3000	Multizone									
3010	Wall mount									
3020	2 @ 3/4 ton cooling	Q-5	1.80	8.889	Ea.	3,375	330		3,705	4,250
5000	Cooling/Heating									
5010	Wall mount									
5110	1 ton cooling	Q-5	1.70	9.412	Ea.	1,300	350		1,650	2,000
5120	1-1/2 ton cooling	"	1.50	10.667	"	1,975	395		2,370	2,825
7000	Accessories for all split ductless systems									
7010	Add for ambient frost control	Q-5	8	2	Ea.	126	74		200	261
7020	Add for tube/wiring kit (Line sets)									
7030	15' kit	Q-5	32	.500	Ea.	100	18.50		118.50	141
7036	25' kit		28	.571		186	21		207	239
7040	35' kit		24	.667		169	24.50		193.50	227
7050	50' kit		20	.800		192	29.50		221.50	260

23 81 43 – Air-Source Unitary Heat Pumps

23 81 43.10 Air-Source Heat Pumps

		Crew	Daily Output	Labor-Hours	Unit	Material	2017 Bare Costs Labor	Equipment	Total	Total Incl O&P
0010	**AIR-SOURCE HEAT PUMPS**, Not including interconnecting tubing									
1000	Air to air, split system, not including curbs, pads, fan coil and ductwork									
1012	Outside condensing unit only, for fan coil see Section 23 82 19.10									
1020	2 ton cooling, 8.5 MBH heat @ 0°F	Q-5	2	8	Ea.	1,650	296		1,946	2,300
1054	4 ton cooling, 24 MBH heat @ 0°F	"	.80	20	"	2,450	740		3,190	3,925
1500	Single package, not including curbs, pads, or plenums									
1520	2 ton cooling, 6.5 MBH heat @ 0°F	Q-5	1.50	10.667	Ea.	3,150	395		3,545	4,100
1580	4 ton cooling, 13 MBH heat @ 0°F	"	.96	16.667	"	4,225	615		4,840	5,675

23 81 46 – Water-Source Unitary Heat Pumps

23 81 46.10 Water Source Heat Pumps

		Crew	Daily Output	Labor-Hours	Unit	Material	2017 Bare Costs Labor	Equipment	Total	Total Incl O&P
0010	**WATER SOURCE HEAT PUMPS**, Not incl. connecting tubing or water source									
2000	Water source to air, single package									
2100	1 ton cooling, 13 MBH heat @ 75°F	Q-5	2	8	Ea.	1,800	296		2,096	2,475
2200	4 ton cooling, 31 MBH heat @ 75°F	"	1.20	13.333	"	3,000	495		3,495	4,125

23 82 Convection Heating and Cooling Units

23 82 19 – Fan Coil Units

23 82 19.10 Fan Coil Air Conditioning

		Crew	Daily Output	Labor-Hours	Unit	Material	2017 Bare Costs Labor	Equipment	Total	Total Incl O&P
0010	**FAN COIL AIR CONDITIONING**									
0030	Fan coil AC, cabinet mounted, filters and controls									
0100	Chilled water, 1/2 ton cooling	Q-5	8	2	Ea.	555	74		629	730
0110	3/4 ton cooling		7	2.286		680	84.50		764.50	890
0120	1 ton cooling		6	2.667		830	98.50		928.50	1,075

23 82 29 – Radiators

23 82 29.10 Hydronic Heating

		Crew	Daily Output	Labor-Hours	Unit	Material	2017 Bare Costs Labor	Equipment	Total	Total Incl O&P
0010	**HYDRONIC HEATING**, Terminal units, not incl. main supply pipe									
1000	Radiation									
1100	Panel, baseboard, C.I., including supports, no covers	Q-5	46	.348	L.F.	40	12.85		52.85	65.50
3000	Radiators, cast iron									
3100	Free standing or wall hung, 6 tube, 25" high	Q-5	96	.167	Section	48	6.15		54.15	63
3200	4 tube, 19" high	"	96	.167	"	31	6.15		37.15	44
3250	Adj. brackets, 2 per wall radiator up to 30 sections	1 Stpi	32	.250	Ea.	55	10.30		65.30	77.50

For customer support on your Residential Costs with RSMeans Data, call 800.448.8182.

591

23 82 Convection Heating and Cooling Units

23 82 36 – Finned-Tube Radiation Heaters

23 82 36.10 Finned Tube Radiation	Crew	Daily Output	Labor-Hours	Unit	Material	2017 Bare Costs Labor	Equipment	Total	Total Incl O&P
0010 **FINNED TUBE RADIATION**, Terminal units, not incl. main supply pipe									
1310 Baseboard, pkgd, 1/2" copper tube, alum. fin, 7" high	Q-5	60	.267	L.F.	11.30	9.85		21.15	28.50
1320 3/4" copper tube, alum. fin, 7" high		58	.276		7.60	10.20		17.80	25
1340 1" copper tube, alum. fin, 8-7/8" high		56	.286		19.25	10.55		29.80	38.50
1360 1-1/4" copper tube, alum. fin, 8-7/8" high	▼	54	.296	▼	28.50	10.95		39.45	49
1500 Note: fin tube may also require corners, caps, etc.									

23 83 Radiant Heating Units

23 83 16 – Radiant-Heating Hydronic Piping

23 83 16.10 Radiant Floor Heating

	Crew	Daily Output	Labor-Hours	Unit	Material	2017 Bare Costs Labor	Equipment	Total	Total Incl O&P
0010 **RADIANT FLOOR HEATING**									
0100 Tubing, PEX (cross-linked polyethylene)									
0110 Oxygen barrier type for systems with ferrous materials									
0120 1/2"	Q-5	800	.020	L.F.	.98	.74		1.72	2.30
0130 3/4"		535	.030		1.39	1.11		2.50	3.35
0140 1"	▼	400	.040	▼	2.16	1.48		3.64	4.82
0200 Non barrier type for ferrous free systems									
0210 1/2"	Q-5	800	.020	L.F.	.50	.74		1.24	1.77
0220 3/4"		535	.030		.92	1.11		2.03	2.83
0230 1"	▼	400	.040	▼	1.58	1.48		3.06	4.18
1000 Manifolds									
1110 Brass									
1120 With supply and return valves, flow meter, thermometer,									
1122 auto air vent and drain/fill valve.									
1130 1", 2 circuit	Q-5	14	1.143	Ea.	281	42.50		323.50	380
1140 1", 3 circuit		13.50	1.185		320	44		364	430
1150 1", 4 circuit		13	1.231		350	45.50		395.50	460
1154 1", 5 circuit		12.50	1.280		415	47.50		462.50	540
1158 1", 6 circuit		12	1.333		455	49.50		504.50	580
1162 1", 7 circuit		11.50	1.391		495	51.50		546.50	630
1166 1", 8 circuit		11	1.455		500	54		554	640
1172 1", 9 circuit		10.50	1.524		590	56.50		646.50	745
1174 1", 10 circuit		10	1.600		635	59		694	800
1178 1", 11 circuit		9.50	1.684		660	62.50		722.50	830
1182 1", 12 circuit	▼	9	1.778	▼	730	66		796	915
1610 Copper manifold header (cut to size)									
1620 1" header, 12 circuit 1/2" sweat outlets	Q-5	3.33	4.805	Ea.	96	178		274	400
1630 1-1/4" header, 12 circuit 1/2" sweat outlets		3.20	5		112	185		297	430
1640 1-1/4" header, 12 circuit 3/4" sweat outlets		3	5.333		120	197		317	455
1650 1-1/2" header, 12 circuit 3/4" sweat outlets		3.10	5.161		144	191		335	475
1660 2" header, 12 circuit 3/4" sweat outlets	▼	2.90	5.517	▼	212	204		416	570
3000 Valves									
3110 Thermostatic zone valve actuator with end switch	Q-5	40	.400	Ea.	42	14.80		56.80	71
3114 Thermostatic zone valve actuator	"	36	.444	"	85.50	16.45		101.95	121
3120 Motorized straight zone valve with operator complete									
3130 3/4"	Q-5	35	.457	Ea.	138	16.90		154.90	179
3140 1"		32	.500		149	18.50		167.50	195
3150 1-1/4"	▼	29.60	.541	▼	189	20		209	241
3500 4 way mixing valve, manual, brass									
3530 1"	Q-5	13.30	1.203	Ea.	191	44.50		235.50	284

23 83 Radiant Heating Units

23 83 16 — Radiant-Heating Hydronic Piping

23 83 16.10 Radiant Floor Heating

		Crew	Daily Output	Labor-Hours	Unit	Material	2017 Bare Costs Labor	Equipment	Total	Total Incl O&P
3540	1-1/4"	Q-5	11.40	1.404	Ea.	207	52		259	315
3550	1-1/2"		11	1.455		264	54		318	380
3560	2"		10.60	1.509		375	56		431	500
3800	Mixing valve motor, 4 way for valves, 1" and 1-1/4"		34	.471		355	17.40		372.40	420
3810	Mixing valve motor, 4 way for valves, 1-1/2" and 2"	↓	30	.533	↓	380	19.75		399.75	450
5000	Radiant floor heating, zone control panel									
5120	4 zone actuator valve control, expandable	Q-5	20	.800	Ea.	149	29.50		178.50	213
5130	6 zone actuator valve control, expandable		18	.889		238	33		271	315
6070	Thermal track, straight panel for long continuous runs, 5.333 S.F.		40	.400		29	14.80		43.80	56.50
6080	Thermal track, utility panel, for direction reverse at run end, 5.333 S.F.		40	.400		29	14.80		43.80	56.50
6090	Combination panel, for direction reverse plus straight run, 5.333 S.F.	↓	40	.400	↓	29	14.80		43.80	56.50
7000	PEX tubing fittings									
7100	Compression type									
7116	Coupling									
7120	1/2" x 1/2"	1 Stpi	27	.296	Ea.	6.30	12.20		18.50	27
7124	3/4" x 3/4"	"	23	.348	"	12.40	14.30		26.70	37
7130	Adapter									
7132	1/2" x female sweat 1/2"	1 Stpi	27	.296	Ea.	4.09	12.20		16.29	24.50
7134	1/2" x female sweat 3/4"		26	.308		4.58	12.65		17.23	26
7136	5/8" x female sweat 3/4"	↓	24	.333	↓	6.55	13.70		20.25	29.50
7140	Elbow									
7142	1/2" x female sweat 1/2"	1 Stpi	27	.296	Ea.	6.25	12.20		18.45	27
7144	1/2" x female sweat 3/4"		26	.308		7.30	12.65		19.95	29
7146	5/8" x female sweat 3/4"	↓	24	.333	↓	8.20	13.70		21.90	31.50
7200	Insert type									
7206	PEX x male NPT									
7210	1/2" x 1/2"	1 Stpi	29	.276	Ea.	2.56	11.35		13.91	21.50
7220	3/4" x 3/4"		27	.296		3.77	12.20		15.97	24
7230	1" x 1"	↓	26	.308		6.35	12.65		19	28
7300	PEX coupling									
7310	1/2" x 1/2"	1 Stpi	30	.267	Ea.	.51	10.95		11.46	18.60
7320	3/4" x 3/4"		29	.276		.72	11.35		12.07	19.50
7330	1" x 1"	↓	28	.286	↓	1.26	11.75		13.01	20.50
7400	PEX stainless crimp ring									
7410	1/2" x 1/2"	1 Stpi	86	.093	Ea.	.44	3.82		4.26	6.80
7420	3/4" x 3/4"		84	.095		.60	3.91		4.51	7.10
7430	1" x 1"	↓	82	.098	↓	.85	4.01		4.86	7.55

23 83 33 — Electric Radiant Heaters

23 83 33.10 Electric Heating

		Crew	Daily Output	Labor-Hours	Unit	Material	2017 Bare Costs Labor	Equipment	Total	Total Incl O&P
0010	**ELECTRIC HEATING**, not incl. conduit or feed wiring									
1100	Rule of thumb: Baseboard units, including control	1 Elec	4.40	1.818	kW	106	73		179	237
1300	Baseboard heaters, 2' long, 350 watt		8	1	Ea.	26	40		66	94.50
1400	3' long, 750 watt		8	1		30	40		70	99
1600	4' long, 1000 watt		6.70	1.194		35	48		83	117
1800	5' long, 935 watt		5.70	1.404		43	56.50		99.50	140
2000	6' long, 1500 watt		5	1.600		49	64.50		113.50	159
2400	8' long, 2000 watt		4	2		59.50	80.50		140	198
2800	10' long, 1875 watt	↓	3.30	2.424	↓	184	97.50		281.50	360
2950	Wall heaters with fan, 120 to 277 volt									
3170	1000 watt	1 Elec	6	1.333	Ea.	84.50	53.50		138	181
3180	1250 watt		5	1.600		84.50	64.50		149	198
3190	1500 watt		4	2		84.50	80.50		165	225

For customer support on your Residential Costs with RSMeans Data, call 800.448.8182.

593

23 83 Radiant Heating Units

23 83 33 - Electric Radiant Heaters

23 83 33.10 Electric Heating	Crew	Daily Output	Labor-Hours	Unit	Material	2017 Bare Costs Labor	Equipment	Total	Total Incl O&P
3600	Thermostats, integral	1 Elec	16	.500	Ea.	27	20		47	62.50
3800	Line voltage, 1 pole		8	1		15.65	40		55.65	83.50
5000	Radiant heating ceiling panels, 2' x 4', 500 watt		16	.500		420	20		440	500
5050	750 watt		16	.500		465	20		485	545
5300	Infrared quartz heaters, 120 volts, 1000 watt		6.70	1.194		300	48		348	410
5350	1500 watt		5	1.600		300	64.50		364.50	435
5400	240 volts, 1500 watt		5	1.600		300	64.50		364.50	435
5450	2000 watt		4	2		300	80.50		380.50	460
5500	3000 watt		3	2.667		385	107		492	595

Estimating Tips
26 05 00 Common Work Results for Electrical

- Conduit should be taken off in three main categories—power distribution, branch power, and branch lighting—so the estimator can concentrate on systems and components, therefore making it easier to ensure all items have been accounted for.

- For cost modifications for elevated conduit installation, add the percentages to labor according to the height of installation and only to the quantities exceeding the different height levels, not to the total conduit quantities. Refer to 26 01 02.20 for labor adjustment factors.

- Remember that aluminum wiring of equal ampacity is larger in diameter than copper and may require larger conduit.

- If more than three wires at a time are being pulled, deduct percentages from the labor hours of that grouping of wires.

- When taking off grounding systems, identify separately the type and size of wire, and list each unique type of ground connection.

- The estimator should take the weights of materials into consideration when completing a takeoff. Topics to consider include: How will the materials be supported? What methods of support are available? How high will the support structure have to reach? Will the final support structure be able to withstand the total burden? Is the support material included or separate from the fixture, equipment, and material specified?

- Do not overlook the costs for equipment used in the installation. If scaffolding or highlifts are available in the field, contractors may use them in lieu of the proposed ladders and rolling staging.

26 20 00 Low-Voltage Electrical Transmission

- Supports and concrete pads may be shown on drawings for the larger equipment, or the support system may be only a piece of plywood for the back of a panelboard. In either case, they must be included in the costs.

26 40 00 Electrical and Cathodic Protection

- When taking off cathodic protection systems, identify the type and size of cable, and list each unique type of anode connection.

26 50 00 Lighting

- Fixtures should be taken off room by room using the fixture schedule, specifications, and the ceiling plan. For large concentrations of lighting fixtures in the same area, deduct the percentages from labor hours.

Reference Numbers

Reference numbers are shown at the beginning of some major classifications. These numbers refer to related items in the Reference Section. The reference information may be an estimating procedure, an alternate pricing method, or technical information.

Note: Not all subdivisions listed here necessarily appear. ■

26 05 05.10 Electrical Demolition	Crew	Daily Output	Labor-Hours	Unit	Material	2017 Bare Costs Labor	Equipment	Total	Total Incl O&P
0010 **ELECTRICAL DEMOLITION**									
0020 Electrical dml, conduit to 10' high, including fittings & hangers									
0100 Rigid galvanized steel, 1/2" to 1" diameter	1 Elec	242	.033	L.F.		1.33		1.33	2.18
0120 1-1/4" to 2"	"	200	.040	"		1.61		1.61	2.63
0270 Armored cable (BX) avg. 50' runs									
0280 #14, 2 wire	1 Elec	690	.012	L.F.		.47		.47	.76
0290 #14, 3 wire		571	.014			.56		.56	.92
0300 #12, 2 wire		605	.013			.53		.53	.87
0310 #12, 3 wire		514	.016			.63		.63	1.02
0320 #10, 2 wire		514	.016			.63		.63	1.02
0330 #10, 3 wire		425	.019			.76		.76	1.24
0340 #8, 3 wire		342	.023			.94		.94	1.54
0350 Non metallic sheathed cable (Romex)									
0360 #14, 2 wire	1 Elec	720	.011	L.F.		.45		.45	.73
0370 #14, 3 wire		657	.012			.49		.49	.80
0380 #12, 2 wire		629	.013			.51		.51	.84
0390 #10, 3 wire		450	.018			.71		.71	1.17
0400 Wiremold raceway, including fittings & hangers									
0420 No. 3000	1 Elec	250	.032	L.F.		1.29		1.29	2.11
0440 No. 4000		217	.037			1.48		1.48	2.43
0460 No. 6000		166	.048			1.94		1.94	3.17
0462 Plugmold with receptacle		114	.070			2.82		2.82	4.62
0465 Telephone/power pole		12	.667	Ea.		27		27	44
0470 Non-metallic, straight section		480	.017	L.F.		.67		.67	1.10
0500 Channels, steel, including fittings & hangers									
0520 3/4" x 1-1/2"	1 Elec	308	.026	L.F.		1.04		1.04	1.71
0540 1-1/2" x 1-1/2"		269	.030			1.20		1.20	1.96
0560 1-1/2" x 1-7/8"		229	.035			1.40		1.40	2.30
1210 Panel boards, incl. removal of all breakers,									
1220 conduit terminations & wire connections									
1230 3 wire, 120/240 V, 100A, to 20 circuits	1 Elec	2.60	3.077	Ea.		124		124	203
1240 200 amps, to 42 circuits	2 Elec	2.60	6.154			247		247	405
1241 225 amps, to 42 circuits		5.60	2.857			115		115	188
1250 400 amps, to 42 circuits		2.20	7.273			292		292	480
1260 4 wire, 120/208 V, 125A, to 20 circuits	1 Elec	2.40	3.333			134		134	220
1270 200 amps, to 42 circuits	2 Elec	2.40	6.667			268		268	440
1720 Junction boxes, 4" sq. & oct.	1 Elec	80	.100			4.02		4.02	6.60
1740 Handy box		107	.075			3.01		3.01	4.92
1760 Switch box		107	.075			3.01		3.01	4.92
1780 Receptacle & switch plates		257	.031			1.25		1.25	2.05
1800 Wire, THW-THWN-THHN, removed from									
1810 in place conduit, to 10' high									
1830 #14	1 Elec	65	.123	C.L.F.		4.95		4.95	8.10
1840 #12		55	.145			5.85		5.85	9.60
1850 #10		45.50	.176			7.05		7.05	11.60
2000 Interior fluorescent fixtures, incl. supports									
2010 & whips, to 10' high									
2100 Recessed drop-in 2' x 2', 2 lamp	2 Elec	35	.457	Ea.		18.40		18.40	30
2110 2' x 2', 4 lamp		30	.533			21.50		21.50	35
2140 2' x 4', 4 lamp		30	.533			21.50		21.50	35
2180 Surface mount, acrylic lens & hinged frame									
2220 2' x 2', 2 lamp	2 Elec	44	.364	Ea.		14.60		14.60	24
2260 2' x 4', 4 lamp	"	33	.485	"		19.50		19.50	32

26 05 Common Work Results for Electrical

26 05 05 – Selective Demolition for Electrical

26 05 05.10 Electrical Demolition

26 05 05.10 Electrical Demolition	Crew	Daily Output	Labor-Hours	Unit	Material	2017 Bare Costs Labor	Equipment	Total	Total Incl O&P
2300	Strip fixtures, surface mount									
2320	4' long, 1 lamp	2 Elec	53	.302	Ea.		12.15		12.15	19.90
2380	8' long, 2 lamp	"	40	.400	"		16.10		16.10	26.50
2460	Interior incandescent, surface, ceiling									
2470	or wall mount, to 12' high									
2480	Metal cylinder type, 75 Watt	2 Elec	62	.258	Ea.		10.35		10.35	17
2600	Exterior fixtures, incandescent, wall mount									
2620	100 Watt	2 Elec	50	.320	Ea.		12.85		12.85	21
3000	Ceiling fan, tear out and remove	1 Elec	24	.333	"		13.40		13.40	22

26 05 19 – Low-Voltage Electrical Power Conductors and Cables

26 05 19.20 Armored Cable

26 05 19.20 Armored Cable	Crew	Daily Output	Labor-Hours	Unit	Material	2017 Bare Costs Labor	Equipment	Total	Total Incl O&P
0010	**ARMORED CABLE**									
0051	600 volt, copper (BX), #14, 2 conductor, solid	1 Elec	240	.033	L.F.	.46	1.34		1.80	2.69
0101	3 conductor, solid		200	.040		.73	1.61		2.34	3.43
0151	#12, 2 conductor, solid		210	.038		.46	1.53		1.99	3.01
0201	3 conductor, solid		180	.044		.75	1.79		2.54	3.75
0251	#10, 2 conductor, solid		180	.044		.87	1.79		2.66	3.89
0301	3 conductor, solid		150	.053		1.21	2.14		3.35	4.85
0351	3 conductor, stranded		120	.067		2.29	2.68		4.97	6.90

26 05 19.55 Non-Metallic Sheathed Cable

26 05 19.55 Non-Metallic Sheathed Cable	Crew	Daily Output	Labor-Hours	Unit	Material	2017 Bare Costs Labor	Equipment	Total	Total Incl O&P
0010	**NON-METALLIC SHEATHED CABLE** 600 volt									
0100	Copper with ground wire (Romex)									
0151	#14, 2 wire	1 Elec	250	.032	L.F.	.21	1.29		1.50	2.35
0201	3 wire		230	.035		.31	1.40		1.71	2.63
0251	#12, 2 wire		220	.036		.33	1.46		1.79	2.75
0301	3 wire		200	.040		.47	1.61		2.08	3.14
0351	#10, 2 wire		200	.040		.50	1.61		2.11	3.19
0401	3 wire		140	.057		.74	2.30		3.04	4.57
0451	#8, 3 conductor		130	.062		1.18	2.47		3.65	5.35
0501	#6, 3 wire		120	.067		1.92	2.68		4.60	6.50
0550	SE type SER aluminum cable, 3 RHW and									
0601	1 bare neutral, 3 #8 & 1 #8	1 Elec	150	.053	L.F.	.69	2.14		2.83	4.27
0651	3 #6 & 1 #6	"	130	.062		.78	2.47		3.25	4.91
0701	3 #4 & 1 #6	2 Elec	220	.073		.87	2.92		3.79	5.75
0751	3 #2 & 1 #4		200	.080		1.29	3.22		4.51	6.65
0801	3 #1/0 & 1 #2		180	.089		1.95	3.57		5.52	8
0851	3 #2/0 & 1 #1		160	.100		2.29	4.02		6.31	9.10
0901	3 #4/0 & 1 #2/0		140	.114		3.27	4.59		7.86	11.15
2401	SEU service entrance cable, copper 2 conductors, #8 + #8 neutral	1 Elec	150	.053		1.07	2.14		3.21	4.69
2601	#6 + #8 neutral		130	.062		1.58	2.47		4.05	5.80
2801	#6 + #6 neutral		130	.062		1.80	2.47		4.27	6.05
3001	#4 + #6 neutral	2 Elec	220	.073		2.48	2.92		5.40	7.50
3201	#4 + #4 neutral		220	.073		2.80	2.92		5.72	7.85
3401	#3 + #5 neutral		210	.076		3.47	3.06		6.53	8.80
6500	Service entrance cap for copper SEU									
6600	100 amp	1 Elec	12	.667	Ea.	8.10	27		35.10	53
6700	150 amp		10	.800		13.80	32		45.80	67.50
6800	200 amp		8	1		21	40		61	89

26 05 19.90 Wire

26 05 19.90 Wire	Crew	Daily Output	Labor-Hours	Unit	Material	2017 Bare Costs Labor	Equipment	Total	Total Incl O&P
0010	**WIRE**									
0021	600 volt, copper type THW, solid, #14	1 Elec	1300	.006	L.F.	.07	.25		.32	.49
0031	#12		1100	.007		.11	.29		.40	.60

For customer support on your Residential Costs with RSMeans Data, call 800.448.8182.

597

26 05 19 – Low-Voltage Electrical Power Conductors and Cables

26 05 19.90 Wire		Crew	Daily Output	Labor-Hours	Unit	Material	2017 Bare Costs Labor	Equipment	Total	Total Incl O&P
0041	#10	1 Elec	1000	.008	L.F.	.17	.32		.49	.71
0050	Stranded, #14		13	.615	C.L.F.	8.20	24.50		32.70	49.50
0100	#12		11	.727		12.55	29		41.55	62
0120	#10		10	.800		19.80	32		51.80	74.50
0161	#6		650	.012	L.F.	.55	.49		1.04	1.42
0181	#4	2 Elec	1060	.015		.85	.61		1.46	1.93
0201	#3		1000	.016		1.06	.64		1.70	2.21
0221	#2		900	.018		1.33	.71		2.04	2.63
0241	#1		800	.020		1.75	.80		2.55	3.25
0261	1/0		660	.024		2.18	.97		3.15	4
0281	2/0		580	.028		2.74	1.11		3.85	4.84
0301	3/0		500	.032		3.44	1.29		4.73	5.90
0351	4/0		440	.036		4.38	1.46		5.84	7.20

26 05 26 – Grounding and Bonding for Electrical Systems

26 05 26.80 Grounding

		Crew	Daily Output	Labor-Hours	Unit	Material	2017 Bare Costs Labor	Equipment	Total	Total Incl O&P
0010	**GROUNDING**									
0030	Rod, copper clad, 8' long, 1/2" diameter	1 Elec	5.50	1.455	Ea.	20	58.50		78.50	118
0040	5/8" diameter		5.50	1.455		19.40	58.50		77.90	118
0050	3/4" diameter		5.30	1.509		34	60.50		94.50	137
0080	10' long, 1/2" diameter		4.80	1.667		22.50	67		89.50	135
0090	5/8" diameter		4.60	1.739		24.50	70		94.50	142
0100	3/4" diameter		4.40	1.818		39	73		112	163
0130	15' long, 3/4" diameter		4	2		51	80.50		131.50	188
0261	Wire, ground bare armored, #8-1 conductor		200	.040	L.F.	.70	1.61		2.31	3.40
0271	#6-1 conductor		180	.044	"	.84	1.79		2.63	3.85
0390	Bare copper wire, stranded, #8		11	.727	C.L.F.	25.50	29		54.50	76
0401	Bare copper, #6 wire		1000	.008	L.F.	.45	.32		.77	1.02
0601	#2 stranded	2 Elec	1000	.016	"	.94	.64		1.58	2.08
1800	Water pipe ground clamps, heavy duty									
2000	Bronze, 1/2" to 1" diameter	1 Elec	8	1	Ea.	24	40		64	92
2100	1-1/4" to 2" diameter		8	1		33	40		73	103
2200	2-1/2" to 3" diameter		6	1.333		44.50	53.50		98	137

26 05 33 – Raceway and Boxes for Electrical Systems

26 05 33.13 Conduit

		Crew	Daily Output	Labor-Hours	Unit	Material	2017 Bare Costs Labor	Equipment	Total	Total Incl O&P
0010	**CONDUIT** To 10' high, includes 2 terminations, 2 elbows,									
0020	11 beam clamps, and 11 couplings per 100 L.F.									
1750	Rigid galvanized steel, 1/2" diameter	1 Elec	90	.089	L.F.	2.50	3.57		6.07	8.60
1770	3/4" diameter		80	.100		4.66	4.02		8.68	11.75
1800	1" diameter		65	.123		7.10	4.95		12.05	15.95
1830	1-1/4" diameter		60	.133		5.10	5.35		10.45	14.40
1850	1-1/2" diameter		55	.145		8	5.85		13.85	18.40
1870	2" diameter		45	.178		10.25	7.15		17.40	23
5000	Electric metallic tubing (EMT), 1/2" diameter		170	.047		.69	1.89		2.58	3.86
5020	3/4" diameter		130	.062		.98	2.47		3.45	5.15
5040	1" diameter		115	.070		1.65	2.80		4.45	6.40
5060	1-1/4" diameter		100	.080		2.66	3.22		5.88	8.15
5080	1-1/2" diameter		90	.089		3.38	3.57		6.95	9.55
9100	PVC, schedule 40, 1/2" diameter		190	.042		.86	1.69		2.55	3.72
9110	3/4" diameter		145	.055		.95	2.22		3.17	4.67
9120	1" diameter		125	.064		2.06	2.57		4.63	6.50
9130	1-1/4" diameter		110	.073		2.53	2.92		5.45	7.55
9140	1-1/2" diameter		100	.080		2.86	3.22		6.08	8.40

26 05 33 – Raceway and Boxes for Electrical Systems

26 05 33.13 Conduit

	Crew	Daily Output	Labor-Hours	Unit	Material	2017 Bare Costs Labor	Equipment	Total	Total Incl O&P
9150	2" diameter	1 Elec	90	.089	L.F.	3.73	3.57		7.30	9.95
9995	Do not include labor when adding couplings to a fitting installation									

26 05 33.16 Boxes for Electrical Systems

	Crew	Daily Output	Labor-Hours	Unit	Material	2017 Bare Costs Labor	Equipment	Total	Total Incl O&P
0010	**BOXES FOR ELECTRICAL SYSTEMS**									
0021	Pressed steel, octagon, 4"	1 Elec	18	.444	Ea.	2.22	17.85		20.07	32
0060	Covers, blank		64	.125		.93	5.05		5.98	9.25
0100	Extension rings		40	.200		3.68	8.05		11.73	17.20
0151	Square 4"		18	.444		2.88	17.85		20.73	32.50
0200	Extension rings		40	.200		3.72	8.05		11.77	17.25
0250	Covers, blank		64	.125		1	5.05		6.05	9.35
0300	Plaster rings		64	.125		2.04	5.05		7.09	10.50
0651	Switchbox		24	.333		3.55	13.40		16.95	26
1100	Concrete, floor, 1 gang		5.30	1.509		89.50	60.50		150	198

26 05 33.17 Outlet Boxes, Plastic

	Crew	Daily Output	Labor-Hours	Unit	Material	2017 Bare Costs Labor	Equipment	Total	Total Incl O&P
0010	**OUTLET BOXES, PLASTIC**									
0051	4" diameter, round, with 2 mounting nails	1 Elec	23	.348	Ea.	2.39	14		16.39	25.50
0101	Bar hanger mounted		23	.348		5.10	14		19.10	28.50
0201	Square with 2 mounting nails		23	.348		4.63	14		18.63	28
0300	Plaster ring		64	.125		1.98	5.05		7.03	10.45
0401	Switch box with 2 mounting nails, 1 gang		27	.296		4.39	11.90		16.29	24.50
0501	2 gang		23	.348		3.33	14		17.33	26.50
0601	3 gang		18	.444		4.19	17.85		22.04	34

26 05 33.18 Pull Boxes

	Crew	Daily Output	Labor-Hours	Unit	Material	2017 Bare Costs Labor	Equipment	Total	Total Incl O&P
0010	**PULL BOXES**									
0100	Steel, pull box, NEMA 1, type SC, 6" W x 6" H x 4" D	1 Elec	8	1	Ea.	9.65	40		49.65	76.50
0200	8" W x 8" H x 4" D		8	1		13.20	40		53.20	80.50
0300	10" W x 12" H x 6" D		5.30	1.509		22.50	60.50		83	125

26 05 33.25 Conduit Fittings for Rigid Galvanized Steel

	Crew	Daily Output	Labor-Hours	Unit	Material	2017 Bare Costs Labor	Equipment	Total	Total Incl O&P
0010	**CONDUIT FITTINGS FOR RIGID GALVANIZED STEEL**									
2280	LB, LR or LL fittings & covers, 1/2" diameter	1 Elec	16	.500	Ea.	9	20		29	43
2290	3/4" diameter		13	.615		11.15	24.50		35.65	53
2300	1" diameter		11	.727		16.25	29		45.25	66
2330	1-1/4" diameter		8	1		25.50	40		65.50	94
2350	1-1/2" diameter		6	1.333		33.50	53.50		87	125
2370	2" diameter		5	1.600		55	64.50		119.50	166
5280	Service entrance cap, 1/2" diameter		16	.500		4.99	20		24.99	38.50
5300	3/4" diameter		13	.615		5.95	24.50		30.45	47
5320	1" diameter		10	.800		7.10	32		39.10	60.50
5340	1-1/4" diameter		8	1		7.70	40		47.70	74.50
5360	1-1/2" diameter		6.50	1.231		14.15	49.50		63.65	96.50
5380	2" diameter		5.50	1.455		20	58.50		78.50	118

26 05 33.35 Flexible Metallic Conduit

	Crew	Daily Output	Labor-Hours	Unit	Material	2017 Bare Costs Labor	Equipment	Total	Total Incl O&P
0010	**FLEXIBLE METALLIC CONDUIT**									
0050	Steel, 3/8" diameter	1 Elec	200	.040	L.F.	.23	1.61		1.84	2.88
0100	1/2" diameter		200	.040		.26	1.61		1.87	2.92
0200	3/4" diameter		160	.050		.36	2.01		2.37	3.69
0250	1" diameter		100	.080		.65	3.22		3.87	5.95
0300	1-1/4" diameter		70	.114		.84	4.59		5.43	8.45
0350	1-1/2" diameter		50	.160		1.37	6.45		7.82	12.05
0370	2" diameter		40	.200		1.67	8.05		9.72	15

For customer support on your Residential Costs with RSMeans Data, call 800.448.8182.

599

26 05 39 – Underfloor Raceways for Electrical Systems

26 05 39.30 Conduit In Concrete Slab

26 05 39.30 Conduit In Concrete Slab	Crew	Daily Output	Labor-Hours	Unit	Material	2017 Bare Costs Labor	Equipment	Total	Total Incl O&P
0010 **CONDUIT IN CONCRETE SLAB** Including terminations,									
0020 fittings and supports									
3230 PVC, schedule 40, 1/2" diameter	1 Elec	270	.030	L.F.	.49	1.19		1.68	2.49
3250 3/4" diameter		230	.035		.56	1.40		1.96	2.91
3270 1" diameter		200	.040		.76	1.61		2.37	3.47
3300 1-1/4" diameter		170	.047		1	1.89		2.89	4.20
3330 1-1/2" diameter		140	.057		1.21	2.30		3.51	5.10
3350 2" diameter		120	.067		1.53	2.68		4.21	6.05
4350 Rigid galvanized steel, 1/2" diameter		200	.040		2.37	1.61		3.98	5.25
4400 3/4" diameter		170	.047		4.34	1.89		6.23	7.90
4450 1" diameter		130	.062		6.70	2.47		9.17	11.40
4500 1-1/4" diameter		110	.073		4.78	2.92		7.70	10.05
4600 1-1/2" diameter		100	.080		7.30	3.22		10.52	13.25
4800 2" diameter	↓	90	.089	↓	9.05	3.57		12.62	15.80

26 05 39.40 Conduit In Trench

26 05 39.40 Conduit In Trench	Crew	Daily Output	Labor-Hours	Unit	Material	2017 Bare Costs Labor	Equipment	Total	Total Incl O&P
0010 **CONDUIT IN TRENCH** Includes terminations and fittings									
0020 Does not include excavation or backfill, see Section 31 23 16									
0200 Rigid galvanized steel, 2" diameter	1 Elec	150	.053	L.F.	8.70	2.14		10.84	13.05
0400 2-1/2" diameter	"	100	.080		12.10	3.22		15.32	18.55
0600 3" diameter	2 Elec	160	.100		14.10	4.02		18.12	22
0800 3-1/2" diameter	"	140	.114	↓	18.35	4.59		22.94	27.50

26 05 80 – Wiring Connections

26 05 80.10 Motor Connections

	Crew	Daily Output	Labor-Hours	Unit	Material	2017 Bare Costs Labor	Equipment	Total	Total Incl O&P
0010 **MOTOR CONNECTIONS**									
0020 Flexible conduit and fittings, 115 volt, 1 phase, up to 1 HP motor	1 Elec	8	1	Ea.	4.92	40		44.92	71.50

26 05 90 – Residential Applications

26 05 90.10 Residential Wiring

	Crew	Daily Output	Labor-Hours	Unit	Material	2017 Bare Costs Labor	Equipment	Total	Total Incl O&P
0010 **RESIDENTIAL WIRING**									
0020 20' avg. runs and #14/2 wiring incl. unless otherwise noted									
1000 Service & panel, includes 24' SE-AL cable, service eye, meter,									
1010 Socket, panel board, main bkr., ground rod, 15 or 20 amp									
1020 1-pole circuit breakers, and misc. hardware									
1100 100 amp, with 10 branch breakers	1 Elec	1.19	6.723	Ea.	490	270		760	985
1110 With PVC conduit and wire		.92	8.696		530	350		880	1,150
1120 With RGS conduit and wire		.73	10.959		745	440		1,185	1,550
1150 150 amp, with 14 branch breakers		1.03	7.767		845	310		1,155	1,450
1170 With PVC conduit and wire		.82	9.756		930	390		1,320	1,675
1180 With RGS conduit and wire		.67	11.940		1,250	480		1,730	2,150
1200 200 amp, with 18 branch breakers	2 Elec	1.80	8.889		1,050	355		1,405	1,750
1220 With PVC conduit and wire		1.46	10.959		1,150	440		1,590	1,975
1230 With RGS conduit and wire		1.24	12.903		1,550	520		2,070	2,550
1800 Lightning surge suppressor	1 Elec	32	.250	↓	50.50	10.05		60.55	72.50
2000 Switch devices									
2100 Single pole, 15 amp, Ivory, with a 1-gang box, cover plate,									
2110 Type NM (Romex) cable	1 Elec	17.10	.468	Ea.	18.70	18.80		37.50	51.50
2120 Type MC (BX) cable		14.30	.559		27.50	22.50		50	67
2130 EMT & wire		5.71	1.401		36	56.50		92.50	132
2150 3-way, #14/3, type NM cable		14.55	.550		12.40	22		34.40	49.50
2170 Type MC cable		12.31	.650		24.50	26		50.50	70
2180 EMT & wire		5	1.600		29	64.50		93.50	137
2200 4-way, #14/3, type NM cable	↓	14.55	.550	↓	21	22		43	59

26 05 90 – Residential Applications

26 05 90.10 Residential Wiring	Crew	Daily Output	Labor-Hours	Unit	Material	2017 Bare Costs Labor	Equipment	Total	Total Incl O&P
2220	Type MC cable	1 Elec	12.31	.650	Ea.	33	26		59	79.50
2230	EMT & wire		5	1.600		37.50	64.50		102	146
2250	S.P., 20 amp, #12/2, type NM cable		13.33	.600		14.75	24		38.75	55.50
2270	Type MC cable		11.43	.700		21	28		49	69
2280	EMT & wire		4.85	1.649		33	66.50		99.50	146
2290	S.P. rotary dimmer, 600W, no wiring		17	.471		32.50	18.90		51.40	66.50
2300	S.P. rotary dimmer, 600W, type NM cable		14.55	.550		36.50	22		58.50	76.50
2320	Type MC cable		12.31	.650		45.50	26		71.50	93
2330	EMT & wire		5	1.600		55	64.50		119.50	166
2350	3-way rotary dimmer, type NM cable		13.33	.600		21	24		45	62.50
2370	Type MC cable		11.43	.700		29.50	28		57.50	78.50
2380	EMT & wire		4.85	1.649		39.50	66.50		106	153
2400	Interval timer wall switch, 20 amp, 1-30 min., #12/2									
2410	Type NM cable	1 Elec	14.55	.550	Ea.	57	22		79	99
2420	Type MC cable		12.31	.650		62	26		88	111
2430	EMT & wire		5	1.600		75.50	64.50		140	188
2500	Decorator style									
2510	S.P., 15 amp, type NM cable	1 Elec	17.10	.468	Ea.	23.50	18.80		42.30	57
2520	Type MC cable		14.30	.559		32.50	22.50		55	72.50
2530	EMT & wire		5.71	1.401		40.50	56.50		97	138
2550	3-way, #14/3, type NM cable		14.55	.550		17.30	22		39.30	55
2570	Type MC cable		12.31	.650		29.50	26		55.50	75.50
2580	EMT & wire		5	1.600		34	64.50		98.50	143
2600	4-way, #14/3, type NM cable		14.55	.550		25.50	22		47.50	64.50
2620	Type MC cable		12.31	.650		38	26		64	85
2630	EMT & wire		5	1.600		42.50	64.50		107	152
2650	S.P., 20 amp, #12/2, type NM cable		13.33	.600		19.65	24		43.65	61
2670	Type MC cable		11.43	.700		26	28		54	74.50
2680	EMT & wire		4.85	1.649		38	66.50		104.50	151
2700	S.P., slide dimmer, type NM cable		17.10	.468		24.50	18.80		43.30	58
2720	Type MC cable		14.30	.559		33	22.50		55.50	73.50
2730	EMT & wire		5.71	1.401		43	56.50		99.50	140
2750	S.P., touch dimmer, type NM cable		17.10	.468		41	18.80		59.80	76
2770	Type MC cable		14.30	.559		50	22.50		72.50	91.50
2780	EMT & wire		5.71	1.401		59.50	56.50		116	158
2800	3-way touch dimmer, type NM cable		13.33	.600		51.50	24		75.50	96
2820	Type MC cable		11.43	.700		60	28		88	112
2830	EMT & wire		4.85	1.649		70	66.50		136.50	186
3000	Combination devices									
3100	S.P. switch/15 amp recpt., Ivory, 1-gang box, plate									
3110	Type NM cable	1 Elec	11.43	.700	Ea.	24	28		52	72.50
3120	Type MC cable		10	.800		33	32		65	88.50
3130	EMT & wire		4.40	1.818		42.50	73		115.50	167
3150	S.P. switch/pilot light, type NM cable		11.43	.700		24.50	28		52.50	73
3170	Type MC cable		10	.800		33	32		65	89
3180	EMT & wire		4.43	1.806		43	72.50		115.50	166
3190	2-S.P. switches, 2-#14/2, no wiring		14	.571		13.70	23		36.70	52.50
3200	2-S.P. switches, 2-#14/2, type NM cables		10	.800		26.50	32		58.50	82
3220	Type MC cable		8.89	.900		40.50	36		76.50	104
3230	EMT & wire		4.10	1.951		45	78.50		123.50	178
3250	3-way switch/15 amp recpt., #14/3, type NM cable		10	.800		31.50	32		63.50	87
3270	Type MC cable		8.89	.900		44	36		80	108
3280	EMT & wire		4.10	1.951		48.50	78.50		127	181

26 05 90.10 Residential Wiring	Crew	Daily Output	Labor-Hours	Unit	Material	2017 Bare Costs Labor	Equipment	Total	Total Incl O&P
3300	2-3 way switches, 2-#14/3, type NM cables	1 Elec	8.89	.900	Ea.	40.50	36		76.50	104
3320	Type MC cable		8	1		61.50	40		101.50	134
3330	EMT & wire		4	2		55	80.50		135.50	193
3350	S.P. switch/20 amp recpt., #12/2, type NM cable		10	.800		31	32		63	87
3370	Type MC cable		8.89	.900		36	36		72	99
3380	EMT & wire		4.10	1.951		49.50	78.50		128	183
3400	Decorator style									
3410	S.P. switch/15 amp recpt., type NM cable	1 Elec	11.43	.700	Ea.	29	28		57	78
3420	Type MC cable		10	.800		37.50	32		69.50	94
3430	EMT & wire		4.40	1.818		47.50	73		120.50	173
3450	S.P. switch/pilot light, type NM cable		11.43	.700		29	28		57	78
3470	Type MC cable		10	.800		38	32		70	94
3480	EMT & wire		4.40	1.818		47.50	73		120.50	173
3500	2-S.P. switches, 2-#14/2, type NM cables		10	.800		31.50	32		63.50	87.50
3520	Type MC cable		8.89	.900		45	36		81	109
3530	EMT & wire		4.10	1.951		50	78.50		128.50	183
3550	3-way/15 amp recpt., #14/3, type NM cable		10	.800		36.50	32		68.50	92.50
3570	Type MC cable		8.89	.900		49	36		85	113
3580	EMT & wire		4.10	1.951		53	78.50		131.50	187
3650	2-3 way switches, 2-#14/3, type NM cables		8.89	.900		45.50	36		81.50	110
3670	Type MC cable		8	1		66	40		106	139
3680	EMT & wire		4	2		60	80.50		140.50	198
3700	S.P. switch/20 amp recpt., #12/2, type NM cable		10	.800		36	32		68	92
3720	Type MC cable		8.89	.900		41	36		77	105
3730	EMT & wire		4.10	1.951		54.50	78.50		133	188
4000	Receptacle devices									
4010	Duplex outlet, 15 amp recpt., Ivory, 1-gang box, plate									
4015	Type NM cable	1 Elec	14.55	.550	Ea.	10.30	22		32.30	47.50
4020	Type MC cable		12.31	.650		19	26		45	64
4030	EMT & wire		5.33	1.501		27.50	60.50		88	129
4050	With #12/2, type NM cable		12.31	.650		12.65	26		38.65	57
4070	Type MC cable		10.67	.750		19	30		49	70.50
4080	EMT & wire		4.71	1.699		31	68.50		99.50	146
4100	20 amp recpt., #12/2, type NM cable		12.31	.650		19.30	26		45.30	64.50
4120	Type MC cable		10.67	.750		25.50	30		55.50	77.50
4130	EMT & wire		4.71	1.699		37.50	68.50		106	154
4140	For GFI see Section 26 05 90.10 line 4300 below									
4150	Decorator style, 15 amp recpt., type NM cable	1 Elec	14.55	.550	Ea.	15.20	22		37.20	53
4170	Type MC cable		12.31	.650		24	26		50	69.50
4180	EMT & wire		5.33	1.501		32.50	60.50		93	135
4200	With #12/2, type NM cable		12.31	.650		17.55	26		43.55	62.50
4220	Type MC cable		10.67	.750		24	30		54	76
4230	EMT & wire		4.71	1.699		36	68.50		104.50	152
4250	20 amp recpt., #12/2, type NM cable		12.31	.650		24	26		50	69.50
4270	Type MC cable		10.67	.750		30.50	30		60.50	83
4280	EMT & wire		4.71	1.699		42.50	68.50		111	159
4300	GFI, 15 amp recpt., type NM cable		12.31	.650		23	26		49	68
4320	Type MC cable		10.67	.750		31.50	30		61.50	84
4330	EMT & wire		4.71	1.699		40	68.50		108.50	156
4350	GFI with #12/2, type NM cable		10.67	.750		25	30		55	77
4370	Type MC cable		9.20	.870		31.50	35		66.50	92
4380	EMT & wire		4.21	1.900		43.50	76.50		120	173
4400	20 amp recpt., #12/2, type NM cable		10.67	.750		51.50	30		81.50	106

26 05 90.10 Residential Wiring	Crew	Daily Output	Labor-Hours	Unit	Material	2017 Bare Costs Labor	Equipment	Total	Total Incl O&P
4420	Type MC cable	1 Elec	9.20	.870	Ea.	58	35		93	121
4430	EMT & wire		4.21	1.900		70	76.50		146.50	202
4500	Weather-proof cover for above receptacles, add	↓	32	.250	↓	2.47	10.05		12.52	19.15
4550	Air conditioner outlet, 20 amp-240 volt recpt.									
4560	30' of #12/2, 2 pole circuit breaker									
4570	Type NM cable	1 Elec	10	.800	Ea.	62	32		94	121
4580	Type MC cable		9	.889		70	35.50		105.50	136
4590	EMT & wire		4	2		80.50	80.50		161	221
4600	Decorator style, type NM cable		10	.800		67	32		99	126
4620	Type MC cable		9	.889		74.50	35.50		110	141
4630	EMT & wire	↓	4	2	↓	85	80.50		165.50	226
4650	Dryer outlet, 30 amp-240 volt recpt., 20' of #10/3									
4660	2 pole circuit breaker									
4670	Type NM cable	1 Elec	6.41	1.248	Ea.	58	50		108	146
4680	Type MC cable		5.71	1.401		64	56.50		120.50	163
4690	EMT & wire	↓	3.48	2.299	↓	74	92.50		166.50	233
4700	Range outlet, 50 amp-240 volt recpt., 30' of #8/3									
4710	Type NM cable	1 Elec	4.21	1.900	Ea.	85	76.50		161.50	219
4720	Type MC cable		4	2		126	80.50		206.50	270
4730	EMT & wire		2.96	2.703		104	109		213	292
4750	Central vacuum outlet, Type NM cable		6.40	1.250		54	50.50		104.50	142
4770	Type MC cable		5.71	1.401		67	56.50		123.50	166
4780	EMT & wire	↓	3.48	2.299	↓	80.50	92.50		173	240
4800	30 amp-110 volt locking recpt., #10/2 circ. bkr.									
4810	Type NM cable	1 Elec	6.20	1.290	Ea.	62	52		114	153
4820	Type MC cable		5.40	1.481		78.50	59.50		138	184
4830	EMT & wire	↓	3.20	2.500	↓	91	101		192	265
4900	Low voltage outlets									
4910	Telephone recpt., 20' of 4/C phone wire	1 Elec	26	.308	Ea.	8.20	12.35		20.55	29.50
4920	TV recpt., 20' of RG59U coax wire, F type connector	"	16	.500	"	15.75	20		35.75	50.50
4950	Door bell chime, transformer, 2 buttons, 60' of bellwire									
4970	Economy model	1 Elec	11.50	.696	Ea.	49.50	28		77.50	101
4980	Custom model		11.50	.696		99	28		127	155
4990	Luxury model, 3 buttons	↓	9.50	.842	↓	201	34		235	277
6000	Lighting outlets									
6050	Wire only (for fixture), type NM cable	1 Elec	32	.250	Ea.	6.35	10.05		16.40	23.50
6070	Type MC cable		24	.333		12.55	13.40		25.95	36
6080	EMT & wire		10	.800		20	32		52	74.50
6100	Box (4"), and wire (for fixture), type NM cable		25	.320		13.90	12.85		26.75	36.50
6120	Type MC cable		20	.400		20	16.10		36.10	48.50
6130	EMT & wire	↓	11	.727	↓	27.50	29		56.50	78.50
6200	Fixtures (use with line 6050 or 6100 above)									
6210	Canopy style, economy grade	1 Elec	40	.200	Ea.	27	8.05		35.05	42.50
6220	Custom grade		40	.200		53.50	8.05		61.55	72
6250	Dining room chandelier, economy grade		19	.421		67.50	16.95		84.45	102
6260	Custom grade		19	.421		315	16.95		331.95	375
6270	Luxury grade		15	.533		820	21.50		841.50	940
6310	Kitchen fixture (fluorescent), economy grade		30	.267		71.50	10.70		82.20	96.50
6320	Custom grade		25	.320		221	12.85		233.85	265
6350	Outdoor, wall mounted, economy grade		30	.267		25.50	10.70		36.20	45.50
6360	Custom grade		30	.267		120	10.70		130.70	150
6370	Luxury grade		25	.320		248	12.85		260.85	294
6410	Outdoor PAR floodlights, 1 lamp, 150 watt	↓	20	.400	↓	27.50	16.10		43.60	56.50

For customer support on your Residential Costs with RSMeans Data, call 800.448.8182.

603

26 05 Common Work Results for Electrical

26 05 90 – Residential Applications

26 05 90.10 Residential Wiring	Crew	Daily Output	Labor-Hours	Unit	Material	2017 Bare Costs Labor	Equipment	Total	Total Incl O&P
6420	2 lamp, 150 watt each	1 Elec	20	.400	Ea.	45.50	16.10		61.60	76.50
6425	Motion sensing, 2 lamp, 150 watt each		20	.400		75.50	16.10		91.60	110
6430	For infrared security sensor, add		32	.250		132	10.05		142.05	161
6450	Outdoor, quartz-halogen, 300 watt flood		20	.400		33	16.10		49.10	63
6600	Recessed downlight, round, pre-wired, 50 or 75 watt trim		30	.267		68	10.70		78.70	92
6610	With shower light trim		30	.267		82.50	10.70		93.20	108
6620	With wall washer trim		28	.286		85	11.50		96.50	112
6630	With eye-ball trim		28	.286		84.50	11.50		96	112
6700	Porcelain lamp holder		40	.200		2.98	8.05		11.03	16.45
6710	With pull switch		40	.200		6.55	8.05		14.60	20.50
6750	Fluorescent strip, 2-20 watt tube, wrap around diffuser, 24"		24	.333		42	13.40		55.40	68.50
6760	1-34 watt tube, 48"		24	.333		100	13.40		113.40	132
6770	2-34 watt tubes, 48"		20	.400		118	16.10		134.10	157
6800	Bathroom heat lamp, 1-250 watt		28	.286		38.50	11.50		50	61
6810	2-250 watt lamps	▼	28	.286	▼	61	11.50		72.50	86.50
6820	For timer switch, see Section 26 05 90.10 line 2400									
6900	Outdoor post lamp, incl. post, fixture, 35' of #14/2									
6910	Type NM cable	1 Elec	3.50	2.286	Ea.	285	92		377	465
6920	Photo-eye, add		27	.296		27.50	11.90		39.40	49.50
6950	Clock dial time switch, 24 hr., w/enclosure, type NM cable		11.43	.700		73	28		101	127
6970	Type MC cable		11	.727		81.50	29		110.50	138
6980	EMT & wire	▼	4.85	1.649	▼	90	66.50		156.50	208
7000	Alarm systems									
7050	Smoke detectors, box, #14/3, type NM cable	1 Elec	14.55	.550	Ea.	34	22		56	73.50
7070	Type MC cable		12.31	.650		44.50	26		70.50	92
7080	EMT & wire	▼	5	1.600		49	64.50		113.50	159
7090	For relay output to security system, add				▼	10.20			10.20	11.20
8000	Residential equipment									
8050	Disposal hook-up, incl. switch, outlet box, 3' of flex									
8060	20 amp-1 pole circ. bkr., and 25' of #12/2									
8070	Type NM cable	1 Elec	10	.800	Ea.	36	32		68	92
8080	Type MC cable		8	1		43	40		83	114
8090	EMT & wire	▼	5	1.600	▼	57.50	64.50		122	168
8100	Trash compactor or dishwasher hook-up, incl. outlet box,									
8110	3' of flex, 15 amp-1 pole circ. bkr., and 25' of #14/2									
8130	Type MC cable	1 Elec	8	1	Ea.	30.50	40		70.50	99.50
8140	EMT & wire	"	5	1.600	"	42.50	64.50		107	152
8150	Hot water sink dispenser hook-up, use line 8100									
8200	Vent/exhaust fan hook-up, type NM cable	1 Elec	32	.250	Ea.	6.35	10.05		16.40	23.50
8220	Type MC cable		24	.333		12.55	13.40		25.95	36
8230	EMT & wire	▼	10	.800	▼	20	32		52	74.50
8250	Bathroom vent fan, 50 CFM (use with above hook-up)									
8260	Economy model	1 Elec	15	.533	Ea.	20	21.50		41.50	57.50
8270	Low noise model		15	.533		43.50	21.50		65	82.50
8280	Custom model	▼	12	.667	▼	131	27		158	188
8300	Bathroom or kitchen vent fan, 110 CFM									
8310	Economy model	1 Elec	15	.533	Ea.	67.50	21.50		89	110
8320	Low noise model	"	15	.533	"	130	21.50		151.50	178
8350	Paddle fan, variable speed (w/o lights)									
8360	Economy model (AC motor)	1 Elec	10	.800	Ea.	109	32		141	173
8362	With light kit		10	.800		150	32		182	218
8370	Custom model (AC motor)		10	.800		262	32		294	340
8372	With light kit		10	.800		305	32		337	390

604

For customer support on your Residential Costs with RSMeans Data, call 800.448.8182.

26 05 Common Work Results for Electrical

26 05 90 – Residential Applications

26 05 90.10 Residential Wiring		Crew	Daily Output	Labor-Hours	Unit	Material	2017 Bare Costs Labor	Equipment	Total	Total Incl O&P
8380	Luxury model (DC motor)	1 Elec	8	1	Ea.	288	40		328	380
8382	With light kit		8	1		330	40		370	425
8390	Remote speed switch for above, add	↓	12	.667	↓	33.50	27		60.50	81
8500	Whole house exhaust fan, ceiling mount, 36", variable speed									
8510	Remote switch, incl. shutters, 20 amp-1 pole circ. bkr.									
8520	30' of #12/2, type NM cable	1 Elec	4	2	Ea.	1,350	80.50		1,430.50	1,600
8530	Type MC cable		3.50	2.286		1,350	92		1,442	1,625
8540	EMT & wire	↓	3	2.667	↓	1,375	107		1,482	1,675
8600	Whirlpool tub hook-up, incl. timer switch, outlet box									
8610	3' of flex, 20 amp-1 pole GFI circ. bkr.									
8620	30' of #12/2, type NM cable	1 Elec	5	1.600	Ea.	113	64.50		177.50	229
8630	Type MC cable		4.20	1.905		116	76.50		192.50	253
8640	EMT & wire	↓	3.40	2.353	↓	128	94.50		222.50	296
8650	Hot water heater hook-up, incl. 1-2 pole circ. bkr., box;									
8660	3' of flex, 20' of #10/2, type NM cable	1 Elec	5	1.600	Ea.	31	64.50		95.50	139
8670	Type MC cable		4.20	1.905		42	76.50		118.50	171
8680	EMT & wire	↓	3.40	2.353	↓	46	94.50		140.50	206
9000	Heating/air conditioning									
9050	Furnace/boiler hook-up, incl. firestat, local on-off switch									
9060	Emergency switch, and 40' of type NM cable	1 Elec	4	2	Ea.	52	80.50		132.50	189
9070	Type MC cable		3.50	2.286		65.50	92		157.50	223
9080	EMT & wire	↓	1.50	5.333		83	214		297	440
9100	Air conditioner hook-up, incl. local 60 amp disc. switch									
9110	3' sealtite, 40 amp, 2 pole circuit breaker									
9130	40' of #8/2, type NM cable	1 Elec	3.50	2.286	Ea.	146	92		238	310
9140	Type MC cable		3	2.667		206	107		313	405
9150	EMT & wire	↓	1.30	6.154	↓	186	247		433	610
9200	Heat pump hook-up, 1-40 & 1-100 amp 2 pole circ. bkr.									
9210	Local disconnect switch, 3' sealtite									
9220	40' of #8/2 & 30' of #3/2									
9230	Type NM cable	1 Elec	1.30	6.154	Ea.	460	247		707	915
9240	Type MC cable		1.08	7.407		515	298		813	1,050
9250	EMT & wire	↓	.94	8.511		520	340		860	1,125
9500	Thermostat hook-up, using low voltage wire									
9520	Heating only, 25' of #18-3	1 Elec	24	.333	Ea.	8	13.40		21.40	31
9530	Heating/cooling, 25' of #18-4	"	20	.400	"	10.50	16.10		26.60	38

26 24 Switchboards and Panelboards

26 24 16 – Panelboards

26 24 16.10 Load Centers

		Crew	Daily Output	Labor-Hours	Unit	Material	2017 Bare Costs Labor	Equipment	Total	Total Incl O&P
0010	**LOAD CENTERS** (residential type)									
0100	3 wire, 120/240 V, 1 phase, including 1 pole plug-in breakers									
0200	100 amp main lugs, indoor, 8 circuits	1 Elec	1.40	5.714	Ea.	126	230		356	515
0300	12 circuits		1.20	6.667		213	268		481	675
0400	Rainproof, 8 circuits		1.40	5.714		155	230		385	545
0500	12 circuits	↓	1.20	6.667		166	268		434	625
0600	200 amp main lugs, indoor, 16 circuits	R-1A	1.80	8.889		214	320		534	760
0700	20 circuits		1.50	10.667		254	385		639	910
0800	24 circuits		1.30	12.308		305	445		750	1,075
1200	Rainproof, 16 circuits		1.80	8.889		248	320		568	795
1300	20 circuits	↓	1.50	10.667		287	385		672	945

For customer support on your Residential Costs with RSMeans Data, call 800.448.8182.

605

26 24 Switchboards and Panelboards

26 24 16 – Panelboards

26 24 16.10 Load Centers

	Crew	Daily Output	Labor-Hours	Unit	Material	2017 Bare Costs Labor	Equipment	Total	Total Incl O&P
1400 24 circuits	R-1A	1.30	12.308	Ea.	350	445		795	1,125

26 24 16.20 Panelboard and Load Center Circuit Breakers

		Crew	Daily Output	Labor-Hours	Unit	Material	2017 Bare Costs Labor	Equipment	Total	Total Incl O&P
0010	**PANELBOARD AND LOAD CENTER CIRCUIT BREAKERS**									
2000	Plug-in panel or load center, 120/240 volt, to 60 amp, 1 pole	1 Elec	12	.667	Ea.	9.90	27		36.90	55
2004	Circuit breaker, 120/240 volt, 20 A, 1 pole with NM cable		6.50	1.231		16.55	49.50		66.05	99
2006	30 A, 1 pole with NM cable		6.50	1.231		16.55	49.50		66.05	99
2010	2 pole		9	.889		26	35.50		61.50	87
2014	50 A, 2 pole with NM cable		5.50	1.455		32.50	58.50		91	132
2020	3 pole		7.50	1.067		77.50	43		120.50	156
2030	100 amp, 2 pole		6	1.333		104	53.50		157.50	202
2040	3 pole		4.50	1.778		115	71.50		186.50	244
2050	150 to 200 amp, 2 pole		3	2.667		218	107		325	415
2060	Plug-in tandem, 120/240 V, 2-15 A, 1 pole		11	.727		37.50	29		66.50	89.50
2070	1-15 A & 1-20 A		11	.727		37.50	29		66.50	89.50
2080	2-20 A		11	.727		37.50	29		66.50	89.50
2300	Ground fault, 240 volt, 30 amp, 1 pole		7	1.143		74	46		120	157
2310	2 pole		6	1.333		132	53.50		185.50	234

26 27 Low-Voltage Distribution Equipment

26 27 13 – Electricity Metering

26 27 13.10 Meter Centers and Sockets

		Crew	Daily Output	Labor-Hours	Unit	Material	2017 Bare Costs Labor	Equipment	Total	Total Incl O&P
0010	**METER CENTERS AND SOCKETS**									
0100	Sockets, single position, 4 terminal, 100 amp	1 Elec	3.20	2.500	Ea.	43	101		144	213
0200	150 amp		2.30	3.478		48	140		188	282
0300	200 amp		1.90	4.211		92	169		261	380
0500	Double position, 4 terminal, 100 amp		2.80	2.857		204	115		319	415
0600	150 amp		2.10	3.810		203	153		356	475
0700	200 amp		1.70	4.706		450	189		639	805
1100	Meter centers and sockets, three phase, single pos, 7 terminal, 100 amp		2.80	2.857		107	115		222	305
1200	200 amp		2.10	3.810		217	153		370	490
1400	400 amp		1.70	4.706		810	189		999	1,200
2590	Basic meter device									
2600	1P 3W 120/240 V 4 jaw 125A sockets, 3 meter	2 Elec	1	16	Ea.	325	645		970	1,400
2610	4 meter		.90	17.778		385	715		1,100	1,600
2620	5 meter		.80	20		465	805		1,270	1,850
2630	6 meter		.60	26.667		610	1,075		1,685	2,425
2640	7 meter		.56	28.571		1,300	1,150		2,450	3,300
2660	10 meter		.48	33.333		1,775	1,350		3,125	4,150
2680	Rainproof 1P 3W 120/240 V 4 jaw 125A sockets									
2690	3 meter	2 Elec	1	16	Ea.	590	645		1,235	1,700
2710	6 meter		.60	26.667		1,025	1,075		2,100	2,875
2730	8 meter		.52	30.769		1,425	1,225		2,650	3,575
2750	1P 3W 120/240 V 4 jaw sockets									
2760	with 125A circuit breaker, 3 meter	2 Elec	1	16	Ea.	1,100	645		1,745	2,275
2780	5 meter		.80	20		1,750	805		2,555	3,250
2800	7 meter		.56	28.571		2,500	1,150		3,650	4,625
2820	10 meter		.48	33.333		3,500	1,350		4,850	6,050
2830	Rainproof 1P 3W 120/240 V 4 jaw sockets									
2840	with 125A circuit breaker, 3 meter	2 Elec	1	16	Ea.	1,100	645		1,745	2,275
2870	6 meter		.60	26.667		2,050	1,075		3,125	4,000
2890	8 meter		.52	30.769		2,800	1,225		4,025	5,100

26 27 Low-Voltage Distribution Equipment

26 27 13 – Electricity Metering

26 27 13.10 Meter Centers and Sockets

		Crew	Daily Output	Labor-Hours	Unit	Material	2017 Bare Costs Labor	Equipment	Total	Total Incl O&P
3250	1P 3W 120/240 V 4 jaw sockets									
3260	with 200A circuit breaker, 3 meter	2 Elec	1	16	Ea.	1,650	645		2,295	2,875
3290	6 meter		.60	26.667		3,325	1,075		4,400	5,400
3310	8 meter		.56	28.571		4,500	1,150		5,650	6,825
3330	Rainproof 1P 3W 120/240 V 4 jaw sockets									
3350	with 200A circuit breaker, 3 meter	2 Elec	1	16	Ea.	1,650	645		2,295	2,875
3380	6 meter		.60	26.667		3,325	1,075		4,400	5,400
3400	8 meter		.52	30.769		4,500	1,225		5,725	6,975

26 27 23 – Indoor Service Poles

26 27 23.40 Surface Raceway

		Crew	Daily Output	Labor-Hours	Unit	Material	2017 Bare Costs Labor	Equipment	Total	Total Incl O&P
0010	**SURFACE RACEWAY**									
0090	Metal, straight section									
0100	No. 500	1 Elec	100	.080	L.F.	1.07	3.22		4.29	6.45
0110	No. 700		100	.080		1.19	3.22		4.41	6.55
0200	No. 1000		90	.089		1.45	3.57		5.02	7.45
0400	No. 1500, small pancake		90	.089		2.20	3.57		5.77	8.25
0600	No. 2000, base & cover, blank		90	.089		2.24	3.57		5.81	8.30
0800	No. 3000, base & cover, blank		75	.107		4.28	4.29		8.57	11.70
2400	Fittings, elbows, No. 500		40	.200	Ea.	2.25	8.05		10.30	15.65
2800	Elbow cover, No. 2000		40	.200		3.25	8.05		11.30	16.75
2880	Tee, No. 500		42	.190		4.10	7.65		11.75	17.05
2900	No. 2000		27	.296		12.10	11.90		24	33
3000	Switch box, No. 500		16	.500		6.20	20		26.20	40
3400	Telephone outlet, No. 1500		16	.500		36	20		56	72.50
3600	Junction box, No. 1500		16	.500		15.75	20		35.75	50.50
3800	Plugmold wired sections, No. 2000									
4000	1 circuit, 6 outlets, 3 ft. long	1 Elec	8	1	Ea.	36.50	40		76.50	106
4100	2 circuits, 8 outlets, 6 ft. long	"	5.30	1.509	"	60	60.50		120.50	166

26 27 26 – Wiring Devices

26 27 26.10 Low Voltage Switching

		Crew	Daily Output	Labor-Hours	Unit	Material	2017 Bare Costs Labor	Equipment	Total	Total Incl O&P
0010	**LOW VOLTAGE SWITCHING**									
3600	Relays, 120 V or 277 V standard	1 Elec	12	.667	Ea.	41	27		68	89
3800	Flush switch, standard		40	.200		11.50	8.05		19.55	26
4000	Interchangeable		40	.200		15.05	8.05		23.10	29.50
4100	Surface switch, standard		40	.200		8.20	8.05		16.25	22
4200	Transformer 115 V to 25 V		12	.667		128	27		155	185
4400	Master control, 12 circuit, manual		4	2		127	80.50		207.50	272
4500	25 circuit, motorized		4	2		141	80.50		221.50	287
4600	Rectifier, silicon		12	.667		46	27		73	94.50
4800	Switchplates, 1 gang, 1, 2 or 3 switch, plastic		80	.100		5	4.02		9.02	12.10
5000	Stainless steel		80	.100		11.35	4.02		15.37	19.10
5400	2 gang, 3 switch, stainless steel		53	.151		23	6.05		29.05	35
5500	4 switch, plastic		53	.151		10.45	6.05		16.50	21.50
5600	2 gang, 4 switch, stainless steel		53	.151		22	6.05		28.05	34
5700	6 switch, stainless steel		53	.151		43.50	6.05		49.55	58
5800	3 gang, 9 switch, stainless steel		32	.250		65.50	10.05		75.55	88.50

26 27 26.20 Wiring Devices Elements

		Crew	Daily Output	Labor-Hours	Unit	Material	2017 Bare Costs Labor	Equipment	Total	Total Incl O&P
0010	**WIRING DEVICES ELEMENTS**									
0200	Toggle switch, quiet type, single pole, 15 amp	1 Elec	40	.200	Ea.	.54	8.05		8.59	13.75
0600	3 way, 15 amp		23	.348		1.90	14		15.90	25
0900	4 way, 15 amp		15	.533		7.75	21.50		29.25	43.50

For customer support on your Residential Costs with RSMeans Data, call 800.448.8182.

607

26 27 Low-Voltage Distribution Equipment

26 27 26 – Wiring Devices

26 27 26.20 Wiring Devices Elements

		Crew	Daily Output	Labor-Hours	Unit	Material	2017 Bare Costs Labor	Equipment	Total	Total Incl O&P
1650	Dimmer switch, 120 volt, incandescent, 600 watt, 1 pole [G]	1 Elec	16	.500	Ea.	22.50	20		42.50	58
2460	Receptacle, duplex, 120 volt, grounded, 15 amp		40	.200		1.26	8.05		9.31	14.55
2470	20 amp		27	.296		7.95	11.90		19.85	28
2490	Dryer, 30 amp		15	.533		4.46	21.50		25.96	40
2500	Range, 50 amp		11	.727		12.15	29		41.15	61.50
2600	Wall plates, stainless steel, 1 gang		80	.100		2.56	4.02		6.58	9.40
2800	2 gang		53	.151		4.33	6.05		10.38	14.70
3200	Lampholder, keyless		26	.308		16.85	12.35		29.20	39
3400	Pullchain with receptacle		22	.364		20.50	14.60		35.10	46.50

26 27 73 – Door Chimes

26 27 73.10 Doorbell System

		Crew	Daily Output	Labor-Hours	Unit	Material	2017 Bare Costs Labor	Equipment	Total	Total Incl O&P
0010	**DOORBELL SYSTEM**, incl. transformer, button & signal									
0100	6" bell	1 Elec	4	2	Ea.	135	80.50		215.50	281
0200	Buzzer		4	2		109	80.50		189.50	252
1000	Door chimes, 2 notes		16	.500		24	20		44	59.50
1020	with ambient light		12	.667		116	27		143	172
1100	Tube type, 3 tube system		12	.667		199	27		226	263
1180	4 tube system		10	.800		440	32		472	540
1900	For transformer & button, add		5	1.600		15.60	64.50		80.10	122
3000	For push button only		24	.333		1.97	13.40		15.37	24

26 28 Low-Voltage Circuit Protective Devices

26 28 16 – Enclosed Switches and Circuit Breakers

26 28 16.10 Circuit Breakers

		Crew	Daily Output	Labor-Hours	Unit	Material	2017 Bare Costs Labor	Equipment	Total	Total Incl O&P
0010	**CIRCUIT BREAKERS** (in enclosure)									
0100	Enclosed (NEMA 1), 600 volt, 3 pole, 30 amp	1 Elec	3.20	2.500	Ea.	490	101		591	705
0200	60 amp		2.80	2.857		605	115		720	855
0400	100 amp		2.30	3.478		690	140		830	990

26 28 16.20 Safety Switches

		Crew	Daily Output	Labor-Hours	Unit	Material	2017 Bare Costs Labor	Equipment	Total	Total Incl O&P
0010	**SAFETY SWITCHES**									
0100	General duty 240 volt, 3 pole NEMA 1, fusible, 30 amp	1 Elec	3.20	2.500	Ea.	64	101		165	236
0200	60 amp		2.30	3.478		109	140		249	350
0300	100 amp		1.90	4.211		186	169		355	480
0400	200 amp		1.30	6.154		400	247		647	845
0500	400 amp	2 Elec	1.80	8.889		980	355		1,335	1,650
9010	Disc. switch, 600 V 3 pole fusible, 30 amp, to 10 HP motor	1 Elec	3.20	2.500		355	101		456	555
9050	60 amp, to 30 HP motor		2.30	3.478		815	140		955	1,125
9070	100 amp, to 60 HP motor		1.90	4.211		815	169		984	1,175

26 28 16.40 Time Switches

		Crew	Daily Output	Labor-Hours	Unit	Material	2017 Bare Costs Labor	Equipment	Total	Total Incl O&P
0010	**TIME SWITCHES**									
0100	Single pole, single throw, 24 hour dial	1 Elec	4	2	Ea.	145	80.50		225.50	292
0200	24 hour dial with reserve power		3.60	2.222		615	89.50		704.50	820
0300	Astronomic dial		3.60	2.222		240	89.50		329.50	410
0400	Astronomic dial with reserve power		3.30	2.424		665	97.50		762.50	890
0500	7 day calendar dial		3.30	2.424		146	97.50		243.50	320
0600	7 day calendar dial with reserve power		3.20	2.500		285	101		386	480
0700	Photo cell 2000 watt		8	1		28.50	40		68.50	97.50

26 32 Packaged Generator Assemblies

26 32 13 – Engine Generators

26 32 13.16 Gas-Engine-Driven Generator Sets	Crew	Daily Output	Labor-Hours	Unit	Material	2017 Bare Costs Labor	Equipment	Total	Total Incl O&P
0010 **GAS-ENGINE-DRIVEN GENERATOR SETS**									
0020 Gas or gasoline operated, includes battery,									
0050 charger, & muffler									
0200 7.5 kW	R-3	.83	24.096	Ea.	8,550	960	166	9,676	11,200
0300 11.5 kW		.71	28.169		12,100	1,125	194	13,419	15,400
0400 20 kW		.63	31.746		14,300	1,275	219	15,794	18,000
0500 35 kW		.55	36.364		17,000	1,450	251	18,701	21,400

26 33 Battery Equipment

26 33 43 – Battery Chargers

26 33 43.55 Electric Vehicle Charging

		Crew	Daily Output	Labor-Hours	Unit	Material	2017 Bare Costs Labor	Equipment	Total	Total Incl O&P
0010 **ELECTRIC VEHICLE CHARGING**										
0020 Level 2, wall mounted										
2100 Light duty, hard wired	G	1 Elec	20.48	.391	Ea.	1,125	15.70		1,140.70	1,250
2110 plug in	G	"	30.72	.260	"	1,125	10.45		1,135.45	1,250

26 36 Transfer Switches

26 36 23 – Automatic Transfer Switches

26 36 23.10 Automatic Transfer Switch Devices

	Crew	Daily Output	Labor-Hours	Unit	Material	2017 Bare Costs Labor	Equipment	Total	Total Incl O&P
0010 **AUTOMATIC TRANSFER SWITCH DEVICES**									
0100 Switches, enclosed 480 volt, 3 pole, 30 amp	1 Elec	2.30	3.478	Ea.	2,400	140		2,540	2,875
0200 60 amp	"	1.90	4.211	"	2,400	169		2,569	2,925

26 41 Facility Lightning Protection

26 41 13 – Lightning Protection for Structures

26 41 13.13 Lightning Protection for Buildings

	Crew	Daily Output	Labor-Hours	Unit	Material	2017 Bare Costs Labor	Equipment	Total	Total Incl O&P
0010 **LIGHTNING PROTECTION FOR BUILDINGS**									
0200 Air terminals & base, copper									
0400 3/8" diameter x 10" (to 75' high)	1 Elec	8	1	Ea.	22.50	40		62.50	90.50
1000 Aluminum, 1/2" diameter x 12" (to 75' high)		8	1		17.65	40		57.65	85.50
1020 1/2" diameter x 24"		7.30	1.096		19.35	44		63.35	93.50
1040 1/2" diameter x 60"		6.70	1.194		26.50	48		74.50	108
2000 Cable, copper, 220 lb. per thousand ft. (to 75' high)		320	.025	L.F.	3.03	1.01		4.04	4.98
2500 Aluminum, 101 lb. per thousand ft. (to 75' high)		280	.029	"	.95	1.15		2.10	2.93
3000 Arrester, 175 volt AC to ground		8	1	Ea.	149	40		189	230

26 51 13 – Interior Lighting Fixtures, Lamps, and Ballasts

26 51 13.50 Interior Lighting Fixtures		Crew	Daily Output	Labor-Hours	Unit	Material	2017 Bare Costs Labor	Equipment	Total	Total Incl O&P
0010	**INTERIOR LIGHTING FIXTURES** Including lamps, mounting									
0030	hardware and connections									
0100	Fluorescent, C.W. lamps, troffer, recess mounted in grid, RS									
0130	Grid ceiling mount									
0200	Acrylic lens, 1'W x 4'L, two 40 watt	1 Elec	5.70	1.404	Ea.	51.50	56.50		108	149
0300	2'W x 2'L, two U40 watt		5.70	1.404		55	56.50		111.50	153
0600	2'W x 4'L, four 40 watt	↓	4.70	1.702	↓	62	68.50		130.50	181
1000	Surface mounted, RS									
1030	Acrylic lens with hinged & latched door frame									
1100	1'W x 4'L, two 40 watt	1 Elec	7	1.143	Ea.	65.50	46		111.50	148
1200	2'W x 2'L, two U40 watt		7	1.143		70.50	46		116.50	153
1500	2'W x 4'L, four 40 watt		5.30	1.509		85	60.50		145.50	193
1501	2'W x 4'L, 6-40W T8	↓	5.20	1.538	↓	85	62		147	195
2100	Strip fixture									
2200	4' long, one 40 watt, RS	1 Elec	8.50	.941	Ea.	31	38		69	96
2300	4' long, two 40 watt, RS	"	8	1		43	40		83	114
2600	8' long, one 75 watt, SL	2 Elec	13.40	1.194		55	48		103	139
2700	8' long, two 75 watt, SL	"	12.40	1.290	↓	66.50	52		118.50	158
4450	Incandescent, high hat can, round alzak reflector, prewired									
4470	100 watt	1 Elec	8	1	Ea.	64.50	40		104.50	137
4480	150 watt		8	1		105	40		145	181
4500	300 watt	↓	6.70	1.194	↓	242	48		290	345
5200	Ceiling, surface mounted, opal glass drum									
5300	8", one 60 watt lamp	1 Elec	10	.800	Ea.	65.50	32		97.50	125
5400	10", two 60 watt lamps		8	1		72.50	40		112.50	146
5500	12", four 60 watt lamps		6.70	1.194		103	48		151	192
6900	Mirror light, fluorescent, RS, acrylic enclosure, two 40 watt		8	1		116	40		156	194
6910	One 40 watt		8	1		96	40		136	172
6920	One 20 watt	↓	12	.667	↓	82.50	27		109.50	135

26 51 13.55 Interior LED Fixtures

26 51 13.55 Interior LED Fixtures			Crew	Daily Output	Labor-Hours	Unit	Material	2017 Bare Costs Labor	Equipment	Total	Total Incl O&P
0010	**INTERIOR LED FIXTURES** Incl. lamps, and mounting hardware										
0100	Downlight, recess mounted, 7.5" diameter, 25 watt	G	1 Elec	8	1	Ea.	335	40		375	430
0120	10" diameter, 36 watt	G		8	1		360	40		400	460
0160	cylinder, 10 watts	G		8	1		102	40		142	178
0180	20 watts	G		8	1		166	40		206	249
1000	Troffer, recess mounted, 2' x 4', 3200 Lumens	G		5.30	1.509		138	60.50		198.50	251
1010	4800 Lumens	G		5	1.600		179	64.50		243.50	300
1020	6400 Lumens	G		4.70	1.702		198	68.50		266.50	330
1100	Troffer retrofit lamp, 38 watt	G		21	.381		238	15.30		253.30	286
1110	60 watt	G		20	.400		340	16.10		356.10	400
1120	100 watt	G		18	.444		510	17.85		527.85	590
1200	Troffer, volumetric recess mounted, 2' x 2'	G		5.70	1.404		279	56.50		335.50	400
2000	Strip, surface mounted, one light bar 4' long, 3500K	G		8.50	.941		260	38		298	350
2010	5000K	G		8	1		260	40		300	350
2020	Two light bar 4' long, 5000K	G		7	1.143		410	46		456	525
3000	Linear, suspended mounted, one light bar 4' long, 37 watt	G	↓	6.70	1.194		153	48		201	247
3010	One light bar 8' long, 74 watt	G	2 Elec	12.20	1.311		283	52.50		335.50	395
3020	Two light bar 4' long, 74 watt	G	1 Elec	5.70	1.404		305	56.50		361.50	430
3030	Two light bar 8' long, 148 watt	G	2 Elec	8.80	1.818		350	73		423	505
4000	High bay, surface mounted, round, 150 watts	G		5.41	2.959		475	119		594	715
4010	2 bars,164 watts	G		5.41	2.959		445	119		564	685
4020	3 bars, 246 watts	G	↓	5.01	3.197		575	129		704	840

26 51 Interior Lighting

26 51 13 – Interior Lighting Fixtures, Lamps, and Ballasts

26 51 13.55 Interior LED Fixtures

		Crew	Daily Output	Labor-Hours	Unit	Material	2017 Bare Costs Labor	Equipment	Total	Total Incl O&P
4030	4 bars, 328 watts	G 2 Elec	4.60	3.478	Ea.	700	140		840	1,000
4040	5 bars, 410 watts	G 3 Elec	4.20	5.716		830	230		1,060	1,300
4050	6 bars, 492 watts	G	3.80	6.324		935	254		1,189	1,450
4060	7 bars, 574 watts	G	3.39	7.075		1,025	284		1,309	1,600
4070	8 bars, 656 watts	G	2.99	8.029		1,125	325		1,450	1,775
5000	Track, lighthead, 6 watt	G 1 Elec	32	.250		54.50	10.05		64.55	76.50
5010	9 watt	G "	32	.250		61.50	10.05		71.55	84
6000	Garage, surface mounted, 103 watts	G 2 Elec	6.50	2.462		970	99		1,069	1,225
6100	pendent mounted, 80 watts	G	6.50	2.462		695	99		794	925
6200	95 watts	G	6.50	2.462		800	99		899	1,050
6300	125 watts	G	6.50	2.462		840	99		939	1,075

26 51 13.70 Residential Fixtures

		Crew	Daily Output	Labor-Hours	Unit	Material	2017 Bare Costs Labor	Equipment	Total	Total Incl O&P
0010	**RESIDENTIAL FIXTURES**									
0400	Fluorescent, interior, surface, circline, 32 watt & 40 watt	1 Elec	20	.400	Ea.	141	16.10		157.10	182
0500	2' x 2', two U-tube 32 watt T8		8	1		165	40		205	247
0700	Shallow under cabinet, two 20 watt		16	.500		71.50	20		91.50	112
0900	Wall mounted, 4'L, two 32 watt T8, with baffle		10	.800		133	32		165	199
2000	Incandescent, exterior lantern, wall mounted, 60 watt		16	.500		60	20		80	99
2100	Post light, 150W, with 7' post		4	2		270	80.50		350.50	430
2500	Lamp holder, weatherproof with 150W PAR		16	.500		32	20		52	68
2550	With reflector and guard		12	.667		56	27		83	106
2600	Interior pendent, globe with shade, 150 watt		20	.400		201	16.10		217.10	248

26 55 Special Purpose Lighting

26 55 59 – Display Lighting

26 55 59.10 Track Lighting

		Crew	Daily Output	Labor-Hours	Unit	Material	2017 Bare Costs Labor	Equipment	Total	Total Incl O&P
0010	**TRACK LIGHTING**									
0100	8' section	2 Elec	10.60	1.509	Ea.	69	60.50		129.50	176
0300	3 circuits, 4' section	1 Elec	6.70	1.194		92.50	48		140.50	181
0400	8' section	2 Elec	10.60	1.509		109	60.50		169.50	220
0500	12' section	"	8.80	1.818		159	73		232	295
1000	Feed kit, surface mounting	1 Elec	16	.500		13	20		33	47.50
1100	End cover		24	.333		5.55	13.40		18.95	28
1200	Feed kit, stem mounting, 1 circuit		16	.500		42	20		62	79
1300	3 circuit		16	.500		42	20		62	79
2000	Electrical joiner, for continuous runs, 1 circuit		32	.250		24	10.05		34.05	43
2100	3 circuit		32	.250		59	10.05		69.05	81.50
2200	Fixtures, spotlight, 75W PAR halogen		16	.500		55.50	20		75.50	94
2210	50W MR16 halogen		16	.500		171	20		191	221
3000	Wall washer, 250 watt tungsten halogen		16	.500		132	20		152	178
3100	Low voltage, 25/50 watt, 1 circuit		16	.500		133	20		153	179
3120	3 circuit		16	.500		198	20		218	251

For customer support on your Residential Costs with RSMeans Data, call 800.448.8182.

611

26 56 Exterior Lighting

26 56 13 – Lighting Poles and Standards

26 56 13.10 Lighting Poles	Crew	Daily Output	Labor-Hours	Unit	Material	2017 Bare Costs Labor	2017 Bare Costs Equipment	Total	Total Incl O&P
0010 **LIGHTING POLES**									
6420 Wood pole, 4-1/2" x 5-1/8", 8' high	1 Elec	6	1.333	Ea.	350	53.50		403.50	475
6440 12' high		5.70	1.404		505	56.50		561.50	655
6460 20' high		4	2		715	80.50		795.50	920

26 56 23 – Area Lighting

26 56 23.10 Exterior Fixtures

	Crew	Daily Output	Labor-Hours	Unit	Material	2017 Bare Costs Labor	2017 Bare Costs Equipment	Total	Total Incl O&P
0010 **EXTERIOR FIXTURES** With lamps									
0400 Quartz, 500 watt	1 Elec	5.30	1.509	Ea.	61.50	60.50		122	167
1100 Wall pack, low pressure sodium, 35 watt		4	2		199	80.50		279.50	350
1150 55 watt		4	2		236	80.50		316.50	390

26 56 26 – Landscape Lighting

26 56 26.20 Landscape Fixtures

	Crew	Daily Output	Labor-Hours	Unit	Material	2017 Bare Costs Labor	2017 Bare Costs Equipment	Total	Total Incl O&P
0010 **LANDSCAPE FIXTURES**									
7380 Landscape recessed uplight, incl. housing, ballast, transformer									
7390 & reflector, not incl. conduit, wire, trench									
7420 Incandescent, 250 watt	1 Elec	5	1.600	Ea.	640	64.50		704.50	810
7440 Quartz, 250 watt	"	5	1.600	"	605	64.50		669.50	775

26 56 26.50 Landscape LED Fixtures

	Crew	Daily Output	Labor-Hours	Unit	Material	2017 Bare Costs Labor	2017 Bare Costs Equipment	Total	Total Incl O&P
0010 **LANDSCAPE LED FIXTURES**									
0100 12 volt alum bullet hooded -BLK	1 Elec	5	1.600	Ea.	96	64.50		160.50	211
0200 12 volt alum bullet hooded -BRZ		5	1.600		96	64.50		160.50	211
0300 12 volt alum bullet hooded -GRN		5	1.600		96	64.50		160.50	211
1000 12 volt alum large bullet hooded -BLK		5	1.600		71	64.50		135.50	183
1100 12 volt alum large bullet hooded -BRZ		5	1.600		71	64.50		135.50	183
1200 12 volt alum large bullet hooded -GRN		5	1.600		71	64.50		135.50	183
2000 12 volt large bullet landscape light fixture		5	1.600		71	64.50		135.50	183
2100 12 volt alum light large bullet		5	1.600		71	64.50		135.50	183
2200 12 volt alum bullet light		5	1.600		71	64.50		135.50	183

26 56 33 – Walkway Lighting

26 56 33.10 Walkway Luminaire

	Crew	Daily Output	Labor-Hours	Unit	Material	2017 Bare Costs Labor	2017 Bare Costs Equipment	Total	Total Incl O&P
0010 **WALKWAY LUMINAIRE**									
6500 Bollard light, lamp & ballast, 42" high with polycarbonate lens									
7200 Incandescent, 150 watt	1 Elec	3	2.667	Ea.	620	107		727	860

26 61 Lighting Systems and Accessories

26 61 23 – Lamps Applications

26 61 23.10 Lamps

	Crew	Daily Output	Labor-Hours	Unit	Material	2017 Bare Costs Labor	2017 Bare Costs Equipment	Total	Total Incl O&P
0010 **LAMPS**									
0081 Fluorescent, rapid start, cool white, 2' long, 20 watt	1 Elec	100	.080	Ea.	3.60	3.22		6.82	9.20
0101 4' long, 40 watt		90	.089		2.75	3.57		6.32	8.90
1351 High pressure sodium, 70 watt		30	.267		26.50	10.70		37.20	46.50
1371 150 watt		30	.267		28.50	10.70		39.20	48.50

Estimating Tips
27 20 00 Data Communications
27 30 00 Voice Communications
27 40 00 Audio-Video Communications

- When estimating material costs for special systems, it is always prudent to obtain manufacturers' quotations for equipment prices and special installation requirements that may affect the total cost.

- For cost modifications for elevated tray installation, add the percentages to labor according to the height of the installation and only to the quantities exceeding the different height levels, not to the total tray quantities. Refer to 26 01 02.20 for labor adjustment factors.

- Do not overlook the costs for equipment used in the installation. If scissor lifts and boom lifts are available in the field, contractors may use them in lieu of the proposed ladders and rolling staging.

Reference Numbers

Reference numbers are shown at the beginning of some major classifications. These numbers refer to related items in the Reference Section. The reference information may be an estimating procedure, an alternate pricing method, or technical information.

Note: Not all subdivisions listed here necessarily appear. ■

27 13 Communications Backbone Cabling

27 13 23 – Communications Optical Fiber Backbone Cabling

27 13 23.13 Communications Optical Fiber

27 13 23.13 Communications Optical Fiber	Crew	Daily Output	Labor-Hours	Unit	Material	2017 Bare Costs Labor	Equipment	Total	Total Incl O&P
0010	**COMMUNICATIONS OPTICAL FIBER**								
0040	Specialized tools & techniques cause installation costs to vary.								
0070	Fiber optic, cable, bulk simplex, single mode	1 Elec	8	1	C.L.F.	24.50	40		64.50	93
0080	Multi mode		8	1		29.50	40		69.50	98.50
0090	4 strand, single mode		7.34	1.090		40.50	44		84.50	117
0095	Multi mode		7.34	1.090		50.50	44		94.50	128
0100	12 strand, single mode		6.67	1.199		78	48		126	165
0105	Multi mode		6.67	1.199		96.50	48		144.50	185
0150	Jumper				Ea.	33			33	36.50
0200	Pigtail					37			37	40.50
0300	Connector	1 Elec	24	.333		27	13.40		40.40	51.50
0350	Finger splice		32	.250		40	10.05		50.05	61
0400	Transceiver (low cost bi-directional)		8	1		480	40		520	590
0450	Rack housing, 4 rack spaces, 12 panels (144 fibers)		2	4		560	161		721	880
1000	Cable, 62.5 microns, direct burial, 4 fiber	R-15	1200	.040	L.F.	.86	1.58	.24	2.68	3.80
1020	Indoor, 2 fiber	R-19	1000	.020		.43	.81		1.24	1.79
1040	Outdoor, aerial/duct	"	1670	.012		.69	.48		1.17	1.55
1060	50 microns, direct burial, 8 fiber	R-22	4000	.009		1.34	.34		1.68	2.03
1080	12 fiber		4000	.009		2.18	.34		2.52	2.96
1100	Indoor, 12 fiber		759	.049		2.07	1.81		3.88	5.25
1120	Connectors, 62.5 micron cable, transmission	R-19	40	.500	Ea.	16.75	20		36.75	51.50
1140	Cable splice		40	.500		18.65	20		38.65	53.50
1160	125 micron cable, transmission		16	1.250		17.50	50.50		68	102
1180	Receiver, 1.2 mile range		20	1		247	40.50		287.50	335
1200	1.9 mile range		20	1		233	40.50		273.50	320
1220	6.2 mile range		5	4		290	161		451	585
1240	Transmitter, 1.2 mile range		20	1		271	40.50		311.50	365
1260	1.9 mile range		20	1		305	40.50		345.50	400
1280	6.2 mile range		5	4		390	161		551	690
1300	Modem, 1.2 mile range		5	4		168	161		329	450
1320	6.2 mile range		5	4		305	161		466	600
1340	1.9 mile range, 12 channel		5	4		1,925	161		2,086	2,375
1360	Repeater, 1.2 mile range		10	2		385	80.50		465.50	555
1380	1.9 mile range		10	2		480	80.50		560.50	660
1400	6.2 mile range		5	4		925	161		1,086	1,300
1420	1.2 mile range, digital		5	4		445	161		606	755

27 41 Audio-Video Systems

27 41 33 – Master Antenna Television Systems

27 41 33.10 T.V. Systems

27 41 33.10 T.V. Systems	Crew	Daily Output	Labor-Hours	Unit	Material	Labor	Equipment	Total	Total Incl O&P
0010	**T.V. SYSTEMS**, not including rough-in wires, cables & conduits									
0100	Master TV antenna system									
0200	VHF reception & distribution, 12 outlets	1 Elec	6	1.333	Outlet	156	53.50		209.50	260
0800	VHF & UHF reception & distribution, 12 outlets		6	1.333	"	233	53.50		286.50	345
5000	Antenna, small		6	1.333	Ea.	51.50	53.50		105	145
5100	Large		4	2		217	80.50		297.50	370
5110	Rotor unit		8	1		63	40		103	136
5120	Single booster		8	1		31.50	40		71.50	101
5130	Antenna pole, 10'		3.20	2.500		20	101		121	187
6100	Satellite TV system	2 Elec	1	16		2,200	645		2,845	3,475
6110	Dish, mesh, 10' diam.	"	2.40	6.667		1,675	268		1,943	2,300

27 41 Audio-Video Systems

27 41 33 – Master Antenna Television Systems

27 41 33.10 T.V. Systems	Crew	Daily Output	Labor-Hours	Unit	Material	2017 Bare Costs Labor	Equipment	Total	Total Incl O&P
6111	Two way RF/IF tapeoff	1 Elec	36	.222	Ea.	3.59	8.95		12.54	18.60
6112	Two way RF/IF splitter		24	.333		14	13.40		27.40	37.50
6113	Line amplifier		24	.333		15.15	13.40		28.55	38.50
6114	Line splitters		36	.222		5.05	8.95		14	20
6115	Line multi switches		8	1		670	40		710	800
6120	Motor unit		2.40	3.333		259	134		393	505
7000	Home theater, widescreen, 42", high definition, TV		10.24	.781		400	31.50		431.50	490
7050	Flat wall mount bracket		10.24	.781		80.50	31.50		112	140
7100	7 channel home theater receiver		10.24	.781		385	31.50		416.50	475
7200	Home theater speakers		10.24	.781	Set	216	31.50		247.50	289
7300	Home theater programmable remote		10.24	.781	Ea.	249	31.50		280.50	325
8000	Main video splitter		4	2		3,200	80.50		3,280.50	3,650
8010	Video distribution units		4	2		140	80.50		220.50	286

Division Notes

		CREW	DAILY OUTPUT	LABOR-HOURS	UNIT	BARE COSTS				TOTAL INCL O&P
						MAT.	LABOR	EQUIP.	TOTAL	

Estimating Tips

- When estimating material costs for electronic safety and security systems, it is always prudent to obtain manufacturers' quotations for equipment prices and special installation requirements that may affect the total cost.

- Fire alarm systems consist of control panels, annunciator panels, batteries with rack, charger, and fire alarm actuating and indicating devices. Some fire alarm systems include speakers, telephone lines, door closer controls, and other components. Be careful not to overlook the costs related to installation for these items. Also be aware of costs for integrated automation instrumentation and terminal devices, control equipment, control wiring, and programming. Insurance underwriters may have specific requirements for the type of materials to be installed or design requirements based on the hazard to be protected. Local jurisdictions may have requirements not covered by code. It is advisable to be aware of any special conditions.

- Security equipment includes items such as CCTV, access control, and other detection and identification systems to perform alert and alarm functions. Be sure to consider the costs related to installation for this security equipment, such as for integrated automation instrumentation and terminal devices, control equipment, control wiring, and programming.

Reference Numbers

Reference numbers are shown at the beginning of some major classifications. These numbers refer to related items in the Reference Section. The reference information may be an estimating procedure, an alternate pricing method, or technical information.

Note: Not all subdivisions listed here necessarily appear. ■

Did you know?

Our online estimating solution gives you the same access to RSMeans' data with 24/7 access:

- Quickly locate costs in the searchable database.

- Build cost lists, estimates, and reports in minutes.

- Adjust costs to any location in the U.S. and Canada with the click of a button.

Start your free trial today at
www.RSMeansOnline.com

28 16 Intrusion Detection

28 16 16 – Intrusion Detection Systems Infrastructure

28 16 16.50 Intrusion Detection	Crew	Daily Output	Labor-Hours	Unit	Material	2017 Bare Costs Labor	Equipment	Total	Total Incl O&P
0010 **INTRUSION DETECTION**, not including wires & conduits									
0100 Burglar alarm, battery operated, mechanical trigger	1 Elec	4	2	Ea.	280	80.50		360.50	440
0200 Electrical trigger		4	2		335	80.50		415.50	500
0400 For outside key control, add		8	1		87	40		127	162
0600 For remote signaling circuitry, add		8	1		138	40		178	218
0800 Card reader, flush type, standard		2.70	2.963		795	119		914	1,075
1000 Multi-code		2.70	2.963		1,200	119		1,319	1,525
1200 Door switches, hinge switch		5.30	1.509		62.50	60.50		123	168
1400 Magnetic switch		5.30	1.509		77	60.50		137.50	184
2800 Ultrasonic motion detector, 12 volt		2.30	3.478		210	140		350	460
3000 Infrared photoelectric detector		4	2		146	80.50		226.50	293
3200 Passive infrared detector		4	2		236	80.50		316.50	390
3420 Switchmats, 30" x 5'		5.30	1.509		105	60.50		165.50	216
3440 30" x 25'		4	2		205	80.50		285.50	355
3460 Police connect panel		4	2		272	80.50		352.50	430
3480 Telephone dialer		5.30	1.509		390	60.50		450.50	525
3500 Alarm bell		4	2		105	80.50		185.50	248
3520 Siren		4	2		147	80.50		227.50	294

28 31 Fire Detection and Alarm

28 31 23 – Fire Detection and Alarm Annunciation Panels and Fire Stations

28 31 23.50 Alarm Panels and Devices

	Crew	Daily Output	Labor-Hours	Unit	Material	2017 Bare Costs Labor	Equipment	Total	Total Incl O&P
0010 **ALARM PANELS AND DEVICES**, not including wires & conduits									
5600 Strobe and horn	1 Elec	5.30	1.509	Ea.	154	60.50		214.50	269
5610 Strobe and horn (ADA type)		5.30	1.509		154	60.50		214.50	269
5620 Visual alarm (ADA type)		6.70	1.194		104	48		152	193
5800 Fire alarm horn		6.70	1.194		61.50	48		109.50	146
6600 Drill switch		8	1		375	40		415	475
6800 Master box		2.70	2.963		6,475	119		6,594	7,325
7000 Break glass station		8	1		61.50	40		101.50	134
7800 Remote annunciator, 8 zone lamp		1.80	4.444		213	179		392	525
8000 12 zone lamp	2 Elec	2.60	6.154		420	247		667	870
8200 16 zone lamp	"	2.20	7.273		380	292		672	900

28 31 46 – Smoke Detection Sensors

28 31 46.50 Smoke Detectors

	Crew	Daily Output	Labor-Hours	Unit	Material	2017 Bare Costs Labor	Equipment	Total	Total Incl O&P
0010 **SMOKE DETECTORS**									
5200 Smoke detector, ceiling type	1 Elec	6.20	1.290	Ea.	130	52		182	228
5240 Smoke detector addressable type		6	1.333		224	53.50		277.50	335
5420 Duct addressable type		3.20	2.500		515	101		616	730
8300 Smoke alarm with w/integrated strobe light 120 V 16DB 60 FPM flash rate		16	.500		92	20		112	134
8310 Photoelectric smoke detector with strobe 120 V 90 DB ceiling mount		12	.667		160	27		187	220
8320 120 V, 90 DB wall mount		12	.667		159	27		186	219

28 31 49 – Carbon-Monoxide Detection Sensors

28 31 49.50 Carbon-Monoxide Detectors

	Crew	Daily Output	Labor-Hours	Unit	Material	2017 Bare Costs Labor	Equipment	Total	Total Incl O&P
0010 **CARBON-MONOXIDE DETECTORS**									
8400 Smoke and carbon monoxide alarm battery operated photoelectric low profile	1 Elec	24	.333	Ea.	46	13.40		59.40	72.50
8410 low profile photoelectric battery powered		24	.333		28.50	13.40		41.90	53.50
8420 photoelectric low profile sealed lithium		24	.333		48.50	13.40		61.90	75
8430 Photoelectric low profile sealed lithium smoke and CO with voice combo		24	.333		38	13.40		51.40	64
8500 Carbon monoxide sensor, wall mount 1Mod 1 relay output smoke & heat		24	.333		530	13.40		543.40	600

28 31 Fire Detection and Alarm

28 31 49 – Carbon-Monoxide Detection Sensors

28 31 49.50 Carbon-Monoxide Detectors	Crew	Daily Output	Labor-Hours	Unit	Material	2017 Bare Costs Labor	Equipment	Total	Total Incl O&P
8700	Carbon monoxide detector, battery operated, wall mounted	1 Elec	16	.500	Ea.	52.50	20		72.50	90.50
8710	Hardwired, wall and ceiling mounted		8	1		101	40		141	177
8720	Duct mounted		8	1		345	40		385	440

Division Notes

		CREW	DAILY OUTPUT	LABOR-HOURS	UNIT	BARE COSTS				TOTAL INCL O&P
						MAT.	LABOR	EQUIP.	TOTAL	

Estimating Tips
31 05 00 Common Work Results for Earthwork

- Estimating the actual cost of performing earthwork requires careful consideration of the variables involved. This includes items such as type of soil, whether water will be encountered, dewatering, whether banks need bracing, disposal of excavated earth, and length of haul to fill or spoil sites, etc. If the project has large quantities of cut or fill, consider raising or lowering the site to reduce costs, while paying close attention to the effect on site drainage and utilities.

- If the project has large quantities of fill, creating a borrow pit on the site can significantly lower the costs.

- It is very important to consider what time of year the project is scheduled for completion. Bad weather can create large cost overruns from dewatering, site repair, and lost productivity from cold weather.

Reference Numbers

Reference numbers are shown at the beginning of some major classifications. These numbers refer to related items in the Reference Section. The reference information may be an estimating procedure, an alternate pricing method, or technical information.

Note: Not all subdivisions listed here necessarily appear. ■

31 05 Common Work Results for Earthwork

31 05 13 – Soils for Earthwork

31 05 13.10 Borrow

		Crew	Daily Output	Labor-Hours	Unit	Material	2017 Bare Costs Labor	Equipment	Total	Total Incl O&P
0010	**BORROW**									
0020	Spread, 200 H.P. dozer, no compaction, 2 mi. RT haul									
0200	Common borrow	B-15	600	.047	C.Y.	12.80	1.53	4.45	18.78	21.50

31 05 16 – Aggregates for Earthwork

31 05 16.10 Borrow

		Crew	Daily Output	Labor-Hours	Unit	Material	2017 Bare Costs Labor	Equipment	Total	Total Incl O&P
0010	**BORROW**									
0020	Spread, with 200 H.P. dozer, no compaction, 2 mi. RT haul									
0100	Bank run gravel	B-15	600	.047	L.C.Y.	18.90	1.53	4.45	24.88	28.50
0300	Crushed stone (1.40 tons per CY), 1-1/2"		600	.047		26	1.53	4.45	31.98	36
0320	3/4"		600	.047		26	1.53	4.45	31.98	36
0340	1/2"		600	.047		29	1.53	4.45	34.98	39
0360	3/8"		600	.047		30.50	1.53	4.45	36.48	41
0400	Sand, washed, concrete		600	.047		38	1.53	4.45	43.98	49
0500	Dead or bank sand		600	.047		18.60	1.53	4.45	24.58	28

31 11 Clearing and Grubbing

31 11 10 – Clearing and Grubbing Land

31 11 10.10 Clear and Grub Site

		Crew	Daily Output	Labor-Hours	Unit	Material	2017 Bare Costs Labor	Equipment	Total	Total Incl O&P
0010	**CLEAR AND GRUB SITE**									
0020	Cut & chip light trees to 6" diam.	B-7	1	48	Acre		1,375	1,775	3,150	4,250
0150	Grub stumps and remove	B-30	2	12			405	1,125	1,530	1,925
0200	Cut & chip medium, trees to 12" diam.	B-7	.70	68.571			1,950	2,525	4,475	6,075
0250	Grub stumps and remove	B-30	1	24			810	2,250	3,060	3,800
0300	Cut & chip heavy, trees to 24" diam.	B-7	.30	160			4,575	5,925	10,500	14,100
0350	Grub stumps and remove	B-30	.50	48			1,625	4,500	6,125	7,625
0400	If burning is allowed, deduct cut & chip								40%	40%

31 13 Selective Tree and Shrub Removal and Trimming

31 13 13 – Selective Tree and Shrub Removal

31 13 13.10 Selective Clearing

		Crew	Daily Output	Labor-Hours	Unit	Material	2017 Bare Costs Labor	Equipment	Total	Total Incl O&P
0010	**SELECTIVE CLEARING**									
0020	Clearing brush with brush saw	A-1C	.25	32	Acre		850	118	968	1,550
0100	By hand	1 Clab	.12	66.667			1,775		1,775	2,975
0300	With dozer, ball and chain, light clearing	B-11A	2	8			252	690	942	1,175
0400	Medium clearing	"	1.50	10.667			335	925	1,260	1,575

31 14 Earth Stripping and Stockpiling

31 14 13 – Soil Stripping and Stockpiling

31 14 13.23 Topsoil Stripping and Stockpiling

		Crew	Daily Output	Labor-Hours	Unit	Material	2017 Bare Costs Labor	Equipment	Total	Total Incl O&P
0010	**TOPSOIL STRIPPING AND STOCKPILING**									
1400	Loam or topsoil, remove and stockpile on site									
1420	6" deep, 200' haul	B-10B	865	.009	C.Y.		.34	1.60	1.94	2.32
1430	300' haul		520	.015			.56	2.66	3.22	3.86
1440	500' haul		225	.036			1.29	6.15	7.44	8.90
1450	Alternate method: 6" deep, 200' haul		5090	.002	S.Y.		.06	.27	.33	.39
1460	500' haul		1325	.006	"		.22	1.04	1.26	1.51
1500	Loam or topsoil, remove/stockpile on site									

31 14 Earth Stripping and Stockpiling

31 14 13 – Soil Stripping and Stockpiling

31 14 13.23 Topsoil Stripping and Stockpiling

		Crew	Daily Output	Labor-Hours	Unit	Material	2017 Bare Costs Labor	2017 Bare Costs Equipment	Total	Total Incl O&P
1510	By hand, 6" deep, 50' haul, less than 100 S.Y.	B-1	100	.240	S.Y.		6.55		6.55	10.95
1520	By skid steer, 6" deep, 100' haul, 101-500 S.Y.	B-62	500	.048			1.41	.34	1.75	2.74
1530	100' haul, 501-900 S.Y.	"	900	.027			.79	.19	.98	1.52
1540	200' haul, 901-1100 S.Y.	B-63	1000	.040			1.06	.17	1.23	1.97
1550	By dozer, 200' haul, 1101-4000 S.Y.	B-10B	4000	.002	▼		.07	.35	.42	.50

31 22 Grading

31 22 16 – Fine Grading

31 22 16.10 Finish Grading

		Crew	Daily Output	Labor-Hours	Unit	Material	2017 Bare Costs Labor	2017 Bare Costs Equipment	Total	Total Incl O&P
0010	**FINISH GRADING**									
0012	Finish grading area to be paved with grader, small area	B-11L	400	.040	S.Y.		1.26	1.70	2.96	3.96
0100	Large area		2000	.008			.25	.34	.59	.79
0200	Grade subgrade for base course, roadways	▼	3500	.005			.14	.19	.33	.45
1020	For large parking lots	B-32C	5000	.010			.31	.46	.77	1.02
1050	For small irregular areas	"	2000	.024			.76	1.15	1.91	2.54
1100	Fine grade for slab on grade, machine	B-11L	1040	.015			.48	.65	1.13	1.52
1150	Hand grading	B-18	700	.034			.94	.06	1	1.63
1200	Fine grade granular base for sidewalks and bikeways	B-62	1200	.020	▼		.59	.14	.73	1.14
2550	Hand grade select gravel	2 Clab	60	.267	C.S.F.		7.10		7.10	11.85
3000	Hand grade select gravel, including compaction, 4" deep	B-18	555	.043	S.Y.		1.18	.08	1.26	2.05
3100	6" deep		400	.060			1.64	.11	1.75	2.86
3120	8" deep	▼	300	.080			2.18	.14	2.32	3.81
3300	Finishing grading slopes, gentle	B-11L	8900	.002			.06	.08	.14	.17
3310	Steep slopes	"	7100	.002	▼		.07	.10	.17	.22

31 23 Excavation and Fill

31 23 16 – Excavation

31 23 16.13 Excavating, Trench

		Crew	Daily Output	Labor-Hours	Unit	Material	2017 Bare Costs Labor	2017 Bare Costs Equipment	Total	Total Incl O&P
0010	**EXCAVATING, TRENCH**									
0011	Or continuous footing									
0050	1' to 4' deep, 3/8 C.Y. excavator	B-11C	150	.107	B.C.Y.		3.36	2.44	5.80	8.30
0060	1/2 C.Y. excavator	B-11M	200	.080			2.52	1.97	4.49	6.35
0090	4' to 6' deep, 1/2 C.Y. excavator	"	200	.080			2.52	1.97	4.49	6.35
0100	5/8 C.Y. excavator	B-12Q	250	.064			2.04	2.46	4.50	6.10
0300	1/2 C.Y. excavator, truck mounted	B-12J	200	.080			2.56	4.55	7.11	9.25
1352	4' to 6' deep, 1/2 C.Y. excavator w/trench box	B-13H	188	.085			2.72	5.25	7.97	10.30
1354	5/8 C.Y. excavator	"	235	.068			2.18	4.22	6.40	8.25
1400	By hand with pick and shovel 2' to 6' deep, light soil	1 Clab	8	1			26.50		26.50	44.50
1500	Heavy soil	"	4	2	▼		53		53	89
5020	Loam & sandy clay with no sheeting or dewatering included									
5050	1' to 4' deep, 3/8 C.Y. tractor loader/backhoe	B-11C	162	.099	B.C.Y.		3.11	2.26	5.37	7.65
5060	1/2 C.Y. excavator	B-11M	216	.074			2.33	1.83	4.16	5.90
5080	4' to 6' deep, 1/2 C.Y. excavator	"	216	.074			2.33	1.83	4.16	5.90
5090	5/8 C.Y. excavator	B-12Q	276	.058			1.85	2.22	4.07	5.55
5130	1/2 C.Y. excavator, truck mounted	B-12J	216	.074			2.37	4.21	6.58	8.55
5352	4' to 6' deep, 1/2 C.Y. excavator w/trench box	B-13H	205	.078			2.49	4.83	7.32	9.45
5354	5/8 C.Y. excavator	"	257	.062			1.99	3.86	5.85	7.55
6020	Sand & gravel with no sheeting or dewatering included									
6050	1' to 4' deep, 3/8 C.Y. excavator	B-11C	165	.097	B.C.Y.		3.05	2.22	5.27	7.50

For customer support on your Residential Costs with RSMeans Data, call 800.448.8182.

623

31 23 Excavation and Fill

31 23 16 – Excavation

31 23 16.13 Excavating, Trench

		Crew	Daily Output	Labor-Hours	Unit	Material	2017 Bare Costs Labor	Equipment	Total	Total Incl O&P
6060	1/2 C.Y. excavator	B-11M	220	.073	B.C.Y.		2.29	1.79	4.08	5.80
6080	4' to 6' deep, 1/2 C.Y. excavator	"	220	.073			2.29	1.79	4.08	5.80
6090	5/8 C.Y. excavator	B-12Q	275	.058			1.86	2.23	4.09	5.55
6130	1/2 C.Y. excavator, truck mounted	B-12J	220	.073			2.32	4.14	6.46	8.40
6352	4' to 6' deep, 1/2 C.Y. excavator w/trench box	B-13H	209	.077			2.45	4.74	7.19	9.25
6354	5/8 C.Y. excavator	"	261	.061			1.96	3.80	5.76	7.45
7020	Dense hard clay with no sheeting or dewatering included									
7050	1' to 4' deep, 3/8 C.Y. excavator	B-11C	132	.121	B.C.Y.		3.82	2.77	6.59	9.40
7060	1/2 C.Y. excavator	B-11M	176	.091			2.86	2.24	5.10	7.25
7080	4' to 6' deep, 1/2 C.Y. excavator	"	176	.091			2.86	2.24	5.10	7.25
7090	5/8 C.Y. excavator	B-12Q	220	.073			2.32	2.79	5.11	6.95
7130	1/2 C.Y. excavator, truck mounted	B-12J	176	.091			2.90	5.15	8.05	10.55

31 23 16.14 Excavating, Utility Trench

		Crew	Daily Output	Labor-Hours	Unit	Material	2017 Bare Costs Labor	Equipment	Total	Total Incl O&P
0010	**EXCAVATING, UTILITY TRENCH**									
0011	Common earth									
0050	Trenching with chain trencher, 12 H.P., operator walking									
0100	4" wide trench, 12" deep	B-53	800	.010	L.F.		.27	.08	.35	.54
1000	Backfill by hand including compaction, add									
1050	4" wide trench, 12" deep	A-1G	800	.010	L.F.		.27	.07	.34	.53

31 23 16.16 Structural Excavation for Minor Structures

		Crew	Daily Output	Labor-Hours	Unit	Material	2017 Bare Costs Labor	Equipment	Total	Total Incl O&P
0010	**STRUCTURAL EXCAVATION FOR MINOR STRUCTURES**									
0015	Hand, pits to 6' deep, sandy soil	1 Clab	8	1	B.C.Y.		26.50		26.50	44.50
0100	Heavy soil or clay		4	2			53		53	89
1100	Hand loading trucks from stock pile, sandy soil		12	.667			17.75		17.75	29.50
1300	Heavy soil or clay		8	1			26.50		26.50	44.50
1500	For wet or muck hand excavation, add to above						50%		50%	50%

31 23 16.42 Excavating, Bulk Bank Measure

		Crew	Daily Output	Labor-Hours	Unit	Material	2017 Bare Costs Labor	Equipment	Total	Total Incl O&P
0010	**EXCAVATING, BULK BANK MEASURE**									
0011	Common earth piled									
0020	For loading onto trucks, add								15%	15%
0200	Excavator, hydraulic, crawler mtd., 1 C.Y. cap. = 100 C.Y./hr.	B-12A	800	.020	B.C.Y.		.64	1	1.64	2.16
0310	Wheel mounted, 1/2 C.Y. cap. = 40 C.Y./hr.	B-12E	320	.050			1.60	1.39	2.99	4.18
1200	Front end loader, track mtd., 1-1/2 C.Y. cap. = 70 C.Y./hr.	B-10N	560	.014			.52	1.02	1.54	1.98
1500	Wheel mounted, 3/4 C.Y. cap. = 45 C.Y./hr.	B-10R	360	.022			.81	.87	1.68	2.30
5000	Excavating, bulk bank measure, sandy clay & loam piled									
5020	For loading onto trucks, add								15%	15%
5100	Excavator, hydraulic, crawler mtd., 1 C.Y. cap. = 120 C.Y./hr.	B-12A	960	.017	B.C.Y.		.53	.83	1.36	1.79
5610	Wheel mounted, 1/2 C.Y. cap. = 44 C.Y./hr.	B-12E	352	.045	"		1.45	1.26	2.71	3.80
8000	For hauling excavated material, see Section 31 23 23.20									

31 23 23 – Fill

31 23 23.13 Backfill

		Crew	Daily Output	Labor-Hours	Unit	Material	2017 Bare Costs Labor	Equipment	Total	Total Incl O&P
0010	**BACKFILL**									
0015	By hand, no compaction, light soil	1 Clab	14	.571	L.C.Y.		15.20		15.20	25.50
0100	Heavy soil		11	.727	"		19.35		19.35	32.50
0300	Compaction in 6" layers, hand tamp, add to above		20.60	.388	E.C.Y.		10.35		10.35	17.30
0400	Roller compaction operator walking, add	B-10A	100	.080			2.91	1.83	4.74	6.80
0500	Air tamp, add	B-9D	190	.211			5.70	1.29	6.99	10.90
0600	Vibrating plate, add	A-1D	60	.133			3.55	.56	4.11	6.55
0800	Compaction in 12" layers, hand tamp, add to above	1 Clab	34	.235			6.25		6.25	10.45
1300	Dozer backfilling, bulk, up to 300' haul, no compaction	B-10B	1200	.007	L.C.Y.		.24	1.15	1.39	1.67
1400	Air tamped, add	B-11B	80	.200	E.C.Y.		6.20	3.42	9.62	14

31 23 Excavation and Fill

31 23 23 – Fill

31 23 23.16 Fill By Borrow and Utility Bedding

	Crew	Daily Output	Labor-Hours	Unit	Material	2017 Bare Costs Labor	2017 Bare Costs Equipment	Total	Total Incl O&P
0010 **FILL BY BORROW AND UTILITY BEDDING**									
0049 Utility bedding, for pipe & conduit, not incl. compaction									
0050 Crushed or screened bank run gravel	B-6	150	.160	L.C.Y.	21.50	4.72	2.44	28.66	34
0100 Crushed stone 3/4" to 1/2"		150	.160		26	4.72	2.44	33.16	39
0200 Sand, dead or bank	A-1D	150	.160		18.60	4.72	2.44	25.76	31
0500 Compacting bedding in trench	A-1D	90	.089	E.C.Y.		2.36	.37	2.73	4.37
0600 If material source exceeds 2 miles, add for extra mileage.									
0610 See Section 31 23 23.20 for hauling mileage add.									

31 23 23.17 General Fill

	Crew	Daily Output	Labor-Hours	Unit	Material	2017 Bare Costs Labor	2017 Bare Costs Equipment	Total	Total Incl O&P
0010 **GENERAL FILL**									
0011 Spread dumped material, no compaction									
0020 By dozer	B-10B	1000	.008	L.C.Y.		.29	1.38	1.67	2
0100 By hand	1 Clab	12	.667	"		17.75		17.75	29.50
0500 Gravel fill, compacted, under floor slabs, 4" deep	B-37	10000	.005	S.F.	.40	.14	.02	.56	.69
0600 6" deep		8600	.006		.60	.16	.02	.78	.94
0700 9" deep		7200	.007		1	.19	.02	1.21	1.44
0800 12" deep		6000	.008		1.40	.23	.03	1.66	1.95
1000 Alternate pricing method, 4" deep		120	.400	E.C.Y.	30	11.35	1.27	42.62	53.50
1100 6" deep		160	.300		30	8.50	.95	39.45	48.50
1200 9" deep		200	.240		30	6.80	.76	37.56	45
1300 12" deep		220	.218		30	6.20	.69	36.89	44

31 23 23.20 Hauling

	Crew	Daily Output	Labor-Hours	Unit	Material	2017 Bare Costs Labor	2017 Bare Costs Equipment	Total	Total Incl O&P
0010 **HAULING**									
0011 Excavated or borrow, loose cubic yards									
0012 no loading equipment, including hauling, waiting, loading/dumping									
0013 time per cycle (wait, load, travel, unload or dump & return)									
0014 8 C.Y. truck, 15 MPH ave, cycle 0.5 miles, 10 min. wait/Ld./Uld.	B-34A	320	.025	L.C.Y.		.81	1.22	2.03	2.67
0016 cycle 1 mile		272	.029			.95	1.44	2.39	3.15
0018 cycle 2 miles		208	.038			1.24	1.88	3.12	4.12
0020 cycle 4 miles		144	.056			1.80	2.72	4.52	5.95
0022 cycle 6 miles		112	.071			2.31	3.49	5.80	7.65
0024 cycle 8 miles		88	.091			2.94	4.44	7.38	9.75
0026 20 MPH ave, cycle 0.5 mile		336	.024			.77	1.16	1.93	2.55
0028 cycle 1 mile		296	.027			.87	1.32	2.19	2.89
0030 cycle 2 miles		240	.033			1.08	1.63	2.71	3.57
0032 cycle 4 miles		176	.045			1.47	2.22	3.69	4.86
0034 cycle 6 miles		136	.059			1.90	2.88	4.78	6.30
0036 cycle 8 miles		112	.071			2.31	3.49	5.80	7.65
0044 25 MPH ave, cycle 4 miles		192	.042			1.35	2.04	3.39	4.46
0046 cycle 6 miles		160	.050			1.62	2.44	4.06	5.35
0048 cycle 8 miles		128	.063			2.02	3.06	5.08	6.70
0050 30 MPH ave, cycle 4 miles		216	.037			1.20	1.81	3.01	3.96
0052 cycle 6 miles		176	.045			1.47	2.22	3.69	4.86
0054 cycle 8 miles		144	.056			1.80	2.72	4.52	5.95
0114 15 MPH ave, cycle 0.5 mile, 15 min. wait/Ld./Uld.		224	.036			1.16	1.75	2.91	3.82
0116 cycle 1 mile		200	.040			1.29	1.96	3.25	4.28
0118 cycle 2 miles		168	.048			1.54	2.33	3.87	5.10
0120 cycle 4 miles		120	.067			2.16	3.26	5.42	7.15
0122 cycle 6 miles		96	.083			2.70	4.07	6.77	8.90
0124 cycle 8 miles		80	.100			3.24	4.89	8.13	10.75
0126 20 MPH ave, cycle 0.5 mile		232	.034			1.12	1.69	2.81	3.69
0128 cycle 1 mile		208	.038			1.24	1.88	3.12	4.12

For customer support on your Residential Costs with RSMeans Data, call 800.448.8182.

625

31 23 23 – Fill

31 23 23.20 Hauling		Crew	Daily Output	Labor-Hours	Unit	Material	2017 Bare Costs Labor	2017 Bare Costs Equipment	Total	Total Incl O&P
0130	cycle 2 miles	B-34A	184	.043	L.C.Y.		1.41	2.13	3.54	4.66
0132	cycle 4 miles		144	.056			1.80	2.72	4.52	5.95
0134	cycle 6 miles		112	.071			2.31	3.49	5.80	7.65
0136	cycle 8 miles		96	.083			2.70	4.07	6.77	8.90
0144	25 MPH ave, cycle 4 miles		152	.053			1.70	2.57	4.27	5.65
0146	cycle 6 miles		128	.063			2.02	3.06	5.08	6.70
0148	cycle 8 miles		112	.071			2.31	3.49	5.80	7.65
0150	30 MPH ave, cycle 4 miles		168	.048			1.54	2.33	3.87	5.10
0152	cycle 6 miles		144	.056			1.80	2.72	4.52	5.95
0154	cycle 8 miles		120	.067			2.16	3.26	5.42	7.15
0214	15 MPH ave, cycle 0.5 mile, 20 min wait/Ld./Uld.		176	.045			1.47	2.22	3.69	4.86
0216	cycle 1 mile		160	.050			1.62	2.44	4.06	5.35
0218	cycle 2 miles		136	.059			1.90	2.88	4.78	6.30
0220	cycle 4 miles		104	.077			2.49	3.76	6.25	8.25
0222	cycle 6 miles		88	.091			2.94	4.44	7.38	9.75
0224	cycle 8 miles		72	.111			3.59	5.45	9.04	11.85
0226	20 MPH ave, cycle 0.5 mile		176	.045			1.47	2.22	3.69	4.86
0228	cycle 1 mile		168	.048			1.54	2.33	3.87	5.10
0230	cycle 2 miles		144	.056			1.80	2.72	4.52	5.95
0232	cycle 4 miles		120	.067			2.16	3.26	5.42	7.15
0234	cycle 6 miles		96	.083			2.70	4.07	6.77	8.90
0236	cycle 8 miles		88	.091			2.94	4.44	7.38	9.75
0244	25 MPH ave, cycle 4 miles		128	.063			2.02	3.06	5.08	6.70
0246	cycle 6 miles		112	.071			2.31	3.49	5.80	7.65
0248	cycle 8 miles		96	.083			2.70	4.07	6.77	8.90
0250	30 MPH ave, cycle 4 miles		136	.059			1.90	2.88	4.78	6.30
0252	cycle 6 miles		120	.067			2.16	3.26	5.42	7.15
0254	cycle 8 miles		104	.077			2.49	3.76	6.25	8.25
0314	15 MPH ave, cycle 0.5 mile, 25 min wait/Ld./Uld.		144	.056			1.80	2.72	4.52	5.95
0316	cycle 1 mile		128	.063			2.02	3.06	5.08	6.70
0318	cycle 2 miles		112	.071			2.31	3.49	5.80	7.65
0320	cycle 4 miles		96	.083			2.70	4.07	6.77	8.90
0322	cycle 6 miles		80	.100			3.24	4.89	8.13	10.75
0324	cycle 8 miles		64	.125			4.04	6.10	10.14	13.35
0326	20 MPH ave, cycle 0.5 mile		144	.056			1.80	2.72	4.52	5.95
0328	cycle 1 mile		136	.059			1.90	2.88	4.78	6.30
0330	cycle 2 miles		120	.067			2.16	3.26	5.42	7.15
0332	cycle 4 miles		104	.077			2.49	3.76	6.25	8.25
0334	cycle 6 miles		88	.091			2.94	4.44	7.38	9.75
0336	cycle 8 miles		80	.100			3.24	4.89	8.13	10.75
0344	25 MPH ave, cycle 4 miles		112	.071			2.31	3.49	5.80	7.65
0346	cycle 6 miles		96	.083			2.70	4.07	6.77	8.90
0348	cycle 8 miles		88	.091			2.94	4.44	7.38	9.75
0350	30 MPH ave, cycle 4 miles		112	.071			2.31	3.49	5.80	7.65
0352	cycle 6 miles		104	.077			2.49	3.76	6.25	8.25
0354	cycle 8 miles		96	.083			2.70	4.07	6.77	8.90
0414	15 MPH ave, cycle 0.5 mile, 30 min wait/Ld./Uld.		120	.067			2.16	3.26	5.42	7.15
0416	cycle 1 mile		112	.071			2.31	3.49	5.80	7.65
0418	cycle 2 miles		96	.083			2.70	4.07	6.77	8.90
0420	cycle 4 miles		80	.100			3.24	4.89	8.13	10.75
0422	cycle 6 miles		72	.111			3.59	5.45	9.04	11.85
0424	cycle 8 miles		64	.125			4.04	6.10	10.14	13.35
0426	20 MPH ave, cycle 0.5 mile		120	.067			2.16	3.26	5.42	7.15

31 23 23.20 Hauling		Crew	Daily Output	Labor-Hours	Unit	Material	2017 Bare Costs Labor	2017 Bare Costs Equipment	Total	Total Incl O&P
0428	cycle 1 mile	B-34A	112	.071	L.C.Y.		2.31	3.49	5.80	7.65
0430	cycle 2 miles		104	.077			2.49	3.76	6.25	8.25
0432	cycle 4 miles		88	.091			2.94	4.44	7.38	9.75
0434	cycle 6 miles		80	.100			3.24	4.89	8.13	10.75
0436	cycle 8 miles		72	.111			3.59	5.45	9.04	11.85
0444	25 MPH ave, cycle 4 miles		96	.083			2.70	4.07	6.77	8.90
0446	cycle 6 miles		88	.091			2.94	4.44	7.38	9.75
0448	cycle 8 miles		80	.100			3.24	4.89	8.13	10.75
0450	30 MPH ave, cycle 4 miles		96	.083			2.70	4.07	6.77	8.90
0452	cycle 6 miles		88	.091			2.94	4.44	7.38	9.75
0454	cycle 8 miles		80	.100			3.24	4.89	8.13	10.75
0514	15 MPH ave, cycle 0.5 mile, 35 min wait/Ld./Uld.		104	.077			2.49	3.76	6.25	8.25
0516	cycle 1 mile		96	.083			2.70	4.07	6.77	8.90
0518	cycle 2 miles		88	.091			2.94	4.44	7.38	9.75
0520	cycle 4 miles		72	.111			3.59	5.45	9.04	11.85
0522	cycle 6 miles		64	.125			4.04	6.10	10.14	13.35
0524	cycle 8 miles		56	.143			4.62	7	11.62	15.30
0526	20 MPH ave, cycle 0.5 mile		104	.077			2.49	3.76	6.25	8.25
0528	cycle 1 mile		96	.083			2.70	4.07	6.77	8.90
0530	cycle 2 miles		96	.083			2.70	4.07	6.77	8.90
0532	cycle 4 miles		80	.100			3.24	4.89	8.13	10.75
0534	cycle 6 miles		72	.111			3.59	5.45	9.04	11.85
0536	cycle 8 miles		64	.125			4.04	6.10	10.14	13.35
0544	25 MPH ave, cycle 4 miles		88	.091			2.94	4.44	7.38	9.75
0546	cycle 6 miles		80	.100			3.24	4.89	8.13	10.75
0548	cycle 8 miles		72	.111			3.59	5.45	9.04	11.85
0550	30 MPH ave, cycle 4 miles		88	.091			2.94	4.44	7.38	9.75
0552	cycle 6 miles		80	.100			3.24	4.89	8.13	10.75
0554	cycle 8 miles		72	.111			3.59	5.45	9.04	11.85
1014	12 C.Y. truck, cycle 0.5 mile, 15 MPH ave, 15 min. wait/Ld./Uld.	B-34B	336	.024			.77	1.91	2.68	3.37
1016	cycle 1 mile		300	.027			.86	2.14	3	3.78
1018	cycle 2 miles		252	.032			1.03	2.55	3.58	4.50
1020	cycle 4 miles		180	.044			1.44	3.57	5.01	6.30
1022	cycle 6 miles		144	.056			1.80	4.46	6.26	7.85
1024	cycle 8 miles		120	.067			2.16	5.35	7.51	9.45
1025	cycle 10 miles		96	.083			2.70	6.70	9.40	11.80
1026	20 MPH ave, cycle 0.5 mile		348	.023			.74	1.85	2.59	3.26
1028	cycle 1 mile		312	.026			.83	2.06	2.89	3.64
1030	cycle 2 miles		276	.029			.94	2.33	3.27	4.11
1032	cycle 4 miles		216	.037			1.20	2.98	4.18	5.25
1034	cycle 6 miles		168	.048			1.54	3.83	5.37	6.75
1036	cycle 8 miles		144	.056			1.80	4.46	6.26	7.85
1038	cycle 10 miles		120	.067			2.16	5.35	7.51	9.45
1040	25 MPH ave, cycle 4 miles		228	.035			1.14	2.82	3.96	4.97
1042	cycle 6 miles		192	.042			1.35	3.35	4.70	5.90
1044	cycle 8 miles		168	.048			1.54	3.83	5.37	6.75
1046	cycle 10 miles		144	.056			1.80	4.46	6.26	7.85
1050	30 MPH ave, cycle 4 miles		252	.032			1.03	2.55	3.58	4.50
1052	cycle 6 miles		216	.037			1.20	2.98	4.18	5.25
1054	cycle 8 miles		180	.044			1.44	3.57	5.01	6.30
1056	cycle 10 miles		156	.051			1.66	4.12	5.78	7.25
1060	35 MPH ave, cycle 4 miles		264	.030			.98	2.43	3.41	4.30
1062	cycle 6 miles		228	.035			1.14	2.82	3.96	4.97

31 23 23.20 Hauling		Crew	Daily Output	Labor-Hours	Unit	Material	2017 Bare Costs Labor	2017 Bare Costs Equipment	Total	Total Incl O&P
1064	cycle 8 miles	B-34B	204	.039	L.C.Y.		1.27	3.15	4.42	5.55
1066	cycle 10 miles		180	.044			1.44	3.57	5.01	6.30
1068	cycle 20 miles		120	.067			2.16	5.35	7.51	9.45
1069	cycle 30 miles		84	.095			3.08	7.65	10.73	13.50
1070	cycle 40 miles		72	.111			3.59	8.95	12.54	15.70
1072	40 MPH ave, cycle 6 miles		240	.033			1.08	2.68	3.76	4.73
1074	cycle 8 miles		216	.037			1.20	2.98	4.18	5.25
1076	cycle 10 miles		192	.042			1.35	3.35	4.70	5.90
1078	cycle 20 miles		120	.067			2.16	5.35	7.51	9.45
1080	cycle 30 miles		96	.083			2.70	6.70	9.40	11.80
1082	cycle 40 miles		72	.111			3.59	8.95	12.54	15.70
1084	cycle 50 miles		60	.133			4.31	10.70	15.01	18.90
1094	45 MPH ave, cycle 8 miles		216	.037			1.20	2.98	4.18	5.25
1096	cycle 10 miles		204	.039			1.27	3.15	4.42	5.55
1098	cycle 20 miles		132	.061			1.96	4.87	6.83	8.60
1100	cycle 30 miles		108	.074			2.40	5.95	8.35	10.50
1102	cycle 40 miles		84	.095			3.08	7.65	10.73	13.50
1104	cycle 50 miles		72	.111			3.59	8.95	12.54	15.70
1106	50 MPH ave, cycle 10 miles		216	.037			1.20	2.98	4.18	5.25
1108	cycle 20 miles		144	.056			1.80	4.46	6.26	7.85
1110	cycle 30 miles		108	.074			2.40	5.95	8.35	10.50
1112	cycle 40 miles		84	.095			3.08	7.65	10.73	13.50
1114	cycle 50 miles		72	.111			3.59	8.95	12.54	15.70
1214	15 MPH ave, cycle 0.5 mile, 20 min. wait/Ld./Uld.		264	.030			.98	2.43	3.41	4.30
1216	cycle 1 mile		240	.033			1.08	2.68	3.76	4.73
1218	cycle 2 miles		204	.039			1.27	3.15	4.42	5.55
1220	cycle 4 miles		156	.051			1.66	4.12	5.78	7.25
1222	cycle 6 miles		132	.061			1.96	4.87	6.83	8.60
1224	cycle 8 miles		108	.074			2.40	5.95	8.35	10.50
1225	cycle 10 miles		96	.083			2.70	6.70	9.40	11.80
1226	20 MPH ave, cycle 0.5 mile		264	.030			.98	2.43	3.41	4.30
1228	cycle 1 mile		252	.032			1.03	2.55	3.58	4.50
1230	cycle 2 miles		216	.037			1.20	2.98	4.18	5.25
1232	cycle 4 miles		180	.044			1.44	3.57	5.01	6.30
1234	cycle 6 miles		144	.056			1.80	4.46	6.26	7.85
1236	cycle 8 miles		132	.061			1.96	4.87	6.83	8.60
1238	cycle 10 miles		108	.074			2.40	5.95	8.35	10.50
1240	25 MPH ave, cycle 4 miles		192	.042			1.35	3.35	4.70	5.90
1242	cycle 6 miles		168	.048			1.54	3.83	5.37	6.75
1244	cycle 8 miles		144	.056			1.80	4.46	6.26	7.85
1246	cycle 10 miles		132	.061			1.96	4.87	6.83	8.60
1250	30 MPH ave, cycle 4 miles		204	.039			1.27	3.15	4.42	5.55
1252	cycle 6 miles		180	.044			1.44	3.57	5.01	6.30
1254	cycle 8 miles		156	.051			1.66	4.12	5.78	7.25
1256	cycle 10 miles		144	.056			1.80	4.46	6.26	7.85
1260	35 MPH ave, cycle 4 miles		216	.037			1.20	2.98	4.18	5.25
1262	cycle 6 miles		192	.042			1.35	3.35	4.70	5.90
1264	cycle 8 miles		168	.048			1.54	3.83	5.37	6.75
1266	cycle 10 miles		156	.051			1.66	4.12	5.78	7.25
1268	cycle 20 miles		108	.074			2.40	5.95	8.35	10.50
1269	cycle 30 miles		72	.111			3.59	8.95	12.54	15.70
1270	cycle 40 miles		60	.133			4.31	10.70	15.01	18.90
1272	40 MPH ave, cycle 6 miles		192	.042			1.35	3.35	4.70	5.90

31 23 Excavation and Fill

31 23 23 – Fill

31 23 23.20 Hauling	Crew	Daily Output	Labor-Hours	Unit	Material	2017 Bare Costs Labor	2017 Bare Costs Equipment	Total	Total Incl O&P
1274	cycle 8 miles	B-34B	180	.044	L.C.Y.		1.44	3.57	5.01	6.30
1276	cycle 10 miles		156	.051			1.66	4.12	5.78	7.25
1278	cycle 20 miles		108	.074			2.40	5.95	8.35	10.50
1280	cycle 30 miles		84	.095			3.08	7.65	10.73	13.50
1282	cycle 40 miles		72	.111			3.59	8.95	12.54	15.70
1284	cycle 50 miles		60	.133			4.31	10.70	15.01	18.90
1294	45 MPH ave, cycle 8 miles		180	.044			1.44	3.57	5.01	6.30
1296	cycle 10 miles		168	.048			1.54	3.83	5.37	6.75
1298	cycle 20 miles		120	.067			2.16	5.35	7.51	9.45
1300	cycle 30 miles		96	.083			2.70	6.70	9.40	11.80
1302	cycle 40 miles		72	.111			3.59	8.95	12.54	15.70
1304	cycle 50 miles		60	.133			4.31	10.70	15.01	18.90
1306	50 MPH ave, cycle 10 miles		180	.044			1.44	3.57	5.01	6.30
1308	cycle 20 miles		132	.061			1.96	4.87	6.83	8.60
1310	cycle 30 miles		96	.083			2.70	6.70	9.40	11.80
1312	cycle 40 miles		84	.095			3.08	7.65	10.73	13.50
1314	cycle 50 miles		72	.111			3.59	8.95	12.54	15.70
1414	15 MPH ave, cycle 0.5 mile, 25 min. wait/Ld./Uld.		204	.039			1.27	3.15	4.42	5.55
1416	cycle 1 mile		192	.042			1.35	3.35	4.70	5.90
1418	cycle 2 miles		168	.048			1.54	3.83	5.37	6.75
1420	cycle 4 miles		132	.061			1.96	4.87	6.83	8.60
1422	cycle 6 miles		120	.067			2.16	5.35	7.51	9.45
1424	cycle 8 miles		96	.083			2.70	6.70	9.40	11.80
1425	cycle 10 miles		84	.095			3.08	7.65	10.73	13.50
1426	20 MPH ave, cycle 0.5 mile		216	.037			1.20	2.98	4.18	5.25
1428	cycle 1 mile		204	.039			1.27	3.15	4.42	5.55
1430	cycle 2 miles		180	.044			1.44	3.57	5.01	6.30
1432	cycle 4 miles		156	.051			1.66	4.12	5.78	7.25
1434	cycle 6 miles		132	.061			1.96	4.87	6.83	8.60
1436	cycle 8 miles		120	.067			2.16	5.35	7.51	9.45
1438	cycle 10 miles		96	.083			2.70	6.70	9.40	11.80
1440	25 MPH ave, cycle 4 miles		168	.048			1.54	3.83	5.37	6.75
1442	cycle 6 miles		144	.056			1.80	4.46	6.26	7.85
1444	cycle 8 miles		132	.061			1.96	4.87	6.83	8.60
1446	cycle 10 miles		108	.074			2.40	5.95	8.35	10.50
1450	30 MPH ave, cycle 4 miles		168	.048			1.54	3.83	5.37	6.75
1452	cycle 6 miles		156	.051			1.66	4.12	5.78	7.25
1454	cycle 8 miles		132	.061			1.96	4.87	6.83	8.60
1456	cycle 10 miles		120	.067			2.16	5.35	7.51	9.45
1460	35 MPH ave, cycle 4 miles		180	.044			1.44	3.57	5.01	6.30
1462	cycle 6 miles		156	.051			1.66	4.12	5.78	7.25
1464	cycle 8 miles		144	.056			1.80	4.46	6.26	7.85
1466	cycle 10 miles		132	.061			1.96	4.87	6.83	8.60
1468	cycle 20 miles		96	.083			2.70	6.70	9.40	11.80
1469	cycle 30 miles		72	.111			3.59	8.95	12.54	15.70
1470	cycle 40 miles		60	.133			4.31	10.70	15.01	18.90
1472	40 MPH ave, cycle 6 miles		168	.048			1.54	3.83	5.37	6.75
1474	cycle 8 miles		156	.051			1.66	4.12	5.78	7.25
1476	cycle 10 miles		144	.056			1.80	4.46	6.26	7.85
1478	cycle 20 miles		96	.083			2.70	6.70	9.40	11.80
1480	cycle 30 miles		84	.095			3.08	7.65	10.73	13.50
1482	cycle 40 miles		60	.133			4.31	10.70	15.01	18.90
1484	cycle 50 miles		60	.133			4.31	10.70	15.01	18.90

For customer support on your Residential Costs with RSMeans Data, call 800.448.8182.

629

31 23 23.20 Hauling		Crew	Daily Output	Labor-Hours	Unit	Material	2017 Bare Costs Labor	Equipment	Total	Total Incl O&P
1494	45 MPH ave, cycle 8 miles	B-34B	156	.051	L.C.Y.		1.66	4.12	5.78	7.25
1496	cycle 10 miles		144	.056			1.80	4.46	6.26	7.85
1498	cycle 20 miles		108	.074			2.40	5.95	8.35	10.50
1500	cycle 30 miles		84	.095			3.08	7.65	10.73	13.50
1502	cycle 40 miles		72	.111			3.59	8.95	12.54	15.70
1504	cycle 50 miles		60	.133			4.31	10.70	15.01	18.90
1506	50 MPH ave, cycle 10 miles		156	.051			1.66	4.12	5.78	7.25
1508	cycle 20 miles		120	.067			2.16	5.35	7.51	9.45
1510	cycle 30 miles		96	.083			2.70	6.70	9.40	11.80
1512	cycle 40 miles		72	.111			3.59	8.95	12.54	15.70
1514	cycle 50 miles		60	.133			4.31	10.70	15.01	18.90
1614	15 MPH ave, cycle 0.5 mile, 30 min. wait/Ld./Uld.		180	.044			1.44	3.57	5.01	6.30
1616	cycle 1 mile		168	.048			1.54	3.83	5.37	6.75
1618	cycle 2 miles		144	.056			1.80	4.46	6.26	7.85
1620	cycle 4 miles		120	.067			2.16	5.35	7.51	9.45
1622	cycle 6 miles		108	.074			2.40	5.95	8.35	10.50
1624	cycle 8 miles		84	.095			3.08	7.65	10.73	13.50
1625	cycle 10 miles		84	.095			3.08	7.65	10.73	13.50
1626	20 MPH ave, cycle 0.5 mile		180	.044			1.44	3.57	5.01	6.30
1628	cycle 1 mile		168	.048			1.54	3.83	5.37	6.75
1630	cycle 2 miles		156	.051			1.66	4.12	5.78	7.25
1632	cycle 4 miles		132	.061			1.96	4.87	6.83	8.60
1634	cycle 6 miles		120	.067			2.16	5.35	7.51	9.45
1636	cycle 8 miles		108	.074			2.40	5.95	8.35	10.50
1638	cycle 10 miles		96	.083			2.70	6.70	9.40	11.80
1640	25 MPH ave, cycle 4 miles		144	.056			1.80	4.46	6.26	7.85
1642	cycle 6 miles		132	.061			1.96	4.87	6.83	8.60
1644	cycle 8 miles		108	.074			2.40	5.95	8.35	10.50
1646	cycle 10 miles		108	.074			2.40	5.95	8.35	10.50
1650	30 MPH ave, cycle 4 miles		144	.056			1.80	4.46	6.26	7.85
1652	cycle 6 miles		132	.061			1.96	4.87	6.83	8.60
1654	cycle 8 miles		120	.067			2.16	5.35	7.51	9.45
1656	cycle 10 miles		108	.074			2.40	5.95	8.35	10.50
1660	35 MPH ave, cycle 4 miles		156	.051			1.66	4.12	5.78	7.25
1662	cycle 6 miles		144	.056			1.80	4.46	6.26	7.85
1664	cycle 8 miles		132	.061			1.96	4.87	6.83	8.60
1666	cycle 10 miles		120	.067			2.16	5.35	7.51	9.45
1668	cycle 20 miles		84	.095			3.08	7.65	10.73	13.50
1669	cycle 30 miles		72	.111			3.59	8.95	12.54	15.70
1670	cycle 40 miles		60	.133			4.31	10.70	15.01	18.90
1672	40 MPH ave, cycle 6 miles		144	.056			1.80	4.46	6.26	7.85
1674	cycle 8 miles		132	.061			1.96	4.87	6.83	8.60
1676	cycle 10 miles		120	.067			2.16	5.35	7.51	9.45
1678	cycle 20 miles		96	.083			2.70	6.70	9.40	11.80
1680	cycle 30 miles		72	.111			3.59	8.95	12.54	15.70
1682	cycle 40 miles		60	.133			4.31	10.70	15.01	18.90
1684	cycle 50 miles		48	.167			5.40	13.40	18.80	23.50
1694	45 MPH ave, cycle 8 miles		144	.056			1.80	4.46	6.26	7.85
1696	cycle 10 miles		132	.061			1.96	4.87	6.83	8.60
1698	cycle 20 miles		96	.083			2.70	6.70	9.40	11.80
1700	cycle 30 miles		84	.095			3.08	7.65	10.73	13.50
1702	cycle 40 miles		60	.133			4.31	10.70	15.01	18.90
1704	cycle 50 miles		60	.133			4.31	10.70	15.01	18.90

31 23 23.20 Hauling	Crew	Daily Output	Labor-Hours	Unit	Material	2017 Bare Costs Labor	Equipment	Total	Total Incl O&P
1706	50 MPH ave, cycle 10 miles	B-34B	132	.061	L.C.Y.		1.96	4.87	6.83	8.60
1708	cycle 20 miles		108	.074			2.40	5.95	8.35	10.50
1710	cycle 30 miles		84	.095			3.08	7.65	10.73	13.50
1712	cycle 40 miles		72	.111			3.59	8.95	12.54	15.70
1714	cycle 50 miles		60	.133			4.31	10.70	15.01	18.90
2000	Hauling, 8 C.Y. truck, small project cost per hour	B-34A	8	1	Hr.		32.50	49	81.50	108
2100	12 C.Y. Truck	B-34B	8	1			32.50	80.50	113	142
2150	16.5 C.Y. Truck	B-34C	8	1			32.50	86	118.50	148
2175	18 C.Y. 8 wheel Truck	B-34I	8	1			32.50	102	134.50	166
2200	20 C.Y. Truck	B-34D	8	1			32.50	88	120.50	150
9014	18 C.Y. truck, 8 wheels,15 min. wait/Ld./Uld.,15 MPH, cycle 0.5 mi.	B-34I	504	.016	L.C.Y.		.51	1.62	2.13	2.63
9016	cycle 1 mile		450	.018			.58	1.81	2.39	2.94
9018	cycle 2 miles		378	.021			.68	2.16	2.84	3.50
9020	cycle 4 miles		270	.030			.96	3.02	3.98	4.90
9022	cycle 6 miles		216	.037			1.20	3.78	4.98	6.10
9024	cycle 8 miles		180	.044			1.44	4.53	5.97	7.35
9025	cycle 10 miles		144	.056			1.80	5.65	7.45	9.20
9026	20 MPH ave, cycle 0.5 mile		522	.015			.50	1.56	2.06	2.54
9028	cycle 1 mile		468	.017			.55	1.74	2.29	2.83
9030	cycle 2 miles		414	.019			.63	1.97	2.60	3.20
9032	cycle 4 miles		324	.025			.80	2.52	3.32	4.09
9034	cycle 6 miles		252	.032			1.03	3.24	4.27	5.25
9036	cycle 8 miles		216	.037			1.20	3.78	4.98	6.10
9038	cycle 10 miles		180	.044			1.44	4.53	5.97	7.35
9040	25 MPH ave, cycle 4 miles		342	.023			.76	2.38	3.14	3.87
9042	cycle 6 miles		288	.028			.90	2.83	3.73	4.60
9044	cycle 8 miles		252	.032			1.03	3.24	4.27	5.25
9046	cycle 10 miles		216	.037			1.20	3.78	4.98	6.10
9050	30 MPH ave, cycle 4 miles		378	.021			.68	2.16	2.84	3.50
9052	cycle 6 miles		324	.025			.80	2.52	3.32	4.09
9054	cycle 8 miles		270	.030			.96	3.02	3.98	4.90
9056	cycle 10 miles		234	.034			1.11	3.49	4.60	5.65
9060	35 MPH ave, cycle 4 miles		396	.020			.65	2.06	2.71	3.35
9062	cycle 6 miles		342	.023			.76	2.38	3.14	3.87
9064	cycle 8 miles		288	.028			.90	2.83	3.73	4.60
9066	cycle 10 miles		270	.030			.96	3.02	3.98	4.90
9068	cycle 20 miles		162	.049			1.60	5.05	6.65	8.20
9070	cycle 30 miles		126	.063			2.05	6.45	8.50	10.50
9072	cycle 40 miles		90	.089			2.88	9.05	11.93	14.70
9074	40 MPH ave, cycle 6 miles		360	.022			.72	2.27	2.99	3.67
9076	cycle 8 miles		324	.025			.80	2.52	3.32	4.09
9078	cycle 10 miles		288	.028			.90	2.83	3.73	4.60
9080	cycle 20 miles		180	.044			1.44	4.53	5.97	7.35
9082	cycle 30 miles		144	.056			1.80	5.65	7.45	9.20
9084	cycle 40 miles		108	.074			2.40	7.55	9.95	12.25
9086	cycle 50 miles		90	.089			2.88	9.05	11.93	14.70
9094	45 MPH ave, cycle 8 miles		324	.025			.80	2.52	3.32	4.09
9096	cycle 10 miles		306	.026			.85	2.67	3.52	4.32
9098	cycle 20 miles		198	.040			1.31	4.12	5.43	6.70
9100	cycle 30 miles		144	.056			1.80	5.65	7.45	9.20
9102	cycle 40 miles		126	.063			2.05	6.45	8.50	10.50
9104	cycle 50 miles		108	.074			2.40	7.55	9.95	12.25
9106	50 MPH ave, cycle 10 miles		324	.025			.80	2.52	3.32	4.09

31 23 23.20 Hauling		Crew	Daily Output	Labor-Hours	Unit	Material	2017 Bare Costs Labor	Equipment	Total	Total Incl O&P
9108	cycle 20 miles	B-34I	216	.037	L.C.Y.		1.20	3.78	4.98	6.10
9110	cycle 30 miles		162	.049			1.60	5.05	6.65	8.20
9112	cycle 40 miles		126	.063			2.05	6.45	8.50	10.50
9114	cycle 50 miles		108	.074			2.40	7.55	9.95	12.25
9214	20 min. wait/Ld./Uld.,15 MPH, cycle 0.5 mi.		396	.020			.65	2.06	2.71	3.35
9216	cycle 1 mile		360	.022			.72	2.27	2.99	3.67
9218	cycle 2 miles		306	.026			.85	2.67	3.52	4.32
9220	cycle 4 miles		234	.034			1.11	3.49	4.60	5.65
9222	cycle 6 miles		198	.040			1.31	4.12	5.43	6.70
9224	cycle 8 miles		162	.049			1.60	5.05	6.65	8.20
9225	cycle 10 miles		144	.056			1.80	5.65	7.45	9.20
9226	20 MPH ave, cycle 0.5 mile		396	.020			.65	2.06	2.71	3.35
9228	cycle 1 mile		378	.021			.68	2.16	2.84	3.50
9230	cycle 2 miles		324	.025			.80	2.52	3.32	4.09
9232	cycle 4 miles		270	.030			.96	3.02	3.98	4.90
9234	cycle 6 miles		216	.037			1.20	3.78	4.98	6.10
9236	cycle 8 miles		198	.040			1.31	4.12	5.43	6.70
9238	cycle 10 miles		162	.049			1.60	5.05	6.65	8.20
9240	25 MPH ave, cycle 4 miles		288	.028			.90	2.83	3.73	4.60
9242	cycle 6 miles		252	.032			1.03	3.24	4.27	5.25
9244	cycle 8 miles		216	.037			1.20	3.78	4.98	6.10
9246	cycle 10 miles		198	.040			1.31	4.12	5.43	6.70
9250	30 MPH ave, cycle 4 miles		306	.026			.85	2.67	3.52	4.32
9252	cycle 6 miles		270	.030			.96	3.02	3.98	4.90
9254	cycle 8 miles		234	.034			1.11	3.49	4.60	5.65
9256	cycle 10 miles		216	.037			1.20	3.78	4.98	6.10
9260	35 MPH ave, cycle 4 miles		324	.025			.80	2.52	3.32	4.09
9262	cycle 6 miles		288	.028			.90	2.83	3.73	4.60
9264	cycle 8 miles		252	.032			1.03	3.24	4.27	5.25
9266	cycle 10 miles		234	.034			1.11	3.49	4.60	5.65
9268	cycle 20 miles		162	.049			1.60	5.05	6.65	8.20
9270	cycle 30 miles		108	.074			2.40	7.55	9.95	12.25
9272	cycle 40 miles		90	.089			2.88	9.05	11.93	14.70
9274	40 MPH ave, cycle 6 miles		288	.028			.90	2.83	3.73	4.60
9276	cycle 8 miles		270	.030			.96	3.02	3.98	4.90
9278	cycle 10 miles		234	.034			1.11	3.49	4.60	5.65
9280	cycle 20 miles		162	.049			1.60	5.05	6.65	8.20
9282	cycle 30 miles		126	.063			2.05	6.45	8.50	10.50
9284	cycle 40 miles		108	.074			2.40	7.55	9.95	12.25
9286	cycle 50 miles		90	.089			2.88	9.05	11.93	14.70
9294	45 MPH ave, cycle 8 miles		270	.030			.96	3.02	3.98	4.90
9296	cycle 10 miles		252	.032			1.03	3.24	4.27	5.25
9298	cycle 20 miles		180	.044			1.44	4.53	5.97	7.35
9300	cycle 30 miles		144	.056			1.80	5.65	7.45	9.20
9302	cycle 40 miles		108	.074			2.40	7.55	9.95	12.25
9304	cycle 50 miles		90	.089			2.88	9.05	11.93	14.70
9306	50 MPH ave, cycle 10 miles		270	.030			.96	3.02	3.98	4.90
9308	cycle 20 miles		198	.040			1.31	4.12	5.43	6.70
9310	cycle 30 miles		144	.056			1.80	5.65	7.45	9.20
9312	cycle 40 miles		126	.063			2.05	6.45	8.50	10.50
9314	cycle 50 miles		108	.074			2.40	7.55	9.95	12.25
9414	25 min. wait/Ld./Uld.,15 MPH, cycle 0.5 mi.		306	.026			.85	2.67	3.52	4.32
9416	cycle 1 mile		288	.028			.90	2.83	3.73	4.60

31 23 Excavation and Fill

31 23 23 – Fill

31 23 23.20 Hauling		Crew	Daily Output	Labor-Hours	Unit	Material	2017 Bare Costs Labor	Equipment	Total	Total Incl O&P
9418	cycle 2 miles	B-34I	252	.032	L.C.Y.		1.03	3.24	4.27	5.25
9420	cycle 4 miles		198	.040			1.31	4.12	5.43	6.70
9422	cycle 6 miles		180	.044			1.44	4.53	5.97	7.35
9424	cycle 8 miles		144	.056			1.80	5.65	7.45	9.20
9425	cycle 10 miles		126	.063			2.05	6.45	8.50	10.50
9426	20 MPH ave, cycle 0.5 mile		324	.025			.80	2.52	3.32	4.09
9428	cycle 1 mile		306	.026			.85	2.67	3.52	4.32
9430	cycle 2 miles		270	.030			.96	3.02	3.98	4.90
9432	cycle 4 miles		234	.034			1.11	3.49	4.60	5.65
9434	cycle 6 miles		198	.040			1.31	4.12	5.43	6.70
9436	cycle 8 miles		180	.044			1.44	4.53	5.97	7.35
9438	cycle 10 miles		144	.056			1.80	5.65	7.45	9.20
9440	25 MPH ave, cycle 4 miles		252	.032			1.03	3.24	4.27	5.25
9442	cycle 6 miles		216	.037			1.20	3.78	4.98	6.10
9444	cycle 8 miles		198	.040			1.31	4.12	5.43	6.70
9446	cycle 10 miles		180	.044			1.44	4.53	5.97	7.35
9450	30 MPH ave, cycle 4 miles		252	.032			1.03	3.24	4.27	5.25
9452	cycle 6 miles		234	.034			1.11	3.49	4.60	5.65
9454	cycle 8 miles		198	.040			1.31	4.12	5.43	6.70
9456	cycle 10 miles		180	.044			1.44	4.53	5.97	7.35
9460	35 MPH ave, cycle 4 miles		270	.030			.96	3.02	3.98	4.90
9462	cycle 6 miles		234	.034			1.11	3.49	4.60	5.65
9464	cycle 8 miles		216	.037			1.20	3.78	4.98	6.10
9466	cycle 10 miles		198	.040			1.31	4.12	5.43	6.70
9468	cycle 20 miles		144	.056			1.80	5.65	7.45	9.20
9470	cycle 30 miles		108	.074			2.40	7.55	9.95	12.25
9472	cycle 40 miles		90	.089			2.88	9.05	11.93	14.70
9474	40 MPH ave, cycle 6 miles		252	.032			1.03	3.24	4.27	5.25
9476	cycle 8 miles		234	.034			1.11	3.49	4.60	5.65
9478	cycle 10 miles		216	.037			1.20	3.78	4.98	6.10
9480	cycle 20 miles		144	.056			1.80	5.65	7.45	9.20
9482	cycle 30 miles		126	.063			2.05	6.45	8.50	10.50
9484	cycle 40 miles		90	.089			2.88	9.05	11.93	14.70
9486	cycle 50 miles		90	.089			2.88	9.05	11.93	14.70
9494	45 MPH ave, cycle 8 miles		234	.034			1.11	3.49	4.60	5.65
9496	cycle 10 miles		216	.037			1.20	3.78	4.98	6.10
9498	cycle 20 miles		162	.049			1.60	5.05	6.65	8.20
9500	cycle 30 miles		126	.063			2.05	6.45	8.50	10.50
9502	cycle 40 miles		108	.074			2.40	7.55	9.95	12.25
9504	cycle 50 miles		90	.089			2.88	9.05	11.93	14.70
9506	50 MPH ave, cycle 10 miles		234	.034			1.11	3.49	4.60	5.65
9508	cycle 20 miles		180	.044			1.44	4.53	5.97	7.35
9510	cycle 30 miles		144	.056			1.80	5.65	7.45	9.20
9512	cycle 40 miles		108	.074			2.40	7.55	9.95	12.25
9514	cycle 50 miles		90	.089			2.88	9.05	11.93	14.70
9614	30 min. wait/Ld./Uld.,15 MPH, cycle 0.5 mi.		270	.030			.96	3.02	3.98	4.90
9616	cycle 1 mile		252	.032			1.03	3.24	4.27	5.25
9618	cycle 2 miles		216	.037			1.20	3.78	4.98	6.10
9620	cycle 4 miles		180	.044			1.44	4.53	5.97	7.35
9622	cycle 6 miles		162	.049			1.60	5.05	6.65	8.20
9624	cycle 8 miles		126	.063			2.05	6.45	8.50	10.50
9625	cycle 10 miles		126	.063			2.05	6.45	8.50	10.50
9626	20 MPH ave, cycle 0.5 mile		270	.030			.96	3.02	3.98	4.90

For customer support on your Residential Costs with RSMeans Data, call 800.448.8182.

31 23 23.20 Hauling

		Crew	Daily Output	Labor-Hours	Unit	Material	Labor	Equipment	Total	Total Incl O&P
							2017 Bare Costs			
9628	cycle 1 mile	B-34I	252	.032	L.C.Y.		1.03	3.24	4.27	5.25
9630	cycle 2 miles		234	.034			1.11	3.49	4.60	5.65
9632	cycle 4 miles		198	.040			1.31	4.12	5.43	6.70
9634	cycle 6 miles		180	.044			1.44	4.53	5.97	7.35
9636	cycle 8 miles		162	.049			1.60	5.05	6.65	8.20
9638	cycle 10 miles		144	.056			1.80	5.65	7.45	9.20
9640	25 MPH ave, cycle 4 miles		216	.037			1.20	3.78	4.98	6.10
9642	cycle 6 miles		198	.040			1.31	4.12	5.43	6.70
9644	cycle 8 miles		180	.044			1.44	4.53	5.97	7.35
9646	cycle 10 miles		162	.049			1.60	5.05	6.65	8.20
9650	30 MPH ave, cycle 4 miles		216	.037			1.20	3.78	4.98	6.10
9652	cycle 6 miles		198	.040			1.31	4.12	5.43	6.70
9654	cycle 8 miles		180	.044			1.44	4.53	5.97	7.35
9656	cycle 10 miles		162	.049			1.60	5.05	6.65	8.20
9660	35 MPH ave, cycle 4 miles		234	.034			1.11	3.49	4.60	5.65
9662	cycle 6 miles		216	.037			1.20	3.78	4.98	6.10
9664	cycle 8 miles		198	.040			1.31	4.12	5.43	6.70
9666	cycle 10 miles		180	.044			1.44	4.53	5.97	7.35
9668	cycle 20 miles		126	.063			2.05	6.45	8.50	10.50
9670	cycle 30 miles		108	.074			2.40	7.55	9.95	12.25
9672	cycle 40 miles		90	.089			2.88	9.05	11.93	14.70
9674	40 MPH ave, cycle 6 miles		216	.037			1.20	3.78	4.98	6.10
9676	cycle 8 miles		198	.040			1.31	4.12	5.43	6.70
9678	cycle 10 miles		180	.044			1.44	4.53	5.97	7.35
9680	cycle 20 miles		144	.056			1.80	5.65	7.45	9.20
9682	cycle 30 miles		108	.074			2.40	7.55	9.95	12.25
9684	cycle 40 miles		90	.089			2.88	9.05	11.93	14.70
9686	cycle 50 miles		72	.111			3.59	11.35	14.94	18.35
9694	45 MPH ave, cycle 8 miles		216	.037			1.20	3.78	4.98	6.10
9696	cycle 10 miles		198	.040			1.31	4.12	5.43	6.70
9698	cycle 20 miles		144	.056			1.80	5.65	7.45	9.20
9700	cycle 30 miles		126	.063			2.05	6.45	8.50	10.50
9702	cycle 40 miles		108	.074			2.40	7.55	9.95	12.25
9704	cycle 50 miles		90	.089			2.88	9.05	11.93	14.70
9706	50 MPH ave, cycle 10 miles		198	.040			1.31	4.12	5.43	6.70
9708	cycle 20 miles		162	.049			1.60	5.05	6.65	8.20
9710	cycle 30 miles		126	.063			2.05	6.45	8.50	10.50
9712	cycle 40 miles		108	.074			2.40	7.55	9.95	12.25
9714	cycle 50 miles		90	.089			2.88	9.05	11.93	14.70

31 23 23.24 Compaction, Structural

		Crew	Daily Output	Labor-Hours	Unit	Material	Labor	Equipment	Total	Total Incl O&P
0010	**COMPACTION, STRUCTURAL**									
0020	Steel wheel tandem roller, 5 tons	B-10E	8	1	Hr.		36.50	19.05	55.55	81
0050	Air tamp, 6" to 8" lifts, common fill	B-9	250	.160	E.C.Y.		4.32	.85	5.17	8.20
0060	Select fill	"	300	.133			3.60	.71	4.31	6.80
0600	Vibratory plate, 8" lifts, common fill	A-1D	200	.040			1.06	.17	1.23	1.96
0700	Select fill	"	216	.037			.99	.16	1.15	1.82

31 25 Erosion and Sedimentation Controls

31 25 14 – Stabilization Measures for Erosion and Sedimentation Control

31 25 14.16 Rolled Erosion Control Mats and Blankets		Crew	Daily Output	Labor-Hours	Unit	Material	2017 Bare Costs Labor	Equipment	Total	Total Incl O&P
0010	**ROLLED EROSION CONTROL MATS AND BLANKETS**									
0020	Jute mesh, 100 S.Y. per roll, 4' wide, stapled	G	B-80A	2400	.010	S.Y.	.77	.27	.11	1.15	1.42
0100	Plastic netting, stapled, 2" x 1" mesh, 20 mil	G	B-1	2500	.010		.29	.26		.55	.76
0120	Revegetation mat, webbed	G	2 Clab	1000	.016		2.91	.43		3.34	3.91
0200	Polypropylene mesh, stapled, 6.5 oz./S.Y.	G	B-1	2500	.010		1.61	.26		1.87	2.21
0300	Tobacco netting, or jute mesh #2, stapled	G	"	2500	.010		.25	.26		.51	.72
1000	Silt fence, install and maintain, remove	G	B-62	1300	.018	L.F.	.55	.54	.13	1.22	1.66
1100	Allow 10% per month for maintenance; 6-month max life										

31 31 Soil Treatment

31 31 16 – Termite Control

31 31 16.13 Chemical Termite Control

		Crew	Daily Output	Labor-Hours	Unit	Material	Labor	Equipment	Total	Total Incl O&P
0010	**CHEMICAL TERMITE CONTROL**									
0020	Slab and walls, residential	1 Skwk	1200	.007	SF Flr.	.32	.24		.56	.75
0030	SS mesh, no chemicals, avg 1400 S.F. home, min	G	1000	.008	"	.32	.29		.61	.83
0400	Insecticides for termite control, minimum		14.20	.563	Gal.	69	20		89	110
0500	Maximum		11	.727	"	118	26		144	174

For customer support on your Residential Costs with RSMeans Data, call 800.448.8182.

635

Division Notes

		CREW	DAILY OUTPUT	LABOR-HOURS	UNIT	BARE COSTS				TOTAL INCL O&P
						MAT.	LABOR	EQUIP.	TOTAL	

Estimating Tips

32 01 00 Operations and Maintenance of Exterior Improvements

- Recycling of asphalt pavement is becoming very popular and is an alternative to removal and replacement. It can be a good value engineering proposal if removed pavement can be recycled, either at the project site or at another site that is reasonably close to the project site. Sections on repair of flexible and rigid pavement are included.

32 10 00 Bases, Ballasts, and Paving

- When estimating paving, keep in mind the project schedule. Also note that prices for asphalt and concrete are generally higher in the cold seasons. Lines for pavement markings, including tactile warning systems and fence lines, are included.

32 90 00 Planting

- The timing of planting and guarantee specifications often dictate the costs for establishing tree and shrub growth and a stand of grass or ground cover. Establish the work performance schedule to coincide with the local planting season. Maintenance and growth guarantees can add from 20%–100% to the total landscaping cost and can be contractually cumbersome. The cost to replace trees and shrubs can be as high as 5% of the total cost, depending on the planting zone, soil conditions, and time of year.

Reference Numbers

Reference numbers are shown at the beginning of some major classifications. These numbers refer to related items in the Reference Section. The reference information may be an estimating procedure, an alternate pricing method, or technical information.

Note: Not all subdivisions listed here necessarily appear. ■

Did you know?

Our online estimating solution gives you the same access to RSMeans' data with 24/7 access:

- Quickly locate costs in the searchable database.

- Build cost lists, estimates, and reports in minutes.

- Adjust costs to any location in the U.S. and Canada with the click of a button.

Start your free trial today at
www.RSMeansOnline.com

32 01 Operation and Maintenance of Exterior Improvements

32 01 13 – Flexible Paving Surface Treatment

32 01 13.66 Fog Seal

		Crew	Daily Output	Labor-Hours	Unit	Material	2017 Bare Costs Labor	Equipment	Total	Total Incl O&P
0010	**FOG SEAL**									
0012	Sealcoating, 2 coat coal tar pitch emulsion over 10,000 S.Y.	B-45	5000	.003	S.Y.	.87	.09	.07	1.03	1.19
0030	1000 to 10,000 S.Y.	"	3000	.005		.87	.16	.11	1.14	1.34
0100	Under 1000 S.Y.	B-1	1050	.023		.87	.62		1.49	2
0300	Petroleum resistant, over 10,000 S.Y.	B-45	5000	.003		1.34	.09	.07	1.50	1.70
0320	1000 to 10,000 S.Y.	"	3000	.005		1.34	.16	.11	1.61	1.85
0400	Under 1000 S.Y.	B-1	1050	.023		1.34	.62		1.96	2.51

32 06 Schedules for Exterior Improvements

32 06 10 – Schedules for Bases, Ballasts, and Paving

32 06 10.10 Sidewalks, Driveways and Patios

		Crew	Daily Output	Labor-Hours	Unit	Material	2017 Bare Costs Labor	Equipment	Total	Total Incl O&P
0010	**SIDEWALKS, DRIVEWAYS AND PATIOS** No base									
0021	Asphaltic concrete, 2" thick	B-37	6480	.007	S.F.	.78	.21	.02	1.01	1.24
0101	2-1/2" thick	"	5950	.008	"	.99	.23	.03	1.25	1.50
0300	Concrete, 3000 psi, CIP, 6 x 6 - W1.4 x W1.4 mesh,									
0310	broomed finish, no base, 4" thick	B-24	600	.040	S.F.	1.97	1.28		3.25	4.28
0350	5" thick		545	.044		2.62	1.41		4.03	5.20
0400	6" thick		510	.047		3.06	1.51		4.57	5.85
0450	For bank run gravel base, 4" thick, add	B-18	2500	.010		.44	.26	.02	.72	.94
0520	8" thick, add	"	1600	.015		.89	.41	.03	1.33	1.69
1000	Crushed stone, 1" thick, white marble	2 Clab	1700	.009		.42	.25		.67	.88
1050	Bluestone	"	1700	.009		.12	.25		.37	.55
1700	Redwood, prefabricated, 4' x 4' sections	2 Carp	316	.051		4.77	1.77		6.54	8.20
1750	Redwood planks, 1" thick, on sleepers	"	240	.067		4.77	2.33		7.10	9.15
2250	Stone dust, 4" thick	B-62	900	.027	S.Y.	3.95	.79	.19	4.93	5.85

32 06 10.20 Steps

		Crew	Daily Output	Labor-Hours	Unit	Material	2017 Bare Costs Labor	Equipment	Total	Total Incl O&P
0010	**STEPS**									
0011	Incl. excav., borrow & concrete base as required									
0100	Brick steps	B-24	35	.686	LF Riser	15.95	22		37.95	54
0200	Railroad ties	2 Clab	25	.640		3.54	17		20.54	32.50
0300	Bluestone treads, 12" x 2" or 12" x 1-1/2"	B-24	30	.800		37.50	25.50		63	83.50
0600	Precast concrete, see Section 03 41 23.50									
4025	Steel edge strips, incl. stakes, 1/4" x 5"	B-1	390	.062	L.F.	4.26	1.68		5.94	7.50
4050	Edging, landscape timber or railroad ties, 6" x 8"	2 Carp	170	.094	"	2.24	3.29		5.53	7.95

32 11 Base Courses

32 11 23 – Aggregate Base Courses

32 11 23.23 Base Course Drainage Layers

		Crew	Daily Output	Labor-Hours	Unit	Material	2017 Bare Costs Labor	Equipment	Total	Total Incl O&P
0010	**BASE COURSE DRAINAGE LAYERS**									
0011	For roadways and large areas									
0051	3/4" stone compacted to 3" deep	B-36	36000	.001	S.F.	.28	.03	.05	.36	.42
0101	6" deep		35100	.001		.56	.04	.05	.65	.73
0201	9" deep		25875	.002		.82	.05	.06	.93	1.05
0305	12" deep		21150	.002		1.40	.06	.08	1.54	1.73
0306	Crushed 1-1/2" stone base, compacted to 4" deep		47000	.001		.05	.03	.04	.12	.14
0307	6" deep		35100	.001		.70	.04	.05	.79	.88
0308	8" deep		27000	.001		.94	.05	.06	1.05	1.18
0309	12" deep		16200	.002		1.40	.08	.10	1.58	1.78
0350	Bank run gravel, spread and compacted									

32 11 Base Courses

32 11 23 – Aggregate Base Courses

32 11 23.23 Base Course Drainage Layers		Crew	Daily Output	Labor-Hours	Unit	Material	2017 Bare Costs Labor	Equipment	Total	Total Incl O&P
0371	6" deep	B-32	54000	.001	S.F.	.41	.02	.04	.47	.53
0391	9" deep	↓	39600	.001		.60	.03	.06	.69	.77
0401	12" deep	↓	32400	.001	↓	.82	.03	.07	.92	1.04
6900	For small and irregular areas, add						50%	50%		

32 11 26 – Asphaltic Base Courses

32 11 26.19 Bituminous-Stabilized Base Courses

		Crew	Daily Output	Labor-Hours	Unit	Material	Labor	Equipment	Total	Total Incl O&P
0010	**BITUMINOUS-STABILIZED BASE COURSES**									
0020	And large paved areas									
0700	Liquid application to gravel base, asphalt emulsion	B-45	6000	.003	Gal.	4.46	.08	.05	4.59	5.10
0800	Prime and seal, cut back asphalt		6000	.003	"	5.25	.08	.05	5.38	6
1000	Macadam penetration crushed stone, 2 gal. per S.Y., 4" thick		6000	.003	S.Y.	8.90	.08	.05	9.03	10
1100	6" thick, 3 gal. per S.Y.		4000	.004		13.40	.12	.08	13.60	15
1200	8" thick, 4 gal. per S.Y.	↓	3000	.005	↓	17.85	.16	.11	18.12	20
8900	For small and irregular areas, add						50%	50%		

32 12 Flexible Paving

32 12 16 – Asphalt Paving

32 12 16.14 Paving Asphaltic Concrete

		Crew	Daily Output	Labor-Hours	Unit	Material	Labor	Equipment	Total	Total Incl O&P
0010	**PAVING ASPHALTIC CONCRETE**									
0020	6" stone base, 2" binder course, 1" topping	B-25C	9000	.005	S.F.	1.80	.16	.27	2.23	2.55
0025	2" binder course, 2" topping		9000	.005		2.24	.16	.27	2.67	3.03
0030	3" binder course, 2" topping		9000	.005		2.64	.16	.27	3.07	3.48
0035	4" binder course, 2" topping		9000	.005		3.04	.16	.27	3.47	3.91
0040	1.5" binder course, 1" topping		9000	.005		1.60	.16	.27	2.03	2.33
0042	3" binder course, 1" topping		9000	.005		2.21	.16	.27	2.64	3
0045	3" binder course, 3" topping		9000	.005		3.09	.16	.27	3.52	3.96
0050	4" binder course, 3" topping		9000	.005		3.48	.16	.27	3.91	4.40
0055	4" binder course, 4" topping		9000	.005		3.92	.16	.27	4.35	4.88
0300	Binder course, 1-1/2" thick		35000	.001		.60	.04	.07	.71	.81
0400	2" thick		25000	.002		.78	.06	.10	.94	1.07
0500	3" thick		15000	.003		1.20	.10	.16	1.46	1.66
0600	4" thick		10800	.004		1.57	.13	.23	1.93	2.20
0800	Sand finish course, 3/4" thick		41000	.001		.31	.04	.06	.41	.48
0900	1" thick	↓	34000	.001		.39	.04	.07	.50	.58
1000	Fill pot holes, hot mix, 2" thick	B-16	4200	.008		.82	.22	.15	1.19	1.43
1100	4" thick		3500	.009		1.20	.26	.18	1.64	1.95
1120	6" thick	↓	3100	.010		1.62	.29	.21	2.12	2.50
1140	Cold patch, 2" thick	B-51	3000	.016		.93	.44	.07	1.44	1.85
1160	4" thick		2700	.018		1.78	.49	.08	2.35	2.87
1180	6" thick	↓	1900	.025	↓	2.77	.70	.11	3.58	4.35

For customer support on your Residential Costs with RSMeans Data, call 800.448.8182.

639

32 13 Rigid Paving

32 13 13 – Concrete Paving

32 13 13.25 Concrete Pavement, Highways	Crew	Daily Output	Labor-Hours	Unit	Material	2017 Bare Costs Labor	2017 Bare Costs Equipment	Total	Total Incl O&P
0010 **CONCRETE PAVEMENT, HIGHWAYS**									
0015 Including joints, finishing and curing									
0021 Fixed form, 12' pass, unreinforced, 6" thick	B-26	18000	.005	S.F.	3.69	.15	.17	4.01	4.50
0101 8" thick	"	13500	.007		4.97	.20	.23	5.40	6.05
0701 Finishing, broom finish small areas	2 Cefi	1215	.013	↓		.46		.46	.74

32 14 Unit Paving

32 14 13 – Precast Concrete Unit Paving

32 14 13.18 Precast Concrete Plantable Pavers

	Crew	Daily Output	Labor-Hours	Unit	Material	2017 Bare Costs Labor	2017 Bare Costs Equipment	Total	Total Incl O&P
0010 **PRECAST CONCRETE PLANTABLE PAVERS** (50% grass)									
0300 3/4" crushed stone base for plantable pavers, 6 inch depth	B-62	1000	.024	S.Y.	3.94	.71	.17	4.82	5.70
0400 8 inch depth		900	.027		5.25	.79	.19	6.23	7.25
0500 10 inch depth		800	.030		6.55	.88	.21	7.64	8.90
0600 12 inch depth	↓	700	.034	↓	7.85	1.01	.24	9.10	10.60
0700 Hydro seeding plantable pavers	B-81A	20	.800	M.S.F.	11.40	23.50	19.65	54.55	73
0800 Apply fertilizer and seed to plantable pavers	1 Clab	8	1	"	40	26.50		66.50	88.50

32 14 16 – Brick Unit Paving

32 14 16.10 Brick Paving

	Crew	Daily Output	Labor-Hours	Unit	Material	2017 Bare Costs Labor	2017 Bare Costs Equipment	Total	Total Incl O&P
0010 **BRICK PAVING**									
0012 4" x 8" x 1-1/2", without joints (4.5 bricks/S.F.)	D-1	110	.145	S.F.	2.25	4.62		6.87	10.20
0100 Grouted, 3/8" joint (3.9 bricks/S.F.)		90	.178		2.02	5.65		7.67	11.70
0200 4" x 8" x 2-1/4", without joints (4.5 bricks/S.F.)		110	.145		2.33	4.62		6.95	10.30
0300 Grouted, 3/8" joint (3.9 bricks/S.F.)		90	.178		2.02	5.65		7.67	11.70
0455 Pervious brick paving, 4" x 8" x 3-1/4", without joints (4.5 bricks/S.F.)	↓	110	.145		3.49	4.62		8.11	11.60
0500 Bedding, asphalt, 3/4" thick	B-25	5130	.017		.66	.51	.55	1.72	2.18
0540 Course washed sand bed, 1" thick	B-18	5000	.005		.36	.13	.01	.50	.63
0580 Mortar, 1" thick	D-1	300	.053		.80	1.69		2.49	3.72
0620 2" thick		200	.080		1.59	2.54		4.13	6
1500 Brick on 1" thick sand bed laid flat, 4.5 per S.F.		100	.160		2.82	5.10		7.92	11.65
2000 Brick pavers, laid on edge, 7.2 per S.F.	↓	70	.229	↓	3.95	7.25		11.20	16.55

32 14 23 – Asphalt Unit Paving

32 14 23.10 Asphalt Blocks

	Crew	Daily Output	Labor-Hours	Unit	Material	2017 Bare Costs Labor	2017 Bare Costs Equipment	Total	Total Incl O&P
0010 **ASPHALT BLOCKS**									
0020 Rectangular, 6" x 12" x 1-1/4", w/bed & neopr. adhesive	D-1	135	.119	S.F.	8.05	3.77		11.82	15.15
0100 3" thick		130	.123		11.25	3.91		15.16	18.95
0300 Hexagonal tile, 8" wide, 1-1/4" thick		135	.119		8.05	3.77		11.82	15.15
0400 2" thick		130	.123		11.25	3.91		15.16	18.95
0500 Square, 8" x 8", 1-1/4" thick		135	.119		8.05	3.77		11.82	15.15
0600 2" thick	↓	130	.123	↓	11.25	3.91		15.16	18.95

32 14 40 – Stone Paving

32 14 40.10 Stone Pavers

	Crew	Daily Output	Labor-Hours	Unit	Material	2017 Bare Costs Labor	2017 Bare Costs Equipment	Total	Total Incl O&P
0010 **STONE PAVERS**									
1100 Flagging, bluestone, irregular, 1" thick,	D-1	81	.198	S.F.	9.15	6.30		15.45	20.50
1150 Snapped random rectangular, 1" thick		92	.174		13.85	5.55		19.40	24.50
1200 1-1/2" thick		85	.188		16.65	6		22.65	28.50
1250 2" thick		83	.193		19.40	6.15		25.55	32
1300 Slate, natural cleft, irregular, 3/4" thick		92	.174		9	5.55		14.55	19.15
1310 1" thick		85	.188		10.50	6		16.50	21.50
1351 Random rectangular, gauged, 1/2" thick	↓	105	.152	↓	19.50	4.84		24.34	29.50

32 14 Unit Paving

32 14 40 – Stone Paving

32 14 40.10 Stone Pavers

32 14 40.10 Stone Pavers	Crew	Daily Output	Labor-Hours	Unit	Material	2017 Bare Costs Labor	Equipment	Total	Total Incl O&P
1400	Random rectangular, butt joint, gauged, 1/4" thick	D-1	150	.107	S.F.	21	3.39		24.39	28.50
1450	For sand rubbed finish, add					9			9	9.90
1500	For interior setting, add					25%			25%	25%
1550	Granite blocks, 3-1/2" x 3-1/2" x 3-1/2"	D-1	92	.174	S.F.	16.95	5.55		22.50	28

32 16 Curbs, Gutters, Sidewalks, and Driveways

32 16 13 – Curbs and Gutters

32 16 13.13 Cast-in-Place Concrete Curbs and Gutters

32 16 13.13 Cast-in-Place Concrete Curbs and Gutters	Crew	Daily Output	Labor-Hours	Unit	Material	2017 Bare Costs Labor	Equipment	Total	Total Incl O&P
0010	**CAST-IN-PLACE CONCRETE CURBS AND GUTTERS**									
0290	Forms only, no concrete									
0300	Concrete, wood forms, 6" x 18", straight	C-2	500	.096	L.F.	3.12	2.98		6.10	8.45
0400	6" x 18", radius	"	200	.240		3.24	7.45		10.69	16.05
0404	Concrete, wood forms, 6" x 18", straight & concrete	C-2A	500	.096		6.45	3.25		9.70	12.45
0406	6" x 18", radius	"	200	.240		6.55	8.10		14.65	20.50

32 16 13.23 Precast Concrete Curbs and Gutters

32 16 13.23 Precast Concrete Curbs and Gutters	Crew	Daily Output	Labor-Hours	Unit	Material	2017 Bare Costs Labor	Equipment	Total	Total Incl O&P
0010	**PRECAST CONCRETE CURBS AND GUTTERS**									
0550	Precast, 6" x 18", straight	B-29	700	.069	L.F.	9.15	1.97	1.30	12.42	14.75
0600	6" x 18", radius	"	325	.148	"	10.15	4.24	2.80	17.19	21.50

32 16 13.33 Asphalt Curbs

32 16 13.33 Asphalt Curbs	Crew	Daily Output	Labor-Hours	Unit	Material	2017 Bare Costs Labor	Equipment	Total	Total Incl O&P
0010	**ASPHALT CURBS**									
0012	Curbs, asphaltic, machine formed, 8" wide, 6" high, 40 L.F./ton	B-27	1000	.032	L.F.	1.66	.87	.31	2.84	3.62
0100	8" wide, 8" high, 30 L.F./ton		900	.036		2.22	.96	.35	3.53	4.44
0150	Asphaltic berm, 12" W, 3" to 6" H, 35 L.F./ton, before pavement		700	.046		.04	1.24	.45	1.73	2.60
0200	12" W, 1-1/2" to 4" H, 60 L.F./ton, laid with pavement	B-2	1050	.038		.02	1.03		1.05	1.75

32 16 13.43 Stone Curbs

32 16 13.43 Stone Curbs	Crew	Daily Output	Labor-Hours	Unit	Material	2017 Bare Costs Labor	Equipment	Total	Total Incl O&P
0010	**STONE CURBS**									
1000	Granite, split face, straight, 5" x 16"	D-13	275	.175	L.F.	14.10	5.85	1.58	21.53	27
1100	6" x 18"	"	250	.192		18.55	6.45	1.74	26.74	33
1300	Radius curbing, 6" x 18", over 10' radius	B-29	260	.185		22.50	5.30	3.50	31.30	37.50
1400	Corners, 2' radius	"	80	.600	Ea.	76	17.25	11.40	104.65	126
1600	Edging, 4-1/2" x 12", straight	D-13	300	.160	L.F.	7.05	5.35	1.45	13.85	18.35
1800	Curb inlets (guttermouth) straight	B-29	41	1.171	Ea.	169	33.50	22	224.50	267
2000	Indian granite (Belgian block)									
2100	Jumbo, 10-1/2" x 7-1/2" x 4", grey	D-1	150	.107	L.F.	7.65	3.39		11.04	14.10
2150	Pink		150	.107		8.35	3.39		11.74	14.90
2200	Regular, 9" x 4-1/2" x 4-1/2", grey		160	.100		4.53	3.18		7.71	10.35
2250	Pink		160	.100		5.95	3.18		9.13	11.90
2300	Cubes, 4" x 4" x 4", grey		175	.091		3.52	2.91		6.43	8.75
2350	Pink		175	.091		3.55	2.91		6.46	8.80
2400	6" x 6" x 6", pink		155	.103		11.75	3.28		15.03	18.40
2500	Alternate pricing method for Indian granite									
2550	Jumbo, 10-1/2" x 7-1/2" x 4" (30 lb.), grey				Ton	435			435	480
2600	Pink					485			485	535
2650	Regular, 9" x 4-1/2" x 4-1/2" (20 lb.), grey					320			320	350
2700	Pink					415			415	460
2750	Cubes, 4" x 4" x 4" (5 lb.), grey					425			425	470
2800	Pink					455			455	500
2850	6" x 6" x 6" (25 lb.), pink					455			455	500
2900	For pallets, add					22			22	24

32 31 Fences and Gates

32 31 13 – Chain Link Fences and Gates

32 31 13.15 Chain Link Fence

		Crew	Daily Output	Labor-Hours	Unit	Material	2017 Bare Costs Labor	2017 Bare Costs Equipment	Total	Total Incl O&P
0010	**CHAIN LINK FENCE**									
0020	1-5/8" post 10' O.C., 1-3/8" top rail, 2" corner post galv. stl., 3' high	B-1	185	.130	L.F.	10.70	3.54		14.24	17.65
0050	4' high		170	.141		9.50	3.85		13.35	16.90
0100	6' high		115	.209		12.25	5.70		17.95	23
0150	Add for gate 3' wide, 1-3/8" frame 3' high		12	2	Ea.	103	54.50		157.50	204
0170	4' high		10	2.400		117	65.50		182.50	238
0190	6' high		10	2.400		141	65.50		206.50	264
0200	Add for gate 4' wide, 1-3/8" frame 3' high		9	2.667		112	72.50		184.50	245
0220	4' high		9	2.667		122	72.50		194.50	256
0240	6' high		8	3		148	82		230	300
0350	Aluminized steel, 9 ga. wire, 3' high		185	.130	L.F.	8.95	3.54		12.49	15.75
0380	4' high		170	.141		9.35	3.85		13.20	16.75
0400	6' high		115	.209		12.20	5.70		17.90	23
0450	Add for gate 3' wide, 1-3/8" frame 3' high		12	2	Ea.	149	54.50		203.50	255
0470	4' high		10	2.400		160	65.50		225.50	285
0490	6' high		10	2.400		202	65.50		267.50	330
0500	Add for gate 4' wide, 1-3/8" frame 3' high		10	2.400		155	65.50		220.50	280
0520	4' high		9	2.667		148	72.50		220.50	285
0540	6' high		8	3		201	82		283	360
0620	Vinyl covered 9 ga. wire, 3' high		185	.130	L.F.	8.70	3.54		12.24	15.45
0640	4' high		170	.141		7.30	3.85		11.15	14.50
0660	6' high		115	.209		9.80	5.70		15.50	20.50
0720	Add for gate 3' wide, 1-3/8" frame 3' high		12	2	Ea.	111	54.50		165.50	213
0740	4' high		10	2.400		125	65.50		190.50	247
0760	6' high		10	2.400		155	65.50		220.50	280
0780	Add for gate 4' wide, 1-3/8" frame 3' high		10	2.400		123	65.50		188.50	244
0800	4' high		9	2.667		129	72.50		201.50	263
0820	6' high		8	3		167	82		249	320
0860	Tennis courts, 11 ga. wire, 2-1/2" post 10' O.C., 1-5/8" top rail									
0900	2-1/2" corner post, 10' high	B-1	95	.253	L.F.	9.05	6.90		15.95	21.50
0920	12' high		80	.300	"	9.35	8.20		17.55	24
1000	Add for gate 3' wide, 1-5/8" frame 10' high		10	2.400	Ea.	240	65.50		305.50	375
1040	Aluminized, 11 ga. wire 10' high		95	.253	L.F.	10.90	6.90		17.80	23.50
1100	12' high		80	.300	"	11.95	8.20		20.15	27
1140	Add for gate 3' wide, 1-5/8" frame, 10' high		10	2.400	Ea.	167	65.50		232.50	292
1250	Vinyl covered 11 ga. wire, 10' high		95	.253	L.F.	9.40	6.90		16.30	22
1300	12' high		80	.300	"	11.30	8.20		19.50	26
1400	Add for gate 3' wide, 1-3/8" frame, 10' high		10	2.400	Ea.	330	65.50		395.50	475

32 31 23 – Plastic Fences and Gates

32 31 23.10 Fence, Vinyl

		Crew	Daily Output	Labor-Hours	Unit	Material	2017 Bare Costs Labor	2017 Bare Costs Equipment	Total	Total Incl O&P
0010	**FENCE, VINYL**									
0011	White, steel reinforced, stainless steel fasteners									
0020	Picket, 4" x 4" posts @ 6'-0" OC, 3' high	B-1	140	.171	L.F.	23	4.67		27.67	33
0030	4' high		130	.185		25	5.05		30.05	36
0040	5' high		120	.200		28	5.45		33.45	40
0100	Board (semi-privacy), 5" x 5" posts @ 7'-6" OC, 5' high		130	.185		25.50	5.05		30.55	36.50
0120	6' high		125	.192		29	5.25		34.25	41
0200	Basketweave, 5" x 5" posts @ 7'-6" OC, 5' high		160	.150		26	4.09		30.09	35.50
0220	6' high		150	.160		29	4.36		33.36	39
0300	Privacy, 5" x 5" posts @ 7'-6" OC, 5' high		130	.185		25	5.05		30.05	36
0320	6' high		150	.160		29	4.36		33.36	39
0350	Gate, 5' high		9	2.667	Ea.	315	72.50		387.50	470

32 31 Fences and Gates

32 31 23 – Plastic Fences and Gates

32 31 23.10 Fence, Vinyl

		Crew	Daily Output	Labor-Hours	Unit	Material	2017 Bare Costs Labor	Equipment	Total	Total Incl O&P
0360	6' high	B-1	9	2.667	Ea.	360	72.50		432.50	520
0400	For posts set in concrete, add		25	.960	↓	9.80	26		35.80	55
0500	Post and rail fence, 2 rail		150	.160	L.F.	6	4.36		10.36	13.90
0510	3 rail		150	.160		7.75	4.36		12.11	15.85
0515	4 rail	↓	150	.160	↓	10.05	4.36		14.41	18.35

32 31 26 – Wire Fences and Gates

32 31 26.10 Fences, Misc. Metal

		Crew	Daily Output	Labor-Hours	Unit	Material	2017 Bare Costs Labor	Equipment	Total	Total Incl O&P
0010	**FENCES, MISC. METAL**									
0012	Chicken wire, posts @ 4', 1" mesh, 4' high	B-80C	410	.059	L.F.	3.40	1.66	.55	5.61	7.10
0100	2" mesh, 6' high		350	.069		3.82	1.94	.64	6.40	8.15
0200	Galv. steel, 12 ga., 2" x 4" mesh, posts 5' O.C., 3' high		300	.080		2.78	2.27	.75	5.80	7.65
0300	5' high		300	.080		3.38	2.27	.75	6.40	8.30
0400	14 ga., 1" x 2" mesh, 3' high		300	.080		3.42	2.27	.75	6.44	8.35
0500	5' high	↓	300	.080	↓	4.57	2.27	.75	7.59	9.65
1000	Kennel fencing, 1-1/2" mesh, 6' long, 3'-6" wide, 6'-2" high	2 Clab	4	4	Ea.	510	106		616	740
1050	12' long		4	4		720	106		826	970
1200	Top covers, 1-1/2" mesh, 6' long		15	1.067		136	28.50		164.50	198
1250	12' long	↓	12	1.333	↓	191	35.50		226.50	270

32 31 29 – Wood Fences and Gates

32 31 29.10 Fence, Wood

		Crew	Daily Output	Labor-Hours	Unit	Material	2017 Bare Costs Labor	Equipment	Total	Total Incl O&P
0010	**FENCE, WOOD**									
0011	Basket weave, 3/8" x 4" boards, 2" x 4"									
0020	stringers on spreaders, 4" x 4" posts									
0050	No. 1 cedar, 6' high	B-80C	160	.150	L.F.	26	4.25	1.41	31.66	37
0070	Treated pine, 6' high		150	.160		34.50	4.53	1.50	40.53	47
0090	Vertical weave, 6' high	↓	145	.166	↓	22.50	4.69	1.55	28.74	34.50
0200	Board fence, 1" x 4" boards, 2" x 4" rails, 4" x 4" post									
0220	Preservative treated, 2 rail, 3' high	B-80C	145	.166	L.F.	9.55	4.69	1.55	15.79	20
0240	4' high		135	.178		11.20	5.05	1.67	17.92	22.50
0260	3 rail, 5' high		130	.185		12.25	5.25	1.73	19.23	24
0300	6' high		125	.192		13.80	5.45	1.80	21.05	26
0320	No. 2 grade western cedar, 2 rail, 3' high		145	.166		10.50	4.69	1.55	16.74	21
0340	4' high		135	.178		11.55	5.05	1.67	18.27	23
0360	3 rail, 5' high		130	.185		13	5.25	1.73	19.98	25
0400	6' high		125	.192		13.85	5.45	1.80	21.10	26.50
0420	No. 1 grade cedar, 2 rail, 3' high		145	.166		13.30	4.69	1.55	19.54	24
0440	4' high		135	.178		14.40	5.05	1.67	21.12	26
0460	3 rail, 5' high		130	.185		17.50	5.25	1.73	24.48	30
0500	6' high	↓	125	.192	↓	19.30	5.45	1.80	26.55	32
0540	Shadow box, 1" x 6" board, 2" x 4" rail, 4" x 4" post									
0560	Pine, pressure treated, 3 rail, 6' high	B-80C	150	.160	L.F.	17.70	4.53	1.50	23.73	28.50
0600	Gate, 3'-6" wide		8	3	Ea.	110	85	28	223	293
0620	No. 1 cedar, 3 rail, 4' high		130	.185	L.F.	18.55	5.25	1.73	25.53	31
0640	6' high		125	.192		23.50	5.45	1.80	30.75	37
0860	Open rail fence, split rails, 2 rail, 3' high, no. 1 cedar		160	.150		12.90	4.25	1.41	18.56	23
0870	No. 2 cedar		160	.150		11.85	4.25	1.41	17.51	21.50
0880	3 rail, 4' high, no. 1 cedar		150	.160		13.35	4.53	1.50	19.38	24
0890	No. 2 cedar		150	.160		9.40	4.53	1.50	15.43	19.55
0920	Rustic rails, 2 rail, 3' high, no. 1 cedar		160	.150		10.30	4.25	1.41	15.96	19.90
0930	No. 2 cedar		160	.150		9.65	4.25	1.41	15.31	19.20
0940	3 rail, 4' high		150	.160		9.85	4.53	1.50	15.88	20
0950	No. 2 cedar	↓	150	.160	↓	8.05	4.53	1.50	14.08	18.05

32 31 Fences and Gates

32 31 29 – Wood Fences and Gates

32 31 29.10 Fence, Wood

	32 31 29.10 Fence, Wood	Crew	Daily Output	Labor-Hours	Unit	Material	2017 Bare Costs Labor	Equipment	Total	Total Incl O&P
0960	Picket fence, gothic, pressure treated pine									
1000	2 rail, 3' high	B-80C	140	.171	L.F.	7.80	4.86	1.61	14.27	18.45
1020	3 rail, 4' high		130	.185	"	8.90	5.25	1.73	15.88	20.50
1040	Gate, 3'-6" wide		9	2.667	Ea.	74	75.50	25	174.50	235
1060	No. 2 cedar, 2 rail, 3' high		140	.171	L.F.	9	4.86	1.61	15.47	19.75
1100	3 rail, 4' high		130	.185	"	9.10	5.25	1.73	16.08	20.50
1120	Gate, 3'-6" wide		9	2.667	Ea.	79	75.50	25	179.50	241
1140	No. 1 cedar, 2 rail, 3' high		140	.171	L.F.	13.70	4.86	1.61	20.17	25
1160	3 rail, 4' high		130	.185		17.85	5.25	1.73	24.83	30
1200	Rustic picket, molded pine, 2 rail, 3' high		140	.171		8.50	4.86	1.61	14.97	19.20
1220	No. 1 cedar, 2 rail, 3' high		140	.171		9.85	4.86	1.61	16.32	20.50
1240	Stockade fence, no. 1 cedar, 3-1/4" rails, 6' high		160	.150		13.15	4.25	1.41	18.81	23
1260	8' high		155	.155		18.10	4.39	1.45	23.94	29
1300	No. 2 cedar, treated wood rails, 6' high		160	.150	↓	13.45	4.25	1.41	19.11	23.50
1320	Gate, 3'-6" wide		8	3	Ea.	89.50	85	28	202.50	271
1360	Treated pine, treated rails, 6' high		160	.150	L.F.	13.95	4.25	1.41	19.61	24
1400	8' high	↓	150	.160	"	19.40	4.53	1.50	25.43	30.50

32 31 29.20 Fence, Wood Rail

	32 31 29.20 Fence, Wood Rail	Crew	Daily Output	Labor-Hours	Unit	Material	2017 Bare Costs Labor	Equipment	Total	Total Incl O&P
0010	**FENCE, WOOD RAIL**									
0012	Picket, No. 2 cedar, Gothic, 2 rail, 3' high	B-1	160	.150	L.F.	8.10	4.09		12.19	15.75
0050	Gate, 3'-6" wide	B-80C	9	2.667	Ea.	78	75.50	25	178.50	239
0400	3 rail, 4' high		150	.160	L.F.	9.10	4.53	1.50	15.13	19.20
0500	Gate, 3'-6" wide		9	2.667	Ea.	95	75.50	25	195.50	258
1200	Stockade, No. 2 cedar, treated wood rails, 6' high		160	.150	L.F.	9.10	4.25	1.41	14.76	18.60
1250	Gate, 3' wide		9	2.667	Ea.	97	75.50	25	197.50	261
1300	No. 1 cedar, 3-1/4" cedar rails, 6' high		160	.150	L.F.	20.50	4.25	1.41	26.16	31
1500	Gate, 3' wide		9	2.667	Ea.	222	75.50	25	322.50	400
2700	Prefabricated redwood or cedar, 4' high		160	.150	L.F.	15.90	4.25	1.41	21.56	26
2800	6' high		150	.160		23.50	4.53	1.50	29.53	35
3300	Board, shadow box, 1" x 6", treated pine, 6' high		160	.150		12.65	4.25	1.41	18.31	22.50
3400	No. 1 cedar, 6' high		150	.160		25	4.53	1.50	31.03	36.50
3900	Basket weave, No. 1 cedar, 6' high	↓	160	.150	↓	34	4.25	1.41	39.66	46
4200	Gate, 3'-6" wide	B-1	9	2.667	Ea.	178	72.50		250.50	320
5000	Fence rail, redwood, 2" x 4", merch. grade, 8'	"	2400	.010	L.F.	2.53	.27		2.80	3.24

32 32 Retaining Walls

32 32 13 – Cast-in-Place Concrete Retaining Walls

32 32 13.10 Retaining Walls, Cast Concrete

	32 32 13.10 Retaining Walls, Cast Concrete	Crew	Daily Output	Labor-Hours	Unit	Material	2017 Bare Costs Labor	Equipment	Total	Total Incl O&P
0010	**RETAINING WALLS, CAST CONCRETE**									
1800	Concrete gravity wall with vertical face including excavation & backfill									
1850	No reinforcing									
1900	6' high, level embankment	C-17C	36	2.306	L.F.	87	83.50	16.85	187.35	254
2000	33° slope embankment	"	32	2.594	"	100	94	18.95	212.95	288
2800	Reinforced concrete cantilever, incl. excavation, backfill & reinf.									
2900	6' high, 33° slope embankment	C-17C	35	2.371	L.F.	78.50	86	17.30	181.80	250

32 32 Retaining Walls

32 32 23 – Segmental Retaining Walls

32 32 23.13 Segmental Conc. Unit Masonry Retaining Walls	Crew	Daily Output	Labor-Hours	Unit	Material	2017 Bare Costs Labor	Equipment	Total	Total Incl O&P
0010 **SEGMENTAL CONC. UNIT MASONRY RETAINING WALLS**									
7100 Segmental Retaining Wall system, incl. pins, and void fill									
7120 base and backfill not included									
7140 Large unit, 8" high x 18" wide x 20" deep, 3 plane split	B-62	300	.080	S.F.	12.40	2.36	.57	15.33	18.20
7150 Straight split		300	.080		12.50	2.36	.57	15.43	18.30
7160 Medium, lt. wt., 8" high x 18" wide x 12" deep, 3 plane split		400	.060		7.10	1.77	.43	9.30	11.20
7170 Straight split		400	.060		9.45	1.77	.43	11.65	13.80
7180 Small unit, 4" x 18" x 10" deep, 3 plane split		400	.060		14.20	1.77	.43	16.40	19
7190 Straight split		400	.060		10.70	1.77	.43	12.90	15.15
7200 Cap unit, 3 plane split		300	.080		13.25	2.36	.57	16.18	19.15
7210 Cap unit, straight split		300	.080		13.25	2.36	.57	16.18	19.15
7250 Geo-grid soil reinforcement 4' x 50'	2 Clab	22500	.001		.68	.02		.70	.78
7255 Geo-grid soil reinforcement 6' x 150'	"	22500	.001		.54	.02		.56	.62

32 32 26 – Metal Crib Retaining Walls

32 32 26.10 Metal Bin Retaining Walls

	Crew	Daily Output	Labor-Hours	Unit	Material	Labor	Equipment	Total	Total Incl O&P
0010 **METAL BIN RETAINING WALLS**									
0011 Aluminized steel bin, excavation									
0020 and backfill not included, 10' wide									
0100 4' high, 5.5' deep	B-13	650	.074	S.F.	27	2.12	1.04	30.16	34
0200 8' high, 5.5' deep		615	.078		31	2.24	1.10	34.34	39
0300 10' high, 7.7' deep		580	.083		34.50	2.38	1.16	38.04	43.50
0400 12' high, 7.7' deep		530	.091		37	2.60	1.27	40.87	46.50
0500 16' high, 7.7' deep		515	.093		39	2.68	1.31	42.99	49

32 32 29 – Timber Retaining Walls

32 32 29.10 Landscape Timber Retaining Walls

	Crew	Daily Output	Labor-Hours	Unit	Material	Labor	Equipment	Total	Total Incl O&P
0010 **LANDSCAPE TIMBER RETAINING WALLS**									
0100 Treated timbers, 6" x 6"	1 Clab	265	.030	L.F.	2.47	.80		3.27	4.06
0110 6" x 8"	"	200	.040	"	5.20	1.06		6.26	7.55
0120 Drilling holes in timbers for fastening, 1/2"	1 Carp	450	.018	Inch		.62		.62	1.04
0130 5/8"	"	450	.018	"		.62		.62	1.04
0140 Reinforcing rods for fastening, 1/2"	1 Clab	312	.026	L.F.	.35	.68		1.03	1.52
0150 5/8"	"	312	.026	"	.54	.68		1.22	1.73
0160 Reinforcing fabric	2 Clab	2500	.006	S.Y.	2.13	.17		2.30	2.62
0170 Gravel backfill		28	.571	C.Y.	17.20	15.20		32.40	44.50
0180 Perforated pipe, 4" diameter with silt sock		1200	.013	L.F.	1.07	.35		1.42	1.77
0190 Galvanized 60d common nails	1 Clab	625	.013	Ea.	.17	.34		.51	.76
0200 20d common nails	"	3800	.002	"	.04	.06		.10	.13

32 32 53 – Stone Retaining Walls

32 32 53.10 Retaining Walls, Stone

	Crew	Daily Output	Labor-Hours	Unit	Material	Labor	Equipment	Total	Total Incl O&P
0010 **RETAINING WALLS, STONE**									
0015 Including excavation, concrete footing and									
0020 stone 3' below grade. Price is exposed face area.									
0200 Decorative random stone, to 6' high, 1'-6" thick, dry set	D-1	35	.457	S.F.	61.50	14.55		76.05	92.50
0300 Mortar set		40	.400		63.50	12.70		76.20	91.50
0500 Cut stone, to 6' high, 1'-6" thick, dry set		35	.457		64	14.55		78.55	94.50
0600 Mortar set		40	.400		64.50	12.70		77.20	92.50
0800 Random stone, 6' to 10' high, 2' thick, dry set		45	.356		69.50	11.30		80.80	95.50
0900 Mortar set		50	.320		72.50	10.15		82.65	96.50
1100 Cut stone, 6' to 10' high, 2' thick, dry set		45	.356		70.50	11.30		81.80	96.50
1200 Mortar set		50	.320		72.50	10.15		82.65	97

32 33 Site Furnishings

32 33 33 – Site Manufactured Planters

32 33 33.10 Planters

		Crew	Daily Output	Labor-Hours	Unit	Material	2017 Bare Costs Labor	2017 Bare Costs Equipment	Total	Total Incl O&P
0010	**PLANTERS**									
0012	Concrete, sandblasted, precast, 48" diameter, 24" high	2 Clab	15	1.067	Ea.	655	28.50		683.50	770
0300	Fiberglass, circular, 36" diameter, 24" high		15	1.067		675	28.50		703.50	795
1200	Wood, square, 48" side, 24" high		15	1.067		1,600	28.50		1,628.50	1,800
1300	Circular, 48" diameter, 30" high		10	1.600		1,075	42.50		1,117.50	1,250
1600	Planter/bench, 72"		5	3.200		3,625	85		3,710	4,125

32 33 43 – Site Seating and Tables

32 33 43.13 Site Seating

		Crew	Daily Output	Labor-Hours	Unit	Material	2017 Bare Costs Labor	2017 Bare Costs Equipment	Total	Total Incl O&P
0010	**SITE SEATING**									
0012	Seating, benches, park, precast conc., w/backs, wood rails, 4' long	2 Clab	5	3.200	Ea.	625	85		710	830
0100	8' long		4	4		1,050	106		1,156	1,325
0500	Steel barstock pedestals w/backs, 2" x 3" wood rails, 4' long		10	1.600		1,325	42.50		1,367.50	1,550
0510	8' long		7	2.286		1,700	61		1,761	1,975
0800	Cast iron pedestals, back & arms, wood slats, 4' long		8	2		435	53		488	570
0820	8' long		5	3.200		1,100	85		1,185	1,350
1700	Steel frame, fir seat, 10' long		10	1.600		395	42.50		437.50	505

32 84 Planting Irrigation

32 84 23 – Underground Sprinklers

32 84 23.10 Sprinkler Irrigation System

		Crew	Daily Output	Labor-Hours	Unit	Material	2017 Bare Costs Labor	2017 Bare Costs Equipment	Total	Total Incl O&P
0010	**SPRINKLER IRRIGATION SYSTEM**									
0011	For lawns									
0800	Residential system, custom, 1" supply	B-20	2000	.012	S.F.	.25	.33		.58	.83
0900	1-1/2" supply	"	1800	.013	"	.46	.36		.82	1.12

32 91 Planting Preparation

32 91 13 – Soil Preparation

32 91 13.16 Mulching

		Crew	Daily Output	Labor-Hours	Unit	Material	2017 Bare Costs Labor	2017 Bare Costs Equipment	Total	Total Incl O&P
0010	**MULCHING**									
0100	Aged barks, 3" deep, hand spread	1 Clab	100	.080	S.Y.	3.57	2.13		5.70	7.50
0150	Skid steer loader	B-63	13.50	2.963	M.S.F.	395	79	12.70	486.70	580
0200	Hay, 1" deep, hand spread	1 Clab	475	.017	S.Y.	.43	.45		.88	1.22
0250	Power mulcher, small	B-64	180	.089	M.S.F.	48	2.60	2	52.60	59
0350	Large	B-65	530	.030	"	48	.88	.98	49.86	55
0400	Humus peat, 1" deep, hand spread	1 Clab	700	.011	S.Y.	2.63	.30		2.93	3.40
0450	Push spreader	"	2500	.003	"	2.63	.09		2.72	3.03
0550	Tractor spreader	B-66	700	.011	M.S.F.	292	.40	.38	292.78	320
0600	Oat straw, 1" deep, hand spread	1 Clab	475	.017	S.Y.	.56	.45		1.01	1.37
0650	Power mulcher, small	B-64	180	.089	M.S.F.	62	2.60	2	66.60	75
0700	Large	B-65	530	.030	"	62	.88	.98	63.86	71
0750	Add for asphaltic emulsion	B-45	1770	.009	Gal.	5.80	.27	.19	6.26	7.05
0800	Peat moss, 1" deep, hand spread	1 Clab	900	.009	S.Y.	2.60	.24		2.84	3.26
0850	Push spreader	"	2500	.003	"	2.60	.09		2.69	3
0950	Tractor spreader	B-66	700	.011	M.S.F.	289	.40	.38	289.78	320
1000	Polyethylene film, 6 mil	2 Clab	2000	.008	S.Y.	.50	.21		.71	.91
1100	Redwood nuggets, 3" deep, hand spread	1 Clab	150	.053	"	2.78	1.42		4.20	5.45
1150	Skid steer loader	B-63	13.50	2.963	M.S.F.	310	79	12.70	401.70	485
1200	Stone mulch, hand spread, ceramic chips, economy	1 Clab	125	.064	S.Y.	6.90	1.70		8.60	10.45
1250	Deluxe	"	95	.084	"	10.60	2.24		12.84	15.40

32 91 Planting Preparation

32 91 13 – Soil Preparation

32 91 13.16 Mulching

		Crew	Daily Output	Labor-Hours	Unit	Material	2017 Bare Costs Labor	Equipment	Total	Total Incl O&P
1300	Granite chips	B-1	10	2.400	C.Y.	60	65.50		125.50	175
1400	Marble chips		10	2.400		189	65.50		254.50	315
1600	Pea gravel		28	.857		109	23.50		132.50	158
1700	Quartz		10	2.400		190	65.50		255.50	320
1800	Tar paper, 15 lb. felt	1 Clab	800	.010	S.Y.	.48	.27		.75	.97
1900	Wood chips, 2" deep, hand spread	"	220	.036	"	1.80	.97		2.77	3.60
1950	Skid steer loader	B-63	20.30	1.970	M.S.F.	200	52.50	8.45	260.95	315

32 91 13.26 Planting Beds

		Crew	Daily Output	Labor-Hours	Unit	Material	2017 Bare Costs Labor	Equipment	Total	Total Incl O&P
0010	**PLANTING BEDS**									
0100	Backfill planting pit, by hand, on site topsoil	2 Clab	18	.889	C.Y.		23.50		23.50	39.50
0200	Prepared planting mix, by hand	"	24	.667			17.75		17.75	29.50
0300	Skid steer loader, on site topsoil	B-62	340	.071			2.08	.50	2.58	4.01
0400	Prepared planting mix	"	410	.059			1.73	.42	2.15	3.33
1000	Excavate planting pit, by hand, sandy soil	2 Clab	16	1			26.50		26.50	44.50
1100	Heavy soil or clay	"	8	2			53		53	89
1200	1/2 C.Y. backhoe, sandy soil	B-11C	150	.107			3.36	2.44	5.80	8.30
1300	Heavy soil or clay	"	115	.139			4.38	3.18	7.56	10.80
2000	Mix planting soil, incl. loam, manure, peat, by hand	2 Clab	60	.267		44	7.10		51.10	60.50
2100	Skid steer loader	B-62	150	.160		44	4.72	1.14	49.86	57.50
3000	Pile sod, skid steer loader	"	2800	.009	S.Y.		.25	.06	.31	.49
3100	By hand	2 Clab	400	.040			1.06		1.06	1.78
4000	Remove sod, F.E. loader	B-10S	2000	.004			.15	.18	.33	.44
4100	Sod cutter	B-12K	3200	.005			.16	.36	.52	.66
4200	By hand	2 Clab	240	.067			1.77		1.77	2.97

32 91 19 – Landscape Grading

32 91 19.13 Topsoil Placement and Grading

		Crew	Daily Output	Labor-Hours	Unit	Material	2017 Bare Costs Labor	Equipment	Total	Total Incl O&P
0010	**TOPSOIL PLACEMENT AND GRADING**									
0300	Fine grade, base course for paving, see Section 32 11 23.23									
0701	Furnish and place, truck dumped, unscreened, 4" deep	B-10S	12000	.001	S.F.	.42	.02	.03	.47	.53
0801	6" deep	"	7400	.001	"	.50	.04	.05	.59	.66
0900	Fine grading and seeding, incl. lime, fertilizer & seed,									
1001	With equipment	B-14	9000	.005	S.F.	.07	.15	.04	.26	.37

32 92 Turf and Grasses

32 92 19 – Seeding

32 92 19.13 Mechanical Seeding

		Crew	Daily Output	Labor-Hours	Unit	Material	2017 Bare Costs Labor	Equipment	Total	Total Incl O&P
0010	**MECHANICAL SEEDING**									
0020	Mechanical seeding, 215 lb./acre	B-66	1.50	5.333	Acre	560	188	179	927	1,125
0100	44 lb./M.S.Y.	"	2500	.003	S.Y.	.20	.11	.11	.42	.53
0101	44 lb./M.S.Y.	1 Clab	13950	.001	S.F.	.02	.02		.04	.05
0300	Fine grading and seeding incl. lime, fertilizer & seed,									
0310	with equipment	B-14	1000	.048	S.Y.	.45	1.36	.37	2.18	3.17
0400	Fertilizer hand push spreader, 35 lb. per M.S.F.	1 Clab	200	.040	M.S.F.	9.85	1.06		10.91	12.65
0600	Limestone hand push spreader, 50 lb. per M.S.F.		180	.044		5.30	1.18		6.48	7.80
0800	Grass seed hand push spreader, 4.5 lb. per M.S.F.		180	.044		22	1.18		23.18	26.50
1000	Hydro or air seeding for large areas, incl. seed and fertilizer	B-81	8900	.002	S.Y.	.51	.05	.07	.63	.73
1100	With wood fiber mulch added	"	8900	.002	"	2.02	.05	.07	2.14	2.39
1300	Seed only, over 100 lb., field seed, minimum				Lb.	1.80			1.80	1.98
1400	Maximum					1.70			1.70	1.87
1500	Lawn seed, minimum					1.40			1.40	1.54

32 92 Turf and Grasses

32 92 19 – Seeding

32 92 19.13 Mechanical Seeding		Crew	Daily Output	Labor-Hours	Unit	Material	2017 Bare Costs Labor	Equipment	Total	Total Incl O&P
1600	Maximum				Lb.	2.50			2.50	2.75
1800	Aerial operations, seeding only, field seed	B-58	50	.480	Acre	585	14.15	63	662.15	740
1900	Lawn seed		50	.480		455	14.15	63	532.15	595
2100	Seed and liquid fertilizer, field seed		50	.480		745	14.15	63	822.15	915
2200	Lawn seed		50	.480		615	14.15	63	692.15	770

32 92 23 – Sodding

32 92 23.10 Sodding Systems

		Crew	Daily Output	Labor-Hours	Unit	Material	Labor	Equipment	Total	Total Incl O&P
0010	**SODDING SYSTEMS**									
0020	Sodding, 1" deep, bluegrass sod, on level ground, over 8 M.S.F.	B-63	22	1.818	M.S.F.	243	48.50	7.80	299.30	355
0200	4 M.S.F.		17	2.353		240	62.50	10.05	312.55	380
0300	1000 S.F.		13.50	2.963		290	79	12.70	381.70	465
0500	Sloped ground, over 8 M.S.F.		6	6.667		243	177	28.50	448.50	595
0600	4 M.S.F.		5	8		240	213	34	487	655
0700	1000 S.F.		4	10		290	266	43	599	810
1000	Bent grass sod, on level ground, over 6 M.S.F.		20	2		255	53	8.55	316.55	380
1100	3 M.S.F.		18	2.222		269	59	9.50	337.50	405
1200	Sodding 1000 S.F. or less		14	2.857		293	76	12.25	381.25	460
1500	Sloped ground, over 6 M.S.F.		15	2.667		255	71	11.40	337.40	415
1600	3 M.S.F.		13.50	2.963		269	79	12.70	360.70	440
1700	1000 S.F.		12	3.333		293	88.50	14.25	395.75	485

32 93 Plants

32 93 13 – Ground Covers

32 93 13.10 Ground Cover Plants

		Crew	Daily Output	Labor-Hours	Unit	Material	Labor	Equipment	Total	Total Incl O&P
0010	**GROUND COVER PLANTS**									
0012	Plants, pachysandra, in prepared beds	B-1	15	1.600	C	84.50	43.50		128	166
0200	Vinca minor, 1 yr., bare root, in prepared beds		12	2	"	72	54.50		126.50	170
0600	Stone chips, in 50 lb. bags, Georgia marble		520	.046	Bag	4.75	1.26		6.01	7.35
0700	Onyx gemstone		260	.092		16	2.52		18.52	22
0800	Quartz		260	.092		16	2.52		18.52	22
0900	Pea gravel, truckload lots		28	.857	Ton	28.50	23.50		52	70

32 93 33 – Shrubs

32 93 33.10 Shrubs and Trees

		Crew	Daily Output	Labor-Hours	Unit	Material	Labor	Equipment	Total	Total Incl O&P
0010	**SHRUBS AND TREES**									
0011	Evergreen, in prepared beds, B & B									
0100	Arborvitae pyramidal, 4'-5'	B-17	30	1.067	Ea.	102	32	25	159	195
0150	Globe, 12"-15"	B-1	96	.250		24.50	6.80		31.30	38.50
0300	Cedar, blue, 8'-10'	B-17	18	1.778		238	53.50	42	333.50	395
0500	Hemlock, Canadian, 2-1/2'-3'	B-1	36	.667		32	18.20		50.20	66
0550	Holly, Savannah, 8'-10' H		9.68	2.479		264	67.50		331.50	405
0600	Juniper, andorra, 18"-24"		80	.300		37.50	8.20		45.70	55
0620	Wiltoni, 15"-18"		80	.300		26.50	8.20		34.70	42.50
0640	Skyrocket, 4-1/2'-5'	B-17	55	.582		109	17.55	13.75	140.30	164
0660	Blue pfitzer, 2'-2-1/2'	B-1	44	.545		39	14.85		53.85	68
0680	Ketleerie, 2-1/2'-3'		50	.480		53.50	13.10		66.60	80.50
0700	Pine, black, 2-1/2'-3'		50	.480		61	13.10		74.10	89
0720	Mugo, 18"-24"		60	.400		61	10.90		71.90	85.50
0740	White, 4'-5'	B-17	75	.427		52.50	12.90	10.10	75.50	90.50
0800	Spruce, blue, 18"-24"	B-1	60	.400		68.50	10.90		79.40	94
0840	Norway, 4'-5'	B-17	75	.427		85.50	12.90	10.10	108.50	127

32 93 Plants

32 93 33 – Shrubs

32 93 33.10 Shrubs and Trees

		Crew	Daily Output	Labor-Hours	Unit	Material	2017 Bare Costs Labor	Equipment	Total	Total Incl O&P
0900	Yew, denisforma, 12"-15"	B-1	60	.400	Ea.	36	10.90		46.90	58
1000	Capitata, 18"-24"		30	.800		33.50	22		55.50	73.50
1100	Hicksi, 2'-2-1/2'		30	.800		80	22		102	125

32 93 33.20 Shrubs

		Crew	Daily Output	Labor-Hours	Unit	Material	2017 Bare Costs Labor	Equipment	Total	Total Incl O&P
0010	**SHRUBS**									
0011	Broadleaf Evergreen, planted in prepared beds									
0100	Andromeda, 15"-18", container	B-1	96	.250	Ea.	33.50	6.80		40.30	48.50
0200	Azalea, 15"-18", container		96	.250		30.50	6.80		37.30	45
0300	Barberry, 9"-12", container		130	.185		18.15	5.05		23.20	28.50
0400	Boxwood, 15"-18", B & B		96	.250		44	6.80		50.80	60
0500	Euonymus, emerald gaiety, 12"-15", container		115	.209		24.50	5.70		30.20	36.50
0600	Holly, 15"-18", B & B		96	.250		37.50	6.80		44.30	52.50
0900	Mount laurel, 18"-24", B & B		80	.300		72.50	8.20		80.70	93.50
1000	Paxistema, 9"-12" high		130	.185		22	5.05		27.05	32.50
1100	Rhododendron, 18"-24", container		48	.500		38.50	13.65		52.15	65.50
1200	Rosemary, 1 gal. container		600	.040		18.25	1.09		19.34	22
2000	Deciduous, planted in prepared beds, amelanchier, 2'-3', B & B		57	.421		123	11.50		134.50	154
2100	Azalea, 15"-18", B & B		96	.250		30	6.80		36.80	44.50
2300	Bayberry, 2'-3', B & B		57	.421		24.50	11.50		36	46
2600	Cotoneaster, 15"-18", B & B		80	.300		27	8.20		35.20	43.50
2800	Dogwood, 3'-4', B & B	B-17	40	.800		33	24	18.95	75.95	97.50
2900	Euonymus, alatus compacta, 15"-18", container	B-1	80	.300		27	8.20		35.20	43
3200	Forsythia, 2'-3', container	"	60	.400		19	10.90		29.90	39.50
3300	Hibiscus, 3'-4', B & B	B-17	75	.427		49.50	12.90	10.10	72.50	87
3400	Honeysuckle, 3'-4', B & B	B-1	60	.400		27	10.90		37.90	48.50
3500	Hydrangea, 2'-3', B & B	"	57	.421		30.50	11.50		42	53
3600	Lilac, 3'-4', B & B	B-17	40	.800		29	24	18.95	71.95	92.50
3900	Privet, bare root, 18"-24"	B-1	80	.300		14.95	8.20		23.15	30
4100	Quince, 2'-3', B & B	"	57	.421		29	11.50		40.50	51
4200	Russian olive, 3'-4', B & B	B-17	75	.427		29.50	12.90	10.10	52.50	65
4400	Spirea, 3'-4', B & B	B-1	70	.343		21	9.35		30.35	38.50
4500	Viburnum, 3'-4', B & B	B-17	40	.800		26	24	18.95	68.95	89.50

32 93 43 – Trees

32 93 43.20 Trees

			Crew	Daily Output	Labor-Hours	Unit	Material	2017 Bare Costs Labor	Equipment	Total	Total Incl O&P
0010	**TREES**										
0011	Deciduous, in prep. beds, balled & burlapped (B&B)										
0100	Ash, 2" caliper	G	B-17	8	4	Ea.	193	121	94.50	408.50	520
0200	Beech, 5'-6'	G		50	.640		189	19.30	15.15	223.45	257
0300	Birch, 6'-8', 3 stems	G		20	1.600		168	48.50	38	254.50	305
0500	Crabapple, 6'-8'	G		20	1.600		140	48.50	38	226.50	276
0600	Dogwood, 4'-5'	G		40	.800		134	24	18.95	176.95	208
0700	Eastern redbud, 4'-5'	G		40	.800		149	24	18.95	191.95	225
0800	Elm, 8'-10'	G		20	1.600		253	48.50	38	339.50	400
0900	Ginkgo, 6'-7'	G		24	1.333		145	40.50	31.50	217	262
1000	Hawthorn, 8'-10', 1" caliper	G		20	1.600		159	48.50	38	245.50	297
1100	Honeylocust, 10'-12', 1-1/2" caliper	G		10	3.200		202	96.50	75.50	374	465
1300	Larch, 8'	G		32	1		124	30	23.50	177.50	213
1400	Linden, 8'-10', 1" caliper	G		20	1.600		141	48.50	38	227.50	277
1500	Magnolia, 4'-5'	G		20	1.600		99	48.50	38	185.50	231
1600	Maple, red, 8'-10', 1-1/2" caliper	G		10	3.200		198	96.50	75.50	370	460
1700	Mountain ash, 8'-10', 1" caliper	G		16	2		172	60.50	47.50	280	340
1800	Oak, 2-1/2"-3" caliper	G		6	5.333		320	161	126	607	755

32 93 Plants

32 93 43 – Trees

32 93 43.20 Trees		Crew	Daily Output	Labor-Hours	Unit	Material	2017 Bare Costs Labor	Equipment	Total	Total Incl O&P
2100	Planetree, 9'-11', 1-1/4" caliper G	B-17	10	3.200	Ea.	231	96.50	75.50	403	500
2200	Plum, 6'-8', 1" caliper G		20	1.600		80.50	48.50	38	167	210
2300	Poplar, 9'-11', 1-1/4" caliper G		10	3.200		141	96.50	75.50	313	400
2500	Sumac, 2'-3' G		75	.427		43	12.90	10.10	66	80
2700	Tulip, 5'-6' G		40	.800		45.50	24	18.95	88.45	111
2800	Willow, 6'-8', 1" caliper G		20	1.600		94	48.50	38	180.50	225

32 94 Planting Accessories

32 94 13 – Landscape Edging

32 94 13.20 Edging

		Crew	Daily Output	Labor-Hours	Unit	Material	2017 Bare Costs Labor	Equipment	Total	Total Incl O&P
0010	**EDGING**									
0050	Aluminum alloy, including stakes, 1/8" x 4", mill finish	B-1	390	.062	L.F.	4	1.68		5.68	7.20
0051	Black paint		390	.062		4.64	1.68		6.32	7.90
0052	Black anodized		390	.062		5.35	1.68		7.03	8.70
0100	Brick, set horizontally, 1-1/2 bricks per L.F.	D-1	370	.043		1.37	1.37		2.74	3.82
0150	Set vertically, 3 bricks per L.F.	"	135	.119		3.54	3.77		7.31	10.20
0200	Corrugated aluminum, roll, 4" wide	1 Carp	650	.012		1.87	.43		2.30	2.78
0250	6" wide	"	550	.015		2.34	.51		2.85	3.42
0600	Railroad ties, 6" x 8"	2 Carp	170	.094		2.24	3.29		5.53	7.95
0650	7" x 9"		136	.118		2.49	4.11		6.60	9.65
0750	Redwood 2" x 4"		330	.048		2.26	1.69		3.95	5.30
0800	Steel edge strips, incl. stakes, 1/4" x 5"	B-1	390	.062		4.26	1.68		5.94	7.50
0850	3/16" x 4"	"	390	.062		3.37	1.68		5.05	6.50

32 94 50 – Tree Guying

32 94 50.10 Tree Guying Systems

		Crew	Daily Output	Labor-Hours	Unit	Material	2017 Bare Costs Labor	Equipment	Total	Total Incl O&P
0010	**TREE GUYING SYSTEMS**									
0015	Tree guying including stakes, guy wire and wrap									
0100	Less than 3" caliper, 2 stakes	2 Clab	35	.457	Ea.	13.20	12.15		25.35	35
0200	3" to 4" caliper, 3 stakes	"	21	.762	"	19.75	20.50		40.25	55.50
1000	Including arrowhead anchor, cable, turnbuckles and wrap									
1100	Less than 3" caliper, 3" anchors	2 Clab	20	.800	Ea.	21.50	21.50		43	59.50
1200	3" to 6" caliper, 4" anchors		15	1.067		31.50	28.50		60	82
1300	6" caliper, 6" anchors		12	1.333		24	35.50		59.50	86
1400	8" caliper, 8" anchors		9	1.778		115	47.50		162.50	206

32 96 Transplanting

32 96 23 – Plant and Bulb Transplanting

32 96 23.23 Planting

		Crew	Daily Output	Labor-Hours	Unit	Material	2017 Bare Costs Labor	Equipment	Total	Total Incl O&P
0010	**PLANTING**									
0012	Moving shrubs on site, 12" ball	B-62	28	.857	Ea.		25.50	6.10	31.60	48.50
0100	24" ball	"	22	1.091	"		32	7.80	39.80	62

32 96 23.43 Moving Trees

		Crew	Daily Output	Labor-Hours	Unit	Material	2017 Bare Costs Labor	Equipment	Total	Total Incl O&P
0010	**MOVING TREES**, On site									
0300	Moving trees on site, 36" ball	B-6	3.75	6.400	Ea.		189	97.50	286.50	420
0400	60" ball	"	1	24	"		705	365	1,070	1,575

Estimating Tips

33 10 00 Water Utilities
33 30 00 Sanitary Sewerage Utilities
33 40 00 Storm Drainage Utilities

- Never assume that the water, sewer, and drainage lines will go in at the early stages of the project. Consider the site access needs before dividing the site in half with open trenches, loose pipe, and machinery obstructions. Always inspect the site to establish that the site drawings are complete. Check off all existing utilities on your drawings as you locate them. Be especially careful with underground utilities because appurtenances are sometimes buried during regrading or repaving operations. If you find any discrepancies, mark up the site plan for further research. Differing site conditions can be very costly if discovered later in the project.

- See also Section 33 01 00 for restoration of pipe where removal/replacement may be undesirable. Use of new types of piping materials can reduce the overall project cost. Owners/design engineers should consider the installing contractor as a valuable source of current information on utility products and local conditions that could lead to significant cost savings.

Reference Numbers

Reference numbers are shown at the beginning of some major classifications. These numbers refer to related items in the Reference Section. The reference information may be an estimating procedure, an alternate pricing method, or technical information.

Note: Not all subdivisions listed here necessarily appear. ■

Did you know?

Our online estimating solution gives you the same access to RSMeans' data with 24/7 access:

- Quickly locate costs in the searchable database.

- Build cost lists, estimates, and reports in minutes.

- Adjust costs to any location in the U.S. and Canada with the click of a button.

Start your free trial today at
www.RSMeansOnline.com

33 05 Common Work Results for Utilities

33 05 16 – Utility Structures

33 05 16.13 Precast Concrete Utility Structures

33 05 16.13 Precast Concrete Utility Structures	Crew	Daily Output	Labor-Hours	Unit	Material	2017 Bare Costs Labor	Equipment	Total	Total Incl O&P
0010 **PRECAST CONCRETE UTILITY STRUCTURES**, 6" thick									
0050 5' x 10' x 6' high, I.D.	B-13	2	24	Ea.	1,800	690	335	2,825	3,500
0350 Hand hole, precast concrete, 1-1/2" thick									
0400 1'-0" x 2'-0" x 1'-9", I.D., light duty	B-1	4	6	Ea.	430	164		594	745
0450 4'-6" x 3'-2" x 2'-0", O.D., heavy duty	B-6	3	8	"	1,525	236	122	1,883	2,200

33 05 23 – Trenchless Utility Installation

33 05 23.19 Microtunneling

0010 **MICROTUNNELING**									
0011 Not including excavation, backfill, shoring,									
0020 or dewatering, average 50'/day, slurry method									
0100 24" to 48" outside diameter, minimum				L.F.				875	965
0110 Adverse conditions, add				%				50%	50%
1000 Rent microtunneling machine, average monthly lease				Month				97,500	107,000
1010 Operating technician				Day				630	690
1100 Mobilization and demobilization, minimum				Job				41,200	45,900
1110 Maximum				"				445,500	490,500

33 11 Water Utility Distribution Piping

33 11 13 – Public Water Utility Distribution Piping

33 11 13.15 Water Supply, Ductile Iron Pipe

	Crew	Daily Output	Labor-Hours	Unit	Material	2017 Bare Costs Labor	Equipment	Total	Total Incl O&P
0010 **WATER SUPPLY, DUCTILE IRON PIPE**									
0020 Not including excavation or backfill									
2000 Pipe, class 50 water piping, 18' lengths									
2020 Mechanical joint, 4" diameter	B-21A	200	.200	L.F.	30.50	6.55	2.18	39.23	47
2040 6" diameter		160	.250		26.50	8.20	2.72	37.42	45.50
3000 Push-on joint, 4" diameter		400	.100		15.50	3.27	1.09	19.86	23.50
3020 6" diameter		333.33	.120		18.25	3.93	1.31	23.49	28
8000 Piping, fittings, mechanical joint, AWWA C110									
8006 90° bend, 4" diameter	B-20A	16	2	Ea.	155	63		218	275
8020 6" diameter		12.80	2.500		229	79		308	385
8200 Wye or tee, 4" diameter		10.67	2.999		375	95		470	570
8220 6" diameter		8.53	3.751		565	119		684	815
8398 45° bend, 4" diameter		16	2		255	63		318	385
8400 6" diameter		12.80	2.500		199	79		278	350
8405 8" diameter		10.67	2.999		291	95		386	475
8450 Decreaser, 6" x 4" diameter		14.22	2.250		207	71		278	345
8460 8" x 6" diameter		11.64	2.749		310	87		397	485
8550 Piping, butterfly valves, cast iron									
8560 4" diameter	B-20	6	4	Ea.	440	109		549	660
8700 Joint restraint, ductile iron mechanical joints									
8710 4" diameter	B-20A	32	1	Ea.	31	31.50		62.50	87
8720 6" diameter		25.60	1.250		36	39.50		75.50	106
8730 8" diameter		21.33	1.500		53.50	47.50		101	137
8740 10" diameter		18.28	1.751		80	55.50		135.50	180
8750 12" diameter		16.84	1.900		112	60		172	223
8760 14" diameter		16	2		151	63		214	272
8770 16" diameter		11.64	2.749		193	87		280	355
8780 18" diameter		11.03	2.901		256	91.50		347.50	435
8785 20" diameter		9.14	3.501		340	111		451	560
8790 24" diameter		7.53	4.250		435	134		569	705

33 11 Water Utility Distribution Piping

33 11 13 – Public Water Utility Distribution Piping

33 11 13.15 Water Supply, Ductile Iron Pipe		Crew	Daily Output	Labor-Hours	Unit	Material	2017 Bare Costs Labor	Equipment	Total	Total Incl O&P
9600	Steel sleeve with tap, 4" diameter	B-20	3	8	Ea.	405	218		623	810
9620	6" diameter	"	2	12	↓	470	325		795	1,075

33 11 13.25 Water Supply, Polyvinyl Chloride Pipe		Crew	Daily Output	Labor-Hours	Unit	Material	Labor	Equipment	Total	Total Incl O&P
0010	**WATER SUPPLY, POLYVINYL CHLORIDE PIPE**									
2100	PVC pipe, Class 150, 1-1/2" diameter	Q-1A	750	.013	L.F.	.47	.53		1	1.40
2120	2" diameter		686	.015		.69	.58		1.27	1.72
2140	2-1/2" diameter	↓	500	.020		1.18	.80		1.98	2.62
2160	3" diameter	B-20	430	.056	↓	1.33	1.52		2.85	4
8700	PVC pipe, joint restraint									
8710	4" diameter	B-20A	32	1	Ea.	42	31.50		73.50	99
8720	6" diameter		25.60	1.250		49.50	39.50		89	120
8730	8" diameter		21.33	1.500		72	47.50		119.50	158
8740	10" diameter		18.28	1.751		146	55.50		201.50	253
8750	12" diameter		16.84	1.900		140	60		200	254
8760	14" diameter		16	2		224	63		287	350
8770	16" diameter		11.64	2.749		300	87		387	475
8780	18" diameter		11.03	2.901		375	91.50		466.50	560
8785	20" diameter		9.14	3.501		460	111		571	695
8790	24" diameter	↓	7.53	4.250	↓	535	134		669	810

33 12 Water Utility Distribution Equipment

33 12 13 – Water Service Connections

33 12 13.15 Tapping, Crosses and Sleeves		Crew	Daily Output	Labor-Hours	Unit	Material	Labor	Equipment	Total	Total Incl O&P
0010	**TAPPING, CROSSES AND SLEEVES**									
4000	Drill and tap pressurized main (labor only)									
4100	6" main, 1" to 2" service	Q-1	3	5.333	Ea.		190		190	315
4150	8" main, 1" to 2" service	"	2.75	5.818	"		207		207	340
4500	Tap and insert gate valve									
4600	8" main, 4" branch	B-21	3.20	8.750	Ea.		251	43	294	470
4650	6" branch		2.70	10.370			298	51	349	550
4700	10" main, 4" branch		2.70	10.370			298	51	349	550
4750	6" branch		2.35	11.915			340	58.50	398.50	635
4800	12" main, 6" branch	↓	2.35	11.915	↓		340	58.50	398.50	635

33 21 Water Supply Wells

33 21 13 – Public Water Supply Wells

33 21 13.10 Wells and Accessories		Crew	Daily Output	Labor-Hours	Unit	Material	Labor	Equipment	Total	Total Incl O&P
0010	**WELLS & ACCESSORIES**									
0011	Domestic									
0100	Drilled, 4" to 6" diameter	B-23	120	.333	L.F.		9	23.50	32.50	41
1500	Pumps, installed in wells to 100' deep, 4" submersible									
1520	3/4 H.P.	Q-1	2.66	6.015	Ea.	855	214		1,069	1,300
1600	1 H.P.	"	2.29	6.987	"	905	249		1,154	1,400

For customer support on your Residential Costs with RSMeans Data, call 800.448.8182.

653

33 31 Sanitary Utility Sewerage Piping

33 31 13 – Public Sanitary Utility Sewerage Piping

33 31 13.15 Sewage Collection, Concrete Pipe	Crew	Daily Output	Labor-Hours	Unit	Material	2017 Bare Costs Labor	Equipment	Total	Total Incl O&P
0010 **SEWAGE COLLECTION, CONCRETE PIPE**									
0020 See Section 33 41 13.60 for sewage/drainage collection, concrete pipe									

33 31 13.25 Sewage Collection, Polyvinyl Chloride Pipe	Crew	Daily Output	Labor-Hours	Unit	Material	2017 Bare Costs Labor	Equipment	Total	Total Incl O&P
0010 **SEWAGE COLLECTION, POLYVINYL CHLORIDE PIPE**									
0020 Not including excavation or backfill									
2000 20' lengths, SDR 35, B&S, 4" diameter	B-20	375	.064	L.F.	1.55	1.75		3.30	4.63
2040 6" diameter		350	.069		3.28	1.87		5.15	6.75
2080 13' lengths, SDR 35, B&S, 8" diameter	↓	335	.072		5.90	1.95		7.85	9.75
2120 10" diameter	B-21	330	.085		10.65	2.44	.42	13.51	16.20
4000 Piping, DWV PVC, no exc./bkfill., 10' L, Sch 40, 4" diameter	B-20	375	.064		3.18	1.75		4.93	6.40
4010 6" diameter		350	.069		6.75	1.87		8.62	10.55
4020 8" diameter		335	.072	↓	10.55	1.95		12.50	14.90
4030 Fittings, 1/4 bend DWV PVC, 4" diameter		19	1.263	Ea.	18.95	34.50		53.45	78.50
4040 6" diameter		12	2		86.50	54.50		141	186
4050 8" diameter		11	2.182		86.50	59.50		146	195
4060 1/8 bend DWV PVC, 4" diameter		19	1.263		15.10	34.50		49.60	74
4070 6" diameter		12	2		58.50	54.50		113	156
4080 8" diameter		11	2.182		168	59.50		227.50	285
4090 Tee DWV PVC, 4" diameter		12	2		26	54.50		80.50	120
4100 6" diameter		10	2.400		103	65.50		168.50	223
4110 8" diameter	↓	9	2.667	↓	229	72.50		301.50	375

33 36 Utility Septic Tanks

33 36 13 – Utility Septic Tank and Effluent Wet Wells

33 36 13.13 Concrete Utility Septic Tank

33 36 13.13 Concrete Utility Septic Tank	Crew	Daily Output	Labor-Hours	Unit	Material	2017 Bare Costs Labor	Equipment	Total	Total Incl O&P
0010 **CONCRETE UTILITY SEPTIC TANK**									
0011 Not including excavation or piping									
0015 Septic tanks, precast, 1,000 gallon	B-21	8	3.500	Ea.	1,025	100	17.25	1,142.25	1,325
0060 1,500 gallon		7	4		1,625	115	19.70	1,759.70	2,025
0100 2,000 gallon	↓	5	5.600		2,325	161	27.50	2,513.50	2,850
0900 Concrete riser 24" x 12" with standard lid	1 Clab	6	1.333		87	35.50		122.50	155
0905 24" x 12" with heavy duty lid		6	1.333		110	35.50		145.50	181
0910 24" x 8" with standard lid		6	1.333		81	35.50		116.50	149
0915 24" x 8" with heavy duty lid		6	1.333		104	35.50		139.50	175
0917 24" x 12" extension		12	.667		58.50	17.75		76.25	94
0920 24" x 8" extension		12	.667		53	17.75		70.75	87.50
0950 HDPE riser 20" x 12" with standard lid		8	1		118	26.50		144.50	174
0951 HDPE 20" x 12" with heavy duty lid		8	1		131	26.50		157.50	189
0955 HDPE 24" x 12" with standard lid		8	1		115	26.50		141.50	171
0956 HDPE 24" x 12" with heavy duty lid		8	1		137	26.50		163.50	196
0960 HDPE 20" x 6" extension		48	.167		26	4.43		30.43	36
0962 HDPE 20" x 12" extension		48	.167		46	4.43		50.43	58
0965 HDPE 24" x 6" extension		48	.167		27	4.43		31.43	37.50
0967 HDPE 24" x 12" extension	↓	48	.167		44.50	4.43		48.93	56.50
1150 Leaching field chambers, 13' x 3'-7" x 1'-4", standard	B-13	16	3		500	86	42	628	740
1420 Leaching pit, precast concrete, 6' dia, 3' deep	B-21	4.70	5.957	↓	815	171	29.50	1,015.50	1,225

33 36 13.19 Polyethylene Utility Septic Tank

33 36 13.19 Polyethylene Utility Septic Tank	Crew	Daily Output	Labor-Hours	Unit	Material	2017 Bare Costs Labor	Equipment	Total	Total Incl O&P
0010 **POLYETHYLENE UTILITY SEPTIC TANK**									
0015 High density polyethylene, 1,000 gallon	B-21	8	3.500	Ea.	1,325	100	17.25	1,442.25	1,625
0020 1,250 gallon	↓	8	3.500	↓	1,300	100	17.25	1,417.25	1,600

33 36 Utility Septic Tanks

33 36 13 - Utility Septic Tank and Effluent Wet Wells

33 36 13.19 Polyethylene Utility Septic Tank	Crew	Daily Output	Labor-Hours	Unit	Material	2017 Bare Costs Labor	Equipment	Total	Total Incl O&P
0025	1,500 gallon	B-21	7	4	Ea.	1,525	115	19.70	1,659.70	1,900

33 36 19 - Utility Septic Tank Effluent Filter

33 36 19.13 Utility Septic Tank Effluent Tube Filter

		Crew	Daily Output	Labor-Hours	Unit	Material	Labor	Equipment	Total	Total Incl O&P
0010	**UTILITY SEPTIC TANK EFFLUENT TUBE FILTER**									
3000	Effluent filter, 4" diameter	1 Skwk	8	1	Ea.	43	36		79	107
3020	6" diameter	"	7	1.143	"	248	41		289	340

33 36 33 - Utility Septic Tank Drainage Field

33 36 33.13 Utility Septic Tank Tile Drainage Field

		Crew	Daily Output	Labor-Hours	Unit	Material	Labor	Equipment	Total	Total Incl O&P
0010	**UTILITY SEPTIC TANK TILE DRAINAGE FIELD**									
0015	Distribution box, concrete, 5 outlets	2 Clab	20	.800	Ea.	92.50	21.50		114	138
0020	7 outlets		16	1		92.50	26.50		119	147
0025	9 outlets		8	2		550	53		603	695
0115	Distribution boxes, HDPE, 5 outlets		20	.800		64.50	21.50		86	107
0117	6 outlets		15	1.067		65	28.50		93.50	119
0118	7 outlets		15	1.067		65	28.50		93.50	119
0120	8 outlets		10	1.600		68.50	42.50		111	147
0240	Distribution boxes, Outlet Flow Leveler	1 Clab	50	.160		2.30	4.26		6.56	9.65
0300	Precast concrete, galley, 4' x 4' x 4'	B-21	16	1.750		236	50	8.65	294.65	355
0350	HDPE infiltration chamber 12" H x 15" W	2 Clab	300	.053	L.F.	6.95	1.42		8.37	10
0351	12" H x 15" W End Cap	1 Clab	32	.250	Ea.	18.65	6.65		25.30	31.50
0355	chamber 12" H x 22" W	2 Clab	300	.053	L.F.	6.65	1.42		8.07	9.65
0356	12" H x 22" W End Cap	1 Clab	32	.250	Ea.	16.75	6.65		23.40	29.50
0360	chamber 13" H x 34" W	2 Clab	300	.053	L.F.	14.15	1.42		15.57	17.95
0361	13" H x 34" W End Cap	1 Clab	32	.250	Ea.	50.50	6.65		57.15	66.50
0365	chamber 16" H x 34" W	2 Clab	300	.053	L.F.	12.70	1.42		14.12	16.30
0366	16" H x 34" W End Cap	1 Clab	32	.250	Ea.	8.15	6.65		14.80	20
0370	chamber 8" H x 16" W	2 Clab	300	.053	L.F.	9.85	1.42		11.27	13.15
0371	8" H x 16" W End Cap	1 Clab	32	.250	Ea.	11	6.65		17.65	23.50

33 36 50 - Drainage Field Systems

33 36 50.10 Drainage Field Excavation and Fill

		Crew	Daily Output	Labor-Hours	Unit	Material	Labor	Equipment	Total	Total Incl O&P
0010	**DRAINAGE FIELD EXCAVATION AND FILL**									
2200	Septic tank & drainage field excavation with 3/4 C.Y. backhoe	B-12F	145	.110	C.Y.		3.53	4.65	8.18	10.95
2400	4' trench for disposal field, 3/4 C.Y. backhoe	"	335	.048	L.F.		1.53	2.01	3.54	4.75
2600	Gravel fill, run of bank	B-6	150	.160	C.Y.	17.20	4.72	2.44	24.36	29.50
2800	Crushed stone, 3/4"	"	150	.160	"	40	4.72	2.44	47.16	54.50

33 41 Storm Utility Drainage Piping

33 41 13 - Public Storm Utility Drainage Piping

33 41 13.60 Sewage/Drainage Collection, Concrete Pipe

		Crew	Daily Output	Labor-Hours	Unit	Material	Labor	Equipment	Total	Total Incl O&P
0010	**SEWAGE/DRAINAGE COLLECTION, CONCRETE PIPE**									
0020	Not including excavation or backfill									
1020	8" diameter	B-14	224	.214	L.F.	8.30	6.10	1.64	16.04	21
1030	10" diameter	"	216	.222	".	9.20	6.30	1.70	17.20	22.50
3780	Concrete slotted pipe, class 4 mortar joint									
3800	12" diameter	B-21	168	.167	L.F.	28	4.78	.82	33.60	40
3840	18" diameter	"	152	.184	"	32	5.30	.91	38.21	45
3900	Concrete slotted pipe, Class 4 O-ring joint									
3940	12" diameter	B-21	168	.167	L.F.	28	4.78	.82	33.60	39.50
3960	18" diameter	"	152	.184	"	32	5.30	.91	38.21	45

For customer support on your Residential Costs with RSMeans Data, call 800.448.8182.

655

33 44 Storm Utility Water Drains

33 44 13 – Utility Area Drains

33 44 13.13 Catch Basins

33 44 13.13 Catch Basins	Crew	Daily Output	Labor-Hours	Unit	Material	2017 Bare Costs Labor	Equipment	Total	Total Incl O&P
0010 **CATCH BASINS**									
0011 Not including footing & excavation									
1600 Frames & grates, C.I., 24" square, 500 lb.	B-6	7.80	3.077	Ea.	350	90.50	47	487.50	590

33 46 Subdrainage

33 46 16 – Subdrainage Piping

33 46 16.25 Piping, Subdrainage, Corrugated Metal

33 46 16.25 Piping, Subdrainage, Corrugated Metal	Crew	Daily Output	Labor-Hours	Unit	Material	2017 Bare Costs Labor	Equipment	Total	Total Incl O&P
0010 **PIPING, SUBDRAINAGE, CORRUGATED METAL**									
0021 Not including excavation and backfill									
2010 Aluminum, perforated									
2020 6" diameter, 18 ga.	B-20	380	.063	L.F.	6.50	1.72		8.22	10.05
2200 8" diameter, 16 ga.	"	370	.065		8.55	1.77		10.32	12.35
2220 10" diameter, 16 ga.	B-21	360	.078	↓	10.70	2.23	.38	13.31	15.90
3000 Uncoated galvanized, perforated									
3020 6" diameter, 18 ga.	B-20	380	.063	L.F.	6.05	1.72		7.77	9.55
3200 8" diameter, 16 ga.	"	370	.065		8.30	1.77		10.07	12.10
3220 10" diameter, 16 ga.	B-21	360	.078		8.80	2.23	.38	11.41	13.85
3240 12" diameter, 16 ga.	"	285	.098	↓	9.80	2.82	.48	13.10	16
4000 Steel, perforated, asphalt coated									
4020 6" diameter, 18 ga.	B-20	380	.063	L.F.	6.65	1.72		8.37	10.20
4030 8" diameter, 18 ga.	"	370	.065		8.75	1.77		10.52	12.55
4040 10" diameter, 16 ga.	B-21	360	.078		10.40	2.23	.38	13.01	15.60
4050 12" diameter, 16 ga.	↓	285	.098		11.50	2.82	.48	14.80	17.90
4060 18" diameter, 16 ga.	↓	205	.137	↓	17.65	3.92	.67	22.24	26.50

33 49 Storm Drainage Structures

33 49 13 – Storm Drainage Manholes, Frames, and Covers

33 49 13.10 Storm Drainage Manholes, Frames and Covers

33 49 13.10 Storm Drainage Manholes, Frames and Covers	Crew	Daily Output	Labor-Hours	Unit	Material	2017 Bare Costs Labor	Equipment	Total	Total Incl O&P
0010 **STORM DRAINAGE MANHOLES, FRAMES & COVERS**									
0020 Excludes footing, excavation, backfill (See line items for frame & cover)									
0050 Brick, 4' inside diameter, 4' deep	D-1	1	16	Ea.	545	510		1,055	1,450
1110 Precast, 4' I.D., 4' deep	B-22	4.10	7.317	"	840	214	50.50	1,104.50	1,325

33 51 Natural-Gas Distribution

33 51 13 – Natural-Gas Piping

33 51 13.10 Piping, Gas Service and Distribution, P.E.

33 51 13.10 Piping, Gas Service and Distribution, P.E.	Crew	Daily Output	Labor-Hours	Unit	Material	2017 Bare Costs Labor	Equipment	Total	Total Incl O&P
0010 **PIPING, GAS SERVICE AND DISTRIBUTION, POLYETHYLENE**									
0020 Not including excavation or backfill									
1000 60 psi coils, compression coupling @ 100', 1/2" diameter, SDR 11	B-20A	608	.053	L.F.	.47	1.66		2.13	3.28
1010 1" diameter, SDR 11		544	.059		1.07	1.86		2.93	4.25
1040 1-1/4" diameter, SDR 11		544	.059		1.53	1.86		3.39	4.76
1100 2" diameter, SDR 11		488	.066		2.13	2.07		4.20	5.80
1160 3" diameter, SDR 11	↓	408	.078		4.43	2.48		6.91	9
1500 60 psi 40' joints with coupling, 3" diameter, SDR 11	B-21A	408	.098		8.85	3.21	1.07	13.13	16.20
1540 4" diameter, SDR 11		352	.114		12.75	3.72	1.24	17.71	21.50
1600 6" diameter, SDR 11		328	.122		31.50	3.99	1.33	36.82	43
1640 8" diameter, SDR 11	↓	272	.147		43.50	4.81	1.60	49.91	58

33 51 Natural-Gas Distribution

33 51 13 – Natural-Gas Piping

33 51 13.20 Piping, Gas Service and Distribution, Steel	Crew	Daily Output	Labor-Hours	Unit	Material	2017 Bare Costs Labor	Equipment	Total	Total Incl O&P
0010 PIPING, GAS SERVICE & DISTRIBUTION, STEEL									
0020 Not including excavation or backfill, tar coated and wrapped									
4000 Pipe schedule 40, plain end									
4040 1" diameter	Q-4	300	.107	L.F.	5.05	4.01	.19	9.25	12.35
4080 2" diameter	"	280	.114	"	7.95	4.30	.21	12.46	16.05

Division Notes

	CREW	DAILY OUTPUT	LABOR-HOURS	UNIT	BARE COSTS				TOTAL INCL O&P
					MAT.	LABOR	EQUIP.	TOTAL	

Estimating Tips

- When estimating costs for the installation of electrical power generation equipment, factors to review include access to the job site, access and setting up at the installation site, required connections, uncrating pads, anchors, leveling, final assembly of the components, and temporary protection from physical damage, such as environmental exposure.

- Be aware of the costs of equipment supports, concrete pads, and vibration isolators. Cross-reference them against other trades' specifications. Also, review site and structural drawings for items that must be included in the estimates.

- It is important to include items that are not documented in the plans and specifications but must be priced. These items include, but are not limited to, testing, dust protection, roof penetration, core drilling concrete floors and walls, patching, cleanup, and final adjustments. Add a contingency or allowance for utility company fees for power hookups, if needed.

- The project size and scope of electrical power generation equipment will have a significant impact on cost. The intent of RSMeans cost data is to provide a benchmark cost so that owners, engineers, and electrical contractors will have a comfortable number with which to start a project. Additionally, there are many websites available to use for research and to obtain a vendor's quote to finalize costs.

Reference Numbers

Reference numbers are shown at the beginning of some major classifications. These numbers refer to related items in the Reference Section. The reference information may be an estimating procedure, an alternate pricing method, or technical information.

Note: Not all subdivisions listed here necessarily appear. ■

Did you know?

Our online estimating solution gives you the same access to RSMeans' data with 24/7 access:

- Quickly locate costs in the searchable database.
- Build cost lists, estimates, and reports in minutes.
- Adjust costs to any location in the U.S. and Canada with the click of a button.

Start your free trial today at
www.RSMeansOnline.com

48 15 Wind Energy Electrical Power Generation Equipment

48 15 13 – Wind Turbines

48 15 13.50 Wind Turbines and Components	Crew	Daily Output	Labor-Hours	Unit	Material	2017 Bare Costs Labor	Equipment	Total	Total Incl O&P
0010 WIND TURBINES & COMPONENTS									
0500 Complete system, grid connected									
1000 20 kW, 31' dia, incl. labor & material	G			System				49,900	49,900
1010 Enhanced	G							55,000	55,000
1500 10 kW, 23' dia, incl. labor & material	G							74,000	74,000
2000 2.4 kW, 12' dia, incl. labor & material	G							18,000	18,000
2900 Component system									
3000 Turbine, 400 watt, 3' dia	G	1 Elec	3.41	2.346	Ea.	550	94.50		644.50	760
3100 600 watt, 3' dia	G		2.56	3.125		710	126		836	985
3200 1000 watt, 9' dia	G		2.05	3.902		1,500	157		1,657	1,900
3400 Mounting hardware									
3500 30' guyed tower kit	G	2 Clab	5.12	3.125	Ea.	410	83		493	590
3505 3' galvanized helical earth screw	G	1 Clab	8	1		49.50	26.50		76	99
3510 Attic mount kit	G	1 Rofc	2.56	3.125		194	93		287	385
3520 Roof mount kit	G	1 Clab	3.41	2.346		320	62.50		382.50	455
8900 Equipment									
9100 DC to AC inverter for, 48 V, 4,000 watt	G	1 Elec	2	4	Ea.	2,275	161		2,436	2,775

Reference Section

All the reference information is in one section, making it easy to find what you need to know . . . and easy to use the data set on a daily basis. This section is visually identified by a vertical black bar on the page edges.

In this Reference Section, we've included Equipment Rental Costs, a listing of rental and operating costs; Crew Listings, a full listing of all crews, equipment, and their costs; Location Factors for adjusting costs to the region you are in; Reference Tables, where you will find explanations, estimating information and procedures, or technical data; an explanation of all the Abbreviations in the data set; and sample Estimating Forms.

Table of Contents

Estimating Tips

- This section contains the average costs to rent and operate hundreds of pieces of construction equipment. This is useful information when estimating the time and material requirements of any particular operation in order to establish a unit or total cost. Bare equipment costs shown on a unit cost line include not only rental, but also operating costs for equipment under normal use.

Rental Costs

- Equipment rental rates are obtained from the following industry sources throughout North America: contractors, suppliers, dealers, manufacturers, and distributors.

- Rental rates vary throughout the country, with larger cities generally having lower rates. Lease plans for new equipment are available for periods in excess of six months, with a percentage of payments applying toward purchase.

- Monthly rental rates vary from 2% to 5% of the purchase price of the equipment depending on the anticipated life of the equipment and its wearing parts.

- Weekly rental rates are about 1/3 of the monthly rates, and daily rental rates are about 1/3 of the weekly rate.

- Rental rates can also be treated as reimbursement costs for contractor-owned equipment. Owned equipment costs include depreciation, loan payments, interest, taxes, insurance, storage, and major repairs.

Operating Costs

- The operating costs include parts and labor for routine servicing, such as the repair and replacement of pumps, filters, and worn lines. Normal operating expendables, such as fuel, lubricants, tires, and electricity (where applicable), are also included.

- Extraordinary operating expendables with highly variable wear patterns, such as diamond bits and blades, are excluded. These costs can be found as material costs in the Unit Price section.

- The hourly operating costs listed do not include the operator's wages.

Equipment Cost/Day

- Any power equipment required by a crew is shown in the Crew Listings with a daily cost.

- This daily cost of equipment needed by a crew includes both the rental cost and the operating cost and is based on dividing the weekly rental rate by 5 (number of working days in the week), and then adding the hourly operating cost times 8 (the number of hours in a day). This "Equipment Cost/Day" is shown in the far right column of the Equipment Rental section.

- If equipment is needed for only one or two days, it is best to develop your own cost by including components for daily rent and hourly operating costs. This is important when the listed Crew for a task does not contain the equipment needed, such as a crane for lifting mechanical heating/cooling equipment up onto a roof.

- If the quantity of work is less than the crew's Daily Output shown for a Unit Price line item that includes a bare unit equipment cost, the recommendation is to estimate one day's rental cost and operating cost for equipment shown in the Crew Listing for that line item.

Mobilization, Demobilization Costs

- The cost to move construction equipment from an equipment yard or rental company to the job site and back again is not included in equipment rental costs listed in the Reference Section, nor in the bare equipment cost of any unit price line item, nor in any equipment costs shown in the Crew Listings.

- Mobilization (to the site) and demobilization (from the site) costs can be found in the Unit Price section.

- If a piece of equipment is already at the job site, it is not appropriate to utilize mobilization, demobilization costs again in an estimate. ■

01 54 33 | Equipment Rental

		UNIT	HOURLY OPER. COST	RENT PER DAY	RENT PER WEEK	RENT PER MONTH	EQUIPMENT COST/DAY	
10	0010	**CONCRETE EQUIPMENT RENTAL** without operators R015433 -10	Ea.	.80	23.50	70	210	20.40	**10**
	0200	Bucket, concrete lightweight, 1/2 C.Y.		.90	28	84	252	24	
	0300	1 C.Y.		1.15	38.50	115	345	32.20	
	0400	1-1/2 C.Y.		1.25	45	135	405	37	
	0500	2 C.Y.		6.15	258	775	2,325	204.20	
	0580	8 C.Y.		3.00	56.50	170	510	58	
	0600	Cart, concrete, self-propelled, operator walking, 10 C.F.		4.95	95	285	855	96.60	
	0700	Operator riding, 18 C.F.		11.35	125	375	1,125	165.80	
	0800	Conveyer for concrete, portable, gas, 16" wide, 26' long		11.70	150	450	1,350	183.60	
	0900	46' long		11.85	158	475	1,425	189.80	
	1000	56' long		1.83	67.50	203	610	55.25	
	1100	Core drill, electric, 2-1/2 H.P., 1" to 8" bit diameter		5.45	118	355	1,075	114.60	
	1150	11 H.P., 8" to 18" cores		10.99	147	440	1,325	175.90	
	1200	Finisher, concrete floor, gas, riding trowel, 96" wide		1.85	20.50	62	186	27.20	
	1300	Gas, walk-behind, 3 blade, 36" trowel		3.62	27.50	83	249	45.55	
	1400	4 blade, 48" trowel		.08	13.35	40	120	8.65	
	1500	Float, hand-operated (Bull float), 48" wide		14.35	263	790	2,375	272.80	
	1570	Curb builder, 14 H.P., gas, single screw		15.30	320	955	2,875	313.40	
	1590	Double screw		2.69	167	500	1,500	121.50	
	1600	Floor grinder, concrete and terrazzo, electric, 22" path		1.03	51.50	155	465	39.25	
	1700	Edger, concrete, electric, 7" path		1.48	81.50	245	735	60.85	
	1750	Vacuum pick-up system for floor grinders, wet/dry		7.85	120	360	1,075	134.80	
	1800	Mixer, powered, mortar and concrete, gas, 6 C.F., 18 H.P.		9.70	145	435	1,300	164.60	
	1900	10 C.F., 25 H.P.		10.00	167	500	1,500	180	
	2000	16 C.F.		7.00	235	705	2,125	197	
	2100	Concrete, stationary, tilt drum, 2 C.Y.		28.30	965	2,900	8,700	806.40	
	2120	Pump, concrete, truck mounted, 4" line, 80' boom		35.55	1,325	4,010	12,000	1,086	
	2140	5" line, 110' boom		6.60	133	400	1,200	132.80	
	2160	Mud jack, 50 C.F. per hr.		8.80	152	455	1,375	161.40	
	2180	225 C.F. per hr.		13.90	232	695	2,075	250.20	
	2190	Shotcrete pump rig, 12 C.Y./hr.		15.90	248	745	2,225	276.20	
	2200	35 C.Y./hr.		5.90	45	135	405	74.20	
	2600	Saw, concrete, manual, gas, 18 H.P.		11.45	103	310	930	153.60	
	2650	Self-propelled, gas, 30 H.P.		2.00	17.65	53	159	26.60	
	2675	V-groove crack chaser, manual, gas, 6 H.P.		.46	8.65	26	78	8.90	
	2700	Vibrators, concrete, electric, 60 cycle, 2 H.P.		.59	11.65	35	105	11.70	
	2800	3 H.P.		1.75	16.35	49	147	23.80	
	2900	Gas engine, 5 H.P.		2.38	15.35	46	138	28.25	
	3000	8 H.P.		2.47	74.50	223	670	64.35	
	3050	Vibrating screed, gas engine, 8 H.P.		57.25	580	1,745	5,225	807	
	3120	Concrete transit mixer, 6 x 4, 250 H.P., 8 C.Y., rear discharge		67.15	715	2,145	6,425	966.20	
	3200	Front discharge		66.20	675	2,030	6,100	935.60	
	3300	6 x 6, 285 H.P., 12 C.Y., rear discharge		69.15	715	2,145	6,425	982.20	
	3400	Front discharge							
20	0010	**EARTHWORK EQUIPMENT RENTAL** without operators R015433 -10	Ea.	2.75	25.50	77	231	37.40	**20**
	0040	Aggregate spreader, push type, 8' to 12' wide		2.65	32.50	98	294	40.80	
	0045	Tailgate type, 8' wide		17.05	445	1,335	4,000	403.40	
	0055	Earth auger, truck mounted, for fence & sign posts, utility poles		43.80	720	2,155	6,475	781.40	
	0060	For borings and monitoring wells		2.77	33.50	100	300	42.15	
	0070	Portable, trailer mounted		89.45	3,100	9,285	27,900	2,573	
	0075	Truck mounted, for caissons, water wells		22.60	207	620	1,850	304.80	
	0080	Horizontal boring machine, 12" to 36" diameter, 45 H.P.		31.15	360	1,080	3,250	465.20	
	0090	12" to 48" diameter, 65 H.P.		.51	6.35	19	57	7.90	
	0095	Auger, for fence posts, gas engine, hand held		23.45	425	1,280	3,850	443.60	
	0100	Excavator, diesel hydraulic, crawler mounted, 1/2 C.Y. cap.		31.75	600	1,800	5,400	614	
	0120	5/8 C.Y. capacity		34.90	660	1,975	5,925	674.20	
	0140	3/4 C.Y. capacity		46.40	710	2,135	6,400	798.20	
	0150	1 C.Y. capacity							

01 54 33 | Equipment Rental

		UNIT	HOURLY OPER. COST	RENT PER DAY	RENT PER WEEK	RENT PER MONTH	EQUIPMENT COST/DAY
0200	1-1/2 C.Y. capacity	Ea.	54.75	880	2,635	7,900	965
0300	2 C.Y. capacity		61.90	1,050	3,140	9,425	1,123
0320	2-1/2 C.Y. capacity		94.70	1,300	3,890	11,700	1,536
0325	3-1/2 C.Y. capacity		134.25	2,200	6,635	19,900	2,401
0330	4-1/2 C.Y. capacity		166.65	2,925	8,755	26,300	3,084
0335	6 C.Y. capacity		214.30	3,125	9,410	28,200	3,596
0340	7 C.Y. capacity		216.45	3,275	9,830	29,500	3,698
0342	Excavator attachments, bucket thumbs		3.25	247	740	2,225	174
0345	Grapples		2.80	195	585	1,750	139.40
0346	Hydraulic hammer for boom mounting, 4000 ft lb.		12.55	355	1,060	3,175	312.40
0347	5000 ft lb.		14.65	430	1,295	3,875	376.20
0348	8000 ft lb.		21.60	635	1,900	5,700	552.80
0349	12,000 ft lb.		23.65	755	2,270	6,800	643.20
0350	Gradall type, truck mounted, 3 ton @ 15' radius, 5/8 C.Y.		52.50	815	2,450	7,350	910
0370	1 C.Y. capacity		61.90	1,075	3,245	9,725	1,144
0400	Backhoe-loader, 40 to 45 H.P., 5/8 C.Y. capacity		14.25	257	770	2,300	268
0450	45 H.P. to 60 H.P., 3/4 C.Y. capacity		22.15	315	945	2,825	366.20
0460	80 H.P., 1-1/4 C.Y. capacity		23.55	345	1,030	3,100	394.40
0470	112 H.P., 1-1/2 C.Y. capacity		37.45	650	1,945	5,825	688.60
0482	Backhoe-loader attachment, compactor, 20,000 lb.		5.90	143	430	1,300	133.20
0485	Hydraulic hammer, 750 ft lb.		3.35	98.50	295	885	85.80
0486	Hydraulic hammer, 1200 ft lb.		6.40	218	655	1,975	182.20
0500	Brush chipper, gas engine, 6" cutter head, 35 H.P.		9.90	107	320	960	143.20
0550	Diesel engine, 12" cutter head, 130 H.P.		26.30	325	970	2,900	404.40
0600	15" cutter head, 165 H.P.		32.05	390	1,170	3,500	490.40
0750	Bucket, clamshell, general purpose, 3/8 C.Y.		1.30	38.50	115	345	33.40
0800	1/2 C.Y.		1.40	45	135	405	38.20
0850	3/4 C.Y.		1.55	55	165	495	45.40
0900	1 C.Y.		1.60	60	180	540	48.80
0950	1-1/2 C.Y.		2.60	81.50	245	735	69.80
1000	2 C.Y.		2.75	90	270	810	76
1010	Bucket, dragline, medium duty, 1/2 C.Y.		.75	23.50	70	210	20
1020	3/4 C.Y.		.75	24.50	74	222	20.80
1030	1 C.Y.		.80	26.50	80	240	22.40
1040	1-1/2 C.Y.		1.25	40	120	360	34
1050	2 C.Y.		1.30	45	135	405	37.40
1070	3 C.Y.		2.00	63.50	190	570	54
1200	Compactor, manually guided 2-drum vibratory smooth roller, 7.5 H.P.		7.10	210	630	1,900	182.80
1250	Rammer/tamper, gas, 8"		2.75	46.50	140	420	50
1260	15"		3.10	53.50	160	480	56.80
1300	Vibratory plate, gas, 18" plate, 3000 lb. blow		2.30	25.50	76	228	33.60
1350	21" plate, 5000 lb. blow		2.85	33.50	100	300	42.80
1370	Curb builder/extruder, 14 H.P., gas, single screw		14.35	263	790	2,375	272.80
1390	Double screw		15.30	320	955	2,875	313.40
1500	Disc harrow attachment, for tractor		.46	76.50	230	690	49.70
1810	Feller buncher, shearing & accumulating trees, 100 H.P.		45.65	780	2,340	7,025	833.20
1860	Grader, self-propelled, 25,000 lb.		38.80	750	2,245	6,725	759.40
1910	30,000 lb.		39.30	605	1,820	5,450	678.40
1920	40,000 lb.		64.30	1,225	3,670	11,000	1,248
1930	55,000 lb.		78.85	1,825	5,455	16,400	1,722
1950	Hammer, pavement breaker, self-propelled, diesel, 1000 to 1250 lb.		30.65	400	1,200	3,600	485.20
2000	1300 to 1500 lb.		45.98	800	2,400	7,200	847.85
2050	Pile driving hammer, steam or air, 4150 ft lb. @ 225 bpm		11.25	550	1,645	4,925	419
2100	8750 ft lb. @ 145 bpm		13.75	765	2,300	6,900	570
2150	15,000 ft lb. @ 60 bpm		14.10	820	2,465	7,400	605.80
2200	24,450 ft lb. @ 111 bpm		15.15	910	2,730	8,200	667.20
2250	Leads, 60' high for pile driving hammers up to 20,000 ft lb.		3.40	81.50	244	730	76
2300	90' high for hammers over 20,000 ft lb.		5.10	142	426	1,275	126

01 54 33 | Equipment Rental

		UNIT	HOURLY OPER. COST	RENT PER DAY	RENT PER WEEK	RENT PER MONTH	EQUIPMENT COST/DAY
2350	Diesel type hammer, 22,400 ft lb.	Ea.	19.00	450	1,345	4,025	421
2400	41,300 ft lb.		28.25	580	1,740	5,225	574
2450	141,000 ft lb.		45.65	915	2,750	8,250	915.20
2500	Vib. elec. hammer/extractor, 200 kW diesel generator, 34 H.P.		50.30	675	2,025	6,075	807.40
2550	80 H.P.		90.70	970	2,915	8,750	1,309
2600	150 H.P.		170.95	1,875	5,630	16,900	2,494
2800	Log chipper, up to 22" diameter, 600 H.P.		57.85	650	1,950	5,850	852.80
2850	Logger, for skidding & stacking logs, 150 H.P.		48.90	800	2,400	7,200	871.20
2860	Mulcher, diesel powered, trailer mounted		21.75	215	645	1,925	303
2900	Rake, spring tooth, with tractor		16.89	350	1,045	3,125	344.10
3000	Roller, vibratory, tandem, smooth drum, 20 H.P.		7.80	150	450	1,350	152.40
3050	35 H.P.		10.20	260	780	2,350	237.60
3100	Towed type vibratory compactor, smooth drum, 50 H.P.		25.30	375	1,125	3,375	427.40
3150	Sheepsfoot, 50 H.P.		26.25	400	1,205	3,625	451
3170	Landfill compactor, 220 H.P.		76.55	1,625	4,860	14,600	1,584
3200	Pneumatic tire roller, 80 H.P.		14.10	405	1,215	3,650	355.80
3250	120 H.P.		21.30	685	2,050	6,150	580.40
3300	Sheepsfoot vibratory roller, 240 H.P.		67.40	1,250	3,785	11,400	1,296
3320	340 H.P.		90.85	1,875	5,590	16,800	1,845
3350	Smooth drum vibratory roller, 75 H.P.		23.80	690	2,075	6,225	605.40
3400	125 H.P.		28.75	755	2,270	6,800	684
3410	Rotary mower, brush, 60", with tractor		21.35	325	975	2,925	365.80
3420	Rototiller, walk-behind, gas, 5 H.P.		1.50	44	132	395	38.40
3422	8 H.P.		2.59	80	240	720	68.70
3440	Scrapers, towed type, 7 C.Y. capacity		5.90	117	350	1,050	117.20
3450	10 C.Y. capacity		6.70	158	475	1,425	148.60
3500	15 C.Y. capacity		7.20	183	550	1,650	167.60
3525	Self-propelled, single engine, 14 C.Y. capacity		141.45	2,150	6,485	19,500	2,429
3550	Dual engine, 21 C.Y. capacity		164.55	2,450	7,340	22,000	2,784
3600	31 C.Y. capacity		217.70	3,400	10,170	30,500	3,776
3640	44 C.Y. capacity		267.35	4,300	12,865	38,600	4,712
3650	Elevating type, single engine, 11 C.Y. capacity		67.70	1,075	3,250	9,750	1,192
3700	22 C.Y. capacity		129.45	2,425	7,270	21,800	2,490
3710	Screening plant, 110 H.P. w/5' x 10' screen		19.53	385	1,155	3,475	387.25
3720	5' x 16' screen		24.83	500	1,495	4,475	497.65
3850	Shovel, crawler-mounted, front-loading, 7 C.Y. capacity		240.65	3,625	10,910	32,700	4,107
3855	12 C.Y. capacity		391.30	5,025	15,110	45,300	6,152
3860	Shovel/backhoe bucket, 1/2 C.Y.		2.50	68.50	205	615	61
3870	3/4 C.Y.		2.60	75	225	675	65.80
3880	1 C.Y.		2.70	85	255	765	72.60
3890	1-1/2 C.Y.		2.80	98.50	295	885	81.40
3910	3 C.Y.		3.15	132	395	1,175	104.20
3950	Stump chipper, 18" deep, 30 H.P.		6.79	215	646	1,950	183.50
4110	Dozer, crawler, torque converter, diesel 80 H.P.		27.95	410	1,225	3,675	468.60
4150	105 H.P.		34.25	555	1,670	5,000	608
4200	140 H.P.		48.40	765	2,300	6,900	847.20
4260	200 H.P.		72.10	1,350	4,035	12,100	1,384
4310	300 H.P.		95.10	1,900	5,695	17,100	1,900
4360	410 H.P.		125.20	2,275	6,830	20,500	2,368
4370	500 H.P.		160.05	3,425	10,310	30,900	3,342
4380	700 H.P.		264.25	5,175	15,520	46,600	5,218
4400	Loader, crawler, torque conv., diesel, 1-1/2 C.Y., 80 H.P.		32.65	510	1,535	4,600	568.20
4450	1-1/2 to 1-3/4 C.Y., 95 H.P.		33.60	655	1,970	5,900	662.80
4510	1-3/4 to 2-1/4 C.Y., 130 H.P.		53.20	920	2,760	8,275	977.60
4530	2-1/2 to 3-1/4 C.Y., 190 H.P.		65.10	1,275	3,800	11,400	1,281
4560	3-1/2 to 5 C.Y., 275 H.P.		82.45	1,450	4,340	13,000	1,528
4610	Front end loader, 4WD, articulated frame, diesel, 1 to 1-1/4 C.Y., 70 H.P.		18.85	270	810	2,425	312.80
4620	1-1/2 to 1-3/4 C.Y., 95 H.P.		23.25	293	880	2,650	362

20

01 54 33 | Equipment Rental

		UNIT	HOURLY OPER. COST	RENT PER DAY	RENT PER WEEK	RENT PER MONTH	EQUIPMENT COST/DAY
20	4650	1-3/4 to 2 C.Y., 130 H.P.	Ea.	24.90	370	1,105	3,325	420.20
	4710	2-1/2 to 3-1/2 C.Y., 145 H.P.		35.40	455	1,365	4,100	556.20
	4730	3 to 4-1/2 C.Y., 185 H.P.		40.70	555	1,660	4,975	657.60
	4760	5-1/4 to 5-3/4 C.Y., 270 H.P.		63.35	955	2,870	8,600	1,081
	4810	7 to 9 C.Y., 475 H.P.		108.10	1,825	5,510	16,500	1,967
	4870	9 to 11 C.Y., 620 H.P.		154.85	3,300	9,925	29,800	3,224
	4880	Skid-steer loader, wheeled, 10 C.F., 30 H.P. gas		9.75	155	465	1,400	171
	4890	1 C.Y., 78 H.P., diesel		18.80	265	795	2,375	309.40
	4892	Skid-steer attachment, auger		.40	66.50	200	600	43.20
	4893	Backhoe		.65	108	325	975	70.20
	4894	Broom		.79	131	393	1,175	84.90
	4895	Forks		.19	31.50	95	285	20.50
	4896	Grapple		.55	92.50	277	830	59.80
	4897	Concrete hammer		1.07	178	535	1,600	115.55
	4898	Tree spade		1.03	172	515	1,550	111.25
	4899	Trencher		.51	85.50	256	770	55.30
	4900	Trencher, chain, boom type, gas, operator walking, 12 H.P.		4.45	46.50	140	420	63.60
	4910	Operator riding, 40 H.P.		18.65	293	880	2,650	325.20
	5000	Wheel type, diesel, 4' deep, 12" wide		80.25	860	2,575	7,725	1,157
	5100	6' deep, 20" wide		90.50	2,000	6,030	18,100	1,930
	5150	Chain type, diesel, 5' deep, 8" wide		27.70	400	1,195	3,575	460.60
	5200	Diesel, 8' deep, 16" wide		116.95	2,550	7,620	22,900	2,460
	5202	Rock trencher, wheel type, 6" wide x 18" deep		38.00	740	2,225	6,675	749
	5206	Chain type, 18" wide x 7' deep		109.44	2,950	8,845	26,500	2,645
	5210	Tree spade, self-propelled		11.28	267	800	2,400	250.25
	5250	Truck, dump, 2-axle, 12 ton, 8 C.Y. payload, 220 H.P.		31.00	238	715	2,150	391
	5300	Three axle dump, 16 ton, 12 C.Y. payload, 400 H.P.		54.70	340	1,025	3,075	642.60
	5310	Four axle dump, 25 ton, 18 C.Y. payload, 450 H.P.		64.70	495	1,490	4,475	815.60
	5350	Dump trailer only, rear dump, 16-1/2 C.Y.		5.50	140	420	1,250	128
	5400	20 C.Y.		5.95	158	475	1,425	142.60
	5450	Flatbed, single axle, 1-1/2 ton rating		22.05	68.50	205	615	217.40
	5500	3 ton rating		26.40	98.50	295	885	270.20
	5550	Off highway rear dump, 25 ton capacity		72.20	1,500	4,490	13,500	1,476
	5600	35 ton capacity		78.15	1,500	4,535	13,600	1,532
	5610	50 ton capacity		101.00	2,000	5,990	18,000	2,006
	5620	65 ton capacity		104.00	2,050	6,160	18,500	2,064
	5630	100 ton capacity		141.00	3,050	9,120	27,400	2,952
	6000	Vibratory plow, 25 H.P., walking		7.45	63.50	190	570	97.60
40	0010	**GENERAL EQUIPMENT RENTAL** without operators						
	0020	Aerial lift, scissor type, to 20' high, 1200 lb. capacity, electric	Ea.	3.15	55	165	495	58.20
	0030	To 30' high, 1200 lb. capacity		3.60	71.50	215	645	71.80
	0040	Over 30' high, 1500 lb. capacity		4.90	130	390	1,175	117.20
	0070	Articulating boom, to 45' high, 500 lb. capacity, diesel		10.05	277	830	2,500	246.40
	0075	To 60' high, 500 lb. capacity		14.05	485	1,460	4,375	404.40
	0080	To 80' high, 500 lb. capacity		16.90	585	1,760	5,275	487.20
	0085	To 125' high, 500 lb. capacity		20.40	690	2,075	6,225	578.20
	0100	Telescoping boom to 40' high, 500 lb. capacity, diesel		11.85	325	970	2,900	288.80
	0105	To 45' high, 500 lb. capacity		12.60	330	995	2,975	299.80
	0110	To 60' high, 500 lb. capacity		16.25	545	1,630	4,900	456
	0115	To 80' high, 500 lb. capacity		22.45	645	1,930	5,800	565.60
	0120	To 100' high, 500 lb. capacity		26.35	795	2,385	7,150	687.80
	0125	To 120' high, 500 lb. capacity		29.80	940	2,815	8,450	801.40
	0195	Air compressor, portable, 6.5 CFM, electric		.88	13.65	41	123	15.25
	0196	Gasoline		.65	20.50	62	186	17.60
	0200	Towed type, gas engine, 60 CFM		12.00	51.50	155	465	127
	0300	160 CFM		13.95	53.50	160	480	143.60
	0400	Diesel engine, rotary screw, 250 CFM		13.90	117	350	1,050	181.20
	0500	365 CFM		18.75	143	430	1,300	236

Reference codes: R015433-10 (line 0020), R015433-15 (line 0075)

01 54 33 | Equipment Rental

	UNIT	HOURLY OPER. COST	RENT PER DAY	RENT PER WEEK	RENT PER MONTH	EQUIPMENT COST/DAY
0550	450 CFM	Ea.	23.80	178	535	1,600	297.40
0600	600 CFM		41.75	247	740	2,225	482
0700	750 CFM	▼	41.90	255	765	2,300	488.20
0800	For silenced models, small sizes, add to rent		3%	5%	5%	5%	
0900	Large sizes, add to rent		5%	7%	7%	7%	
0930	Air tools, breaker, pavement, 60 lb.	Ea.	.50	10.35	31	93	10.20
0940	80 lb.		.55	10.65	32	96	10.80
0950	Drills, hand (jackhammer), 65 lb.		.60	18.35	55	165	15.80
0960	Track or wagon, swing boom, 4" drifter		56.05	945	2,840	8,525	1,016
0970	5" drifter		65.70	1,150	3,425	10,300	1,211
0975	Track mounted quarry drill, 6" diameter drill		109.15	1,725	5,145	15,400	1,902
0980	Dust control per drill		1.03	25.50	77	231	23.65
0990	Hammer, chipping, 12 lb.		.60	26	78	234	20.40
1000	Hose, air with couplings, 50' long, 3/4" diameter		.03	5	15	45	3.25
1100	1" diameter		.04	6.35	19	57	4.10
1200	1-1/2" diameter		.05	9	27	81	5.80
1300	2" diameter		.07	12	36	108	7.75
1400	2-1/2" diameter		.11	19	57	171	12.30
1410	3" diameter		.14	23	69	207	14.90
1450	Drill, steel, 7/8" x 2'		.05	8.65	26	78	5.60
1460	7/8" x 6'		.05	9	27	81	5.80
1520	Moil points		.02	3.67	11	33	2.35
1525	Pneumatic nailer w/accessories		.49	32.50	97	291	23.30
1530	Sheeting driver for 60 lb. breaker		.04	6	18	54	3.90
1540	For 90 lb. breaker		.12	8	24	72	5.75
1550	Spade, 25 lb.		.50	7.35	22	66	8.40
1560	Tamper, single, 35 lb.		.55	36.50	109	325	26.20
1570	Triple, 140 lb.		.82	54.50	164	490	39.35
1580	Wrenches, impact, air powered, up to 3/4" bolt		.40	13	39	117	11
1590	Up to 1-1/4" bolt		.50	24.50	73	219	18.60
1600	Barricades, barrels, reflectorized, 1 to 99 barrels		.03	4.60	13.80	41.50	3
1610	100 to 200 barrels		.02	3.53	10.60	32	2.30
1620	Barrels with flashers, 1 to 99 barrels		.03	5.25	15.80	47.50	3.40
1630	100 to 200 barrels		.03	4.20	12.60	38	2.75
1640	Barrels with steady burn type C lights		.04	7	21	63	4.50
1650	Illuminated board, trailer mounted, with generator		3.45	130	390	1,175	105.60
1670	Portable barricade, stock, with flashers, 1 to 6 units		.03	5.25	15.80	47.50	3.40
1680	25 to 50 units		.03	4.90	14.70	44	3.20
1685	Butt fusion machine, wheeled, 1.5 HP electric, 2" - 8" diameter pipe		2.63	167	500	1,500	121.05
1690	Tracked, 20 HP diesel, 4"-12" diameter pipe		10.89	545	1,640	4,925	415.10
1695	83 HP diesel, 8" - 24" diameter pipe		47.24	2,400	7,215	21,600	1,821
1700	Carts, brick, hand powered, 1000 lb. capacity		.47	78.50	235	705	50.75
1800	Gas engine, 1500 lb., 7-1/2' lift		3.55	115	345	1,025	97.40
1822	Dehumidifier, medium, 6 lb./hr., 150 CFM		1.11	69.50	209	625	50.70
1824	Large, 18 lb./hr., 600 CFM		2.12	133	398	1,200	96.55
1830	Distributor, asphalt, trailer mounted, 2000 gal., 38 H.P. diesel		10.25	360	1,075	3,225	297
1840	3000 gal., 38 H.P. diesel		11.80	390	1,165	3,500	327.40
1850	Drill, rotary hammer, electric		1.06	27	81	243	24.70
1860	Carbide bit, 1-1/2" diameter, add to electric rotary hammer		.03	4.67	14	42	3.05
1865	Rotary, crawler, 250 H.P.		142.30	2,300	6,925	20,800	2,523
1870	Emulsion sprayer, 65 gal., 5 H.P. gas engine		2.75	104	312	935	84.40
1880	200 gal., 5 H.P. engine		7.35	173	520	1,550	162.80
1900	Floor auto-scrubbing machine, walk-behind, 28" path		5.03	325	980	2,950	236.25
1930	Floodlight, mercury vapor, or quartz, on tripod, 1000 watt		.45	21.50	64	192	16.40
1940	2000 watt		.85	43	129	385	32.60
1950	Floodlights, trailer mounted with generator, 1 - 300 watt light		3.60	73.50	220	660	72.80
1960	2 - 1000 watt lights		4.70	98.50	295	885	96.60
2000	4 - 300 watt lights		4.45	93.50	280	840	91.60

01 54 33 | Equipment Rental

		UNIT	HOURLY OPER. COST	RENT PER DAY	RENT PER WEEK	RENT PER MONTH	EQUIPMENT COST/DAY	
2005	Foam spray rig, incl. box trailer, compressor, generator, proportioner	Ea.	28.70	520	1,565	4,700	542.60	40
2015	Forklift, pneumatic tire, rough terr, straight mast, 5000 lb, 12' lift, gas		22.35	212	635	1,900	305.80	
2025	8000 lb, 12' lift		26.00	285	855	2,575	379	
2030	5000 lb, 12' lift, diesel		17.40	238	715	2,150	282.20	
2035	8000 lb, 12' lift, diesel		18.45	270	810	2,425	309.60	
2045	All terrain, telescoping boom, diesel, 5000 lb, 10' reach, 19' lift		18.25	330	985	2,950	343	
2055	6600 lb, 29' reach, 42' lift		22.25	385	1,155	3,475	409	
2065	10,000 lb, 31' reach, 45' lift		26.20	520	1,555	4,675	520.60	
2070	Cushion tire, smooth floor, gas, 5000 lb capacity		9.55	83.50	250	750	126.40	
2075	8000 lb capacity		13.65	103	310	930	171.20	
2085	Diesel, 5000 lb capacity		8.75	90	270	810	124	
2090	12,000 lb capacity		13.55	142	425	1,275	193.40	
2095	20,000 lb capacity		19.75	178	535	1,600	265	
2100	Generator, electric, gas engine, 1.5 kW to 3 kW		3.15	12.65	38	114	32.80	
2200	5 kW		4.10	16	48	144	42.40	
2300	10 kW		7.70	36.50	110	330	83.60	
2400	25 kW		8.75	90	270	810	124	
2500	Diesel engine, 20 kW		10.05	78.50	235	705	127.40	
2600	50 kW		19.15	105	315	945	216.20	
2700	100 kW		35.30	142	425	1,275	367.40	
2800	250 kW		69.45	268	805	2,425	716.60	
2850	Hammer, hydraulic, for mounting on boom, to 500 ft lb.		2.60	76.50	230	690	66.80	
2860	1000 ft lb.		4.54	128	385	1,150	113.30	
2900	Heaters, space, oil or electric, 50 MBH		1.39	8	24	72	15.90	
3000	100 MBH		2.52	10.65	32	96	26.55	
3100	300 MBH		7.36	38.50	115	345	81.90	
3150	500 MBH		11.95	45	135	405	122.60	
3200	Hose, water, suction with coupling, 20' long, 2" diameter		.02	3	9	27	1.95	
3210	3" diameter		.03	4.67	14	42	3.05	
3220	4" diameter		.03	5.35	16	48	3.45	
3230	6" diameter		.11	18.35	55	165	11.90	
3240	8" diameter		.34	56	168	505	36.30	
3250	Discharge hose with coupling, 50' long, 2" diameter		.01	1.33	4	12	.90	
3260	3" diameter		.02	2.67	8	24	1.75	
3270	4" diameter		.02	3.67	11	33	2.35	
3280	6" diameter		.06	9.65	29	87	6.30	
3290	8" diameter		.18	30	90	270	19.45	
3295	Insulation blower		.78	6.35	19	57	10.05	
3300	Ladders, extension type, 16' to 36' long		.14	22.50	68	204	14.70	
3400	40' to 60' long		.19	31	93	279	20.10	
3405	Lance for cutting concrete		2.13	55.50	167	500	50.45	
3407	Lawn mower, rotary, 22", 5 H.P.		1.35	33.50	101	305	31	
3408	48" self-propelled		2.90	95	285	855	80.20	
3410	Level, electronic, automatic, with tripod and leveling rod		.87	57.50	173	520	41.55	
3430	Laser type, for pipe and sewer line and grade		.73	48.50	145	435	34.85	
3440	Rotating beam for interior control		.80	53	159	475	38.20	
3460	Builder's optical transit, with tripod and rod		.09	14.65	44	132	9.50	
3500	Light towers, towable, with diesel generator, 2000 watt		4.45	93.50	280	840	91.60	
3600	4000 watt		4.70	98.50	295	885	96.60	
3700	Mixer, powered, plaster and mortar, 6 C.F., 7 H.P.		2.30	20	60	180	30.40	
3800	10 C.F., 9 H.P.		2.45	32.50	98	294	39.20	
3850	Nailer, pneumatic		.49	32.50	97	291	23.30	
3900	Paint sprayers complete, 8 CFM		1.06	70.50	211	635	50.70	
4000	17 CFM		1.89	126	378	1,125	90.70	
4020	Pavers, bituminous, rubber tires, 8' wide, 50 H.P., diesel		30.50	540	1,615	4,850	567	
4030	10' wide, 150 H.P.		97.10	1,950	5,875	17,600	1,952	
4050	Crawler, 8' wide, 100 H.P., diesel		85.85	2,050	6,165	18,500	1,920	
4060	10' wide, 150 H.P.		104.85	2,425	7,290	21,900	2,297	

		UNIT	HOURLY OPER. COST	RENT PER DAY	RENT PER WEEK	RENT PER MONTH	EQUIPMENT COST/DAY	
01 54 33 | Equipment Rental								
4070	Concrete paver, 12' to 24' wide, 250 H.P.	Ea.	96.45	1,575	4,730	14,200	1,718	**40**
4080	Placer-spreader-trimmer, 24' wide, 300 H.P.		133.20	2,300	6,934	20,800	2,452	
4100	Pump, centrifugal gas pump, 1-1/2" diam., 65 GPM		3.75	50	150	450	60	
4200	2" diameter, 130 GPM		5.00	60	180	540	76	
4300	3" diameter, 250 GPM		5.20	61.50	185	555	78.60	
4400	6" diameter, 1500 GPM		25.80	198	595	1,775	325.40	
4500	Submersible electric pump, 1-1/4" diameter, 55 GPM		.41	17.65	53	159	13.90	
4600	1-1/2" diameter, 83 GPM		.45	20.50	61	183	15.80	
4700	2" diameter, 120 GPM		1.54	25.50	76	228	27.50	
4800	3" diameter, 300 GPM		2.78	45	135	405	49.25	
4900	4" diameter, 560 GPM		14.43	172	515	1,550	218.45	
5000	6" diameter, 1590 GPM		21.57	227	680	2,050	308.55	
5100	Diaphragm pump, gas, single, 1-1/2" diameter		1.06	52	156	470	39.70	
5200	2" diameter		4.00	65	195	585	71	
5300	3" diameter		4.00	65	195	585	71	
5400	Double, 4" diameter		5.90	112	335	1,000	114.20	
5450	Pressure washer 5 GPM, 3000 psi		4.25	53.50	160	480	66	
5460	7 GPM, 3000 psi		5.50	63.50	190	570	82	
5500	Trash pump, self-priming, gas, 2" diameter		4.00	22.50	67	201	45.40	
5600	Diesel, 4" diameter		7.65	96.50	290	870	119.20	
5650	Diesel, 6" diameter		20.65	172	515	1,550	268.20	
5655	Grout Pump		24.05	275	825	2,475	357.40	
5700	Salamanders, L.P. gas fired, 100,000 Btu		2.72	13.65	41	123	29.95	
5705	50,000 Btu		1.59	10.65	32	96	19.10	
5720	Sandblaster, portable, open top, 3 C.F. capacity		.60	27.50	83	249	21.40	
5730	6 C.F. capacity		.95	41.50	125	375	32.60	
5740	Accessories for above		.13	22.50	67	201	14.45	
5750	Sander, floor		.89	23.50	71	213	21.30	
5760	Edger		.53	16	48	144	13.85	
5800	Saw, chain, gas engine, 18" long		2.00	22.50	67	201	29.40	
5900	Hydraulic powered, 36" long		.75	65	195	585	45	
5950	60" long		.75	66.50	200	600	46	
6000	Masonry, table mounted, 14" diameter, 5 H.P.		1.32	56.50	170	510	44.55	
6050	Portable cut-off, 8 H.P.		2.15	35	105	315	38.20	
6100	Circular, hand held, electric, 7-1/4" diameter		.23	4.67	14	42	4.65	
6200	12" diameter		.23	8.35	25	75	6.85	
6250	Wall saw, w/hydraulic power, 10 H.P.		8.30	61.50	185	555	103.40	
6275	Shot blaster, walk-behind, 20" wide		4.80	305	910	2,725	220.40	
6280	Sidewalk broom, walk-behind		2.21	74.50	224	670	62.50	
6300	Steam cleaner, 100 gallons per hour		3.40	80	240	720	75.20	
6310	200 gallons per hour		4.60	98.50	295	885	95.80	
6340	Tar Kettle/Pot, 400 gallons		14.21	76.50	230	690	159.70	
6350	Torch, cutting, acetylene-oxygen, 150' hose, excludes gases		.30	16	48	144	12	
6360	Hourly operating cost includes tips and gas		21.00				168	
6410	Toilet, portable chemical		.13	21.50	65	195	14.05	
6420	Recycle flush type		.16	26.50	79	237	17.10	
6430	Toilet, fresh water flush, garden hose,		.19	31.50	95	285	20.50	
6440	Hoisted, non-flush, for high rise		.15	25.50	77	231	16.60	
6465	Tractor, farm with attachment		20.65	335	1,010	3,025	367.20	
6480	Trailers, platform, flush deck, 2 axle, 3 ton capacity		1.50	20	60	180	24	
6500	25 ton capacity		6.05	133	400	1,200	128.40	
6600	40 ton capacity		7.75	188	565	1,700	175	
6700	3 axle, 50 ton capacity		8.40	208	625	1,875	192.20	
6800	75 ton capacity		10.65	275	825	2,475	250.20	
6810	Trailer mounted cable reel for high voltage line work		5.68	270	811	2,425	207.65	
6820	Trailer mounted cable tensioning rig		11.27	535	1,610	4,825	412.15	
6830	Cable pulling rig		71.16	3,000	9,030	27,100	2,375	
6850	Portable cable/wire puller, 8000 lb max pulling capacity		3.71	167	502	1,500	130.10	

01 54 33 | Equipment Rental

		UNIT	HOURLY OPER. COST	RENT PER DAY	RENT PER WEEK	RENT PER MONTH	EQUIPMENT COST/DAY	
40								**40**
6900	Water tank trailer, engine driven discharge, 5000 gallons	Ea.	7.00	145	435	1,300	143	
6925	10,000 gallons		9.55	200	600	1,800	196.40	
6950	Water truck, off highway, 6000 gallons		82.10	785	2,350	7,050	1,127	
7010	Tram car for high voltage line work, powered, 2 conductor		6.64	147	440	1,325	141.10	
7020	Transit (builder's level) with tripod		.09	14.65	44	132	9.50	
7030	Trench box, 3000 lb., 6' x 8'		.56	93.50	280	840	60.50	
7040	7200 lb., 6' x 20'		.75	125	375	1,125	81	
7050	8000 lb., 8' x 16'		1.08	180	540	1,625	116.65	
7060	9500 lb., 8' x 20'		1.21	201	603	1,800	130.30	
7065	11,000 lb., 8' x 24'		1.27	211	633	1,900	136.75	
7070	12,000 lb., 10' x 20'		1.50	251	752	2,250	162.40	
7100	Truck, pickup, 3/4 ton, 2 wheel drive		11.80	58.50	175	525	129.40	
7200	4 wheel drive		12.00	73.50	220	660	140	
7250	Crew carrier, 9 passenger		16.70	86.50	260	780	185.60	
7290	Flat bed truck, 20,000 lb. GVW		19.50	127	380	1,150	232	
7300	Tractor, 4 x 2, 220 H.P.		27.20	198	595	1,775	336.60	
7410	330 H.P.		40.20	273	820	2,450	485.60	
7500	6 x 4, 380 H.P.		46.10	320	955	2,875	559.80	
7600	450 H.P.		56.10	385	1,155	3,475	679.80	
7610	Tractor, with A frame, boom and winch, 225 H.P.		30.10	278	835	2,500	407.80	
7620	Vacuum truck, hazardous material, 2500 gallons		12.20	293	880	2,650	273.60	
7625	5,000 gallons		12.65	410	1,230	3,700	347.20	
7650	Vacuum, HEPA, 16 gallon, wet/dry		.84	19	57	171	18.10	
7655	55 gallon, wet/dry		.82	28.50	86	258	23.75	
7660	Water tank, portable		.16	26.50	80	240	17.30	
7690	Sewer/catch basin vacuum, 14 C.Y., 1500 gallons		16.99	615	1,850	5,550	505.90	
7700	Welder, electric, 200 amp		3.81	17.35	52	156	40.90	
7800	300 amp		5.67	21.50	64	192	58.15	
7900	Gas engine, 200 amp		12.30	26.50	80	240	114.40	
8000	300 amp		14.10	28.50	85	255	129.80	
8100	Wheelbarrow, any size		.08	12.65	38	114	8.25	
8200	Wrecking ball, 4000 lb.		2.35	70	210	630	60.80	
50	**HIGHWAY EQUIPMENT RENTAL** without operators							**50**
0010		R015433 -10						
0050	Asphalt batch plant, portable drum mixer, 100 ton/hr.	Ea.	80.67	1,500	4,535	13,600	1,552	
0060	200 ton/hr.		92.19	1,600	4,810	14,400	1,700	
0070	300 ton/hr.		109.71	1,875	5,660	17,000	2,010	
0100	Backhoe attachment, long stick, up to 185 H.P., 10.5' long		.36	24	72	216	17.30	
0140	Up to 250 H.P., 12' long		.40	26.50	79	237	19	
0180	Over 250 H.P., 15' long		.55	36.50	109	325	26.20	
0200	Special dipper arm, up to 100 H.P., 32' long		1.12	74.50	223	670	53.55	
0240	Over 100 H.P., 33' long		1.39	92.50	278	835	66.70	
0280	Catch basin/sewer cleaning truck, 3 ton, 9 C.Y., 1000 gal.		38.00	390	1,175	3,525	539	
0300	Concrete batch plant, portable, electric, 200 C.Y./hr.		23.11	525	1,570	4,700	498.90	
0520	Grader/dozer attachment, ripper/scarifier, rear mounted, up to 135 H.P.		3.00	60	180	540	60	
0540	Up to 180 H.P.		3.95	90	270	810	85.60	
0580	Up to 250 H.P.		5.60	142	425	1,275	129.80	
0700	Pvmt. removal bucket, for hyd. excavator, up to 90 H.P.		1.95	53.50	160	480	47.60	
0740	Up to 200 H.P.		2.10	68.50	205	615	57.80	
0780	Over 200 H.P.		2.30	86.50	260	780	70.40	
0900	Aggregate spreader, self-propelled, 187 H.P.		50.25	690	2,075	6,225	817	
1000	Chemical spreader, 3 C.Y.		3.15	43.50	130	390	51.20	
1900	Hammermill, traveling, 250 H.P.		66.08	2,175	6,490	19,500	1,827	
2000	Horizontal borer, 3" diameter, 13 H.P. gas driven		5.65	58.50	175	525	80.20	
2150	Horizontal directional drill, 20,000 lb. thrust, 78 H.P. diesel		28.20	710	2,130	6,400	651.60	
2160	30,000 lb. thrust, 115 H.P.		34.75	1,075	3,255	9,775	929	
2170	50,000 lb. thrust, 170 H.P.		49.65	1,375	4,160	12,500	1,229	
2190	Mud trailer for HDD, 1500 gallons, 175 H.P., gas		27.45	153	460	1,375	311.60	
2200	Hydromulcher, diesel, 3000 gallon, for truck mounting		21.10	248	745	2,225	317.80	

For customer support on your Residential Costs with RSMeans Data, call 800.448.8182.

671

01 54 33 | Equipment Rental

		UNIT	HOURLY OPER. COST	RENT PER DAY	RENT PER WEEK	RENT PER MONTH	EQUIPMENT COST/DAY	
50	2300	Gas, 600 gallon	Ea.	7.80	100	300	900	122.40	**50**
	2400	Joint & crack cleaner, walk behind, 25 H.P.		3.45	50	150	450	57.60	
	2500	Filler, trailer mounted, 400 gallons, 20 H.P.		9.10	212	635	1,900	199.80	
	3000	Paint striper, self-propelled, 40 gallon, 22 H.P.		6.90	157	470	1,400	149.20	
	3100	120 gallon, 120 H.P.		20.55	400	1,195	3,575	403.40	
	3200	Post drivers, 6" I-Beam frame, for truck mounting		16.90	385	1,150	3,450	365.20	
	3400	Road sweeper, self-propelled, 8' wide, 90 H.P.		39.10	645	1,940	5,825	700.80	
	3450	Road sweeper, vacuum assisted, 4 C.Y., 220 gallons		68.85	630	1,885	5,650	927.80	
	4000	Road mixer, self-propelled, 130 H.P.		44.90	840	2,520	7,550	863.20	
	4100	310 H.P.		76.55	2,225	6,650	20,000	1,942	
	4220	Cold mix paver, incl. pug mill and bitumen tank, 165 H.P.		92.95	2,500	7,535	22,600	2,251	
	4240	Pavement brush, towed		3.25	93.50	280	840	82	
	4250	Paver, asphalt, wheel or crawler, 130 H.P., diesel		92.60	2,500	7,470	22,400	2,235	
	4300	Paver, road widener, gas, 1' to 6', 67 H.P.		46.00	945	2,830	8,500	934	
	4400	Diesel, 2' to 14', 88 H.P.		57.45	1,125	3,385	10,200	1,137	
	4600	Slipform pavers, curb and gutter, 2 track, 75 H.P.		62.00	1,175	3,490	10,500	1,194	
	4700	4 track, 165 H.P.		40.30	800	2,400	7,200	802.40	
	4800	Median barrier, 215 H.P.		63.25	1,225	3,695	11,100	1,245	
	4901	Trailer, low bed, 75 ton capacity		10.80	260	780	2,350	242.40	
	5000	Road planer, walk behind, 10" cutting width, 10 H.P.		3.30	33.50	100	300	46.40	
	5100	Self-propelled, 12" cutting width, 64 H.P.		8.95	113	340	1,025	139.60	
	5120	Traffic line remover, metal ball blaster, truck mounted, 115 H.P.		46.35	840	2,515	7,550	873.80	
	5140	Grinder, truck mounted, 115 H.P.		51.30	900	2,705	8,125	951.40	
	5160	Walk-behind, 11 H.P.		3.75	53.50	160	480	62	
	5200	Pavement profiler, 4' to 6' wide, 450 H.P.		225.65	3,500	10,525	31,600	3,910	
	5300	8' to 10' wide, 750 H.P.		349.00	4,600	13,805	41,400	5,553	
	5400	Roadway plate, steel, 1" x 8' x 20'		.08	14	42	126	9.05	
	5600	Stabilizer, self-propelled, 150 H.P.		43.90	715	2,150	6,450	781.20	
	5700	310 H.P.		83.60	1,975	5,960	17,900	1,861	
	5800	Striper, truck mounted, 120 gallon paint, 460 H.P.		55.20	490	1,465	4,400	734.60	
	5900	Thermal paint heating kettle, 115 gallons		7.26	25.50	77	231	73.50	
	6000	Tar kettle, 330 gallon, trailer mounted		10.97	58.50	175	525	122.75	
	7000	Tunnel locomotive, diesel, 8 to 12 ton		29.80	610	1,835	5,500	605.40	
	7005	Electric, 10 ton		26.90	700	2,105	6,325	636.20	
	7010	Muck cars, 1/2 C.Y. capacity		2.10	25.50	76	228	32	
	7020	1 C.Y. capacity		2.30	33.50	100	300	38.40	
	7030	2 C.Y. capacity		2.45	40	120	360	43.60	
	7040	Side dump, 2 C.Y. capacity		2.65	46.50	140	420	49.20	
	7050	3 C.Y. capacity		3.60	53.50	160	480	60.80	
	7060	5 C.Y. capacity		5.15	68.50	205	615	82.20	
	7100	Ventilating blower for tunnel, 7-1/2 H.P.		2.08	53.50	160	480	48.65	
	7110	10 H.P.		2.26	55	165	495	51.10	
	7120	20 H.P.		3.58	71.50	215	645	71.65	
	7140	40 H.P.		5.75	102	305	915	107	
	7160	60 H.P.		8.83	158	475	1,425	165.65	
	7175	75 H.P.		11.60	218	655	1,975	223.80	
	7180	200 H.P.		23.76	315	950	2,850	380.10	
	7800	Windrow loader, elevating		53.10	1,375	4,145	12,400	1,254	
60	0010	**LIFTING AND HOISTING EQUIPMENT RENTAL** without operators R015433 -10	Ea.						**60**
	0150	Crane, flatbed mounted, 3 ton capacity		14.60	218	655	1,975	247.80	
	0200	Crane, climbing, 106' jib, 6000 lb. capacity, 410 fpm R312316 -45		40.06	1,725	5,160	15,500	1,352	
	0300	101' jib, 10,250 lb. capacity, 270 fpm		46.96	2,175	6,540	19,600	1,684	
	0500	Tower, static, 130' high, 106' jib, 6200 lb. capacity at 400 fpm		44.06	1,975	5,960	17,900	1,544	
	0600	Crawler mounted, lattice boom, 1/2 C.Y., 15 tons at 12' radius		37.97	755	2,270	6,800	757.75	
	0700	3/4 C.Y., 20 tons at 12' radius		50.63	945	2,835	8,500	972.05	
	0800	1 C.Y., 25 tons at 12' radius		67.50	1,250	3,780	11,300	1,296	
	0900	1-1/2 C.Y., 40 tons at 12' radius		67.95	1,275	3,845	11,500	1,313	
	1000	2 C.Y., 50 tons at 12' radius		80.20	1,725	5,168	15,500	1,675	

01 54 33	Equipment Rental	UNIT	HOURLY OPER. COST	RENT PER DAY	RENT PER WEEK	RENT PER MONTH	EQUIPMENT COST/DAY	
1100	3 C.Y., 75 tons at 12' radius	Ea.	77.65	1,700	5,120	15,400	1,645	60
1200	100 ton capacity, 60' boom		88.00	1,825	5,500	16,500	1,804	
1300	165 ton capacity, 60' boom		108.25	2,275	6,825	20,500	2,231	
1400	200 ton capacity, 70' boom		143.85	2,900	8,730	26,200	2,897	
1500	350 ton capacity, 80' boom		187.45	4,200	12,600	37,800	4,020	
1600	Truck mounted, lattice boom, 6 x 4, 20 tons at 10' radius		39.35	1,275	3,800	11,400	1,075	
1700	25 tons at 10' radius		42.61	1,375	4,135	12,400	1,168	
1800	8 x 4, 30 tons at 10' radius		45.99	1,475	4,400	13,200	1,248	
1900	40 tons at 12' radius		48.87	1,525	4,600	13,800	1,311	
2000	60 tons at 15' radius		54.26	1,625	4,870	14,600	1,408	
2050	82 tons at 15' radius		60.22	1,725	5,200	15,600	1,522	
2100	90 tons at 15' radius		67.15	1,900	5,670	17,000	1,671	
2200	115 tons at 15' radius		75.69	2,100	6,335	19,000	1,873	
2300	150 tons at 18' radius		83.25	2,225	6,670	20,000	2,000	
2350	165 tons at 18' radius		88.09	2,350	7,070	21,200	2,119	
2400	Truck mounted, hydraulic, 12 ton capacity		35.35	485	1,450	4,350	572.80	
2500	25 ton capacity		40.60	580	1,745	5,225	673.80	
2550	33 ton capacity		49.70	775	2,330	7,000	863.60	
2560	40 ton capacity		55.05	915	2,745	8,225	989.40	
2600	55 ton capacity		63.75	945	2,830	8,500	1,076	
2700	80 ton capacity		83.75	1,575	4,730	14,200	1,616	
2720	100 ton capacity		93.00	1,700	5,085	15,300	1,761	
2740	120 ton capacity		107.35	1,825	5,495	16,500	1,958	
2760	150 ton capacity		113.30	2,225	6,700	20,100	2,246	
2800	Self-propelled, 4 x 4, with telescoping boom, 5 ton		15.50	253	760	2,275	276	
2900	12-1/2 ton capacity		26.95	365	1,100	3,300	435.60	
3000	15 ton capacity		36.50	455	1,365	4,100	565	
3050	20 ton capacity		29.85	525	1,575	4,725	553.80	
3100	25 ton capacity		31.20	595	1,780	5,350	605.60	
3150	40 ton capacity		47.40	660	1,985	5,950	776.20	
3200	Derricks, guy, 20 ton capacity, 60' boom, 75' mast		22.29	420	1,263	3,800	430.90	
3300	100' boom, 115' mast		35.37	725	2,170	6,500	716.95	
3400	Stiffleg, 20 ton capacity, 70' boom, 37' mast		24.93	545	1,640	4,925	527.45	
3500	100' boom, 47' mast		38.59	875	2,630	7,900	834.70	
3550	Helicopter, small, lift to 1250 lb. maximum, w/pilot		94.10	3,400	10,200	30,600	2,793	
3600	Hoists, chain type, overhead, manual, 3/4 ton		.15	.33	1	3	1.40	
3900	10 ton		.75	6.65	20	60	10	
4000	Hoist and tower, 5000 lb. cap., portable electric, 40' high		5.06	242	727	2,175	185.90	
4100	For each added 10' section, add		.11	19	57	171	12.30	
4200	Hoist and single tubular tower, 5000 lb. electric, 100' high		6.86	340	1,016	3,050	258.10	
4300	For each added 6'-6" section, add		.20	33	99	297	21.40	
4400	Hoist and double tubular tower, 5000 lb., 100' high		7.38	375	1,119	3,350	282.85	
4500	For each added 6'-6" section, add		.22	36.50	109	325	23.55	
4550	Hoist and tower, mast type, 6000 lb., 100' high		7.94	385	1,160	3,475	295.50	
4570	For each added 10' section, add		.13	22.50	67	201	14.45	
4600	Hoist and tower, personnel, electric, 2000 lb., 100' @ 125 fpm		16.88	1,025	3,090	9,275	753.05	
4700	3000 lb., 100' @ 200 fpm		19.28	1,175	3,500	10,500	854.25	
4800	3000 lb., 150' @ 300 fpm		21.38	1,300	3,920	11,800	955.05	
4900	4000 lb., 100' @ 300 fpm		22.14	1,325	4,000	12,000	977.10	
5000	6000 lb., 100' @ 275 fpm		23.80	1,400	4,190	12,600	1,028	
5100	For added heights up to 500', add	L.F.	.01	1.67	5	15	1.10	
5200	Jacks, hydraulic, 20 ton	Ea.	.05	2	6	18	1.60	
5500	100 ton		.40	12	36	108	10.40	
6100	Jacks, hydraulic, climbing w/50' jackrods, control console, 30 ton cap.		2.09	139	418	1,250	100.30	
6150	For each added 10' jackrod section, add		.05	3.33	10	30	2.40	
6300	50 ton capacity		3.36	224	672	2,025	161.30	
6350	For each added 10' jackrod section, add		.06	4	12	36	2.90	
6500	125 ton capacity		8.75	585	1,750	5,250	420	

			UNIT	HOURLY OPER. COST	RENT PER DAY	RENT PER WEEK	RENT PER MONTH	EQUIPMENT COST/DAY	
01 54 33 | Equipment Rental									
60	6550	For each added 10' jackrod section, add	Ea.	.60	39.50	119	355	28.60	60
	6600	Cable jack, 10 ton capacity with 200' cable		1.75	117	350	1,050	84	
	6650	For each added 50' of cable, add	↓	.21	14	42	126	10.10	
70	0010	**WELLPOINT EQUIPMENT RENTAL** without operators R015433 -10							70
	0020	Based on 2 months rental							
	0100	Combination jetting & wellpoint pump, 60 H.P. diesel	Ea.	15.32	345	1,036	3,100	329.75	
	0200	High pressure gas jet pump, 200 H.P., 300 psi	"	33.10	295	885	2,650	441.80	
	0300	Discharge pipe, 8" diameter	L.F.	.01	.56	1.68	5.05	.40	
	0350	12" diameter		.01	.83	2.48	7.45	.60	
	0400	Header pipe, flows up to 150 GPM, 4" diameter		.01	.51	1.53	4.59	.40	
	0500	400 GPM, 6" diameter		.01	.60	1.79	5.35	.45	
	0600	800 GPM, 8" diameter		.01	.83	2.48	7.45	.60	
	0700	1500 GPM, 10" diameter		.01	.87	2.61	7.85	.60	
	0800	2500 GPM, 12" diameter		.02	1.64	4.93	14.80	1.15	
	0900	4500 GPM, 16" diameter		.03	2.10	6.31	18.95	1.50	
	0950	For quick coupling aluminum and plastic pipe, add	↓	.03	2.18	6.54	19.60	1.55	
	1100	Wellpoint, 25' long, with fittings & riser pipe, 1-1/2" or 2" diameter	Ea.	.07	4.35	13.05	39	3.15	
	1200	Wellpoint pump, diesel powered, 4" suction, 20 H.P.		6.87	199	597	1,800	174.35	
	1300	6" suction, 30 H.P.		9.22	247	741	2,225	221.95	
	1400	8" suction, 40 H.P.		12.49	340	1,016	3,050	303.10	
	1500	10" suction, 75 H.P.		18.40	395	1,187	3,550	384.60	
	1600	12" suction, 100 H.P.		26.68	630	1,890	5,675	591.45	
	1700	12" suction, 175 H.P.	↓	38.17	695	2,090	6,275	723.35	
80	0010	**MARINE EQUIPMENT RENTAL** without operators R015433 -10							80
	0200	Barge, 400 Ton, 30' wide x 90' long	Ea.	17.65	1,100	3,265	9,800	794.20	
	0240	800 Ton, 45' wide x 90' long		21.40	1,325	3,980	11,900	967.20	
	2000	Tugboat, diesel, 100 H.P.		35.00	220	660	1,975	412	
	2040	250 H.P.		71.15	395	1,190	3,575	807.20	
	2080	380 H.P.		145.20	1,200	3,575	10,700	1,877	
	3000	Small work boat, gas, 16-foot, 50 H.P.		14.75	61.50	185	555	155	
	4000	Large, diesel, 48-foot, 200 H.P.	↓	84.45	1,275	3,815	11,400	1,439	

Crew A-1

Crew No.	Hr.	Daily	Hr.	Daily	Bare Costs	Incl. O&P
1 Building Laborer	$26.60	$212.80	$44.50	$356.00	$26.60	$44.50
1 Concrete Saw, Gas Manual		74.20		81.62	9.28	10.20
8 L.H., Daily Totals		$287.00		$437.62	$35.88	$54.70

Crew A-1A

Crew No.	Hr.	Daily	Hr.	Daily	Bare Costs	Incl. O&P
1 Skilled Worker	$35.75	$286.00	$60.00	$480.00	$35.75	$60.00
1 Shot Blaster, 20"		220.40		242.44	27.55	30.31
8 L.H., Daily Totals		$506.40		$722.44	$63.30	$90.31

Crew A-1B

Crew No.	Hr.	Daily	Hr.	Daily	Bare Costs	Incl. O&P
1 Building Laborer	$26.60	$212.80	$44.50	$356.00	$26.60	$44.50
1 Concrete Saw		153.60		168.96	19.20	21.12
8 L.H., Daily Totals		$366.40		$524.96	$45.80	$65.62

Crew A-1C

Crew No.	Hr.	Daily	Hr.	Daily	Bare Costs	Incl. O&P
1 Building Laborer	$26.60	$212.80	$44.50	$356.00	$26.60	$44.50
1 Chain Saw, Gas, 18"		29.40		32.34	3.67	4.04
8 L.H., Daily Totals		$242.20		$388.34	$30.27	$48.54

Crew A-1D

Crew No.	Hr.	Daily	Hr.	Daily	Bare Costs	Incl. O&P
1 Building Laborer	$26.60	$212.80	$44.50	$356.00	$26.60	$44.50
1 Vibrating Plate, Gas, 18"		33.60		36.96	4.20	4.62
8 L.H., Daily Totals		$246.40		$392.96	$30.80	$49.12

Crew A-1E

Crew No.	Hr.	Daily	Hr.	Daily	Bare Costs	Incl. O&P
1 Building Laborer	$26.60	$212.80	$44.50	$356.00	$26.60	$44.50
1 Vibrating Plate, Gas, 21"		42.80		47.08	5.35	5.88
8 L.H., Daily Totals		$255.60		$403.08	$31.95	$50.38

Crew A-1F

Crew No.	Hr.	Daily	Hr.	Daily	Bare Costs	Incl. O&P
1 Building Laborer	$26.60	$212.80	$44.50	$356.00	$26.60	$44.50
1 Rammer/Tamper, Gas, 8"		50.00		55.00	6.25	6.88
8 L.H., Daily Totals		$262.80		$411.00	$32.85	$51.38

Crew A-1G

Crew No.	Hr.	Daily	Hr.	Daily	Bare Costs	Incl. O&P
1 Building Laborer	$26.60	$212.80	$44.50	$356.00	$26.60	$44.50
1 Rammer/Tamper, Gas, 15"		56.80		62.48	7.10	7.81
8 L.H., Daily Totals		$269.60		$418.48	$33.70	$52.31

Crew A-1H

Crew No.	Hr.	Daily	Hr.	Daily	Bare Costs	Incl. O&P
1 Building Laborer	$26.60	$212.80	$44.50	$356.00	$26.60	$44.50
1 Exterior Steam Cleaner		75.20		82.72	9.40	10.34
8 L.H., Daily Totals		$288.00		$438.72	$36.00	$54.84

Crew A-1J

Crew No.	Hr.	Daily	Hr.	Daily	Bare Costs	Incl. O&P
1 Building Laborer	$26.60	$212.80	$44.50	$356.00	$26.60	$44.50
1 Cultivator, Walk-Behind, 5 H.P.		38.40		42.24	4.80	5.28
8 L.H., Daily Totals		$251.20		$398.24	$31.40	$49.78

Crew A-1K

Crew No.	Hr.	Daily	Hr.	Daily	Bare Costs	Incl. O&P
1 Building Laborer	$26.60	$212.80	$44.50	$356.00	$26.60	$44.50
1 Cultivator, Walk-Behind, 8 H.P.		68.70		75.57	8.59	9.45
8 L.H., Daily Totals		$281.50		$431.57	$35.19	$53.95

Crew A-1M

Crew No.	Hr.	Daily	Hr.	Daily	Bare Costs	Incl. O&P
1 Building Laborer	$26.60	$212.80	$44.50	$356.00	$26.60	$44.50
1 Snow Blower, Walk-Behind		62.50		68.75	7.81	8.59
8 L.H., Daily Totals		$275.30		$424.75	$34.41	$53.09

Crew A-2

Crew No.	Hr.	Daily	Hr.	Daily	Bare Costs	Incl. O&P
2 Laborers	$26.60	$425.60	$44.50	$712.00	$28.33	$47.13
1 Truck Driver (light)	31.80	254.40	52.40	419.20		
1 Flatbed Truck, Gas, 1.5 Ton		217.40		239.14	9.06	9.96
24 L.H., Daily Totals		$897.40		$1370.34	$37.39	$57.10

Crew A-2A

Crew No.	Hr.	Daily	Hr.	Daily	Bare Costs	Incl. O&P
2 Laborers	$26.60	$425.60	$44.50	$712.00	$28.33	$47.13
1 Truck Driver (light)	31.80	254.40	52.40	419.20		
1 Flatbed Truck, Gas, 1.5 Ton		217.40		239.14		
1 Concrete Saw		153.60		168.96	15.46	17.00
24 L.H., Daily Totals		$1051.00		$1539.30	$43.79	$64.14

Crew A-2B

Crew No.	Hr.	Daily	Hr.	Daily	Bare Costs	Incl. O&P
1 Truck Driver (light)	$31.80	$254.40	$52.40	$419.20	$31.80	$52.40
1 Flatbed Truck, Gas, 1.5 Ton		217.40		239.14	27.18	29.89
8 L.H., Daily Totals		$471.80		$658.34	$58.98	$82.29

Crew A-3A

Crew No.	Hr.	Daily	Hr.	Daily	Bare Costs	Incl. O&P
1 Equip. Oper. (light)	$35.20	$281.60	$58.20	$465.60	$35.20	$58.20
1 Pickup Truck, 4x4, 3/4 Ton		140.00		154.00	17.50	19.25
8 L.H., Daily Totals		$421.60		$619.60	$52.70	$77.45

Crew A-3B

Crew No.	Hr.	Daily	Hr.	Daily	Bare Costs	Incl. O&P
1 Equip. Oper. (medium)	$36.40	$291.20	$60.15	$481.20	$34.38	$56.73
1 Truck Driver (heavy)	32.35	258.80	53.30	426.40		
1 Dump Truck, 12 C.Y., 400 H.P.		642.60		706.86		
1 F.E. Loader, W.M., 2.5 C.Y.		556.20		611.82	74.92	82.42
16 L.H., Daily Totals		$1748.80		$2226.28	$109.30	$139.14

Crew A-3C

Crew No.	Hr.	Daily	Hr.	Daily	Bare Costs	Incl. O&P
1 Equip. Oper. (light)	$35.20	$281.60	$58.20	$465.60	$35.20	$58.20
1 Loader, Skid Steer, 78 H.P.		309.40		340.34	38.67	42.54
8 L.H., Daily Totals		$591.00		$805.94	$73.88	$100.74

Crew A-3D

Crew No.	Hr.	Daily	Hr.	Daily	Bare Costs	Incl. O&P
1 Truck Driver (light)	$31.80	$254.40	$52.40	$419.20	$31.80	$52.40
1 Pickup Truck, 4x4, 3/4 Ton		140.00		154.00		
1 Flatbed Trailer, 25 Ton		128.40		141.24	33.55	36.91
8 L.H., Daily Totals		$522.80		$714.44	$65.35	$89.31

Crew A-3E

Crew No.	Hr.	Daily	Hr.	Daily	Bare Costs	Incl. O&P
1 Equip. Oper. (crane)	$37.30	$298.40	$61.65	$493.20	$34.83	$57.48
1 Truck Driver (heavy)	32.35	258.80	53.30	426.40		
1 Pickup Truck, 4x4, 3/4 Ton		140.00		154.00	8.75	9.63
16 L.H., Daily Totals		$697.20		$1073.60	$43.58	$67.10

Crew A-3F

Crew No.	Hr.	Daily	Hr.	Daily	Bare Costs	Incl. O&P
1 Equip. Oper. (crane)	$37.30	$298.40	$61.65	$493.20	$34.83	$57.48
1 Truck Driver (heavy)	32.35	258.80	53.30	426.40		
1 Pickup Truck, 4x4, 3/4 Ton		140.00		154.00		
1 Truck Tractor, 6x4, 380 H.P.		559.80		615.78		
1 Lowbed Trailer, 75 Ton		242.40		266.64	58.89	64.78
16 L.H., Daily Totals		$1499.40		$1956.02	$93.71	$122.25

For customer support on your Residential Costs with RSMeans Data, call 800.448.8182.

675

Crews - Residential

Crew A-3G

Crew No.	Hr.	Daily	Hr.	Daily	Bare Costs	Incl. O&P
1 Equip. Oper. (crane)	$37.30	$298.40	$61.65	$493.20	$34.83	$57.48
1 Truck Driver (heavy)	32.35	258.80	53.30	426.40		
1 Pickup Truck, 4x4, 3/4 Ton		140.00		154.00		
1 Truck Tractor, 6x4, 450 H.P.		679.80		747.78		
1 Lowbed Trailer, 75 Ton		242.40		266.64	66.39	73.03
16 L.H., Daily Totals		$1619.40		$2088.02	$101.21	$130.50

Crew A-3H

Crew No.	Hr.	Daily	Hr.	Daily	Bare Costs	Incl. O&P
1 Equip. Oper. (crane)	$37.30	$298.40	$61.65	$493.20	$37.30	$61.65
1 Hyd. Crane, 12 Ton (Daily)		767.80		844.58	95.97	105.57
8 L.H., Daily Totals		$1066.20		$1337.78	$133.28	$167.22

Crew A-3I

Crew No.	Hr.	Daily	Hr.	Daily	Bare Costs	Incl. O&P
1 Equip. Oper. (crane)	$37.30	$298.40	$61.65	$493.20	$37.30	$61.65
1 Hyd. Crane, 25 Ton (Daily)		904.80		995.28	113.10	124.41
8 L.H., Daily Totals		$1203.20		$1488.48	$150.40	$186.06

Crew A-3J

Crew No.	Hr.	Daily	Hr.	Daily	Bare Costs	Incl. O&P
1 Equip. Oper. (crane)	$37.30	$298.40	$61.65	$493.20	$37.30	$61.65
1 Hyd. Crane, 40 Ton (Daily)		1354.00		1489.40	169.25	186.18
8 L.H., Daily Totals		$1652.40		$1982.60	$206.55	$247.82

Crew A-3K

Crew No.	Hr.	Daily	Hr.	Daily	Bare Costs	Incl. O&P
1 Equip. Oper. (crane)	$37.30	$298.40	$61.65	$493.20	$34.98	$57.80
1 Equip. Oper. (oiler)	32.65	261.20	53.95	431.60		
1 Hyd. Crane, 55 Ton (Daily)		1455.00		1600.50		
1 P/U Truck, 3/4 Ton (Daily)		154.40		169.84	100.59	110.65
16 L.H., Daily Totals		$2169.00		$2695.14	$135.56	$168.45

Crew A-3L

Crew No.	Hr.	Daily	Hr.	Daily	Bare Costs	Incl. O&P
1 Equip. Oper. (crane)	$37.30	$298.40	$61.65	$493.20	$34.98	$57.80
1 Equip. Oper. (oiler)	32.65	261.20	53.95	431.60		
1 Hyd. Crane, 80 Ton (Daily)		2245.00		2469.50		
1 P/U Truck, 3/4 Ton (Daily)		154.40		169.84	149.96	164.96
16 L.H., Daily Totals		$2959.00		$3564.14	$184.94	$222.76

Crew A-3M

Crew No.	Hr.	Daily	Hr.	Daily	Bare Costs	Incl. O&P
1 Equip. Oper. (crane)	$37.30	$298.40	$61.65	$493.20	$34.98	$57.80
1 Equip. Oper. (oiler)	32.65	261.20	53.95	431.60		
1 Hyd. Crane, 100 Ton (Daily)		2439.00		2682.90		
1 P/U Truck, 3/4 Ton (Daily)		154.40		169.84	162.09	178.30
16 L.H., Daily Totals		$3153.00		$3777.54	$197.06	$236.10

Crew A-3N

Crew No.	Hr.	Daily	Hr.	Daily	Bare Costs	Incl. O&P
1 Equip. Oper. (crane)	$37.30	$298.40	$61.65	$493.20	$37.30	$61.65
1 Tower Crane (monthly)		1166.00		1282.60	145.75	160.32
8 L.H., Daily Totals		$1464.40		$1775.80	$183.05	$221.97

Crew A-3P

Crew No.	Hr.	Daily	Hr.	Daily	Bare Costs	Incl. O&P
1 Equip. Oper. (light)	$35.20	$281.60	$58.20	$465.60	$35.20	$58.20
1 A.T. Forklift, 31' reach, 45' lift		520.60		572.66	65.08	71.58
8 L.H., Daily Totals		$802.20		$1038.26	$100.28	$129.78

Crew A-3Q

Crew No.	Hr.	Daily	Hr.	Daily	Bare Costs	Incl. O&P
1 Equip. Oper. (light)	$35.20	$281.60	$58.20	$465.60	$35.20	$58.20
1 Pickup Truck, 4x4, 3/4 Ton		140.00		154.00		
1 Flatbed Trailer, 3 Ton		24.00		26.40	20.50	22.55
8 L.H., Daily Totals		$445.60		$646.00	$55.70	$80.75

Crew A-3R

Crew No.	Hr.	Daily	Hr.	Daily	Bare Costs	Incl. O&P
1 Equip. Oper. (light)	$35.20	$281.60	$58.20	$465.60	$35.20	$58.20
1 Forklift, Smooth Floor, 8,000 Lb.		171.20		188.32	21.40	23.54
8 L.H., Daily Totals		$452.80		$653.92	$56.60	$81.74

Crew A-4

Crew No.	Hr.	Daily	Hr.	Daily	Bare Costs	Incl. O&P
2 Carpenters	$34.95	$559.20	$58.45	$935.20	$33.03	$55.03
1 Painter, Ordinary	29.20	233.60	48.20	385.60		
24 L.H., Daily Totals		$792.80		$1320.80	$33.03	$55.03

Crew A-5

Crew No.	Hr.	Daily	Hr.	Daily	Bare Costs	Incl. O&P
2 Laborers	$26.60	$425.60	$44.50	$712.00	$27.18	$45.38
.25 Truck Driver (light)	31.80	63.60	52.40	104.80		
.25 Flatbed Truck, Gas, 1.5 Ton		54.35		59.78	3.02	3.32
18 L.H., Daily Totals		$543.55		$876.59	$30.20	$48.70

Crew A-6

Crew No.	Hr.	Daily	Hr.	Daily	Bare Costs	Incl. O&P
1 Instrument Man	$35.75	$286.00	$60.00	$480.00	$34.85	$58.20
1 Rodman/Chainman	33.95	271.60	56.40	451.20		
1 Level, Electronic		41.55		45.70	2.60	2.86
16 L.H., Daily Totals		$599.15		$976.90	$37.45	$61.06

Crew A-7

Crew No.	Hr.	Daily	Hr.	Daily	Bare Costs	Incl. O&P
1 Chief of Party	$41.40	$331.20	$68.70	$549.60	$37.03	$61.70
1 Instrument Man	35.75	286.00	60.00	480.00		
1 Rodman/Chainman	33.95	271.60	56.40	451.20		
1 Level, Electronic		41.55		45.70	1.73	1.90
24 L.H., Daily Totals		$930.35		$1526.51	$38.76	$63.60

Crew A-8

Crew No.	Hr.	Daily	Hr.	Daily	Bare Costs	Incl. O&P
1 Chief of Party	$41.40	$331.20	$68.70	$549.60	$36.26	$60.38
1 Instrument Man	35.75	286.00	60.00	480.00		
2 Rodmen/Chainmen	33.95	543.20	56.40	902.40		
1 Level, Electronic		41.55		45.70	1.30	1.43
32 L.H., Daily Totals		$1201.95		$1977.70	$37.56	$61.80

Crew A-9

Crew No.	Hr.	Daily	Hr.	Daily	Bare Costs	Incl. O&P
1 Asbestos Foreman	$36.30	$290.40	$61.50	$492.00	$35.86	$60.76
7 Asbestos Workers	35.80	2004.80	60.65	3396.40		
64 L.H., Daily Totals		$2295.20		$3888.40	$35.86	$60.76

Crew A-10A

Crew No.	Hr.	Daily	Hr.	Daily	Bare Costs	Incl. O&P
1 Asbestos Foreman	$36.30	$290.40	$61.50	$492.00	$35.97	$60.93
2 Asbestos Workers	35.80	572.80	60.65	970.40		
24 L.H., Daily Totals		$863.20		$1462.40	$35.97	$60.93

Crew A-10B

Crew No.	Hr.	Daily	Hr.	Daily	Bare Costs	Incl. O&P
1 Asbestos Foreman	$36.30	$290.40	$61.50	$492.00	$35.92	$60.86
3 Asbestos Workers	35.80	859.20	60.65	1455.60		
32 L.H., Daily Totals		$1149.60		$1947.60	$35.92	$60.86

Crew A-10C

Crew No.	Hr.	Daily	Hr.	Daily	Bare Costs	Incl. O&P
3 Asbestos Workers	$35.80	$859.20	$60.65	$1455.60	$35.80	$60.65
1 Flatbed Truck, Gas, 1.5 Ton		217.40		239.14	9.06	9.96
24 L.H., Daily Totals		$1076.60		$1694.74	$44.86	$70.61

For customer support on your Residential Costs with RSMeans Data, call 800.448.8182.

Crews - Residential

Crew A-10D

Crew No.	Bare Costs Hr.	Daily	Incl. Subs O&P Hr.	Daily	Cost Per Labor-Hour Bare Costs	Incl. O&P
2 Asbestos Workers	$35.80	$572.80	$60.65	$970.40	$35.39	$59.23
1 Equip. Oper. (crane)	37.30	298.40	61.65	493.20		
1 Equip. Oper. (oiler)	32.65	261.20	53.95	431.60		
1 Hydraulic Crane, 33 Ton		863.60		949.96	26.99	29.69
32 L.H., Daily Totals		$1996.00		$2845.16	$62.38	$88.91

Crew A-11

Crew No.	Bare Costs Hr.	Daily	Incl. Subs O&P Hr.	Daily	Cost Per Labor-Hour Bare Costs	Incl. O&P
1 Asbestos Foreman	$36.30	$290.40	$61.50	$492.00	$35.86	$60.76
7 Asbestos Workers	35.80	2004.80	60.65	3396.40		
2 Chip. Hammers, 12 Lb., Elec.		40.80		44.88	0.64	0.70
64 L.H., Daily Totals		$2336.00		$3933.28	$36.50	$61.46

Crew A-12

Crew No.	Bare Costs Hr.	Daily	Incl. Subs O&P Hr.	Daily	Cost Per Labor-Hour Bare Costs	Incl. O&P
1 Asbestos Foreman	$36.30	$290.40	$61.50	$492.00	$35.86	$60.76
7 Asbestos Workers	35.80	2004.80	60.65	3396.40		
1 Trk-Mtd Vac, 14 CY, 1500 Gal.		505.90		556.49		
1 Flatbed Truck, 20,000 GVW		232.00		255.20	11.53	12.68
64 L.H., Daily Totals		$3033.10		$4700.09	$47.39	$73.44

Crew A-13

Crew No.	Bare Costs Hr.	Daily	Incl. Subs O&P Hr.	Daily	Cost Per Labor-Hour Bare Costs	Incl. O&P
1 Equip. Oper. (light)	$35.20	$281.60	$58.20	$465.60	$35.20	$58.20
1 Trk-Mtd Vac, 14 CY, 1500 Gal.		505.90		556.49		
1 Flatbed Truck, 20,000 GVW		232.00		255.20	92.24	101.46
8 L.H., Daily Totals		$1019.50		$1277.29	$127.44	$159.66

Crew B-1

Crew No.	Bare Costs Hr.	Daily	Incl. Subs O&P Hr.	Daily	Cost Per Labor-Hour Bare Costs	Incl. O&P
1 Labor Foreman (outside)	$28.60	$228.80	$47.80	$382.40	$27.27	$45.60
2 Laborers	26.60	425.60	44.50	712.00		
24 L.H., Daily Totals		$654.40		$1094.40	$27.27	$45.60

Crew B-1A

Crew No.	Bare Costs Hr.	Daily	Incl. Subs O&P Hr.	Daily	Cost Per Labor-Hour Bare Costs	Incl. O&P
1 Labor Foreman (outside)	$28.60	$228.80	$47.80	$382.40	$27.27	$45.60
2 Laborers	26.60	425.60	44.50	712.00		
2 Cutting Torches		24.00		26.40		
2 Sets of Gases		336.00		369.60	15.00	16.50
24 L.H., Daily Totals		$1014.40		$1490.40	$42.27	$62.10

Crew B-1B

Crew No.	Bare Costs Hr.	Daily	Incl. Subs O&P Hr.	Daily	Cost Per Labor-Hour Bare Costs	Incl. O&P
1 Labor Foreman (outside)	$28.60	$228.80	$47.80	$382.40	$29.77	$49.61
2 Laborers	26.60	425.60	44.50	712.00		
1 Equip. Oper. (crane)	37.30	298.40	61.65	493.20		
2 Cutting Torches		24.00		26.40		
2 Sets of Gases		336.00		369.60		
1 Hyd. Crane, 12 Ton		572.80		630.08	29.15	32.06
32 L.H., Daily Totals		$1885.60		$2613.68	$58.92	$81.68

Crew B-1C

Crew No.	Bare Costs Hr.	Daily	Incl. Subs O&P Hr.	Daily	Cost Per Labor-Hour Bare Costs	Incl. O&P
1 Labor Foreman (outside)	$28.60	$228.80	$47.80	$382.40	$27.27	$45.60
2 Laborers	26.60	425.60	44.50	712.00		
1 Telescoping Boom Lift, to 60'		456.00		501.60	19.00	20.90
24 L.H., Daily Totals		$1110.40		$1596.00	$46.27	$66.50

Crew B-1D

Crew No.	Bare Costs Hr.	Daily	Incl. Subs O&P Hr.	Daily	Cost Per Labor-Hour Bare Costs	Incl. O&P
2 Laborers	$26.60	$425.60	$44.50	$712.00	$26.60	$44.50
1 Small Work Boat, Gas, 50 H.P.		155.00		170.50		
1 Pressure Washer, 7 GPM		82.00		90.20	14.81	16.29
16 L.H., Daily Totals		$662.60		$972.70	$41.41	$60.79

Crew B-1E

Crew No.	Bare Costs Hr.	Daily	Incl. Subs O&P Hr.	Daily	Cost Per Labor-Hour Bare Costs	Incl. O&P
1 Labor Foreman (outside)	$28.60	$228.80	$47.80	$382.40	$27.10	$45.33
3 Laborers	26.60	638.40	44.50	1068.00		
1 Work Boat, Diesel, 200 H.P.		1439.00		1582.90		
2 Pressure Washers, 7 GPM		164.00		180.40	50.09	55.10
32 L.H., Daily Totals		$2470.20		$3213.70	$77.19	$100.43

Crew B-1F

Crew No.	Bare Costs Hr.	Daily	Incl. Subs O&P Hr.	Daily	Cost Per Labor-Hour Bare Costs	Incl. O&P
2 Skilled Workers	$35.75	$572.00	$60.00	$960.00	$32.70	$54.83
1 Laborer	26.60	212.80	44.50	356.00		
1 Small Work Boat, Gas, 50 H.P.		155.00		170.50		
1 Pressure Washer, 7 GPM		82.00		90.20	9.88	10.86
24 L.H., Daily Totals		$1021.80		$1576.70	$42.58	$65.70

Crew B-1G

Crew No.	Bare Costs Hr.	Daily	Incl. Subs O&P Hr.	Daily	Cost Per Labor-Hour Bare Costs	Incl. O&P
2 Laborers	$26.60	$425.60	$44.50	$712.00	$26.60	$44.50
1 Small Work Boat, Gas, 50 H.P.		155.00		170.50	9.69	10.66
16 L.H., Daily Totals		$580.60		$882.50	$36.29	$55.16

Crew B-1H

Crew No.	Bare Costs Hr.	Daily	Incl. Subs O&P Hr.	Daily	Cost Per Labor-Hour Bare Costs	Incl. O&P
2 Skilled Workers	$35.75	$572.00	$60.00	$960.00	$32.70	$54.83
1 Laborer	26.60	212.80	44.50	356.00		
1 Small Work Boat, Gas, 50 H.P.		155.00		170.50	6.46	7.10
24 L.H., Daily Totals		$939.80		$1486.50	$39.16	$61.94

Crew B-1J

Crew No.	Bare Costs Hr.	Daily	Incl. Subs O&P Hr.	Daily	Cost Per Labor-Hour Bare Costs	Incl. O&P
1 Labor Foreman (inside)	$27.10	$216.80	$45.30	$362.40	$26.85	$44.90
1 Laborer	26.60	212.80	44.50	356.00		
16 L.H., Daily Totals		$429.60		$718.40	$26.85	$44.90

Crew B-1K

Crew No.	Bare Costs Hr.	Daily	Incl. Subs O&P Hr.	Daily	Cost Per Labor-Hour Bare Costs	Incl. O&P
1 Carpenter Foreman (inside)	$35.45	$283.60	$59.25	$474.00	$35.20	$58.85
1 Carpenter	34.95	279.60	58.45	467.60		
16 L.H., Daily Totals		$563.20		$941.60	$35.20	$58.85

Crew B-2

Crew No.	Bare Costs Hr.	Daily	Incl. Subs O&P Hr.	Daily	Cost Per Labor-Hour Bare Costs	Incl. O&P
1 Labor Foreman (outside)	$28.60	$228.80	$47.80	$382.40	$27.00	$45.16
4 Laborers	26.60	851.20	44.50	1424.00		
40 L.H., Daily Totals		$1080.00		$1806.40	$27.00	$45.16

Crew B-2A

Crew No.	Bare Costs Hr.	Daily	Incl. Subs O&P Hr.	Daily	Cost Per Labor-Hour Bare Costs	Incl. O&P
1 Labor Foreman (outside)	$28.60	$228.80	$47.80	$382.40	$27.27	$45.60
2 Laborers	26.60	425.60	44.50	712.00		
1 Telescoping Boom Lift, to 60'		456.00		501.60	19.00	20.90
24 L.H., Daily Totals		$1110.40		$1596.00	$46.27	$66.50

Crew B-3

Crew No.	Bare Costs Hr.	Daily	Incl. Subs O&P Hr.	Daily	Cost Per Labor-Hour Bare Costs	Incl. O&P
1 Labor Foreman (outside)	$28.60	$228.80	$47.80	$382.40	$30.48	$50.59
2 Laborers	26.60	425.60	44.50	712.00		
1 Equip. Oper. (medium)	36.40	291.20	60.15	481.20		
2 Truck Drivers (heavy)	32.35	517.60	53.30	852.80		
1 Crawler Loader, 3 C.Y.		1281.00		1409.10		
2 Dump Trucks, 12 C.Y., 400 H.P.		1285.20		1413.72	53.46	58.81
48 L.H., Daily Totals		$4029.40		$5251.22	$83.95	$109.40

Crew B-3A

Crew No.	Bare Costs Hr.	Daily	Incl. Subs O&P Hr.	Daily	Cost Per Labor-Hour Bare Costs	Incl. O&P
4 Laborers	$26.60	$851.20	$44.50	$1424.00	$28.56	$47.63
1 Equip. Oper. (medium)	36.40	291.20	60.15	481.20		
1 Hyd. Excavator, 1.5 C.Y.		965.00		1061.50	24.13	26.54
40 L.H., Daily Totals		$2107.40		$2966.70	$52.69	$74.17

For customer support on your Residential Costs with RSMeans Data, call 800.448.8182.

677

Crew B-3B	Hr.	Daily	Hr.	Daily	Bare Costs	Incl. O&P
2 Laborers	$26.60	$425.60	$44.50	$712.00	$30.49	$50.61
1 Equip. Oper. (medium)	36.40	291.20	60.15	481.20		
1 Truck Driver (heavy)	32.35	258.80	53.30	426.40		
1 Backhoe Loader, 80 H.P.		394.40		433.84		
1 Dump Truck, 12 C.Y., 400 H.P.		642.60		706.86	32.41	35.65
32 L.H., Daily Totals		$2012.60		$2760.30	$62.89	$86.26

Crew B-3C	Hr.	Daily	Hr.	Daily	Bare Costs	Incl. O&P
3 Laborers	$26.60	$638.40	$44.50	$1068.00	$29.05	$48.41
1 Equip. Oper. (medium)	36.40	291.20	60.15	481.20		
1 Crawler Loader, 4 C.Y.		1528.00		1680.80	47.75	52.52
32 L.H., Daily Totals		$2457.60		$3230.00	$76.80	$100.94

Crew B-4	Hr.	Daily	Hr.	Daily	Bare Costs	Incl. O&P
1 Labor Foreman (outside)	$28.60	$228.80	$47.80	$382.40	$27.89	$46.52
4 Laborers	26.60	851.20	44.50	1424.00		
1 Truck Driver (heavy)	32.35	258.80	53.30	426.40		
1 Truck Tractor, 220 H.P.		336.60		370.26		
1 Flatbed Trailer, 40 Ton		175.00		192.50	10.66	11.72
48 L.H., Daily Totals		$1850.40		$2795.56	$38.55	$58.24

Crew B-5	Hr.	Daily	Hr.	Daily	Bare Costs	Incl. O&P
1 Labor Foreman (outside)	$28.60	$228.80	$47.80	$382.40	$28.96	$48.29
3 Laborers	26.60	638.40	44.50	1068.00		
1 Equip. Oper. (medium)	36.40	291.20	60.15	481.20		
1 Air Compressor, 250 cfm		181.20		199.32		
2 Breakers, Pavement, 60 lb.		20.40		22.44		
2 -50' Air Hoses, 1.5"		11.60		12.76		
1 Crawler Loader, 3 C.Y.		1281.00		1409.10	37.35	41.09
40 L.H., Daily Totals		$2652.60		$3575.22	$66.31	$89.38

Crew B-5A	Hr.	Daily	Hr.	Daily	Bare Costs	Incl. O&P
1 Labor Foreman (outside)	$28.60	$228.80	$47.80	$382.40	$30.07	$49.99
6 Laborers	26.60	1276.80	44.50	2136.00		
2 Equip. Oper. (medium)	36.40	582.40	60.15	962.40		
1 Equip. Oper. (light)	35.20	281.60	58.20	465.60		
2 Truck Drivers (heavy)	32.35	517.60	53.30	852.80		
1 Air Compressor, 365 cfm		236.00		259.60		
2 Breakers, Pavement, 60 lb.		20.40		22.44		
8 -50' Air Hoses, 1"		32.80		36.08		
2 Dump Trucks, 8 C.Y., 220 H.P.		782.00		860.20	11.16	12.27
96 L.H., Daily Totals		$3958.40		$5977.52	$41.23	$62.27

Crew B-5B	Hr.	Daily	Hr.	Daily	Bare Costs	Incl. O&P
1 Powderman	$35.75	$286.00	$60.00	$480.00	$34.27	$56.70
2 Equip. Oper. (medium)	36.40	582.40	60.15	962.40		
3 Truck Drivers (heavy)	32.35	776.40	53.30	1279.20		
1 F.E. Loader, W.M., 2.5 C.Y.		556.20		611.82		
3 Dump Trucks, 12 C.Y., 400 H.P.		1927.80		2120.58		
1 Air Compressor, 365 CFM		236.00		259.60	56.67	62.33
48 L.H., Daily Totals		$4364.80		$5713.60	$90.93	$119.03

Crew B-5C	Hr.	Daily	Hr.	Daily	Bare Costs	Incl. O&P
3 Laborers	$26.60	$638.40	$44.50	$1068.00	$31.36	$51.98
1 Equip. Oper. (medium)	36.40	291.20	60.15	481.20		
2 Truck Drivers (heavy)	32.35	517.60	53.30	852.80		
1 Equip. Oper. (crane)	37.30	298.40	61.65	493.20		
1 Equip. Oper. (oiler)	32.65	261.20	53.95	431.60		
2 Dump Trucks, 12 C.Y., 400 H.P.		1285.20		1413.72		
1 Crawler Loader, 4 C.Y.		1528.00		1680.80		
1 S.P. Crane, 4x4, 25 Ton		605.60		666.16	53.42	58.76
64 L.H., Daily Totals		$5425.60		$7087.48	$84.78	$110.74

Crew B-5D	Hr.	Daily	Hr.	Daily	Bare Costs	Incl. O&P
1 Labor Foreman (outside)	$28.60	$228.80	$47.80	$382.40	$29.52	$49.13
3 Laborers	26.60	638.40	44.50	1068.00		
1 Equip. Oper. (medium)	36.40	291.20	60.15	481.20		
1 Truck Driver (heavy)	32.35	258.80	53.30	426.40		
1 Air Compressor, 250 cfm		181.20		199.32		
2 Breakers, Pavement, 60 lb.		20.40		22.44		
2 -50' Air Hoses, 1.5"		11.60		12.76		
1 Crawler Loader, 3 C.Y.		1281.00		1409.10		
1 Dump Truck, 12 C.Y., 400 H.P.		642.60		706.86	44.52	48.97
48 L.H., Daily Totals		$3554.00		$4708.48	$74.04	$98.09

Crew B-6	Hr.	Daily	Hr.	Daily	Bare Costs	Incl. O&P
2 Laborers	$26.60	$425.60	$44.50	$712.00	$29.47	$49.07
1 Equip. Oper. (light)	35.20	281.60	58.20	465.60		
1 Backhoe Loader, 48 H.P.		366.20		402.82	15.26	16.78
24 L.H., Daily Totals		$1073.40		$1580.42	$44.73	$65.85

Crew B-6B	Hr.	Daily	Hr.	Daily	Bare Costs	Incl. O&P
2 Labor Foremen (outside)	$28.60	$457.60	$47.80	$764.80	$27.27	$45.60
4 Laborers	26.60	851.20	44.50	1424.00		
1 S.P. Crane, 4x4, 5 Ton		276.00		303.60		
1 Flatbed Truck, Gas, 1.5 Ton		217.40		239.14		
1 Butt Fusion Mach., 4"-12" diam.		415.10		456.61	18.93	20.82
48 L.H., Daily Totals		$2217.30		$3188.15	$46.19	$66.42

Crew B-6C	Hr.	Daily	Hr.	Daily	Bare Costs	Incl. O&P
2 Labor Foremen (outside)	$28.60	$457.60	$47.80	$764.80	$27.27	$45.60
4 Laborers	26.60	851.20	44.50	1424.00		
1 S.P. Crane, 4x4, 12 Ton		435.60		479.16		
1 Flatbed Truck, Gas, 3 Ton		270.20		297.22		
1 Butt Fusion Mach., 8"-24" diam.		1821.00		2003.10	52.64	57.91
48 L.H., Daily Totals		$3835.60		$4968.28	$79.91	$103.51

Crew B-7	Hr.	Daily	Hr.	Daily	Bare Costs	Incl. O&P
1 Labor Foreman (outside)	$28.60	$228.80	$47.80	$382.40	$28.57	$47.66
4 Laborers	26.60	851.20	44.50	1424.00		
1 Equip. Oper. (medium)	36.40	291.20	60.15	481.20		
1 Brush Chipper, 12", 130 H.P.		404.40		444.84		
1 Crawler Loader, 3 C.Y.		1281.00		1409.10		
2 Chain Saws, Gas, 36" Long		90.00		99.00	36.99	40.69
48 L.H., Daily Totals		$3146.60		$4240.54	$65.55	$88.34

Crew B-7A	Hr.	Daily	Hr.	Daily	Bare Costs	Incl. O&P
2 Laborers	$26.60	$425.60	$44.50	$712.00	$29.47	$49.07
1 Equip. Oper. (light)	35.20	281.60	58.20	465.60		
1 Rake w/Tractor		344.10		378.51		
2 Chain Saws, Gas, 18"		58.80		64.68	16.79	18.47
24 L.H., Daily Totals		$1110.10		$1620.79	$46.25	$67.53

Crew No.	Bare Costs		Incl. Subs O&P		Cost Per Labor-Hour	

Crew B-7B	Hr.	Daily	Hr.	Daily	Bare Costs	Incl. O&P
1 Labor Foreman (outside)	$28.60	$228.80	$47.80	$382.40	$29.11	$48.46
4 Laborers	26.60	851.20	44.50	1424.00		
1 Equip. Oper. (medium)	36.40	291.20	60.15	481.20		
1 Truck Driver (heavy)	32.35	258.80	53.30	426.40		
1 Brush Chipper, 12", 130 H.P.		404.40		444.84		
1 Crawler Loader, 3 C.Y.		1281.00		1409.10		
2 Chain Saws, Gas, 36" Long		90.00		99.00		
1 Dump Truck, 8 C.Y., 220 H.P.		391.00		430.10	38.69	42.55
56 L.H., Daily Totals		$3796.40		$5097.04	$67.79	$91.02

Crew B-7C	Hr.	Daily	Hr.	Daily	Bare Costs	Incl. O&P
1 Labor Foreman (outside)	$28.60	$228.80	$47.80	$382.40	$29.11	$48.46
4 Laborers	26.60	851.20	44.50	1424.00		
1 Equip. Oper. (medium)	36.40	291.20	60.15	481.20		
1 Truck Driver (heavy)	32.35	258.80	53.30	426.40		
1 Brush Chipper, 12", 130 H.P.		404.40		444.84		
1 Crawler Loader, 3 C.Y.		1281.00		1409.10		
2 Chain Saws, Gas, 36" Long		90.00		99.00		
1 Dump Truck, 12 C.Y., 400 H.P.		642.60		706.86	43.18	47.50
56 L.H., Daily Totals		$4048.00		$5373.80	$72.29	$95.96

Crew B-8	Hr.	Daily	Hr.	Daily	Bare Costs	Incl. O&P
1 Labor Foreman (outside)	$28.60	$228.80	$47.80	$382.40	$31.33	$51.96
2 Laborers	26.60	425.60	44.50	712.00		
2 Equip. Oper. (medium)	36.40	582.40	60.15	962.40		
2 Truck Drivers (heavy)	32.35	517.60	53.30	852.80		
1 Hyd. Crane, 25 Ton		673.80		741.18		
1 Crawler Loader, 3 C.Y.		1281.00		1409.10		
2 Dump Trucks, 12 C.Y., 400 H.P.		1285.20		1413.72	57.86	63.64
56 L.H., Daily Totals		$4994.40		$6473.60	$89.19	$115.60

Crew B-9	Hr.	Daily	Hr.	Daily	Bare Costs	Incl. O&P
1 Labor Foreman (outside)	$28.60	$228.80	$47.80	$382.40	$27.00	$45.16
4 Laborers	26.60	851.20	44.50	1424.00		
1 Air Compressor, 250 cfm		181.20		199.32		
2 Breakers, Pavement, 60 lb.		20.40		22.44		
2 -50' Air Hoses, 1.5"		11.60		12.76	5.33	5.86
40 L.H., Daily Totals		$1293.20		$2040.92	$32.33	$51.02

Crew B-9A	Hr.	Daily	Hr.	Daily	Bare Costs	Incl. O&P
2 Laborers	$26.60	$425.60	$44.50	$712.00	$28.52	$47.43
1 Truck Driver (heavy)	32.35	258.80	53.30	426.40		
1 Water Tank Trailer, 5000 Gal.		143.00		157.30		
1 Truck Tractor, 220 H.P.		336.60		370.26		
2 -50' Discharge Hoses, 3"		3.50		3.85	20.13	22.14
24 L.H., Daily Totals		$1167.50		$1669.81	$48.65	$69.58

Crew B-9B	Hr.	Daily	Hr.	Daily	Bare Costs	Incl. O&P
2 Laborers	$26.60	$425.60	$44.50	$712.00	$28.52	$47.43
1 Truck Driver (heavy)	32.35	258.80	53.30	426.40		
2 -50' Discharge Hoses, 3"		3.50		3.85		
1 Water Tank Trailer, 5000 Gal.		143.00		157.30		
1 Truck Tractor, 220 H.P.		336.60		370.26		
1 Pressure Washer		66.00		72.60	22.88	25.17
24 L.H., Daily Totals		$1233.50		$1742.41	$51.40	$72.60

Crew B-9D	Hr.	Daily	Hr.	Daily	Bare Costs	Incl. O&P
1 Labor Foreman (outside)	$28.60	$228.80	$47.80	$382.40	$27.00	$45.16
4 Common Laborers	26.60	851.20	44.50	1424.00		
1 Air Compressor, 250 cfm		181.20		199.32		
2 -50' Air Hoses, 1.5"		11.60		12.76		
2 Air Powered Tampers		52.40		57.64	6.13	6.74
40 L.H., Daily Totals		$1325.20		$2076.12	$33.13	$51.90

Crew B-10	Hr.	Daily	Hr.	Daily	Bare Costs	Incl. O&P
1 Equip. Oper. (medium)	36.40	291.20	60.15	481.20	36.40	60.15
8 L.H., Daily Totals		$291.20		$481.20	$36.40	$60.15

Crew B-10A	Hr.	Daily	Hr.	Daily	Bare Costs	Incl. O&P
1 Equip. Oper. (medium)	$36.40	$291.20	$60.15	$481.20	$36.40	$60.15
1 Roller, 2-Drum, W.B., 7.5 H.P.		182.80		201.08	22.85	25.14
8 L.H., Daily Totals		$474.00		$682.28	$59.25	$85.28

Crew B-10B	Hr.	Daily	Hr.	Daily	Bare Costs	Incl. O&P
1 Equip. Oper. (medium)	$36.40	$291.20	$60.15	$481.20	$36.40	$60.15
1 Dozer, 200 H.P.		1384.00		1522.40	173.00	190.30
8 L.H., Daily Totals		$1675.20		$2003.60	$209.40	$250.45

Crew B-10C	Hr.	Daily	Hr.	Daily	Bare Costs	Incl. O&P
1 Equip. Oper. (medium)	$36.40	$291.20	$60.15	$481.20	$36.40	$60.15
1 Dozer, 200 H.P.		1384.00		1522.40		
1 Vibratory Roller, Towed, 23 Ton		427.40		470.14	226.43	249.07
8 L.H., Daily Totals		$2102.60		$2473.74	$262.82	$309.22

Crew B-10D	Hr.	Daily	Hr.	Daily	Bare Costs	Incl. O&P
1 Equip. Oper. (medium)	$36.40	$291.20	$60.15	$481.20	$36.40	$60.15
1 Dozer, 200 H.P.		1384.00		1522.40		
1 Sheepsft. Roller, Towed		451.00		496.10	229.38	252.31
8 L.H., Daily Totals		$2126.20		$2499.70	$265.77	$312.46

Crew B-10E	Hr.	Daily	Hr.	Daily	Bare Costs	Incl. O&P
1 Equip. Oper. (medium)	$36.40	$291.20	$60.15	$481.20	$36.40	$60.15
1 Tandem Roller, 5 Ton		152.40		167.64	19.05	20.95
8 L.H., Daily Totals		$443.60		$648.84	$55.45	$81.11

Crew B-10F	Hr.	Daily	Hr.	Daily	Bare Costs	Incl. O&P
1 Equip. Oper. (medium)	$36.40	$291.20	$60.15	$481.20	$36.40	$60.15
1 Tandem Roller, 10 Ton		237.60		261.36	29.70	32.67
8 L.H., Daily Totals		$528.80		$742.56	$66.10	$92.82

Crew B-10G	Hr.	Daily	Hr.	Daily	Bare Costs	Incl. O&P
1 Equip. Oper. (medium)	$36.40	$291.20	$60.15	$481.20	$36.40	$60.15
1 Sheepsfoot Roller, 240 H.P.		1296.00		1425.60	162.00	178.20
8 L.H., Daily Totals		$1587.20		$1906.80	$198.40	$238.35

Crew B-10H	Hr.	Daily	Hr.	Daily	Bare Costs	Incl. O&P
1 Equip. Oper. (medium)	$36.40	$291.20	$60.15	$481.20	$36.40	$60.15
1 Diaphragm Water Pump, 2"		71.00		78.10		
1 -20' Suction Hose, 2"		1.95		2.15		
2 -50' Discharge Hoses, 2"		1.80		1.98	9.34	10.28
8 L.H., Daily Totals		$365.95		$563.42	$45.74	$70.43

For customer support on your Residential Costs with RSMeans Data, call 800.448.8182.

679

Crew No.	Bare Costs Hr.	Daily	Incl. Subs O&P Hr.	Daily	Cost Per Labor-Hour Bare Costs	Incl. O&P
Crew B-10I	Hr.	Daily	Hr.	Daily	Bare Costs	Incl. O&P
1 Equip. Oper. (medium)	$36.40	$291.20	$60.15	$481.20	$36.40	$60.15
1 Diaphragm Water Pump, 4"		114.20		125.62		
1 -20' Suction Hose, 4"		3.45		3.79		
2 -50' Discharge Hoses, 4"		4.70		5.17	15.29	16.82
8 L.H., Daily Totals		$413.55		$615.78	$51.69	$76.97

Crew No.	Bare Costs Hr.	Daily	Incl. Subs O&P Hr.	Daily	Bare Costs	Incl. O&P
Crew B-10J	Hr.	Daily	Hr.	Daily	Bare Costs	Incl. O&P
1 Equip. Oper. (medium)	$36.40	$291.20	$60.15	$481.20	$36.40	$60.15
1 Centrifugal Water Pump, 3"		78.60		86.46		
1 -20' Suction Hose, 3"		3.05		3.36		
2 -50' Discharge Hoses, 3"		3.50		3.85	10.64	11.71
8 L.H., Daily Totals		$376.35		$574.87	$47.04	$71.86

Crew B-10K	Hr.	Daily	Hr.	Daily	Bare Costs	Incl. O&P
1 Equip. Oper. (medium)	$36.40	$291.20	$60.15	$481.20	$36.40	$60.15
1 Centr. Water Pump, 6"		325.40		357.94		
1 -20' Suction Hose, 6"		11.90		13.09		
2 -50' Discharge Hoses, 6"		12.60		13.86	43.74	48.11
8 L.H., Daily Totals		$641.10		$866.09	$80.14	$108.26

Crew B-10L	Hr.	Daily	Hr.	Daily	Bare Costs	Incl. O&P
1 Equip. Oper. (medium)	$36.40	$291.20	$60.15	$481.20	$36.40	$60.15
1 Dozer, 80 H.P.		468.60		515.46	58.58	64.43
8 L.H., Daily Totals		$759.80		$996.66	$94.97	$124.58

Crew B-10M	Hr.	Daily	Hr.	Daily	Bare Costs	Incl. O&P
1 Equip. Oper. (medium)	$36.40	$291.20	$60.15	$481.20	$36.40	$60.15
1 Dozer, 300 H.P.		1900.00		2090.00	237.50	261.25
8 L.H., Daily Totals		$2191.20		$2571.20	$273.90	$321.40

Crew B-10N	Hr.	Daily	Hr.	Daily	Bare Costs	Incl. O&P
1 Equip. Oper. (medium)	$36.40	$291.20	$60.15	$481.20	$36.40	$60.15
1 F.E. Loader, T.M., 1.5 C.Y.		568.20		625.02	71.03	78.13
8 L.H., Daily Totals		$859.40		$1106.22	$107.43	$138.28

Crew B-10O	Hr.	Daily	Hr.	Daily	Bare Costs	Incl. O&P
1 Equip. Oper. (medium)	$36.40	$291.20	$60.15	$481.20	$36.40	$60.15
1 F.E. Loader, T.M., 2.25 C.Y.		977.60		1075.36	122.20	134.42
8 L.H., Daily Totals		$1268.80		$1556.56	$158.60	$194.57

Crew B-10P	Hr.	Daily	Hr.	Daily	Bare Costs	Incl. O&P
1 Equip. Oper. (medium)	$36.40	$291.20	$60.15	$481.20	$36.40	$60.15
1 Crawler Loader, 3 C.Y.		1281.00		1409.10	160.13	176.14
8 L.H., Daily Totals		$1572.20		$1890.30	$196.53	$236.29

Crew B-10Q	Hr.	Daily	Hr.	Daily	Bare Costs	Incl. O&P
1 Equip. Oper. (medium)	$36.40	$291.20	$60.15	$481.20	$36.40	$60.15
1 Crawler Loader, 4 C.Y.		1528.00		1680.80	191.00	210.10
8 L.H., Daily Totals		$1819.20		$2162.00	$227.40	$270.25

Crew B-10R	Hr.	Daily	Hr.	Daily	Bare Costs	Incl. O&P
1 Equip. Oper. (medium)	$36.40	$291.20	$60.15	$481.20	$36.40	$60.15
1 F.E. Loader, W.M., 1 C.Y.		312.80		344.08	39.10	43.01
8 L.H., Daily Totals		$604.00		$825.28	$75.50	$103.16

Crew B-10S	Hr.	Daily	Hr.	Daily	Bare Costs	Incl. O&P
1 Equip. Oper. (medium)	$36.40	$291.20	$60.15	$481.20	$36.40	$60.15
1 F.E. Loader, W.M., 1.5 C.Y.		362.00		398.20	45.25	49.77
8 L.H., Daily Totals		$653.20		$879.40	$81.65	$109.93

Crew B-10T	Hr.	Daily	Hr.	Daily	Bare Costs	Incl. O&P
1 Equip. Oper. (medium)	$36.40	$291.20	$60.15	$481.20	$36.40	$60.15
1 F.E. Loader, W.M., 2.5 C.Y.		556.20		611.82	69.53	76.48
8 L.H., Daily Totals		$847.40		$1093.02	$105.93	$136.63

Crew B-10U	Hr.	Daily	Hr.	Daily	Bare Costs	Incl. O&P
1 Equip. Oper. (medium)	$36.40	$291.20	$60.15	$481.20	$36.40	$60.15
1 F.E. Loader, W.M., 5.5 C.Y.		1081.00		1189.10	135.13	148.64
8 L.H., Daily Totals		$1372.20		$1670.30	$171.53	$208.79

Crew B-10V	Hr.	Daily	Hr.	Daily	Bare Costs	Incl. O&P
1 Equip. Oper. (medium)	$36.40	$291.20	$60.15	$481.20	$36.40	$60.15
1 Dozer, 700 H.P.		5218.00		5739.80	652.25	717.48
8 L.H., Daily Totals		$5509.20		$6221.00	$688.65	$777.63

Crew B-10W	Hr.	Daily	Hr.	Daily	Bare Costs	Incl. O&P
1 Equip. Oper. (medium)	$36.40	$291.20	$60.15	$481.20	$36.40	$60.15
1 Dozer, 105 H.P.		608.00		668.80	76.00	83.60
8 L.H., Daily Totals		$899.20		$1150.00	$112.40	$143.75

Crew B-10X	Hr.	Daily	Hr.	Daily	Bare Costs	Incl. O&P
1 Equip. Oper. (medium)	$36.40	$291.20	$60.15	$481.20	$36.40	$60.15
1 Dozer, 410 H.P.		2368.00		2604.80	296.00	325.60
8 L.H., Daily Totals		$2659.20		$3086.00	$332.40	$385.75

Crew B-10Y	Hr.	Daily	Hr.	Daily	Bare Costs	Incl. O&P
1 Equip. Oper. (medium)	$36.40	$291.20	$60.15	$481.20	$36.40	$60.15
1 Vibr. Roller, Towed, 12 Ton		605.40		665.94	75.67	83.24
8 L.H., Daily Totals		$896.60		$1147.14	$112.08	$143.39

Crew B-11A	Hr.	Daily	Hr.	Daily	Bare Costs	Incl. O&P
1 Equipment Oper. (med.)	$36.40	$291.20	$60.15	$481.20	$31.50	$52.33
1 Laborer	26.60	212.80	44.50	356.00		
1 Dozer, 200 H.P.		1384.00		1522.40	86.50	95.15
16 L.H., Daily Totals		$1888.00		$2359.60	$118.00	$147.47

Crew B-11B	Hr.	Daily	Hr.	Daily	Bare Costs	Incl. O&P
1 Equipment Oper. (light)	$35.20	$281.60	$58.20	$465.60	$30.90	$51.35
1 Laborer	26.60	212.80	44.50	356.00		
1 Air Powered Tamper		26.20		28.82		
1 Air Compressor, 365 cfm		236.00		259.60		
2 -50' Air Hoses, 1.5"		11.60		12.76	17.11	18.82
16 L.H., Daily Totals		$768.20		$1122.78	$48.01	$70.17

Crew B-11C	Hr.	Daily	Hr.	Daily	Bare Costs	Incl. O&P
1 Equipment Oper. (med.)	$36.40	$291.20	$60.15	$481.20	$31.50	$52.33
1 Laborer	26.60	212.80	44.50	356.00		
1 Backhoe Loader, 48 H.P.		366.20		402.82	22.89	25.18
16 L.H., Daily Totals		$870.20		$1240.02	$54.39	$77.50

Crew B-11K	Hr.	Daily	Hr.	Daily	Bare Costs	Incl. O&P
1 Equipment Oper. (med.)	$36.40	$291.20	$60.15	$481.20	$31.50	$52.33
1 Laborer	26.60	212.80	44.50	356.00		
1 Trencher, Chain Type, 8' D		2460.00		2706.00	153.75	169.13
16 L.H., Daily Totals		$2964.00		$3543.20	$185.25	$221.45

Crews - Residential

Crew B-11L

	Hr.	Daily	Hr.	Daily	Bare Costs	Incl. O&P
1 Equipment Oper. (med.)	$36.40	$291.20	$60.15	$481.20	$31.50	$52.33
1 Laborer	26.60	212.80	44.50	356.00		
1 Grader, 30,000 Lbs.		678.40		746.24	42.40	46.64
16 L.H., Daily Totals		$1182.40		$1583.44	$73.90	$98.97

Crew B-11M

	Hr.	Daily	Hr.	Daily	Bare Costs	Incl. O&P
1 Equipment Oper. (med.)	$36.40	$291.20	$60.15	$481.20	$31.50	$52.33
1 Laborer	26.60	212.80	44.50	356.00		
1 Backhoe Loader, 80 H.P.		394.40		433.84	24.65	27.11
16 L.H., Daily Totals		$898.40		$1271.04	$56.15	$79.44

Crew B-11W

	Hr.	Daily	Hr.	Daily	Bare Costs	Incl. O&P
1 Equipment Operator (med.)	$36.40	$291.20	$60.15	$481.20	$32.21	$53.14
1 Common Laborer	26.60	212.80	44.50	356.00		
10 Truck Drivers (heavy)	32.35	2588.00	53.30	4264.00		
1 Dozer, 200 H.P.		1384.00		1522.40		
1 Vibratory Roller, Towed, 23 Ton		427.40		470.14		
10 Dump Trucks, 8 C.Y., 220 H.P.		3910.00		4301.00	59.60	65.56
96 L.H., Daily Totals		$8813.40		$11394.74	$91.81	$118.70

Crew B-11Y

	Hr.	Daily	Hr.	Daily	Bare Costs	Incl. O&P
1 Labor Foreman (outside)	$28.60	$228.80	$47.80	$382.40	$30.09	$50.08
5 Common Laborers	26.60	1064.00	44.50	1780.00		
3 Equipment Operators (med.)	36.40	873.60	60.15	1443.60		
1 Dozer, 80 H.P.		468.60		515.46		
2 Rollers, 2-Drum, W.B., 7.5 H.P.		365.60		402.16		
4 Vibrating Plates, Gas, 21"		171.20		188.32	13.96	15.36
72 L.H., Daily Totals		$3171.80		$4711.94	$44.05	$65.44

Crew B-12A

	Hr.	Daily	Hr.	Daily	Bare Costs	Incl. O&P
1 Equip. Oper. (crane)	$37.30	$298.40	$61.65	$493.20	$31.95	$53.08
1 Laborer	26.60	212.80	44.50	356.00		
1 Hyd. Excavator, 1 C.Y.		798.20		878.02	49.89	54.88
16 L.H., Daily Totals		$1309.40		$1727.22	$81.84	$107.95

Crew B-12B

	Hr.	Daily	Hr.	Daily	Bare Costs	Incl. O&P
1 Equip. Oper. (crane)	$37.30	$298.40	$61.65	$493.20	$31.95	$53.08
1 Laborer	26.60	212.80	44.50	356.00		
1 Hyd. Excavator, 1.5 C.Y.		965.00		1061.50	60.31	66.34
16 L.H., Daily Totals		$1476.20		$1910.70	$92.26	$119.42

Crew B-12C

	Hr.	Daily	Hr.	Daily	Bare Costs	Incl. O&P
1 Equip. Oper. (crane)	$37.30	$298.40	$61.65	$493.20	$31.95	$53.08
1 Laborer	26.60	212.80	44.50	356.00		
1 Hyd. Excavator, 2 C.Y.		1123.00		1235.30	70.19	77.21
16 L.H., Daily Totals		$1634.20		$2084.50	$102.14	$130.28

Crew B-12D

	Hr.	Daily	Hr.	Daily	Bare Costs	Incl. O&P
1 Equip. Oper. (crane)	$37.30	$298.40	$61.65	$493.20	$31.95	$53.08
1 Laborer	26.60	212.80	44.50	356.00		
1 Hyd. Excavator, 3.5 C.Y.		2401.00		2641.10	150.06	165.07
16 L.H., Daily Totals		$2912.20		$3490.30	$182.01	$218.14

Crew B-12E

	Hr.	Daily	Hr.	Daily	Bare Costs	Incl. O&P
1 Equip. Oper. (crane)	$37.30	$298.40	$61.65	$493.20	$31.95	$53.08
1 Laborer	26.60	212.80	44.50	356.00		
1 Hyd. Excavator, .5 C.Y.		443.60		487.96	27.73	30.50
16 L.H., Daily Totals		$954.80		$1337.16	$59.67	$83.57

Crew B-12F

	Hr.	Daily	Hr.	Daily	Bare Costs	Incl. O&P
1 Equip. Oper. (crane)	$37.30	$298.40	$61.65	$493.20	$31.95	$53.08
1 Laborer	26.60	212.80	44.50	356.00		
1 Hyd. Excavator, .75 C.Y.		674.20		741.62	42.14	46.35
16 L.H., Daily Totals		$1185.40		$1590.82	$74.09	$99.43

Crew B-12G

	Hr.	Daily	Hr.	Daily	Bare Costs	Incl. O&P
1 Equip. Oper. (crane)	$37.30	$298.40	$61.65	$493.20	$31.95	$53.08
1 Laborer	26.60	212.80	44.50	356.00		
1 Crawler Crane, 15 Ton		757.75		833.52		
1 Clamshell Bucket, .5 C.Y.		38.20		42.02	49.75	54.72
16 L.H., Daily Totals		$1307.15		$1724.74	$81.70	$107.80

Crew B-12H

	Hr.	Daily	Hr.	Daily	Bare Costs	Incl. O&P
1 Equip. Oper. (crane)	$37.30	$298.40	$61.65	$493.20	$31.95	$53.08
1 Laborer	26.60	212.80	44.50	356.00		
1 Crawler Crane, 25 Ton		1296.00		1425.60		
1 Clamshell Bucket, 1 C.Y.		48.80		53.68	84.05	92.45
16 L.H., Daily Totals		$1856.00		$2328.48	$116.00	$145.53

Crew B-12I

	Hr.	Daily	Hr.	Daily	Bare Costs	Incl. O&P
1 Equip. Oper. (crane)	$37.30	$298.40	$61.65	$493.20	$31.95	$53.08
1 Laborer	26.60	212.80	44.50	356.00		
1 Crawler Crane, 20 Ton		972.05		1069.26		
1 Dragline Bucket, .75 C.Y.		20.80		22.88	62.05	68.26
16 L.H., Daily Totals		$1504.05		$1941.34	$94.00	$121.33

Crew B-12J

	Hr.	Daily	Hr.	Daily	Bare Costs	Incl. O&P
1 Equip. Oper. (crane)	$37.30	$298.40	$61.65	$493.20	$31.95	$53.08
1 Laborer	26.60	212.80	44.50	356.00		
1 Gradall, 5/8 C.Y.		910.00		1001.00	56.88	62.56
16 L.H., Daily Totals		$1421.20		$1850.20	$88.83	$115.64

Crew B-12K

	Hr.	Daily	Hr.	Daily	Bare Costs	Incl. O&P
1 Equip. Oper. (crane)	$37.30	$298.40	$61.65	$493.20	$31.95	$53.08
1 Laborer	26.60	212.80	44.50	356.00		
1 Gradall, 3 Ton, 1 C.Y.		1144.00		1258.40	71.50	78.65
16 L.H., Daily Totals		$1655.20		$2107.60	$103.45	$131.72

Crew B-12L

	Hr.	Daily	Hr.	Daily	Bare Costs	Incl. O&P
1 Equip. Oper. (crane)	$37.30	$298.40	$61.65	$493.20	$31.95	$53.08
1 Laborer	26.60	212.80	44.50	356.00		
1 Crawler Crane, 15 Ton		757.75		833.52		
1 F.E. Attachment, .5 C.Y.		61.00		67.10	51.17	56.29
16 L.H., Daily Totals		$1329.95		$1749.83	$83.12	$109.36

Crew B-12M

	Hr.	Daily	Hr.	Daily	Bare Costs	Incl. O&P
1 Equip. Oper. (crane)	$37.30	$298.40	$61.65	$493.20	$31.95	$53.08
1 Laborer	26.60	212.80	44.50	356.00		
1 Crawler Crane, 20 Ton		972.05		1069.26		
1 F.E. Attachment, .75 C.Y.		65.80		72.38	64.87	71.35
16 L.H., Daily Totals		$1549.05		$1990.84	$96.82	$124.43

Crew B-12N

	Hr.	Daily	Hr.	Daily	Bare Costs	Incl. O&P
1 Equip. Oper. (crane)	$37.30	$298.40	$61.65	$493.20	$31.95	$53.08
1 Laborer	26.60	212.80	44.50	356.00		
1 Crawler Crane, 25 Ton		1296.00		1425.60		
1 F.E. Attachment, 1 C.Y.		72.60		79.86	85.54	94.09
16 L.H., Daily Totals		$1879.80		$2354.66	$117.49	$147.17

For customer support on your Residential Costs with RSMeans Data, call 800.448.8182.

681

Crew B-120

Crew No.	Bare Costs Hr.	Bare Costs Daily	Incl. Subs O&P Hr.	Incl. Subs O&P Daily	Cost Per Labor-Hour Bare Costs	Cost Per Labor-Hour Incl. O&P
1 Equip. Oper. (crane)	$37.30	$298.40	$61.65	$493.20	$31.95	$53.08
1 Laborer	26.60	212.80	44.50	356.00		
1 Crawler Crane, 40 Ton		1313.00		1444.30		
1 F.E. Attachment, 1.5 C.Y.		81.40		89.54	87.15	95.86
16 L.H., Daily Totals		$1905.60		$2383.04	$119.10	$148.94

Crew B-12P

Crew No.	Bare Costs Hr.	Bare Costs Daily	Incl. Subs O&P Hr.	Incl. Subs O&P Daily	Cost Per Labor-Hour Bare Costs	Cost Per Labor-Hour Incl. O&P
1 Equip. Oper. (crane)	$37.30	$298.40	$61.65	$493.20	$31.95	$53.08
1 Laborer	26.60	212.80	44.50	356.00		
1 Crawler Crane, 40 Ton		1313.00		1444.30		
1 Dragline Bucket, 1.5 C.Y.		34.00		37.40	84.19	92.61
16 L.H., Daily Totals		$1858.20		$2330.90	$116.14	$145.68

Crew B-12Q

Crew No.	Bare Costs Hr.	Bare Costs Daily	Incl. Subs O&P Hr.	Incl. Subs O&P Daily	Cost Per Labor-Hour Bare Costs	Cost Per Labor-Hour Incl. O&P
1 Equip. Oper. (crane)	$37.30	$298.40	$61.65	$493.20	$31.95	$53.08
1 Laborer	26.60	212.80	44.50	356.00		
1 Hyd. Excavator, 5/8 C.Y.		614.00		675.40	38.38	42.21
16 L.H., Daily Totals		$1125.20		$1524.60	$70.33	$95.29

Crew B-12S

Crew No.	Bare Costs Hr.	Bare Costs Daily	Incl. Subs O&P Hr.	Incl. Subs O&P Daily	Cost Per Labor-Hour Bare Costs	Cost Per Labor-Hour Incl. O&P
1 Equip. Oper. (crane)	$37.30	$298.40	$61.65	$493.20	$31.95	$53.08
1 Laborer	26.60	212.80	44.50	356.00		
1 Hyd. Excavator, 2.5 C.Y.		1536.00		1689.60	96.00	105.60
16 L.H., Daily Totals		$2047.20		$2538.80	$127.95	$158.68

Crew B-12T

Crew No.	Bare Costs Hr.	Bare Costs Daily	Incl. Subs O&P Hr.	Incl. Subs O&P Daily	Cost Per Labor-Hour Bare Costs	Cost Per Labor-Hour Incl. O&P
1 Equip. Oper. (crane)	$37.30	$298.40	$61.65	$493.20	$31.95	$53.08
1 Laborer	26.60	212.80	44.50	356.00		
1 Crawler Crane, 75 Ton		1645.00		1809.50		
1 F.E. Attachment, 3 C.Y.		104.20		114.62	109.33	120.26
16 L.H., Daily Totals		$2260.40		$2773.32	$141.28	$173.33

Crew B-12V

Crew No.	Bare Costs Hr.	Bare Costs Daily	Incl. Subs O&P Hr.	Incl. Subs O&P Daily	Cost Per Labor-Hour Bare Costs	Cost Per Labor-Hour Incl. O&P
1 Equip. Oper. (crane)	$37.30	$298.40	$61.65	$493.20	$31.95	$53.08
1 Laborer	26.60	212.80	44.50	356.00		
1 Crawler Crane, 75 Ton		1645.00		1809.50		
1 Dragline Bucket, 3 C.Y.		54.00		59.40	106.19	116.81
16 L.H., Daily Totals		$2210.20		$2718.10	$138.14	$169.88

Crew B-12Y

Crew No.	Bare Costs Hr.	Bare Costs Daily	Incl. Subs O&P Hr.	Incl. Subs O&P Daily	Cost Per Labor-Hour Bare Costs	Cost Per Labor-Hour Incl. O&P
1 Equip. Oper. (crane)	$37.30	$298.40	$61.65	$493.20	$30.17	$50.22
2 Laborers	26.60	425.60	44.50	712.00		
1 Hyd. Excavator, 3.5 C.Y.		2401.00		2641.10	100.04	110.05
24 L.H., Daily Totals		$3125.00		$3846.30	$130.21	$160.26

Crew B-12Z

Crew No.	Bare Costs Hr.	Bare Costs Daily	Incl. Subs O&P Hr.	Incl. Subs O&P Daily	Cost Per Labor-Hour Bare Costs	Cost Per Labor-Hour Incl. O&P
1 Equip. Oper. (crane)	$37.30	$298.40	$61.65	$493.20	$30.17	$50.22
2 Laborers	26.60	425.60	44.50	712.00		
1 Hyd. Excavator, 2.5 C.Y.		1536.00		1689.60	64.00	70.40
24 L.H., Daily Totals		$2260.00		$2894.80	$94.17	$120.62

Crew B-13

Crew No.	Bare Costs Hr.	Bare Costs Daily	Incl. Subs O&P Hr.	Incl. Subs O&P Daily	Cost Per Labor-Hour Bare Costs	Cost Per Labor-Hour Incl. O&P
1 Labor Foreman (outside)	$28.60	$228.80	$47.80	$382.40	$28.72	$47.91
4 Laborers	26.60	851.20	44.50	1424.00		
1 Equip. Oper. (crane)	37.30	298.40	61.65	493.20		
1 Hyd. Crane, 25 Ton		673.80		741.18	14.04	15.44
48 L.H., Daily Totals		$2052.20		$3040.78	$42.75	$63.35

Crew B-13A

Crew No.	Bare Costs Hr.	Bare Costs Daily	Incl. Subs O&P Hr.	Incl. Subs O&P Daily	Cost Per Labor-Hour Bare Costs	Cost Per Labor-Hour Incl. O&P
1 Labor Foreman (outside)	$28.60	$228.80	$47.80	$382.40	$31.33	$51.96
2 Laborers	26.60	425.60	44.50	712.00		
2 Equipment Operators (med.)	36.40	582.40	60.15	962.40		
2 Truck Drivers (heavy)	32.35	517.60	53.30	852.80		
1 Crawler Crane, 75 Ton		1645.00		1809.50		
1 Crawler Loader, 4 C.Y.		1528.00		1680.80		
2 Dump Trucks, 8 C.Y., 220 H.P.		782.00		860.20	70.63	77.69
56 L.H., Daily Totals		$5709.40		$7260.10	$101.95	$129.64

Crew B-13B

Crew No.	Bare Costs Hr.	Bare Costs Daily	Incl. Subs O&P Hr.	Incl. Subs O&P Daily	Cost Per Labor-Hour Bare Costs	Cost Per Labor-Hour Incl. O&P
1 Labor Foreman (outside)	$28.60	$228.80	$47.80	$382.40	$29.28	$48.77
4 Laborers	26.60	851.20	44.50	1424.00		
1 Equip. Oper. (crane)	37.30	298.40	61.65	493.20		
1 Equip. Oper. (oiler)	32.65	261.20	53.95	431.60		
1 Hyd. Crane, 55 Ton		1076.00		1183.60	19.21	21.14
56 L.H., Daily Totals		$2715.60		$3914.80	$48.49	$69.91

Crew B-13C

Crew No.	Bare Costs Hr.	Bare Costs Daily	Incl. Subs O&P Hr.	Incl. Subs O&P Daily	Cost Per Labor-Hour Bare Costs	Cost Per Labor-Hour Incl. O&P
1 Labor Foreman (outside)	$28.60	$228.80	$47.80	$382.40	$29.28	$48.77
4 Laborers	26.60	851.20	44.50	1424.00		
1 Equip. Oper. (crane)	37.30	298.40	61.65	493.20		
1 Equip. Oper. (oiler)	32.65	261.20	53.95	431.60		
1 Crawler Crane, 100 Ton		1804.00		1984.40	32.21	35.44
56 L.H., Daily Totals		$3443.60		$4715.60	$61.49	$84.21

Crew B-13D

Crew No.	Bare Costs Hr.	Bare Costs Daily	Incl. Subs O&P Hr.	Incl. Subs O&P Daily	Cost Per Labor-Hour Bare Costs	Cost Per Labor-Hour Incl. O&P
1 Laborer	$26.60	$212.80	$44.50	$356.00	$31.95	$53.08
1 Equip. Oper. (crane)	37.30	298.40	61.65	493.20		
1 Hyd. Excavator, 1 C.Y.		798.20		878.02		
1 Trench Box		81.00		89.10	54.95	60.45
16 L.H., Daily Totals		$1390.40		$1816.32	$86.90	$113.52

Crew B-13E

Crew No.	Bare Costs Hr.	Bare Costs Daily	Incl. Subs O&P Hr.	Incl. Subs O&P Daily	Cost Per Labor-Hour Bare Costs	Cost Per Labor-Hour Incl. O&P
1 Laborer	$26.60	$212.80	$44.50	$356.00	$31.95	$53.08
1 Equip. Oper. (crane)	37.30	298.40	61.65	493.20		
1 Hyd. Excavator, 1.5 C.Y.		965.00		1061.50		
1 Trench Box		81.00		89.10	65.38	71.91
16 L.H., Daily Totals		$1557.20		$1999.80	$97.33	$124.99

Crew B-13F

Crew No.	Bare Costs Hr.	Bare Costs Daily	Incl. Subs O&P Hr.	Incl. Subs O&P Daily	Cost Per Labor-Hour Bare Costs	Cost Per Labor-Hour Incl. O&P
1 Laborer	$26.60	$212.80	$44.50	$356.00	$31.95	$53.08
1 Equip. Oper. (crane)	37.30	298.40	61.65	493.20		
1 Hyd. Excavator, 3.5 C.Y.		2401.00		2641.10		
1 Trench Box		81.00		89.10	155.13	170.64
16 L.H., Daily Totals		$2993.20		$3579.40	$187.07	$223.71

Crew B-13G

Crew No.	Bare Costs Hr.	Bare Costs Daily	Incl. Subs O&P Hr.	Incl. Subs O&P Daily	Cost Per Labor-Hour Bare Costs	Cost Per Labor-Hour Incl. O&P
1 Laborer	$26.60	$212.80	$44.50	$356.00	$31.95	$53.08
1 Equip. Oper. (crane)	37.30	298.40	61.65	493.20		
1 Hyd. Excavator, .75 C.Y.		674.20		741.62		
1 Trench Box		81.00		89.10	47.20	51.92
16 L.H., Daily Totals		$1266.40		$1679.92	$79.15	$105.00

Crew B-13H

Crew No.	Bare Costs Hr.	Bare Costs Daily	Incl. Subs O&P Hr.	Incl. Subs O&P Daily	Cost Per Labor-Hour Bare Costs	Cost Per Labor-Hour Incl. O&P
1 Laborer	$26.60	$212.80	$44.50	$356.00	$31.95	$53.08
1 Equip. Oper. (crane)	37.30	298.40	61.65	493.20		
1 Gradall, 5/8 C.Y.		910.00		1001.00		
1 Trench Box		81.00		89.10	61.94	68.13
16 L.H., Daily Totals		$1502.20		$1939.30	$93.89	$121.21

For customer support on your Residential Costs with RSMeans Data, call 800.448.8182.

Crew No.	Bare Costs		Incl. Subs O&P		Cost Per Labor-Hour	

Crew B-13I	Hr.	Daily	Hr.	Daily	Bare Costs	Incl. O&P
1 Laborer	$26.60	$212.80	$44.50	$356.00	$31.95	$53.08
1 Equip. Oper. (crane)	37.30	298.40	61.65	493.20		
1 Gradall, 3 Ton, 1 C.Y.		1144.00		1258.40		
1 Trench Box		81.00		89.10	76.56	84.22
16 L.H., Daily Totals		$1736.20		$2196.70	$108.51	$137.29

Crew B-13J	Hr.	Daily	Hr.	Daily	Bare Costs	Incl. O&P
1 Laborer	$26.60	$212.80	$44.50	$356.00	$31.95	$53.08
1 Equip. Oper. (crane)	37.30	298.40	61.65	493.20		
1 Hyd. Excavator, 2.5 C.Y.		1536.00		1689.60		
1 Trench Box		81.00		89.10	101.06	111.17
16 L.H., Daily Totals		$2128.20		$2627.90	$133.01	$164.24

Crew B-13K	Hr.	Daily	Hr.	Daily	Bare Costs	Incl. O&P
2 Equip. Opers. (crane)	$37.30	$596.80	$61.65	$986.40	$37.30	$61.65
1 Hyd. Excavator, .75 C.Y.		674.20		741.62		
1 Hyd. Hammer, 4000 ft-lb		312.40		343.64		
1 Hyd. Excavator, .75 C.Y.		674.20		741.62	103.80	114.18
16 L.H., Daily Totals		$2257.60		$2813.28	$141.10	$175.83

Crew B-13L	Hr.	Daily	Hr.	Daily	Bare Costs	Incl. O&P
2 Equip. Opers. (crane)	$37.30	$596.80	$61.65	$986.40	$37.30	$61.65
1 Hyd. Excavator, 1.5 C.Y.		965.00		1061.50		
1 Hyd. Hammer, 5000 ft-lb		376.20		413.82		
1 Hyd. Excavator, .75 C.Y.		674.20		741.62	125.96	138.56
16 L.H., Daily Totals		$2612.20		$3203.34	$163.26	$200.21

Crew B-13M	Hr.	Daily	Hr.	Daily	Bare Costs	Incl. O&P
2 Equip. Opers. (crane)	$37.30	$596.80	$61.65	$986.40	$37.30	$61.65
1 Hyd. Excavator, 2.5 C.Y.		1536.00		1689.60		
1 Hyd. Hammer, 8000 ft-lb		552.80		608.08		
1 Hyd. Excavator, 1.5 C.Y.		965.00		1061.50	190.86	209.95
16 L.H., Daily Totals		$3650.60		$4345.58	$228.16	$271.60

Crew B-13N	Hr.	Daily	Hr.	Daily	Bare Costs	Incl. O&P
2 Equip. Opers. (crane)	$37.30	$596.80	$61.65	$986.40	$37.30	$61.65
1 Hyd. Excavator, 3.5 C.Y.		2401.00		2641.10		
1 Hyd. Hammer, 12,000 ft-lb		643.20		707.52		
1 Hyd. Excavator, 1.5 C.Y.		965.00		1061.50	250.57	275.63
16 L.H., Daily Totals		$4606.00		$5396.52	$287.88	$337.28

Crew B-14	Hr.	Daily	Hr.	Daily	Bare Costs	Incl. O&P
1 Labor Foreman (outside)	$28.60	$228.80	$47.80	$382.40	$28.37	$47.33
4 Laborers	26.60	851.20	44.50	1424.00		
1 Equip. Oper. (light)	35.20	281.60	58.20	465.60		
1 Backhoe Loader, 48 H.P.		366.20		402.82	7.63	8.39
48 L.H., Daily Totals		$1727.80		$2674.82	$36.00	$55.73

Crew B-14A	Hr.	Daily	Hr.	Daily	Bare Costs	Incl. O&P
1 Equip. Oper. (crane)	$37.30	$298.40	$61.65	$493.20	$33.73	$55.93
.5 Laborer	26.60	106.40	44.50	178.00		
1 Hyd. Excavator, 4.5 C.Y.		3084.00		3392.40	257.00	282.70
12 L.H., Daily Totals		$3488.80		$4063.60	$290.73	$338.63

Crew B-14B	Hr.	Daily	Hr.	Daily	Bare Costs	Incl. O&P
1 Equip. Oper. (crane)	$37.30	$298.40	$61.65	$493.20	$33.73	$55.93
.5 Laborer	26.60	106.40	44.50	178.00		
1 Hyd. Excavator, 6 C.Y.		3596.00		3955.60	299.67	329.63
12 L.H., Daily Totals		$4000.80		$4626.80	$333.40	$385.57

Crew B-14C	Hr.	Daily	Hr.	Daily	Bare Costs	Incl. O&P
1 Equip. Oper. (crane)	$37.30	$298.40	$61.65	$493.20	$33.73	$55.93
.5 Laborer	26.60	106.40	44.50	178.00		
1 Hyd. Excavator, 7 C.Y.		3698.00		4067.80	308.17	338.98
12 L.H., Daily Totals		$4102.80		$4739.00	$341.90	$394.92

Crew B-14F	Hr.	Daily	Hr.	Daily	Bare Costs	Incl. O&P
1 Equip. Oper. (crane)	$37.30	$298.40	$61.65	$493.20	$33.73	$55.93
.5 Laborer	26.60	106.40	44.50	178.00		
1 Hyd. Shovel, 7 C.Y.		4107.00		4517.70	342.25	376.48
12 L.H., Daily Totals		$4511.80		$5188.90	$375.98	$432.41

Crew B-14G	Hr.	Daily	Hr.	Daily	Bare Costs	Incl. O&P
1 Equip. Oper. (crane)	$37.30	$298.40	$61.65	$493.20	$33.73	$55.93
.5 Laborer	26.60	106.40	44.50	178.00		
1 Hyd. Shovel, 12 C.Y.		6152.00		6767.20	512.67	563.93
12 L.H., Daily Totals		$6556.80		$7438.40	$546.40	$619.87

Crew B-14J	Hr.	Daily	Hr.	Daily	Bare Costs	Incl. O&P
1 Equip. Oper. (medium)	$36.40	$291.20	$60.15	$481.20	$33.13	$54.93
.5 Laborer	26.60	106.40	44.50	178.00		
1 F.E. Loader, 8 C.Y.		1967.00		2163.70	163.92	180.31
12 L.H., Daily Totals		$2364.60		$2822.90	$197.05	$235.24

Crew B-14K	Hr.	Daily	Hr.	Daily	Bare Costs	Incl. O&P
1 Equip. Oper. (medium)	$36.40	$291.20	$60.15	$481.20	$33.13	$54.93
.5 Laborer	26.60	106.40	44.50	178.00		
1 F.E. Loader, 10 C.Y.		3224.00		3546.40	268.67	295.53
12 L.H., Daily Totals		$3621.60		$4205.60	$301.80	$350.47

Crew B-15	Hr.	Daily	Hr.	Daily	Bare Costs	Incl. O&P
1 Equipment Oper. (med.)	$36.40	$291.20	$60.15	$481.20	$32.69	$54.00
.5 Laborer	26.60	106.40	44.50	178.00		
2 Truck Drivers (heavy)	32.35	517.60	53.30	852.80		
2 Dump Trucks, 12 C.Y., 400 H.P.		1285.20		1413.72		
1 Dozer, 200 H.P.		1384.00		1522.40	95.33	104.86
28 L.H., Daily Totals		$3584.40		$4448.12	$128.01	$158.86

Crew B-16	Hr.	Daily	Hr.	Daily	Bare Costs	Incl. O&P
1 Labor Foreman (outside)	$28.60	$228.80	$47.80	$382.40	$28.54	$47.52
2 Laborers	26.60	425.60	44.50	712.00		
1 Truck Driver (heavy)	32.35	258.80	53.30	426.40		
1 Dump Truck, 12 C.Y., 400 H.P.		642.60		706.86	20.08	22.09
32 L.H., Daily Totals		$1555.80		$2227.66	$48.62	$69.61

Crew B-17	Hr.	Daily	Hr.	Daily	Bare Costs	Incl. O&P
2 Laborers	$26.60	$425.60	$44.50	$712.00	$30.19	$50.13
1 Equip. Oper. (light)	35.20	281.60	58.20	465.60		
1 Truck Driver (heavy)	32.35	258.80	53.30	426.40		
1 Backhoe Loader, 48 H.P.		366.20		402.82		
1 Dump Truck, 8 C.Y., 220 H.P.		391.00		430.10	23.66	26.03
32 L.H., Daily Totals		$1723.20		$2436.92	$53.85	$76.15

Crew B-17A	Hr.	Daily	Hr.	Daily	Bare Costs	Incl. O&P
2 Labor Foremen (outside)	$28.60	$457.60	$47.80	$764.80	$29.03	$48.60
6 Laborers	26.60	1276.80	44.50	2136.00		
1 Skilled Worker Foreman (out)	37.75	302.00	63.40	507.20		
1 Skilled Worker	35.75	286.00	60.00	480.00		
80 L.H., Daily Totals		$2322.40		$3888.00	$29.03	$48.60

For customer support on your Residential Costs with RSMeans Data, call 800.448.8182.

683

Crew B-17B

Crew No.	Bare Costs Hr.	Bare Costs Daily	Incl. Subs O&P Hr.	Incl. Subs O&P Daily	Cost Per Labor-Hour Bare Costs	Cost Per Labor-Hour Incl. O&P
2 Laborers	$26.60	$425.60	$44.50	$712.00	$30.19	$50.13
1 Equip. Oper. (light)	35.20	281.60	58.20	465.60		
1 Truck Driver (heavy)	32.35	258.80	53.30	426.40		
1 Backhoe Loader, 48 H.P.		366.20		402.82		
1 Dump Truck, 12 C.Y., 400 H.P.		642.60		706.86	31.52	34.68
32 L.H., Daily Totals		$1974.80		$2713.68	$61.71	$84.80

Crew B-18

Crew No.	Bare Costs Hr.	Bare Costs Daily	Incl. Subs O&P Hr.	Incl. Subs O&P Daily	Cost Per Labor-Hour Bare Costs	Cost Per Labor-Hour Incl. O&P
1 Labor Foreman (outside)	$28.60	$228.80	$47.80	$382.40	$27.27	$45.60
2 Laborers	26.60	425.60	44.50	712.00		
1 Vibrating Plate, Gas, 21"		42.80		47.08	1.78	1.96
24 L.H., Daily Totals		$697.20		$1141.48	$29.05	$47.56

Crew B-19

Crew No.	Bare Costs Hr.	Bare Costs Daily	Incl. Subs O&P Hr.	Incl. Subs O&P Daily	Cost Per Labor-Hour Bare Costs	Cost Per Labor-Hour Incl. O&P
1 Pile Driver Foreman (outside)	$37.15	$297.20	$64.20	$513.60	$34.52	$59.05
4 Pile Drivers	35.15	1124.80	60.75	1944.00		
1 Equip. Oper. (crane)	37.30	298.40	61.65	493.20		
1 Building Laborer	26.60	212.80	44.50	356.00		
1 Crawler Crane, 40 Ton		1313.00		1444.30		
1 Lead, 90' High		126.00		138.60		
1 Hammer, Diesel, 22k ft-lb		421.00		463.10	33.21	36.54
56 L.H., Daily Totals		$3793.20		$5352.80	$67.74	$95.59

Crew B-19A

Crew No.	Bare Costs Hr.	Bare Costs Daily	Incl. Subs O&P Hr.	Incl. Subs O&P Daily	Cost Per Labor-Hour Bare Costs	Cost Per Labor-Hour Incl. O&P
1 Pile Driver Foreman (outside)	$37.15	$297.20	$64.20	$513.60	$34.52	$59.05
4 Pile Drivers	35.15	1124.80	60.75	1944.00		
1 Equip. Oper. (crane)	37.30	298.40	61.65	493.20		
1 Common Laborer	26.60	212.80	44.50	356.00		
1 Crawler Crane, 75 Ton		1645.00		1809.50		
1 Lead, 90' high		126.00		138.60		
1 Hammer, Diesel, 41k ft-lb		574.00		631.40	41.88	46.06
56 L.H., Daily Totals		$4278.20		$5886.30	$76.40	$105.11

Crew B-19B

Crew No.	Bare Costs Hr.	Bare Costs Daily	Incl. Subs O&P Hr.	Incl. Subs O&P Daily	Cost Per Labor-Hour Bare Costs	Cost Per Labor-Hour Incl. O&P
1 Pile Driver Foreman (outside)	$37.15	$297.20	$64.20	$513.60	$34.52	$59.05
4 Pile Drivers	35.15	1124.80	60.75	1944.00		
1 Equip. Oper. (crane)	37.30	298.40	61.65	493.20		
1 Common Laborer	26.60	212.80	44.50	356.00		
1 Crawler Crane, 40 Ton		1313.00		1444.30		
1 Lead, 90' High		126.00		138.60		
1 Hammer, Diesel, 22k ft-lb		421.00		463.10		
1 Barge, 400 Ton		794.20		873.62	47.40	52.14
56 L.H., Daily Totals		$4587.40		$6226.42	$81.92	$111.19

Crew B-19C

Crew No.	Bare Costs Hr.	Bare Costs Daily	Incl. Subs O&P Hr.	Incl. Subs O&P Daily	Cost Per Labor-Hour Bare Costs	Cost Per Labor-Hour Incl. O&P
1 Pile Driver Foreman (outside)	$37.15	$297.20	$64.20	$513.60	$34.52	$59.05
4 Pile Drivers	35.15	1124.80	60.75	1944.00		
1 Equip. Oper. (crane)	37.30	298.40	61.65	493.20		
1 Common Laborer	26.60	212.80	44.50	356.00		
1 Crawler Crane, 75 Ton		1645.00		1809.50		
1 Lead, 90' High		126.00		138.60		
1 Hammer, Diesel, 41k ft-lb		574.00		631.40		
1 Barge, 400 Ton		794.20		873.62	56.06	61.66
56 L.H., Daily Totals		$5072.40		$6759.92	$90.58	$120.71

Crew B-20

Crew No.	Bare Costs Hr.	Bare Costs Daily	Incl. Subs O&P Hr.	Incl. Subs O&P Daily	Cost Per Labor-Hour Bare Costs	Cost Per Labor-Hour Incl. O&P
1 Labor Foreman (outside)	$28.60	$228.80	$47.80	$382.40	$27.27	$45.60
2 Laborers	26.60	425.60	44.50	712.00		
24 L.H., Daily Totals		$654.40		$1094.40	$27.27	$45.60

Crew B-20A

Crew No.	Bare Costs Hr.	Bare Costs Daily	Incl. Subs O&P Hr.	Incl. Subs O&P Daily	Cost Per Labor-Hour Bare Costs	Cost Per Labor-Hour Incl. O&P
1 Labor Foreman (outside)	$28.60	$228.80	$47.80	$382.40	$31.60	$52.42
1 Laborer	26.60	212.80	44.50	356.00		
1 Plumber	39.55	316.40	65.20	521.60		
1 Plumber Apprentice	31.65	253.20	52.20	417.60		
32 L.H., Daily Totals		$1011.20		$1677.60	$31.60	$52.42

Crew B-21

Crew No.	Bare Costs Hr.	Bare Costs Daily	Incl. Subs O&P Hr.	Incl. Subs O&P Daily	Cost Per Labor-Hour Bare Costs	Cost Per Labor-Hour Incl. O&P
1 Labor Foreman (outside)	$28.60	$228.80	$47.80	$382.40	$28.70	$47.89
2 Laborers	26.60	425.60	44.50	712.00		
.5 Equip. Oper. (crane)	37.30	149.20	61.65	246.60		
.5 S.P. Crane, 4x4, 5 Ton		138.00		151.80	4.93	5.42
28 L.H., Daily Totals		$941.60		$1492.80	$33.63	$53.31

Crew B-21A

Crew No.	Bare Costs Hr.	Bare Costs Daily	Incl. Subs O&P Hr.	Incl. Subs O&P Daily	Cost Per Labor-Hour Bare Costs	Cost Per Labor-Hour Incl. O&P
1 Labor Foreman (outside)	$28.60	$228.80	$47.80	$382.40	$32.74	$54.27
1 Laborer	26.60	212.80	44.50	356.00		
1 Plumber	39.55	316.40	65.20	521.60		
1 Plumber Apprentice	31.65	253.20	52.20	417.60		
1 Equip. Oper. (crane)	37.30	298.40	61.65	493.20		
1 S.P. Crane, 4x4, 12 Ton		435.60		479.16	10.89	11.98
40 L.H., Daily Totals		$1745.20		$2649.96	$43.63	$66.25

Crew B-21B

Crew No.	Bare Costs Hr.	Bare Costs Daily	Incl. Subs O&P Hr.	Incl. Subs O&P Daily	Cost Per Labor-Hour Bare Costs	Cost Per Labor-Hour Incl. O&P
1 Labor Foreman (outside)	$28.60	$228.80	$47.80	$382.40	$29.14	$48.59
3 Laborers	26.60	638.40	44.50	1068.00		
1 Equip. Oper. (crane)	37.30	298.40	61.65	493.20		
1 Hyd. Crane, 12 Ton		572.80		630.08	14.32	15.75
40 L.H., Daily Totals		$1738.40		$2573.68	$43.46	$64.34

Crew B-21C

Crew No.	Bare Costs Hr.	Bare Costs Daily	Incl. Subs O&P Hr.	Incl. Subs O&P Daily	Cost Per Labor-Hour Bare Costs	Cost Per Labor-Hour Incl. O&P
1 Labor Foreman (outside)	$28.60	$228.80	$47.80	$382.40	$29.28	$48.77
4 Laborers	26.60	851.20	44.50	1424.00		
1 Equip. Oper. (crane)	37.30	298.40	61.65	493.20		
1 Equip. Oper. (oiler)	32.65	261.20	53.95	431.60		
2 Cutting Torches		24.00		26.40		
2 Sets of Gases		336.00		369.60		
1 Lattice Boom Crane, 90 Ton		1671.00		1838.10	36.27	39.89
56 L.H., Daily Totals		$3670.60		$4965.30	$65.55	$88.67

Crew B-22

Crew No.	Bare Costs Hr.	Bare Costs Daily	Incl. Subs O&P Hr.	Incl. Subs O&P Daily	Cost Per Labor-Hour Bare Costs	Cost Per Labor-Hour Incl. O&P
1 Labor Foreman (outside)	$28.60	$228.80	$47.80	$382.40	$29.27	$48.81
2 Laborers	26.60	425.60	44.50	712.00		
.75 Equip. Oper. (crane)	37.30	223.80	61.65	369.90		
.75 S.P. Crane, 4x4, 5 Ton		207.00		227.70	6.90	7.59
30 L.H., Daily Totals		$1085.20		$1692.00	$36.17	$56.40

Crew B-22A

Crew No.	Bare Costs Hr.	Bare Costs Daily	Incl. Subs O&P Hr.	Incl. Subs O&P Daily	Cost Per Labor-Hour Bare Costs	Cost Per Labor-Hour Incl. O&P
1 Labor Foreman (outside)	$28.60	$228.80	$47.80	$382.40	$30.97	$51.69
1 Skilled Worker	35.75	286.00	60.00	480.00		
2 Laborers	26.60	425.60	44.50	712.00		
1 Equipment Operator, Crane	37.30	298.40	61.65	493.20		
1 S.P. Crane, 4x4, 5 Ton		276.00		303.60		
1 Butt Fusion Mach., 4"-12" diam.		415.10		456.61	17.28	19.01
40 L.H., Daily Totals		$1929.90		$2827.81	$48.25	$70.70

Crews - Residential

Crew B-22B

Crew No.	Bare Costs Hr.	Daily	Incl. Subs O&P Hr.	Daily	Cost Per Labor-Hour Bare Costs	Incl. O&P
1 Labor Foreman (outside)	$28.60	$228.80	$47.80	$382.40	$30.97	$51.69
1 Skilled Worker	35.75	286.00	60.00	480.00		
2 Laborers	26.60	425.60	44.50	712.00		
1 Equip. Oper. (crane)	37.30	298.40	61.65	493.20		
1 S.P. Crane, 4x4, 5 Ton		276.00		303.60		
1 Butt Fusion Mach., 8"-24" diam.		1821.00		2003.10	52.42	57.67
40 L.H., Daily Totals		$3335.80		$4374.30	$83.39	$109.36

Crew B-22C

Crew No.	Bare Costs Hr.	Daily	Incl. Subs O&P Hr.	Daily	Cost Per Labor-Hour Bare Costs	Incl. O&P
1 Skilled Worker	$35.75	$286.00	$60.00	$480.00	$31.18	$52.25
1 Laborer	26.60	212.80	44.50	356.00		
1 Butt Fusion Mach., 2"-8" diam.		121.05		133.16	7.57	8.32
16 L.H., Daily Totals		$619.85		$969.15	$38.74	$60.57

Crew B-23

Crew No.	Bare Costs Hr.	Daily	Incl. Subs O&P Hr.	Daily	Cost Per Labor-Hour Bare Costs	Incl. O&P
1 Labor Foreman (outside)	$28.60	$228.80	$47.80	$382.40	$27.00	$45.16
4 Laborers	26.60	851.20	44.50	1424.00		
1 Drill Rig, Truck-Mounted		2573.00		2830.30		
1 Flatbed Truck, Gas, 3 Ton		270.20		297.22	71.08	78.19
40 L.H., Daily Totals		$3923.20		$4933.92	$98.08	$123.35

Crew B-23A

Crew No.	Bare Costs Hr.	Daily	Incl. Subs O&P Hr.	Daily	Cost Per Labor-Hour Bare Costs	Incl. O&P
1 Labor Foreman (outside)	$28.60	$228.80	$47.80	$382.40	$30.53	$50.82
1 Laborer	26.60	212.80	44.50	356.00		
1 Equip. Oper. (medium)	36.40	291.20	60.15	481.20		
1 Drill Rig, Truck-Mounted		2573.00		2830.30		
1 Pickup Truck, 3/4 Ton		129.40		142.34	112.60	123.86
24 L.H., Daily Totals		$3435.20		$4192.24	$143.13	$174.68

Crew B-23B

Crew No.	Bare Costs Hr.	Daily	Incl. Subs O&P Hr.	Daily	Cost Per Labor-Hour Bare Costs	Incl. O&P
1 Labor Foreman (outside)	$28.60	$228.80	$47.80	$382.40	$30.53	$50.82
1 Laborer	26.60	212.80	44.50	356.00		
1 Equip. Oper. (medium)	36.40	291.20	60.15	481.20		
1 Drill Rig, Truck-Mounted		2573.00		2830.30		
1 Pickup Truck, 3/4 Ton		129.40		142.34		
1 Centr. Water Pump, 6"		325.40		357.94	126.16	138.77
24 L.H., Daily Totals		$3760.60		$4550.18	$156.69	$189.59

Crew B-24

Crew No.	Bare Costs Hr.	Daily	Incl. Subs O&P Hr.	Daily	Cost Per Labor-Hour Bare Costs	Incl. O&P
1 Cement Finisher	$34.65	$277.20	$56.40	$451.20	$32.07	$53.12
1 Laborer	26.60	212.80	44.50	356.00		
1 Carpenter	34.95	279.60	58.45	467.60		
24 L.H., Daily Totals		$769.60		$1274.80	$32.07	$53.12

Crew B-25

Crew No.	Bare Costs Hr.	Daily	Incl. Subs O&P Hr.	Daily	Cost Per Labor-Hour Bare Costs	Incl. O&P
1 Labor Foreman (outside)	$28.60	$228.80	$47.80	$382.40	$29.45	$49.07
7 Laborers	26.60	1489.60	44.50	2492.00		
3 Equip. Oper. (medium)	36.40	873.60	60.15	1443.60		
1 Asphalt Paver, 130 H.P.		2235.00		2458.50		
1 Tandem Roller, 10 Ton		237.60		261.36		
1 Roller, Pneum. Whl., 12 Ton		355.80		391.38	32.14	35.35
88 L.H., Daily Totals		$5420.40		$7429.24	$61.60	$84.42

Crew B-25B

Crew No.	Bare Costs Hr.	Daily	Incl. Subs O&P Hr.	Daily	Cost Per Labor-Hour Bare Costs	Incl. O&P
1 Labor Foreman (outside)	$28.60	$228.80	$47.80	$382.40	$30.03	$49.99
7 Laborers	26.60	1489.60	44.50	2492.00		
4 Equip. Oper. (medium)	36.40	1164.80	60.15	1924.80		
1 Asphalt Paver, 130 H.P.		2235.00		2458.50		
2 Tandem Rollers, 10 Ton		475.20		522.72		
1 Roller, Pneum. Whl., 12 Ton		355.80		391.38	31.94	35.13
96 L.H., Daily Totals		$5949.20		$8171.80	$61.97	$85.12

Crew B-25C

Crew No.	Bare Costs Hr.	Daily	Incl. Subs O&P Hr.	Daily	Cost Per Labor-Hour Bare Costs	Incl. O&P
1 Labor Foreman (outside)	$28.60	$228.80	$47.80	$382.40	$30.20	$50.27
3 Laborers	26.60	638.40	44.50	1068.00		
2 Equip. Oper. (medium)	36.40	582.40	60.15	962.40		
1 Asphalt Paver, 130 H.P.		2235.00		2458.50		
1 Tandem Roller, 10 Ton		237.60		261.36	51.51	56.66
48 L.H., Daily Totals		$3922.20		$5132.66	$81.71	$106.93

Crew B-25D

Crew No.	Bare Costs Hr.	Daily	Incl. Subs O&P Hr.	Daily	Cost Per Labor-Hour Bare Costs	Incl. O&P
1 Labor Foreman (outside)	$28.60	$228.80	$47.80	$382.40	$30.37	$50.52
3 Laborers	26.60	638.40	44.50	1068.00		
2.125 Equip. Oper. (medium)	36.40	618.80	60.15	1022.55		
.125 Truck Driver (heavy)	32.35	32.35	53.30	53.30		
.125 Truck Tractor, 6x4, 380 H.P.		69.97		76.97		
.125 Dist. Tanker, 3000 Gallon		40.92		45.02		
1 Asphalt Paver, 130 H.P.		2235.00		2458.50		
1 Tandem Roller, 10 Ton		237.60		261.36	51.67	56.84
50 L.H., Daily Totals		$4101.85		$5368.10	$82.04	$107.36

Crew B-25E

Crew No.	Bare Costs Hr.	Daily	Incl. Subs O&P Hr.	Daily	Cost Per Labor-Hour Bare Costs	Incl. O&P
1 Labor Foreman (outside)	$28.60	$228.80	$47.80	$382.40	$30.52	$50.76
3 Laborers	26.60	638.40	44.50	1068.00		
2.250 Equip. Oper. (medium)	36.40	655.20	60.15	1082.70		
.25 Truck Driver (heavy)	32.35	64.70	53.30	106.60		
.25 Truck Tractor, 6x4, 380 H.P.		139.95		153.94		
.25 Dist. Tanker, 3000 Gallon		81.85		90.03		
1 Asphalt Paver, 130 H.P.		2235.00		2458.50		
1 Tandem Roller, 10 Ton		237.60		261.36	51.82	57.00
52 L.H., Daily Totals		$4281.50		$5603.54	$82.34	$107.76

Crew B-26

Crew No.	Bare Costs Hr.	Daily	Incl. Subs O&P Hr.	Daily	Cost Per Labor-Hour Bare Costs	Incl. O&P
1 Labor Foreman (outside)	$28.60	$228.80	$47.80	$382.40	$30.38	$50.57
6 Laborers	26.60	1276.80	44.50	2136.00		
2 Equip. Oper. (medium)	36.40	582.40	60.15	962.40		
1 Rodman (reinf.)	38.55	308.40	64.80	518.40		
1 Cement Finisher	34.65	277.20	56.40	451.20		
1 Grader, 30,000 Lbs.		678.40		746.24		
1 Paving Mach. & Equip.		2452.00		2697.20	35.57	39.13
88 L.H., Daily Totals		$5804.00		$7893.84	$65.95	$89.70

Crew B-26A

Crew No.	Bare Costs Hr.	Daily	Incl. Subs O&P Hr.	Daily	Cost Per Labor-Hour Bare Costs	Incl. O&P
1 Labor Foreman (outside)	$28.60	$228.80	$47.80	$382.40	$30.38	$50.57
6 Laborers	26.60	1276.80	44.50	2136.00		
2 Equip. Oper. (medium)	36.40	582.40	60.15	962.40		
1 Rodman (reinf.)	38.55	308.40	64.80	518.40		
1 Cement Finisher	34.65	277.20	56.40	451.20		
1 Grader, 30,000 Lbs.		678.40		746.24		
1 Paving Mach. & Equip.		2452.00		2697.20		
1 Concrete Saw		153.60		168.96	37.32	41.05
88 L.H., Daily Totals		$5957.60		$8062.80	$67.70	$91.62

Crew B-26B

Crew No.	Bare Costs Hr.	Daily	Incl. Subs O&P Hr.	Daily	Cost Per Labor-Hour Bare Costs	Incl. O&P
1 Labor Foreman (outside)	$28.60	$228.80	$47.80	$382.40	$30.88	$51.37
6 Laborers	26.60	1276.80	44.50	2136.00		
3 Equip. Oper. (medium)	36.40	873.60	60.15	1443.60		
1 Rodman (reinf.)	38.55	308.40	64.80	518.40		
1 Cement Finisher	34.65	277.20	56.40	451.20		
1 Grader, 30,000 Lbs.		678.40		746.24		
1 Paving Mach. & Equip.		2452.00		2697.20		
1 Concrete Pump, 110' Boom		1086.00		1194.60	43.92	48.31
96 L.H., Daily Totals		$7181.20		$9569.64	$74.80	$99.68

For customer support on your Residential Costs with RSMeans Data, call 800.448.8182.

685

Crew No.	Bare Costs Hr.	Daily	Incl. Subs O&P Hr.	Daily	Cost Per Labor-Hour Bare Costs	Incl. O&P
Crew B-26C	Hr.	Daily	Hr.	Daily	Bare Costs	Incl. O&P
1 Labor Foreman (outside)	$28.60	$228.80	$47.80	$382.40	$29.78	$49.62
6 Laborers	26.60	1276.80	44.50	2136.00		
1 Equip. Oper. (medium)	36.40	291.20	60.15	481.20		
1 Rodman (reinf.)	38.55	308.40	64.80	518.40		
1 Cement Finisher	34.65	277.20	56.40	451.20		
1 Paving Mach. & Equip.		2452.00		2697.20		
1 Concrete Saw		153.60		168.96	32.57	35.83
80 L.H., Daily Totals		$4988.00		$6835.36	$62.35	$85.44

Crew B-27	Hr.	Daily	Hr.	Daily	Bare Costs	Incl. O&P
1 Labor Foreman (outside)	$28.60	$228.80	$47.80	$382.40	$27.10	$45.33
3 Laborers	26.60	638.40	44.50	1068.00		
1 Berm Machine		313.40		344.74	9.79	10.77
32 L.H., Daily Totals		$1180.60		$1795.14	$36.89	$56.10

Crew B-28	Hr.	Daily	Hr.	Daily	Bare Costs	Incl. O&P
2 Carpenters	$34.95	$559.20	$58.45	$935.20	$32.17	$53.80
1 Laborer	26.60	212.80	44.50	356.00		
24 L.H., Daily Totals		$772.00		$1291.20	$32.17	$53.80

Crew B-29	Hr.	Daily	Hr.	Daily	Bare Costs	Incl. O&P
1 Labor Foreman (outside)	$28.60	$228.80	$47.80	$382.40	$28.72	$47.91
4 Laborers	26.60	851.20	44.50	1424.00		
1 Equip. Oper. (crane)	37.30	298.40	61.65	493.20		
1 Gradall, 5/8 C.Y.		910.00		1001.00	18.96	20.85
48 L.H., Daily Totals		$2288.40		$3300.60	$47.67	$68.76

Crew B-30	Hr.	Daily	Hr.	Daily	Bare Costs	Incl. O&P
1 Equip. Oper. (medium)	$36.40	$291.20	$60.15	$481.20	$33.70	$55.58
2 Truck Drivers (heavy)	32.35	517.60	53.30	852.80		
1 Hyd. Excavator, 1.5 C.Y.		965.00		1061.50		
2 Dump Trucks, 12 C.Y., 400 H.P.		1285.20		1413.72	93.76	103.13
24 L.H., Daily Totals		$3059.00		$3809.22	$127.46	$158.72

Crew B-31	Hr.	Daily	Hr.	Daily	Bare Costs	Incl. O&P
1 Labor Foreman (outside)	$28.60	$228.80	$47.80	$382.40	$27.00	$45.16
4 Laborers	26.60	851.20	44.50	1424.00		
1 Air Compressor, 250 cfm		181.20		199.32		
1 Sheeting Driver		5.75		6.33		
2 -50' Air Hoses, 1.5"		11.60		12.76	4.96	5.46
40 L.H., Daily Totals		$1278.55		$2024.81	$31.96	$50.62

Crew B-32	Hr.	Daily	Hr.	Daily	Bare Costs	Incl. O&P
1 Laborer	$26.60	$212.80	$44.50	$356.00	$33.95	$56.24
3 Equip. Oper. (medium)	36.40	873.60	60.15	1443.60		
1 Grader, 30,000 Lbs.		678.40		746.24		
1 Tandem Roller, 10 Ton		237.60		261.36		
1 Dozer, 200 H.P.		1384.00		1522.40	71.88	79.06
32 L.H., Daily Totals		$3386.40		$4329.60	$105.83	$135.30

Crew B-32A	Hr.	Daily	Hr.	Daily	Bare Costs	Incl. O&P
1 Laborer	$26.60	$212.80	$44.50	$356.00	$33.13	$54.93
2 Equip. Oper. (medium)	36.40	582.40	60.15	962.40		
1 Grader, 30,000 Lbs.		678.40		746.24		
1 Roller, Vibratory, 25 Ton		684.00		752.40	56.77	62.44
24 L.H., Daily Totals		$2157.60		$2817.04	$89.90	$117.38

Crew B-32B	Hr.	Daily	Hr.	Daily	Bare Costs	Incl. O&P
1 Laborer	$26.60	$212.80	$44.50	$356.00	$33.13	$54.93
2 Equip. Oper. (medium)	36.40	582.40	60.15	962.40		
1 Dozer, 200 H.P.		1384.00		1522.40		
1 Roller, Vibratory, 25 Ton		684.00		752.40	86.17	94.78
24 L.H., Daily Totals		$2863.20		$3593.20	$119.30	$149.72

Crew B-32C	Hr.	Daily	Hr.	Daily	Bare Costs	Incl. O&P
1 Labor Foreman (outside)	$28.60	$228.80	$47.80	$382.40	$31.83	$52.88
2 Laborers	26.60	425.60	44.50	712.00		
3 Equip. Oper. (medium)	36.40	873.60	60.15	1443.60		
1 Grader, 30,000 Lbs.		678.40		746.24		
1 Tandem Roller, 10 Ton		237.60		261.36		
1 Dozer, 200 H.P.		1384.00		1522.40	47.92	52.71
48 L.H., Daily Totals		$3828.00		$5068.00	$79.75	$105.58

Crew B-33A	Hr.	Daily	Hr.	Daily	Bare Costs	Incl. O&P
1 Equip. Oper. (medium)	$36.40	$291.20	$60.15	$481.20	$36.40	$60.15
.25 Equip. Oper. (medium)	36.40	72.80	60.15	120.30		
1 Scraper, Towed, 7 C.Y.		117.20		128.92		
1.250 Dozers, 300 H.P.		2375.00		2612.50	249.22	274.14
10 L.H., Daily Totals		$2856.20		$3342.92	$285.62	$334.29

Crew B-33B	Hr.	Daily	Hr.	Daily	Bare Costs	Incl. O&P
1 Equip. Oper. (medium)	$36.40	$291.20	$60.15	$481.20	$36.40	$60.15
.25 Equip. Oper. (medium)	36.40	72.80	60.15	120.30		
1 Scraper, Towed, 10 C.Y.		148.60		163.46		
1.250 Dozers, 300 H.P.		2375.00		2612.50	252.36	277.60
10 L.H., Daily Totals		$2887.60		$3377.46	$288.76	$337.75

Crew B-33C	Hr.	Daily	Hr.	Daily	Bare Costs	Incl. O&P
1 Equip. Oper. (medium)	$36.40	$291.20	$60.15	$481.20	$36.40	$60.15
.25 Equip. Oper. (medium)	36.40	72.80	60.15	120.30		
1 Scraper, Towed, 15 C.Y.		167.60		184.36		
1.250 Dozers, 300 H.P.		2375.00		2612.50	254.26	279.69
10 L.H., Daily Totals		$2906.60		$3398.36	$290.66	$339.84

Crew B-33D	Hr.	Daily	Hr.	Daily	Bare Costs	Incl. O&P
1 Equip. Oper. (medium)	$36.40	$291.20	$60.15	$481.20	$36.40	$60.15
.25 Equip. Oper. (medium)	36.40	72.80	60.15	120.30		
1 S.P. Scraper, 14 C.Y.		2429.00		2671.90		
.25 Dozer, 300 H.P.		475.00		522.50	290.40	319.44
10 L.H., Daily Totals		$3268.00		$3795.90	$326.80	$379.59

Crew B-33E	Hr.	Daily	Hr.	Daily	Bare Costs	Incl. O&P
1 Equip. Oper. (medium)	$36.40	$291.20	$60.15	$481.20	$36.40	$60.15
.25 Equip. Oper. (medium)	36.40	72.80	60.15	120.30		
1 S.P. Scraper, 21 C.Y.		2784.00		3062.40		
.25 Dozer, 300 H.P.		475.00		522.50	325.90	358.49
10 L.H., Daily Totals		$3623.00		$4186.40	$362.30	$418.64

Crew B-33F	Hr.	Daily	Hr.	Daily	Bare Costs	Incl. O&P
1 Equip. Oper. (medium)	$36.40	$291.20	$60.15	$481.20	$36.40	$60.15
.25 Equip. Oper. (medium)	36.40	72.80	60.15	120.30		
1 Elev. Scraper, 11 C.Y.		1192.00		1311.20		
.25 Dozer, 300 H.P.		475.00		522.50	166.70	183.37
10 L.H., Daily Totals		$2031.00		$2435.20	$203.10	$243.52

Crew No.	Bare Costs Hr.	Bare Costs Daily	Incl. Subs O&P Hr.	Incl. Subs O&P Daily	Cost Per Labor-Hour Bare Costs	Cost Per Labor-Hour Incl. O&P
Crew B-33G						
1 Equip. Oper. (medium)	$36.40	$291.20	$60.15	$481.20	$36.40	$60.15
.25 Equip. Oper. (medium)	36.40	72.80	60.15	120.30		
1 Elev. Scraper, 22 C.Y.		2490.00		2739.00		
.25 Dozer, 300 H.P.		475.00		522.50	296.50	326.15
10 L.H., Daily Totals		$3329.00		$3863.00	$332.90	$386.30
Crew B-33K						
1 Equipment Operator (med.)	$36.40	$291.20	$60.15	$481.20	$33.60	$55.68
.25 Equipment Operator (med.)	36.40	72.80	60.15	120.30		
.5 Laborer	26.60	106.40	44.50	178.00		
1 S.P. Scraper, 31 C.Y.		3776.00		4153.60		
.25 Dozer, 410 H.P.		592.00		651.20	312.00	343.20
14 L.H., Daily Totals		$4838.40		$5584.30	$345.60	$398.88
Crew B-34A						
1 Truck Driver (heavy)	$32.35	$258.80	$53.30	$426.40	$32.35	$53.30
1 Dump Truck, 8 C.Y., 220 H.P.		391.00		430.10	48.88	53.76
8 L.H., Daily Totals		$649.80		$856.50	$81.22	$107.06
Crew B-34B						
1 Truck Driver (heavy)	$32.35	$258.80	$53.30	$426.40	$32.35	$53.30
1 Dump Truck, 12 C.Y., 400 H.P.		642.60		706.86	80.33	88.36
8 L.H., Daily Totals		$901.40		$1133.26	$112.68	$141.66
Crew B-34C						
1 Truck Driver (heavy)	$32.35	$258.80	$53.30	$426.40	$32.35	$53.30
1 Truck Tractor, 6x4, 380 H.P.		559.80		615.78		
1 Dump Trailer, 16.5 C.Y.		128.00		140.80	85.97	94.57
8 L.H., Daily Totals		$946.60		$1182.98	$118.33	$147.87
Crew B-34D						
1 Truck Driver (heavy)	$32.35	$258.80	$53.30	$426.40	$32.35	$53.30
1 Truck Tractor, 6x4, 380 H.P.		559.80		615.78		
1 Dump Trailer, 20 C.Y.		142.60		156.86	87.80	96.58
8 L.H., Daily Totals		$961.20		$1199.04	$120.15	$149.88
Crew B-34E						
1 Truck Driver (heavy)	$32.35	$258.80	$53.30	$426.40	$32.35	$53.30
1 Dump Truck, Off Hwy., 25 Ton		1476.00		1623.60	184.50	202.95
8 L.H., Daily Totals		$1734.80		$2050.00	$216.85	$256.25
Crew B-34F						
1 Truck Driver (heavy)	$32.35	$258.80	$53.30	$426.40	$32.35	$53.30
1 Dump Truck, Off Hwy., 35 Ton		1532.00		1685.20	191.50	210.65
8 L.H., Daily Totals		$1790.80		$2111.60	$223.85	$263.95
Crew B-34G						
1 Truck Driver (heavy)	$32.35	$258.80	$53.30	$426.40	$32.35	$53.30
1 Dump Truck, Off Hwy., 50 Ton		2006.00		2206.60	250.75	275.82
8 L.H., Daily Totals		$2264.80		$2633.00	$283.10	$329.13
Crew B-34H						
1 Truck Driver (heavy)	$32.35	$258.80	$53.30	$426.40	$32.35	$53.30
1 Dump Truck, Off Hwy., 65 Ton		2064.00		2270.40	258.00	283.80
8 L.H., Daily Totals		$2322.80		$2696.80	$290.35	$337.10

Crew No.	Bare Costs Hr.	Bare Costs Daily	Incl. Subs O&P Hr.	Incl. Subs O&P Daily	Cost Per Labor-Hour Bare Costs	Cost Per Labor-Hour Incl. O&P
Crew B-34I						
1 Truck Driver (heavy)	$32.35	$258.80	$53.30	$426.40	$32.35	$53.30
1 Dump Truck, 18 C.Y., 450 H.P.		815.60		897.16	101.95	112.15
8 L.H., Daily Totals		$1074.40		$1323.56	$134.30	$165.44
Crew B-34J						
1 Truck Driver (heavy)	$32.35	$258.80	$53.30	$426.40	$32.35	$53.30
1 Dump Truck, Off Hwy., 100 Ton		2952.00		3247.20	369.00	405.90
8 L.H., Daily Totals		$3210.80		$3673.60	$401.35	$459.20
Crew B-34K						
1 Truck Driver (heavy)	$32.35	$258.80	$53.30	$426.40	$32.35	$53.30
1 Truck Tractor, 6x4, 450 H.P.		679.80		747.78		
1 Lowbed Trailer, 75 Ton		242.40		266.64	115.28	126.80
8 L.H., Daily Totals		$1181.00		$1440.82	$147.63	$180.10
Crew B-34L						
1 Equip. Oper. (light)	$35.20	$281.60	$58.20	$465.60	$35.20	$58.20
1 Flatbed Truck, Gas, 1.5 Ton		217.40		239.14	27.18	29.89
8 L.H., Daily Totals		$499.00		$704.74	$62.38	$88.09
Crew B-34M						
1 Equip. Oper. (light)	$35.20	$281.60	$58.20	$465.60	$35.20	$58.20
1 Flatbed Truck, Gas, 3 Ton		270.20		297.22	33.77	37.15
8 L.H., Daily Totals		$551.80		$762.82	$68.97	$95.35
Crew B-34N						
1 Truck Driver (heavy)	$32.35	$258.80	$53.30	$426.40	$34.38	$56.73
1 Equip. Oper. (medium)	36.40	291.20	60.15	481.20		
1 Truck Tractor, 6x4, 380 H.P.		559.80		615.78		
1 Flatbed Trailer, 40 Ton		175.00		192.50	45.92	50.52
16 L.H., Daily Totals		$1284.80		$1715.88	$80.30	$107.24
Crew B-34P						
1 Pipe Fitter	$41.10	$328.80	$67.75	$542.00	$36.43	$60.10
1 Truck Driver (light)	31.80	254.40	52.40	419.20		
1 Equip. Oper. (medium)	36.40	291.20	60.15	481.20		
1 Flatbed Truck, Gas, 3 Ton		270.20		297.22		
1 Backhoe Loader, 48 H.P.		366.20		402.82	26.52	29.17
24 L.H., Daily Totals		$1510.80		$2142.44	$62.95	$89.27
Crew B-34Q						
1 Pipe Fitter	$41.10	$328.80	$67.75	$542.00	$36.73	$60.60
1 Truck Driver (light)	31.80	254.40	52.40	419.20		
1 Equip. Oper. (crane)	37.30	298.40	61.65	493.20		
1 Flatbed Trailer, 25 Ton		128.40		141.24		
1 Dump Truck, 8 C.Y., 220 H.P.		391.00		430.10		
1 Hyd. Crane, 25 Ton		673.80		741.18	49.72	54.69
24 L.H., Daily Totals		$2074.80		$2766.92	$86.45	$115.29
Crew B-34R						
1 Pipe Fitter	$41.10	$328.80	$67.75	$542.00	$36.73	$60.60
1 Truck Driver (light)	31.80	254.40	52.40	419.20		
1 Equip. Oper. (crane)	37.30	298.40	61.65	493.20		
1 Flatbed Trailer, 25 Ton		128.40		141.24		
1 Dump Truck, 8 C.Y., 220 H.P.		391.00		430.10		
1 Hyd. Crane, 25 Ton		673.80		741.18		
1 Hyd. Excavator, 1 C.Y.		798.20		878.02	82.97	91.27
24 L.H., Daily Totals		$2873.00		$3644.94	$119.71	$151.87

Crew No.	Bare Costs Hr.	Bare Costs Daily	Incl. Subs O&P Hr.	Incl. Subs O&P Daily	Cost Per Labor-Hour Bare Costs	Cost Per Labor-Hour Incl. O&P
Crew B-34S	Hr.	Daily	Hr.	Daily	Bare Costs	Incl. O&P
2 Pipe Fitters	$41.10	$657.60	$67.75	$1084.00	$37.96	$62.61
1 Truck Driver (heavy)	32.35	258.80	53.30	426.40		
1 Equip. Oper. (crane)	37.30	298.40	61.65	493.20		
1 Flatbed Trailer, 40 Ton		175.00		192.50		
1 Truck Tractor, 6x4, 380 H.P.		559.80		615.78		
1 Hyd. Crane, 80 Ton		1616.00		1777.60		
1 Hyd. Excavator, 2 C.Y.		1123.00		1235.30	108.56	119.41
32 L.H., Daily Totals		$4688.60		$5824.78	$146.52	$182.02
Crew B-34T	Hr.	Daily	Hr.	Daily	Bare Costs	Incl. O&P
2 Pipe Fitters	$41.10	$657.60	$67.75	$1084.00	$37.96	$62.61
1 Truck Driver (heavy)	32.35	258.80	53.30	426.40		
1 Equip. Oper. (crane)	37.30	298.40	61.65	493.20		
1 Flatbed Trailer, 40 Ton		175.00		192.50		
1 Truck Tractor, 6x4, 380 H.P.		559.80		615.78		
1 Hyd. Crane, 80 Ton		1616.00		1777.60	73.46	80.81
32 L.H., Daily Totals		$3565.60		$4589.48	$111.43	$143.42
Crew B-34U	Hr.	Daily	Hr.	Daily	Bare Costs	Incl. O&P
1 Truck Driver (heavy)	$32.35	$258.80	$53.30	$426.40	$33.77	$55.75
1 Equip. Oper. (light)	35.20	281.60	58.20	465.60		
1 Truck Tractor, 220 H.P.		336.60		370.26		
1 Flatbed Trailer, 25 Ton		128.40		141.24	29.06	31.97
16 L.H., Daily Totals		$1005.40		$1403.50	$62.84	$87.72
Crew B-34V	Hr.	Daily	Hr.	Daily	Bare Costs	Incl. O&P
1 Truck Driver (heavy)	$32.35	$258.80	$53.30	$426.40	$34.95	$57.72
1 Equip. Oper. (crane)	37.30	298.40	61.65	493.20		
1 Equip. Oper. (light)	35.20	281.60	58.20	465.60		
1 Truck Tractor, 6x4, 450 H.P.		679.80		747.78		
1 Equipment Trailer, 50 Ton		192.20		211.42		
1 Pickup Truck, 4x4, 3/4 Ton		140.00		154.00	42.17	46.38
24 L.H., Daily Totals		$1850.80		$2498.40	$77.12	$104.10
Crew B-34W	Hr.	Daily	Hr.	Daily	Bare Costs	Incl. O&P
5 Truck Drivers (heavy)	$32.35	$1294.00	$53.30	$2132.00	$33.37	$55.12
2 Equip. Opers. (crane)	37.30	596.80	61.65	986.40		
1 Equip. Oper. (mechanic)	37.40	299.20	61.80	494.40		
1 Laborer	26.60	212.80	44.50	356.00		
4 Truck Tractors, 6x4, 380 H.P.		2239.20		2463.12		
2 Equipment Trailers, 50 Ton		384.40		422.84		
2 Flatbed Trailers, 40 Ton		350.00		385.00		
1 Pickup Truck, 4x4, 3/4 Ton		140.00		154.00		
1 S.P. Crane, 4x4, 20 Ton		553.80		609.18	50.94	56.03
72 L.H., Daily Totals		$6070.20		$8002.94	$84.31	$111.15
Crew B-35	Hr.	Daily	Hr.	Daily	Bare Costs	Incl. O&P
1 Labor Foreman (outside)	$28.60	$228.80	$47.80	$382.40	$33.56	$55.83
1 Skilled Worker	35.75	286.00	60.00	480.00		
1 Welder (plumber)	39.55	316.40	65.20	521.60		
1 Laborer	26.60	212.80	44.50	356.00		
1 Equip. Oper. (crane)	37.30	298.40	61.65	493.20		
1 Welder, Electric, 300 amp		58.15		63.97		
1 Hyd. Excavator, .75 C.Y.		674.20		741.62	18.31	20.14
40 L.H., Daily Totals		$2074.75		$3038.78	$51.87	$75.97

Crew No.	Bare Costs Hr.	Bare Costs Daily	Incl. Subs O&P Hr.	Incl. Subs O&P Daily	Cost Per Labor-Hour Bare Costs	Cost Per Labor-Hour Incl. O&P
Crew B-35A	Hr.	Daily	Hr.	Daily	Bare Costs	Incl. O&P
1 Labor Foreman (outside)	$28.60	$228.80	$47.80	$382.40	$32.44	$53.94
2 Laborers	26.60	425.60	44.50	712.00		
1 Skilled Worker	35.75	286.00	60.00	480.00		
1 Welder (plumber)	39.55	316.40	65.20	521.60		
1 Equip. Oper. (crane)	37.30	298.40	61.65	493.20		
1 Equip. Oper. (oiler)	32.65	261.20	53.95	431.60		
1 Welder, Gas Engine, 300 amp		129.80		142.78		
1 Crawler Crane, 75 Ton		1645.00		1809.50	31.69	34.86
56 L.H., Daily Totals		$3591.20		$4973.08	$64.13	$88.81
Crew B-36	Hr.	Daily	Hr.	Daily	Bare Costs	Incl. O&P
1 Labor Foreman (outside)	$28.60	$228.80	$47.80	$382.40	$30.92	$51.42
2 Laborers	26.60	425.60	44.50	712.00		
2 Equip. Oper. (medium)	36.40	582.40	60.15	962.40		
1 Dozer, 200 H.P.		1384.00		1522.40		
1 Aggregate Spreader		37.40		41.14		
1 Tandem Roller, 10 Ton		237.60		261.36	41.48	45.62
40 L.H., Daily Totals		$2895.80		$3881.70	$72.39	$97.04
Crew B-36A	Hr.	Daily	Hr.	Daily	Bare Costs	Incl. O&P
1 Labor Foreman (outside)	$28.60	$228.80	$47.80	$382.40	$32.49	$53.91
2 Laborers	26.60	425.60	44.50	712.00		
4 Equip. Oper. (medium)	36.40	1164.80	60.15	1924.80		
1 Dozer, 200 H.P.		1384.00		1522.40		
1 Aggregate Spreader		37.40		41.14		
1 Tandem Roller, 10 Ton		237.60		261.36		
1 Roller, Pneum. Whl., 12 Ton		355.80		391.38	35.98	39.58
56 L.H., Daily Totals		$3834.00		$5235.48	$68.46	$93.49
Crew B-36B	Hr.	Daily	Hr.	Daily	Bare Costs	Incl. O&P
1 Labor Foreman (outside)	$28.60	$228.80	$47.80	$382.40	$32.47	$53.84
2 Laborers	26.60	425.60	44.50	712.00		
4 Equip. Oper. (medium)	36.40	1164.80	60.15	1924.80		
1 Truck Driver (heavy)	32.35	258.80	53.30	426.40		
1 Grader, 30,000 Lbs.		678.40		746.24		
1 F.E. Loader, Crl, 1.5 C.Y.		662.80		729.08		
1 Dozer, 300 H.P.		1900.00		2090.00		
1 Roller, Vibratory, 25 Ton		684.00		752.40		
1 Truck Tractor, 6x4, 450 H.P.		679.80		747.78		
1 Water Tank Trailer, 5000 Gal.		143.00		157.30	74.19	81.61
64 L.H., Daily Totals		$6826.00		$8668.40	$106.66	$135.44
Crew B-36C	Hr.	Daily	Hr.	Daily	Bare Costs	Incl. O&P
1 Labor Foreman (outside)	$28.60	$228.80	$47.80	$382.40	$34.03	$56.31
3 Equip. Oper. (medium)	36.40	873.60	60.15	1443.60		
1 Truck Driver (heavy)	32.35	258.80	53.30	426.40		
1 Grader, 30,000 Lbs.		678.40		746.24		
1 Dozer, 300 H.P.		1900.00		2090.00		
1 Roller, Vibratory, 25 Ton		684.00		752.40		
1 Truck Tractor, 6x4, 450 H.P.		679.80		747.78		
1 Water Tank Trailer, 5000 Gal.		143.00		157.30	102.13	112.34
40 L.H., Daily Totals		$5446.40		$6746.12	$136.16	$168.65

Crews - Residential

Crew No.	Bare Costs		Incl. Subs O&P		Cost Per Labor-Hour	

Crew B-36E	Hr.	Daily	Hr.	Daily	Bare Costs	Incl. O&P
1 Labor Foreman (outside)	$28.60	$228.80	$47.80	$382.40	$34.42	$56.95
4 Equip. Oper. (medium)	36.40	1164.80	60.15	1924.80		
1 Truck Driver (heavy)	32.35	258.80	53.30	426.40		
1 Grader, 30,000 Lbs.		678.40		746.24		
1 Dozer, 300 H.P.		1900.00		2090.00		
1 Roller, Vibratory, 25 Ton		684.00		752.40		
1 Truck Tractor, 6x4, 380 H.P.		559.80		615.78		
1 Dist. Tanker, 3000 Gallon		327.40		360.14	86.45	95.09
48 L.H., Daily Totals		$5802.00		$7298.16	$120.88	$152.04

Crew B-37	Hr.	Daily	Hr.	Daily	Bare Costs	Incl. O&P
1 Labor Foreman (outside)	$28.60	$228.80	$47.80	$382.40	$28.37	$47.33
4 Laborers	26.60	851.20	44.50	1424.00		
1 Equip. Oper. (light)	35.20	281.60	58.20	465.60		
1 Tandem Roller, 5 Ton		152.40		167.64	3.17	3.49
48 L.H., Daily Totals		$1514.00		$2439.64	$31.54	$50.83

Crew B-37A	Hr.	Daily	Hr.	Daily	Bare Costs	Incl. O&P
2 Laborers	$26.60	$425.60	$44.50	$712.00	$28.33	$47.13
1 Truck Driver (light)	31.80	254.40	52.40	419.20		
1 Flatbed Truck, Gas, 1.5 Ton		217.40		239.14		
1 Tar Kettle, T.M.		122.75		135.03	14.17	15.59
24 L.H., Daily Totals		$1020.15		$1505.37	$42.51	$62.72

Crew B-37B	Hr.	Daily	Hr.	Daily	Bare Costs	Incl. O&P
3 Laborers	$26.60	$638.40	$44.50	$1068.00	$27.90	$46.48
1 Truck Driver (light)	31.80	254.40	52.40	419.20		
1 Flatbed Truck, Gas, 1.5 Ton		217.40		239.14		
1 Tar Kettle, T.M.		122.75		135.03	10.63	11.69
32 L.H., Daily Totals		$1232.95		$1861.37	$38.53	$58.17

Crew B-37C	Hr.	Daily	Hr.	Daily	Bare Costs	Incl. O&P
2 Laborers	$26.60	$425.60	$44.50	$712.00	$29.20	$48.45
2 Truck Drivers (light)	31.80	508.80	52.40	838.40		
2 Flatbed Trucks, Gas, 1.5 Ton		434.80		478.28		
1 Tar Kettle, T.M.		122.75		135.03	17.42	19.17
32 L.H., Daily Totals		$1491.95		$2163.70	$46.62	$67.62

Crew B-37D	Hr.	Daily	Hr.	Daily	Bare Costs	Incl. O&P
1 Laborer	$26.60	$212.80	$44.50	$356.00	$29.20	$48.45
1 Truck Driver (light)	31.80	254.40	52.40	419.20		
1 Pickup Truck, 3/4 Ton		129.40		142.34	8.09	8.90
16 L.H., Daily Totals		$596.60		$917.54	$37.29	$57.35

Crew B-37E	Hr.	Daily	Hr.	Daily	Bare Costs	Incl. O&P
3 Laborers	$26.60	$638.40	$44.50	$1068.00	$30.71	$50.95
1 Equip. Oper. (light)	35.20	281.60	58.20	465.60		
1 Equip. Oper. (medium)	36.40	291.20	60.15	481.20		
2 Truck Drivers (light)	31.80	508.80	52.40	838.40		
4 Barrels w/ Flasher		13.60		14.96		
1 Concrete Saw		153.60		168.96		
1 Rotary Hammer Drill		24.70		27.17		
1 Hammer Drill Bit		3.05		3.36		
1 Loader, Skid Steer, 30 H.P.		171.00		188.10		
1 Conc. Hammer Attach.		115.55		127.11		
1 Vibrating Plate, Gas, 18"		33.60		36.96		
2 Flatbed Trucks, Gas, 1.5 Ton		434.80		478.28	16.96	18.66
56 L.H., Daily Totals		$2669.90		$3898.09	$47.68	$69.61

Crew B-37F	Hr.	Daily	Hr.	Daily	Bare Costs	Incl. O&P
3 Laborers	$26.60	$638.40	$44.50	$1068.00	$27.90	$46.48
1 Truck Driver (light)	31.80	254.40	52.40	419.20		
4 Barrels w/ Flasher		13.60		14.96		
1 Concrete Mixer, 10 C.F.		164.60		181.06		
1 Air Compressor, 60 cfm		127.00		139.70		
1 -50' Air Hose, 3/4"		3.25		3.58		
1 Spade (Chipper)		8.40		9.24		
1 Flatbed Truck, Gas, 1.5 Ton		217.40		239.14	16.70	18.36
32 L.H., Daily Totals		$1427.05		$2074.88	$44.60	$64.84

Crew B-37G	Hr.	Daily	Hr.	Daily	Bare Costs	Incl. O&P
1 Labor Foreman (outside)	$28.60	$228.80	$47.80	$382.40	$28.37	$47.33
4 Laborers	26.60	851.20	44.50	1424.00		
1 Equip. Oper. (light)	35.20	281.60	58.20	465.60		
1 Berm Machine		313.40		344.74		
1 Tandem Roller, 5 Ton		152.40		167.64	9.70	10.67
48 L.H., Daily Totals		$1827.40		$2784.38	$38.07	$58.01

Crew B-37H	Hr.	Daily	Hr.	Daily	Bare Costs	Incl. O&P
1 Labor Foreman (outside)	$28.60	$228.80	$47.80	$382.40	$28.37	$47.33
4 Laborers	26.60	851.20	44.50	1424.00		
1 Equip. Oper. (light)	35.20	281.60	58.20	465.60		
1 Tandem Roller, 5 Ton		152.40		167.64		
1 Flatbed Truck, Gas, 1.5 Ton		217.40		239.14		
1 Tar Kettle, T.M.		122.75		135.03	10.26	11.29
48 L.H., Daily Totals		$1854.15		$2813.80	$38.63	$58.62

Crew B-37I	Hr.	Daily	Hr.	Daily	Bare Costs	Incl. O&P
3 Laborers	$26.60	$638.40	$44.50	$1068.00	$30.71	$50.95
1 Equip. Oper. (light)	35.20	281.60	58.20	465.60		
1 Equip. Oper. (medium)	36.40	291.20	60.15	481.20		
2 Truck Drivers (light)	31.80	508.80	52.40	838.40		
4 Barrels w/ Flasher		13.60		14.96		
1 Concrete Saw		153.60		168.96		
1 Rotary Hammer Drill		24.70		27.17		
1 Hammer Drill Bit		3.05		3.36		
1 Air Compressor, 60 cfm		127.00		139.70		
1 -50' Air Hose, 3/4"		3.25		3.58		
1 Spade (Chipper)		8.40		9.24		
1 Loader, Skid Steer, 30 H.P.		171.00		188.10		
1 Conc. Hammer Attach.		115.55		127.11		
1 Concrete Mixer, 10 C.F.		164.60		181.06		
1 Vibrating Plate, Gas, 18"		33.60		36.96		
2 Flatbed Trucks, Gas, 1.5 Ton		434.80		478.28	22.38	24.62
56 L.H., Daily Totals		$2973.15		$4231.67	$53.09	$75.57

Crew B-37J	Hr.	Daily	Hr.	Daily	Bare Costs	Incl. O&P
1 Labor Foreman (outside)	$28.60	$228.80	$47.80	$382.40	$28.37	$47.33
4 Laborers	26.60	851.20	44.50	1424.00		
1 Equip. Oper. (light)	35.20	281.60	58.20	465.60		
1 Air Compressor, 60 cfm		127.00		139.70		
1 -50' Air Hose, 3/4"		3.25		3.58		
2 Concrete Mixers, 10 C.F.		329.20		362.12		
2 Flatbed Trucks, Gas, 1.5 Ton		434.80		478.28		
1 Shot Blaster, 20"		220.40		242.44	23.22	25.54
48 L.H., Daily Totals		$2476.25		$3498.11	$51.59	$72.88

For customer support on your Residential Costs with RSMeans Data, call 800.448.8182.

689

| Crew No. | Bare Costs | | Incl. Subs O&P | | Cost Per Labor-Hour | |

Crew B-37K

Crew B-37K	Hr.	Daily	Hr.	Daily	Bare Costs	Incl. O&P
1 Labor Foreman (outside)	$28.60	$228.80	$47.80	$382.40	$28.37	$47.33
4 Laborers	26.60	851.20	44.50	1424.00		
1 Equip. Oper. (light)	35.20	281.60	58.20	465.60		
1 Air Compressor, 60 cfm		127.00		139.70		
1 -50' Air Hose, 3/4"		3.25		3.58		
2 Flatbed Trucks, Gas, 1.5 Ton		434.80		478.28		
1 Shot Blaster, 20"		220.40		242.44	16.36	18.00
48 L.H., Daily Totals		$2147.05		$3135.99	$44.73	$65.33

Crew B-38

Crew B-38	Hr.	Daily	Hr.	Daily	Bare Costs	Incl. O&P
2 Laborers	$26.60	$425.60	$44.50	$712.00	$29.47	$49.07
1 Equip. Oper. (light)	35.20	281.60	58.20	465.60		
1 Backhoe Loader, 48 H.P.		366.20		402.82		
1 Hyd. Hammer (1200 lb.)		182.20		200.42	22.85	25.14
24 L.H., Daily Totals		$1255.60		$1780.84	$52.32	$74.20

Crew B-39

Crew B-39	Hr.	Daily	Hr.	Daily	Bare Costs	Incl. O&P
1 Labor Foreman (outside)	$28.60	$228.80	$47.80	$382.40	$26.93	$45.05
5 Laborers	26.60	1064.00	44.50	1780.00		
1 Air Compressor, 250 cfm		181.20		199.32		
2 Breakers, Pavement, 60 lb.		20.40		22.44		
2 -50' Air Hoses, 1.5"		11.60		12.76	4.44	4.89
48 L.H., Daily Totals		$1506.00		$2396.92	$31.38	$49.94

Crew B-40

Crew B-40	Hr.	Daily	Hr.	Daily	Bare Costs	Incl. O&P
1 Pile Driver Foreman (outside)	$37.15	$297.20	$64.20	$513.60	$34.52	$59.05
4 Pile Drivers	35.15	1124.80	60.75	1944.00		
1 Building Laborer	26.60	212.80	44.50	356.00		
1 Equip. Oper. (crane)	37.30	298.40	61.65	493.20		
1 Crawler Crane, 40 Ton		1313.00		1444.30		
1 Vibratory Hammer & Gen.		2494.00		2743.40	67.98	74.78
56 L.H., Daily Totals		$5740.20		$7494.50	$102.50	$133.83

Crew B-40B

Crew B-40B	Hr.	Daily	Hr.	Daily	Bare Costs	Incl. O&P
1 Labor Foreman (outside)	$28.60	$228.80	$47.80	$382.40	$29.73	$49.48
3 Laborers	26.60	638.40	44.50	1068.00		
1 Equip. Oper. (crane)	37.30	298.40	61.65	493.20		
1 Equip. Oper. (oiler)	32.65	261.20	53.95	431.60		
1 Lattice Boom Crane, 40 Ton		1311.00		1442.10	27.31	30.04
48 L.H., Daily Totals		$2737.80		$3817.30	$57.04	$79.53

Crew B-41

Crew B-41	Hr.	Daily	Hr.	Daily	Bare Costs	Incl. O&P
1 Labor Foreman (outside)	$28.60	$228.80	$47.80	$382.40	$27.73	$46.31
4 Laborers	26.60	851.20	44.50	1424.00		
.25 Equip. Oper. (crane)	37.30	74.60	61.65	123.30		
.25 Equip. Oper. (oiler)	32.65	65.30	53.95	107.90		
.25 Crawler Crane, 40 Ton		328.25		361.07	7.46	8.21
44 L.H., Daily Totals		$1548.15		$2398.68	$35.19	$54.52

Crew B-42

Crew B-42	Hr.	Daily	Hr.	Daily	Bare Costs	Incl. O&P
1 Labor Foreman (outside)	$28.60	$228.80	$47.80	$382.40	$30.26	$50.38
4 Laborers	26.60	851.20	44.50	1424.00		
1 Equip. Oper. (crane)	37.30	298.40	61.65	493.20		
1 Welder	39.55	316.40	65.20	521.60		
1 Hyd. Crane, 25 Ton		673.80		741.18		
1 Welder, Gas Engine, 300 amp		129.80		142.78		
1 Horz. Boring Csg. Mch.		465.20		511.72	22.66	24.92
56 L.H., Daily Totals		$2963.60		$4216.88	$52.92	$75.30

Crew B-43

Crew B-43	Hr.	Daily	Hr.	Daily	Bare Costs	Incl. O&P
1 Labor Foreman (outside)	$28.60	$228.80	$47.80	$382.40	$27.00	$45.16
4 Laborers	26.60	851.20	44.50	1424.00		
1 Drill Rig, Truck-Mounted		2573.00		2830.30	64.33	70.76
40 L.H., Daily Totals		$3653.00		$4636.70	$91.33	$115.92

Crew B-44

Crew B-44	Hr.	Daily	Hr.	Daily	Bare Costs	Incl. O&P
1 Pile Driver Foreman (outside)	$37.15	$297.20	$64.20	$513.60	$33.53	$57.23
4 Pile Drivers	35.15	1124.80	60.75	1944.00		
1 Equip. Oper. (crane)	37.30	298.40	61.65	493.20		
2 Laborers	26.60	425.60	44.50	712.00		
1 Crawler Crane, 40 Ton		1313.00		1444.30		
1 Lead, 60' High		76.00		83.60		
1 Hammer, Diesel, 15K ft.-lbs.		605.80		666.38	31.17	34.29
64 L.H., Daily Totals		$4140.80		$5857.08	$64.70	$91.52

Crew B-45

Crew B-45	Hr.	Daily	Hr.	Daily	Bare Costs	Incl. O&P
1 Building Laborer	$26.60	$212.80	$44.50	$356.00	$29.48	$48.90
1 Truck Driver (heavy)	32.35	258.80	53.30	426.40		
1 Dist. Tanker, 3000 Gallon		327.40		360.14	20.46	22.51
16 L.H., Daily Totals		$799.00		$1142.54	$49.94	$71.41

Crew B-46

Crew B-46	Hr.	Daily	Hr.	Daily	Bare Costs	Incl. O&P
1 Pile Driver Foreman (outside)	$37.15	$297.20	$64.20	$513.60	$31.21	$53.20
2 Pile Drivers	35.15	562.40	60.75	972.00		
3 Laborers	26.60	638.40	44.50	1068.00		
1 Chain Saw, Gas, 36" Long		45.00		49.50	0.94	1.03
48 L.H., Daily Totals		$1543.00		$2603.10	$32.15	$54.23

Crew B-47

Crew B-47	Hr.	Daily	Hr.	Daily	Bare Costs	Incl. O&P
1 Blast Foreman (outside)	$28.60	$228.80	$47.80	$382.40	$27.60	$46.15
1 Driller	26.60	212.80	44.50	356.00		
1 Air Track Drill, 4"		1016.00		1117.60		
1 Air Compressor, 600 cfm		482.00		530.20		
2 -50' Air Hoses, 3"		29.80		32.78	95.49	105.04
16 L.H., Daily Totals		$1969.40		$2418.98	$123.09	$151.19

Crew B-47A

Crew B-47A	Hr.	Daily	Hr.	Daily	Bare Costs	Incl. O&P
1 Drilling Foreman (outside)	$28.60	$228.80	$47.80	$382.40	$32.85	$54.47
1 Equip. Oper. (heavy)	37.30	298.40	61.65	493.20		
1 Equip. Oper. (oiler)	32.65	261.20	53.95	431.60		
1 Air Track Drill, 5"		1211.00		1332.10	50.46	55.50
24 L.H., Daily Totals		$1999.40		$2639.30	$83.31	$109.97

Crew B-47C

Crew B-47C	Hr.	Daily	Hr.	Daily	Bare Costs	Incl. O&P
1 Laborer	$26.60	$212.80	$44.50	$356.00	$30.90	$51.35
1 Equip. Oper. (light)	35.20	281.60	58.20	465.60		
1 Air Compressor, 750 cfm		488.20		537.02		
2 -50' Air Hoses, 3"		29.80		32.78		
1 Air Track Drill, 4"		1016.00		1117.60	95.88	105.46
16 L.H., Daily Totals		$2028.40		$2509.00	$126.78	$156.81

Crew B-47E

Crew B-47E	Hr.	Daily	Hr.	Daily	Bare Costs	Incl. O&P
1 Labor Foreman (outside)	$28.60	$228.80	$47.80	$382.40	$27.10	$45.33
3 Laborers	26.60	638.40	44.50	1068.00		
1 Flatbed Truck, Gas, 3 Ton		270.20		297.22	8.44	9.29
32 L.H., Daily Totals		$1137.40		$1747.62	$35.54	$54.61

Crew B-47G

Crew No.	Bare Costs Hr.	Daily	Incl. Subs O&P Hr.	Daily	Cost Per Labor-Hour Bare Costs	Incl. O&P
1 Labor Foreman (outside)	$28.60	$228.80	$47.80	$382.40	$27.27	$45.60
2 Laborers	26.60	425.60	44.50	712.00		
1 Air Track Drill, 4"		1016.00		1117.60		
1 Air Compressor, 600 cfm		482.00		530.20		
2 -50' Air Hoses, 3"		29.80		32.78		
1 Gunite Pump Rig		357.40		393.14	78.55	86.41
24 L.H., Daily Totals		$2539.60		$3168.12	$105.82	$132.01

Crew B-47H

Crew No.	Bare Costs Hr.	Daily	Incl. Subs O&P Hr.	Daily	Cost Per Labor-Hour Bare Costs	Incl. O&P
1 Skilled Worker Foreman (out)	$37.75	$302.00	$63.40	$507.20	$36.25	$60.85
3 Skilled Workers	35.75	858.00	60.00	1440.00		
1 Flatbed Truck, Gas, 3 Ton		270.20		297.22	8.44	9.29
32 L.H., Daily Totals		$1430.20		$2244.42	$44.69	$70.14

Crew B-48

Crew No.	Bare Costs Hr.	Daily	Incl. Subs O&P Hr.	Daily	Cost Per Labor-Hour Bare Costs	Incl. O&P
1 Labor Foreman (outside)	$28.60	$228.80	$47.80	$382.40	$28.72	$47.91
4 Laborers	26.60	851.20	44.50	1424.00		
1 Equip. Oper. (crane)	37.30	298.40	61.65	493.20		
1 Centr. Water Pump, 6"		325.40		357.94		
1 -20' Suction Hose, 6"		11.90		13.09		
1 -50' Discharge Hose, 6"		6.30		6.93		
1 Drill Rig, Truck-Mounted		2573.00		2830.30	60.76	66.84
48 L.H., Daily Totals		$4295.00		$5507.86	$89.48	$114.75

Crew B-49

Crew No.	Bare Costs Hr.	Daily	Incl. Subs O&P Hr.	Daily	Cost Per Labor-Hour Bare Costs	Incl. O&P
1 Labor Foreman (outside)	$28.60	$228.80	$47.80	$382.40	$29.91	$50.38
5 Laborers	26.60	1064.00	44.50	1780.00		
1 Equip. Oper. (crane)	37.30	298.40	61.65	493.20		
2 Pile Drivers	35.15	562.40	60.75	972.00		
1 Hyd. Crane, 25 Ton		673.80		741.18		
1 Centr. Water Pump, 6"		325.40		357.94		
1 -20' Suction Hose, 6"		11.90		13.09		
1 -50' Discharge Hose, 6"		6.30		6.93		
1 Drill Rig, Truck-Mounted		2573.00		2830.30	49.87	54.85
72 L.H., Daily Totals		$5744.00		$7577.04	$79.78	$105.24

Crew B-50

Crew No.	Bare Costs Hr.	Daily	Incl. Subs O&P Hr.	Daily	Cost Per Labor-Hour Bare Costs	Incl. O&P
1 Pile Driver Foreman (outside)	$37.15	$297.20	$64.20	$513.60	$32.18	$54.83
6 Pile Drivers	35.15	1687.20	60.75	2916.00		
1 Equip. Oper. (crane)	37.30	298.40	61.65	493.20		
5 Laborers	26.60	1064.00	44.50	1780.00		
1 Crawler Crane, 40 Ton		1313.00		1444.30		
1 Lead, 60' High		76.00		83.60		
1 Hammer, Diesel, 15K ft.-lbs.		605.80		666.38		
1 Air Compressor, 600 cfm		482.00		530.20		
2 -50' Air Hoses, 3"		29.80		32.78		
1 Chain Saw, Gas, 36" Long		45.00		49.50	24.53	26.99
104 L.H., Daily Totals		$5898.40		$8509.56	$56.72	$81.82

Crew B-51

Crew No.	Bare Costs Hr.	Daily	Incl. Subs O&P Hr.	Daily	Cost Per Labor-Hour Bare Costs	Incl. O&P
1 Labor Foreman (outside)	$28.60	$228.80	$47.80	$382.40	$27.80	$46.37
4 Laborers	26.60	851.20	44.50	1424.00		
1 Truck Driver (light)	31.80	254.40	52.40	419.20		
1 Flatbed Truck, Gas, 1.5 Ton		217.40		239.14	4.53	4.98
48 L.H., Daily Totals		$1551.80		$2464.74	$32.33	$51.35

Crew B-52

Crew No.	Bare Costs Hr.	Daily	Incl. Subs O&P Hr.	Daily	Cost Per Labor-Hour Bare Costs	Incl. O&P
1 Labor Foreman (outside)	$28.60	$228.80	$47.80	$382.40	$29.63	$49.53
1 Carpenter	34.95	279.60	58.45	467.60		
4 Laborers	26.60	851.20	44.50	1424.00		
.5 Rodman (reinf.)	38.55	154.20	64.80	259.20		
.5 Equip. Oper. (medium)	36.40	145.60	60.15	240.60		
.5 Crawler Loader, 3 C.Y.		640.50		704.55	11.44	12.58
56 L.H., Daily Totals		$2299.90		$3478.35	$41.07	$62.11

Crew B-53

Crew No.	Bare Costs Hr.	Daily	Incl. Subs O&P Hr.	Daily	Cost Per Labor-Hour Bare Costs	Incl. O&P
1 Building Laborer	$26.60	$212.80	$44.50	$356.00	$26.60	$44.50
1 Trencher, Chain, 12 H.P.		63.60		69.96	7.95	8.74
8 L.H., Daily Totals		$276.40		$425.96	$34.55	$53.24

Crew B-54

Crew No.	Bare Costs Hr.	Daily	Incl. Subs O&P Hr.	Daily	Cost Per Labor-Hour Bare Costs	Incl. O&P
1 Equip. Oper. (light)	$35.20	$281.60	$58.20	$465.60	$35.20	$58.20
1 Trencher, Chain, 40 H.P.		325.20		357.72	40.65	44.72
8 L.H., Daily Totals		$606.80		$823.32	$75.85	$102.92

Crew B-54A

Crew No.	Bare Costs Hr.	Daily	Incl. Subs O&P Hr.	Daily	Cost Per Labor-Hour Bare Costs	Incl. O&P
.17 Labor Foreman (outside)	$28.60	$38.90	$47.80	$65.01	$35.27	$58.36
1 Equipment Operator (med.)	36.40	291.20	60.15	481.20		
1 Wheel Trencher, 67 H.P.		1157.00		1272.70	123.61	135.97
9.36 L.H., Daily Totals		$1487.10		$1818.91	$158.88	$194.33

Crew B-54B

Crew No.	Bare Costs Hr.	Daily	Incl. Subs O&P Hr.	Daily	Cost Per Labor-Hour Bare Costs	Incl. O&P
.25 Labor Foreman (outside)	$28.60	$57.20	$47.80	$95.60	$34.84	$57.68
1 Equipment Operator (med.)	36.40	291.20	60.15	481.20		
1 Wheel Trencher, 150 H.P.		1930.00		2123.00	193.00	212.30
10 L.H., Daily Totals		$2278.40		$2699.80	$227.84	$269.98

Crew B-54D

Crew No.	Bare Costs Hr.	Daily	Incl. Subs O&P Hr.	Daily	Cost Per Labor-Hour Bare Costs	Incl. O&P
1 Laborer	$26.60	$212.80	$44.50	$356.00	$31.50	$52.33
1 Equipment Operator (med.)	36.40	291.20	60.15	481.20		
1 Rock Trencher, 6" Width		749.00		823.90	46.81	51.49
16 L.H., Daily Totals		$1253.00		$1661.10	$78.31	$103.82

Crew B-54E

Crew No.	Bare Costs Hr.	Daily	Incl. Subs O&P Hr.	Daily	Cost Per Labor-Hour Bare Costs	Incl. O&P
1 Laborer	$26.60	$212.80	$44.50	$356.00	$31.50	$52.33
1 Equipment Operator (med.)	36.40	291.20	60.15	481.20		
1 Rock Trencher, 18" Width		2645.00		2909.50	165.31	181.84
16 L.H., Daily Totals		$3149.00		$3746.70	$196.81	$234.17

Crew B-55

Crew No.	Bare Costs Hr.	Daily	Incl. Subs O&P Hr.	Daily	Cost Per Labor-Hour Bare Costs	Incl. O&P
1 Laborer	$26.60	$212.80	$44.50	$356.00	$29.20	$48.45
1 Truck Driver (light)	31.80	254.40	52.40	419.20		
1 Truck-Mounted Earth Auger		781.40		859.54		
1 Flatbed Truck, Gas, 3 Ton		270.20		297.22	65.72	72.30
16 L.H., Daily Totals		$1518.80		$1931.96	$94.92	$120.75

Crew B-56

Crew No.	Bare Costs Hr.	Daily	Incl. Subs O&P Hr.	Daily	Cost Per Labor-Hour Bare Costs	Incl. O&P
2 Laborers	$26.60	$425.60	$44.50	$712.00	$26.60	$44.50
1 Air Track Drill, 4"		1016.00		1117.60		
1 Air Compressor, 600 cfm		482.00		530.20		
1 -50' Air Hose, 3"		14.90		16.39	94.56	104.01
16 L.H., Daily Totals		$1938.50		$2376.19	$121.16	$148.51

For customer support on your Residential Costs with RSMeans Data, call 800.448.8182.

691

Crew No.	Bare Costs		Incl. Subs O&P		Cost Per Labor-Hour	

Crew B-57	Hr.	Daily	Hr.	Daily	Bare Costs	Incl. O&P
1 Labor Foreman (outside)	$28.60	$228.80	$47.80	$382.40	$29.14	$48.59
3 Laborers	26.60	638.40	44.50	1068.00		
1 Equip. Oper. (crane)	37.30	298.40	61.65	493.20		
1 Barge, 400 Ton		794.20		873.62		
1 Crawler Crane, 25 Ton		1296.00		1425.60		
1 Clamshell Bucket, 1 C.Y.		48.80		53.68		
1 Centr. Water Pump, 6"		325.40		357.94		
1 -20' Suction Hose, 6"		11.90		13.09		
20 -50' Discharge Hoses, 6"		126.00		138.60	65.06	71.56
40 L.H., Daily Totals		$3767.90		$4806.13	$94.20	$120.15

Crew B-58	Hr.	Daily	Hr.	Daily	Bare Costs	Incl. O&P
2 Laborers	$26.60	$425.60	$44.50	$712.00	$29.47	$49.07
1 Equip. Oper. (light)	35.20	281.60	58.20	465.60		
1 Backhoe Loader, 48 H.P.		366.20		402.82		
1 Small Helicopter, w/ Pilot		2793.00		3072.30	131.63	144.80
24 L.H., Daily Totals		$3866.40		$4652.72	$161.10	$193.86

Crew B-59	Hr.	Daily	Hr.	Daily	Bare Costs	Incl. O&P
1 Truck Driver (heavy)	$32.35	$258.80	$53.30	$426.40	$32.35	$53.30
1 Truck Tractor, 220 H.P.		336.60		370.26		
1 Water Tank Trailer, 5000 Gal.		143.00		157.30	59.95	65.94
8 L.H., Daily Totals		$738.40		$953.96	$92.30	$119.25

Crew B-60	Hr.	Daily	Hr.	Daily	Bare Costs	Incl. O&P
1 Labor Foreman (outside)	$28.60	$228.80	$47.80	$382.40	$30.15	$50.19
3 Laborers	26.60	638.40	44.50	1068.00		
1 Equip. Oper. (crane)	37.30	298.40	61.65	493.20		
1 Equip. Oper. (light)	35.20	281.60	58.20	465.60		
1 Crawler Crane, 40 Ton		1313.00		1444.30		
1 Lead, 60' High		76.00		83.60		
1 Hammer, Diesel, 15K ft.-lbs.		605.80		666.38		
1 Backhoe Loader, 48 H.P.		366.20		402.82	49.19	54.11
48 L.H., Daily Totals		$3808.20		$5006.30	$79.34	$104.30

Crew B-61	Hr.	Daily	Hr.	Daily	Bare Costs	Incl. O&P
1 Labor Foreman (outside)	$28.60	$228.80	$47.80	$382.40	$27.00	$45.16
4 Laborers	26.60	851.20	44.50	1424.00		
1 Cement Mixer, 2 C.Y.		197.00		216.70		
1 Air Compressor, 160 cfm		143.60		157.96	8.52	9.37
40 L.H., Daily Totals		$1420.60		$2181.06	$35.52	$54.53

Crew B-62	Hr.	Daily	Hr.	Daily	Bare Costs	Incl. O&P
2 Laborers	$26.60	$425.60	$44.50	$712.00	$29.47	$49.07
1 Equip. Oper. (light)	35.20	281.60	58.20	465.60		
1 Loader, Skid Steer, 30 H.P.		171.00		188.10	7.13	7.84
24 L.H., Daily Totals		$878.20		$1365.70	$36.59	$56.90

Crew B-62A	Hr.	Daily	Hr.	Daily	Bare Costs	Incl. O&P
2 Laborers	$26.60	$425.60	$44.50	$712.00	$29.47	$49.07
1 Equip. Oper. (light)	35.20	281.60	58.20	465.60		
1 Loader, Skid Steer, 30 H.P.		171.00		188.10		
1 Trencher Attachment		55.30		60.83	9.43	10.37
24 L.H., Daily Totals		$933.50		$1426.53	$38.90	$59.44

Crew B-63	Hr.	Daily	Hr.	Daily	Bare Costs	Incl. O&P
5 Laborers	$26.60	$1064.00	$44.50	$1780.00	$26.60	$44.50
1 Loader, Skid Steer, 30 H.P.		171.00		188.10	4.28	4.70
40 L.H., Daily Totals		$1235.00		$1968.10	$30.88	$49.20

Crew B-63B	Hr.	Daily	Hr.	Daily	Bare Costs	Incl. O&P
1 Labor Foreman (inside)	$27.10	$216.80	$45.30	$362.40	$28.88	$48.13
2 Laborers	26.60	425.60	44.50	712.00		
1 Equip. Oper. (light)	35.20	281.60	58.20	465.60		
1 Loader, Skid Steer, 78 H.P.		309.40		340.34	9.67	10.64
32 L.H., Daily Totals		$1233.40		$1880.34	$38.54	$58.76

Crew B-64	Hr.	Daily	Hr.	Daily	Bare Costs	Incl. O&P
1 Laborer	$26.60	$212.80	$44.50	$356.00	$29.20	$48.45
1 Truck Driver (light)	31.80	254.40	52.40	419.20		
1 Power Mulcher (small)		143.20		157.52		
1 Flatbed Truck, Gas, 1.5 Ton		217.40		239.14	22.54	24.79
16 L.H., Daily Totals		$827.80		$1171.86	$51.74	$73.24

Crew B-65	Hr.	Daily	Hr.	Daily	Bare Costs	Incl. O&P
1 Laborer	$26.60	$212.80	$44.50	$356.00	$29.20	$48.45
1 Truck Driver (light)	31.80	254.40	52.40	419.20		
1 Power Mulcher (Large)		303.00		333.30		
1 Flatbed Truck, Gas, 1.5 Ton		217.40		239.14	32.52	35.78
16 L.H., Daily Totals		$987.60		$1347.64	$61.73	$84.23

Crew B-66	Hr.	Daily	Hr.	Daily	Bare Costs	Incl. O&P
1 Equip. Oper. (light)	$35.20	$281.60	$58.20	$465.60	$35.20	$58.20
1 Loader-Backhoe, 40 H.P.		268.00		294.80	33.50	36.85
8 L.H., Daily Totals		$549.60		$760.40	$68.70	$95.05

Crew B-67	Hr.	Daily	Hr.	Daily	Bare Costs	Incl. O&P
1 Millwright	$37.10	$296.80	$59.55	$476.40	$36.15	$58.88
1 Equip. Oper. (light)	35.20	281.60	58.20	465.60		
1 R.T. Forklift, 5,000 Lb., diesel		282.20		310.42	17.64	19.40
16 L.H., Daily Totals		$860.60		$1252.42	$53.79	$78.28

Crew B-67B	Hr.	Daily	Hr.	Daily	Bare Costs	Incl. O&P
1 Millwright Foreman (inside)	$37.60	$300.80	$60.35	$482.80	$37.35	$59.95
1 Millwright	37.10	296.80	59.55	476.40		
16 L.H., Daily Totals		$597.60		$959.20	$37.35	$59.95

Crew B-68	Hr.	Daily	Hr.	Daily	Bare Costs	Incl. O&P
2 Millwrights	$37.10	$593.60	$59.55	$952.80	$36.47	$59.10
1 Equip. Oper. (light)	35.20	281.60	58.20	465.60		
1 R.T. Forklift, 5,000 Lb., diesel		282.20		310.42	11.76	12.93
24 L.H., Daily Totals		$1157.40		$1728.82	$48.23	$72.03

Crew B-68A	Hr.	Daily	Hr.	Daily	Bare Costs	Incl. O&P
1 Millwright Foreman (inside)	$37.60	$300.80	$60.35	$482.80	$37.27	$59.82
2 Millwrights	37.10	593.60	59.55	952.80		
1 Forklift, Smooth Floor, 8,000 Lb.		171.20		188.32	7.13	7.85
24 L.H., Daily Totals		$1065.60		$1623.92	$44.40	$67.66

Crew B-68B	Hr.	Daily	Hr.	Daily	Bare Costs	Incl. O&P
1 Millwright Foreman (inside)	$37.60	$300.80	$60.35	$482.80	$38.76	$63.08
2 Millwrights	37.10	593.60	59.55	952.80		
2 Electricians	40.20	643.20	65.85	1053.60		
2 Plumbers	39.55	632.80	65.20	1043.20		
1 R.T. Forklift, 5,000 Lb., gas		305.80		336.38	5.46	6.01
56 L.H., Daily Totals		$2476.20		$3868.78	$44.22	$69.09

692

Crews - Residential

Crew No.	Bare Costs Hr.	Bare Costs Daily	Incl. Subs O&P Hr.	Incl. Subs O&P Daily	Cost Per Labor-Hour Bare Costs	Cost Per Labor-Hour Incl. O&P
Crew B-68C	Hr.	Daily	Hr.	Daily	Bare Costs	Incl. O&P
1 Millwright Foreman (inside)	$37.60	$300.80	$60.35	$482.80	$38.61	$62.74
1 Millwright	37.10	296.80	59.55	476.40		
1 Electrician	40.20	321.60	65.85	526.80		
1 Plumber	39.55	316.40	65.20	521.60		
1 R.T. Forklift, 5,000 Lb., gas		305.80		336.38	9.56	10.51
32 L.H., Daily Totals		$1541.40		$2343.98	$48.17	$73.25
Crew B-68D	Hr.	Daily	Hr.	Daily	Bare Costs	Incl. O&P
1 Labor Foreman (inside)	$27.10	$216.80	$45.30	$362.40	$29.63	$49.33
1 Laborer	26.60	212.80	44.50	356.00		
1 Equip. Oper. (light)	35.20	281.60	58.20	465.60		
1 R.T. Forklift, 5,000 Lb., gas		305.80		336.38	12.74	14.02
24 L.H., Daily Totals		$1017.00		$1520.38	$42.38	$63.35
Crew B-68E	Hr.	Daily	Hr.	Daily	Bare Costs	Incl. O&P
1 Struc. Steel Foreman (inside)	$39.05	$312.40	$70.55	$564.40	$38.65	$69.83
3 Struc. Steel Workers	38.55	925.20	69.65	1671.60		
1 Welder	38.55	308.40	69.65	557.20		
1 Forklift, Smooth Floor, 8,000 Lb.		171.20		188.32	4.28	4.71
40 L.H., Daily Totals		$1717.20		$2981.52	$42.93	$74.54
Crew B-68F	Hr.	Daily	Hr.	Daily	Bare Costs	Incl. O&P
1 Skilled Worker Foreman (out)	$37.75	$302.00	$63.40	$507.20	$36.42	$61.13
2 Skilled Workers	35.75	572.00	60.00	960.00		
1 R.T. Forklift, 5,000 Lb., gas		305.80		336.38	12.74	14.02
24 L.H., Daily Totals		$1179.80		$1803.58	$49.16	$75.15
Crew B-68G	Hr.	Daily	Hr.	Daily	Bare Costs	Incl. O&P
2 Structural Steel Workers	$38.55	$616.80	$69.65	$1114.40	$38.55	$69.65
1 R.T. Forklift, 5,000 Lb., gas		305.80		336.38	19.11	21.02
16 L.H., Daily Totals		$922.60		$1450.78	$57.66	$90.67
Crew B-69	Hr.	Daily	Hr.	Daily	Bare Costs	Incl. O&P
1 Labor Foreman (outside)	$28.60	$228.80	$47.80	$382.40	$29.73	$49.48
3 Laborers	26.60	638.40	44.50	1068.00		
1 Equip. Oper. (crane)	37.30	298.40	61.65	493.20		
1 Equip. Oper. (oiler)	32.65	261.20	53.95	431.60		
1 Hyd. Crane, 80 Ton		1616.00		1777.60	33.67	37.03
48 L.H., Daily Totals		$3042.80		$4152.80	$63.39	$86.52
Crew B-69A	Hr.	Daily	Hr.	Daily	Bare Costs	Incl. O&P
1 Labor Foreman (outside)	$28.60	$228.80	$47.80	$382.40	$29.91	$49.64
3 Laborers	26.60	638.40	44.50	1068.00		
1 Equip. Oper. (medium)	36.40	291.20	60.15	481.20		
1 Concrete Finisher	34.65	277.20	56.40	451.20		
1 Curb/Gutter Paver, 2-Track		1194.00		1313.40	24.88	27.36
48 L.H., Daily Totals		$2629.60		$3696.20	$54.78	$77.00
Crew B-69B	Hr.	Daily	Hr.	Daily	Bare Costs	Incl. O&P
1 Labor Foreman (outside)	$28.60	$228.80	$47.80	$382.40	$29.91	$49.64
3 Laborers	26.60	638.40	44.50	1068.00		
1 Equip. Oper. (medium)	36.40	291.20	60.15	481.20		
1 Cement Finisher	34.65	277.20	56.40	451.20		
1 Curb/Gutter Paver, 4-Track		802.40		882.64	16.72	18.39
48 L.H., Daily Totals		$2238.00		$3265.44	$46.63	$68.03

Crew No.	Bare Costs Hr.	Bare Costs Daily	Incl. Subs O&P Hr.	Incl. Subs O&P Daily	Cost Per Labor-Hour Bare Costs	Cost Per Labor-Hour Incl. O&P
Crew B-70	Hr.	Daily	Hr.	Daily	Bare Costs	Incl. O&P
1 Labor Foreman (outside)	$28.60	$228.80	$47.80	$382.40	$31.09	$51.68
3 Laborers	26.60	638.40	44.50	1068.00		
3 Equip. Oper. (medium)	36.40	873.60	60.15	1443.60		
1 Grader, 30,000 Lbs.		678.40		746.24		
1 Ripper, Beam & 1 Shank		85.60		94.16		
1 Road Sweeper, S.P., 8' wide		700.80		770.88		
1 F.E. Loader, W.M., 1.5 C.Y.		362.00		398.20	32.62	35.88
56 L.H., Daily Totals		$3567.60		$4903.48	$63.71	$87.56
Crew B-71	Hr.	Daily	Hr.	Daily	Bare Costs	Incl. O&P
1 Labor Foreman (outside)	$28.60	$228.80	$47.80	$382.40	$31.09	$51.68
3 Laborers	26.60	638.40	44.50	1068.00		
3 Equip. Oper. (medium)	36.40	873.60	60.15	1443.60		
1 Pvmt. Profiler, 750 H.P.		5553.00		6108.30		
1 Road Sweeper, S.P., 8' wide		700.80		770.88		
1 F.E. Loader, W.M., 1.5 C.Y.		362.00		398.20	118.14	129.95
56 L.H., Daily Totals		$8356.60		$10171.38	$149.22	$181.63
Crew B-72	Hr.	Daily	Hr.	Daily	Bare Costs	Incl. O&P
1 Labor Foreman (outside)	$28.60	$228.80	$47.80	$382.40	$31.75	$52.74
3 Laborers	26.60	638.40	44.50	1068.00		
4 Equip. Oper. (medium)	36.40	1164.80	60.15	1924.80		
1 Pvmt. Profiler, 750 H.P.		5553.00		6108.30		
1 Hammermill, 250 H.P.		1827.00		2009.70		
1 Windrow Loader		1254.00		1379.40		
1 Mix Paver, 165 H.P.		2251.00		2476.10		
1 Roller, Pneum. Whl., 12 Ton		355.80		391.38	175.64	193.20
64 L.H., Daily Totals		$13272.80		$15740.08	$207.39	$245.94
Crew B-73	Hr.	Daily	Hr.	Daily	Bare Costs	Incl. O&P
1 Labor Foreman (outside)	$28.60	$228.80	$47.80	$382.40	$32.98	$54.69
2 Laborers	26.60	425.60	44.50	712.00		
5 Equip. Oper. (medium)	36.40	1456.00	60.15	2406.00		
1 Road Mixer, 310 H.P.		1942.00		2136.20		
1 Tandem Roller, 10 Ton		237.60		261.36		
1 Hammermill, 250 H.P.		1827.00		2009.70		
1 Grader, 30,000 Lbs.		678.40		746.24		
.5 F.E. Loader, W.M., 1.5 C.Y.		181.00		199.10		
.5 Truck Tractor, 220 H.P.		168.30		185.13		
.5 Water Tank Trailer, 5000 Gal.		71.50		78.65	79.78	87.76
64 L.H., Daily Totals		$7216.20		$9116.78	$112.75	$142.45
Crew B-74	Hr.	Daily	Hr.	Daily	Bare Costs	Incl. O&P
1 Labor Foreman (outside)	$28.60	$228.80	$47.80	$382.40	$33.19	$54.94
1 Laborer	26.60	212.80	44.50	356.00		
4 Equip. Oper. (medium)	36.40	1164.80	60.15	1924.80		
2 Truck Drivers (heavy)	32.35	517.60	53.30	852.80		
1 Grader, 30,000 Lbs.		678.40		746.24		
1 Ripper, Beam & 1 Shank		85.60		94.16		
2 Stabilizers, 310 H.P.		3722.00		4094.20		
1 Flatbed Truck, Gas, 3 Ton		270.20		297.22		
1 Chem. Spreader, Towed		51.20		56.32		
1 Roller, Vibratory, 25 Ton		684.00		752.40		
1 Water Tank Trailer, 5000 Gal.		143.00		157.30		
1 Truck Tractor, 220 H.P.		336.60		370.26	93.30	102.63
64 L.H., Daily Totals		$8095.00		$10084.10	$126.48	$157.56

For customer support on your Residential Costs with RSMeans Data, call 800.448.8182.

693

Crew No.	Bare Costs		Incl. Subs O&P		Cost Per Labor-Hour	

Crew B-75

Crew B-75	Hr.	Daily	Hr.	Daily	Bare Costs	Incl. O&P
1 Labor Foreman (outside)	$28.60	$228.80	$47.80	$382.40	$33.31	$55.17
1 Laborer	26.60	212.80	44.50	356.00		
4 Equip. Oper. (medium)	36.40	1164.80	60.15	1924.80		
1 Truck Driver (heavy)	32.35	258.80	53.30	426.40		
1 Grader, 30,000 Lbs.		678.40		746.24		
1 Ripper, Beam & 1 Shank		85.60		94.16		
2 Stabilizers, 310 H.P.		3722.00		4094.20		
1 Dist. Tanker, 3000 Gallon		327.40		360.14		
1 Truck Tractor, 6x4, 380 H.P.		559.80		615.78		
1 Roller, Vibratory, 25 Ton		684.00		752.40	108.16	118.98
56 L.H., Daily Totals		$7922.40		$9752.52	$141.47	$174.15

Crew B-76

Crew B-76	Hr.	Daily	Hr.	Daily	Bare Costs	Incl. O&P
1 Dock Builder Foreman (outside)	$37.15	$297.20	$64.20	$513.60	$35.57	$60.58
5 Dock Builders	35.15	1406.00	60.75	2430.00		
2 Equip. Oper. (crane)	37.30	596.80	61.65	986.40		
1 Equip. Oper. (oiler)	32.65	261.20	53.95	431.60		
1 Crawler Crane, 50 Ton		1675.00		1842.50		
1 Barge, 400 Ton		794.20		873.62		
1 Hammer, Diesel, 15K ft.-lbs.		605.80		666.38		
1 Lead, 60' High		76.00		83.60		
1 Air Compressor, 600 cfm		482.00		530.20		
2 -50' Air Hoses, 3"		29.80		32.78	50.87	55.96
72 L.H., Daily Totals		$6224.00		$8390.68	$86.44	$116.54

Crew B-76A

Crew B-76A	Hr.	Daily	Hr.	Daily	Bare Costs	Incl. O&P
1 Labor Foreman (outside)	$28.60	$228.80	$47.80	$382.40	$28.94	$48.24
5 Laborers	26.60	1064.00	44.50	1780.00		
1 Equip. Oper. (crane)	37.30	298.40	61.65	493.20		
1 Equip. Oper. (oiler)	32.65	261.20	53.95	431.60		
1 Crawler Crane, 50 Ton		1675.00		1842.50		
1 Barge, 400 Ton		794.20		873.62	38.58	42.44
64 L.H., Daily Totals		$4321.60		$5803.32	$67.53	$90.68

Crew B-77

Crew B-77	Hr.	Daily	Hr.	Daily	Bare Costs	Incl. O&P
1 Labor Foreman (outside)	$28.60	$228.80	$47.80	$382.40	$28.04	$46.74
3 Laborers	26.60	638.40	44.50	1068.00		
1 Truck Driver (light)	31.80	254.40	52.40	419.20		
1 Crack Cleaner, 25 H.P.		57.60		63.36		
1 Crack Filler, Trailer Mtd.		199.80		219.78		
1 Flatbed Truck, Gas, 3 Ton		270.20		297.22	13.19	14.51
40 L.H., Daily Totals		$1649.20		$2449.96	$41.23	$61.25

Crew B-78

Crew B-78	Hr.	Daily	Hr.	Daily	Bare Costs	Incl. O&P
1 Labor Foreman (outside)	$28.60	$228.80	$47.80	$382.40	$27.00	$45.16
4 Laborers	26.60	851.20	44.50	1424.00		
1 Paint Striper, S.P., 40 Gallon		149.20		164.12		
1 Flatbed Truck, Gas, 3 Ton		270.20		297.22		
1 Pickup Truck, 3/4 Ton		129.40		142.34	13.72	15.09
40 L.H., Daily Totals		$1628.80		$2410.08	$40.72	$60.25

Crew B-78B

Crew B-78B	Hr.	Daily	Hr.	Daily	Bare Costs	Incl. O&P
2 Laborers	$26.60	$425.60	$44.50	$712.00	$27.56	$46.02
.25 Equip. Oper. (light)	35.20	70.40	58.20	116.40		
1 Pickup Truck, 3/4 Ton		129.40		142.34		
1 Line Rem.,11 H.P.,Walk Behind		62.00		68.20		
.25 Road Sweeper, S.P., 8' wide		175.20		192.72	20.37	22.40
18 L.H., Daily Totals		$862.60		$1231.66	$47.92	$68.43

Crew B-78C

Crew B-78C	Hr.	Daily	Hr.	Daily	Bare Costs	Incl. O&P
1 Labor Foreman (outside)	$28.60	$228.80	$47.80	$382.40	$27.80	$46.37
4 Laborers	26.60	851.20	44.50	1424.00		
1 Truck Driver (light)	31.80	254.40	52.40	419.20		
1 Paint Striper, T.M., 120 Gal.		734.60		808.06		
1 Flatbed Truck, Gas, 3 Ton		270.20		297.22		
1 Pickup Truck, 3/4 Ton		129.40		142.34	23.63	25.99
48 L.H., Daily Totals		$2468.60		$3473.22	$51.43	$72.36

Crew B-78D

Crew B-78D	Hr.	Daily	Hr.	Daily	Bare Costs	Incl. O&P
2 Labor Foremen (outside)	$28.60	$457.60	$47.80	$764.80	$27.52	$45.95
7 Laborers	26.60	1489.60	44.50	2492.00		
1 Truck Driver (light)	31.80	254.40	52.40	419.20		
1 Paint Striper, T.M., 120 Gal.		734.60		808.06		
1 Flatbed Truck, Gas, 3 Ton		270.20		297.22		
3 Pickup Trucks, 3/4 Ton		388.20		427.02		
1 Air Compressor, 60 cfm		127.00		139.70		
1 -50' Air Hose, 3/4"		3.25		3.58		
1 Breaker, Pavement, 60 lb.		10.20		11.22	19.17	21.08
80 L.H., Daily Totals		$3735.05		$5362.80	$46.69	$67.03

Crew B-78E

Crew B-78E	Hr.	Daily	Hr.	Daily	Bare Costs	Incl. O&P
2 Labor Foremen (outside)	$28.60	$457.60	$47.80	$764.80	$27.37	$45.71
9 Laborers	26.60	1915.20	44.50	3204.00		
1 Truck Driver (light)	31.80	254.40	52.40	419.20		
1 Paint Striper, T.M., 120 Gal.		734.60		808.06		
1 Flatbed Truck, Gas, 3 Ton		270.20		297.22		
4 Pickup Trucks, 3/4 Ton		517.60		569.36		
2 Air Compressors, 60 cfm		254.00		279.40		
2 -50' Air Hoses, 3/4"		6.50		7.15		
2 Breakers, Pavement, 60 lb.		20.40		22.44	18.78	20.66
96 L.H., Daily Totals		$4430.50		$6371.63	$46.15	$66.37

Crew B-78F

Crew B-78F	Hr.	Daily	Hr.	Daily	Bare Costs	Incl. O&P
2 Labor Foremen (outside)	$28.60	$457.60	$47.80	$764.80	$27.26	$45.54
11 Laborers	26.60	2340.80	44.50	3916.00		
1 Truck Driver (light)	31.80	254.40	52.40	419.20		
1 Paint Striper, T.M., 120 Gal.		734.60		808.06		
1 Flatbed Truck, Gas, 3 Ton		270.20		297.22		
7 Pickup Trucks, 3/4 Ton		905.80		996.38		
3 Air Compressors, 60 cfm		381.00		419.10		
3 -50' Air Hoses, 3/4"		9.75		10.73		
3 Breakers, Pavement, 60 lb.		30.60		33.66	20.82	22.90
112 L.H., Daily Totals		$5384.75		$7665.15	$48.08	$68.44

Crew B-79

Crew B-79	Hr.	Daily	Hr.	Daily	Bare Costs	Incl. O&P
1 Labor Foreman (outside)	$28.60	$228.80	$47.80	$382.40	$28.04	$46.74
3 Laborers	26.60	638.40	44.50	1068.00		
1 Truck Driver (light)	31.80	254.40	52.40	419.20		
1 Paint Striper, T.M., 120 Gal.		734.60		808.06		
1 Heating Kettle, 115 Gallon		73.50		80.85		
1 Flatbed Truck, Gas, 3 Ton		270.20		297.22		
2 Pickup Trucks, 3/4 Ton		258.80		284.68	33.43	36.77
40 L.H., Daily Totals		$2458.70		$3340.41	$61.47	$83.51

Crew B-79B

Crew B-79B	Hr.	Daily	Hr.	Daily	Bare Costs	Incl. O&P
1 Laborer	$26.60	$212.80	$44.50	$356.00	$26.60	$44.50
1 Set of Gases		168.00		184.80	21.00	23.10
8 L.H., Daily Totals		$380.80		$540.80	$47.60	$67.60

For customer support on your Residential Costs with RSMeans Data, call 800.448.8182.

Crew No.	Bare Costs		Incl. Subs O&P		Cost Per Labor-Hour	

Crew B-79C

Crew B-79C	Hr.	Daily	Hr.	Daily	Bare Costs	Incl. O&P
1 Labor Foreman (outside)	$28.60	$228.80	$47.80	$382.40	$27.63	$46.10
5 Laborers	26.60	1064.00	44.50	1780.00		
1 Truck Driver (light)	31.80	254.40	52.40	419.20		
1 Paint Striper, T.M., 120 Gal.		734.60		808.06		
1 Heating Kettle, 115 Gallon		73.50		80.85		
1 Flatbed Truck, Gas, 3 Ton		270.20		297.22		
3 Pickup Trucks, 3/4 Ton		388.20		427.02		
1 Air Compressor, 60 cfm		127.00		139.70		
1 -50' Air Hose, 3/4"		3.25		3.58		
1 Breaker, Pavement, 60 lb.		10.20		11.22	28.70	31.57
56 L.H., Daily Totals		$3154.15		$4349.24	$56.32	$77.67

Crew B-79D

Crew B-79D	Hr.	Daily	Hr.	Daily	Bare Costs	Incl. O&P
2 Labor Foremen (outside)	$28.60	$457.60	$47.80	$764.80	$27.75	$46.31
5 Laborers	26.60	1064.00	44.50	1780.00		
1 Truck Driver (light)	31.80	254.40	52.40	419.20		
1 Paint Striper, T.M., 120 Gal.		734.60		808.06		
1 Heating Kettle, 115 Gallon		73.50		80.85		
1 Flatbed Truck, Gas, 3 Ton		270.20		297.22		
4 Pickup Trucks, 3/4 Ton		517.60		569.36		
1 Air Compressor, 60 cfm		127.00		139.70		
1 -50' Air Hose, 3/4"		3.25		3.58		
1 Breaker, Pavement, 60 lb.		10.20		11.22	27.13	29.84
64 L.H., Daily Totals		$3512.35		$4873.98	$54.88	$76.16

Crew B-79E

Crew B-79E	Hr.	Daily	Hr.	Daily	Bare Costs	Incl. O&P
2 Labor Foremen (outside)	$28.60	$457.60	$47.80	$764.80	$27.52	$45.95
7 Laborers	26.60	1489.60	44.50	2492.00		
1 Truck Driver (light)	31.80	254.40	52.40	419.20		
1 Paint Striper, T.M., 120 Gal.		734.60		808.06		
1 Heating Kettle, 115 Gallon		73.50		80.85		
1 Flatbed Truck, Gas, 3 Ton		270.20		297.22		
5 Pickup Trucks, 3/4 Ton		647.00		711.70		
2 Air Compressors, 60 cfm		254.00		279.40		
2 -50' Air Hoses, 3/4"		6.50		7.15		
2 Breakers, Pavement, 60 lb.		20.40		22.44	25.08	27.59
80 L.H., Daily Totals		$4207.80		$5882.82	$52.60	$73.54

Crew B-80

Crew B-80	Hr.	Daily	Hr.	Daily	Bare Costs	Incl. O&P
1 Labor Foreman (outside)	$28.60	$228.80	$47.80	$382.40	$27.27	$45.60
2 Laborers	26.60	425.60	44.50	712.00		
1 Flatbed Truck, Gas, 3 Ton		270.20		297.22		
1 Earth Auger, Truck-Mtd.		403.40		443.74	28.07	30.87
24 L.H., Daily Totals		$1328.00		$1835.36	$55.33	$76.47

Crew B-80A

Crew B-80A	Hr.	Daily	Hr.	Daily	Bare Costs	Incl. O&P
3 Laborers	$26.60	$638.40	$44.50	$1068.00	$26.60	$44.50
1 Flatbed Truck, Gas, 3 Ton		270.20		297.22	11.26	12.38
24 L.H., Daily Totals		$908.60		$1365.22	$37.86	$56.88

Crew B-80B

Crew B-80B	Hr.	Daily	Hr.	Daily	Bare Costs	Incl. O&P
3 Laborers	$26.60	$638.40	$44.50	$1068.00	$28.75	$47.92
1 Equip. Oper. (light)	35.20	281.60	58.20	465.60		
1 Crane, Flatbed Mounted, 3 Ton		247.80		272.58	7.74	8.52
32 L.H., Daily Totals		$1167.80		$1806.18	$36.49	$56.44

Crew B-80C

Crew B-80C	Hr.	Daily	Hr.	Daily	Bare Costs	Incl. O&P
2 Laborers	$26.60	$425.60	$44.50	$712.00	$28.33	$47.13
1 Truck Driver (light)	31.80	254.40	52.40	419.20		
1 Flatbed Truck, Gas, 1.5 Ton		217.40		239.14		
1 Manual Fence Post Auger, Gas		7.90		8.69	9.39	10.33
24 L.H., Daily Totals		$905.30		$1379.03	$37.72	$57.46

Crew B-81

Crew B-81	Hr.	Daily	Hr.	Daily	Bare Costs	Incl. O&P
1 Laborer	$26.60	$212.80	$44.50	$356.00	$29.48	$48.90
1 Truck Driver (heavy)	32.35	258.80	53.30	426.40		
1 Hydromulcher, T.M., 3000 Gal.		317.80		349.58		
1 Truck Tractor, 220 H.P.		336.60		370.26	40.90	44.99
16 L.H., Daily Totals		$1126.00		$1502.24	$70.38	$93.89

Crew B-81A

Crew B-81A	Hr.	Daily	Hr.	Daily	Bare Costs	Incl. O&P
1 Laborer	$26.60	$212.80	$44.50	$356.00	$29.20	$48.45
1 Truck Driver (light)	31.80	254.40	52.40	419.20		
1 Hydromulcher, T.M., 600 Gal.		122.40		134.64		
1 Flatbed Truck, Gas, 3 Ton		270.20		297.22	24.54	26.99
16 L.H., Daily Totals		$859.80		$1207.06	$53.74	$75.44

Crew B-82

Crew B-82	Hr.	Daily	Hr.	Daily	Bare Costs	Incl. O&P
1 Laborer	$26.60	$212.80	$44.50	$356.00	$30.90	$51.35
1 Equip. Oper. (light)	35.20	281.60	58.20	465.60		
1 Horiz. Borer, 6 H.P.		80.20		88.22	5.01	5.51
16 L.H., Daily Totals		$574.60		$909.82	$35.91	$56.86

Crew B-82A

Crew B-82A	Hr.	Daily	Hr.	Daily	Bare Costs	Incl. O&P
2 Laborers	$26.60	$425.60	$44.50	$712.00	$30.90	$51.35
2 Equip. Opers. (light)	35.20	563.20	58.20	931.20		
2 Dump Truck, 8 C.Y., 220 H.P.		782.00		860.20		
1 Flatbed Trailer, 25 Ton		128.40		141.24		
1 Horiz. Dir. Drill, 20k lb. Thrust		651.60		716.76		
1 Mud Trailer for HDD, 1500 Gal.		311.60		342.76		
1 Pickup Truck, 4x4, 3/4 Ton		140.00		154.00		
1 Flatbed Trailer, 3 Ton		24.00		26.40		
1 Loader, Skid Steer, 78 H.P.		309.40		340.34	73.34	80.68
32 L.H., Daily Totals		$3335.80		$4224.90	$104.24	$132.03

Crew B-82B

Crew B-82B	Hr.	Daily	Hr.	Daily	Bare Costs	Incl. O&P
2 Laborers	$26.60	$425.60	$44.50	$712.00	$30.90	$51.35
2 Equip. Opers. (light)	35.20	563.20	58.20	931.20		
2 Dump Truck, 8 C.Y., 220 H.P.		782.00		860.20		
1 Flatbed Trailer, 25 Ton		128.40		141.24		
1 Horiz. Dir. Drill, 30k lb. Thrust		929.00		1021.90		
1 Mud Trailer for HDD, 1500 Gal.		311.60		342.76		
1 Pickup Truck, 4x4, 3/4 Ton		140.00		154.00		
1 Flatbed Trailer, 3 Ton		24.00		26.40		
1 Loader, Skid Steer, 78 H.P.		309.40		340.34	82.01	90.21
32 L.H., Daily Totals		$3613.20		$4530.04	$112.91	$141.56

Crew B-82C

Crew B-82C	Hr.	Daily	Hr.	Daily	Bare Costs	Incl. O&P
2 Laborers	$26.60	$425.60	$44.50	$712.00	$30.90	$51.35
2 Equip. Opers. (light)	35.20	563.20	58.20	931.20		
2 Dump Truck, 8 C.Y., 220 H.P.		782.00		860.20		
1 Flatbed Trailer, 25 Ton		128.40		141.24		
1 Horiz. Dir. Drill, 50k lb. Thrust		1229.00		1351.90		
1 Mud Trailer for HDD, 1500 Gal.		311.60		342.76		
1 Pickup Truck, 4x4, 3/4 Ton		140.00		154.00		
1 Flatbed Trailer, 3 Ton		24.00		26.40		
1 Loader, Skid Steer, 78 H.P.		309.40		340.34	91.39	100.53
32 L.H., Daily Totals		$3913.20		$4860.04	$122.29	$151.88

Crew No.	Bare Costs		Incl. Subs O&P		Cost Per Labor-Hour	

Crew B-82D

	Hr.	Daily	Hr.	Daily	Bare Costs	Incl. O&P
1 Equip. Oper. (light)	$35.20	$281.60	$58.20	$465.60	$35.20	$58.20
1 Mud Trailer for HDD, 1500 Gal.		311.60		342.76	38.95	42.84
8 L.H., Daily Totals		$593.20		$808.36	$74.15	$101.05

Crew B-83

	Hr.	Daily	Hr.	Daily	Bare Costs	Incl. O&P
1 Tugboat Captain	$36.40	$291.20	$60.15	$481.20	$31.50	$52.33
1 Tugboat Hand	26.60	212.80	44.50	356.00		
1 Tugboat, 250 H.P.		807.20		887.92	50.45	55.49
16 L.H., Daily Totals		$1311.20		$1725.12	$81.95	$107.82

Crew B-84

	Hr.	Daily	Hr.	Daily	Bare Costs	Incl. O&P
1 Equip. Oper. (medium)	$36.40	$291.20	$60.15	$481.20	$36.40	$60.15
1 Rotary Mower/Tractor		365.80		402.38	45.73	50.30
8 L.H., Daily Totals		$657.00		$883.58	$82.13	$110.45

Crew B-85

	Hr.	Daily	Hr.	Daily	Bare Costs	Incl. O&P
3 Laborers	$26.60	$638.40	$44.50	$1068.00	$29.71	$49.39
1 Equip. Oper. (medium)	36.40	291.20	60.15	481.20		
1 Truck Driver (heavy)	32.35	258.80	53.30	426.40		
1 Telescoping Boom Lift, to 80'		565.60		622.16		
1 Brush Chipper, 12", 130 H.P.		404.40		444.84		
1 Pruning Saw, Rotary		6.85		7.54	24.42	26.86
40 L.H., Daily Totals		$2165.25		$3050.14	$54.13	$76.25

Crew B-86

	Hr.	Daily	Hr.	Daily	Bare Costs	Incl. O&P
1 Equip. Oper. (medium)	$36.40	$291.20	$60.15	$481.20	$36.40	$60.15
1 Stump Chipper, S.P.		183.50		201.85	22.94	25.23
8 L.H., Daily Totals		$474.70		$683.05	$59.34	$85.38

Crew B-86A

	Hr.	Daily	Hr.	Daily	Bare Costs	Incl. O&P
1 Equip. Oper. (medium)	$36.40	$291.20	$60.15	$481.20	$36.40	$60.15
1 Grader, 30,000 Lbs.		678.40		746.24	84.80	93.28
8 L.H., Daily Totals		$969.60		$1227.44	$121.20	$153.43

Crew B-86B

	Hr.	Daily	Hr.	Daily	Bare Costs	Incl. O&P
1 Equip. Oper. (medium)	$36.40	$291.20	$60.15	$481.20	$36.40	$60.15
1 Dozer, 200 H.P.		1384.00		1522.40	173.00	190.30
8 L.H., Daily Totals		$1675.20		$2003.60	$209.40	$250.45

Crew B-87

	Hr.	Daily	Hr.	Daily	Bare Costs	Incl. O&P
1 Laborer	$26.60	$212.80	$44.50	$356.00	$34.44	$57.02
4 Equip. Oper. (medium)	36.40	1164.80	60.15	1924.80		
2 Feller Bunchers, 100 H.P.		1666.40		1833.04		
1 Log Chipper, 22" Tree		852.80		938.08		
1 Dozer, 105 H.P.		608.00		668.80		
1 Chain Saw, Gas, 36" Long		45.00		49.50	79.31	87.24
40 L.H., Daily Totals		$4549.80		$5770.22	$113.75	$144.26

Crew B-88

	Hr.	Daily	Hr.	Daily	Bare Costs	Incl. O&P
1 Laborer	$26.60	$212.80	$44.50	$356.00	$35.00	$57.91
6 Equip. Oper. (medium)	36.40	1747.20	60.15	2887.20		
2 Feller Bunchers, 100 H.P.		1666.40		1833.04		
1 Log Chipper, 22" Tree		852.80		938.08		
2 Log Skidders, 50 H.P.		1742.40		1916.64		
1 Dozer, 105 H.P.		608.00		668.80		
1 Chain Saw, Gas, 36" Long		45.00		49.50	87.76	96.54
56 L.H., Daily Totals		$6874.60		$8649.26	$122.76	$154.45

Crew B-89

	Hr.	Daily	Hr.	Daily	Bare Costs	Incl. O&P
1 Skilled Worker	$35.75	$286.00	$60.00	$480.00	$31.18	$52.25
1 Building Laborer	26.60	212.80	44.50	356.00		
1 Flatbed Truck, Gas, 3 Ton		270.20		297.22		
1 Concrete Saw		153.60		168.96		
1 Water Tank, 65 Gal.		17.30		19.03	27.57	30.33
16 L.H., Daily Totals		$939.90		$1321.21	$58.74	$82.58

Crew B-89A

	Hr.	Daily	Hr.	Daily	Bare Costs	Incl. O&P
1 Skilled Worker	$35.75	$286.00	$60.00	$480.00	$31.18	$52.25
1 Laborer	26.60	212.80	44.50	356.00		
1 Core Drill (Large)		114.60		126.06	7.16	7.88
16 L.H., Daily Totals		$613.40		$962.06	$38.34	$60.13

Crew B-89B

	Hr.	Daily	Hr.	Daily	Bare Costs	Incl. O&P
1 Equip. Oper. (light)	$35.20	$281.60	$58.20	$465.60	$33.50	$55.30
1 Truck Driver (light)	31.80	254.40	52.40	419.20		
1 Wall Saw, Hydraulic, 10 H.P.		103.40		113.74		
1 Generator, Diesel, 100 kW		367.40		404.14		
1 Water Tank, 65 Gal.		17.30		19.03		
1 Flatbed Truck, Gas, 3 Ton		270.20		297.22	47.39	52.13
16 L.H., Daily Totals		$1294.30		$1718.93	$80.89	$107.43

Crew B-90

	Hr.	Daily	Hr.	Daily	Bare Costs	Incl. O&P
1 Labor Foreman (outside)	$28.60	$228.80	$47.80	$382.40	$30.44	$50.54
3 Laborers	26.60	638.40	44.50	1068.00		
2 Equip. Oper. (light)	35.20	563.20	58.20	931.20		
2 Truck Drivers (heavy)	32.35	517.60	53.30	852.80		
1 Road Mixer, 310 H.P.		1942.00		2136.20		
1 Dist. Truck, 2000 Gal.		297.00		326.70	34.98	38.48
64 L.H., Daily Totals		$4187.00		$5697.30	$65.42	$89.02

Crew B-90A

	Hr.	Daily	Hr.	Daily	Bare Costs	Incl. O&P
1 Labor Foreman (outside)	$28.60	$228.80	$47.80	$382.40	$32.49	$53.91
2 Laborers	26.60	425.60	44.50	712.00		
4 Equip. Oper. (medium)	36.40	1164.80	60.15	1924.80		
2 Graders, 30,000 Lbs.		1356.80		1492.48		
1 Tandem Roller, 10 Ton		237.60		261.36		
1 Roller, Pneum. Whl., 12 Ton		355.80		391.38	34.83	38.31
56 L.H., Daily Totals		$3769.40		$5164.42	$67.31	$92.22

Crew B-90B

	Hr.	Daily	Hr.	Daily	Bare Costs	Incl. O&P
1 Labor Foreman (outside)	$28.60	$228.80	$47.80	$382.40	$31.83	$52.88
2 Laborers	26.60	425.60	44.50	712.00		
3 Equip. Oper. (medium)	36.40	873.60	60.15	1443.60		
1 Roller, Pneum. Whl., 12 Ton		355.80		391.38		
1 Road Mixer, 310 H.P.		1942.00		2136.20	47.87	52.66
48 L.H., Daily Totals		$3825.80		$5065.58	$79.70	$105.53

Crew B-90C

	Hr.	Daily	Hr.	Daily	Bare Costs	Incl. O&P
1 Labor Foreman (outside)	$28.60	$228.80	$47.80	$382.40	$31.02	$51.47
4 Laborers	26.60	851.20	44.50	1424.00		
3 Equip. Oper. (medium)	36.40	873.60	60.15	1443.60		
3 Truck Drivers (heavy)	32.35	776.40	53.30	1279.20		
3 Road Mixers, 310 H.P.		5826.00		6408.60	66.20	72.83
88 L.H., Daily Totals		$8556.00		$10937.80	$97.23	$124.29

Crew No.	Bare Costs		Incl. Subs O&P		Cost Per Labor-Hour	
Crew B-90D	Hr.	Daily	Hr.	Daily	Bare Costs	Incl. O&P
1 Labor Foreman (outside)	$28.60	$228.80	$47.80	$382.40	$30.34	$50.40
6 Laborers	26.60	1276.80	44.50	2136.00		
3 Equip. Oper. (medium)	36.40	873.60	60.15	1443.60		
3 Truck Drivers (heavy)	32.35	776.40	53.30	1279.20		
3 Road Mixers, 310 H.P.		5826.00		6408.60	56.02	61.62
104 L.H., Daily Totals		$8981.60		$11649.80	$86.36	$112.02

Crew No.	Bare Costs		Incl. Subs O&P		Cost Per Labor-Hour	
Crew B-90E	Hr.	Daily	Hr.	Daily	Bare Costs	Incl. O&P
1 Labor Foreman (outside)	$28.60	$228.80	$47.80	$382.40	$30.73	$51.06
4 Laborers	26.60	851.20	44.50	1424.00		
3 Equip. Oper. (medium)	36.40	873.60	60.15	1443.60		
1 Truck Driver (heavy)	32.35	258.80	53.30	426.40		
1 Road Mixer, 310 H.P.		1942.00		2136.20	26.97	29.67
72 L.H., Daily Totals		$4154.40		$5812.60	$57.70	$80.73

Crew No.	Bare Costs		Incl. Subs O&P		Cost Per Labor-Hour	
Crew B-91	Hr.	Daily	Hr.	Daily	Bare Costs	Incl. O&P
1 Labor Foreman (outside)	$28.60	$228.80	$47.80	$382.40	$32.47	$53.84
2 Laborers	26.60	425.60	44.50	712.00		
4 Equip. Oper. (medium)	36.40	1164.80	60.15	1924.80		
1 Truck Driver (heavy)	32.35	258.80	53.30	426.40		
1 Dist. Tanker, 3000 Gallon		327.40		360.14		
1 Truck Tractor, 6x4, 380 H.P.		559.80		615.78		
1 Aggreg. Spreader, S.P.		817.00		898.70		
1 Roller, Pneum. Whl., 12 Ton		355.80		391.38		
1 Tandem Roller, 10 Ton		237.60		261.36	35.90	39.49
64 L.H., Daily Totals		$4375.60		$5972.96	$68.37	$93.33

Crew No.	Bare Costs		Incl. Subs O&P		Cost Per Labor-Hour	
Crew B-91B	Hr.	Daily	Hr.	Daily	Bare Costs	Incl. O&P
1 Laborer	$26.60	$212.80	$44.50	$356.00	$31.50	$52.33
1 Equipment Oper. (med.)	36.40	291.20	60.15	481.20		
1 Road Sweeper, Vac. Assist.		927.80		1020.58	57.99	63.79
16 L.H., Daily Totals		$1431.80		$1857.78	$89.49	$116.11

Crew No.	Bare Costs		Incl. Subs O&P		Cost Per Labor-Hour	
Crew B-91C	Hr.	Daily	Hr.	Daily	Bare Costs	Incl. O&P
1 Laborer	$26.60	$212.80	$44.50	$356.00	$29.20	$48.45
1 Truck Driver (light)	31.80	254.40	52.40	419.20		
1 Catch Basin Cleaning Truck		539.00		592.90	33.69	37.06
16 L.H., Daily Totals		$1006.20		$1368.10	$62.89	$85.51

Crew No.	Bare Costs		Incl. Subs O&P		Cost Per Labor-Hour	
Crew B-91D	Hr.	Daily	Hr.	Daily	Bare Costs	Incl. O&P
1 Labor Foreman (outside)	$28.60	$228.80	$47.80	$382.40	$31.41	$52.13
5 Laborers	26.60	1064.00	44.50	1780.00		
5 Equip. Oper. (medium)	36.40	1456.00	60.15	2406.00		
2 Truck Drivers (heavy)	32.35	517.60	53.30	852.80		
1 Aggreg. Spreader, S.P.		817.00		898.70		
2 Truck Tractors, 6x4, 380 H.P.		1119.60		1231.56		
2 Dist. Tankers, 3000 Gallon		654.80		720.28		
2 Pavement Brushes, Towed		164.00		180.40		
2 Rollers Pneum. Whl., 12 Ton		711.60		782.76	33.34	36.67
104 L.H., Daily Totals		$6733.40		$9234.90	$64.74	$88.80

Crew No.	Bare Costs		Incl. Subs O&P		Cost Per Labor-Hour	
Crew B-92	Hr.	Daily	Hr.	Daily	Bare Costs	Incl. O&P
1 Labor Foreman (outside)	$28.60	$228.80	$47.80	$382.40	$27.10	$45.33
3 Laborers	26.60	638.40	44.50	1068.00		
1 Crack Cleaner, 25 H.P.		57.60		63.36		
1 Air Compressor, 60 cfm		127.00		139.70		
1 Tar Kettle, T.M.		122.75		135.03		
1 Flatbed Truck, Gas, 3 Ton		270.20		297.22	18.05	19.85
32 L.H., Daily Totals		$1444.75		$2085.70	$45.15	$65.18

Crew No.	Bare Costs		Incl. Subs O&P		Cost Per Labor-Hour	
Crew B-93	Hr.	Daily	Hr.	Daily	Bare Costs	Incl. O&P
1 Equip. Oper. (medium)	$36.40	$291.20	$60.15	$481.20	$36.40	$60.15
1 Feller Buncher, 100 H.P.		833.20		916.52	104.15	114.57
8 L.H., Daily Totals		$1124.40		$1397.72	$140.55	$174.72

Crew No.	Bare Costs		Incl. Subs O&P		Cost Per Labor-Hour	
Crew B-94A	Hr.	Daily	Hr.	Daily	Bare Costs	Incl. O&P
1 Laborer	$26.60	$212.80	$44.50	$356.00	$26.60	$44.50
1 Diaphragm Water Pump, 2"		71.00		78.10		
1 -20' Suction Hose, 2"		1.95		2.15		
2 -50' Discharge Hoses, 2"		1.80		1.98	9.34	10.28
8 L.H., Daily Totals		$287.55		$438.23	$35.94	$54.78

Crew No.	Bare Costs		Incl. Subs O&P		Cost Per Labor-Hour	
Crew B-94B	Hr.	Daily	Hr.	Daily	Bare Costs	Incl. O&P
1 Laborer	$26.60	$212.80	$44.50	$356.00	$26.60	$44.50
1 Diaphragm Water Pump, 4"		114.20		125.62		
1 -20' Suction Hose, 4"		3.45		3.79		
2 -50' Discharge Hoses, 4"		4.70		5.17	15.29	16.82
8 L.H., Daily Totals		$335.15		$490.58	$41.89	$61.32

Crew No.	Bare Costs		Incl. Subs O&P		Cost Per Labor-Hour	
Crew B-94C	Hr.	Daily	Hr.	Daily	Bare Costs	Incl. O&P
1 Laborer	$26.60	$212.80	$44.50	$356.00	$26.60	$44.50
1 Centrifugal Water Pump, 3"		78.60		86.46		
1 -20' Suction Hose, 3"		3.05		3.36		
2 -50' Discharge Hoses, 3"		3.50		3.85	10.64	11.71
8 L.H., Daily Totals		$297.95		$449.67	$37.24	$56.21

Crew No.	Bare Costs		Incl. Subs O&P		Cost Per Labor-Hour	
Crew B-94D	Hr.	Daily	Hr.	Daily	Bare Costs	Incl. O&P
1 Laborer	$26.60	$212.80	$44.50	$356.00	$26.60	$44.50
1 Centr. Water Pump, 6"		325.40		357.94		
1 -20' Suction Hose, 6"		11.90		13.09		
2 -50' Discharge Hoses, 6"		12.60		13.86	43.74	48.11
8 L.H., Daily Totals		$562.70		$740.89	$70.34	$92.61

Crew No.	Bare Costs		Incl. Subs O&P		Cost Per Labor-Hour	
Crew C-1	Hr.	Daily	Hr.	Daily	Bare Costs	Incl. O&P
2 Carpenters	$34.95	$559.20	$58.45	$935.20	$30.76	$51.58
1 Carpenter Helper	26.55	212.40	44.90	359.20		
1 Laborer	26.60	212.80	44.50	356.00		
32 L.H., Daily Totals		$984.40		$1650.40	$30.76	$51.58

Crew No.	Bare Costs		Incl. Subs O&P		Cost Per Labor-Hour	
Crew C-2	Hr.	Daily	Hr.	Daily	Bare Costs	Incl. O&P
1 Carpenter Foreman (outside)	$36.95	$295.60	$61.80	$494.40	$31.09	$52.17
2 Carpenters	34.95	559.20	58.45	935.20		
2 Carpenter Helpers	26.55	424.80	44.90	718.40		
1 Laborer	26.60	212.80	44.50	356.00		
48 L.H., Daily Totals		$1492.40		$2504.00	$31.09	$52.17

Crew No.	Bare Costs		Incl. Subs O&P		Cost Per Labor-Hour	
Crew C-2A	Hr.	Daily	Hr.	Daily	Bare Costs	Incl. O&P
1 Carpenter Foreman (outside)	$36.95	$295.60	$61.80	$494.40	$33.84	$56.34
3 Carpenters	34.95	838.80	58.45	1402.80		
1 Cement Finisher	34.65	277.20	56.40	451.20		
1 Laborer	26.60	212.80	44.50	356.00		
48 L.H., Daily Totals		$1624.40		$2704.40	$33.84	$56.34

Crew No.	Bare Costs		Incl. Subs O&P		Cost Per Labor-Hour	
Crew C-3	Hr.	Daily	Hr.	Daily	Bare Costs	Incl. O&P
1 Rodman Foreman (outside)	$40.55	$324.40	$68.15	$545.20	$33.90	$56.78
3 Rodmen (reinf.)	38.55	925.20	64.80	1555.20		
1 Equip. Oper. (light)	35.20	281.60	58.20	465.60		
3 Laborers	26.60	638.40	44.50	1068.00		
3 Stressing Equipment		31.20		34.32		
.5 Grouting Equipment		80.70		88.77	1.75	1.92
64 L.H., Daily Totals		$2281.50		$3757.09	$35.65	$58.70

Crew No.	Bare Costs		Incl. Subs O&P		Cost Per Labor-Hour	

Crew C-4

Crew C-4	Hr.	Daily	Hr.	Daily	Bare Costs	Incl. O&P
1 Rodman Foreman (outside)	$40.55	$324.40	$68.15	$545.20	$36.06	$60.56
2 Rodmen (reinf.)	38.55	616.80	64.80	1036.80		
1 Building Laborer	26.60	212.80	44.50	356.00		
3 Stressing Equipment		31.20		34.32	0.97	1.07
32 L.H., Daily Totals		$1185.20		$1972.32	$37.04	$61.63

Crew C-4A	Hr.	Daily	Hr.	Daily	Bare Costs	Incl. O&P
2 Rodmen (reinf.)	$38.55	$616.80	$64.80	$1036.80	$38.55	$64.80
4 Stressing Equipment		41.60		45.76	2.60	2.86
16 L.H., Daily Totals		$658.40		$1082.56	$41.15	$67.66

Crew C-5	Hr.	Daily	Hr.	Daily	Bare Costs	Incl. O&P
1 Rodman Foreman (outside)	$40.55	$324.40	$68.15	$545.20	$34.69	$58.07
2 Rodmen (reinf.)	38.55	616.80	64.80	1036.80		
1 Equip. Oper. (crane)	37.30	298.40	61.65	493.20		
2 Building Laborers	26.60	425.60	44.50	712.00		
1 Hyd. Crane, 25 Ton		673.80		741.18	14.04	15.44
48 L.H., Daily Totals		$2339.00		$3528.38	$48.73	$73.51

Crew C-6	Hr.	Daily	Hr.	Daily	Bare Costs	Incl. O&P
1 Labor Foreman (outside)	$28.60	$228.80	$47.80	$382.40	$28.27	$47.03
4 Laborers	26.60	851.20	44.50	1424.00		
1 Cement Finisher	34.65	277.20	56.40	451.20		
2 Gas Engine Vibrators		56.50		62.15	1.18	1.29
48 L.H., Daily Totals		$1413.70		$2319.75	$29.45	$48.33

Crew C-7	Hr.	Daily	Hr.	Daily	Bare Costs	Incl. O&P
1 Labor Foreman (outside)	$28.60	$228.80	$47.80	$382.40	$29.48	$48.98
5 Laborers	26.60	1064.00	44.50	1780.00		
1 Cement Finisher	34.65	277.20	56.40	451.20		
1 Equip. Oper. (medium)	36.40	291.20	60.15	481.20		
1 Equip. Oper. (oiler)	32.65	261.20	53.95	431.60		
2 Gas Engine Vibrators		56.50		62.15		
1 Concrete Bucket, 1 C.Y.		24.00		26.40		
1 Hyd. Crane, 55 Ton		1076.00		1183.60	16.06	17.67
72 L.H., Daily Totals		$3278.90		$4798.55	$45.54	$66.65

Crew C-8	Hr.	Daily	Hr.	Daily	Bare Costs	Incl. O&P
1 Labor Foreman (outside)	$28.60	$228.80	$47.80	$382.40	$30.59	$50.61
3 Laborers	26.60	638.40	44.50	1068.00		
2 Cement Finishers	34.65	554.40	56.40	902.40		
1 Equip. Oper. (medium)	36.40	291.20	60.15	481.20		
1 Concrete Pump (Small)		806.40		887.04	14.40	15.84
56 L.H., Daily Totals		$2519.20		$3721.04	$44.99	$66.45

Crew C-8A	Hr.	Daily	Hr.	Daily	Bare Costs	Incl. O&P
1 Labor Foreman (outside)	$28.60	$228.80	$47.80	$382.40	$29.62	$49.02
3 Laborers	26.60	638.40	44.50	1068.00		
2 Cement Finishers	34.65	554.40	56.40	902.40		
48 L.H., Daily Totals		$1421.60		$2352.80	$29.62	$49.02

Crew C-8B	Hr.	Daily	Hr.	Daily	Bare Costs	Incl. O&P
1 Labor Foreman (outside)	$28.60	$228.80	$47.80	$382.40	$28.96	$48.29
3 Laborers	26.60	638.40	44.50	1068.00		
1 Equip. Oper. (medium)	36.40	291.20	60.15	481.20		
1 Vibrating Power Screed		64.35		70.78		
1 Roller, Vibratory, 25 Ton		684.00		752.40		
1 Dozer, 200 H.P.		1384.00		1522.40	53.31	58.64
40 L.H., Daily Totals		$3290.75		$4277.19	$82.27	$106.93

Crew C-8C	Hr.	Daily	Hr.	Daily	Bare Costs	Incl. O&P
1 Labor Foreman (outside)	$28.60	$228.80	$47.80	$382.40	$29.91	$49.64
3 Laborers	26.60	638.40	44.50	1068.00		
1 Cement Finisher	34.65	277.20	56.40	451.20		
1 Equip. Oper. (medium)	36.40	291.20	60.15	481.20		
1 Shotcrete Rig, 12 C.Y./hr		250.20		275.22		
1 Air Compressor, 160 cfm		143.60		157.96		
4 -50' Air Hoses, 1"		16.40		18.04		
4 -50' Air Hoses, 2"		31.00		34.10	9.19	10.11
48 L.H., Daily Totals		$1876.80		$2868.12	$39.10	$59.75

Crew C-8D	Hr.	Daily	Hr.	Daily	Bare Costs	Incl. O&P
1 Labor Foreman (outside)	$28.60	$228.80	$47.80	$382.40	$31.26	$51.73
1 Laborer	26.60	212.80	44.50	356.00		
1 Cement Finisher	34.65	277.20	56.40	451.20		
1 Equipment Oper. (light)	35.20	281.60	58.20	465.60		
1 Air Compressor, 250 cfm		181.20		199.32		
2 -50' Air Hoses, 1"		8.20		9.02	5.92	6.51
32 L.H., Daily Totals		$1189.80		$1863.54	$37.18	$58.24

Crew C-8E	Hr.	Daily	Hr.	Daily	Bare Costs	Incl. O&P
1 Labor Foreman (outside)	$28.60	$228.80	$47.80	$382.40	$29.71	$49.32
3 Laborers	26.60	638.40	44.50	1068.00		
1 Cement Finisher	34.65	277.20	56.40	451.20		
1 Equipment Oper. (light)	35.20	281.60	58.20	465.60		
1 Shotcrete Rig, 35 C.Y./hr		276.20		303.82		
1 Air Compressor, 250 cfm		181.20		199.32		
4 -50' Air Hoses, 1"		16.40		18.04		
4 -50' Air Hoses, 2"		31.00		34.10	10.52	11.57
48 L.H., Daily Totals		$1930.80		$2922.48	$40.23	$60.88

Crew C-10	Hr.	Daily	Hr.	Daily	Bare Costs	Incl. O&P
1 Laborer	$26.60	$212.80	$44.50	$356.00	$31.97	$52.43
2 Cement Finishers	34.65	554.40	56.40	902.40		
24 L.H., Daily Totals		$767.20		$1258.40	$31.97	$52.43

Crew C-10B	Hr.	Daily	Hr.	Daily	Bare Costs	Incl. O&P
3 Laborers	$26.60	$638.40	$44.50	$1068.00	$29.82	$49.26
2 Cement Finishers	34.65	554.40	56.40	902.40		
1 Concrete Mixer, 10 C.F.		164.60		181.06		
2 Trowels, 48" Walk-Behind		91.10		100.21	6.39	7.03
40 L.H., Daily Totals		$1448.50		$2251.67	$36.21	$56.29

Crew C-10C	Hr.	Daily	Hr.	Daily	Bare Costs	Incl. O&P
1 Laborer	$26.60	$212.80	$44.50	$356.00	$31.97	$52.43
2 Cement Finishers	34.65	554.40	56.40	902.40		
1 Trowel, 48" Walk-Behind		45.55		50.10	1.90	2.09
24 L.H., Daily Totals		$812.75		$1308.51	$33.86	$54.52

Crew C-10D	Hr.	Daily	Hr.	Daily	Bare Costs	Incl. O&P
1 Laborer	$26.60	$212.80	$44.50	$356.00	$31.97	$52.43
2 Cement Finishers	34.65	554.40	56.40	902.40		
1 Vibrating Power Screed		64.35		70.78		
1 Trowel, 48" Walk-Behind		45.55		50.10	4.58	5.04
24 L.H., Daily Totals		$877.10		$1379.29	$36.55	$57.47

Crew C-10E	Hr.	Daily	Hr.	Daily	Bare Costs	Incl. O&P
1 Laborer	$26.60	$212.80	$44.50	$356.00	$31.97	$52.43
2 Cement Finishers	34.65	554.40	56.40	902.40		
1 Vibrating Power Screed		64.35		70.78		
1 Cement Trowel, 96" Ride-On		175.90		193.49	10.01	11.01
24 L.H., Daily Totals		$1007.45		$1522.68	$41.98	$63.44

Crews - Residential

Crew C-10F

Crew No.	Bare Costs Hr.	Bare Costs Daily	Incl. Subs O&P Hr.	Incl. Subs O&P Daily	Cost Per Labor-Hour Bare Costs	Cost Per Labor-Hour Incl. O&P
1 Laborer	$26.60	$212.80	$44.50	$356.00	$31.97	$52.43
2 Cement Finishers	34.65	554.40	56.40	902.40		
1 Telescoping Boom Lift, to 60'		456.00		501.60	19.00	20.90
24 L.H., Daily Totals		$1223.20		$1760.00	$50.97	$73.33

Crew C-11

Crew No.	Bare Costs Hr.	Bare Costs Daily	Incl. Subs O&P Hr.	Incl. Subs O&P Daily	Cost Per Labor-Hour Bare Costs	Cost Per Labor-Hour Incl. O&P
1 Skilled Worker Foreman	$37.75	$302.00	$63.40	$507.20	$36.26	$60.72
5 Skilled Workers	35.75	1430.00	60.00	2400.00		
1 Equip. Oper. (crane)	37.30	298.40	61.65	493.20		
1 Lattice Boom Crane, 150 Ton		2000.00		2200.00	35.71	39.29
56 L.H., Daily Totals		$4030.40		$5600.40	$71.97	$100.01

Crew C-12

Crew No.	Bare Costs Hr.	Bare Costs Daily	Incl. Subs O&P Hr.	Incl. Subs O&P Daily	Cost Per Labor-Hour Bare Costs	Cost Per Labor-Hour Incl. O&P
1 Carpenter Foreman (outside)	$36.95	$295.60	$61.80	$494.40	$34.28	$57.22
3 Carpenters	34.95	838.80	58.45	1402.80		
1 Laborer	26.60	212.80	44.50	356.00		
1 Equip. Oper. (crane)	37.30	298.40	61.65	493.20		
1 Hyd. Crane, 12 Ton		572.80		630.08	11.93	13.13
48 L.H., Daily Totals		$2218.40		$3376.48	$46.22	$70.34

Crew C-13

Crew No.	Bare Costs Hr.	Bare Costs Daily	Incl. Subs O&P Hr.	Incl. Subs O&P Daily	Cost Per Labor-Hour Bare Costs	Cost Per Labor-Hour Incl. O&P
2 Struc. Steel Workers	$38.55	$616.80	$69.65	$1114.40	$37.35	$65.92
1 Carpenter	34.95	279.60	58.45	467.60		
1 Welder, Gas Engine, 300 amp		129.80		142.78	5.41	5.95
24 L.H., Daily Totals		$1026.20		$1724.78	$42.76	$71.87

Crew C-14

Crew No.	Bare Costs Hr.	Bare Costs Daily	Incl. Subs O&P Hr.	Incl. Subs O&P Daily	Cost Per Labor-Hour Bare Costs	Cost Per Labor-Hour Incl. O&P
1 Carpenter Foreman (outside)	$36.95	$295.60	$61.80	$494.40	$31.65	$52.87
3 Carpenters	34.95	838.80	58.45	1402.80		
2 Carpenter Helpers	26.55	424.80	44.90	718.40		
4 Laborers	26.60	851.20	44.50	1424.00		
2 Rodmen (reinf.)	38.55	616.80	64.80	1036.80		
2 Rodman Helpers	26.55	424.80	44.90	718.40		
2 Cement Finishers	34.65	554.40	56.40	902.40		
1 Equip. Oper. (crane)	37.30	298.40	61.65	493.20		
1 Hyd. Crane, 80 Ton		1616.00		1777.60	11.88	13.07
136 L.H., Daily Totals		$5920.80		$8968.00	$43.54	$65.94

Crew C-14A

Crew No.	Bare Costs Hr.	Bare Costs Daily	Incl. Subs O&P Hr.	Incl. Subs O&P Daily	Cost Per Labor-Hour Bare Costs	Cost Per Labor-Hour Incl. O&P
1 Carpenter Foreman (outside)	$36.95	$295.60	$61.80	$494.40	$34.98	$58.47
16 Carpenters	34.95	4473.60	58.45	7481.60		
4 Rodmen (reinf.)	38.55	1233.60	64.80	2073.60		
2 Laborers	26.60	425.60	44.50	712.00		
1 Cement Finisher	34.65	277.20	56.40	451.20		
1 Equip. Oper. (medium)	36.40	291.20	60.15	481.20		
1 Gas Engine Vibrator		28.25		31.07		
1 Concrete Pump (Small)		806.40		887.04	4.17	4.59
200 L.H., Daily Totals		$7831.45		$12612.12	$39.16	$63.06

Crew C-14B

Crew No.	Bare Costs Hr.	Bare Costs Daily	Incl. Subs O&P Hr.	Incl. Subs O&P Daily	Cost Per Labor-Hour Bare Costs	Cost Per Labor-Hour Incl. O&P
1 Carpenter Foreman (outside)	$36.95	$295.60	$61.80	$494.40	$34.97	$58.39
16 Carpenters	34.95	4473.60	58.45	7481.60		
4 Rodmen (reinf.)	38.55	1233.60	64.80	2073.60		
2 Laborers	26.60	425.60	44.50	712.00		
2 Cement Finishers	34.65	554.40	56.40	902.40		
1 Equip. Oper. (medium)	36.40	291.20	60.15	481.20		
1 Gas Engine Vibrator		28.25		31.07		
1 Concrete Pump (Small)		806.40		887.04	4.01	4.41
208 L.H., Daily Totals		$8108.65		$13063.32	$38.98	$62.80

Crew C-14C

Crew No.	Bare Costs Hr.	Bare Costs Daily	Incl. Subs O&P Hr.	Incl. Subs O&P Daily	Cost Per Labor-Hour Bare Costs	Cost Per Labor-Hour Incl. O&P
1 Carpenter Foreman (outside)	$36.95	$295.60	$61.80	$494.40	$33.20	$55.46
6 Carpenters	34.95	1677.60	58.45	2805.60		
2 Rodmen (reinf.)	38.55	616.80	64.80	1036.80		
4 Laborers	26.60	851.20	44.50	1424.00		
1 Cement Finisher	34.65	277.20	56.40	451.20		
1 Gas Engine Vibrator		28.25		31.07	0.25	0.28
112 L.H., Daily Totals		$3746.65		$6243.07	$33.45	$55.74

Crew C-14D

Crew No.	Bare Costs Hr.	Bare Costs Daily	Incl. Subs O&P Hr.	Incl. Subs O&P Daily	Cost Per Labor-Hour Bare Costs	Cost Per Labor-Hour Incl. O&P
1 Carpenter Foreman (outside)	$36.95	$295.60	$61.80	$494.40	$34.70	$57.96
18 Carpenters	34.95	5032.80	58.45	8416.80		
2 Rodmen (reinf.)	38.55	616.80	64.80	1036.80		
2 Laborers	26.60	425.60	44.50	712.00		
1 Cement Finisher	34.65	277.20	56.40	451.20		
1 Equip. Oper. (medium)	36.40	291.20	60.15	481.20		
1 Gas Engine Vibrator		28.25		31.07		
1 Concrete Pump (Small)		806.40		887.04	4.17	4.59
200 L.H., Daily Totals		$7773.85		$12510.51	$38.87	$62.55

Crew C-14E

Crew No.	Bare Costs Hr.	Bare Costs Daily	Incl. Subs O&P Hr.	Incl. Subs O&P Daily	Cost Per Labor-Hour Bare Costs	Cost Per Labor-Hour Incl. O&P
1 Carpenter Foreman (outside)	$36.95	$295.60	$61.80	$494.40	$34.14	$57.07
2 Carpenters	34.95	559.20	58.45	935.20		
4 Rodmen (reinf.)	38.55	1233.60	64.80	2073.60		
3 Laborers	26.60	638.40	44.50	1068.00		
1 Cement Finisher	34.65	277.20	56.40	451.20		
1 Gas Engine Vibrator		28.25		31.07	0.32	0.35
88 L.H., Daily Totals		$3032.25		$5053.48	$34.46	$57.43

Crew C-14F

Crew No.	Bare Costs Hr.	Bare Costs Daily	Incl. Subs O&P Hr.	Incl. Subs O&P Daily	Cost Per Labor-Hour Bare Costs	Cost Per Labor-Hour Incl. O&P
1 Labor Foreman (outside)	$28.60	$228.80	$47.80	$382.40	$32.19	$52.80
2 Laborers	26.60	425.60	44.50	712.00		
6 Cement Finishers	34.65	1663.20	56.40	2707.20		
1 Gas Engine Vibrator		28.25		31.07	0.39	0.43
72 L.H., Daily Totals		$2345.85		$3832.68	$32.58	$53.23

Crew C-14G

Crew No.	Bare Costs Hr.	Bare Costs Daily	Incl. Subs O&P Hr.	Incl. Subs O&P Daily	Cost Per Labor-Hour Bare Costs	Cost Per Labor-Hour Incl. O&P
1 Labor Foreman (outside)	$28.60	$228.80	$47.80	$382.40	$31.49	$51.77
2 Laborers	26.60	425.60	44.50	712.00		
4 Cement Finishers	34.65	1108.80	56.40	1804.80		
1 Gas Engine Vibrator		28.25		31.07	0.50	0.55
56 L.H., Daily Totals		$1791.45		$2930.28	$31.99	$52.33

Crew C-14H

Crew No.	Bare Costs Hr.	Bare Costs Daily	Incl. Subs O&P Hr.	Incl. Subs O&P Daily	Cost Per Labor-Hour Bare Costs	Cost Per Labor-Hour Incl. O&P
1 Carpenter Foreman (outside)	$36.95	$295.60	$61.80	$494.40	$34.44	$57.40
2 Carpenters	34.95	559.20	58.45	935.20		
1 Rodman (reinf.)	38.55	308.40	64.80	518.40		
1 Laborer	26.60	212.80	44.50	356.00		
1 Cement Finisher	34.65	277.20	56.40	451.20		
1 Gas Engine Vibrator		28.25		31.07	0.59	0.65
48 L.H., Daily Totals		$1681.45		$2786.28	$35.03	$58.05

Crew C-14L

Crew No.	Bare Costs Hr.	Bare Costs Daily	Incl. Subs O&P Hr.	Incl. Subs O&P Daily	Cost Per Labor-Hour Bare Costs	Cost Per Labor-Hour Incl. O&P
1 Carpenter Foreman (outside)	$36.95	$295.60	$61.80	$494.40	$32.31	$53.91
6 Carpenters	34.95	1677.60	58.45	2805.60		
4 Laborers	26.60	851.20	44.50	1424.00		
1 Cement Finisher	34.65	277.20	56.40	451.20		
1 Gas Engine Vibrator		28.25		31.07	0.29	0.32
96 L.H., Daily Totals		$3129.85		$5206.27	$32.60	$54.23

For customer support on your Residential Costs with RSMeans Data, call 800.448.8182.

699

Crew No.	Bare Costs Hr.	Bare Costs Daily	Incl. Subs O&P Hr.	Incl. Subs O&P Daily	Cost Per Labor-Hour Bare Costs	Cost Per Labor-Hour Incl. O&P
Crew C-14M	Hr.	Daily	Hr.	Daily	Bare Costs	Incl. O&P
1 Carpenter Foreman (outside)	$36.95	$295.60	$61.80	$494.40	$33.71	$56.13
2 Carpenters	34.95	559.20	58.45	935.20		
1 Rodman (reinf.)	38.55	308.40	64.80	518.40		
2 Laborers	26.60	425.60	44.50	712.00		
1 Cement Finisher	34.65	277.20	56.40	451.20		
1 Equip. Oper. (medium)	36.40	291.20	60.15	481.20		
1 Gas Engine Vibrator		28.25		31.07		
1 Concrete Pump (Small)		806.40		887.04	13.04	14.35
64 L.H., Daily Totals		$2991.85		$4510.52	$46.75	$70.48
Crew C-15	Hr.	Daily	Hr.	Daily	Bare Costs	Incl. O&P
1 Carpenter Foreman (outside)	$36.95	$295.60	$61.80	$494.40	$32.72	$54.42
2 Carpenters	34.95	559.20	58.45	935.20		
3 Laborers	26.60	638.40	44.50	1068.00		
2 Cement Finishers	34.65	554.40	56.40	902.40		
1 Rodman (reinf.)	38.55	308.40	64.80	518.40		
72 L.H., Daily Totals		$2356.00		$3918.40	$32.72	$54.42
Crew C-16	Hr.	Daily	Hr.	Daily	Bare Costs	Incl. O&P
1 Labor Foreman (outside)	$28.60	$228.80	$47.80	$382.40	$30.59	$50.61
3 Laborers	26.60	638.40	44.50	1068.00		
2 Cement Finishers	34.65	554.40	56.40	902.40		
1 Equip. Oper. (medium)	36.40	291.20	60.15	481.20		
1 Gunite Pump Rig		357.40		393.14		
2 -50' Air Hoses, 3/4"		6.50		7.15		
2 -50' Air Hoses, 2"		15.50		17.05	6.78	7.45
56 L.H., Daily Totals		$2092.20		$3251.34	$37.36	$58.06
Crew C-16A	Hr.	Daily	Hr.	Daily	Bare Costs	Incl. O&P
1 Laborer	$26.60	$212.80	$44.50	$356.00	$33.08	$54.36
2 Cement Finishers	34.65	554.40	56.40	902.40		
1 Equip. Oper. (medium)	36.40	291.20	60.15	481.20		
1 Gunite Pump Rig		357.40		393.14		
2 -50' Air Hoses, 3/4"		6.50		7.15		
2 -50' Air Hoses, 2"		15.50		17.05		
1 Telescoping Boom Lift, to 60'		456.00		501.60	26.11	28.72
32 L.H., Daily Totals		$1893.80		$2658.54	$59.18	$83.08
Crew C-17	Hr.	Daily	Hr.	Daily	Bare Costs	Incl. O&P
2 Skilled Worker Foremen (out)	$37.75	$604.00	$63.40	$1014.40	$36.15	$60.68
8 Skilled Workers	35.75	2288.00	60.00	3840.00		
80 L.H., Daily Totals		$2892.00		$4854.40	$36.15	$60.68
Crew C-17A	Hr.	Daily	Hr.	Daily	Bare Costs	Incl. O&P
2 Skilled Worker Foremen (out)	$37.75	$604.00	$63.40	$1014.40	$36.16	$60.69
8 Skilled Workers	35.75	2288.00	60.00	3840.00		
.125 Equip. Oper. (crane)	37.30	37.30	61.65	61.65		
.125 Hyd. Crane, 80 Ton		202.00		222.20	2.49	2.74
81 L.H., Daily Totals		$3131.30		$5138.25	$38.66	$63.44
Crew C-17B	Hr.	Daily	Hr.	Daily	Bare Costs	Incl. O&P
2 Skilled Worker Foremen (out)	$37.75	$604.00	$63.40	$1014.40	$36.18	$60.70
8 Skilled Workers	35.75	2288.00	60.00	3840.00		
.25 Equip. Oper. (crane)	37.30	74.60	61.65	123.30		
.25 Hyd. Crane, 80 Ton		404.00		444.40		
.25 Trowel, 48" Walk-Behind		11.39		12.53	5.07	5.57
82 L.H., Daily Totals		$3381.99		$5434.63	$41.24	$66.28

Crew No.	Bare Costs Hr.	Bare Costs Daily	Incl. Subs O&P Hr.	Incl. Subs O&P Daily	Cost Per Labor-Hour Bare Costs	Cost Per Labor-Hour Incl. O&P
Crew C-17C	Hr.	Daily	Hr.	Daily	Bare Costs	Incl. O&P
2 Skilled Worker Foremen (out)	$37.75	$604.00	$63.40	$1014.40	$36.19	$60.72
8 Skilled Workers	35.75	2288.00	60.00	3840.00		
.375 Equip. Oper. (crane)	37.30	111.90	61.65	184.95		
.375 Hyd. Crane, 80 Ton		606.00		666.60	7.30	8.03
83 L.H., Daily Totals		$3609.90		$5705.95	$43.49	$68.75
Crew C-17D	Hr.	Daily	Hr.	Daily	Bare Costs	Incl. O&P
2 Skilled Worker Foremen (out)	$37.75	$604.00	$63.40	$1014.40	$36.20	$60.73
8 Skilled Workers	35.75	2288.00	60.00	3840.00		
.5 Equip. Oper. (crane)	37.30	149.20	61.65	246.60		
.5 Hyd. Crane, 80 Ton		808.00		888.80	9.62	10.58
84 L.H., Daily Totals		$3849.20		$5989.80	$45.82	$71.31
Crew C-17E	Hr.	Daily	Hr.	Daily	Bare Costs	Incl. O&P
2 Skilled Worker Foremen (out)	$37.75	$604.00	$63.40	$1014.40	$36.15	$60.68
8 Skilled Workers	35.75	2288.00	60.00	3840.00		
1 Hyd. Jack with Rods		100.30		110.33	1.25	1.38
80 L.H., Daily Totals		$2992.30		$4964.73	$37.40	$62.06
Crew C-18	Hr.	Daily	Hr.	Daily	Bare Costs	Incl. O&P
.125 Labor Foreman (outside)	$28.60	$28.60	$47.80	$47.80	$26.82	$44.87
1 Laborer	26.60	212.80	44.50	356.00		
1 Concrete Cart, 10 C.F.		58.00		63.80	6.44	7.09
9 L.H., Daily Totals		$299.40		$467.60	$33.27	$51.96
Crew C-19	Hr.	Daily	Hr.	Daily	Bare Costs	Incl. O&P
.125 Labor Foreman (outside)	$28.60	$28.60	$47.80	$47.80	$26.82	$44.87
1 Laborer	26.60	212.80	44.50	356.00		
1 Concrete Cart, 18 C.F.		96.60		106.26	10.73	11.81
9 L.H., Daily Totals		$338.00		$510.06	$37.56	$56.67
Crew C-20	Hr.	Daily	Hr.	Daily	Bare Costs	Incl. O&P
1 Labor Foreman (outside)	$28.60	$228.80	$47.80	$382.40	$29.08	$48.36
5 Laborers	26.60	1064.00	44.50	1780.00		
1 Cement Finisher	34.65	277.20	56.40	451.20		
1 Equip. Oper. (medium)	36.40	291.20	60.15	481.20		
2 Gas Engine Vibrators		56.50		62.15		
1 Concrete Pump (Small)		806.40		887.04	13.48	14.83
64 L.H., Daily Totals		$2724.10		$4043.99	$42.56	$63.19
Crew C-21	Hr.	Daily	Hr.	Daily	Bare Costs	Incl. O&P
1 Labor Foreman (outside)	$28.60	$228.80	$47.80	$382.40	$29.08	$48.36
5 Laborers	26.60	1064.00	44.50	1780.00		
1 Cement Finisher	34.65	277.20	56.40	451.20		
1 Equip. Oper. (medium)	36.40	291.20	60.15	481.20		
2 Gas Engine Vibrators		56.50		62.15		
1 Concrete Conveyer		189.80		208.78	3.85	4.23
64 L.H., Daily Totals		$2107.50		$3365.73	$32.93	$52.59
Crew C-22	Hr.	Daily	Hr.	Daily	Bare Costs	Incl. O&P
1 Rodman Foreman (outside)	$40.55	$324.40	$68.15	$545.20	$38.76	$65.10
4 Rodmen (reinf.)	38.55	1233.60	64.80	2073.60		
.125 Equip. Oper. (crane)	37.30	37.30	61.65	61.65		
.125 Equip. Oper. (oiler)	32.65	32.65	53.95	53.95		
.125 Hyd. Crane, 25 Ton		84.22		92.65	2.01	2.21
42 L.H., Daily Totals		$1712.18		$2827.05	$40.77	$67.31

For customer support on your Residential Costs with RSMeans Data, call 800.448.8182.

Crews - Residential

Crew No.	Hr.	Daily	Hr.	Daily	Bare Costs	Incl. O&P
Crew C-23	Hr.	Daily	Hr.	Daily	Bare Costs	Incl. O&P
2 Skilled Worker Foremen (out)	$37.75	$604.00	$63.40	$1014.40	$35.99	$60.24
6 Skilled Workers	35.75	1716.00	60.00	2880.00		
1 Equip. Oper. (crane)	37.30	298.40	61.65	493.20		
1 Equip. Oper. (oiler)	32.65	261.20	53.95	431.60		
1 Lattice Boom Crane, 90 Ton		1671.00		1838.10	20.89	22.98
80 L.H., Daily Totals		$4550.60		$6657.30	$56.88	$83.22
Crew C-24	Hr.	Daily	Hr.	Daily	Bare Costs	Incl. O&P
2 Skilled Worker Foremen (out)	$37.75	$604.00	$63.40	$1014.40	$35.99	$60.24
6 Skilled Workers	35.75	1716.00	60.00	2880.00		
1 Equip. Oper. (crane)	37.30	298.40	61.65	493.20		
1 Equip. Oper. (oiler)	32.65	261.20	53.95	431.60		
1 Lattice Boom Crane, 150 Ton		2000.00		2200.00	25.00	27.50
80 L.H., Daily Totals		$4879.60		$7019.20	$60.99	$87.74
Crew C-25	Hr.	Daily	Hr.	Daily	Bare Costs	Incl. O&P
2 Rodmen (reinf.)	$38.55	$616.80	$64.80	$1036.80	$30.50	$53.05
2 Rodmen Helpers	22.45	359.20	41.30	660.80		
32 L.H., Daily Totals		$976.00		$1697.60	$30.50	$53.05
Crew C-27	Hr.	Daily	Hr.	Daily	Bare Costs	Incl. O&P
2 Cement Finishers	$34.65	$554.40	$56.40	$902.40	$34.65	$56.40
1 Concrete Saw		153.60		168.96	9.60	10.56
16 L.H., Daily Totals		$708.00		$1071.36	$44.25	$66.96
Crew C-28	Hr.	Daily	Hr.	Daily	Bare Costs	Incl. O&P
1 Cement Finisher	$34.65	$277.20	$56.40	$451.20	$34.65	$56.40
1 Portable Air Compressor, Gas		17.60		19.36	2.20	2.42
8 L.H., Daily Totals		$294.80		$470.56	$36.85	$58.82
Crew C-29	Hr.	Daily	Hr.	Daily	Bare Costs	Incl. O&P
1 Laborer	$26.60	$212.80	$44.50	$356.00	$26.60	$44.50
1 Pressure Washer		66.00		72.60	8.25	9.07
8 L.H., Daily Totals		$278.80		$428.60	$34.85	$53.58
Crew C-30	Hr.	Daily	Hr.	Daily	Bare Costs	Incl. O&P
1 Laborer	$26.60	$212.80	$44.50	$356.00	$26.60	$44.50
1 Concrete Mixer, 10 C.F.		164.60		181.06	20.57	22.63
8 L.H., Daily Totals		$377.40		$537.06	$47.17	$67.13
Crew C-31	Hr.	Daily	Hr.	Daily	Bare Costs	Incl. O&P
1 Cement Finisher	$34.65	$277.20	$56.40	$451.20	$34.65	$56.40
1 Grout Pump		357.40		393.14	44.67	49.14
8 L.H., Daily Totals		$634.60		$844.34	$79.33	$105.54
Crew C-32	Hr.	Daily	Hr.	Daily	Bare Costs	Incl. O&P
1 Cement Finisher	$34.65	$277.20	$56.40	$451.20	$30.63	$50.45
1 Laborer	26.60	212.80	44.50	356.00		
1 Crack Chaser Saw, Gas, 6 H.P.		26.60		29.26		
1 Vacuum Pick-Up System		60.85		66.94	5.47	6.01
16 L.H., Daily Totals		$577.45		$903.39	$36.09	$56.46
Crew D-1	Hr.	Daily	Hr.	Daily	Bare Costs	Incl. O&P
1 Bricklayer	$34.85	$278.80	$58.50	$468.00	$31.77	$53.33
1 Bricklayer Helper	28.70	229.60	48.15	385.20		
16 L.H., Daily Totals		$508.40		$853.20	$31.77	$53.33
Crew D-2	Hr.	Daily	Hr.	Daily	Bare Costs	Incl. O&P
3 Bricklayers	$34.85	$836.40	$58.50	$1404.00	$32.39	$54.36
2 Bricklayer Helpers	28.70	459.20	48.15	770.40		
40 L.H., Daily Totals		$1295.60		$2174.40	$32.39	$54.36
Crew D-3	Hr.	Daily	Hr.	Daily	Bare Costs	Incl. O&P
3 Bricklayers	$34.85	$836.40	$58.50	$1404.00	$32.51	$54.55
2 Bricklayer Helpers	28.70	459.20	48.15	770.40		
.25 Carpenter	34.95	69.90	58.45	116.90		
42 L.H., Daily Totals		$1365.50		$2291.30	$32.51	$54.55
Crew D-4	Hr.	Daily	Hr.	Daily	Bare Costs	Incl. O&P
1 Bricklayer	$34.85	$278.80	$58.50	$468.00	$29.51	$49.49
3 Bricklayer Helpers	28.70	688.80	48.15	1155.60		
1 Building Laborer	26.60	212.80	44.50	356.00		
1 Grout Pump, 50 C.F./hr.		132.80		146.08	3.32	3.65
40 L.H., Daily Totals		$1313.20		$2125.68	$32.83	$53.14
Crew D-5	Hr.	Daily	Hr.	Daily	Bare Costs	Incl. O&P
1 Block Mason Helper	28.70	229.60	48.15	385.20	28.70	48.15
8 L.H., Daily Totals		$229.60		$385.20	$28.70	$48.15
Crew D-6	Hr.	Daily	Hr.	Daily	Bare Costs	Incl. O&P
3 Bricklayers	$34.85	$836.40	$58.50	$1404.00	$31.77	$53.33
3 Bricklayer Helpers	28.70	688.80	48.15	1155.60		
48 L.H., Daily Totals		$1525.20		$2559.60	$31.77	$53.33
Crew D-7	Hr.	Daily	Hr.	Daily	Bare Costs	Incl. O&P
1 Tile Layer	$33.45	$267.60	$54.30	$434.40	$29.80	$48.38
1 Tile Layer Helper	26.15	209.20	42.45	339.60		
16 L.H., Daily Totals		$476.80		$774.00	$29.80	$48.38
Crew D-8	Hr.	Daily	Hr.	Daily	Bare Costs	Incl. O&P
3 Bricklayers	$34.85	$836.40	$58.50	$1404.00	$32.39	$54.36
2 Bricklayer Helpers	28.70	459.20	48.15	770.40		
40 L.H., Daily Totals		$1295.60		$2174.40	$32.39	$54.36
Crew D-9	Hr.	Daily	Hr.	Daily	Bare Costs	Incl. O&P
3 Bricklayers	$34.85	$836.40	$58.50	$1404.00	$31.77	$53.33
3 Bricklayer Helpers	28.70	688.80	48.15	1155.60		
48 L.H., Daily Totals		$1525.20		$2559.60	$31.77	$53.33
Crew D-10	Hr.	Daily	Hr.	Daily	Bare Costs	Incl. O&P
1 Bricklayer Foreman (outside)	$36.85	$294.80	$61.85	$494.80	$34.42	$57.54
1 Bricklayer	34.85	278.80	58.50	468.00		
1 Bricklayer Helper	28.70	229.60	48.15	385.20		
1 Equip. Oper. (crane)	37.30	298.40	61.65	493.20		
1 S.P. Crane, 4x4, 12 Ton		435.60		479.16	13.61	14.97
32 L.H., Daily Totals		$1537.20		$2320.36	$48.04	$72.51
Crew D-11	Hr.	Daily	Hr.	Daily	Bare Costs	Incl. O&P
2 Bricklayers	$34.85	$557.60	$58.50	$936.00	$32.80	$55.05
1 Bricklayer Helper	28.70	229.60	48.15	385.20		
24 L.H., Daily Totals		$787.20		$1321.20	$32.80	$55.05
Crew D-12	Hr.	Daily	Hr.	Daily	Bare Costs	Incl. O&P
2 Bricklayers	$34.85	$557.60	$58.50	$936.00	$31.77	$53.33
2 Bricklayer Helpers	28.70	459.20	48.15	770.40		
32 L.H., Daily Totals		$1016.80		$1706.40	$31.77	$53.33

For customer support on your Residential Costs with RSMeans Data, call 800.448.8182.

701

Crew D-13

Crew No.	Bare Costs Hr.	Bare Costs Daily	Incl. Subs O&P Hr.	Incl. Subs O&P Daily	Cost Per Labor-Hour Bare Costs	Cost Per Labor-Hour Incl. O&P
					$33.54	$56.13
1 Bricklayer Foreman (outside)	$36.85	$294.80	$61.85	$494.80		
2 Bricklayers	34.85	557.60	58.50	936.00		
2 Bricklayer Helpers	28.70	459.20	48.15	770.40		
1 Equip. Oper. (crane)	37.30	298.40	61.65	493.20		
1 S.P. Crane, 4x4, 12 Ton		435.60		479.16	9.07	9.98
48 L.H., Daily Totals		$2045.60		$3173.56	$42.62	$66.12

Crew D-14

Crew No.	Bare Costs Hr.	Bare Costs Daily	Incl. Subs O&P Hr.	Incl. Subs O&P Daily	Cost Per Labor-Hour Bare Costs	Cost Per Labor-Hour Incl. O&P
					$33.31	$55.91
3 Bricklayers	$34.85	$836.40	$58.50	$1404.00		
1 Bricklayer Helper	28.70	229.60	48.15	385.20		
32 L.H., Daily Totals		$1066.00		$1789.20	$33.31	$55.91

Crew E-1

Crew No.	Bare Costs Hr.	Bare Costs Daily	Incl. Subs O&P Hr.	Incl. Subs O&P Daily	Cost Per Labor-Hour Bare Costs	Cost Per Labor-Hour Incl. O&P
					$38.55	$69.65
2 Struc. Steel Workers	$38.55	$616.80	$69.65	$1114.40		
1 Welder, Gas Engine, 300 amp		129.80		142.78	8.11	8.92
16 L.H., Daily Totals		$746.60		$1257.18	$46.66	$78.57

Crew E-2

Crew No.	Bare Costs Hr.	Bare Costs Daily	Incl. Subs O&P Hr.	Incl. Subs O&P Daily	Cost Per Labor-Hour Bare Costs	Cost Per Labor-Hour Incl. O&P
					$38.67	$68.92
1 Struc. Steel Foreman (outside)	$40.55	$324.40	$73.25	$586.00		
4 Struc. Steel Workers	38.55	1233.60	69.65	2228.80		
1 Equip. Oper. (crane)	37.30	298.40	61.65	493.20		
1 Lattice Boom Crane, 90 Ton		1671.00		1838.10	34.81	38.29
48 L.H., Daily Totals		$3527.40		$5146.10	$73.49	$107.21

Crew E-3

Crew No.	Bare Costs Hr.	Bare Costs Daily	Incl. Subs O&P Hr.	Incl. Subs O&P Daily	Cost Per Labor-Hour Bare Costs	Cost Per Labor-Hour Incl. O&P
					$39.22	$70.85
1 Struc. Steel Foreman (outside)	$40.55	$324.40	$73.25	$586.00		
2 Struc. Steel Workers	38.55	616.80	69.65	1114.40		
1 Welder, Gas Engine, 300 amp		129.80		142.78	5.41	5.95
24 L.H., Daily Totals		$1071.00		$1843.18	$44.63	$76.80

Crew E-3A

Crew No.	Bare Costs Hr.	Bare Costs Daily	Incl. Subs O&P Hr.	Incl. Subs O&P Daily	Cost Per Labor-Hour Bare Costs	Cost Per Labor-Hour Incl. O&P
					$39.22	$70.85
1 Struc. Steel Foreman (outside)	$40.55	$324.40	$73.25	$586.00		
2 Struc. Steel Workers	38.55	616.80	69.65	1114.40		
1 Welder, Gas Engine, 300 amp		129.80		142.78		
1 Telescoping Boom Lift, to 40'		288.80		317.68	17.44	19.19
24 L.H., Daily Totals		$1359.80		$2160.86	$56.66	$90.04

Crew E-4

Crew No.	Bare Costs Hr.	Bare Costs Daily	Incl. Subs O&P Hr.	Incl. Subs O&P Daily	Cost Per Labor-Hour Bare Costs	Cost Per Labor-Hour Incl. O&P
					$39.05	$70.55
1 Struc. Steel Foreman (outside)	$40.55	$324.40	$73.25	$586.00		
3 Struc. Steel Workers	38.55	925.20	69.65	1671.60		
1 Welder, Gas Engine, 300 amp		129.80		142.78	4.06	4.46
32 L.H., Daily Totals		$1379.40		$2400.38	$43.11	$75.01

Crew E-5

Crew No.	Bare Costs Hr.	Bare Costs Daily	Incl. Subs O&P Hr.	Incl. Subs O&P Daily	Cost Per Labor-Hour Bare Costs	Cost Per Labor-Hour Incl. O&P
					$38.63	$69.16
1 Struc. Steel Foreman (outside)	$40.55	$324.40	$73.25	$586.00		
7 Struc. Steel Workers	38.55	2158.80	69.65	3900.40		
1 Equip. Oper. (crane)	37.30	298.40	61.65	493.20		
1 Lattice Boom Crane, 90 Ton		1671.00		1838.10		
1 Welder, Gas Engine, 300 amp		129.80		142.78	25.01	27.51
72 L.H., Daily Totals		$4582.40		$6960.48	$63.64	$96.67

Crew E-6

Crew No.	Bare Costs Hr.	Bare Costs Daily	Incl. Subs O&P Hr.	Incl. Subs O&P Daily	Cost Per Labor-Hour Bare Costs	Cost Per Labor-Hour Incl. O&P
					$38.38	$68.59
1 Struc. Steel Foreman (outside)	$40.55	$324.40	$73.25	$586.00		
12 Struc. Steel Workers	38.55	3700.80	69.65	6686.40		
1 Equip. Oper. (crane)	37.30	298.40	61.65	493.20		
1 Equip. Oper. (light)	35.20	281.60	58.20	465.60		
1 Lattice Boom Crane, 90 Ton		1671.00		1838.10		
1 Welder, Gas Engine, 300 amp		129.80		142.78		
1 Air Compressor, 160 cfm		143.60		157.96		
2 Impact Wrenches		37.20		40.92	16.51	18.16
120 L.H., Daily Totals		$6586.80		$10410.96	$54.89	$86.76

Crew E-7

Crew No.	Bare Costs Hr.	Bare Costs Daily	Incl. Subs O&P Hr.	Incl. Subs O&P Daily	Cost Per Labor-Hour Bare Costs	Cost Per Labor-Hour Incl. O&P
					$38.63	$69.16
1 Struc. Steel Foreman (outside)	$40.55	$324.40	$73.25	$586.00		
7 Struc. Steel Workers	38.55	2158.80	69.65	3900.40		
1 Equip. Oper. (crane)	37.30	298.40	61.65	493.20		
1 Lattice Boom Crane, 90 Ton		1671.00		1838.10		
2 Welder, Gas Engine, 300 amp		259.60		285.56	26.81	29.50
72 L.H., Daily Totals		$4712.20		$7103.26	$65.45	$98.66

Crew E-8

Crew No.	Bare Costs Hr.	Bare Costs Daily	Incl. Subs O&P Hr.	Incl. Subs O&P Daily	Cost Per Labor-Hour Bare Costs	Cost Per Labor-Hour Incl. O&P
					$38.62	$69.25
1 Struc. Steel Foreman (outside)	$40.55	$324.40	$73.25	$586.00		
9 Struc. Steel Workers	38.55	2775.60	69.65	5014.80		
1 Equip. Oper. (crane)	37.30	298.40	61.65	493.20		
1 Lattice Boom Crane, 90 Ton		1671.00		1838.10		
4 Welder, Gas Engine, 300 amp		519.20		571.12	24.89	27.38
88 L.H., Daily Totals		$5588.60		$8503.22	$63.51	$96.63

Crew E-9

Crew No.	Bare Costs Hr.	Bare Costs Daily	Incl. Subs O&P Hr.	Incl. Subs O&P Daily	Cost Per Labor-Hour Bare Costs	Cost Per Labor-Hour Incl. O&P
					$38.27	$68.13
2 Struc. Steel Foremen (outside)	$40.55	$648.80	$73.25	$1172.00		
5 Struc. Steel Workers	38.55	1542.00	69.65	2786.00		
1 Welder Foreman (outside)	40.55	324.40	73.25	586.00		
5 Welders	38.55	1542.00	69.65	2786.00		
1 Equip. Oper. (crane)	37.30	298.40	61.65	493.20		
1 Equip. Oper. (oiler)	32.65	261.20	53.95	431.60		
1 Equip. Oper. (light)	35.20	281.60	58.20	465.60		
1 Lattice Boom Crane, 90 Ton		1671.00		1838.10		
5 Welder, Gas Engine, 300 amp		649.00		713.90	18.13	19.94
128 L.H., Daily Totals		$7218.40		$11272.40	$56.39	$88.07

Crew E-10

Crew No.	Bare Costs Hr.	Bare Costs Daily	Incl. Subs O&P Hr.	Incl. Subs O&P Daily	Cost Per Labor-Hour Bare Costs	Cost Per Labor-Hour Incl. O&P
					$39.22	$70.85
1 Struc. Steel Foreman (outside)	$40.55	$324.40	$73.25	$586.00		
2 Struc. Steel Workers	38.55	616.80	69.65	1114.40		
1 Welder, Gas Engine, 300 amp		129.80		142.78		
1 Flatbed Truck, Gas, 3 Ton		270.20		297.22	16.67	18.33
24 L.H., Daily Totals		$1341.20		$2140.40	$55.88	$89.18

Crew E-11

Crew No.	Bare Costs Hr.	Bare Costs Daily	Incl. Subs O&P Hr.	Incl. Subs O&P Daily	Cost Per Labor-Hour Bare Costs	Cost Per Labor-Hour Incl. O&P
					$30.27	$52.80
2 Painters, Struc. Steel	$29.65	$474.40	$54.25	$868.00		
1 Building Laborer	26.60	212.80	44.50	356.00		
1 Equip. Oper. (light)	35.20	281.60	58.20	465.60		
1 Air Compressor, 250 cfm		181.20		199.32		
1 Sandblaster, Portable, 3 C.F.		21.40		23.54		
1 Set Sand Blasting Accessories		14.45		15.90	6.78	7.46
32 L.H., Daily Totals		$1185.85		$1928.36	$37.06	$60.26

Crew E-11A

Crew No.	Bare Costs Hr.	Daily	Incl. Subs O&P Hr.	Daily	Bare Costs	Incl. O&P
2 Painters, Struc. Steel	$29.65	$474.40	$54.25	$868.00	$30.27	$52.80
1 Building Laborer	26.60	212.80	44.50	356.00		
1 Equip. Oper. (light)	35.20	281.60	58.20	465.60		
1 Air Compressor, 250 cfm		181.20		199.32		
1 Sandblaster, Portable, 3 C.F.		21.40		23.54		
1 Set Sand Blasting Accessories		14.45		15.90		
1 Telescoping Boom Lift, to 60'		456.00		501.60	21.03	23.14
32 L.H., Daily Totals		$1641.85		$2429.95	$51.31	$75.94

Crew E-11B

Crew No.	Bare Costs Hr.	Daily	Incl. Subs O&P Hr.	Daily	Bare Costs	Incl. O&P
2 Painters, Struc. Steel	$29.65	$474.40	$54.25	$868.00	$28.63	$51.00
1 Building Laborer	26.60	212.80	44.50	356.00		
2 Paint Sprayer, 8 C.F.M.		101.40		111.54		
1 Telescoping Boom Lift, to 60'		456.00		501.60	23.23	25.55
24 L.H., Daily Totals		$1244.60		$1837.14	$51.86	$76.55

Crew E-12

Crew No.	Bare Costs Hr.	Daily	Incl. Subs O&P Hr.	Daily	Bare Costs	Incl. O&P
1 Welder Foreman (outside)	$40.55	$324.40	$73.25	$586.00	$37.88	$65.72
1 Equip. Oper. (light)	35.20	281.60	58.20	465.60		
1 Welder, Gas Engine, 300 amp		129.80		142.78	8.11	8.92
16 L.H., Daily Totals		$735.80		$1194.38	$45.99	$74.65

Crew E-13

Crew No.	Bare Costs Hr.	Daily	Incl. Subs O&P Hr.	Daily	Bare Costs	Incl. O&P
1 Welder Foreman (outside)	$40.55	$324.40	$73.25	$586.00	$38.77	$68.23
.5 Equip. Oper. (light)	35.20	140.80	58.20	232.80		
1 Welder, Gas Engine, 300 amp		129.80		142.78	10.82	11.90
12 L.H., Daily Totals		$595.00		$961.58	$49.58	$80.13

Crew E-14

Crew No.	Bare Costs Hr.	Daily	Incl. Subs O&P Hr.	Daily	Bare Costs	Incl. O&P
1 Struc. Steel Worker	$38.55	$308.40	$69.65	$557.20	$38.55	$69.65
1 Welder, Gas Engine, 300 amp		129.80		142.78	16.23	17.85
8 L.H., Daily Totals		$438.20		$699.98	$54.77	$87.50

Crew E-16

Crew No.	Bare Costs Hr.	Daily	Incl. Subs O&P Hr.	Daily	Bare Costs	Incl. O&P
1 Welder Foreman (outside)	$40.55	$324.40	$73.25	$586.00	$39.55	$71.45
1 Welder	38.55	308.40	69.65	557.20		
1 Welder, Gas Engine, 300 amp		129.80		142.78	8.11	8.92
16 L.H., Daily Totals		$762.60		$1285.98	$47.66	$80.37

Crew E-17

Crew No.	Bare Costs Hr.	Daily	Incl. Subs O&P Hr.	Daily	Bare Costs	Incl. O&P
1 Struc. Steel Foreman (outside)	$40.55	$324.40	$73.25	$586.00	$39.55	$71.45
1 Structural Steel Worker	38.55	308.40	69.65	557.20		
16 L.H., Daily Totals		$632.80		$1143.20	$39.55	$71.45

Crew E-18

Crew No.	Bare Costs Hr.	Daily	Incl. Subs O&P Hr.	Daily	Bare Costs	Incl. O&P
1 Struc. Steel Foreman (outside)	$40.55	$324.40	$73.25	$586.00	$38.52	$68.47
3 Structural Steel Workers	38.55	925.20	69.65	1671.60		
1 Equipment Operator (med.)	36.40	291.20	60.15	481.20		
1 Lattice Boom Crane, 20 Ton		1075.00		1182.50	26.88	29.56
40 L.H., Daily Totals		$2615.80		$3921.30	$65.39	$98.03

Crew E-19

Crew No.	Bare Costs Hr.	Daily	Incl. Subs O&P Hr.	Daily	Bare Costs	Incl. O&P
1 Struc. Steel Foreman (outside)	$40.55	$324.40	$73.25	$586.00	$38.10	$67.03
1 Structural Steel Worker	38.55	308.40	69.65	557.20		
1 Equip. Oper. (light)	35.20	281.60	58.20	465.60		
1 Lattice Boom Crane, 20 Ton		1075.00		1182.50	44.79	49.27
24 L.H., Daily Totals		$1989.40		$2791.30	$82.89	$116.30

Crew E-20

Crew No.	Bare Costs Hr.	Daily	Incl. Subs O&P Hr.	Daily	Bare Costs	Incl. O&P
1 Struc. Steel Foreman (outside)	$40.55	$324.40	$73.25	$586.00	$37.91	$67.14
5 Structural Steel Workers	38.55	1542.00	69.65	2786.00		
1 Equip. Oper. (crane)	37.30	298.40	61.65	493.20		
1 Equip. Oper. (oiler)	32.65	261.20	53.95	431.60		
1 Lattice Boom Crane, 40 Ton		1311.00		1442.10	20.48	22.53
64 L.H., Daily Totals		$3737.00		$5738.90	$58.39	$89.67

Crew E-22

Crew No.	Bare Costs Hr.	Daily	Incl. Subs O&P Hr.	Daily	Bare Costs	Incl. O&P
1 Skilled Worker Foreman (out)	$37.75	$302.00	$63.40	$507.20	$36.42	$61.13
2 Skilled Workers	35.75	572.00	60.00	960.00		
24 L.H., Daily Totals		$874.00		$1467.20	$36.42	$61.13

Crew E-24

Crew No.	Bare Costs Hr.	Daily	Incl. Subs O&P Hr.	Daily	Bare Costs	Incl. O&P
3 Structural Steel Workers	$38.55	$925.20	$69.65	$1671.60	$38.01	$67.28
1 Equipment Operator (med.)	36.40	291.20	60.15	481.20		
1 Hyd. Crane, 25 Ton		673.80		741.18	21.06	23.16
32 L.H., Daily Totals		$1890.20		$2893.98	$59.07	$90.44

Crew E-25

Crew No.	Bare Costs Hr.	Daily	Incl. Subs O&P Hr.	Daily	Bare Costs	Incl. O&P
1 Welder	$38.55	$308.40	$69.65	$557.20	$38.55	$69.65
1 Cutting Torch		12.00		13.20	1.50	1.65
8 L.H., Daily Totals		$320.40		$570.40	$40.05	$71.30

Crew E-26

Crew No.	Bare Costs Hr.	Daily	Incl. Subs O&P Hr.	Daily	Bare Costs	Incl. O&P
1 Struc. Steel Foreman (outside)	$40.55	$324.40	$73.25	$586.00	$39.31	$70.09
1 Struc. Steel Worker	38.55	308.40	69.65	557.20		
1 Welder	38.55	308.40	69.65	557.20		
.25 Electrician	40.20	80.40	65.85	131.70		
.25 Plumber	39.55	79.10	65.20	130.40		
1 Welder, Gas Engine, 300 amp		129.80		142.78	4.64	5.10
28 L.H., Daily Totals		$1230.50		$2105.28	$43.95	$75.19

Crew E-27

Crew No.	Bare Costs Hr.	Daily	Incl. Subs O&P Hr.	Daily	Bare Costs	Incl. O&P
1 Struc. Steel Foreman (outside)	$40.55	$324.40	$73.25	$586.00	$38.64	$69.10
6 Struc. Steel Workers	38.55	1850.40	69.65	3343.20		
1 Equip. Oper. (crane)	37.30	298.40	61.65	493.20		
1 Hyd. Crane, 12 Ton		572.80		630.08		
1 Hyd. Crane, 80 Ton		1616.00		1777.60	34.20	37.62
64 L.H., Daily Totals		$4662.00		$6830.08	$72.84	$106.72

Crew F-3

Crew No.	Bare Costs Hr.	Daily	Incl. Subs O&P Hr.	Daily	Bare Costs	Incl. O&P
2 Carpenters	$34.95	$559.20	$58.45	$935.20	$32.06	$53.67
2 Carpenter Helpers	26.55	424.80	44.90	718.40		
1 Equip. Oper. (crane)	37.30	298.40	61.65	493.20		
1 Hyd. Crane, 12 Ton		572.80		630.08	14.32	15.75
40 L.H., Daily Totals		$1855.20		$2776.88	$46.38	$69.42

Crew F-4

Crew No.	Bare Costs Hr.	Daily	Incl. Subs O&P Hr.	Daily	Bare Costs	Incl. O&P
2 Carpenters	$34.95	$559.20	$58.45	$935.20	$32.06	$53.67
2 Carpenter Helpers	26.55	424.80	44.90	718.40		
1 Equip. Oper. (crane)	37.30	298.40	61.65	493.20		
1 Hyd. Crane, 55 Ton		1076.00		1183.60	26.90	29.59
40 L.H., Daily Totals		$2358.40		$3330.40	$58.96	$83.26

Crew F-5

Crew No.	Bare Costs Hr.	Daily	Incl. Subs O&P Hr.	Daily	Bare Costs	Incl. O&P
2 Carpenters	$34.95	$559.20	$58.45	$935.20	$30.75	$51.67
2 Carpenter Helpers	26.55	424.80	44.90	718.40		
32 L.H., Daily Totals		$984.00		$1653.60	$30.75	$51.67

For customer support on your Residential Costs with RSMeans Data, call 800.448.8182.

703

Crew F-6	Bare Costs Hr.	Bare Costs Daily	Incl. Subs O&P Hr.	Incl. Subs O&P Daily	Cost Per Labor-Hour Bare Costs	Cost Per Labor-Hour Incl. O&P
2 Carpenters	$34.95	$559.20	$58.45	$935.20	$32.08	$53.51
2 Building Laborers	26.60	425.60	44.50	712.00		
1 Equip. Oper. (crane)	37.30	298.40	61.65	493.20		
1 Hyd. Crane, 12 Ton		572.80		630.08	14.32	15.75
40 L.H., Daily Totals		$1856.00		$2770.48	$46.40	$69.26

Crew F-7	Bare Costs Hr.	Bare Costs Daily	Incl. Subs O&P Hr.	Incl. Subs O&P Daily	Cost Per Labor-Hour Bare Costs	Cost Per Labor-Hour Incl. O&P
2 Carpenters	$34.95	$559.20	$58.45	$935.20	$30.77	$51.48
2 Building Laborers	26.60	425.60	44.50	712.00		
32 L.H., Daily Totals		$984.80		$1647.20	$30.77	$51.48

Crew G-1	Bare Costs Hr.	Bare Costs Daily	Incl. Subs O&P Hr.	Incl. Subs O&P Daily	Cost Per Labor-Hour Bare Costs	Cost Per Labor-Hour Incl. O&P
1 Roofer Foreman (outside)	$31.75	$254.00	$58.40	$467.20	$27.95	$51.43
4 Roofers Composition	29.75	952.00	54.75	1752.00		
2 Roofer Helpers	22.45	359.20	41.30	660.80		
1 Application Equipment		183.60		201.96		
1 Tar Kettle/Pot		159.70		175.67		
1 Crew Truck		185.60		204.16	9.44	10.39
56 L.H., Daily Totals		$2094.10		$3461.79	$37.39	$61.82

Crew G-2	Bare Costs Hr.	Bare Costs Daily	Incl. Subs O&P Hr.	Incl. Subs O&P Daily	Cost Per Labor-Hour Bare Costs	Cost Per Labor-Hour Incl. O&P
1 Plasterer	$33.95	$271.60	$55.70	$445.60	$29.82	$49.20
1 Plasterer Helper	28.90	231.20	47.40	379.20		
1 Building Laborer	26.60	212.80	44.50	356.00		
1 Grout Pump, 50 C.F./hr.		132.80		146.08	5.53	6.09
24 L.H., Daily Totals		$848.40		$1326.88	$35.35	$55.29

Crew G-2A	Bare Costs Hr.	Bare Costs Daily	Incl. Subs O&P Hr.	Incl. Subs O&P Daily	Cost Per Labor-Hour Bare Costs	Cost Per Labor-Hour Incl. O&P
1 Roofer Composition	$29.75	$238.00	$54.75	$438.00	$26.27	$46.85
1 Roofer Helper	22.45	179.60	41.30	330.40		
1 Building Laborer	26.60	212.80	44.50	356.00		
1 Foam Spray Rig, Trailer-Mtd.		542.60		596.86		
1 Pickup Truck, 3/4 Ton		129.40		142.34	28.00	30.80
24 L.H., Daily Totals		$1302.40		$1863.60	$54.27	$77.65

Crew G-3	Bare Costs Hr.	Bare Costs Daily	Incl. Subs O&P Hr.	Incl. Subs O&P Daily	Cost Per Labor-Hour Bare Costs	Cost Per Labor-Hour Incl. O&P
2 Sheet Metal Workers	$38.30	$612.80	$64.00	$1024.00	$32.45	$54.25
2 Building Laborers	26.60	425.60	44.50	712.00		
32 L.H., Daily Totals		$1038.40		$1736.00	$32.45	$54.25

Crew G-4	Bare Costs Hr.	Bare Costs Daily	Incl. Subs O&P Hr.	Incl. Subs O&P Daily	Cost Per Labor-Hour Bare Costs	Cost Per Labor-Hour Incl. O&P
1 Labor Foreman (outside)	$28.60	$228.80	$47.80	$382.40	$27.27	$45.60
2 Building Laborers	26.60	425.60	44.50	712.00		
1 Flatbed Truck, Gas, 1.5 Ton		217.40		239.14		
1 Air Compressor, 160 cfm		143.60		157.96	15.04	16.55
24 L.H., Daily Totals		$1015.40		$1491.50	$42.31	$62.15

Crew G-5	Bare Costs Hr.	Bare Costs Daily	Incl. Subs O&P Hr.	Incl. Subs O&P Daily	Cost Per Labor-Hour Bare Costs	Cost Per Labor-Hour Incl. O&P
1 Roofer Foreman (outside)	$31.75	$254.00	$58.40	$467.20	$27.23	$50.10
2 Roofers Composition	29.75	476.00	54.75	876.00		
2 Roofer Helpers	22.45	359.20	41.30	660.80		
1 Application Equipment		183.60		201.96	4.59	5.05
40 L.H., Daily Totals		$1272.80		$2205.96	$31.82	$55.15

Crew G-6A	Bare Costs Hr.	Bare Costs Daily	Incl. Subs O&P Hr.	Incl. Subs O&P Daily	Cost Per Labor-Hour Bare Costs	Cost Per Labor-Hour Incl. O&P
2 Roofers Composition	$29.75	$476.00	$54.75	$876.00	$29.75	$54.75
1 Small Compressor, Electric		15.25		16.77		
2 Pneumatic Nailers		46.60		51.26	3.87	4.25
16 L.H., Daily Totals		$537.85		$944.03	$33.62	$59.00

Crew G-7	Bare Costs Hr.	Bare Costs Daily	Incl. Subs O&P Hr.	Incl. Subs O&P Daily	Cost Per Labor-Hour Bare Costs	Cost Per Labor-Hour Incl. O&P
1 Carpenter	$34.95	$279.60	$58.45	$467.60	$34.95	$58.45
1 Small Compressor, Electric		15.25		16.77		
1 Pneumatic Nailer		23.30		25.63	4.82	5.30
8 L.H., Daily Totals		$318.15		$510.01	$39.77	$63.75

Crew H-1	Bare Costs Hr.	Bare Costs Daily	Incl. Subs O&P Hr.	Incl. Subs O&P Daily	Cost Per Labor-Hour Bare Costs	Cost Per Labor-Hour Incl. O&P
2 Glaziers	$33.95	$543.20	$56.40	$902.40	$36.25	$63.02
2 Struc. Steel Workers	38.55	616.80	69.65	1114.40		
32 L.H., Daily Totals		$1160.00		$2016.80	$36.25	$63.02

Crew H-2	Bare Costs Hr.	Bare Costs Daily	Incl. Subs O&P Hr.	Incl. Subs O&P Daily	Cost Per Labor-Hour Bare Costs	Cost Per Labor-Hour Incl. O&P
2 Glaziers	$33.95	$543.20	$56.40	$902.40	$31.50	$52.43
1 Building Laborer	26.60	212.80	44.50	356.00		
24 L.H., Daily Totals		$756.00		$1258.40	$31.50	$52.43

Crew H-3	Bare Costs Hr.	Bare Costs Daily	Incl. Subs O&P Hr.	Incl. Subs O&P Daily	Cost Per Labor-Hour Bare Costs	Cost Per Labor-Hour Incl. O&P
1 Glazier	$33.95	$271.60	$56.40	$451.20	$30.25	$50.65
1 Helper	26.55	212.40	44.90	359.20		
16 L.H., Daily Totals		$484.00		$810.40	$30.25	$50.65

Crew H-4	Bare Costs Hr.	Bare Costs Daily	Incl. Subs O&P Hr.	Incl. Subs O&P Daily	Cost Per Labor-Hour Bare Costs	Cost Per Labor-Hour Incl. O&P
1 Carpenter	$34.95	$279.60	$58.45	$467.60	$32.64	$54.51
1 Carpenter Helper	26.55	212.40	44.90	359.20		
.5 Electrician	40.20	160.80	65.85	263.40		
20 L.H., Daily Totals		$652.80		$1090.20	$32.64	$54.51

Crew J-1	Bare Costs Hr.	Bare Costs Daily	Incl. Subs O&P Hr.	Incl. Subs O&P Daily	Cost Per Labor-Hour Bare Costs	Cost Per Labor-Hour Incl. O&P
3 Plasterers	$33.95	$814.80	$55.70	$1336.80	$31.93	$52.38
2 Plasterer Helpers	28.90	462.40	47.40	758.40		
1 Mixing Machine, 6 C.F.		134.80		148.28	3.37	3.71
40 L.H., Daily Totals		$1412.00		$2243.48	$35.30	$56.09

Crew J-2	Bare Costs Hr.	Bare Costs Daily	Incl. Subs O&P Hr.	Incl. Subs O&P Daily	Cost Per Labor-Hour Bare Costs	Cost Per Labor-Hour Incl. O&P
3 Plasterers	$33.95	$814.80	$55.70	$1336.80	$32.36	$52.97
2 Plasterer Helpers	28.90	462.40	47.40	758.40		
1 Lather	34.50	276.00	55.90	447.20		
1 Mixing Machine, 6 C.F.		134.80		148.28	2.81	3.09
48 L.H., Daily Totals		$1688.00		$2690.68	$35.17	$56.06

Crew J-3	Bare Costs Hr.	Bare Costs Daily	Incl. Subs O&P Hr.	Incl. Subs O&P Daily	Cost Per Labor-Hour Bare Costs	Cost Per Labor-Hour Incl. O&P
1 Terrazzo Worker	$33.55	$268.40	$54.50	$436.00	$30.93	$50.23
1 Terrazzo Helper	28.30	226.40	45.95	367.60		
1 Floor Grinder, 22" Path		121.50		133.65		
1 Terrazzo Mixer		180.00		198.00	18.84	20.73
16 L.H., Daily Totals		$796.30		$1135.25	$49.77	$70.95

Crew J-4	Bare Costs Hr.	Bare Costs Daily	Incl. Subs O&P Hr.	Incl. Subs O&P Daily	Cost Per Labor-Hour Bare Costs	Cost Per Labor-Hour Incl. O&P
2 Cement Finishers	$34.65	$554.40	$56.40	$902.40	$31.97	$52.43
1 Laborer	26.60	212.80	44.50	356.00		
1 Floor Grinder, 22" Path		121.50		133.65		
1 Floor Edger, 7" Path		39.25		43.17		
1 Vacuum Pick-Up System		60.85		66.94	9.23	10.16
24 L.H., Daily Totals		$988.80		$1502.16	$41.20	$62.59

Crew No.	Bare Costs		Incl. Subs O&P		Cost Per Labor-Hour	
	Hr.	Daily	Hr.	Daily	Bare Costs	Incl. O&P
Crew J-4A						
2 Cement Finishers	$34.65	$554.40	$56.40	$902.40	$30.63	$50.45
2 Laborers	26.60	425.60	44.50	712.00		
1 Floor Grinder, 22" Path		121.50		133.65		
1 Floor Edger, 7" Path		39.25		43.17		
1 Vacuum Pick-Up System		60.85		66.94		
1 Floor Auto Scrubber		236.25		259.88	14.31	15.74
32 L.H., Daily Totals		$1437.85		$2118.03	$44.93	$66.19
Crew J-4B	Hr.	Daily	Hr.	Daily	Bare Costs	Incl. O&P
1 Laborer	$26.60	$212.80	$44.50	$356.00	$26.60	$44.50
1 Floor Auto Scrubber		236.25		259.88	29.53	32.48
8 L.H., Daily Totals		$449.05		$615.88	$56.13	$76.98
Crew J-6	Hr.	Daily	Hr.	Daily	Bare Costs	Incl. O&P
2 Painters	$29.20	$467.20	$48.20	$771.20	$30.05	$49.77
1 Building Laborer	26.60	212.80	44.50	356.00		
1 Equip. Oper. (light)	35.20	281.60	58.20	465.60		
1 Air Compressor, 250 cfm		181.20		199.32		
1 Sandblaster, Portable, 3 C.F.		21.40		23.54		
1 Set Sand Blasting Accessories		14.45		15.90	6.78	7.46
32 L.H., Daily Totals		$1178.65		$1831.56	$36.83	$57.24
Crew J-7	Hr.	Daily	Hr.	Daily	Bare Costs	Incl. O&P
2 Painters	$29.20	$467.20	$48.20	$771.20	$29.20	$48.20
1 Floor Belt Sander		21.30		23.43		
1 Floor Sanding Edger		13.85		15.23	2.20	2.42
16 L.H., Daily Totals		$502.35		$809.87	$31.40	$50.62
Crew K-1	Hr.	Daily	Hr.	Daily	Bare Costs	Incl. O&P
1 Carpenter	$34.95	$279.60	$58.45	$467.60	$33.38	$55.42
1 Truck Driver (light)	31.80	254.40	52.40	419.20		
1 Flatbed Truck, Gas, 3 Ton		270.20		297.22	16.89	18.58
16 L.H., Daily Totals		$804.20		$1184.02	$50.26	$74.00
Crew K-2	Hr.	Daily	Hr.	Daily	Bare Costs	Incl. O&P
1 Struc. Steel Foreman (outside)	$40.55	$324.40	$73.25	$586.00	$36.97	$65.10
1 Struc. Steel Worker	38.55	308.40	69.65	557.20		
1 Truck Driver (light)	31.80	254.40	52.40	419.20		
1 Flatbed Truck, Gas, 3 Ton		270.20		297.22	11.26	12.38
24 L.H., Daily Totals		$1157.40		$1859.62	$48.23	$77.48
Crew L-1	Hr.	Daily	Hr.	Daily	Bare Costs	Incl. O&P
.25 Electrician	$40.20	$80.40	$65.85	$131.70	$39.68	$65.33
1 Plumber	39.55	316.40	65.20	521.60		
10 L.H., Daily Totals		$396.80		$653.30	$39.68	$65.33
Crew L-2	Hr.	Daily	Hr.	Daily	Bare Costs	Incl. O&P
1 Carpenter	$34.95	$279.60	$58.45	$467.60	$30.75	$51.67
1 Carpenter Helper	26.55	212.40	44.90	359.20		
16 L.H., Daily Totals		$492.00		$826.80	$30.75	$51.67
Crew L-3	Hr.	Daily	Hr.	Daily	Bare Costs	Incl. O&P
1 Carpenter	$34.95	$279.60	$58.45	$467.60	$36.00	$59.93
.25 Electrician	40.20	80.40	65.85	131.70		
10 L.H., Daily Totals		$360.00		$599.30	$36.00	$59.93
Crew L-3A	Hr.	Daily	Hr.	Daily	Bare Costs	Incl. O&P
1 Carpenter Foreman (outside)	$36.95	$295.60	$61.80	$494.40	$37.40	$62.53
.5 Sheet Metal Worker	38.30	153.20	64.00	256.00		
12 L.H., Daily Totals		$448.80		$750.40	$37.40	$62.53

Crew No.	Bare Costs		Incl. Subs O&P		Cost Per Labor-Hour	
	Hr.	Daily	Hr.	Daily	Bare Costs	Incl. O&P
Crew L-4						
1 Skilled Worker	$35.75	$286.00	$60.00	$480.00	$31.15	$52.45
1 Helper	26.55	212.40	44.90	359.20		
16 L.H., Daily Totals		$498.40		$839.20	$31.15	$52.45
Crew L-5	Hr.	Daily	Hr.	Daily	Bare Costs	Incl. O&P
1 Struc. Steel Foreman (outside)	$40.55	$324.40	$73.25	$586.00	$38.66	$69.02
5 Struc. Steel Workers	38.55	1542.00	69.65	2786.00		
1 Equip. Oper. (crane)	37.30	298.40	61.65	493.20		
1 Hyd. Crane, 25 Ton		673.80		741.18	12.03	13.24
56 L.H., Daily Totals		$2838.60		$4606.38	$50.69	$82.26
Crew L-5A	Hr.	Daily	Hr.	Daily	Bare Costs	Incl. O&P
1 Struc. Steel Foreman (outside)	$40.55	$324.40	$73.25	$586.00	$38.74	$68.55
2 Structural Steel Workers	38.55	616.80	69.65	1114.40		
1 Equip. Oper. (crane)	37.30	298.40	61.65	493.20		
1 S.P. Crane, 4x4, 25 Ton		605.60		666.16	18.93	20.82
32 L.H., Daily Totals		$1845.20		$2859.76	$57.66	$89.37
Crew L-5B	Hr.	Daily	Hr.	Daily	Bare Costs	Incl. O&P
1 Struc. Steel Foreman (outside)	$40.55	$324.40	$73.25	$586.00	$38.24	$65.10
2 Structural Steel Workers	38.55	616.80	69.65	1114.40		
2 Electricians	40.20	643.20	65.85	1053.60		
2 Steamfitters/Pipefitters	41.10	657.60	67.75	1084.00		
1 Equip. Oper. (crane)	37.30	298.40	61.65	493.20		
1 Common Laborer	26.60	212.80	44.50	356.00		
1 Hyd. Crane, 80 Ton		1616.00		1777.60	22.44	24.69
72 L.H., Daily Totals		$4369.20		$6464.80	$60.68	$89.79
Crew L-6	Hr.	Daily	Hr.	Daily	Bare Costs	Incl. O&P
1 Plumber	$39.55	$316.40	$65.20	$521.60	$39.77	$65.42
.5 Electrician	40.20	160.80	65.85	263.40		
12 L.H., Daily Totals		$477.20		$785.00	$39.77	$65.42
Crew L-7	Hr.	Daily	Hr.	Daily	Bare Costs	Incl. O&P
1 Carpenter	$34.95	$279.60	$58.45	$467.60	$30.18	$50.68
2 Carpenter Helpers	26.55	424.80	44.90	718.40		
.25 Electrician	40.20	80.40	65.85	131.70		
26 L.H., Daily Totals		$784.80		$1317.70	$30.18	$50.68
Crew L-8	Hr.	Daily	Hr.	Daily	Bare Costs	Incl. O&P
1 Carpenter	$34.95	$279.60	$58.45	$467.60	$32.51	$54.38
1 Carpenter Helper	26.55	212.40	44.90	359.20		
.5 Plumber	39.55	158.20	65.20	260.80		
20 L.H., Daily Totals		$650.20		$1087.60	$32.51	$54.38
Crew L-9	Hr.	Daily	Hr.	Daily	Bare Costs	Incl. O&P
1 Skilled Worker Foreman	$37.75	$302.00	$63.40	$507.20	$32.60	$54.69
1 Skilled Worker	35.75	286.00	60.00	480.00		
2 Helpers	26.55	424.80	44.90	718.40		
.5 Electrician	40.20	160.80	65.85	263.40		
36 L.H., Daily Totals		$1173.60		$1969.00	$32.60	$54.69
Crew L-10	Hr.	Daily	Hr.	Daily	Bare Costs	Incl. O&P
1 Struc. Steel Foreman (outside)	$40.55	$324.40	$73.25	$586.00	$38.80	$68.18
1 Structural Steel Worker	38.55	308.40	69.65	557.20		
1 Equip. Oper. (crane)	37.30	298.40	61.65	493.20		
1 Hyd. Crane, 12 Ton		572.80		630.08	23.87	26.25
24 L.H., Daily Totals		$1504.00		$2266.48	$62.67	$94.44

Crews - Residential

Crew L-11

Crew L-11	Hr.	Daily	Hr.	Daily	Bare Costs	Incl. O&P
2 Wreckers	$27.00	$432.00	$47.00	$752.00	$31.63	$53.46
1 Equip. Oper. (crane)	37.30	298.40	61.65	493.20		
1 Equip. Oper. (light)	35.20	281.60	58.20	465.60		
1 Hyd. Excavator, 2.5 C.Y.		1536.00		1689.60		
1 Loader, Skid Steer, 78 H.P.		309.40		340.34	57.67	63.44
32 L.H., Daily Totals		$2857.40		$3740.74	$89.29	$116.90

Crew M-1

Crew M-1	Hr.	Daily	Hr.	Daily	Bare Costs	Incl. O&P
3 Elevator Constructors	$54.00	$1296.00	$88.20	$2116.80	$51.30	$83.79
1 Elevator Apprentice	43.20	345.60	70.55	564.40		
5 Hand Tools		50.00		55.00	1.56	1.72
32 L.H., Daily Totals		$1691.60		$2736.20	$52.86	$85.51

Crew M-3

Crew M-3	Hr.	Daily	Hr.	Daily	Bare Costs	Incl. O&P
1 Electrician Foreman (outside)	$42.20	$337.60	$69.10	$552.80	$41.20	$67.62
1 Common Laborer	26.60	212.80	44.50	356.00		
.25 Equipment Operator (med.)	36.40	72.80	60.15	120.30		
1 Elevator Constructor	54.00	432.00	88.20	705.60		
1 Elevator Apprentice	43.20	345.60	70.55	564.40		
.25 S.P. Crane, 4x4, 20 Ton		138.45		152.29	4.07	4.48
34 L.H., Daily Totals		$1539.25		$2451.40	$45.27	$72.10

Crew M-4

Crew M-4	Hr.	Daily	Hr.	Daily	Bare Costs	Incl. O&P
1 Electrician Foreman (outside)	$42.20	$337.60	$69.10	$552.80	$40.77	$66.94
1 Common Laborer	26.60	212.80	44.50	356.00		
.25 Equipment Operator, Crane	37.30	74.60	61.65	123.30		
.25 Equip. Oper. (oiler)	32.65	65.30	53.95	107.90		
1 Elevator Constructor	54.00	432.00	88.20	705.60		
1 Elevator Apprentice	43.20	345.60	70.55	564.40		
.25 S.P. Crane, 4x4, 40 Ton		194.05		213.46	5.39	5.93
36 L.H., Daily Totals		$1661.95		$2623.45	$46.17	$72.87

Crew Q-1

Crew Q-1	Hr.	Daily	Hr.	Daily	Bare Costs	Incl. O&P
1 Plumber	$39.55	$316.40	$65.20	$521.60	$35.60	$58.70
1 Plumber Apprentice	31.65	253.20	52.20	417.60		
16 L.H., Daily Totals		$569.60		$939.20	$35.60	$58.70

Crew Q-1A

Crew Q-1A	Hr.	Daily	Hr.	Daily	Bare Costs	Incl. O&P
.25 Plumber Foreman (outside)	$41.55	$83.10	$68.50	$137.00	$39.95	$65.86
1 Plumber	39.55	316.40	65.20	521.60		
10 L.H., Daily Totals		$399.50		$658.60	$39.95	$65.86

Crew Q-1C

Crew Q-1C	Hr.	Daily	Hr.	Daily	Bare Costs	Incl. O&P
1 Plumber	$39.55	$316.40	$65.20	$521.60	$35.87	$59.18
1 Plumber Apprentice	31.65	253.20	52.20	417.60		
1 Equip. Oper. (medium)	36.40	291.20	60.15	481.20		
1 Trencher, Chain Type, 8' D		2460.00		2706.00	102.50	112.75
24 L.H., Daily Totals		$3320.80		$4126.40	$138.37	$171.93

Crew Q-2

Crew Q-2	Hr.	Daily	Hr.	Daily	Bare Costs	Incl. O&P
1 Plumber	$39.55	$316.40	$65.20	$521.60	$34.28	$56.53
2 Plumber Apprentices	31.65	506.40	52.20	835.20		
24 L.H., Daily Totals		$822.80		$1356.80	$34.28	$56.53

Crew Q-3

Crew Q-3	Hr.	Daily	Hr.	Daily	Bare Costs	Incl. O&P
2 Plumbers	$39.55	$632.80	$65.20	$1043.20	$35.60	$58.70
2 Plumber Apprentices	31.65	506.40	52.20	835.20		
32 L.H., Daily Totals		$1139.20		$1878.40	$35.60	$58.70

Crew Q-4

Crew Q-4	Hr.	Daily	Hr.	Daily	Bare Costs	Incl. O&P
2 Plumbers	$39.55	$632.80	$65.20	$1043.20	$37.58	$61.95
1 Welder (plumber)	39.55	316.40	65.20	521.60		
1 Plumber Apprentice	31.65	253.20	52.20	417.60		
1 Welder, Electric, 300 amp		58.15		63.97	1.82	2.00
32 L.H., Daily Totals		$1260.55		$2046.37	$39.39	$63.95

Crew Q-5

Crew Q-5	Hr.	Daily	Hr.	Daily	Bare Costs	Incl. O&P
1 Steamfitter	$41.10	$328.80	$67.75	$542.00	$37.00	$61.00
1 Steamfitter Apprentice	32.90	263.20	54.25	434.00		
16 L.H., Daily Totals		$592.00		$976.00	$37.00	$61.00

Crew Q-6

Crew Q-6	Hr.	Daily	Hr.	Daily	Bare Costs	Incl. O&P
1 Steamfitter	$41.10	$328.80	$67.75	$542.00	$35.63	$58.75
2 Steamfitter Apprentices	32.90	526.40	54.25	868.00		
24 L.H., Daily Totals		$855.20		$1410.00	$35.63	$58.75

Crew Q-7

Crew Q-7	Hr.	Daily	Hr.	Daily	Bare Costs	Incl. O&P
2 Steamfitters	$41.10	$657.60	$67.75	$1084.00	$37.00	$61.00
2 Steamfitter Apprentices	32.90	526.40	54.25	868.00		
32 L.H., Daily Totals		$1184.00		$1952.00	$37.00	$61.00

Crew Q-8

Crew Q-8	Hr.	Daily	Hr.	Daily	Bare Costs	Incl. O&P
2 Steamfitters	$41.10	$657.60	$67.75	$1084.00	$39.05	$64.38
1 Welder (steamfitter)	41.10	328.80	67.75	542.00		
1 Steamfitter Apprentice	32.90	263.20	54.25	434.00		
1 Welder, Electric, 300 amp		58.15		63.97	1.82	2.00
32 L.H., Daily Totals		$1307.75		$2123.97	$40.87	$66.37

Crew Q-9

Crew Q-9	Hr.	Daily	Hr.	Daily	Bare Costs	Incl. O&P
1 Sheet Metal Worker	$38.30	$306.40	$64.00	$512.00	$34.48	$57.60
1 Sheet Metal Apprentice	30.65	245.20	51.20	409.60		
16 L.H., Daily Totals		$551.60		$921.60	$34.48	$57.60

Crew Q-10

Crew Q-10	Hr.	Daily	Hr.	Daily	Bare Costs	Incl. O&P
2 Sheet Metal Workers	$38.30	$612.80	$64.00	$1024.00	$35.75	$59.73
1 Sheet Metal Apprentice	30.65	245.20	51.20	409.60		
24 L.H., Daily Totals		$858.00		$1433.60	$35.75	$59.73

Crew Q-11

Crew Q-11	Hr.	Daily	Hr.	Daily	Bare Costs	Incl. O&P
2 Sheet Metal Workers	$38.30	$612.80	$64.00	$1024.00	$34.48	$57.60
2 Sheet Metal Apprentices	30.65	490.40	51.20	819.20		
32 L.H., Daily Totals		$1103.20		$1843.20	$34.48	$57.60

Crew Q-12

Crew Q-12	Hr.	Daily	Hr.	Daily	Bare Costs	Incl. O&P
1 Sprinkler Installer	$38.95	$311.60	$64.40	$515.20	$35.05	$57.95
1 Sprinkler Apprentice	31.15	249.20	51.50	412.00		
16 L.H., Daily Totals		$560.80		$927.20	$35.05	$57.95

Crew Q-13

Crew Q-13	Hr.	Daily	Hr.	Daily	Bare Costs	Incl. O&P
2 Sprinkler Installers	$38.95	$623.20	$64.40	$1030.40	$35.05	$57.95
2 Sprinkler Apprentices	31.15	498.40	51.50	824.00		
32 L.H., Daily Totals		$1121.60		$1854.40	$35.05	$57.95

Crew Q-14

Crew Q-14	Hr.	Daily	Hr.	Daily	Bare Costs	Incl. O&P
1 Asbestos Worker	$35.80	$286.40	$60.65	$485.20	$32.23	$54.60
1 Asbestos Apprentice	28.65	229.20	48.55	388.40		
16 L.H., Daily Totals		$515.60		$873.60	$32.23	$54.60

Crew Q-15	Bare Costs Hr.	Daily	Incl. Subs O&P Hr.	Daily	Cost Per Labor-Hour Bare Costs	Incl. O&P
1 Plumber	$39.55	$316.40	$65.20	$521.60	$35.60	$58.70
1 Plumber Apprentice	31.65	253.20	52.20	417.60		
1 Welder, Electric, 300 amp		58.15		63.97	3.63	4.00
16 L.H., Daily Totals		$627.75		$1003.17	$39.23	$62.70

Crew Q-16	Hr.	Daily	Hr.	Daily	Bare Costs	Incl. O&P
2 Plumbers	$39.55	$632.80	$65.20	$1043.20	$36.92	$60.87
1 Plumber Apprentice	31.65	253.20	52.20	417.60		
1 Welder, Electric, 300 amp		58.15		63.97	2.42	2.67
24 L.H., Daily Totals		$944.15		$1524.77	$39.34	$63.53

Crew Q-17	Hr.	Daily	Hr.	Daily	Bare Costs	Incl. O&P
1 Steamfitter	$41.10	$328.80	$67.75	$542.00	$37.00	$61.00
1 Steamfitter Apprentice	32.90	263.20	54.25	434.00		
1 Welder, Electric, 300 amp		58.15		63.97	3.63	4.00
16 L.H., Daily Totals		$650.15		$1039.96	$40.63	$65.00

Crew Q-17A	Hr.	Daily	Hr.	Daily	Bare Costs	Incl. O&P
1 Steamfitter	$41.10	$328.80	$67.75	$542.00	$37.10	$61.22
1 Steamfitter Apprentice	32.90	263.20	54.25	434.00		
1 Equip. Oper. (crane)	37.30	298.40	61.65	493.20		
1 Hyd. Crane, 12 Ton		572.80		630.08		
1 Welder, Electric, 300 amp		58.15		63.97	26.29	28.92
24 L.H., Daily Totals		$1521.35		$2163.24	$63.39	$90.14

Crew Q-18	Hr.	Daily	Hr.	Daily	Bare Costs	Incl. O&P
2 Steamfitters	$41.10	$657.60	$67.75	$1084.00	$38.37	$63.25
1 Steamfitter Apprentice	32.90	263.20	54.25	434.00		
1 Welder, Electric, 300 amp		58.15		63.97	2.42	2.67
24 L.H., Daily Totals		$978.95		$1581.96	$40.79	$65.92

Crew Q-19	Hr.	Daily	Hr.	Daily	Bare Costs	Incl. O&P
1 Steamfitter	$41.10	$328.80	$67.75	$542.00	$38.07	$62.62
1 Steamfitter Apprentice	32.90	263.20	54.25	434.00		
1 Electrician	40.20	321.60	65.85	526.80		
24 L.H., Daily Totals		$913.60		$1502.80	$38.07	$62.62

Crew Q-20	Hr.	Daily	Hr.	Daily	Bare Costs	Incl. O&P
1 Sheet Metal Worker	$38.30	$306.40	$64.00	$512.00	$35.62	$59.25
1 Sheet Metal Apprentice	30.65	245.20	51.20	409.60		
.5 Electrician	40.20	160.80	65.85	263.40		
20 L.H., Daily Totals		$712.40		$1185.00	$35.62	$59.25

Crew Q-21	Hr.	Daily	Hr.	Daily	Bare Costs	Incl. O&P
2 Steamfitters	$41.10	$657.60	$67.75	$1084.00	$38.83	$63.90
1 Steamfitter Apprentice	32.90	263.20	54.25	434.00		
1 Electrician	40.20	321.60	65.85	526.80		
32 L.H., Daily Totals		$1242.40		$2044.80	$38.83	$63.90

Crew Q-22	Hr.	Daily	Hr.	Daily	Bare Costs	Incl. O&P
1 Plumber	$39.55	$316.40	$65.20	$521.60	$35.60	$58.70
1 Plumber Apprentice	31.65	253.20	52.20	417.60		
1 Hyd. Crane, 12 Ton		572.80		630.08	35.80	39.38
16 L.H., Daily Totals		$1142.40		$1569.28	$71.40	$98.08

Crew Q-22A	Hr.	Daily	Hr.	Daily	Bare Costs	Incl. O&P
1 Plumber	$39.55	$316.40	$65.20	$521.60	$33.77	$55.89
1 Plumber Apprentice	31.65	253.20	52.20	417.60		
1 Laborer	26.60	212.80	44.50	356.00		
1 Equip. Oper. (crane)	37.30	298.40	61.65	493.20		
1 Hyd. Crane, 12 Ton		572.80		630.08	17.90	19.69
32 L.H., Daily Totals		$1653.60		$2418.48	$51.67	$75.58

Crew Q-23	Hr.	Daily	Hr.	Daily	Bare Costs	Incl. O&P
1 Plumber Foreman (outside)	$41.55	$332.40	$68.50	$548.00	$39.17	$64.62
1 Plumber	39.55	316.40	65.20	521.60		
1 Equip. Oper. (medium)	36.40	291.20	60.15	481.20		
1 Lattice Boom Crane, 20 Ton		1075.00		1182.50	44.79	49.27
24 L.H., Daily Totals		$2015.00		$2733.30	$83.96	$113.89

Crew R-1	Hr.	Daily	Hr.	Daily	Bare Costs	Incl. O&P
1 Electrician Foreman	$40.70	$325.60	$66.65	$533.20	$37.60	$61.58
3 Electricians	40.20	964.80	65.85	1580.40		
2 Electrician Apprentices	32.15	514.40	52.65	842.40		
48 L.H., Daily Totals		$1804.80		$2956.00	$37.60	$61.58

Crew R-1A	Hr.	Daily	Hr.	Daily	Bare Costs	Incl. O&P
1 Electrician	$40.20	$321.60	$65.85	$526.80	$36.17	$59.25
1 Electrician Apprentice	32.15	257.20	52.65	421.20		
16 L.H., Daily Totals		$578.80		$948.00	$36.17	$59.25

Crew R-1B	Hr.	Daily	Hr.	Daily	Bare Costs	Incl. O&P
1 Electrician	$40.20	$321.60	$65.85	$526.80	$34.83	$57.05
2 Electrician Apprentices	32.15	514.40	52.65	842.40		
24 L.H., Daily Totals		$836.00		$1369.20	$34.83	$57.05

Crew R-1C	Hr.	Daily	Hr.	Daily	Bare Costs	Incl. O&P
2 Electricians	$40.20	$643.20	$65.85	$1053.60	$36.17	$59.25
2 Electrician Apprentices	32.15	514.40	52.65	842.40		
1 Portable cable puller, 8000 lb.		130.10		143.11	4.07	4.47
32 L.H., Daily Totals		$1287.70		$2039.11	$40.24	$63.72

Crew R-2	Hr.	Daily	Hr.	Daily	Bare Costs	Incl. O&P
1 Electrician Foreman	$40.70	$325.60	$66.65	$533.20	$37.56	$61.59
3 Electricians	40.20	964.80	65.85	1580.40		
2 Electrician Apprentices	32.15	514.40	52.65	842.40		
1 Equip. Oper. (crane)	37.30	298.40	61.65	493.20		
1 S.P. Crane, 4x4, 5 Ton		276.00		303.60	4.93	5.42
56 L.H., Daily Totals		$2379.20		$3752.80	$42.49	$67.01

Crew R-3	Hr.	Daily	Hr.	Daily	Bare Costs	Incl. O&P
1 Electrician Foreman	$40.70	$325.60	$66.65	$533.20	$39.82	$65.33
1 Electrician	40.20	321.60	65.85	526.80		
.5 Equip. Oper. (crane)	37.30	149.20	61.65	246.60		
.5 S.P. Crane, 4x4, 5 Ton		138.00		151.80	6.90	7.59
20 L.H., Daily Totals		$934.40		$1458.40	$46.72	$72.92

Crew R-4	Hr.	Daily	Hr.	Daily	Bare Costs	Incl. O&P
1 Struc. Steel Foreman (outside)	$40.55	$324.40	$73.25	$586.00	$39.28	$69.61
3 Struc. Steel Workers	38.55	925.20	69.65	1671.60		
1 Electrician	40.20	321.60	65.85	526.80		
1 Welder, Gas Engine, 300 amp		129.80		142.78	3.25	3.57
40 L.H., Daily Totals		$1701.00		$2927.18	$42.52	$73.18

For customer support on your Residential Costs with RSMeans Data, call 800.448.8182.

707

Crew R-5	Hr.	Daily	Hr.	Daily	Bare Costs	Incl. O&P
1 Electrician Foreman	$40.70	$325.60	$66.65	$533.20	$35.28	$58.30
4 Electrician Linemen	40.20	1286.40	65.85	2107.20		
2 Electrician Operators	40.20	643.20	65.85	1053.60		
4 Electrician Groundmen	26.55	849.60	44.90	1436.80		
1 Crew Truck		185.60		204.16		
1 Flatbed Truck, 20,000 GVW		232.00		255.20		
1 Pickup Truck, 3/4 Ton		129.40		142.34		
.2 Hyd. Crane, 55 Ton		215.20		236.72		
.2 Hyd. Crane, 12 Ton		114.56		126.02		
.2 Earth Auger, Truck-Mtd.		80.68		88.75		
1 Tractor w/Winch		407.80		448.58	15.51	17.07
88 L.H., Daily Totals		$4470.04		$6632.56	$50.80	$75.37

Crew R-6	Hr.	Daily	Hr.	Daily	Bare Costs	Incl. O&P
1 Electrician Foreman	$40.70	$325.60	$66.65	$533.20	$35.28	$58.30
4 Electrician Linemen	40.20	1286.40	65.85	2107.20		
2 Electrician Operators	40.20	643.20	65.85	1053.60		
4 Electrician Groundmen	26.55	849.60	44.90	1436.80		
1 Crew Truck		185.60		204.16		
1 Flatbed Truck, 20,000 GVW		232.00		255.20		
1 Pickup Truck, 3/4 Ton		129.40		142.34		
.2 Hyd. Crane, 55 Ton		215.20		236.72		
.2 Hyd. Crane, 12 Ton		114.56		126.02		
.2 Earth Auger, Truck-Mtd.		80.68		88.75		
1 Tractor w/Winch		407.80		448.58		
3 Cable Trailers		622.95		685.25		
.5 Tensioning Rig		206.07		226.68		
.5 Cable Pulling Rig		1187.50		1306.25	38.43	42.27
88 L.H., Daily Totals		$6486.56		$8850.74	$73.71	$100.58

Crew R-7	Hr.	Daily	Hr.	Daily	Bare Costs	Incl. O&P
1 Electrician Foreman	$40.70	$325.60	$66.65	$533.20	$28.91	$48.52
5 Electrician Groundmen	26.55	1062.00	44.90	1796.00		
1 Crew Truck		185.60		204.16	3.87	4.25
48 L.H., Daily Totals		$1573.20		$2533.36	$32.77	$52.78

Crew R-8	Hr.	Daily	Hr.	Daily	Bare Costs	Incl. O&P
1 Electrician Foreman	$40.70	$325.60	$66.65	$533.20	$35.73	$59.00
3 Electrician Linemen	40.20	964.80	65.85	1580.40		
2 Electrician Groundmen	26.55	424.80	44.90	718.40		
1 Pickup Truck, 3/4 Ton		129.40		142.34		
1 Crew Truck		185.60		204.16	6.56	7.22
48 L.H., Daily Totals		$2030.20		$3178.50	$42.30	$66.22

Crew R-9	Hr.	Daily	Hr.	Daily	Bare Costs	Incl. O&P
1 Electrician Foreman	$40.70	$325.60	$66.65	$533.20	$33.44	$55.48
1 Electrician Lineman	40.20	321.60	65.85	526.80		
2 Electrician Operators	40.20	643.20	65.85	1053.60		
4 Electrician Groundmen	26.55	849.60	44.90	1436.80		
1 Pickup Truck, 3/4 Ton		129.40		142.34		
1 Crew Truck		185.60		204.16	4.92	5.41
64 L.H., Daily Totals		$2455.00		$3896.90	$38.36	$60.89

Crew R-10	Hr.	Daily	Hr.	Daily	Bare Costs	Incl. O&P
1 Electrician Foreman	$40.70	$325.60	$66.65	$533.20	$38.01	$62.49
4 Electrician Linemen	40.20	1286.40	65.85	2107.20		
1 Electrician Groundman	26.55	212.40	44.90	359.20		
1 Crew Truck		185.60		204.16		
3 Tram Cars		423.30		465.63	12.69	13.95
48 L.H., Daily Totals		$2433.30		$3669.39	$50.69	$76.45

Crew R-11	Hr.	Daily	Hr.	Daily	Bare Costs	Incl. O&P
1 Electrician Foreman	$40.70	$325.60	$66.65	$533.20	$37.91	$62.31
4 Electricians	40.20	1286.40	65.85	2107.20		
1 Equip. Oper. (crane)	37.30	298.40	61.65	493.20		
1 Common Laborer	26.60	212.80	44.50	356.00		
1 Crew Truck		185.60		204.16		
1 Hyd. Crane, 12 Ton		572.80		630.08	13.54	14.90
56 L.H., Daily Totals		$2881.60		$4323.84	$51.46	$77.21

Crew R-12	Hr.	Daily	Hr.	Daily	Bare Costs	Incl. O&P
1 Carpenter Foreman (inside)	$35.45	$283.60	$59.25	$474.00	$32.42	$54.62
4 Carpenters	34.95	1118.40	58.45	1870.40		
4 Common Laborers	26.60	851.20	44.50	1424.00		
1 Equip. Oper. (medium)	36.40	291.20	60.15	481.20		
1 Steel Worker	38.55	308.40	69.65	557.20		
1 Dozer, 200 H.P.		1384.00		1522.40		
1 Pickup Truck, 3/4 Ton		129.40		142.34	17.20	18.92
88 L.H., Daily Totals		$4366.20		$6471.54	$49.62	$73.54

Crew R-13	Hr.	Daily	Hr.	Daily	Bare Costs	Incl. O&P
1 Electrician Foreman	$40.70	$325.60	$66.65	$533.20	$38.72	$63.54
3 Electricians	40.20	964.80	65.85	1580.40		
.25 Equip. Oper. (crane)	37.30	74.60	61.65	123.30		
1 Equipment Oiler	32.65	261.20	53.95	431.60		
.25 Hydraulic Crane, 33 Ton		215.90		237.49	5.14	5.65
42 L.H., Daily Totals		$1842.10		$2905.99	$43.86	$69.19

Crew R-15	Hr.	Daily	Hr.	Daily	Bare Costs	Incl. O&P
1 Electrician Foreman	$40.70	$325.60	$66.65	$533.20	$39.45	$64.71
4 Electricians	40.20	1286.40	65.85	2107.20		
1 Equipment Oper. (light)	35.20	281.60	58.20	465.60		
1 Telescoping Boom Lift, to 40'		288.80		317.68	6.02	6.62
48 L.H., Daily Totals		$2182.40		$3423.68	$45.47	$71.33

Crew R-15A	Hr.	Daily	Hr.	Daily	Bare Costs	Incl. O&P
1 Electrician Foreman	$40.70	$325.60	$66.65	$533.20	$34.92	$57.59
2 Electricians	40.20	643.20	65.85	1053.60		
2 Common Laborers	26.60	425.60	44.50	712.00		
1 Equip. Oper. (light)	35.20	281.60	58.20	465.60		
1 Telescoping Boom Lift, to 40'		288.80		317.68	6.02	6.62
48 L.H., Daily Totals		$1964.80		$3082.08	$40.93	$64.21

Crew R-18	Hr.	Daily	Hr.	Daily	Bare Costs	Incl. O&P
.25 Electrician Foreman	$40.70	$81.40	$66.65	$133.30	$35.28	$57.79
1 Electrician	40.20	321.60	65.85	526.80		
2 Electrician Apprentices	32.15	514.40	52.65	842.40		
26 L.H., Daily Totals		$917.40		$1502.50	$35.28	$57.79

Crew R-19	Hr.	Daily	Hr.	Daily	Bare Costs	Incl. O&P
.5 Electrician Foreman	$40.70	$162.80	$66.65	$266.60	$40.30	$66.01
2 Electricians	40.20	643.20	65.85	1053.60		
20 L.H., Daily Totals		$806.00		$1320.20	$40.30	$66.01

Crew R-21	Hr.	Daily	Hr.	Daily	Bare Costs	Incl. O&P
1 Electrician Foreman	$40.70	$325.60	$66.65	$533.20	$40.23	$65.91
3 Electricians	40.20	964.80	65.85	1580.40		
.1 Equip. Oper. (medium)	36.40	29.12	60.15	48.12		
.1 S.P. Crane, 4x4, 25 Ton		60.56		66.62	1.85	2.03
32.8 L.H., Daily Totals		$1380.08		$2228.34	$42.08	$67.94

For customer support on your Residential Costs with RSMeans Data, call 800.448.8182.

Crews - Residential

Crew No.	Bare Costs		Incl. Subs O & P		Cost Per Labor-Hour	

Crew R-22	Hr.	Daily	Hr.	Daily	Bare Costs	Incl. O&P
.66 Electrician Foreman	$40.70	$214.90	$66.65	$351.91	$36.82	$60.30
2 Electricians	40.20	643.20	65.85	1053.60		
2 Electrician Apprentices	32.15	514.40	52.65	842.40		
37.28 L.H., Daily Totals		$1372.50		$2247.91	$36.82	$60.30

Crew R-30	Hr.	Daily	Hr.	Daily	Bare Costs	Incl. O&P
.25 Electrician Foreman (outside)	$42.20	$84.40	$69.10	$138.20	$31.98	$52.96
1 Electrician	40.20	321.60	65.85	526.80		
2 Laborers (Semi-Skilled)	26.60	425.60	44.50	712.00		
26 L.H., Daily Totals		$831.60		$1377.00	$31.98	$52.96

Location Factors - Residential

Costs shown in *Residential Costs with RSMeans Data* are based on national averages for materials and installation. To adjust these costs to a specific location, simply multiply the base cost by the factor for that city. The data is arranged alphabetically by state and postal zip code numbers. For a city not listed, use the factor for a nearby city with similar economic characteristics.

STATE	CITY	Residential
ALABAMA		
350-352	Birmingham	.84
354	Tuscaloosa	.85
355	Jasper	.84
356	Decatur	.84
357-358	Huntsville	.84
359	Gadsden	.82
360-361	Montgomery	.83
362	Anniston	.82
363	Dothan	.86
364	Evergreen	.81
365-366	Mobile	.84
367	Selma	.83
368	Phenix City	.84
369	Butler	.82
ALASKA		
995-996	Anchorage	1.22
997	Fairbanks	1.27
998	Juneau	1.24
999	Ketchikan	1.27
ARIZONA		
850,853	Phoenix	.85
851,852	Mesa/Tempe	.86
855	Globe	.86
856-857	Tucson	.84
859	Show Low	.87
860	Flagstaff	.87
863	Prescott	.87
864	Kingman	.85
865	Chambers	.88
ARKANSAS		
716	Pine Bluff	.77
717	Camden	.76
718	Texarkana	.79
719	Hot Springs	.75
720-722	Little Rock	.80
723	West Memphis	.79
724	Jonesboro	.78
725	Batesville	.75
726	Harrison	.77
727	Fayetteville	.75
728	Russellville	.76
729	Fort Smith	.80
CALIFORNIA		
900-902	Los Angeles	1.15
903-905	Inglewood	1.13
906-908	Long Beach	1.13
910-912	Pasadena	1.12
913-916	Van Nuys	1.15
917-918	Alhambra	1.16
919-921	San Diego	1.10
922	Palm Springs	1.12
923-924	San Bernardino	1.13
925	Riverside	1.14
926-927	Santa Ana	1.14
928	Anaheim	1.14
930	Oxnard	1.14
931	Santa Barbara	1.13
932-933	Bakersfield	1.12
934	San Luis Obispo	1.15
935	Mojave	1.13
936-938	Fresno	1.17
939	Salinas	1.21
940-941	San Francisco	1.31
942,956-958	Sacramento	1.18
943	Palo Alto	1.26
944	San Mateo	1.29
945	Vallejo	1.23
946	Oakland	1.28
947	Berkeley	1.31
948	Richmond	1.30
949	San Rafael	1.30
950	Santa Cruz	1.25
951	San Jose	1.30
952	Stockton	1.19
953	Modesto	1.18

STATE	CITY	Residential
CALIFORNIA (CONT'D)		
954	Santa Rosa	1.27
955	Eureka	1.23
959	Marysville	1.20
960	Redding	1.24
961	Susanville	1.23
COLORADO		
800-802	Denver	.87
803	Boulder	.91
804	Golden	.86
805	Fort Collins	.89
806	Greeley	.89
807	Fort Morgan	.86
808-809	Colorado Springs	.84
810	Pueblo	.83
811	Alamosa	.82
812	Salida	.82
813	Durango	.85
814	Montrose	.81
815	Grand Junction	.93
816	Glenwood Springs	.82
CONNECTICUT		
060	New Britain	1.11
061	Hartford	1.09
062	Willimantic	1.11
063	New London	1.10
064	Meriden	1.11
065	New Haven	1.11
066	Bridgeport	1.12
067	Waterbury	1.11
068	Norwalk	1.12
069	Stamford	1.12
D.C.		
200-205	Washington	.90
DELAWARE		
197	Newark	1.02
198	Wilmington	1.01
199	Dover	1.02
FLORIDA		
320,322	Jacksonville	.82
321	Daytona Beach	.84
323	Tallahassee	.82
324	Panama City	.77
325	Pensacola	.85
326,344	Gainesville	.81
327-328,347	Orlando	.83
329	Melbourne	.84
330-332,340	Miami	.81
333	Fort Lauderdale	.81
334,349	West Palm Beach	.82
335-336,346	Tampa	.83
337	St. Petersburg	.82
338	Lakeland	.80
339,341	Fort Myers	.80
342	Sarasota	.83
GEORGIA		
300-303,399	Atlanta	.89
304	Statesboro	.79
305	Gainesville	.82
306	Athens	.81
307	Dalton	.80
308-309	Augusta	.88
310-312	Macon	.80
313-314	Savannah	.87
315	Waycross	.82
316	Valdosta	.76
317,398	Albany	.84
318-319	Columbus	.86
HAWAII		
967	Hilo	1.18
968	Honolulu	1.21

Location Factors - Residential

STATE	CITY	Residential
STATES & POSS.		
969	Guam	.96
IDAHO		
832	Pocatello	.89
833	Twin Falls	.83
834	Idaho Falls	.87
835	Lewiston	.98
836-837	Boise	.90
838	Coeur d'Alene	.98
ILLINOIS		
600-603	North Suburban	1.24
604	Joliet	1.25
605	South Suburban	1.24
606-608	Chicago	1.24
609	Kankakee	1.17
610-611	Rockford	1.13
612	Rock Island	.98
613	La Salle	1.14
614	Galesburg	1.04
615-616	Peoria	1.08
617	Bloomington	1.04
618-619	Champaign	1.04
620-622	East St. Louis	1.02
623	Quincy	1.03
624	Effingham	1.04
625	Decatur	1.04
626-627	Springfield	1.05
628	Centralia	1.02
629	Carbondale	1.01
INDIANA		
460	Anderson	.91
461-462	Indianapolis	.92
463-464	Gary	1.06
465-466	South Bend	.90
467-468	Fort Wayne	.88
469	Kokomo	.91
470	Lawrenceburg	.87
471	New Albany	.87
472	Columbus	.92
473	Muncie	.91
474	Bloomington	.93
475	Washington	.91
476-477	Evansville	.91
478	Terre Haute	.91
479	Lafayette	.91
IOWA		
500-503,509	Des Moines	.92
504	Mason City	.86
505	Fort Dodge	.85
506-507	Waterloo	.84
508	Creston	.89
510-511	Sioux City	.89
512	Sibley	.75
513	Spencer	.77
514	Carroll	.88
515	Council Bluffs	.87
516	Shenandoah	.82
520	Dubuque	.88
521	Decorah	.88
522-524	Cedar Rapids	.94
525	Ottumwa	.88
526	Burlington	.91
527-528	Davenport	.97
KANSAS		
660-662	Kansas City	.99
664-666	Topeka	.86
667	Fort Scott	.91
668	Emporia	.85
669	Belleville	.83
670-672	Wichita	.84
673	Independence	.91
674	Salina	.82
675	Hutchinson	.81
676	Hays	.83
677	Colby	.86
678	Dodge City	.84
679	Liberal	.80
KENTUCKY		
400-402	Louisville	.87
403-405	Lexington	.87

STATE	CITY	Residential
KENTUCKY (CONT'D)		
406	Frankfort	.85
407-409	Corbin	.82
410	Covington	.86
411-412	Ashland	.90
413-414	Campton	.84
415-416	Pikeville	.87
417-418	Hazard	.84
420	Paducah	.88
421-422	Bowling Green	.87
423	Owensboro	.88
424	Henderson	.88
425-426	Somerset	.83
427	Elizabethtown	.84
LOUISIANA		
700-701	New Orleans	.86
703	Thibodaux	.83
704	Hammond	.79
705	Lafayette	.86
706	Lake Charles	.87
707-708	Baton Rouge	.86
710-711	Shreveport	.78
712	Monroe	.80
713-714	Alexandria	.82
MAINE		
039	Kittery	.86
040-041	Portland	.91
042	Lewiston	.91
043	Augusta	.86
044	Bangor	.90
045	Bath	.87
046	Machias	.88
047	Houlton	.88
048	Rockland	.88
049	Waterville	.85
MARYLAND		
206	Waldorf	.89
207-208	College Park	.88
209	Silver Spring	.89
210-212	Baltimore	.92
214	Annapolis	.91
215	Cumberland	.91
216	Easton	.86
217	Hagerstown	.91
218	Salisbury	.84
219	Elkton	.92
MASSACHUSETTS		
010-011	Springfield	1.06
012	Pittsfield	1.05
013	Greenfield	1.04
014	Fitchburg	1.11
015-016	Worcester	1.12
017	Framingham	1.13
018	Lowell	1.14
019	Lawrence	1.15
020-022, 024	Boston	1.19
023	Brockton	1.12
025	Buzzards Bay	1.10
026	Hyannis	1.09
027	New Bedford	1.12
MICHIGAN		
480,483	Royal Oak	.99
481	Ann Arbor	1.00
482	Detroit	1.03
484-485	Flint	.93
486	Saginaw	.90
487	Bay City	.91
488-489	Lansing	.92
490	Battle Creek	.88
491	Kalamazoo	.88
492	Jackson	.90
493,495	Grand Rapids	.89
494	Muskegon	.86
496	Traverse City	.83
497	Gaylord	.86
498-499	Iron Mountain	.87
MINNESOTA		
550-551	Saint Paul	1.05
553-555	Minneapolis	1.06
556-558	Duluth	.99

STATE	CITY	Residential
MINNESOTA (CONT'D)		
559	Rochester	.98
560	Mankato	.96
561	Windom	.89
562	Willmar	.91
563	St. Cloud	.98
564	Brainerd	.93
565	Detroit Lakes	.91
566	Bemidji	.92
567	Thief River Falls	.90
MISSISSIPPI		
386	Clarksdale	.74
387	Greenville	.82
388	Tupelo	.75
389	Greenwood	.78
390-392	Jackson	.84
393	Meridian	.81
394	Laurel	.79
395	Biloxi	.84
396	McComb	.75
397	Columbus	.76
MISSOURI		
630-631	St. Louis	1.04
633	Bowling Green	.98
634	Hannibal	.95
635	Kirksville	.90
636	Flat River	.98
637	Cape Girardeau	.91
638	Sikeston	.90
639	Poplar Bluff	.90
640-641	Kansas City	1.04
644-645	St. Joseph	.98
646	Chillicothe	.97
647	Harrisonville	1.00
648	Joplin	.91
650-651	Jefferson City	.91
652	Columbia	.91
653	Sedalia	.91
654-655	Rolla	.96
656-658	Springfield	.89
MONTANA		
590-591	Billings	.88
592	Wolf Point	.85
593	Miles City	.86
594	Great Falls	.88
595	Havre	.82
596	Helena	.85
597	Butte	.85
598	Missoula	.84
599	Kalispell	.84
NEBRASKA		
680-681	Omaha	.89
683-685	Lincoln	.89
686	Columbus	.89
687	Norfolk	.89
688	Grand Island	.88
689	Hastings	.90
690	McCook	.83
691	North Platte	.86
692	Valentine	.83
693	Alliance	.82
NEVADA		
889-891	Las Vegas	1.01
893	Ely	1.01
894-895	Reno	.90
897	Carson City	.90
898	Elko	.92
NEW HAMPSHIRE		
030	Nashua	.98
031	Manchester	.96
032-033	Concord	.96
034	Keene	.91
035	Littleton	.93
036	Charleston	.89
037	Claremont	.89
038	Portsmouth	.95

STATE	CITY	Residential
NEW JERSEY		
070-071	Newark	1.20
072	Elizabeth	1.22
073	Jersey City	1.19
074-075	Paterson	1.20
076	Hackensack	1.19
077	Long Branch	1.19
078	Dover	1.19
079	Summit	1.20
080,083	Vineland	1.18
081	Camden	1.20
082,084	Atlantic City	1.22
085-086	Trenton	1.20
087	Point Pleasant	1.19
088-089	New Brunswick	1.22
NEW MEXICO		
870-872	Albuquerque	.83
873	Gallup	.83
874	Farmington	.83
875	Santa Fe	.84
877	Las Vegas	.83
878	Socorro	.83
879	Truth/Consequences	.82
880	Las Cruces	.82
881	Clovis	.83
882	Roswell	.84
883	Carrizozo	.83
884	Tucumcari	.84
NEW YORK		
100-102	New York	1.41
103	Staten Island	1.34
104	Bronx	1.38
105	Mount Vernon	1.19
106	White Plains	1.22
107	Yonkers	1.26
108	New Rochelle	1.23
109	Suffern	1.21
110	Queens	1.38
111	Long Island City	1.41
112	Brooklyn	1.40
113	Flushing	1.40
114	Jamaica	1.39
115,117,118	Hicksville	1.28
116	Far Rockaway	1.39
119	Riverhead	1.29
120-122	Albany	1.02
123	Schenectady	1.04
124	Kingston	1.15
125-126	Poughkeepsie	1.27
127	Monticello	1.15
128	Glens Falls	.97
129	Plattsburgh	1.02
130-132	Syracuse	1.01
133-135	Utica	.99
136	Watertown	.97
137-139	Binghamton	1.00
140-142	Buffalo	1.10
143	Niagara Falls	1.06
144-146	Rochester	1.02
147	Jamestown	.95
148-149	Elmira	.98
NORTH CAROLINA		
270,272-274	Greensboro	.96
271	Winston-Salem	.96
275-276	Raleigh	.94
277	Durham	.96
278	Rocky Mount	.93
279	Elizabeth City	.92
280	Gastonia	.98
281-282	Charlotte	.96
283	Fayetteville	.96
284	Wilmington	.95
285	Kinston	.94
286	Hickory	.95
287-288	Asheville	.96
289	Murphy	.97
NORTH DAKOTA		
580-581	Fargo	.88
582	Grand Forks	.88
583	Devils Lake	.91
584	Jamestown	.89
585	Bismarck	.89

Location Factors - Residential

STATE	CITY	Residential
NORTH DAKOTA (CONT'D)		
586	Dickinson	.88
587	Minot	.87
588	Williston	.88
OHIO		
430-432	Columbus	.91
433	Marion	.90
434-436	Toledo	.96
437-438	Zanesville	.88
439	Steubenville	.92
440	Lorain	.94
441	Cleveland	.98
442-443	Akron	.97
444-445	Youngstown	.94
446-447	Canton	.92
448-449	Mansfield	.90
450	Hamilton	.89
451-452	Cincinnati	.89
453-454	Dayton	.89
455	Springfield	.91
456	Chillicothe	.93
457	Athens	.92
458	Lima	.89
OKLAHOMA		
730-731	Oklahoma City	.82
734	Ardmore	.82
735	Lawton	.84
736	Clinton	.82
737	Enid	.83
738	Woodward	.78
739	Guymon	.83
740-741	Tulsa	.82
743	Miami	.81
744	Muskogee	.81
745	McAlester	.74
746	Ponca City	.80
747	Durant	.79
748	Shawnee	.80
749	Poteau	.79
OREGON		
970-972	Portland	.99
973	Salem	.98
974	Eugene	.99
975	Medford	.97
976	Klamath Falls	.98
977	Bend	1.00
978	Pendleton	.98
979	Vale	.96
PENNSYLVANIA		
150-152	Pittsburgh	1.02
153	Washington	.97
154	Uniontown	.94
155	Bedford	.92
156	Greensburg	.97
157	Indiana	.95
158	Dubois	.92
159	Johnstown	.92
160	Butler	.93
161	New Castle	.95
162	Kittanning	.94
163	Oil City	.94
164-165	Erie	.96
166	Altoona	.91
167	Bradford	.97
168	State College	.93
169	Wellsboro	.93
170-171	Harrisburg	.96
172	Chambersburg	.91
173-174	York	.92
175-176	Lancaster	.95
177	Williamsport	.92
178	Sunbury	.93
179	Pottsville	.94
180	Lehigh Valley	1.07
181	Allentown	1.05
182	Hazleton	.93
183	Stroudsburg	.98
184-185	Scranton	.98
186-187	Wilkes-Barre	.95
188	Montrose	.94
189	Doylestown	1.08

STATE	CITY	Residential
PENNSYLVANIA (CONT'D)		
190-191	Philadelphia	1.17
193	Westchester	1.10
194	Norristown	1.10
195-196	Reading	.98
PUERTO RICO		
009	San Juan	.76
RHODE ISLAND		
028	Newport	1.08
029	Providence	1.08
SOUTH CAROLINA		
290-292	Columbia	.95
293	Spartanburg	.95
294	Charleston	.96
295	Florence	.91
296	Greenville	.94
297	Rock Hill	.94
298	Aiken	.95
299	Beaufort	.84
SOUTH DAKOTA		
570-571	Sioux Falls	.82
572	Watertown	.73
573	Mitchell	.74
574	Aberdeen	.75
575	Pierre	.79
576	Mobridge	.74
577	Rapid City	.82
TENNESSEE		
370-372	Nashville	.86
373-374	Chattanooga	.83
375,380-381	Memphis	.84
376	Johnson City	.77
377-379	Knoxville	.81
382	McKenzie	.72
383	Jackson	.76
384	Columbia	.79
385	Cookeville	.70
TEXAS		
750	McKinney	.81
751	Waxahackie	.81
752-753	Dallas	.84
754	Greenville	.81
755	Texarkana	.83
756	Longview	.80
757	Tyler	.82
758	Palestine	.78
759	Lufkin	.80
760-761	Fort Worth	.82
762	Denton	.84
763	Wichita Falls	.84
764	Eastland	.83
765	Temple	.80
766-767	Waco	.85
768	Brownwood	.80
769	San Angelo	.79
770-772	Houston	.82
773	Huntsville	.80
774	Wharton	.80
775	Galveston	.81
776-777	Beaumont	.85
778	Bryan	.78
779	Victoria	.81
780	Laredo	.81
781-782	San Antonio	.81
783-784	Corpus Christi	.84
785	McAllen	.84
786-787	Austin	.79
788	Del Rio	.81
789	Giddings	.80
790-791	Amarillo	.80
792	Childress	.81
793-794	Lubbock	.81
795-796	Abilene	.83
797	Midland	.85
798-799,885	El Paso	.79
UTAH		
840-841	Salt Lake City	.82
842,844	Ogden	.80
843	Logan	.80

STATE	CITY	Residential
UTAH (CONT'D)		
845	Price	.78
846-847	Provo	.81
VERMONT		
050	White River Jct.	.95
051	Bellows Falls	1.01
052	Bennington	1.00
053	Brattleboro	1.01
054	Burlington	.93
056	Montpelier	.98
057	Rutland	.93
058	St. Johnsbury	.96
059	Guildhall	.96
VIRGINIA		
220-221	Fairfax	1.01
222	Arlington	1.03
223	Alexandria	1.04
224-225	Fredericksburg	1.01
226	Winchester	1.02
227	Culpeper	1.00
228	Harrisonburg	.85
229	Charlottesville	.88
230-232	Richmond	.96
233-235	Norfolk	.94
236	Newport News	.95
237	Portsmouth	.88
238	Petersburg	.95
239	Farmville	.85
240-241	Roanoke	.94
242	Bristol	.81
243	Pulaski	.81
244	Staunton	.84
245	Lynchburg	.91
246	Grundy	.79
WASHINGTON		
980-981,987	Seattle	1.04
982	Everett	1.05
983-984	Tacoma	1.02
985	Olympia	1.00
986	Vancouver	.97
988	Wenatchee	.94
989	Yakima	.99
990-992	Spokane	.97
993	Richland	.97
994	Clarkston	.94
WEST VIRGINIA		
247-248	Bluefield	.92
249	Lewisburg	.91
250-253	Charleston	.95
254	Martinsburg	.90
255-257	Huntington	.96
258-259	Beckley	.92
260	Wheeling	.93
261	Parkersburg	.91
262	Buckhannon	.93
263-264	Clarksburg	.93
265	Morgantown	.93
266	Gassaway	.94
267	Romney	.90
268	Petersburg	.91
WISCONSIN		
530,532	Milwaukee	1.06
531	Kenosha	1.06
534	Racine	1.04
535	Beloit	.99
537	Madison	1.00
538	Lancaster	.98
539	Portage	.95
540	New Richmond	.96
541-543	Green Bay	1.04
544	Wausau	.98
545	Rhinelander	.94
546	La Crosse	.98
547	Eau Claire	1.01
548	Superior	.96
549	Oshkosh	.94
WYOMING		
820	Cheyenne	.85
821	Yellowstone Nat. Pk.	.83
822	Wheatland	.80

STATE	CITY	Residential
WYOMING (CONT'D)		
823	Rawlins	.87
824	Worland	.84
825	Riverton	.83
826	Casper	.81
827	Newcastle	.86
828	Sheridan	.86
829-831	Rock Springs	.89
CANADIAN FACTORS (reflect Canadian currency)		
ALBERTA		
	Calgary	1.09
	Edmonton	1.09
	Fort McMurray	1.11
	Lethbridge	1.09
	Lloydminster	1.04
	Medicine Hat	1.04
	Red Deer	1.04
BRITISH COLUMBIA		
	Kamloops	1.01
	Prince George	1.01
	Vancouver	1.04
	Victoria	1.03
MANITOBA		
	Brandon	1.09
	Portage la Prairie	.98
	Winnipeg	.96
NEW BRUNSWICK		
	Bathurst	.90
	Dalhousie	.91
	Fredericton	.95
	Moncton	.92
	Newcastle	.91
	St. John	1.00
NEWFOUNDLAND		
	Corner Brook	1.01
	St. Johns	1.06
NORTHWEST TERRITORIES		
	Yellowknife	1.13
NOVA SCOTIA		
	Bridgewater	.95
	Dartmouth	1.04
	Halifax	1.00
	New Glasgow	1.03
	Sydney	1.02
	Truro	.94
	Yarmouth	1.03
ONTARIO		
	Barrie	1.12
	Brantford	1.11
	Cornwall	1.10
	Hamilton	1.06
	Kingston	1.10
	Kitchener	1.05
	London	1.07
	North Bay	1.18
	Oshawa	1.08
	Ottawa	1.08
	Owen Sound	1.11
	Peterborough	1.08
	Sarnia	1.11
	Sault Ste. Marie	1.05
	St. Catharines	1.06
	Sudbury	1.04
	Thunder Bay	1.08
	Timmins	1.08
	Toronto	1.10
	Windsor	1.07
PRINCE EDWARD ISLAND		
	Charlottetown	.90
	Summerside	.97
QUEBEC		
	Cap-de-la-Madeleine	1.08
	Charlesbourg	1.08
	Chicoutimi	1.11
	Gatineau	1.08
	Granby	1.08

Location Factors - Residential

STATE	CITY	Residential
QUEBEC (CONT'D)		
	Hull	1.08
	Joliette	1.08
	Laval	1.08
	Montreal	1.05
	Quebec City	1.07
	Rimouski	1.11
	Rouyn-Noranda	1.08
	Saint-Hyacinthe	1.08
	Sherbrooke	1.08
	Sorel	1.08
	Saint-Jerome	1.08
	Trois-Rivieres	1.20
SASKATCHEWAN		
	Moose Jaw	.91
	Prince Albert	.89
	Regina	1.05
	Saskatoon	1.03
YUKON		
	Whitehorse	1.04

R011105-05 Tips for Accurate Estimating

1. Use pre-printed or columnar forms for orderly sequence of dimensions and locations and for recording telephone quotations.

2. Use only the front side of each paper or form except for certain pre-printed summary forms.

3. Be consistent in listing dimensions: For example, length x width x height. This helps in rechecking to ensure that, the total length of partitions is appropriate for the building area.

4. Use printed (rather than measured) dimensions where given.

5. Add up multiple printed dimensions for a single entry where possible.

6. Measure all other dimensions carefully.

7. Use each set of dimensions to calculate multiple related quantities.

8. Convert foot and inch measurements to decimal feet when listing. Memorize decimal equivalents to .01 parts of a foot (1/8″ equals approximately .01′).

9. Do not "round off" quantities until the final summary.

10. Mark drawings with different colors as items are taken off.

11. Keep similar items together, different items separate.

12. Identify location and drawing numbers to aid in future checking for completeness.

13. Measure or list everything on the drawings or mentioned in the specifications.

14. It may be necessary to list items not called for to make the job complete.

15. Be alert for: Notes on plans such as N.T.S. (not to scale); changes in scale throughout the drawings; reduced size drawings; discrepancies between the specifications and the drawings.

16. Develop a consistent pattern of performing an estimate. For example:
    a. Start the quantity takeoff at the lower floor and move to the next higher floor.
    b. Proceed from the main section of the building to the wings.
    c. Proceed from south to north or vice versa, clockwise or counterclockwise.
    d. Take off floor plan quantities first, elevations next, then detail drawings.

17. List all gross dimensions that can be either used again for different quantities, or used as a rough check of other quantities for verification (exterior perimeter, gross floor area, individual floor areas, etc.).

18. Utilize design symmetry or repetition (repetitive floors, repetitive wings, symmetrical design around a center line, similar room layouts, etc.). Note: Extreme caution is needed here so as not to omit or duplicate an area.

19. Do not convert units until the final total is obtained. For instance, when estimating concrete work, keep all units to the nearest cubic foot, then summarize and convert to cubic yards.

20. When figuring alternatives, it is best to total all items involved in the basic system, then total all items involved in the alternates. Therefore you work with positive numbers in all cases. When adds and deducts are used, it is often confusing whether to add or subtract a portion of an item; especially on a complicated or involved alternate.

R011105-50   Metric Conversion Factors

Description: This table is primarily for converting customary U.S. units in the left hand column to SI metric units in the right hand column. In addition, conversion factors for some commonly encountered Canadian and non-SI metric units are included.

	If You Know		Multiply By		To Find
Length	Inches	x	25.4[a]	=	Millimeters
	Feet	x	0.3048[a]	=	Meters
	Yards	x	0.9144[a]	=	Meters
	Miles (statute)	x	1.609	=	Kilometers
Area	Square inches	x	645.2	=	Square millimeters
	Square feet	x	0.0929	=	Square meters
	Square yards	x	0.8361	=	Square meters
Volume (Capacity)	Cubic inches	x	16,387	=	Cubic millimeters
	Cubic feet	x	0.02832	=	Cubic meters
	Cubic yards	x	0.7646	=	Cubic meters
	Gallons (U.S. liquids)[b]	x	0.003785	=	Cubic meters[c]
	Gallons (Canadian liquid)[b]	x	0.004546	=	Cubic meters[c]
	Ounces (U.S. liquid)[b]	x	29.57	=	Milliliters[c, d]
	Quarts (U.S. liquid)[b]	x	0.9464	=	Liters[c, d]
	Gallons (U.S. liquid)[b]	x	3.785	=	Liters[c, d]
Force	Kilograms force[d]	x	9.807	=	Newtons
	Pounds force	x	4.448	=	Newtons
	Pounds force	x	0.4536	=	Kilograms force[d]
	Kips	x	4448	=	Newtons
	Kips	x	453.6	=	Kilograms force[d]
Pressure, Stress, Strength (Force per unit area)	Kilograms force per square centimeter[d]	x	0.09807	=	Megapascals
	Pounds force per square inch (psi)	x	0.006895	=	Megapascals
	Kips per square inch	x	6.895	=	Megapascals
	Pounds force per square inch (psi)	x	0.07031	=	Kilograms force per square centimeter[d]
	Pounds force per square foot	x	47.88	=	Pascals
	Pounds force per square foot	x	4.882	=	Kilograms force per square meter[d]
Flow	Cubic feet per minute	x	0.4719	=	Liters per second
	Gallons per minute	x	0.0631	=	Liters per second
	Gallons per hour	x	1.05	=	Milliliters per second
Bending Moment Or Torque	Inch-pounds force	x	0.01152	=	Meter-kilograms force[d]
	Inch-pounds force	x	0.1130	=	Newton-meters
	Foot-pounds force	x	0.1383	=	Meter-kilograms force[d]
	Foot-pounds force	x	1.356	=	Newton-meters
	Meter-kilograms force[d]	x	9.807	=	Newton-meters
Mass	Ounces (avoirdupois)	x	28.35	=	Grams
	Pounds (avoirdupois)	x	0.4536	=	Kilograms
	Tons (metric)	x	1000	=	Kilograms
	Tons, short (2000 pounds)	x	907.2	=	Kilograms
	Tons, short (2000 pounds)	x	0.9072	=	Megagrams[e]
Mass per Unit Volume	Pounds mass per cubic foot	x	16.02	=	Kilograms per cubic meter
	Pounds mass per cubic yard	x	0.5933	=	Kilograms per cubic meter
	Pounds mass per gallon (U.S. liquid)[b]	x	119.8	=	Kilograms per cubic meter
	Pounds mass per gallon (Canadian liquid)[b]	x	99.78	=	Kilograms per cubic meter
Temperature	Degrees Fahrenheit	(F-32)/1.8		=	Degrees Celsius
	Degrees Fahrenheit	(F+459.67)/1.8		=	Degrees Kelvin
	Degrees Celsius	C+273.15		=	Degrees Kelvin

[a]The factor given is exact
[b]One U.S. gallon = 0.8327 Canadian gallon
[c]1 liter = 1000 milliliters = 1000 cubic centimeters
 1 cubic decimeter = 0.001 cubic meter

[d]Metric but not SI unit
[e]Called "tonne" in England and "metric ton" in other metric countries

717

R011105-60 Weights and Measures

Measures of Length
1 Mile = 1760 Yards = 5280 Feet
1 Yard = 3 Feet = 36 inches
1 Foot = 12 Inches
1 Mil = 0.001 Inch
1 Fathom = 2 Yards = 6 Feet
1 Rod = 5.5 Yards = 16.5 Feet
1 Hand = 4 Inches
1 Span = 9 Inches
1 Micro-inch = One Millionth Inch or 0.000001 Inch
1 Micron = One Millionth Meter + 0.00003937 Inch

Surveyor's Measure
1 Mile = 8 Furlongs = 80 Chains
1 Furlong = 10 Chains = 220 Yards
1 Chain = 4 Rods = 22 Yards = 66 Feet = 100 Links
1 Link = 7.92 Inches

Square Measure
1 Square Mile = 640 Acres = 6400 Square Chains
1 Acre = 10 Square Chains = 4840 Square Yards =
  43,560 Sq. Ft.
1 Square Chain = 16 Square Rods = 484 Square Yards =
  4356 Sq. Ft.
1 Square Rod = 30.25 Square Yards = 272.25 Square Feet = 625 Square
  Lines
1 Square Yard = 9 Square Feet
1 Square Foot = 144 Square Inches
An Acre equals a Square 208.7 Feet per Side

Cubic Measure
1 Cubic Yard = 27 Cubic Feet
1 Cubic Foot = 1728 Cubic Inches
1 Cord of Wood = 4 x 4 x 8 Feet = 128 Cubic Feet
1 Perch of Masonry = 16½ x 1½ x 1 Foot = 24.75 Cubic Feet

Avoirdupois or Commercial Weight
1 Gross or Long Ton = 2240 Pounds
1 Net or Short Ton = 2000 Pounds
1 Pound = 16 Ounces = 7000 Grains
1 Ounce = 16 Drachms = 437.5 Grains
1 Stone = 14 Pounds

Power
1 British Thermal Unit per Hour = 0.2931 Watts
1 Ton (Refrigeration) = 3.517 Kilowatts
1 Horsepower (Boiler) = 9.81 Kilowatts
1 Horsepower (550 ft-lb/s) = 0.746 Kilowatts

Shipping Measure
For Measuring Internal Capacity of a Vessel:
  1 Register Ton = 100 Cubic Feet

For Measurement of Cargo:
  Approximately 40 Cubic Feet of Merchandise is considered a Shipping
  Ton, unless that bulk would weigh more than 2000 Pounds, in which case
  Freight Charge may be based upon weight.

40 Cubic Feet = 32.143 U.S. Bushels = 31.16 Imp. Bushels

Liquid Measure
1 Imperial Gallon = 1.2009 U.S. Gallon = 277.42 Cu. In.
1 Cubic Foot = 7.48 U.S. Gallons

R011110-10 Architectural Fees

Tabulated below are typical percentage fees by project size, for good professional architectural service. Fees may vary from those listed depending upon degree of design difficulty and economic conditions in any particular area.

Rates can be interpolated horizontally and vertically. Various portions of the same project requiring different rates should be adjusted proportionately. For alterations, add 50% to the fee for the first $500,000 of project cost and add 25% to the fee for project cost over $500,000.

Architectural fees tabulated below include Structural, Mechanical and Electrical Engineering Fees. They do not include the fees for special consultants such as kitchen planning, security, acoustical, interior design, etc.

Civil Engineering fees are included in the Architectural fee for project sites requiring minimal design such as city sites. However, separate Civil Engineering fees must be added when utility connections require design, drainage calculations are needed, stepped foundations are required, or provisions are required to protect adjacent wetlands.

Building Types	Total Project Size in Thousands of Dollars						
	100	250	500	1,000	5,000	10,000	50,000
Factories, garages, warehouses, repetitive housing	9.0%	8.0%	7.0%	6.2%	5.3%	4.9%	4.5%
Apartments, banks, schools, libraries, offices, municipal buildings	12.2	12.3	9.2	8.0	7.0	6.6	6.2
Churches, hospitals, homes, laboratories, museums, research	15.0	13.6	12.7	11.9	9.5	8.8	8.0
Memorials, monumental work, decorative furnishings	—	16.0	14.5	13.1	10.0	9.0	8.3

R012909-80   Sales Tax by State

State sales tax on materials is tabulated below (5 states have no sales tax). Many states allow local jurisdictions, such as a county or city, to levy additional sales tax.

Some projects may be sales tax exempt, particularly those constructed with public funds.

State	Tax (%)	State	Tax (%)	State	Tax (%)	State	Tax (%)
Alabama	4	Illinois	6.25	Montana	0	Rhode Island	7
Alaska	0	Indiana	7	Nebraska	5.5	South Carolina	6
Arizona	5.6	Iowa	6	Nevada	6.85	South Dakota	4
Arkansas	6.5	Kansas	6.5	New Hampshire	0	Tennessee	7
California	7.5	Kentucky	6	New Jersey	7	Texas	6.25
Colorado	2.9	Louisiana	4	New Mexico	5.125	Utah	5.95
Connecticut	6.35	Maine	5.5	New York	4	Vermont	6
Delaware	0	Maryland	6	North Carolina	4.75	Virginia	5.3
District of Columbia	5.75	Massachusetts	6.25	North Dakota	5	Washington	6.5
Florida	6	Michigan	6	Ohio	5.75	West Virginia	6
Georgia	4	Minnesota	6.875	Oklahoma	4.5	Wisconsin	5
Hawaii	4	Mississippi	7	Oregon	0	Wyoming	4
Idaho	6	Missouri	4.225	Pennsylvania	6	Average	5.09%

Sales Tax by Province (Canada)

GST - a value-added tax, which the government imposes on most goods and services provided in or imported into Canada. PST - a retail sales tax, which five of the provinces impose on the prices of most goods and some services. QST - a value-added tax, similar to the federal GST, which Quebec imposes. HST - Three provinces have combined their retail sales taxes with the federal GST into one harmonized tax.

Province	PST (%)	QST (%)	GST(%)	HST(%)
Alberta	0	0	5	0
British Columbia	7	0	5	0
Manitoba	8	0	5	0
New Brunswick	0	0	0	13
Newfoundland	0	0	0	13
Northwest Territories	0	0	5	0
Nova Scotia	0	0	0	15
Ontario	0	0	0	13
Prince Edward Island	0	0	0	14
Quebec	0	9.975	5	0
Saskatchewan	5	0	5	0
Yukon	0	0	5	0

R012909-85   Unemployment Taxes and Social Security Taxes

State unemployment tax rates vary not only from state to state, but also with the experience rating of the contractor. The federal unemployment tax rate is 6.0% of the first $7,000 of wages. This is reduced by a credit of up to 5.4% for timely payment to the state. The minimum federal unemployment tax is 0.6% after all credits.

Social security (FICA) for 2017 is estimated at time of publication to be 7.65% of wages up to $118,500.

719

R012909-86   Unemployment Tax by State

Information is from the U.S. Department of Labor, state unemployment tax rates.

State	Tax (%)	State	Tax (%)	State	Tax (%)	State	Tax (%)
Alabama	7.1	Illinois	8.15	Montana	6.12	Rhode Island	9.79
Alaska	5.4	Indiana	7.5	Nebraska	5.4	South Carolina	6.03
Arizona	7.79	Iowa	7.5	Nevada	5.4	South Dakota	9.5
Arkansas	6.8	Kansas	7.4	New Hampshire	6	Tennessee	10
California	6.2	Kentucky	10	New Jersey	7	Texas	7.49
Colorado	8.2	Louisiana	6.2	New Mexico	6.4	Utah	7.3
Connecticut	6.8	Maine	6.86	New York	8.9	Vermont	8.4
Delaware	8.2	Maryland	9	North Carolina	5.76	Virginia	6.54
District of Columbia	7.2	Massachusetts	11.13	North Dakota	9.7	Washington	5.84
Florida	5.4	Michigan	10.3	Ohio	8.6	West Virginia	7.5
Georgia	5.4	Minnesota	9.1	Oklahoma	5.5	Wisconsin	12
Hawaii	5.8	Mississippi	5.6	Oregon	5.4	Wyoming	10
Idaho	5.4	Missouri	9.75	Pennsylvania	10.89	Median	7.3 %

R013113-40   Builder's Risk Insurance

Builder's risk insurance is insurance on a building during construction. Premiums are paid by the owner or the contractor. Blasting, collapse and underground insurance would raise total insurance costs.

R013113-50   General Contractor's Overhead

There are two distinct types of overhead on a construction project: Project overhead and main office overhead. Project overhead includes those costs at a construction site not directly associated with the installation of construction materials. Examples of project overhead costs include the following:

1. Superintendent
2. Construction office and storage trailers
3. Temporary sanitary facilities
4. Temporary utilities
5. Security fencing
6. Photographs
7. Cleanup
8. Performance and payment bonds

The above project overhead items are also referred to as general requirements and therefore are estimated in Division 1. Division 1 is the first division listed in the CSI MasterFormat but it is usually the last division estimated. The sum of the costs in Divisions 1 through 49 is referred to as the sum of the direct costs.

All construction projects also include indirect costs. The primary components of indirect costs are the contractor's main office overhead and profit. The amount of the main office overhead expense varies depending on the following:

1. Owner's compensation
2. Project managers' and estimators' wages
3. Clerical support wages
4. Office rent and utilities
5. Corporate legal and accounting costs
6. Advertising
7. Automobile expenses
8. Association dues
9. Travel and entertainment expenses

These costs are usually calculated as a percentage of annual sales volume. This percentage can range from 35% for a small contractor doing less than $500,000 to 5% for a large contractor with sales in excess of $100 million.

R013113-55   Installing Contractor's Overhead

Installing contractors (subcontractors) also incur costs for general requirements and main office overhead.

Included within the total incl. overhead and profit costs is a percent mark-up for overhead that includes:

1. Compensation and benefits for office staff and project managers
2. Office rent, utilities, business equipment, and maintenance
3. Corporate legal and accounting costs

4. Advertising
5. Vehicle expenses (for office staff and project managers)
6. Association dues
7. Travel, entertainment
8. Insurance
9. Small tools and equipment

R013113-60   Workers' Compensation Insurance Rates by Trade

The table below tabulates the national averages for workers' compensation insurance rates by trade and type of building. The average "Insurance Rate" is multiplied by the "% of Building Cost" for each trade. This produces the "Workers' Compensation" cost by % of total labor cost, to be added for each trade by building type to determine the weighted average workers' compensation rate for the building types analyzed.

Trade	Insurance Rate (% Labor Cost)			% of Building Cost			Workers' Compensation		
	Range		Average	Office Bldgs.	Schools & Apts.	Mfg.	Office Bldgs.	Schools & Apts.	Mfg.
Excavation, Grading, etc.	3.3 % to	20.7%	9.0%	4.8%	4.9%	4.5%	0.43%	0.44%	0.41%
Piles & Foundations	6.3 to	34.3	14.5	7.1	5.2	8.7	1.03	0.75	1.26
Concrete	4.5 to	32.5	12.4	5.0	14.8	3.7	0.62	1.84	0.46
Masonry	4.4 to	43.4	14.5	6.9	7.5	1.9	1.00	1.09	0.28
Structural Steel	6.3 to	71.0	24.4	10.7	3.9	17.6	2.61	0.95	4.29
Miscellaneous & Ornamental Metals	4.4 to	28.9	11.3	2.8	4.0	3.6	0.32	0.45	0.41
Carpentry & Millwork	4.7 to	39.7	13.9	3.7	4.0	0.5	0.51	0.56	0.07
Metal or Composition Siding	6.3 to	92.8	19.1	2.3	0.3	4.3	0.44	0.06	0.82
Roofing	6.3 to	108.8	30.7	2.3	2.6	3.1	0.71	0.80	0.95
Doors & Hardware	3.9 to	39.7	11.6	0.9	1.4	0.4	0.10	0.16	0.05
Sash & Glazing	4.5 to	29.4	12.9	3.5	4.0	1.0	0.45	0.52	0.13
Lath & Plaster	3.2 to	42.3	10.7	3.3	6.9	0.8	0.35	0.74	0.09
Tile, Marble & Floors	2.9 to	22.4	9.1	2.6	3.0	0.5	0.24	0.27	0.05
Acoustical Ceilings	2.6 to	43.8	8.7	2.4	0.2	0.3	0.21	0.02	0.03
Painting	4.6 to	35.9	11.7	1.5	1.6	1.6	0.18	0.19	0.19
Interior Partitions	4.7 to	39.7	13.9	3.9	4.3	4.4	0.54	0.60	0.61
Miscellaneous Items	2.1 to	97.7	11.9	5.2	3.7	9.7	0.62	0.44	1.16
Elevators	1.4 to	14.4	5.0	2.1	1.1	2.2	0.11	0.06	0.11
Sprinklers	2.3 to	23.4	7.1	0.5	—	2.0	0.04	—	0.14
Plumbing	1.8 to	17.8	6.6	4.9	7.2	5.2	0.32	0.48	0.34
Heat., Vent., Air Conditioning	3.3 to	19.2	8.8	13.5	11.0	12.9	1.19	0.97	1.14
Electrical	2.2 to	14.4	5.5	10.1	8.4	11.1	0.56	0.46	0.61
Total	1.4 % to	108.8%	—	100.0%	100.0%	100.0%	12.58%	11.85%	13.60%
					Overall Weighted Average	12.68%			

Workers' Compensation Insurance Rates by States

The table below lists the weighted average Workers' Compensation base rate for each state with a factor comparing this with the national average of 12.6%.

State	Weighted Average	Factor	State	Weighted Average	Factor	State	Weighted Average	Factor
Alabama	17.8%	141	Kentucky	10.5%	83	North Dakota	7.2%	57
Alaska	10.6	84	Louisiana	19.2	152	Ohio	7.7	61
Arizona	11.2	89	Maine	11.3	90	Oklahoma	11.1	88
Arkansas	7.0	56	Maryland	12.3	98	Oregon	10.0	79
California	29.4	233	Massachusetts	11.4	90	Pennsylvania	19.5	155
Colorado	7.8	62	Michigan	9.2	73	Rhode Island	13.8	110
Connecticut	20.9	166	Minnesota	19.7	156	South Carolina	15.6	124
Delaware	14.1	112	Mississippi	11.9	94	South Dakota	12.5	99
District of Columbia	10.2	81	Missouri	13.5	107	Tennessee	10.2	81
Florida	9.6	76	Montana	8.2	65	Texas	7.3	58
Georgia	31.3	248	Nebraska	14.1	112	Utah	8.3	66
Hawaii	8.6	68	Nevada	8.4	67	Vermont	12.0	95
Idaho	9.7	77	New Hampshire	13.8	110	Virginia	7.9	63
Illinois	23.7	188	New Jersey	15.3	121	Washington	9.8	78
Indiana	4.8	38	New Mexico	14.7	117	West Virginia	5.7	45
Iowa	15.2	121	New York	18.4	146	Wisconsin	14.1	112
Kansas	7.2	57	North Carolina	16.5	131	Wyoming	6.4	51
			Weighted Average for U.S. is	12.7% of payroll = 100%				

The weighted average skilled worker rate for 35 trades is 12.6%. For bidding purposes, apply the full value of Workers' Compensation directly to total labor costs, or if labor is 38%, materials 42% and overhead and profit 20% of total cost, carry 38/80 x 12.6% = 6.0% of cost (before overhead and profit)

into overhead. Rates vary not only from state to state but also with the experience rating of the contractor.

Rates are the most current available at the time of publication.

721

R015423-10   Steel Tubular Scaffolding

On new construction, tubular scaffolding is efficient up to 60' high or five stories. Above this it is usually better to use a hung scaffolding if construction permits. Swing scaffolding operations may interfere with tenants. In this case, the tubular is more practical at all heights.

In repairing or cleaning the front of an existing building the cost of tubular scaffolding per S.F. of building front increases as the height increases above the first tier. The first tier cost is relatively high due to leveling and alignment.

The minimum efficient crew for erecting and dismantling is three workers. They can set up and remove 18 frame sections per day up to 5 stories high. For 6 to 12 stories high, a crew of four is most efficient. Use two or more on top and two on the bottom for handing up or hoisting. They can

also set up and remove 18 frame sections per day. At 7' horizontal spacing, this will run about 800 S.F. per day of erecting and dismantling. Time for placing and removing planks must be added to the above. A crew of three can place and remove 72 planks per day up to 5 stories. For over 5 stories, a crew of four can place and remove 80 planks per day.

The table below shows the number of pieces required to erect tubular steel scaffolding for 1000 S.F. of building frontage. This area is made up of a scaffolding system that is 12 frames (11 bays) long by 2 frames high.

For jobs under twenty-five frames, add 50% to rental cost. Rental rates will be lower for jobs over three months duration. Large quantities for long periods can reduce rental rates by 20%.

Description of Component	Number of Pieces for 1000 S.F. of Building Front	Unit
5' Wide Standard Frame, 6'-4" High	24	Ea.
Leveling Jack & Plate	24	
Cross Brace	44	
Side Arm Bracket, 21"	12	
Guardrail Post	12	
Guardrail, 7' section	22	
Stairway Section	2	
Stairway Starter Bar	1	
Stairway Inside Handrail	2	
Stairway Outside Handrail	2	
Walk-Thru Frame Guardrail	2	

Scaffolding is often used as falsework over 15' high during construction of cast-in-place concrete beams and slabs. Two foot wide scaffolding is generally used for heavy beam construction. The span between frames depends upon the load to be carried with a maximum span of 5'.

Heavy duty shoring frames with a capacity of 10,000#/leg can be spaced up to 10' O.C. depending upon form support design and loading.

Scaffolding used as horizontal shoring requires less than half the material required with conventional shoring.

On new construction, erection is done by carpenters.

Rolling towers supporting horizontal shores can reduce labor and speed the job. For maintenance work, catwalks with spans up to 70' can be supported by the rolling towers.

R015423-20   Pump Staging

Pump staging is generally not available for rent. The table below shows the number of pieces required to erect pump staging for 2400 S.F. of building frontage. This area is made up of a pump jack system that is 3 poles (2 bays) wide by 2 poles high.

Item	Number of Pieces for 2400 S.F. of Building Front	Unit
Aluminum pole section, 24' long	6	Ea.
Aluminum splice joint, 6' long	3	
Aluminum foldable brace	3	
Aluminum pump jack	3	
Aluminum support for workbench/back safety rail	3	
Aluminum scaffold plank/workbench, 14" wide x 24' long	4	
Safety net, 22' long	2	
Aluminum plank end safety rail	2	

The cost in place for this 2400 S.F. will depend on how many uses are realized during the life of the equipment.

R015436-50   Mobilization

Costs to move rented construction equipment to a job site from an equipment dealer's or contractor's yard (mobilization) or off the job site (demobilization) are not included in the rental or operating rates, nor in the equipment cost on a unit price line or in a crew listing. These costs can be found consolidated in the Mobilization section of the data and elsewhere in particular site work sections. If a piece of

equipment is already on the job site, it is not appropriate to include mob/demob costs in a new estimate that requires use of that equipment. The following table identifies approximate sizes of rented construction equipment that would be hauled on a towed trailer. Because this listing is not all-encompassing, the user can infer as to what size trailer might be required for a piece of equipment not listed.

3-ton Trailer	20-ton Trailer	40-ton Trailer	50-ton Trailer
20 H.P. Excavator	110 H.P. Excavator	200 H.P. Excavator	270 H.P. Excavator
50 H.P. Skid Steer	165 H.P. Dozer	300 H.P. Dozer	Small Crawler Crane
35 H.P. Roller	150 H.P. Roller	400 H.P. Scraper	500 H.P. Scraper
40 H.P. Trencher	Backhoe	450 H.P. Art. Dump Truck	500 H.P. Art. Dump Truck

R024119-10   Demolition Defined

Whole Building Demolition - Demolition of the whole building with no concern for any particular building element, component, or material type being demolished. This type of demolition is accomplished with large pieces of construction equipment that break up the structure, load it into trucks and haul it to a disposal site, but disposal or dump fees are not included. Demolition of below-grade foundation elements, such as footings, foundation walls, grade beams, slabs on grade, etc., is not included. Certain mechanical equipment containing flammable liquids or ozone-depleting refrigerants, electric lighting elements, communication equipment components, and other building elements may contain hazardous waste, and must be removed, either selectively or carefully, as hazardous waste before the building can be demolished.

Foundation Demolition - Demolition of below-grade foundation footings, foundation walls, grade beams, and slabs on grade. This type of demolition is accomplished by hand or pneumatic hand tools, and does not include saw cutting, or handling, loading, hauling, or disposal of the debris.

Gutting - Removal of building interior finishes and electrical/mechanical systems down to the load-bearing and sub-floor elements of the rough building frame, with no concern for any particular building element, component, or material type being demolished. This type of demolition is accomplished by hand or pneumatic hand tools, and includes loading into trucks, but not hauling, disposal or dump fees, scaffolding, or shoring. Certain mechanical equipment containing flammable liquids or ozone-depleting refrigerants, electric lighting elements, communication equipment components, and other building elements may contain hazardous waste, and must be removed, either selectively or carefully, as hazardous waste, before the building is gutted.

Selective Demolition - Demolition of a selected building element, component, or finish, with some concern for surrounding or adjacent elements, components, or finishes (see the first Subdivision (s) at the beginning of appropriate Divisions). This type of demolition is accomplished by hand or pneumatic hand tools, and does not include handling, loading,

storing, hauling, or disposal of the debris, scaffolding, or shoring. "Gutting" methods may be used in order to save time, but damage that is caused to surrounding or adjacent elements, components, or finishes may have to be repaired at a later time.

Careful Removal - Removal of a piece of service equipment, building element or component, or material type, with great concern for both the removed item and surrounding or adjacent elements, components or finishes. The purpose of careful removal may be to protect the removed item for later re-use, preserve a higher salvage value of the removed item, or replace an item while taking care to protect surrounding or adjacent elements, components, connections, or finishes from cosmetic and/or structural damage. An approximation of the time required to perform this type of removal is 1/3 to 1/2 the time it would take to install a new item of like kind. This type of removal is accomplished by hand or pneumatic hand tools, and does not include loading, hauling, or storing the removed item, scaffolding, shoring, or lifting equipment.

Cutout Demolition - Demolition of a small quantity of floor, wall, roof, or other assembly, with concern for the appearance and structural integrity of the surrounding materials. This type of demolition is accomplished by hand or pneumatic hand tools, and does not include saw cutting, handling, loading, hauling, or disposal of debris, scaffolding, or shoring.

Rubbish Handling - Work activities that involve handling, loading or hauling of debris. Generally, the cost of rubbish handling must be added to the cost of all types of demolition, with the exception of whole building demolition.

Minor Site Demolition - Demolition of site elements outside the footprint of a building. This type of demolition is accomplished by hand or pneumatic hand tools, or with larger pieces of construction equipment, and may include loading a removed item onto a truck (check the Crew for equipment used). It does not include saw cutting, hauling or disposal of debris, and, sometimes, handling or loading.

R024119-20   Dumpsters

Dumpster rental costs on construction sites are presented in two ways.

The cost per week rental includes the delivery of the dumpster; its pulling or emptying once per week, and its final removal. The assumption is made that the dumpster contractor could choose to empty a dumpster by simply bringing in an empty unit and removing the full one. These costs also include the disposal of the materials in the dumpster.

The Alternate Pricing can be used when actual planned conditions are not approximated by the weekly numbers. For example, these lines can be used when a dumpster is needed for 4 weeks and will need to be emptied 2 or 3 times per week. Conversely the Alternate Pricing lines can be used when a dumpster will be rented for several weeks or months but needs to be emptied only a few times over this period.

R040130-10   Cleaning Face Brick

On smooth brick a person can clean 70 S.F. an hour; on rough brick 50 S.F. per hour. Use one gallon muriatic acid to 20 gallons of water for 1000

S.F. Do not use acid solution until wall is at least seven days old, but a mild soap solution may be used after two days.

Time has been allowed for clean-up in brick prices.

R040513-10   Cement Mortar (material only)

Type N - 1:1:6 mix by volume. Use everywhere above grade except as noted below. - 1:3 mix using conventional masonry cement which saves handling two separate bagged materials.

Type M - 1:1/4:3 mix by volume, or 1 part cement, 1/4 (10% by wt.) lime, 3 parts sand. Use for heavy loads and where earthquakes or hurricanes may occur. Also for reinforced brick, sewers, manholes and everywhere below grade.

Mix Proportions by Volume and Compressive Strength of Mortar

Where Used	Mortar Type	Allowable Proportions by Volume				Compressive Strength @ 28 days
		Portland Cement	Masonry Cement	Hydrated Lime	Masonry Sand	
Plain Masonry	M	1	1	—	6	
		1	—	1/4	3	2500 psi
	S	1/2	1	—	4	
		1	—	1/4 to 1/2	4	1800 psi
	N	—	1	—	3	
		1	—	1/2 to 1-1/4	6	750 psi
	O	—	1	—	3	
		1	—	1-1/4 to 2-1/2	9	350 psi
	K	1	—	2-1/2 to 4	12	75 psi
Reinforced Masonry	PM	1	1	—	6	2500 psi
	PL	1	—	1/4 to 1/2	4	2500 psi

Note: The total aggregate should be between 2.25 to 3 times the sum of the cement and lime used.

The labor cost to mix the mortar is included in the productivity and labor cost of unit price lines in unit cost sections for brickwork, blockwork and stonework.

The material cost of mixed mortar is included in the material cost of those same unit price lines and includes the cost of renting and operating a 10 C.F. mixer at the rate of 200 C.F. per day.

There are two types of mortar color used. One type is the inert additive type with about 100 lbs. per M brick as the typical quantity required. These colors are also available in smaller-batch-sized bags (1 lb. to 15 lb.) which can be placed directly into the mixer without measuring. The other type is premixed and replaces the masonry cement. Dark green color has the highest cost.

R040519-50   Masonry Reinforcing

Horizontal joint reinforcing helps prevent wall cracks where wall movement may occur and in many locations is required by code. Horizontal joint reinforcing is generally not considered to be structural reinforcing and an unreinforced wall may still contain joint reinforcing.

Reinforcing strips come in 10' and 12' lengths and in truss and ladder shapes, with and without drips. Field labor runs between 2.7 to 5.3 hours per 1000 L.F. for wall thicknesses up to 12".

The wire meets ASTM A82 for cold drawn steel wire and the typical size is 9 ga. sides and ties with 3/16" diameter also available. Typical finish is mill galvanized with zinc coating at .10 oz. per S.F. Class I (.40 oz. per S.F.) and Class III (.80 oz. per S.F.) are also available, as is hot dipped galvanizing at 1.50 oz. per S.F.

R042110-10   Economy in Bricklaying

Have adequate supervision. Be sure bricklayers are always supplied with materials so there is no waiting. Place experienced bricklayers at corners and openings.

Use only screened sand for mortar. Otherwise, labor time will be wasted picking out pebbles. Use seamless metal tubs for mortar as they do not leak or catch the trowel. Locate stack and mortar for easy wheeling.

Have brick delivered for stacking. This makes for faster handling, reduces chipping and breakage, and requires less storage space. Many dealers will deliver select common in 2' x 3' x 4' pallets or face brick packaged. This affords quick handling with a crane or forklift and easy tonging in units of ten, which reduces waste.

Use wider bricks for one wythe wall construction. Keep scaffolding away from the wall to allow mortar to fall clear and not stain the wall.

On large jobs develop specialized crews for each type of masonry unit.

Consider designing for prefabricated panel construction on high rise projects.

Avoid excessive corners or openings. Each opening adds about 50% to the labor cost for area of opening.

Bolting stone panels and using window frames as stops reduce labor costs and speed up erection.

R042110-20   Common and Face Brick

Common building brick manufactured according to ASTM C62 and facing brick manufactured according to ASTM C216 are the two standard bricks available for general building use.

Building brick is made in three grades: SW, where high resistance to damage caused by cyclic freezing is required; MW, where moderate resistance to cyclic freezing is needed; and NW, where little resistance to cyclic freezing is needed. Facing brick is made in only the two grades SW and MW. Additionally, facing brick is available in three types: FBS, for general use; FBX, for general use where a higher degree of precision and lower permissible variation in size than FBS are needed; and FBA, for general use to produce characteristic architectural effects resulting from non-uniformity in size and texture of the units.

In figuring the material cost of brickwork, an allowance of 25% mortar waste and 3% brick breakage was included. If bricks are delivered palletized

with 280 to 300 per pallet, or packaged, allow only 1-1/2% for breakage. Packaged or palletized delivery is practical when a job is big enough to have a crane or other equipment available to handle a package of brick. This is so on all industrial work but not always true on small commercial buildings.

The use of buff and gray face is increasing, and there is a continuing trend to the Norman, Roman, Jumbo and SCR brick.

Common red clay brick for backup is not used that often. Concrete block is the most usual backup material with occasional use of sand lime or cement brick. Building brick is commonly used in solid walls for strength and as a fire stop.

Brick panels built on the ground and then crane erected to the upper floors have proven to be economical. This allows the work to be done under cover and without scaffolding.

R042110-50   Brick, Block & Mortar Quantities

	Running Bond							For Other Bonds Standard Size Add to S.F. Quantities in Table to Left		
	Number of Brick per S.F. of Wall - Single Wythe with 3/8" Joints					C.F. of Mortar per M Bricks, Waste Included				
Type Brick	Nominal Size (incl. mortar) L H W			Modular Coursing	Number of Brick per S.F.	3/8" Joint	1/2" Joint	Bond Type	Description	Factor
Standard	8 x 2-2/3 x 4			3C=8"	6.75	10.3	12.9	Common	full header every fifth course	+20%
Economy	8 x 4 x 4			1C=4"	4.50	11.4	14.6		full header every sixth course	+16.7%
Engineer	8 x 3-1/5 x 4			5C=16"	5.63	10.6	13.6	English	full header every second course	+50%
Fire	9 x 2-1/2 x 4-1/2			2C=5"	6.40	550 # Fireclay	—	Flemish	alternate headers every course	+33.3%
Jumbo	12 x 4 x 6 or 8			1C=4"	3.00	23.8	30.8		every sixth course	+5.6%
Norman	12 x 2-2/3 x 4			3C=8"	4.50	14.0	17.9	Header = W x H exposed		+100%
Norwegian	12 x 3-1/5 x 4			5C=16"	3.75	14.6	18.6	Rowlock = H x W exposed		+100%
Roman	12 x 2 x 4			2C=4"	6.00	13.4	17.0	Rowlock stretcher = L x W exposed		+33.3%
SCR	12 x 2-2/3 x 6			3C=8"	4.50	21.8	28.0	Soldier = H x L exposed		—
Utility	12 x 4 x 4			1C=4"	3.00	15.4	19.6	Sailor = W x L exposed		-33.3%

Concrete Blocks Nominal Size		Approximate Weight per S.F.		Blocks per 100 S.F.	Mortar per M block, waste included	
		Standard	Lightweight		Partitions	Back up
2"	x 8" x 16"	20 PSF	15 PSF	113	27 C.F.	36 C.F.
4"		30	20		41	51
6"		42	30		56	66
8"		55	38		72	82
10"		70	47		87	97
12"		85	55		102	112

Brick & Mortar Quantities
©Brick Industry Association. 2009 Feb. Technical Notes on
Brick Construction 10:
    Dimensioning and Estimating Brick Masonry. Reston (VA): BIA. Table 1
    Modular Brick Sizes and Table 4 Quantity Estimates for Brick Masonry.

R042210-20   Concrete Block

The material cost of special block such as corner, jamb and head block can be figured at the same price as ordinary block of equal size. Labor on specials is about the same as equal-sized regular block.

Bond beams and 16″ high lintel blocks are more expensive than regular units of equal size. Lintel blocks are 8″ long and either 8″ or 16″ high.

Use of a motorized mortar spreader box will speed construction of continuous walls.

Hollow non-load-bearing units are made according to ASTM C129 and hollow load-bearing units according to ASTM C90.

R053100-10   Decking Descriptions

General - All Deck Products

A steel deck is made by cold forming structural grade sheet steel into a repeating pattern of parallel ribs. The strength and stiffness of the panels are the result of the ribs and the material properties of the steel. Deck lengths can be varied to suit job conditions, but because of shipping considerations, are usually less than 40 feet. Standard deck width varies with the product used but full sheets are usually 12″, 18″, 24″, 30″, or 36″. The deck is typically furnished in a standard width with the ends cut square. Any cutting for width, such as at openings or for angular fit, is done at the job site.

The deck is typically attached to the building frame with arc puddle welds, self-drilling screws, or powder or pneumatically driven pins. Sheet to sheet fastening is done with screws, button punching (crimping), or welds.

Composite Floor Deck

After installation and adequate fastening, a floor deck serves several purposes. It (a) acts as a working platform, (b) stabilizes the frame, (c) serves as a concrete form for the slab, and (d) reinforces the slab to carry the design loads applied during the life of the building. Composite decks are distinguished by the presence of shear connector devices as part of the deck. These devices are designed to mechanically lock the concrete and deck together so that the concrete and the deck work together to carry subsequent floor loads. These shear connector devices can be rolled-in embossments, lugs, holes, or wires welded to the panels. The deck profile can also be used to interlock concrete and steel.

Composite deck finishes are either galvanized (zinc coated) or phosphatized/painted. Galvanized deck has a zinc coating on both the top and bottom surfaces. The phosphatized/painted deck has a bare (phosphatized) top surface that will come into contact with the concrete. This bare top surface can be expected to develop rust before the concrete is placed. The bottom side of the deck has a primer coat of paint.

A composite floor deck is normally installed so the panel ends do not overlap on the supporting beams. Shear lugs or panel profile shapes often prevent a tight metal to metal fit if the panel ends overlap; the air gap caused by overlapping will prevent proper fusion with the structural steel supports when the panel end laps are shear stud welded.

Adequate end bearing of the deck must be obtained as shown on the drawings. If bearing is actually less in the field than shown on the drawings, further investigation is required.

Roof Deck

A roof deck is not designed to act compositely with other materials. A roof deck acts alone in transferring horizontal and vertical loads into the building frame. Roof deck rib openings are usually narrower than floor deck rib openings. This provides adequate support of the rigid thermal insulation board.

A roof deck is typically installed to endlap approximately 2″ over supports. However, it can be butted (or lapped more than 2″) to solve field fit problems. Since designers frequently use the installed deck system as part of the horizontal bracing system (the deck as a diaphragm), any fastening substitution or change should be approved by the designer. Continuous perimeter support of the deck is necessary to limit edge deflection in the finished roof and may be required for diaphragm shear transfer.

Standard roof deck finishes are galvanized or primer painted. The standard factory applied paint for roof decks is a primer paint and is not intended to weather for extended periods of time. Field painting or touching up of abrasions and deterioration of the primer coat or other protective finishes is the responsibility of the contractor.

Cellular Deck

A cellular deck is made by attaching a bottom steel sheet to a roof deck or composite floor deck panel. A cellular deck can be used in the same manner as a floor deck. Electrical, telephone, and data wires are easily run through the chase created between the deck panel and the bottom sheet.

When used as part of the electrical distribution system, the cellular deck must be installed so that the ribs line up and create a smooth cell transition at abutting ends. The joint that occurs at butting cell ends must be taped or otherwise sealed to prevent wet concrete from seeping into the cell. Cell interiors must be free of welding burrs, or other sharp intrusions, to prevent damage to wires.

When used as a roof deck, the bottom flat plate is usually left exposed to view. Care must be maintained during erection to keep good alignment and prevent damage.

A cellular deck is sometimes used with the flat plate on the top side to provide a flat working surface. Installation of the deck for this purpose requires special methods for attachment to the frame because the flat plate, now on the top, can prevent direct access to the deck material that is bearing on the structural steel. It may be advisable to treat the flat top surface to prevent slipping.

A cellular deck is always furnished galvanized or painted over galvanized.

Form Deck

A form deck can be any floor or roof deck product used as a concrete form. Connections to the frame are by the same methods used to anchor floor and roof decks. Welding washers are recommended when welding a deck that is less than 20 gauge thickness.

A form deck is furnished galvanized, prime painted, or uncoated. A galvanized deck must be used for those roof deck systems where a form deck is used to carry a lightweight insulating concrete fill.

R061110-30   Lumber Product Material Prices

The price of forest products fluctuates widely from location to location and from season to season depending upon economic conditions. The bare material prices in the unit cost sections of the data set show the National Average material prices in effect Jan. 1 of this data year. It must be noted that lumber prices in general may change significantly during the year.

Availability of certain items depends upon geographic location and must be checked prior to firm-price bidding.

R061636-20   Plywood

There are two types of plywood used in construction: interior, which is moisture-resistant but not waterproofed, and exterior, which is waterproofed.

The grade of the exterior surface of the plywood sheets is designated by the first letter: A, for smooth surface with patches allowed; B, for solid surface with patches and plugs allowed; C, which may be surface plugged or may have knot holes up to 1″ wide; and D, which is used only for interior type plywood and may have knot holes up to 2-1/2″ wide. "Structural Grade" is specifically designed for engineered applications such as box beams. All CC & DD grades have roof and floor spans marked on them.

Underlayment-grade plywood runs from 1/4″ to 1-1/4″ thick. Thicknesses 5/8″ and over have optional tongue and groove joints which eliminate the need for blocking the edges. Underlayment 19/32″ and over may be referred to as Sturd-i-Floor.

The price of plywood can fluctuate widely due to geographic and economic conditions.

Typical uses for various plywood grades are as follows:

AA-AD Interior — cupboards, shelving, paneling, furniture

BB Plyform — concrete form plywood

CDX — wall and roof sheathing

Structural — box beams, girders, stressed skin panels

AA-AC Exterior — fences, signs, siding, soffits, etc.

Underlayment — base for resilient floor coverings

Overlaid HDO — high density for concrete forms & highway signs

Overlaid MDO — medium density for painting, siding, soffits & signs

303 Siding — exterior siding, textured, striated, embossed, etc.

R073126-20   Roof Slate

16″, 18″ and 20″ are standard lengths, and slate usually comes in random widths. For standard 3/16″ thickness use 1-1/2″ copper nails. Allow for 3% breakage.

R075213-30   Modified Bitumen Roofing

The cost of modified bitumen roofing is highly dependent on the type of installation that is planned. Installation is based on the type of modifier used in the bitumen. The two most popular modifiers are atactic polypropylene (APP) and styrene butadiene styrene (SBS). The modifiers are added to heated bitumen during the manufacturing process to change its characteristics. A polyethylene, polyester or fiberglass reinforcing sheet is then sandwiched between layers of this bitumen. When completed, the result is a pre-assembled, built-up roof that has increased elasticity and weatherability. Some manufacturers include a surfacing material such as ceramic or mineral granules, metal particles or sand.

The preferred method of adhering SBS-modified bitumen roofing to the substrate is with hot-mopped asphalt (much the same as built-up roofing). This installation method requires a tar kettle/pot to heat the asphalt, as well as the labor, tools and equipment necessary to distribute and spread the hot asphalt.

The alternative method for applying APP and SBS modified bitumen is as follows. A skilled installer uses a torch to melt a small pool of bitumen off the membrane. This pool must form across the entire roll for proper adhesion. The installer must unroll the roofing at a pace slow enough to melt the bitumen, but fast enough to prevent damage to the rest of the membrane.

Modified bitumen roofing provides the advantages of both built-up and single-ply roofing. Labor costs are reduced over those of built-up roofing because only a single ply is necessary. The elasticity of single-ply roofing is attained with the reinforcing sheet and polymer modifiers. Modifieds have some self-healing characteristics and because of their multi-layer construction, they offer the reliability and safety of built-up roofing.

Openings   R0813 Metal Doors

R081313-20   Steel Door Selection Guide

Standard steel doors are classified into four levels, as recommended by the Steel Door Institute in the chart below. Each of the four levels offers a range of construction models and designs to meet architectural requirements for preference and appearance, including full flush, seamless, and stile & rail. Recommended minimum gauge requirements are also included.

For complete standard steel door construction specifications and available sizes, refer to the Steel Door Institute Technical Data Series, ANSI A250.8-98 (SDI-100), and ANSI A250.4-94 Test Procedure and Acceptance Criteria for Physical Endurance of Steel Door and Hardware Reinforcements.

Level		Model	Construction	For Full Flush or Seamless		
				Min. Gauge	Thickness (in)	Thickness (mm)
I	Standard Duty	1	Full Flush	20	0.032	0.8
		2	Seamless			
II	Heavy Duty	1	Full Flush	18	0.042	1.0
		2	Seamless			
III	Extra Heavy Duty	1	Full Flush	16	0.053	1.3
		2	Seamless			
		3	*Stile & Rail			
IV	Maximum Duty	1	Full Flush	14	0.067	1.6
		2	Seamless			

*Stiles & rails are 16 gauge; flush panels, when specified, are 18 gauge.

Openings   R0852 Wood Windows

R085216-10   Window Estimates

To ensure a complete window estimate, be sure to include the material and labor costs for each window, as well as the material and labor costs for an interior wood trim set.

Openings   R0853 Plastic Windows

R085313-20   Replacement Windows

Replacement windows are typically measured per United Inch.

United Inches are calculated by rounding the width and height of the window opening up to the nearest inch, then adding the two figures.

The labor cost for replacement windows includes removal of sash, existing sash balance or weights, parting bead where necessary and installation of new window.

Debris hauling and dump fees are not included.

729

For customer support on your Residential Costs with RSMeans Data, call 800.448.8182.

R087110-10   Hardware Finishes

This table describes hardware finishes used throughout the industry. It also shows the base metal and the respective symbols in the three predominate systems of identification. Many of these are used in pricing descriptions in Division Eight.

US″	BMHA*	CDN^	Base	Description
US P	600	CP	Steel	Primed for Painting
US 1B	601	C1B	Steel	Bright Black Japanned
US 2C	602	C2C	Steel	Zinc Plated
US 2G	603	C2G	Steel	Zinc Plated
US 3	605	C3	Brass	Bright Brass, Clear Coated
US 4	606	C4	Brass	Satin Brass, Clear Coated
US 5	609	C5	Brass	Satin Brass, Blackened, Satin Relieved, Clear Coated
US 7	610	C7	Brass	Satin Brass, Blackened, Bright Relieved, Clear Coated
US 9	611	C9	Bronze	Bright Bronze, Clear Coated
US 10	612	C10	Bronze	Satin Bronze, Clear Coated
US 10A	641	C10A	Steel	Antiqued Bronze, Oiled and Lacquered
US 10B	613	C10B	Bronze	Antiqued Bronze, Oiled
US 11	616	C11	Bronze	Satin Bronze, Blackened, Satin Relieved, Clear Coated
US 14	618	C14	Brass/Bronze	Bright Nickel Plated, Clear Coated
US 15	619	C15	Brass/Bronze	Satin Nickel, Clear Coated
US 15A	620	C15A	Brass/Bronze	Satin Nickel Plated, Blackened, Satin Relieved, Clear Coated
US 17A	621	C17A	Brass/Bronze	Nickel Plated, Blackened, Relieved, Clear Coated
US 19	622	C19	Brass/Bronze	Flat Black Coated
US 20	623	C20	Brass/Bronze	Statuary Bronze, Light
US 20A	624	C20A	Brass/Bronze	Statuary Bronze, Dark
US 26	625	C26	Brass/Bronze	Bright Chromium
US 26D	626	C26D	Brass/Bronze	Satin Chromium
US 20	627	C27	Aluminum	Satin Aluminum Clear
US 28	628	C28	Aluminum	Anodized Dull Aluminum
US 32	629	C32	Stainless Steel	Bright Stainless Steel
US 32D	630	C32D	Stainless Steel	Stainless Steel
US 3	632	C3	Steel	Bright Brass Plated, Clear Coated
US 4	633	C4	Steel	Satin Brass, Clear Coated
US 7	636	C7	Steel	Satin Brass Plated, Blackened, Bright Relieved, Clear Coated
US 9	637	C9	Steel	Bright Bronze Plated, Clear Coated
US 5	638	C5	Steel	Satin Brass Plated, Blackened, Bright Relieved, Clear Coated
US 10	639	C10	Steel	Satin Bronze Plated, Clear Coated
US 10B	640	C10B	Steel	Antique Bronze, Oiled
US 10A	641	C10A	Steel	Antiqued Bronze, Oiled and Lacquered
US 11	643	C11	Steel	Satin Bronze Plated, Blackened, Bright Relieved, Clear Coated
US 14	645	C14	Steel	Bright Nickel Plated, Clear Coated
US 15	646	C15	Steel	Satin Nickel Plated, Clear Coated
US 15A	647	C15A	Steel	Nickel Plated, Blackened, Bright Relieved, Clear Coated
US 17A	648	C17A	Steel	Nickel Plated, Blackened, Relieved, Clear Coated
US 20	649	C20	Steel	Statuary Bronze, Light
US 20A	650	C20A	Steel	Statuary Bronze, Dark
US 26	651	C26	Steel	Bright Chromium Plated
US 26D	652	C26D	Steel	Satin Chromium Plated

* - BMHA Builders Hardware Manufacturing Association

″ - US Equivalent

^ - Canadian Equivalent

Japanning is imitating Asian lacquer work

R092000-50 Lath, Plaster and Gypsum Board

Gypsum board lath is available in 3/8″ thick x 16″ wide x 4′ long sheets as a base material for multi-layer plaster applications. It is also available as a base for either multi-layer or veneer plaster applications in 1/2″ and 5/8″ thick–4′ wide x 8′, 10′ or 12′ long sheets. Fasteners are screws or blued ring shank nails for wood framing and screws for metal framing.

Metal lath is available in diamond mesh patterns with flat or self-furring profiles. Paper backing is available for applications where excessive plaster waste needs to be avoided. A slotted mesh ribbed lath should be used in areas where the span between structural supports is greater than normal. Most metal lath comes in 27″ x 96″ sheets. Diamond mesh weighs 1.75, 2.5 or 3.4 pounds per square yard, slotted mesh lath weighs 2.75 or 3.4 pounds per square yard. Metal lath can be nailed, screwed or tied in place.

Many **accessories** are available. Corner beads, flat reinforcing strips, casing beads, control and expansion joints, furring brackets and channels are some examples. Note that accessories are not included in plaster or stucco line items.

Plaster is defined as a material or combination of materials that when mixed with a suitable amount of water, forms a plastic mass or paste. When applied to a surface, the paste adheres to it and subsequently hardens, preserving in a rigid state the form or texture imposed during the period of elasticity.

Gypsum plaster is made from ground calcined gypsum. It is mixed with aggregates and water for use as a base coat plaster.

Vermiculite plaster is a fire-retardant plaster covering used on steel beams, concrete slabs and other heavy construction materials. Vermiculite is a group name for certain clay minerals, hydrous silicates or aluminum, magnesium and iron that have been expanded by heat.

Perlite plaster is a plaster using perlite as an aggregate instead of sand. Perlite is a volcanic glass that has been expanded by heat.

Gauging plaster is a mix of gypsum plaster and lime putty that when applied produces a quick drying finish coat.

Veneer plaster is a one or two component gypsum plaster used as a thin finish coat over special gypsum board.

Keenes cement is a white cementitious material manufactured from gypsum that has been burned at a high temperature and ground to a fine powder. Alum is added to accelerate the set. The resulting plaster is hard and strong and accepts and maintains a high polish, hence it is used as a finishing plaster.

Stucco is a Portland cement based plaster used primarily as an exterior finish.

Plaster is used on both interior and exterior surfaces. Generally it is applied in multiple-coat systems. A three-coat system uses the terms scratch, brown and finish to identify each coat. A two-coat system uses base and finish to describe each coat. Each type of plaster and application system has attributes that are chosen by the designer to best fit the intended use.

Gypsum Plaster Quantities for 100 S.Y.	2 Coat, 5/8″ Thick		3 Coat, 3/4″ Thick		
	Base	Finish	Scratch	Brown	Finish
	1:3 Mix	2:1 Mix	1:2 Mix	1:3 Mix	2:1 Mix
Gypsum plaster	1,300 lb.		1,350 lb.	650 lb.	
Sand	1.75 C.Y.		1.85 C.Y.	1.35 C.Y.	
Finish hydrated lime		340 lb.			340 lb.
Gauging plaster		170 lb.			170 lb.

Vermiculite or Perlite Plaster Quantities for 100 S.Y.	2 Coat, 5/8″ Thick		3 Coat, 3/4″ Thick		
	Base	Finish	Scratch	Brown	Finish
Gypsum plaster	1,250 lb.		1,450 lb.	800 lb.	
Vermiculite or perlite	7.8 bags		8.0 bags	3.3 bags	
Finish hydrated lime		340 lb.			340 lb.
Gauging plaster		170 lb.			170 lb.

Stucco–Three-Coat System Quantities for 100 S.Y.	On Wood Frame	On Masonry
Portland cement	29 bags	21 bags
Sand	2.6 C.Y.	2.0 C.Y.
Hydrated lime	180 lb.	120 lb.

731

Finishes

R092910-10   Levels of Gypsum Board Finish

In the past, contract documents often used phrases such as "industry standard" and "workmanlike finish" to specify the expected quality of gypsum board wall and ceiling installations. The vagueness of these descriptions led to unacceptable work and disputes.

In order to resolve this problem, four major trade associations concerned with the manufacture, erection, finish and decoration of gypsum board wall and ceiling systems developed an industry-wide *Recommended Levels of Gypsum Board Finish.*

The finish of gypsum board walls and ceilings for specific final decoration is dependent on a number of factors. A primary consideration is the location of the surface and the degree of decorative treatment desired. Painted and unpainted surfaces in warehouses and other areas where appearance is normally not critical may simply require the taping of wallboard joints and 'spotting' of fastener heads. Blemish-free, smooth, monolithic surfaces often intended for painted and decorated walls and ceilings in habitated structures, ranging from single-family dwellings through monumental buildings, require additional finishing prior to the application of the final decoration.

Other factors to be considered in determining the level of finish of the gypsum board surface are (1) the type of angle of surface illumination (both natural and artificial lighting), and (2) the paint and method of application or the type and finish of wallcovering specified as the final decoration. Critical lighting conditions, gloss paints, and thin wall coverings require a higher level of gypsum board finish than heavily textured surfaces which are subsequently painted or surfaces which are to be decorated with heavy grade wall coverings.

The following descriptions were developed by the Association of the Wall and Ceiling Industries-International (AWCI), Ceiling & Interior Systems Construction Association (CISCA), Gypsum Association (GA), and Painting and Decorating Contractors of America (PDCA) as a guide.

Level 0: Used in temporary construction or wherever the final decoration has not been determined. Unfinished. No taping, finishing or corner beads are required. Also could be used where non-predecorated panels will be used in demountable-type partitions that are to be painted as a final finish. .

Level 1: Frequently used in plenum areas above ceilings, in attics, in areas where the assembly would generally be concealed, or in building service corridors and other areas not normally open to public view. Some degree of sound and smoke control is provided; in some geographic areas, this level of finish is referred to as "fire-taping," although this level of finish does not typically meet fire-resistant assembly requirements. Where a fire resistance rating is required for the gypsum board assembly, details of construction should be in accordance with reports of fire tests of assemblies that have met the requirements of the fire rating acceptable.

All joints and interior angles shall have tape embedded in joint compound. Accessories are optional at specifier discretion in corridors and other areas with pedestrian traffic. Tape and fastener heads need not be covered with joint compound. Surface shall be free of excess joint compound. Tool marks and ridges are acceptable.

Level 2: It may be specified for standard gypsum board surfaces in garages, warehouse storage, or other similar areas where surface appearance is not of primary importance.

All joints and interior angles shall have tape embedded in joint compound and shall be immediately wiped with a joint knife or trowel, leaving a thin coating of joint compound over all joints and interior angles. Fastener heads and accessories shall be covered with a coat of joint compound. Surface shall be free of excess joint compound. Tool marks and ridges are acceptable.

Level 3: Typically used in areas receiving heavy texture (spray or hand applied) finishes before final painting, or where commercial-grade (heavy duty) wall coverings are to be applied as the final decoration. This level of finish should not be used where smooth painted surfaces or where lighter weight wall coverings are specified. The prepared surface shall be coated with a drywall primer prior to the application of final finishes.

All joints and interior angles shall have tape embedded in joint compound and shall be immediately wiped with a joint knife or trowel, leaving a thin coating of joint compound over all joints and interior angles. One additional coat of joint compound shall be applied over all joints and interior angles. Fastener heads and accessories shall be covered with two separate coats of joint compound. All joint compounds shall be smooth and free of tool marks and ridges. The prepared surface shall be covered with a drywall primer prior to the application of the final decoration.

Level 4: This level should be used where residential grade (light duty) wall coverings, flat paints, or light textures are to be applied. The prepared surface shall be coated with a drywall primer prior to the application of final finishes. Release agents for wall coverings are specifically formulated to minimize damage if coverings are subsequently removed.

The weight, texture, and sheen level of the wall covering material selected should be taken into consideration when specifying wall coverings over this level of drywall treatment. Joints and fasteners must be sufficiently concealed if the wall covering material is lightweight, contains limited pattern, has a glossy finish, or has any combination of these features. In critical lighting areas, flat paints applied over light textures tend to reduce joint photographing. Gloss, semi-gloss, and enamel paints are not recommended over this level of finish.

All joints and interior angles shall have tape embedded in joint compound and shall be immediately wiped with a joint knife or trowel, leaving a thin coating of joint compound over all joints and interior angles. In addition, two separate coats of joint compound shall be applied over all flat joints and one separate coat of joint compound applied over interior angles. Fastener heads and accessories shall be covered with three separate coats of joint compound. All joint compounds shall be smooth and free of tool marks and ridges. The prepared surface shall be covered with a drywall primer like Sheetrock first coat prior to the application of the final decoration.

Level 5: The highest quality finish is the most effective method to provide a uniform surface and minimize the possibility of joint photographing and of fasteners showing through the final decoration. This level of finish is required where gloss, semi-gloss, or enamel is specified; when flat joints are specified over an untextured surface; or where critical lighting conditions occur. The prepared surface shall be coated with a drywall primer prior to the application of the final decoration.

All joints and interior angles shall have tape embedded in joint compound and be immediately wiped with a joint knife or trowel, leaving a thin coating of joint compound over all joints and interior angles. Two separate coats of joint compound shall be applied over all flat joints and one separate coat of joint compound applied over interior angles. Fastener heads and accessories shall be covered with three separate coats of joint compound.

A thin skim coat of joint compound shall be trowel applied to the entire surface. Excess compound is immediately troweled off, leaving a film or skim coating of compound completely covering the paper. As an alternative to a skim coat, a material manufactured especially for this purpose may be applied such as Sheetrock Tuff-Hide primer surfacer. The surface must be smooth and free of tool marks and ridges. The prepared surface shall be covered with a drywall primer prior to the application of the final decoration.

R097223-10 Wall Covering

The table below lists the quantities required for 100 S.F. of wall covering.

Description	Medium-Priced Paper	Expensive Paper
Paper	1.6 dbl. rolls	1.6 dbl. rolls
Wall sizing	0.25 gallon	0.25 gallon
Vinyl wall paste	0.6 gallon	0.6 gallon
Apply sizing	0.3 hour	0.3 hour
Apply paper	1.2 hours	1.5 hours

Most wallpapers now come in double rolls only.
To remove old paper, allow 1.3 hours per 100 S.F.

R099100-10 Painting Estimating Techniques

Proper estimating methodology is needed to obtain an accurate painting estimate. There is no known reliable shortcut or square foot method. The following steps should be followed:

- List all surfaces to be painted, with an accurate quantity (area) of each. Items having similar surface condition, finish, application method and accessibility may be grouped together.
- List all the tasks required for each surface to be painted, including surface preparation, masking, and protection of adjacent surfaces. Surface preparation may include minor repairs, washing, sanding and puttying.
- Select the proper Means line for each task. Review and consider all adjustments to labor and materials for type of paint and location of work. Apply the height adjustment carefully. For instance, when applying the adjustment for work over 8' high to a wall that is 12' high, apply the adjustment only to the area between 8' and 12' high, and not to the entire wall.

When applying more than one percent (%) adjustment, apply each to the base cost of the data, rather than applying one percentage adjustment on top of the other.

When estimating the cost of painting walls and ceilings remember to add the brushwork for all cut-ins at inside corners and around windows and doors as a LF measure. One linear foot of cut-in with a brush equals one square foot of painting.

All items for spray painting include the labor for roll-back.

Deduct for openings greater than 100 SF or openings that extend from floor to ceiling and are greater than 5' wide. Do not deduct small openings.

The cost of brushes, rollers, ladders and spray equipment are considered part of a painting contractor's overhead, and should not be added to the estimate. The cost of rented equipment such as scaffolding and swing staging should be added to the estimate.

R099100-20 Painting

Item	Coat	One Gallon Covers			In 8 Hours a Laborer Covers			Labor-Hours per 100 S.F.		
		Brush	Roller	Spray	Brush	Roller	Spray	Brush	Roller	Spray
Paint wood siding	prime	250 S.F.	225 S.F.	290 S.F.	1150 S.F.	1300 S.F.	2275 S.F.	.695	.615	.351
	others	270	250	290	1300	1625	2600	.615	.492	.307
Paint exterior trim	prime	400	—	—	650	—	—	1.230	—	—
	1st	475	—	—	800	—	—	1.000	—	—
	2nd	520	—	—	975	—	—	.820	—	—
Paint shingle siding	prime	270	255	300	650	975	1950	1.230	.820	.410
	others	360	340	380	800	1150	2275	1.000	.695	.351
Stain shingle siding	1st	180	170	200	750	1125	2250	1.068	.711	.355
	2nd	270	250	290	900	1325	2600	.888	.603	.307
Paint brick masonry	prime	180	135	160	750	800	1800	1.066	1.000	.444
	1st	270	225	290	815	975	2275	.981	.820	.351
	2nd	340	305	360	815	1150	2925	.981	.695	.273
Paint interior plaster or drywall	prime	400	380	495	1150	2000	3250	.695	.400	.246
	others	450	425	495	1300	2300	4000	.615	.347	.200
Paint interior doors and windows	prime	400	—	—	650	—	—	1.230	—	—
	1st	425	—	—	800	—	—	1.000	—	—
	2nd	450	—	—	975	—	—	.820	—	—

733

R131113-20   Swimming Pools

Pool prices given per square foot of surface area include pool structure, filter and chlorination equipment, pumps, related piping, ladders/steps, maintenance kit, skimmer and vacuum system. Decks and electrical service to equipment are not included.

Residential in-ground pool construction can be divided into two categories: vinyl lined and gunite. Vinyl lined pool walls are constructed of different materials including wood, concrete, plastic or metal. The bottom is often graded with sand over which the vinyl liner is installed. Vermiculite or soil cement bottoms may be substituted for an added cost.

Gunite pool construction is used both in residential and municipal installations. These structures are steel reinforced for strength and finished with a white cement limestone plaster.

Municipal pools will have a higher cost because plumbing codes require more expensive materials, chlorination equipment and higher filtration rates.

Municipal pools greater than 1,800 S.F. require gutter systems to control waves. This gutter may be formed into the concrete wall. Often a vinyl/stainless steel gutter or gutter/wall system is specified, which will raise the pool cost.

Competition pools usually require tile bottoms and sides with contrasting lane striping, which will also raise the pool cost.

R221113-50 Pipe Material Considerations

1. Malleable fittings should be used for gas service.
2. Malleable fittings are used where there are stresses/strains due to expansion and vibration.
3. Cast fittings may be broken as an aid to disassembling heating lines frozen by long use, temperature and minerals.
4. A cast iron pipe is extensively used for underground and submerged service.
5. Type M (light wall) copper tubing is available in hard temper only and is used for nonpressure and less severe applications than K and L.
6. Type L (medium wall) copper tubing, available hard or soft for interior service.
7. Type K (heavy wall) copper tubing, available in hard or soft temper for use where conditions are severe. For underground and interior service.
8. Hard drawn tubing requires fewer hangers or supports but should not be bent. Silver brazed fittings are recommended, but soft solder is normally used.
9. Type DMV (very light wall) copper tubing designed for drainage, waste and vent plus other non-critical pressure services.

Domestic/Imported Pipe and Fittings Costs

The prices shown in this publication for steel/cast iron pipe and steel, cast iron, and malleable iron fittings are based on domestic production sold at the normal trade discounts. The above listed items of foreign manufacture may be available at prices 1/3 to 1/2 of those shown. Some imported items after minor machining or finishing operations are being sold as domestic to further complicate the system.

Caution: Most pipe prices in this data set also include a coupling and pipe hangers which for the larger sizes can add significantly to the per foot cost and should be taken into account when comparing "book cost" with the quoted supplier's cost.

R329219-50 Seeding

The type of grass is determined by light, shade and moisture content of soil plus intended use. Fertilizer should be disked 4" before seeding. For steep slopes disk five tons of mulch and lay two tons of hay or straw on surface per acre after seeding. Surface mulch can be staked, lightly disked or tar emulsion sprayed. Material for mulch can be wood chips, peat moss, partially rotted hay or straw, wood fibers and sprayed emulsions. Hemp seed blankets with fertilizer are also available. For spring seeding, watering is necessary. Late fall seeding may have to be reseeded in the spring. Hydraulic seeding, power mulching, and aerial seeding can be used on large areas.

735

For customer support on your Residential Costs with RSMeans Data, call 800.448.8182.

R331113-80   Piping Designations

There are several systems currently in use to describe pipe and fittings. The following paragraphs will help to identify and clarify classifications of piping systems used for water distribution.

Piping may be classified by schedule. Piping schedules include 5S, 10S, 10, 20, 30, Standard, 40, 60, Extra Strong, 80, 100, 120, 140, 160 and Double Extra Strong. These schedules are dependent upon the pipe wall thickness. The wall thickness of a particular schedule may vary with pipe size.

Ductile iron pipe for water distribution is classified by Pressure Classes such as Class 150, 200, 250, 300 and 350. These classes are actually the rated water working pressure of the pipe in pounds per square inch (psi). The pipe in these pressure classes is designed to withstand the rated water working pressure plus a surge allowance of 100 psi.

The American Water Works Association (AWWA) provides standards for various types of **plastic pipe.** C-900 is the specification for polyvinyl chloride (PVC) piping used for water distribution in sizes ranging from 4″ through 12″. C-901 is the specification for polyethylene (PE) pressure pipe, tubing and fittings used for water distribution in sizes ranging from 1/2″ through 3″. C-905 is the specification for PVC piping sizes 14″ and greater.

PVC pressure-rated pipe is identified using the standard dimensional ratio (SDR) method. This method is defined by the American Society for Testing and Materials (ASTM) Standard D 2241. This pipe is available in SDR numbers 64, 41, 32.5, 26, 21, 17, and 13.5. A pipe with an SDR of 64 will have the thinnest wall while a pipe with an SDR of 13.5 will have the thickest wall. When the pressure rating (PR) of a pipe is given in psi, it is based on a line supplying water at 73 degrees F.

The National Sanitation Foundation (NSF) seal of approval is applied to products that can be used with potable water. These products have been tested to ANSI/NSF Standard 14.

Valves and strainers are classified by American National Standards Institute (ANSI) Classes. These Classes are 125, 150, 200, 250, 300, 400, 600, 900, 1500 and 2500. Within each class there is an operating pressure range dependent upon temperature. Design parameters should be compared to the appropriate material dependent, pressure-temperature rating chart for accurate valve selection.

Abbreviation	Definition
A	Area Square Feet; Ampere
AAFES	Army and Air Force Exchange Service
ABS	Acrylonitrile Butadiene Stryrene; Asbestos Bonded Steel
A.C., AC	Alternating Current; Air-Conditioning; Asbestos Cement; Plywood Grade A & C
ACI	American Concrete Institute
ACR	Air Conditioning Refrigeration
ADA	Americans with Disabilities Act
AD	Plywood, Grade A & D
Addit.	Additional
Adj.	Adjustable
af	Audio-frequency
AFFF	Aqueous Film Forming Foam
AFUE	Annual Fuel Utilization Efficiency
AGA	American Gas Association
Agg.	Aggregate
A.H., Ah	Ampere Hours
A hr.	Ampere-hour
A.H.U., AHU	Air Handling Unit
A.I.A.	American Institute of Architects
AIC	Ampere Interrupting Capacity
Allow.	Allowance
alt., alt	Alternate
Alum.	Aluminum
a.m.	Ante Meridiem
Amp.	Ampere
Anod.	Anodized
ANSI	American National Standards Institute
APA	American Plywood Association
Approx.	Approximate
Apt.	Apartment
Asb.	Asbestos
A.S.B.C.	American Standard Building Code
Asbe.	Asbestos Worker
ASCE	American Society of Civil Engineers
A.S.H.R.A.E.	American Society of Heating, Refrig. & AC Engineers
ASME	American Society of Mechanical Engineers
ASTM	American Society for Testing and Materials
Attchmt.	Attachment
Avg., Ave.	Average
AWG	American Wire Gauge
AWWA	American Water Works Assoc.
Bbl.	Barrel
B&B, BB	Grade B and Better; Balled & Burlapped
B&S	Bell and Spigot
B.&W.	Black and White
b.c.c.	Body-centered Cubic
B.C.Y.	Bank Cubic Yards
BE	Bevel End
B.F.	Board Feet
Bg. cem.	Bag of Cement
BHP	Boiler Horsepower; Brake Horsepower
B.I.	Black Iron
bidir.	bidirectional
Bit., Bitum.	Bituminous
Bit., Conc.	Bituminous Concrete
Bk.	Backed
Bkrs.	Breakers
Bldg., bldg	Building
Blk.	Block
Bm.	Beam
Boil.	Boilermaker
bpm	Blows per Minute
BR	Bedroom
Brg., brng.	Bearing
Brhe.	Bricklayer Helper
Bric.	Bricklayer
Brk., brk	Brick
brkt	Bracket
Brs.	Brass
Brz.	Bronze
Bsn.	Basin
Btr.	Better
BTU	British Thermal Unit
BTUH	BTU per Hour
Bu.	Bushels
BUR	Built-up Roofing
BX	Interlocked Armored Cable
°C	Degree Centigrade
c	Conductivity, Copper Sweat
C	Hundred; Centigrade
C/C	Center to Center, Cedar on Cedar
C-C	Center to Center
Cab	Cabinet
Cair.	Air Tool Laborer
Cal.	Caliper
Calc	Calculated
Cap.	Capacity
Carp.	Carpenter
C.B.	Circuit Breaker
C.C.A.	Chromate Copper Arsenate
C.C.F.	Hundred Cubic Feet
cd	Candela
cd/sf	Candela per Square Foot
CD	Grade of Plywood Face & Back
CDX	Plywood, Grade C & D, exterior glue
Cefi.	Cement Finisher
Cem.	Cement
CF	Hundred Feet
C.F.	Cubic Feet
CFM	Cubic Feet per Minute
CFRP	Carbon Fiber Reinforced Plastic
c.g.	Center of Gravity
CHW	Chilled Water; Commercial Hot Water
C.I., CI	Cast Iron
C.I.P., CIP	Cast in Place
Circ.	Circuit
C.L.	Carload Lot
CL	Chain Link
Clab.	Common Laborer
Clam	Common Maintenance Laborer
C.L.F.	Hundred Linear Feet
CLF	Current Limiting Fuse
CLP	Cross Linked Polyethylene
cm	Centimeter
CMP	Corr. Metal Pipe
CMU	Concrete Masonry Unit
CN	Change Notice
Col.	Column
CO_2	Carbon Dioxide
Comb.	Combination
comm.	Commercial, Communication
Compr.	Compressor
Conc.	Concrete
Cont., cont	Continuous; Continued, Container
Corr.	Corrugated
Cos	Cosine
Cot	Cotangent
Cov.	Cover
C/P	Cedar on Paneling
CPA	Control Point Adjustment
Cplg.	Coupling
CPM	Critical Path Method
CPVC	Chlorinated Polyvinyl Chloride
C.Pr.	Hundred Pair
CRC	Cold Rolled Channel
Creos.	Creosote
Crpt.	Carpet & Linoleum Layer
CRT	Cathode-ray Tube
CS	Carbon Steel, Constant Shear Bar Joist
Csc	Cosecant
C.S.F.	Hundred Square Feet
CSI	Construction Specifications Institute
CT	Current Transformer
CTS	Copper Tube Size
Cu	Copper, Cubic
Cu. Ft.	Cubic Foot
cw	Continuous Wave
C.W.	Cool White; Cold Water
Cwt.	100 Pounds
C.W.X.	Cool White Deluxe
C.Y.	Cubic Yard (27 cubic feet)
C.Y./Hr.	Cubic Yard per Hour
Cyl.	Cylinder
d	Penny (nail size)
D	Deep; Depth; Discharge
Dis., Disch.	Discharge
Db	Decibel
Dbl.	Double
DC	Direct Current
DDC	Direct Digital Control
Demob.	Demobilization
d.f.t.	Dry Film Thickness
d.f.u.	Drainage Fixture Units
D.H.	Double Hung
DHW	Domestic Hot Water
DI	Ductile Iron
Diag.	Diagonal
Diam., Dia	Diameter
Distrib.	Distribution
Div.	Division
Dk.	Deck
D.L.	Dead Load; Diesel
DLH	Deep Long Span Bar Joist
dlx	Deluxe
Do.	Ditto
DOP	Dioctyl Phthalate Penetration Test (Air Filters)
Dp., dp	Depth
D.P.S.T.	Double Pole, Single Throw
Dr.	Drive
DR	Dimension Ratio
Drink.	Drinking
D.S.	Double Strength
D.S.A.	Double Strength A Grade
D.S.B.	Double Strength B Grade
Dty.	Duty
DWV	Drain Waste Vent
DX	Deluxe White, Direct Expansion
dyn	Dyne
e	Eccentricity
E	Equipment Only; East; Emissivity
Ea.	Each
EB	Encased Burial
Econ.	Economy
E.C.Y	Embankment Cubic Yards
EDP	Electronic Data Processing
EIFS	Exterior Insulation Finish System
E.D.R.	Equiv. Direct Radiation
Eq.	Equation
EL	Elevation
Elec.	Electrician; Electrical
Elev.	Elevator; Elevating
EMT	Electrical Metallic Conduit; Thin Wall Conduit
Eng.	Engine, Engineered
EPDM	Ethylene Propylene Diene Monomer
EPS	Expanded Polystyrene
Eqhv.	Equip. Oper., Heavy
Eqlt.	Equip. Oper., Light
Eqmd.	Equip. Oper., Medium
Eqmm.	Equip. Oper., Master Mechanic
Eqol.	Equip. Oper., Oilers
Equip.	Equipment
ERW	Electric Resistance Welded

E.S.	Energy Saver
Est.	Estimated
esu	Electrostatic Units
E.W.	Each Way
EWT	Entering Water Temperature
Excav.	Excavation
excl	Excluding
Exp., exp	Expansion, Exposure
Ext., ext	Exterior; Extension
Extru.	Extrusion
f.	Fiber Stress
F	Fahrenheit; Female; Fill
Fab., fab	Fabricated; Fabric
FBGS	Fiberglass
F.C.	Footcandles
f.c.c.	Face-centered Cubic
f'c.	Compressive Stress in Concrete; Extreme Compressive Stress
F.E.	Front End
FEP	Fluorinated Ethylene Propylene (Teflon)
F.G.	Flat Grain
F.H.A.	Federal Housing Administration
Fig.	Figure
Fin.	Finished
FIPS	Female Iron Pipe Size
Fixt.	Fixture
FJP	Finger jointed and primed
Fl. Oz.	Fluid Ounces
Flr.	Floor
FM	Frequency Modulation; Factory Mutual
Fmg.	Framing
FM/UL	Factory Mutual/Underwriters Labs
Fdn.	Foundation
FNPT	Female National Pipe Thread
Fori.	Foreman, Inside
Foro.	Foreman, Outside
Fount.	Fountain
fpm	Feet per Minute
FPT	Female Pipe Thread
Fr	Frame
F.R.	Fire Rating
FRK	Foil Reinforced Kraft
FSK	Foil/Scrim/Kraft
FRP	Fiberglass Reinforced Plastic
FS	Forged Steel
FSC	Cast Body; Cast Switch Box
Ft., ft	Foot; Feet
Ftng.	Fitting
Ftg.	Footing
Ft lb	Foot Pound
Furn.	Furniture
FVNR	Full Voltage Non-Reversing
FVR	Full Voltage Reversing
FXM	Female by Male
Fy.	Minimum Yield Stress of Steel
g	Gram
G	Gauss
Ga.	Gauge
Gal., gal.	Gallon
Galv., galv	Galvanized
GC/MS	Gas Chromatograph/Mass Spectrometer
Gen.	General
GFI	Ground Fault Interrupter
GFRC	Glass Fiber Reinforced Concrete
Glaz.	Glazier
GPD	Gallons per Day
gpf	Gallon per Flush
GPH	Gallons per Hour
gpm, GPM	Gallons per Minute
GR	Grade
Gran.	Granular
Grnd.	Ground
GVW	Gross Vehicle Weight
GWB	Gypsum Wall Board

H	High Henry
HC	High Capacity
H.D., HD	Heavy Duty; High Density
H.D.O.	High Density Overlaid
HDPE	High Density Polyethylene Plastic
Hdr.	Header
Hdwe.	Hardware
H.I.D., HID	High Intensity Discharge
Help.	Helper Average
HEPA	High Efficiency Particulate Air Filter
Hg	Mercury
HIC	High Interrupting Capacity
HM	Hollow Metal
HMWPE	High Molecular Weight Polyethylene
HO	High Output
Horiz.	Horizontal
H.P., HP	Horsepower; High Pressure
H.P.F.	High Power Factor
Hr.	Hour
Hrs./Day	Hours per Day
HSC	High Short Circuit
Ht.	Height
Htg.	Heating
Htrs.	Heaters
HVAC	Heating, Ventilation & Air-Conditioning
Hvy.	Heavy
HW	Hot Water
Hyd.; Hydr.	Hydraulic
Hz	Hertz (cycles)
I.	Moment of Inertia
IBC	International Building Code
I.C.	Interrupting Capacity
ID	Inside Diameter
I.D.	Inside Dimension; Identification
I.F.	Inside Frosted
I.M.C.	Intermediate Metal Conduit
In.	Inch
Incan.	Incandescent
Incl.	Included; Including
Int.	Interior
Inst.	Installation
Insul., insul	Insulation/Insulated
I.P.	Iron Pipe
I.P.S., IPS	Iron Pipe Size
IPT	Iron Pipe Threaded
I.W.	Indirect Waste
J	Joule
J.I.C.	Joint Industrial Council
K	Thousand; Thousand Pounds; Heavy Wall Copper Tubing, Kelvin
K.A.H.	Thousand Amp. Hours
kcmil	Thousand Circular Mils
KD	Knock Down
K.D.A.T.	Kiln Dried After Treatment
kg	Kilogram
kG	Kilogauss
kgf	Kilogram Force
kHz	Kilohertz
Kip	1000 Pounds
KJ	Kilojoule
K.L.	Effective Length Factor
K.L.F.	Kips per Linear Foot
Km	Kilometer
KO	Knock Out
K.S.F.	Kips per Square Foot
K.S.I.	Kips per Square Inch
kV	Kilovolt
kVA	Kilovolt Ampere
kVAR	Kilovar (Reactance)
KW	Kilowatt
KWh	Kilowatt-hour
L	Labor Only; Length; Long; Medium Wall Copper Tubing
Lab.	Labor
lat	Latitude

Lath.	Lather
Lav.	Lavatory
lb.; #	Pound
L.B., LB	Load Bearing; L Conduit Body
L. & E.	Labor & Equipment
lb./hr.	Pounds per Hour
lb./L.F.	Pounds per Linear Foot
lbf/sq.in.	Pound-force per Square Inch
L.C.L.	Less than Carload Lot
L.C.Y.	Loose Cubic Yard
Ld.	Load
LE	Lead Equivalent
LED	Light Emitting Diode
L.F.	Linear Foot
L.F. Nose	Linear Foot of Stair Nosing
L.F. Rsr	Linear Foot of Stair Riser
Lg.	Long; Length; Large
L & H	Light and Heat
LH	Long Span Bar Joist
L.H.	Labor Hours
L.L., LL	Live Load
L.L.D.	Lamp Lumen Depreciation
lm	Lumen
lm/sf	Lumen per Square Foot
lm/W	Lumen per Watt
LOA	Length Over All
log	Logarithm
L-O-L	Lateralolet
long.	Longitude
L.P., LP	Liquefied Petroleum; Low Pressure
L.P.F.	Low Power Factor
LR	Long Radius
L.S.	Lump Sum
Lt.	Light
Lt. Ga.	Light Gauge
L.T.L.	Less than Truckload Lot
Lt. Wt.	Lightweight
L.V.	Low Voltage
M	Thousand; Material; Male; Light Wall Copper Tubing
M²CA	Meters Squared Contact Area
m/hr.; M.H.	Man-hour
mA	Milliampere
Mach.	Machine
Mag. Str.	Magnetic Starter
Maint.	Maintenance
Marb.	Marble Setter
Mat; Mat'l.	Material
Max.	Maximum
MBF	Thousand Board Feet
MBH	Thousand BTU's per hr.
MC	Metal Clad Cable
MCC	Motor Control Center
M.C.F.	Thousand Cubic Feet
MCFM	Thousand Cubic Feet per Minute
M.C.M.	Thousand Circular Mils
MCP	Motor Circuit Protector
MD	Medium Duty
MDF	Medium-density fibreboard
M.D.O.	Medium Density Overlaid
Med.	Medium
MF	Thousand Feet
M.F.B.M.	Thousand Feet Board Measure
Mfg.	Manufacturing
Mfrs.	Manufacturers
mg	Milligram
MGD	Million Gallons per Day
MGPH	Million Gallons per Hour
MH, M.H.	Manhole; Metal Halide; Man-Hour
MHz	Megahertz
Mi.	Mile
MI	Malleable Iron; Mineral Insulated
MIPS	Male Iron Pipe Size
mj	Mechanical Joint
m	Meter
mm	Millimeter
Mill.	Millwright
Min., min.	Minimum, Minute

Abbreviations

Misc.	Miscellaneous	PCM	Phase Contrast Microscopy	SBS	Styrene Butadiere Styrene
ml	Milliliter, Mainline	PDCA	Painting and Decorating	SC	Screw Cover
M.L.F.	Thousand Linear Feet		Contractors of America	SCFM	Standard Cubic Feet per Minute
Mo.	Month	P.E., PE	Professional Engineer;	Scaf.	Scaffold
Mobil.	Mobilization		Porcelain Enamel;	Sch., Sched.	Schedule
Mog.	Mogul Base		Polyethylene; Plain End	S.C.R.	Modular Brick
MPH	Miles per Hour	P.E.C.I.	Porcelain Enamel on Cast Iron	S.D.	Sound Deadening
MPT	Male Pipe Thread	Perf.	Perforated	SDR	Standard Dimension Ratio
MRGWB	Moisture Resistant Gypsum	PEX	Cross Linked Polyethylene	S.E.	Surfaced Edge
	Wallboard	Ph.	Phase	Sel.	Select
MRT	Mile Round Trip	P.I.	Pressure Injected	SER, SEU	Service Entrance Cable
ms	Millisecond	Pile.	Pile Driver	S.F.	Square Foot
M.S.F.	Thousand Square Feet	Pkg.	Package	S.F.C.A.	Square Foot Contact Area
Mstz.	Mosaic & Terrazzo Worker	Pl.	Plate	S.F. Flr.	Square Foot of Floor
M.S.Y.	Thousand Square Yards	Plah.	Plasterer Helper	S.F.G.	Square Foot of Ground
Mtd., mtd., mtd	Mounted	Plas.	Plasterer	S.F. Hor.	Square Foot Horizontal
Mthe.	Mosaic & Terrazzo Helper	plf	Pounds Per Linear Foot	SFR	Square Feet of Radiation
Mtng.	Mounting	Pluh.	Plumber Helper	S.F. Shlf.	Square Foot of Shelf
Mult.	Multi; Multiply	Plum.	Plumber	S4S	Surface 4 Sides
MUTCD	Manual on Uniform Traffic Control	Ply.	Plywood	Shee.	Sheet Metal Worker
	Devices	p.m.	Post Meridiem	Sin.	Sine
M.V.A.	Million Volt Amperes	Pntd.	Painted	Skwk.	Skilled Worker
M.V.A.R.	Million Volt Amperes Reactance	Pord.	Painter, Ordinary	SL	Saran Lined
MV	Megavolt	pp	Pages	S.L.	Slimline
MW	Megawatt	PP, PPL	Polypropylene	Sldr.	Solder
MXM	Male by Male	P.P.M.	Parts per Million	SLH	Super Long Span Bar Joist
MYD	Thousand Yards	Pr.	Pair	S.N.	Solid Neutral
N	Natural; North	P.E.S.B.	Pre-engineered Steel Building	SO	Stranded with oil resistant inside
nA	Nanoampere	Prefab.	Prefabricated		insulation
NA	Not Available; Not Applicable	Prefin.	Prefinished	S-O-L	Socketolet
N.B.C.	National Building Code	Prop.	Propelled	sp	Standpipe
NC	Normally Closed	PSF, psf	Pounds per Square Foot	S.P.	Static Pressure; Single Pole; Self-
NEMA	National Electrical Manufacturers	PSI, psi	Pounds per Square Inch		Propelled
	Assoc.	PSIG	Pounds per Square Inch Gauge	Spri.	Sprinkler Installer
NEHB	Bolted Circuit Breaker to 600V.	PSP	Plastic Sewer Pipe	spwg	Static Pressure Water Gauge
NFPA	National Fire Protection Association	Pspr.	Painter, Spray	S.P.D.T.	Single Pole, Double Throw
NLB	Non-Load-Bearing	Psst.	Painter, Structural Steel	SPF	Spruce Pine Fir; Sprayed
NM	Non-Metallic Cable	P.T.	Potential Transformer		Polyurethane Foam
nm	Nanometer	P. & T.	Pressure & Temperature	S.P.S.T.	Single Pole, Single Throw
No.	Number	Ptd.	Painted	SPT	Standard Pipe Thread
NO	Normally Open	Ptns.	Partitions	Sq.	Square; 100 Square Feet
N.O.C.	Not Otherwise Classified	Pu	Ultimate Load	Sq. Hd.	Square Head
Nose.	Nosing	PVC	Polyvinyl Chloride	Sq. In.	Square Inch
NPT	National Pipe Thread	Pvmt.	Pavement	S.S.	Single Strength; Stainless Steel
NQOD	Combination Plug-on/Bolt on	PRV	Pressure Relief Valve	S.S.B.	Single Strength B Grade
	Circuit Breaker to 240V.	Pwr.	Power	sst, ss	Stainless Steel
N.R.C., NRC	Noise Reduction Coefficient/	Q	Quantity Heat Flow	Sswk.	Structural Steel Worker
	Nuclear Regulator Commission	Qt.	Quart	Sswl.	Structural Steel Welder
N.R.S.	Non Rising Stem	Quan., Qty.	Quantity	St.; Stl.	Steel
ns	Nanosecond	Q.C.	Quick Coupling	STC	Sound Transmission Coefficient
NTP	Notice to Proceed	r	Radius of Gyration	Std.	Standard
nW	Nanowatt	R	Resistance	Stg.	Staging
OB	Opposing Blade	R.C.P.	Reinforced Concrete Pipe	STK	Select Tight Knot
OC	On Center	Rect.	Rectangle	STP	Standard Temperature & Pressure
OD	Outside Diameter	recpt.	Receptacle	Stpi.	Steamfitter, Pipefitter
O.D.	Outside Dimension	Reg.	Regular	Str.	Strength; Starter; Straight
ODS	Overhead Distribution System	Reinf.	Reinforced	Strd.	Stranded
O.G.	Ogee	Req'd.	Required	Struct.	Structural
O.H.	Overhead	Res.	Resistant	Sty.	Story
O&P	Overhead and Profit	Resi.	Residential	Subj.	Subject
Oper.	Operator	RF	Radio Frequency	Subs.	Subcontractors
Opng.	Opening	RFID	Radio-frequency Identification	Surf.	Surface
Orna.	Ornamental	Rgh.	Rough	Sw.	Switch
OSB	Oriented Strand Board	RGS	Rigid Galvanized Steel	Swbd.	Switchboard
OS&Y	Outside Screw and Yoke	RHW	Rubber, Heat & Water Resistant;	S.Y.	Square Yard
OSHA	Occupational Safety and Health		Residential Hot Water	Syn.	Synthetic
	Act	rms	Root Mean Square	S.Y.P.	Southern Yellow Pine
Ovhd.	Overhead	Rnd.	Round	Sys.	System
OWG	Oil, Water or Gas	Rodm.	Rodman	t.	Thickness
Oz.	Ounce	Rofc.	Roofer, Composition	T	Temperature; Ton
P.	Pole; Applied Load; Projection	Rofp.	Roofer, Precast	Tan	Tangent
p.	Page	Rohe.	Roofer Helpers (Composition)	T.C.	Terra Cotta
Pape.	Paperhanger	Rots.	Roofer, Tile & Slate	T & C	Threaded and Coupled
P.A.P.R.	Powered Air Purifying Respirator	R.O.W.	Right of Way	T.D.	Temperature Difference
PAR	Parabolic Reflector	RPM	Revolutions per Minute	TDD	Telecommunications Device for
P.B., PB	Push Button	R.S.	Rapid Start		the Deaf
Pc., Pcs.	Piece, Pieces	Rsr	Riser	T.E.M.	Transmission Electron Microscopy
P.C.	Portland Cement; Power Connector	RT	Round Trip	temp	Temperature, Tempered, Temporary
P.C.F.	Pounds per Cubic Foot	S.	Suction; Single Entrance; South	TFFN	Nylon Jacketed Wire

Abbreviations

TFE	Tetrafluoroethylene (Teflon)	U.L., UL	Underwriters Laboratory	w/	With
T. & G.	Tongue & Groove;	Uld.	Unloading	W.C., WC	Water Column; Water Closet
	Tar & Gravel	Unfin.	Unfinished	W.F.	Wide Flange
Th., Thk.	Thick	UPS	Uninterruptible Power Supply	W.G.	Water Gauge
Thn.	Thin	URD	Underground Residential	Wldg.	Welding
Thrded	Threaded		Distribution	W. Mile	Wire Mile
Tilf.	Tile Layer, Floor	US	United States	W-O-L	Weldolet
Tilh.	Tile Layer, Helper	USGBC	U.S. Green Building Council	W.R.	Water Resistant
THHN	Nylon Jacketed Wire	USP	United States Primed	Wrck.	Wrecker
THW.	Insulated Strand Wire	UTMCD	Uniform Traffic Manual For Control	WSFU	Water Supply Fixture Unit
THWN	Nylon Jacketed Wire		Devices	W.S.P.	Water, Steam, Petroleum
T.L., TL	Truckload	UTP	Unshielded Twisted Pair	WT., Wt.	Weight
T.M.	Track Mounted	V	Volt	WWF	Welded Wire Fabric
Tot.	Total	VA	Volt Amperes	XFER	Transfer
T-O-L	Threadolet	VAT	Vinyl Asbestos Tile	XFMR	Transformer
tmpd	Tempered	V.C.T.	Vinyl Composition Tile	XHD	Extra Heavy Duty
TPO	Thermoplastic Polyolefin	VAV	Variable Air Volume	XHHW	Cross-Linked Polyethylene Wire
T.S.	Trigger Start	VC	Veneer Core	XLPE	Insulation
Tr.	Trade	VDC	Volts Direct Current	XLP	Cross-linked Polyethylene
Transf.	Transformer	Vent.	Ventilation	Xport	Transport
Trhv.	Truck Driver, Heavy	Vert.	Vertical	Y	Wye
Trlr	Trailer	V.F.	Vinyl Faced	yd	Yard
Trlt.	Truck Driver, Light	V.G.	Vertical Grain	yr	Year
TTY	Teletypewriter	VHF	Very High Frequency	Δ	Delta
TV	Television	VHO	Very High Output	%	Percent
T.W.	Thermoplastic Water Resistant	Vib.	Vibrating	~	Approximately
	Wire	VLF	Vertical Linear Foot	Ø	Phase; diameter
UCI	Uniform Construction Index	VOC	Volatile Organic Compound	@	At
UF	Underground Feeder	Vol.	Volume	#	Pound; Number
UGND	Underground Feeder	VRP	Vinyl Reinforced Polyester	<	Less Than
UHF	Ultra High Frequency	W	Wire; Watt; Wide; West	>	Greater Than
U.I.	United Inch			Z	Zone

RESIDENTIAL
COST ESTIMATE

OWNER'S NAME: _____

APPRAISER: _____

RESIDENCE ADDRESS: _____

PROJECT: _____

CITY, STATE, ZIP CODE: _____

DATE: _____

CLASS OF CONSTRUCTION
- ☐ ECONOMY
- ☐ AVERAGE
- ☐ CUSTOM
- ☐ LUXURY

RESIDENCE TYPE
- ☐ 1 STORY
- ☐ 1-1/2 STORY
- ☐ 2 STORY
- ☐ 2-1/2 STORY
- ☐ 3 STORY
- ☐ BI-LEVEL
- ☐ TRI-LEVEL

CONFIGURATION
- ☐ DETACHED
- ☐ TOWN/ROW HOUSE
- ☐ SEMI-DETACHED

OCCUPANCY
- ☐ ONE STORY
- ☐ TWO FAMILY
- ☐ THREE FAMILY
- ☐ OTHER _____

EXTERIOR WALL SYSTEM
- ☐ WOOD SIDING—WOOD FRAME
- ☐ BRICK VENEER—WOOD FRAME
- ☐ STUCCO ON WOOD FRAME
- ☐ PAINTED CONCRETE BLOCK
- ☐ SOLID MASONRY (AVERAGE & CUSTOM)
- ☐ STONE VENEER—WOOD FRAME
- ☐ SOLID BRICK (LUXURY)
- ☐ SOLID STONE (LUXURY)

*LIVING AREA (Main Building)

First Level _____ S.F.
Second Level _____ S.F.
Third Level _____ S.F.
_____
Total _____ S.F.

*LIVING AREA (Wing or Ell) (   )

First Level _____ S.F.
Second Level _____ S.F.
Third Level _____ S.F.

Total _____ S.F.

*LIVING AREA (Wing or Ell) (   )

First Level _____ S.F.
Second Level _____ S.F.
Third Level _____ S.F.

Total _____ S.F.

*Basement Area is not part of living area.

MAIN BUILDING	COSTS PER S.F. LIVING AREA
Cost per Square Foot of Living Area, from Page _____	$
Basement Addition: _____ % Finished, _____ % Unfinished	+
Roof Cover Adjustment: _____ Type, Page _____ (Add or Deduct)	( )
Central Air Conditioning: ☐ Separate Ducts ☐ Heating Ducts, Page _____	+
Heating System Adjustment: _____ Type, Page _____ (Add or Deduct)	( )
Main Building: Adjusted Cost per S.F. of Living Area	$

MAIN BUILDING TOTAL COST

$ _____ /S.F. × _____ S.F. × _____ = $ _____

Cost per S.F. Living Area | Living Area | Town/Row House Multiplier (Use 1 for Detached) | TOTAL COST

WING OR ELL ( ) _____ STORY	COSTS PER S.F. LIVING AREA
Cost per Square Foot of Living Area, from Page _____	$
Basement Addition: _____ % Finished, _____ % Unfinished	+
Roof Cover Adjustment: _____ Type, Page _____ (Add or Deduct)	( )
Central Air Conditioning: ☐ Separate Ducts ☐ Heating Ducts, Page _____	+
Heating System Adjustment: _____ Type, Page _____ (Add or Deduct)	( )
Wing or Ell ( ): Adjusted Cost per S.F. of Living Area	$

WING OR ELL (   ) TOTAL COST

$ _____ /S.F. × _____ S.F. = $ _____

Cost per S.F. Living Area | Living Area | TOTAL COST

WING OR ELL ( ) _____ STORY	COSTS PER S.F. LIVING AREA
Cost per Square Foot of Living Area, from Page _____	$
Basement Addition: _____ % Finished, _____ % Unfinished	+
Roof Cover Adjustment: _____ Type, Page _____ (Add or Deduct)	( )
Central Air Conditioning: ☐ Separate Ducts ☐ Heating Ducts, Page _____	+
Heating System Adjustment: _____ Type, Page _____ (Add or Deduct)	( )
Wing or Ell ( ): Adjusted Cost per S.F. of Living Area	$

WING OR ELL (   ) TOTAL COST

$ _____ /S.F. × _____ S.F. = $ _____

Cost per S.F. Living Area | Living Area | TOTAL COST

TOTAL THIS PAGE [_____]

Page 1 of 2

RESIDENTIAL COST ESTIMATE

Total Page 1			$
	QUANTITY	UNIT COST	
Additional Bathrooms: _____ Full, _____ Half			
Finished Attic: _____ Ft. x _____ Ft.	S.F.		+
Breezeway: ☐ Open ☐ Enclosed _____ Ft. x _____ Ft.	S.F.		+
Covered Porch: ☐ Open ☐ Enclosed _____ Ft. x _____ Ft.	S.F.		+
Fireplace: ☐ Interior Chimney ☐ Exterior Chimney ☐ No. of Flues ☐ Additional Fireplaces			+
Appliances:			+
Kitchen Cabinets Adjustment: (+/−)			
☐ Garage ☐ Carport: _____ Car(s) Description _____ (+/−)			
Miscellaneous:			+

ADJUSTED TOTAL BUILDING COST $ _____

REPLACEMENT COST	
ADJUSTED TOTAL BUILDING COST	$ _____
Site Improvements	
(A) Paving & Sidewalks	$ _____
(B) Landscaping	$ _____
(C) Fences	$ _____
(D) Swimming Pool	$ _____
(E) Miscellaneous	$ _____
TOTAL	$ _____
Location Factor	x _____
Location Replacement Cost	$ _____
Depreciation	−$ _____
LOCAL DEPRECIATED COST	$ _____

INSURANCE COST	
ADJUSTED TOTAL BUILDING COST	$ _____
Insurance Exclusions	
(A) Footings, Site Work, Underground Piping	−$ _____
(B) Architects' Fees	−$ _____
Total Building Cost Less Exclusion	$ _____
Location Factor	x _____
LOCAL INSURABLE REPLACEMENT COST	$ _____

SKETCH AND ADDITIONAL CALCULATIONS

743

For customer support on your Residential Costs with RSMeans Data, call 800.448.8182.

Index

746

Index

For customer support on your Residential Costs with RSMeans Data, call 800.448.8182.

753

757

Index

Division Notes

	CREW	DAILY OUTPUT	LABOR-HOURS	UNIT	BARE COSTS				TOTAL INCL O&P
					MAT.	LABOR	EQUIP.	TOTAL	

Division Notes

	CREW	DAILY OUTPUT	LABOR-HOURS	UNIT	BARE COSTS				TOTAL INCL O&P
					MAT.	LABOR	EQUIP.	TOTAL	

Division Notes

	CREW	DAILY OUTPUT	LABOR-HOURS	UNIT	BARE COSTS				TOTAL INCL O&P
					MAT.	LABOR	EQUIP.	TOTAL	

ost Data Selection Guide

following table provides definitive information on the content of each cost data publication. The number of lines of data provided in each unit price or mblies division, as well as the number of crews, is listed for each data set. The presence of other elements such as reference tables, square foot models, ipment rental costs, historical cost indexes, and city cost indexes, is also indicated. You can use the table to help select the RSMeans data set that has quantity and type of information you most need in your work.

t Cost isions	Building Construction	Mechanical	Electrical	Commercial Renovation	Square Foot	Site Work Landsc.	Green Building	Interior	Concrete Masonry	Open Shop	Heavy Construction	Light Commercial	Facilities Construction	Plumbing	Residential
1	595	414	431	535	0	527	207	334	476	594	527	278	1071	424	180
2	777	280	86	733	0	992	207	399	214	776	734	481	1221	287	274
3	1691	340	230	1084	0	1483	986	354	2037	1691	1693	482	1791	316	389
4	960	21	0	920	0	725	180	615	1158	928	615	533	1175	0	447
5	1901	158	155	1093	0	852	1799	1106	729	1901	1037	979	1918	204	746
6	2453	18	18	2111	0	110	589	1528	281	2449	123	2141	2125	22	2662
7	1596	215	128	1634	0	580	763	532	523	1593	26	1329	1697	227	1049
8	2131	80	44	2711	0	255	1140	1793	105	2119	0	2301	2954	0	1540
9	2006	86	45	1830	0	309	452	2092	394	1948	15	1671	2255	54	1440
10	1063	17	10	657	0	217	27	873	138	1063	30	554	1154	234	224
11	1096	201	166	540	0	135	56	924	29	1063	0	231	1116	164	110
12	548	0	2	299	0	219	147	1551	14	515	0	273	1574	23	217
13	744	149	158	253	0	369	122	254	78	720	267	109	760	115	104
14	273	36	0	223	0	0	0	257	0	273	0	12	293	16	6
21	130	0	41	37	0	0	0	296	0	130	0	121	669	689	259
22	1168	7559	160	1227	0	1572	1066	849	20	1157	1681	875	7507	9411	719
23	1179	6972	579	930	0	157	900	779	38	1173	110	880	5211	1920	469
26	1505	490	10389	1160	0	812	639	1158	55	1437	596	1360	10301	399	636
27	94	0	419	83	0	0	0	71	0	94	39	67	378	0	56
28	125	79	193	107	0	0	27	90	0	110	0	56	182	57	41
31	1510	733	610	806	0	3262	288	7	1217	1455	3276	604	1569	660	613
32	814	49	8	882	0	4410	353	405	292	785	1827	421	1688	142	468
33	529	1076	538	252	0	2173	41	0	236	522	2157	128	1697	1283	154
34	107	0	47	4	0	190	0	0	31	62	212	0	136	0	0
35	18	0	0	0	0	327	0	0	0	18	442	0	84	0	0
41	60	0	0	33	0	8	0	22	0	61	31	0	68	14	0
44	75	79	0	0	0	0	0	0	0	0	0	0	75	75	0
46	23	16	0	0	0	274	261	0	0	23	264	0	33	33	0
48	12	0	25	0	0	0	25	0	0	12	17	12	12	0	12
Totals	25183	19068	14482	20144	0	19958	10275	16289	8065	24672	15719	15898	50714	16769	12815

sem Div	Building Construction	Mechanical	Electrical	Commercial Renovation	Square Foot	Site Work Landscape	Assemblies	Green Building	Interior	Concrete Masonry	Heavy Construction	Light Commercial	Facilities Construction	Plumbing	Asm Div	Residential
A		15	0	188	150	577	598	0	0	536	571	154	24	0	1	378
B		0	0	848	2503	0	5662	56	329	1976	368	2095	174	0	2	211
C		0	0	647	929	0	1310	0	1632	146	0	818	251	0	3	588
D		1069	941	712	1861	72	2540	330	827	0	0	1348	1107	1088	4	850
E		0	0	86	261	0	301	0	5	0	0	258	5	0	5	391
F		0	0	0	114	0	143	0	0	0	0	114	0	0	6	357
G		527	447	318	311	3363	791	0	0	534	1349	205	293	677	7	307
															8	760
															9	80
															10	0
															11	0
															12	0
tals		1611	1388	2799	6129	4012	11345	386	2793	3192	2288	4992	1854	1765		3922

eference Section	Building Construction Costs	Mechanical	Electrical	Commercial Renovation	Square Foot	Site Work Landscape	Assem.	Green Building	Interior	Concrete Masonry	Open Shop	Heavy Construction	Light Commercial	Facilities Construction	Plumbing	Resi.
ference bles	yes	yes	yes	yes	no	yes	yes	yes	yes	yes	yes	yes	yes	yes	yes	yes
odels					111		25						50			28
ews	578	578	578	556		578		578	578	578	555	578	555	556	578	555
uipment ntal Costs	yes	yes	yes	yes		yes		yes	yes	yes	yes	yes	yes	yes	yes	yes
storical st dexes	yes	yes	yes	yes	yes	yes	yes	yes	yes	yes	yes	yes	yes	yes	yes	no
y Cost dexes	yes	yes	yes	yes	yes	yes	yes	yes	yes	yes	yes	yes	yes	yes	yes	yes

Online   Book   CD   eBook   Online add-on available for additional fee

For more information visit our website at www.RSMeans.cc

Unit prices according to the latest MasterFormat

Annual Cost Guides

766

Building Construction Costs with RSMeans Data 2017

Offers you unchallenged unit price reliability in an easy-to-use format. Whether used for verifying complete, finished estimates or for periodic checks, it supplies more cost facts better and faster than any comparable source. The City Cost Indexes and Location Factors cover more than 930 areas for indexing to any project location in North America. Order and get RSMeans Quarterly Update Service FREE.

Green Building Costs with RSMeans Data 2017

Estimate, plan, and budget the costs of green building for both new commercial construction and renovation work with this seventh edition of *Green Building Costs with RSMeans Data*. More than 10,000 unit costs for a wide array of green building products plus assemblies costs. Easily identified cross references to LEED and Green Globes building rating systems criteria.

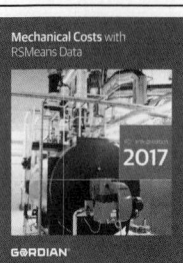

Mechanical Costs with RSMeans Data 2017

Total unit and systems price guidance for mechanical construction—materials, parts, fittings, and complete labor cost information. Includes prices for piping, heating, air conditioning, ventilation, and all related construction.

Plus new 2017 unit costs for:

- Thousands of installed HVAC/controls, sub-assemblies and assemblies
- "On-site" Location Factors for more than 930 cities and towns in the U.S. and Canada
- Crews, labor, and equipment

Facilities Construction Costs with RSMeans Data 2017

For the maintenance and construction of commercial industrial, municipal, and institutional properties. Co are shown for new and remodeling construction and are broken down into materials, labor, equipment, an overhead and profit. Special emphasis is given to sect on mechanical, electrical, furnishings, site work, buil maintenance, finish work, and demolition.

More than 49,800 unit costs, plus assemblies costs a comprehensive Reference Section are included.

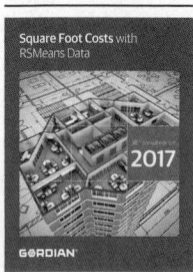

Square Foot Costs with RSMeans Data 2017
Accurate and Easy-to-Use

- Updated price information based on nationwide figures from suppliers, estimators, labor experts, and contractors.
- Green building models
- Realistic graphics, offering true-to-life illustrations of building projects
- Extensive information on using square foot cost data, including sample estimates and alternate pricing methods

Commercial Renovation Costs wit RSMeans Data 2017
Commercial/Multi-family Residential

Use this valuable tool to estimate commercial and multi-family residential renovation and remodeling.

Includes: Updated costs for hundreds of unique methods, materials, and conditions that only come up in repair and remodeling, PLUS:

- Unit costs for more than 19,600 construction components
- Installed costs for more than 2,700 assemblies
- More than 930 "on-site" localization factors for th U.S. and Canada

Electrical Costs with RSMeans Data 2017

Pricing information for every part of electrical cost planning. More than 13,800 unit and systems costs with design tables; clear specifications and drawings; engineering guides; illustrated estimating procedures; complete labor-hour and materials costs for better scheduling and procurement; and the latest electrical products and construction methods.

- A variety of special electrical systems, including cathodic protection
- Costs for maintenance, demolition, HVAC/mechanical, specialties, equipment, and more

Electrical Change Order Costs with RSMeans Data 2017

Electrical Change Order Costs with RSMeans Data provides you with electrical unit prices exclusively for pricing change orders. Analyze and check your own change order estimates against those prepared when using RSMeans cost data. It also covers productivity analysis and change order cost justifications. With useful information for calculating the effects of chang orders and dealing with their administration.

Assemblies Costs with RSMeans Data 2017

Assemblies Costs with RSMeans Data takes the guesswork out of preliminary or conceptual estimates. Now you don't have to try to calculate the assembled cost by working up individual component costs. We've done all the work for you.

Presents detailed illustrations, descriptions, specifications, and costs for every conceivable building assembly—over 350 types in all—arranged in the easy-to-use UNIFORMAT II system. Each illustrated "assembled" cost includes a complete grouping of materials and associated installation costs, including the installing contractor's overhead and profit.

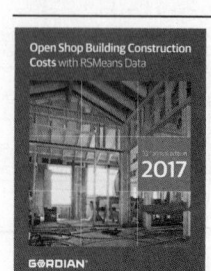

Open Shop Building Construction Costs with RSMeans Data 2017

The latest costs for accurate budgeting and estimating of new commercial and residential construction, renovation work, change orders, and cos engineering.

Open Shop "BCCD" with RSMeans Data will assist you to:

- Develop benchmark prices for change orders.
- Plug gaps in preliminary estimates and budgets.
- Estimate complex projects.
- Substantiate invoices on contracts.
- Price ADA-related renovations.

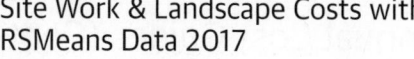
For more information visit our website at www.RSMeans.com

Residential Costs with RSMeans Data 2017

Contains square foot costs for 28 basic home models with the look of today, plus hundreds of custom additions and modifications you can quote right off the page. Includes more than 3,900 costs for 89 residential systems. Complete with blank estimating forms, sample estimates, and step-by-step instructions.

Contains line items for cultured stone and brick, PVC trim, lumber, and TPO roofing.

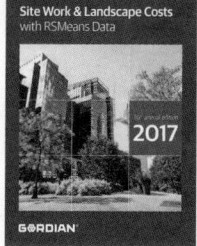

Site Work & Landscape Costs with RSMeans Data 2017

Includes unit and assemblies costs for earthwork, sewerage, piped utilities, site improvements, drainage, paving, trees and shrubs, street openings/repairs, underground tanks, and more. Contains more than 60 types of assemblies costs for accurate conceptual estimates.

Includes:

- Estimating for infrastructure improvements
- Environmentally-oriented construction
- ADA-mandated handicapped access
- Hazardous waste line items

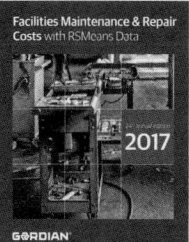

Facilities Maintenance & Repair Costs with RSMeans Data 2017

Facilities Maintenance & Repair Costs with RSMeans Data gives you a complete system to manage and plan your facility repair and maintenance costs and budget efficiently. Guidelines for auditing a facility and developing an annual maintenance plan. Budgeting is included, along with reference tables on cost and management, and information on frequency and productivity of maintenance operations.

The only nationally recognized source of maintenance and repair costs. Developed in cooperation with the Civil Engineering Research Laboratory (CERL) of the Army Corps of Engineers.

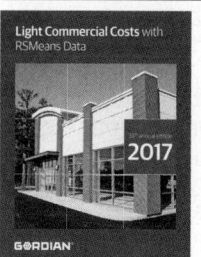

Light Commercial Costs with RSMeans Data 2017

Specifically addresses the light commercial market, which is a specialized niche in the construction industry. Aids you, the owner/designer/contractor, in preparing all types of estimates—from budgets to detailed bids. Includes new advances in methods and materials.

The Assemblies section allows you to evaluate alternatives in the early stages of design/planning.

More than 15,500 unit costs ensure that you have the prices you need, when you need them.

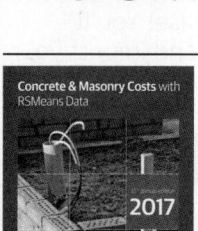

Concrete & Masonry Costs with RSMeans Data 2017

Provides you with cost facts for virtually all concrete/masonry estimating needs, from complicated formwork to various sizes and face finishes of brick and block—all in great detail. The comprehensive Unit Price Section contains more than 8,000 selected entries. Also contains an Assemblies [Cost] Section, and a detailed Reference Section that supplements the cost data.

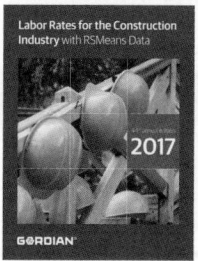

Labor Rates for the Construction Industry with RSMeans Data 2017

Complete information for estimating labor costs, making comparisons, and negotiating wage rates by trade for more than 300 U.S. and Canadian cities. With 46 construction trades in each city and historical wage rates included for comparison. Each city chart lists the county and is alphabetically arranged with handy visual flip tabs for quick reference.

Square Foot Renovation Costs with RSMeans Data 2017

For conceptual estimating of renovation projects, *Square Foot Renovation Costs with RSMeans Data* provides whole building and assembly level renovation costs at varying levels for 44 building models. Renovation costs are unique to each model and adjust with the intensity of renovation work being represented. Levels of renovation are:

Level 1 - Cosmetics
Level 2 - Plus Non-Masonry Partitions
Level 3 - Plus Masonry Partitions
Level 4 - Plus Bathrooms, Kitchens
Level 5 - Plus Equip, Ext Doors & Windows

Interior Costs with RSMeans Data 2017

Provides you with prices and guidance needed to make accurate interior work estimates. Contains costs on materials, equipment, hardware, custom installations, furnishings, and labor for new and remodel commercial and industrial interior construction, including updated information on office furnishings, as well as reference information.

Heavy Construction Costs with RSMeans Data 2017

A comprehensive guide to heavy construction costs. Includes costs for highly specialized projects such as tunnels, dams, highways, airports, and waterways. Information on labor rates, equipment, and materials costs is included. Features unit price costs, systems costs, and numerous reference tables for costs and design.

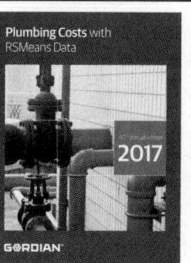

Plumbing Costs with RSMeans Data 2017

Comprehensive unit prices and assemblies for plumbing, irrigation systems, commercial and residential fire protection, point-of-use water heaters, and the latest approved materials. This publication and its companion, *Mechanical Costs with RSMeans Data*, provide full-range cost estimating coverage for all the mechanical trades.

Contains updated costs for potable water, radiant heat systems, and high efficiency fixtures.

For more information visit our website at www.RSMeans.com

Annual Cost Guides (Continued)
Construction Cost Indexes with RSMeans Data 2017

What materials and labor costs will change unexpectedly this year? By how much?
- Breakdowns for 318 major cities
- National averages for 30 key cities
- Expanded five major city indexes

Our Online Estimating Solution
Competitive Cost Estimates Made Easy

Our online estimating solution is a web-based service that provides accurate and up-to-date cost information to help you build competitive estimates or budgets in less time.

Quick, intuitive, easy to use and automatically updated, you'll gain instant access to hundreds of thousands of material, labor, and equipment costs from RSMeans' comprehensive database, delivering the information you need to build budgets and competitive estimates every time.

With our online estimating solutions, you can perform quick searches to locate specific costs and adjust costs to reflect prices in your geographic area. Tag and store your favorites for fast access to your frequently used line items and assemblies and clone estimates to save time. System notifications will alert you as updated data becomes available. This data is automatically updated throughout the year.

Our visual, interactive estimating features help you create, manage, save and share estimates with ease! You'll enjoy increased flexibility with customizable advanced reports. Easily edit custom report templates and import your company logo onto your estimates.

	Core	Advanced	Complete
Unit Prices	✓	✓	✓
Assemblies	X	✓	✓
Sq Ft Models	X	X	✓
Editable Sq Foot Models	X	X	✓
Editable Assembly Components	X	✓	✓
Custom Cost Data	X	✓	✓
User Defined Components	X	✓	✓
Advanced Reporting & Customization	X	✓	✓
Union Labor Type	✓	✓	✓
Open Shop*	Available for add-on at $249.99	Available for add-on at $249.99	✓
History (3-year lookback)**	Available for add-on at $249.99	Available for add-on at $249.99	Available for add-on at $249.99
Full History (2007)	Available for add-on at $499.99	Available for add-on at $499.99	Available for add-on at $499.99
Life Cycle Costing***	X	Available for add-on at $999.99	Available for add-on at $999.99
Alerts	Available for add-on at $299.99	Available for add-on at $299.99	Available for add-on at $299.99

*Open shop included in Complete Library & Bundles   **3-year history look back included with complete library
***Not available as add-on with Residential data set

Continue to check our website at www.RSMeans.com for more product offerings.

Online Estimating Solution   Unit prices according to the latest MasterFormat

stimate with Precision

nd everything you need to develop complete, accurate
timates.
Verified costs for construction materials
Equipment rental costs
Crew sizing, labor hours and labor rates
Localized costs for U.S. and Canada

ave Time & Increase Efficiency

ake cost estimating and calculating faster and easier
an ever with secure, online estimating tools.
Quickly locate costs in the searchable database
Create estimates in minutes with RSMeans cost lines
Tag and store favorites for fast access to frequently
used items

Improve Planning & Decision-Making

Back your estimates with complete, accurate and up-to-
date cost data for informed business decisions.
- Verify construction costs from third parties
- Check validity of subcontractor proposals
- Evaluate material and assembly alternatives

Increase Profits

Use our online estimating solution to estimate projects
quickly and accurately, so you can gain an edge over your
competition.
- Create accurate and competitive bids
- Minimize the risk of cost overruns
- Reduce variability

O Day Free Trial

egister for a free trial at www.RSMeans.com/Trial
Access to unit prices, building assemblies and facilities repair and
remodeling items covering every category of construction
Powerful tools to customize, save and share cost lists, estimates and
reports with ease
Access to square foot models for quick conceptual estimates
Allows up to 10 users to evaluate the full range of collaborative
functionality.

2017 Seminar Schedule

ote: call for exact dates and details.

Location	Dates	Location	Dates
Seattle, WA	January and August	San Francisco, CA	June
Dallas/Ft. Worth, TX	January	Bethesda, MD	June
Austin, TX	February	El Segundo, CA	August
Anchorage, AK	March and September	Dallas, TX	September
Las Vegas, NV	March	Raleigh, NC	October
New Orleans, LA	March	Salt Lake City, UT	October
Washington, DC	April and September	Baltimore, MD	November
Phoenix, AZ	April	Orlando, FL	November
Toronto	May	San Diego, CA	December
Denver, CO	May	San Antonio, TX	December

☎ 877-620-6245

ordian also offers a suite of online RSMeans data self-paced offerings. Check our website www.RSMeans.com for
nore information.

Professional Development

eLearning Training Sessions

earn how to use our RSMeans online estimating
olution from the convenience of your home or office.
Our eLearning training sessions let you join a training
conference call and share the instructors' desktops,
o you can view the presentation and step-by-step
nstructions on your own computer screen. The live
webinars are held from 9 a.m. to 5 p.m. or 11 a.m. to
 p.m. eastern standard time, with a one-hour break
or lunch.

For these sessions, you must have a computer with
high speed Internet access and a compatible Web
browser. Learn more at www.RSMeansOnline.com
or call for a schedule: 781-422-5115. Webinars are
generally held on selected Wednesdays each month.

Training for our Online Estimating Solution

Construction estimating is vital to the decision-making process at each state of every project. Our online solution works the way you do. It's systematic, flexible and intuitive. In this one-day class you will see how you can estimate any phase of any project faster and better.

Some of what you'll learn:
- Customizing our online estimating solution
- Making the most of RSMeans "Circle Reference" numbers
- How to integrate your cost data
- Generating reports, exporting estimates to MS Excel, sharing, collaborating and more

Also available: Online estimating solution training webinar or a self-paced training program.

Facilities Construction Estimating

In this two-day course, professionals working in facilities management can get help with their daily challenges to establish budgets for all phases of a project.

Some of what you'll learn:
- Determining the full scope of a project
- Identifying the scope of risks and opportunities
- Creative solutions to estimating issues
- Organizing estimates for presentation and discussion
- Special techniques for repair/remodel and maintenance projects
- Negotiating project change orders

Who should attend: facility managers, engineers, contractors, facility tradespeople, planners, and project managers.

Construction Cost Estimating: Concepts and Practice

This one-day introductory course to improve estimating skills and effectiveness starts with the details of interpreting bid documents and ends with the summary of the estimate and bid submission.

Some of what you'll learn:
- Using the plans and specifications to create estimates
- The takeoff process—deriving all tasks with correct quantities
- Developing pricing using various sources; how subcontractor pricing fits in
- Summarizing the estimate to arrive at the final number
- Formulas for area and cubic measure, adding waste and adjusting productivity to specific projects
- Evaluating subcontractors' proposals and prices
- Adding insurance and bonds
- Understanding how labor costs are calculated
- Submitting bids and proposals

Who should attend: project managers, architects, engineers, owners' representatives, contractors, and anyone who's responsible for budgeting or estimating construction projects.

Maintenance & Repair Estimating for Facilities

This two-day course teaches attendees how to plan, budget, and estimate the cost of ongoing and preventive maintenance and repair for existing buildings and grounds.

Some of what you'll learn:
- The most financially favorable maintenance, repair, and replacement scheduling and estimating
- Auditing and value engineering facilities
- Preventive planning and facilities upgrading
- Determining both in-house and contract-out service cost
- Annual, asset-protecting M&R plan

Who should attend: facility managers, maintenance supervisors, buildings and grounds superintendents, plant managers, planners, estimators, and others involved in facilities planning and budgeting.

Practical Project Management for Construction Professionals

In this two-day course, acquire the essential knowledge an develop the skills to effectively and efficiently execute the day-to-day responsibilities of the construction project manager.

Some of what you'll learn:
- General conditions of the construction contract
- Contract modifications: change orders and construction change directives
- Negotiations with subcontractors and vendors
- Effective writing: notification and communications
- Dispute resolution: claims and liens

Who should attend: architects, engineers, owners' representatives, and project managers.

Mechanical & Electrical Estimating

This two-day course teaches attendees how to prepare more accurate and complete mechanical/electrical estimates, avoid the pitfalls of omission and double-counting, and understand the composition and rationale within the RSMeans mechanical/electrical database.

Some of what you'll learn:
- The unique way mechanical and electrical systems are interrelated
- M&E estimates—conceptual, planning, budgeting, and bidding stages
- Order of magnitude, square foot, assemblies, and unit price estimating
- Comparative cost analysis of equipment and design alternatives

Who should attend: architects, engineers, facilities managers, mechanical and electrical contractors, and others who need a highly reliable method for developing, understanding, and evaluating mechanical and electrical contracts.

Unit Price Estimating

This interactive two-day seminar teaches attendees how to interpret project information and process it into final, detailed estimates with the greatest accuracy level.

The most important credential an estimator can take to the job is the ability to visualize construction and estimate accurately.

Some of what you'll learn:
- Interpreting the design in terms of cost
- The most detailed, time-tested methodology for accurate pricing
- Key cost drivers—material, labor, equipment, staging, and subcontracts
- Understanding direct and indirect costs for accurate job cost accounting and change order management

Who should attend: corporate and government estimators and purchasers, architects, engineers, and others who need to produce accurate project estimates.

Training for our CD Estimating Solution

This one-day course helps users become more familiar with the functionality of the CD. Each menu, icon, screen, and function found in the program is explained in depth. Time is devoted to hands-on estimating exercises.

Some of what you'll learn:
- Searching the database using all navigation methods
- Exporting RSMeans data to your preferred spreadsheet format
- Viewing crews, assembly components, and much more
- Automatically regionalizing the database

This training session requires you to bring a laptop computer to class.

When you register for this course you will receive an outline for your laptop requirements.

Also offered as a self-paced training program!

Facilities Estimating Using the CD

Combines hands-on skill building with best estimating practices and real-life problems. Brings you up-to-date with key concepts and provides tips, pointers, and guidelines to save time and avoid cost oversights and errors in this two-day class.

Some of what you'll learn:
- Estimating process concepts
- Customizing and adapting RSMeans cost data
- Establishing scope of work to account for all known variables
- Budget estimating: when, why, and how
- Site visits: what to look for—what you can't afford to overlook
- How to estimate repair and remodeling variables

This training session requires you to bring a laptop computer to class.

Who should attend: facility managers, architects, engineers, contractors, facility tradespeople, planners, project managers, and anyone involved with JOC, SABRE, or IDIQ.

Conceptual Estimating Using the CD

This two-day class uses the leading industry data and a powerful software package to develop highly accurate conceptual estimates for your construction projects. All attendees must bring a laptop computer loaded with the current year Square Foot Costs with RSMeans Data and Assemblies Costs with RSMeans Data.

Some of what you'll learn:
- Introduction to conceptual estimating
- Types of conceptual estimates
- Helpful hints
- Order of magnitude estimating
- Square foot estimating
- Assemblies estimating

Who should attend: architects, engineers, contractors, construction estimators, owners' representatives, and anyone looking for an electronic method for performing square foot estimating.

Assessing Scope of Work for Facility Construction Estimating

This two-day practical training program addresses the vital importance of understanding the scope of projects in order to produce accurate cost estimates for facility repair and remodeling.

Some of what you'll learn:
- Discussions of site visits, plans/specs, record drawings of facilities, and site-specific lists
- Review of CSI divisions, including means, methods, materials, and the challenges of scoping each topic
- Exercises in scope identification and scope writing for accurate estimating of projects
- Hands-on exercises that require scope, take-off, and pricing

Who should attend: corporate and government estimators, planners, facility managers, and others who need to produce accurate project estimates.

Building Systems and the Construction Process

This one-day course was written to assist novices and those outside the industry in obtaining a solid understanding of the construction process - from both a building systems and construction administration approach.

Some of what you'll learn:
- Various systems used and how components come together to create a building
- Start with foundation and end with the physical systems of the structure such as HVAC and Electrical
- Focus on the process from start of design through project closeout

This training session requires you to bring a laptop computer to class.

Who should attend: building professionals or novices to help make the crossover to the construction industry; suited for anyone responsible for providing high level oversight on construction projects.

Professional Development

771

Professional Development

For more information visit our website at www.RSMeans.com

Self-Paced Professional Development Courses

Training and professional development courses on RSMeans data are now offered in a convenient self-paced format allowing more flexibility to learn around your busy schedule.

These self-paced training courses can be completed over the course of 45 days and most are comprised of 10 lessons complete with documentation, video presentation, assessment quizzes and certificate of completion.

To view and register for the currently offered self-paced course, visit https://rsmeans.myabsorb.com.

Registration Information

Register early and save up to $100!
Register 30 days before the start date of a seminar and save $100 off your total fee. Note: This discount can be applied only once per order. It cannot be applied to team discount registrations or any other special offer.

How to register
By Phone
Register by phone at 877-620-6245

Online
Register online at
www.RSMeans.com/products/seminars.aspx

Note: Purchase Orders or Credits Cards are required to register.

Two-day seminar registration fee - $995. One-day CD or online training registration fee - $395.

One-Day Construction Cost Estimating or Building Systems and the Construction Process - $600.

Government pricing
All federal government employees save off the regular seminar price. Other promotional discounts cannot be combined with the government discount.

Team discount program
For over five attendee registrations. Call for pricing: 781-422-5115

Refund policy
Cancellations will be accepted up to ten business days prior to the seminar start. There are no refunds for cancellations received later than ten working days prior to the first day of the seminar. A $150 processing fee will be applied for all cancellations. Written notice of the cancellation is required. Substitutions can be made at any time before the session starts. No-shows are subject to the full seminar fee.

Note: Pricing subject to change.

AACE approved courses
Many seminars described and offered here have been approved for 14 hours (1.4 recertification credits) of credit by the AACE International Certification Board toward meeting the continuing education requirements for recertification as a Certified Cost Engineer/Certified Cost Consultant.

AIA Continuing Education
We are registered with the AIA Continuing Education System (AIA/CES) and are committed to developing quality learning activities in accordance with the CES criteria. Many seminars meet the AIA/CES criteria for Quality Level 2. AIA members may receive 14 learning units (LUs) for each two-day RSMeans course.

Daily course schedule
The first day of each seminar session begins at 8:30 a.m. and ends at 4:30 p.m. The second day begins at 8:00 a.m. and ends at 4:00 p.m. Participants are urged to bring a hand-held calculator since many actual problems will be worked out in each session.

Continental breakfast
Your registration includes the cost of a continental breakfast and a morning and afternoon refreshment break. These informal segments allow you to discuss topics of mutual interest with other seminar attendees. (You are free to make your own lunch and dinner arrangements.)

Hotel/transportation arrangements
We arrange to hold a block of rooms at most host hotels. To take advantage of special group rates when making your reservation, be sure to mention that you are attending the RSMeans Institute data seminar. You are, of course, free to stay at the lodging place of your choice. (Hotel reservations and transportation arrangements should be made directly by seminar attendees.)

Important
Class sizes are limited, so please register as soon as possible.